THE HORMONES

PHYSIOLOGY, CHEMISTRY AND APPLICATIONS

VOLUME III

THE HORMONES

Physiology, Chemistry and Applications

Edited by

GREGORY PINCUS

Worcester Foundation for Experimental
Biology, Shrewsbury, Massachusetts

KENNETH V. THIMANN

Harvard University
Cambridge, Massachusetts

VOLUME III

1955

ACADEMIC PRESS INC. PUBLISHERS

NEW YORK

Contributors to Volume III

E. B. ASTWOOD, *New England Center Hospital, Boston, Massachusetts*

BEN BLOOM, *National Institute of Arthritis and Metabolic Diseases, National Institutes of Health, Bethesda, Maryland*

A. T. COWIE, *National Institute for Research in Dairying, Shinfield, Reading, England*

RALPH I. DORFMAN, *Worcester Foundation for Experimental Biology, Shrewsbury, Massachusetts*

S. J. FOLLEY, *National Institute for Research in Dairying, Shinfield, Reading, England*

ROY O. GREEP, *Department of Anatomy, Harvard School of Dental Medicine, Boston, Massachusetts*

EDWIN E. HAYS, *Research Department, The Armour Laboratories, Chicago, Illinois*

H. HIRSCHMANN, *Lakeside Hospital, Cleveland, Ohio*

ALEXANDER D. KENNY, *Department of Pharmacology, Harvard School of Dental Medicine, Boston, Massachusetts*

B. KETTERER, *Department of Pharmacology, Welsh National School of Medicine, Cardiff, Wales*

F. W. LANDGREBE, *Department of Pharmacology, Welsh National School of Medicine, Cardiff, Wales*

A. CARL LEOPOLD, *Department of Horticulture, Agricultural Experiment Station, Purdue University, Lafayette, Indiana*

R. L. NOBLE, *Department of Physiology, University of Western Ontario, London, Ontario, Canada*

K. E. PASCHKIS, *Department of Physiology, Jefferson Medical College of Philadelphia, Philadelphia, Pennsylvania*

GREGORY PINCUS, *Worcester Foundation for Experimental Biology, Shrewsbury, Massachusetts*

A. E. RAKOFF, *Department of Physiology, Jefferson Medical College of Philadelphia, Philadelphia, Pennsylvania*

JOSEPH E. RALL, *Memorial Center for Cancer and Allied Diseases, New York, N. Y.*

RULON W. RAWSON, *Memorial Center for Cancer and Allied Diseases, New York, N. Y.*

BERTA SCHARRER, *Department of Anatomy, Albert Einstein College of Medicine, New York, N. Y.*

MARTIN SONENBERG, *Memorial Center for Cancer and Allied Diseases, New York, N. Y.*

SANFORD L. STEELMAN, *Research Department, The Armour Laboratories, Chicago, Illinois*

DEWITT STETTEN, JR., *National Institute of Arthritis and Metabolic Diseases, National Institutes of Health, Bethesda, Maryland*

KENNETH V. THIMANN, *The Biological Laboratories, Harvard University, Cambridge, Massachusetts*

H. WARING, *Department of Zoology, University of Western Australia, Nedlands, Western Australia*

JOHN H. WELSH, *The Biological Laboratories, Harvard University, Cambridge, Massachusetts*

Preface to Volume III

Seven years have passed since the appearance of Volume I of The Hormones. At that time it was suggested that the subject might have completed its first unfolding—virtually all the major hormones, especially in the mammals and man, having been discovered, bioassayed, and at least partially identified chemically. The subsequent period, it was felt, would be one first of consolidation, then of increasing emphasis upon physiological problems and the inner mechanism of the action of hormones. This prognostication, it now appears, was true only in part. It was true for the hormones of the thyroid, anterior pituitary, and gonads, which have always occupied so central a position in research and application. To a lesser extent it was true in other areas. But as regards the hormones of the invertebrates and insects, and in the realms of the posterior pituitary and the nervous systems, the appearance of new facts and ideas has opened new horizons. The concept of nerves as secreting and transmitting hormones, as well as the long-awaited isolation of the pure posterior pituitary hormones themselves, are both notable. Even in the plants, the discovery that auxin plays a role in flowering brings what was thought to be a growth hormone into relationship with the reproduction process. Not less to be regarded as new departures are the discoveries concerning the pituitary-adrenal axis and the widespread medical applications, just touched on in Volume II, which have followed.

The expected emphasis upon mechanism of action, on the contrary, has not yet developed to the degree expected, and the major discoveries in this direction are still probably for the future, although there have been interesting and suggestive developments. In the case of the animal hormones particularly, intensive investigations of their metabolic fate have been considered necessary preludes to studies of their specific roles in biochemical reactions; in several instances it has been indicated that a metabolite of the secretory product rather than the secreted substance itself may be responsible for the presumed specific effects. Furthermore, with the broadening of our knowledge of hormone interaction, the need for distinction between primary and secondary effects of a given hormone has become more evident. For example, the adrenocorticomimetic effects of estrogens are cited in the text; the effects are presumably exerted through stimulating the secretion of ACTH from the anterior pituitary. Another complication which has emerged with clarity is that mammals differ more widely in their physiology than was formerly thought. For this reason, any attempt to study mechanisms of action as problems in general physiology must recognize species differences in response to hormones, and the past septennium has unearthed additional remarkable hormonal responses occurring in one species and completely absent in another.

For all these reasons the present volume is not merely a supplement to Volumes I and II; that is, it is not merely a chronicle of recent experiments, extending in detail what has already been laid down in outline. Instead, some parts of the volume supplant their predecessors, and certainly the majority of the chapters at least modify or recast the picture which had been presented. While part of its information is certainly supplementary an important part must be regarded as revision or perhaps as reassessment.

The partition of subject matter between the authors and the planned content of the individual chapters has been somewhat revised from that of the previous volumes to allow of more unification and changed emphasis. Some of the authors are those who already reviewed their subjects in Volumes I and II, but the regrouping of the subject matter, as well as death, retirement, or preoccupation with other affairs, has necessitated a number of changes. In any event the chapters reflect individual viewpoints as much as ever. It is hoped that the elements both of variety and of uniformity will combine to make the book a useful tool in the difficult task of integrating modern biology.

G. PINCUS
K. V. THIMANN

June, 1955

Contents

Contents of Volume II

Contents of Volume I

CHAPTER I

Plant Growth Hormones

By KENNETH V. THIMANN and A. CARL LEOPOLD

CONTENTS

I. Introduction

The progress of any field of science is highly irregular; some parts may make a major break-through, whereas other parts—apparently no more complex—seem blocked by some difficulty of procedure or of concepts, so that ideas and experiments proceed in spirals without advancing. The study of plant hormones has shown the expected irregularity of advance during the six years since the appearance of Volume I of *The Hormones*. Some aspects, like that of the inhibition of the growth of buds, have not undergone any really fundamental change, whereas the role of auxin in flowering and the mechanism of auxin action in growth have developed with great rapidity. Recent evidence for an *in vitro* action of auxin, and

1

greatly increased clarity as to the naturally occurring substances which alter auxin action, strengthen the hope that a reasonable picture of the biochemical control of plant growth may become available rather soon.

Numerous books and reviews have appeared recently. A reissue of Chapters II and III of Volume I (290) with bibliography bringing the subject up through 1950, appeared early in 1952. The 1949 Wisconsin Centenary volume, *Plant Growth Substances*, edited by F. Skoog and with 39 individual contributions, appeared in 1951. In a monograph on "Growth and Differentiation in Plants," edited by W. E. Loomis, about half of the 18 contributed chapters deal in one way or another with hormone action. The Brookhaven Symposium, "Abnormal and Pathological Plant Growth" (44), though concentrating on abnormalities, is necessarily much concerned with the action not only of auxins but also of other growth factors, known and postulated. Finally, three full-length treatments of the whole field of plant hormones have appeared, one by H. Söding, *Die Wuchsstofflehre* in 1952, one by L. J. Audus, *Plant Growth Substances* in 1953, and one by A. C. Leopold, *Auxins and Plant Growth* in 1955. The several shorter reviews, published in the Annual Reviews of Plant Physiology and elsewhere, are referred to here and there in the following sections.

The matter of definitions was taken up in Volume I. The definitions there suggested have been accepted by Audus (10), and, with an interesting discussion of alternatives, by Gordon (98). There is therefore no reason to discuss the matter further in this chapter, though the proposal to name the compounds that cause root elongation "root auxins" should be noted (116). The term "shoot auxins" would be used for compounds stimulating elongation and multiplication of shoot cells and inhibiting the same processes in root cells. Problems of antiauxin terminology have been discussed by Burström (53).

II. Assay Methods

The speed and the direction in which an area of study proceeds are determined largely by the methods available for research in that field, and in the past few years a new set of tools has become available in the study of plant hormones. These new tools center around the chromatographic separation of auxins and related compounds.

Paper chromatography was first employed in the study of plant growth hormones by Jerchel and Müller (136) and Pacheco (224), who demonstrated the presence of indoleacetic acid in several plants, and by Bennet-Clark and co-workers (17, 18), who showed that growth-promoting and growth-inhibiting substances are present in several parts of the chromatogram. The compounds can be detected on the paper by color reactions (see below), by their fluorescence characteristics (261), and by bio-assay tests (13, 17, 18, 76, 77, 114, 281, 286).

Other techniques which have been recently developed for the separation of growth substances include column chromatography (180), countercurrent distribution (128), and electrophoresis of the paper chromatograph (76,77).

Another technique which has greatly facilitated research in the study of auxins is the development of color assays, especially for indole-acetic acid and 2,4-D. The Salkowski color reaction for indoleacetic acid and related compounds, which had been used as a qualitative test in many earlier researches, was first used quantitatively by Tang and Bonner (285) and improved by Gordon and Weber (100). This simple technique is used now almost to the exclusion of other tests in the study of the destruction of auxin. However, its sensitivity to interfering substances necessitates reservations in some instances (u)[1]. A number of other color reactions have been used in paper chromatography (17, 18, 281, 337). A color test for 2,4-D has been described (86) and subsequently improved (172).

The methods of bio-assay for auxins have undergone some changes, most of them minor. Improved methods for obtaining auxins by diffusion have been worked out, utilizing cyanide as a poison to prevent enzymatic destruction (276) or providing ascorbic acid as an alternative substrate (330). A fair number of workers have turned to the use of roots as an assay material. It has been known since the earliest days of the study of auxins that roots were the most sensitive material to auxins, and because of their sensitivity they have provided some very de'icate assay methods (205, 334). It is a little unfortunate that most root assays utilize the inhibitory functions of auxins, while the action on shoots is typically growth promotion. In screening synthetic compounds, distinction between auxins (i.e., "shoot auxins") and growth inhibitors is not easily made. By the proper selection of material, however, or by the use of isolated sections, root tests have been carried out using the growth promotion which results from very low auxin concentrations (205, 164, and see Section IV). Some variability in the sensitivity of the root promotion has been noted (205, 227) owing to the age of the roots or to some quality of the seed. For this reason it is not always possible to obtain consistent root growth promotions, though where they are obtainable they present valuable assay material. In a number of instances, synthetic compounds have been found to promote root growth over a wide range of concentrations and/or to remove the inhibition caused by auxins. These substances have been considered as "root auxins" or antiauxins (see 53). The removal of the auxin inhibition of root growth constitutes the best bioassay for antiauxin activity (see Section IV).

[1] The abbreviation (u) indicates unpublished data from the laboratories of the authors or supplied by correspondence.

The increasing array of chemical and biological techniques for assay has introduced some confusion, as might be expected. This will doubtless be removed as the new methods facilitate progress.

III. Natural Auxins

For some years one of the major problems of plant physiology has been the chemical identity of the native growth hormone, or auxin. With the passage of time, this problem has become broader, and certainly not simpler. Twenty years ago, when auxins *a* and *b* (di-*sec*-butylcyclopentene derivatives) and indoleacetic acid were isolated, the problem was merely to know which of these functioned in plants. Simple experiments on crude diffusates pointed to one of the two first-named, and indoleacetic acid (IAA) was relegated to the role of "heteroauxin," a substance formed by fungi but not by higher plants, and entering the growth process in higher plants only by some biochemical "backdoor." Ten years ago, indoleacetic acid began to be isolated from a few higher plants, and indirect evidence for its presence was obtained in many more. Indoleacetaldehyde was identified in several seedlings and in pineapple leaves. The isolation of auxins *a* and *b*, on the other hand, could not be confirmed, in spite of numerous trials. It seemed reasonable to conclude in Volume I (290), therefore, that "indoleacetic acid is widely distributed in higher plants, perhaps more widely than auxin *a* and *b*, and it is evidently a true plant hormone." In the last few years, however, the trend of opinion has gone further.

In the first place, the continued failure to reisolate auxins *a* and *b* has made their general occurrence very improbable.

In the second place, the study of analogues has not lent support to previous conceptions of these compounds. The cyclopentenyl (*i.e.*, unsubstituted) analogue of auxin *b* lactone has been synthesized in two laboratories (45, 145). The stability of this compound in the lactone form forced Jones and associates to the conclusion that the open-chain, free-acid structure could not exist as previously formulated. This casts fundamental doubt on the structures assigned. Furthermore, comparison of the structures with those of other compounds possessing auxin activity indicates that auxins *a* and *b* would not be expected to be appreciably active (291) for the following reasons: (*1*) No compound in which the ring structure is five-membered has so far shown appreciable activity; (*2*) side chains longer than three carbon atoms are associated with only low activity; (*3*) substitution of large alkyl groups on the ring lowers activity; and (*4*) the presence of hydroxyl groups on the side chain always drastically lowers activity. Yet auxins *a* and *b* have all four of these features.

In the third place, the original basis for identifying the auxin of such classical objects as the oat coleoptile with auxin *a* has been set aside. The molecular weight of over 300, obtained by the diffusion method, has been found to fall to about 206 after a single ether extraction (332). (The calculated value for auxin a is 336, and for indoleacetic acid, 175.) The auxin of tomato shoots gave, as the mean of 24 careful determinations, a molecular weight of 202 (147), and a more recent study of the oat coleoptile auxin (236) gave values below 200 for both the acid and neutral fractions. The coleoptile auxin is destroyed by hot acid, as is indoleacetic acid (275). Because of the small discrepancy in the molecular weight, however, as well as other differences in behavior, Söding and Raadts concluded that the oat coleoptile contains, in addition to indoleacetic acid, a second auxin, chemically related, but of higher molecular weight. Terpstra (286) also found another auxin besides IAA in the coleoptile.

Although some of this evidence is circumstantial and might be set aside by new isolations, its cumulative weight appears now sufficient to justify the omission of auxins a and b from the present consideration of native plant hormones.

Indole compounds, on the other hand, have become much more important. In addition to the earlier isolations of indoleacetic acid (I), this compound has been identified by the Salkowski color reaction in oat coleoptiles (332) and by chromatographic methods in a wide variety of species. Its ethyl ester has recently been identified in apple seeds (288) and actually isolated from immature maize kernels (241). In the latter case, however, because the starting material was an ethanol extract, made by standing the corn in cold 95% alcohol, it is possible that esterification might have occurred during the extraction; Willstätter found ethyl chlorophyllide to be readily formed when leaves were similarly extracted with cold ethanol.

The wide occurrence of indoleacetaldehyde (II) appears to be well supported. First identified by Larsen (155) as a neutral material of very low activity, it was later found to be converted to a highly active acid auxin on treatment with soil or with aldehyde oxidase preparations (157). It has been found in etiolated seedlings of *Pisum* (155, 156, 157), in potato (120), in corn germ (337), and especially in pineapple leaves (99). A brei from these leaves converted tryptophane to neutral and acid auxins and also gave increased yields of auxin from tryptamine and from indolepyruvic acid. The preparation of Larsen formed an addition product with bisulfite, and that of Gordon and Nieva with dimedon as well. The bisulfite compound is, however, not specific, since indole forms a similar derivative (126). The acid auxin formed on oxidation of the aldehyde had a molecular weight close to that of indoleacetic acid (155). Both indole-3-acetaldehyde and naphthalene-1-acetaldehyde are converted to the corresponding acids by the juice of coleoptiles (158).

Next, the occurrence of indoleacetonitrile (III) has been established. This compound was isolated from cabbage in a yield of about 2 mg. per kilogram, crystallized, thoroughly characterized, and compared with a synthetic sample (124). Besides the cabbage and Brussels sprouts used in these experiments, broccoli contains a neutral auxin which is probably the nitrile (180), and chromatographic methods developed by Bennet-Clark and co-workers (17, 18) indicate its presence in potatoes, apple seeds, and rhizomes; it has been detected as well in young shoots of peach trees (*u*). A point of interest is that the nitrile is not destroyed on heating with 1 *N* acid at 100°C.—a character which has often been considered as *prima facie* evidence for the presence of auxin *a* (124).

Whether the nitrile is really a true auxin is not certain. Although it is more active on *Avena* coleoptiles than is indoleacetic acid, it is converted to indoleacetic acid in good yield during the test, and the conversion has been proved by both biological and chemical means (294, 295, 281). It is almost totally inactive on pea stems (another standard test object) (21), and on corn coleoptiles and lupine hypocotyls it has only a low activity which is not proportional to concentration (294, 295). This behavior indicates that its activity is limited in these plants by the extent of its conversion to indoleacetic acid. Since the substance is quite stable in solution, the conversion must be enzymatic. Its activity in the agar-block test with *Avena* is lower than that of indoleacetic acid—a fact which may explain the apparent increase in yield of auxin (assayed by this test) which was long ago reported to occur on heating various plant materials with alkali.

Lastly, the presence of indolepyruvic acid (IV) has been shown in corn (var. Country Gentleman) by chromatographic methods (280, 281). Its chromatographic behavior, however, is such as to suggest strongly that it is identical with active substances observed by other workers in various plant materials, including *Avena* coleoptiles themselves (286), wheat roots (177), and broad bean seedlings (17).   Söding and Raadts' conclusion (275) that *Avena* contains, besides indoleacetic acid, another auxin of molecular weight about 200 could also be considered to support the presence of indolepyruvic acid (molecular weight, 203).   Kramer and Went's value of 202 (above) agrees remarkably well.   The value of about 360 sometimes found in fresh extracts has been ascribed to the possible occurrence of a dimer (enol ester) of indolepyruvic acid (281).   The activity of indolepyruvic acid, though much lower than that of indoleacetic, appears to be exerted in all tests so far studied.   The extent to which it is due to conversion to I is not known and would be difficult to assess because conversion takes place spontaneously in solution.

The corn variety Country Gentleman is probably exceptionally rich in IV, since another variety, Silver Bantam, yielded no evidence for it (315). In a third variety, Yamaki and Nakamura (337) found indoleacetaldehyde, II.   The material was identified chromatographically and shown to be active (presumably by conversion to IAA) in the *Avena* test.   However, in view of the ease with which pyruvic acid is decarboxylated, it seems not improbable that its indole derivative, IV, may provide a source for the aldehyde, II, which seems to occur widely in plants.   Recently also, IV has been identified chromatographically in leaves of soybeans and tobacco (315a), particularly when these were grown under short-day conditions. The amounts of both I and IV seemed to be greatly reduced by long light periods.

IV. Synthetic Auxins

In recent years, the work on synthetic compounds having auxin activity has been less haphazard and more specifically directed towards the testing of theoretical ideas.   It will be recalled (ref. 290, p. 19) that the earlier work demonstrated that growth-promoting activity involves two functions: *primary activity*, or the ability to cause cell enlargement when present in the cell, and *secondary activity*, or the ability to enter, to be stable in the cell, and to be transported from one cell to another.   The requirements for primary activity were stated to be: (*1*) a ring system as nucleus, (*2*) a double bond in the ring, (*3*) a side chain containing a carboxyl (or an ester or amide readily convertible to a carboxyl) or certain other weakly acidic groups, (*4*) a distance of at least one carbon atom between this group and the ring, and (*5*) a particular spatial relationship between the acid group and the ring.   Point (*4*) must now be abandoned, and much of the newer work bears on the last point.   Some of it has already been reviewed in detail (291, 310).

A. The Relation between Structure and Activity

The effect of geometrical isomerism in the side chain is very clear. The activity of *cis*-cinnamic acid (V) and its derivatives, and the inactivity of the *trans*- isomer (VII), have been paralleled by the cases of tetralidene-1-acetic acid and naphthalene-1-acrylic acid (311), in both of which the *cis*-isomer is the only one with activity (119, 308). A further confirmation of this point is given by the 2-phenylcyclopropane-1-carboxylic acids, of which one form, shown indirectly to be the *cis*- isomer (VI) is active, the other (VIII) inactive (312).

The association of activity with the *cis*- configuration was at first ascribed by Veldstra (307) to the necessity for the side chain to be as nearly as possible at right angles to the plane of the ring. More recently, this concept has been broadened to mean that the carboxyl is so situated that "on adsorption of the active molecule to a boundary (the non-polar part playing the most important role), this functional group will be situated as peripherally as possible" (310). Such an interpretation was applied to the nitrophenoxyacetic acids, in which only the *meta*-nitro form is active (308), and to the hydronaphthoic acids (313). α-Naphthoic acid, IX, which is the parent compound of these, has slight activity (which might be considered due to a spatial resemblance to phenylacetic acid) but its 1,2,3,4-tetrahydro derivative, X, is much more active. On the other hand, XI, which compares only to 2,3-dimethylbenzoic acid, is inactive. Also β-naphthoic acid and its reduced derivatives are inactive. All these effects were ascribed to the "puckering"of the reduced ring, which allows the carboxyl to leave the plane of the aromatic ring. However, introduction of a methyl group at position 8, which should much more strongly swing the COOH out of the plane of the ring (XII), did not increase the activity at all. This rather critical test opposes the theory. So does the rather high activity of acenapthene-1-carboxylic acid, whose COOH would be expected to lie in the plane of the ring (137a). Other aspects of the theory have been discussed previously (291).

IX   X   XI   XII

The most striking development in connection with all such theories of molecular orientation is the demonstration that certain substituted benzoic acids are active. The first reports of this, with 2-bromo-3-nitrobenzoic acid (338, 339), were with relatively unspecific biological tests, and could have been due to interaction with auxin in the green auxin-rich plants used. However, it is now clear that 2,5,- and 2,6,-dichloro-, and especially 2,3,6-trichlorobenzoic acids (XIII, XIV, and XV) have true auxin activity on etiolated, auxin-poor, test plants, (20, 210, 293). The corresponding aldehyde has weak activity (20), which is probably due to conversion to the acid, while several other substituted derivatives have weak activity (211). The 2,4- and 3,4-dichlorobenzoic acids (XVI and XVII) are inactive. Activity in this series can be quite high, that of 2,3,6-trichlorobenzoic acid being about twice that of indoleacetic acid in the pea test (293). The 2-chloro-, 2-bromo- and 2-nitro-benzoic acids also have distinct activity on *Avena*.

	XIII	XIV	XV	XVI	XVII	XVIII
Pisum:	—	—	200	0	0	0.2
Avena:	1.0	0.1	—	0	—	0.1[2]

[2] See page 12.

Some of the data on pea curvature (293) and *Avena* straight growth (211) are given herewith, activities being expressed as per cent of that of indole-acetic acid. The relative activity of XVIII is much higher in another test.

Much of Veldstra's earlier reasoning was based on the idea that the auxin functions in a surface membrane, where the "planarity" of the molecule would be of importance. However, this view has been largely abandoned (308). Another of his suggestions was that activity requires a certain balance between lipophilic and hydrophilic parts of the molecule (309); thus, increased activity of phenoxyacetic acid on chlorine-substitution was ascribed to increased lipophily, but the decrease in activity when more than three chlorine atoms were introduced was held to indicate a degree of lipophily above the "optimum." Since the optimum remains undefined, and is probably different for each molecular type, this view is very flexible. Recently it has been again invoked to explain the fact that compounds with two COOH groups are always inactive or nearly so. Thus 2-carboxymethoxy-naphthalene-1-acetic acid, XIX, contains the side chains of two highly active compounds, yet has very low activity (137b). Similarly the compound XX, which has one COOH added to the highly active "MCPA," is quite inactive (137b). Numerous aryloxy-succinic acids are also inactive (137d). It is true that the extra COOH would give more hydrophily, but one would expect that 2,4,5-trichlorination would redress the balance somewhat; it does not. The effect of a second acid group therefore probably has another explanation.

CH₂COOH
—OCH₂COOH
XIX

CH₂COOH
Cl—OCH₂COOH
XX

Optical isomerism, like geometrical isomerism, has a great influence on activity. The first case of this, with the (+) and (−) forms of α-(3-indole)-propionic acid (146), was ascribed to an effect of the optical activity on transport of the auxin in the plant, since the two enantiomorphs were equally active when the coleoptile sections were immersed in the test solution. However, the case of α-(dichlorophenoxy)-propionic acid is different; here the (+) form is twice as active as the racemic, which means the (−) form is virtually inactive, and this holds in the pea test, carried out in solution, where transport is not a critical factor (291). Similar considerations hold for the enantiomorphs of X and of the corresponding 1,4-dihydro compound (312, 203, 204), and of α-allyl-phenylacetic acid (312).

Clear differences exist in the optical and biological activities of several other compounds of the α-aryloxy propionic type (2, 273, 5, 321).

Recently an extensive study of this whole subject, undertaken by Fredga and collaborators in Sweden, has been reported in detail (2, 3, 197; also 84, 85). In this work, some 19 pairs of phenoxy and naphthoxy compounds have been resolved into their enantiomorphs and tested, principally against growth of flax roots. In most cases the optical activity has been sterically connected to that of glyceraldehyde. The main conclusion is that the D-forms of all the compounds are more active than the L-. The ratio of

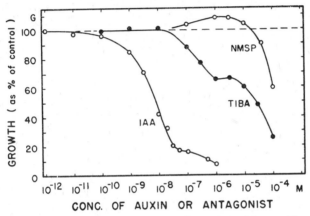

FIG. 1. Effects of three compounds on root elongation of flax seedlings. Concentrations molar and on logarithmic scale. IAA, indoleacetic acid, inhibition only (auxin action). N.M.S.P., α(1-napthylmethyl-sulfide)-propionic acid, promotion at low concentrations, inhibition at high (auxin antagonist). TIBA; 2,3,5-triiodobenzoic acid, shape of curve ascribed to synergism with auxin. From Åberg, 1953 (2).

biological activity, D:L, varies from 2 to over 1000; even when the ratio is high, however, the activity of the L-form seems not to be due to optical impurity, but to persist through very careful repeated fractionation (197). The highest activities found were for D-α-(2-methyl,4-chloro-phenoxy)-propionic acid and D-α-(2-naphthoxy)-propionic acid (XXI, p. 15). In a number of instances the L-forms acted as auxin antagonists, i.e., they restored the growth of roots which were inhibited by 2,4-D or other auxins (2, 3). These antagonists included especially the 2-naphthoxy, 2-methyl-4-chlorophenoxy, and the trichlorophenoxy compounds. In contrast, the L-forms of phenoxy and 2,4-dichlorophenoxy compounds were inactive both as auxins and as antagonists. The antagonists generally gave root growth promotion at subinhibiting concentrations (cf. Fig. 1). Introduction of an isopropyl or a n-butyl group at the asymmetric carbon atom greatly reduces auxin activity, but in many cases leaves the substances with a marked auxin-antagonistic action. All these facts point strongly toward the existence of multiple points of attachment between the auxin and its substrate (3; see below).

Substitution in the ring has, of course, a large effect on activity, and the above work adds many instances of this. Other compounds have been made and tested by many workers (see 310, 137a–f). With certain exceptions (see below), their activity confirms or extends the principles already discussed (290, 291), but one new theory has been suggested. Because 2,6-dichloro- and 2,4,6-trichloro-phenoxyacetic acids are much less active than the other di- and tri-substituted acids, Muir and Hansch (209–212) have proposed that combination takes place with the substrate at the position *ortho* to the side chain. Thus compounds with both *ortho* positions substituted would be unable to combine. The postulated auxin-substrate complexes involve formation of a ring with (*1*) the carboxyl group, (*2*) cysteine or a similar sulfur-containing residue in the presumed substrate, and (*3*) the *ortho* carbon of the ring; the suggested rings contain up to 11 atoms, which should make their formation somewhat difficult.

The evidence for this proposal has been examined critically, and it has been pointed out that actually 2,6-dichlorophenoxyacetic acid is far from inactive, having about 4% of the activity of indoleacetic acid in the pea test (293). Also 2,6-dimethylphenoxyacetic acid is active (322). Even 2,6-dimethylbenzoic acid, XVIII, has real, though weak, activity. Furthermore, when tested on slit coleoptiles by the curvature method, its relative activity is some 40 times greater than that shown for straight growth (*u*). Thus, both phenoxy and benzoic acid derivatives can be active when both groups *ortho* to the side chain are occupied. The activity of 2,6-dichlorobenzoic acid (XIV above) was ascribed to liberation of one of the Cl atoms in the reaction (115), but this explanation could hardly apply to methyl groups. Besides, it was shown that 2,4-dichlorobenzoic acid, which is inactive, liberates almost as much chlorine as the 2,6 acid. Equally difficult for this theory is the fact that 3,5-dichlorophenoxyacetic acid, which has *both ortho* positions free, and therefore should have full activity, is in fact totally inactive (293; *cf.* also 322). The low activity of the 2,6-disubstituted phenoxy acids may alternatively be due to steric blocking of the free rotation about the ring-oxygen bond. While 2,4,6-trichloro- and 2,4,6-tribromophenoxyacetic acids admittedly have extremely low activity, yet the 2,4-dichloro-6-fluoro and 2,4-dibromo-6-fluoro acids are reported highly active (321). These facts clearly point away from any absolute requirement for the unsubstituted *ortho* position as far as chemical reactivity is concerned.

The increase of activity by introduction of methyl groups into the ring is important in this connection, for it has been pointed out (293) that halogen atoms, which generally confer auxin activity, are known to organic chemists as the least effective substituents in "deactivating" the benzene ring, whereas methyl groups are the least effective in "activating" it. Thus, these two types come nearest to merely occupying a position on the ring. If the ring has to combine with some substrate it was suggested that it may do so at the 2, 4, or 6 positions, and hence occupation of any one of these would promote activity at the others. This, of course, would explain the activity of 2,4- or 2,6-di-substituted chlorophenoxy acids and the inactivity of the 3,5 acid mentioned above. It also would explain the high activity of the 2,4,5-trichloro- and the virtual inactivity of the 2,4,6-trichlorophenoxyacetic acids. In general, the only groups other than halogens which confer activity are CH_3 groups. Although Muir and Hansch (212) draw the opposite conclusion, their data show this effect very clearly; the activity of phenoxyacetic acid in their test is increased some 7 times by *ortho* methylation and 2 times by *meta* or *para* methylation, 17 times by 2,4-dimethyl substitution, and 7 times by 2,5-dimethyl substitution. *Para* methyl substitution also imparts auxin activity against roots (4). The great activity as a weed killer of 2-methyl-4-chlorophenoxyacetic acid, "MCPA," is a familiar example of the same principle. The difference between phenoxy acids and benzoic acids falls into line with this view also. In the benzoic acids 2,6 di-substitution *favors* activity, which means the 3- or 4-position is probably the one most favorable for combination with the substrate (293); in the phenoxy series 2,6 di-substitution, although it does not prevent activity, does reduce it, *i.e.*, the 2-position is favored for combination with the substrate. The distance d between the carboxyl and the presumed point of attachment would be essentially the same in each case:

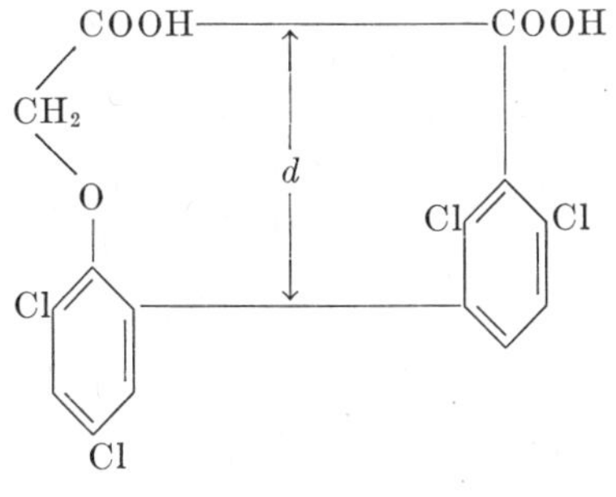

The oxygen atom in the side chain is of course not simply an inert "spacer." Its place can be taken by sulfur in some phenylthioacetic acids (291). In other compounds both —S— and —SO—, but not —SO$_2$—, could take its place without serious loss in activity (137, 138). However,

—NH—, which has properties very different from —O— or —S—, will apparently not substitute for it, since the chlorinated derivatives of γ-phenylaminocrotonic acid are quite inactive (137f), while the corresponding derivatives of γ-phenoxycrotonic acid are active (137e). In tests on roots, substitution of —O— by —S— or —NH— lowers, but does not abolish, the activity (2, 3). Many thio-acids cause callus formation (138).

The influence of side-chain length, per se, is, however, somewhat puzzling. Activity usually alternates with increasing numbers of CH_2 groups in the side chain; indoleacetic and indolebutyric acids have long been known to have much higher activity than indole-carboxylic, -propionic, or -valeric acids, etc. In the chlorinated phenoxy series the same is true, the acetic, butyric, and even caproic acids being active, the propionic and valeric inactive. Fawcett et al. (81) have related the inactivity of the unsubstituted phenoxy acids of uneven numbers of carbon atoms in the side chain to the ease with which such acids are metabolized down to phenol. The acids with even numbers of carbons (acetic, n-butyric, n-caproic, etc.) were not metabolized to phenol to any appreciable extent, and presumably were oxidized only to the acetic level, there exerting their auxin action. 1-substituted propionic acids, like XXI, in which such oxidation is blocked, are generally highly active. However, in the unchlorinated phenoxy series the order is reversed, the acetic and butyric acids being inactive, the propionic and valeric active (321). At the other end of the molecule, long chains introduced in the para or 4-position oppose auxin activity, and with increasing chain length the antiauxin activity on roots increases steadily (4). Branched chains and alkoxy groups act similarly.

It is evident that the combination of the auxin with its substrate has real "chemical" specificity and cannot be wholly explained in simple physicochemical terms of absorption on to membranes, etc. It is also evident that the explanations so far advanced for the nature of the combination are in general too simple, and that a full explanation must involve both electrical and spatial considerations.

B. Phenomena of Antagonism and Synergism

As long ago as 1942 it was shown (271) that γ-phenylbutyric acid, itself virtually inactive, could oppose the action of indoleacetic acid in the Avena curvature test. Since that time, a number of compounds having structures similar to that of the auxins have been found to promote or reduce the action of auxin. Promotion is termed synergism, and inhibition is termed antagonism. Weak auxins, in concentrations too low to show growth promotion by themselves, greatly increase curvature in the pea test (329). So do many compounds which have all but one of the structural requirements for auxin activity (329). At first it was thought that these compounds had to be applied before the auxin, to "prepare" the plant, but it seems now that synergism is as good or better when both compounds are applied together (293). 2,3,5-Triiodobenzoic acid (TIBA) is particularly potent, causing very large synergism in the pea test, smaller effects in other tests, and clear antagonism in still others (89, 297, 21). Its role in promoting flower formation in some plants was discussed in Volume I (see also Section VI,C); its production of tumors may be due to synergism (241a).

It is essential to establish that the antagonism is really competitive with auxin, for in some instances "antagonism" has been claimed, which was only nonspecific inhibition, such as is produced by enzyme inhibitors. The inhibition by 2,4-dichloroanisole has been ascribed to this latter type (12, but see 192). In the cases of 2,6-dichlorophenoxyacetic acid, which is virtually inactive on *Avena* (191), and *trans*-cinnamic acid, which is inactive in the pea test (223), the interaction between indoleacetic acid and the antagonist seems, however, to be well supported.

Antagonism is particularly clear in roots, for auxins produce only very slight growth promotion therein (sometimes none at all) and only at a narrow range of low concentrations; all higher concentrations inhibit growth. Hence an auxin antagonist is readily detected by its ability to restore growth in roots inhibited by auxin (48, 49). Such effects are exerted not only by compounds of the same general structure as auxins, but very strongly by the optical isomers of auxins discussed above. In the 2-naphthyl and phenyl derivatives the L(−) forms are active as antagonists (or antiauxins) whereas in the phenoxy series the L(−) forms are simply without any activity, positive or negative (3). In the straight growth of *Avena* sections, similar behavior appears, the (+) isomer of α-(2,4,5-trichlorophenoxy)-propionic acid, XXII, being strongly antagonized by its (−) isomer, to give only one example (321).

XXI   XXII

Phenoxyacetic acid is inactive, but the introduction of a large alkyl group in the *para* position makes for strong auxin antagonism (4). A methyl group in the same position makes the molecule an auxin, suggesting that the *para* position plays an important part in the growth reaction.

These phenomena naturally indicate that the auxin and its antagonist compete for the same locus. Skoog and co-workers in 1942 suggested that the auxin, acting as a kind of coenzyme, had to combine with both enzyme and substrate and pointed out that excess of auxin would mean that different molecules of auxin could combine separately with the enzyme and with the substrate. Hence these two materials would not be brought together, and inhibition would result at high auxin concentrations. Thimann (291) envisaged a combination similar to that between succinic dehydrogenase and a protective agent like maleic acid and pointed out that growth promotion or inhibition would then depend on the relative affinities (for the enzyme) of the auxin and its natural antagonist in the plant. Both views require combination at not less than two points on the auxin molecule (see Section X,A), but Wain (321) concluded from the importance of optical activity that three points of attachment must be involved, namely, the ring, the carboxyl, and the H atom of the side chain. Supporting this is the fact that some compounds in which the side chain does not contain a free H atom, like α,α-dimethyl toluic acid, XXIV, and α-(2-naphthoxy)-isobutyric acid, XXV (321), are inactive. Others, in which a methylene group is substituted for 2 H atoms, however, as in XXIII, have definite, though low, activity, and this makes the suggested need for a free H atom less attractive.

On the other hand, Åberg (2, 3) has laid stress on the varying effects, in different aromatic series, of the change in configuration, i.e., the fact that some enantiomorphs antagonize and some do not, etc. For these reasons, he believes that there are probably numerous points of attachment and contact between the auxin and its receptor molecules. Burström (53) in a valuable discussion, concludes that in roots antagonism must be exerted not only at the site of growth action, but also at the sites of uptake or transport; the very numerous data cannot be explained on a simpler basis.

All in all, it seems that the study of the relation between structure and activity has come to a point where some definite lead from another direction is called for. Evidence of such a type, as to the systems with which the auxin combines, will be discussed in Section X.

XXIII　　　　　　XXIV　　　　　　XXV

V. The Transport of Auxin

Two types of auxin transport have long been recognized—an apex-to-base polar transport, which is linked to metabolism, and an "upward" transport, occurring mainly in the transpiration stream. The former moves indoleacetic acid at a rate of about 1 cm. per hour, and synthetic auxins more slowly; the latter may involve rates enormously higher and essentially independent of the nature of the auxin. Any solute which penetrates to the xylem will, of course, be carried upward in the transpiration stream.

In addition to these two types, there is now evidence that nonpolar transport may occur in other ways. Much of this evidence, but not all, has been obtained with 2,4-D, whose transport by the polar system is very slight. From the observation that darkened plants were unable to transport 2,4-D (244), it was suggested that light may serve to permit this transport through the production of photosynthetic products (251). To verify this concept, the leaves of darkened plants to which 2,4-D had been applied were treated with sugar; auxin transport took place at once, even without light. A wide variety of sugars can invoke auxin transport in this way, and it is indicated that auxins are transported by a translocation system which normally carries sugars (179, 324). Indeed, the application of auxins can even bring about an increase in carbohydrate translocation (314). Borate, which accelerates the rate of sugar transport, also influences the rate of movement of 2,4-D (202).

It has been calculated that the rate of carbohydrate translocation is in the vicinity of 80 cm. per hour (314, and many earlier researches) and the nonpolar transport of auxin has been estimated to be in the same range (74). The values were arrived at by applying 2,4-D at different time intervals to each of two opposite bean leaves. Application to one leaf was made at the leaf base and application to the other leaf was made at a point 4 cm. distal to the base. If the two applications were made simultaneously, the plant would curve first away from the leaf with the basal application. If the distal application were made sufficiently earlier than the basal one, the auxin from the two applications would be transported to the stem simultaneously and no curvature would result. Such a lack of curvature was obtained when a 5-minute interval was permitted to elapse between the two applications. It is deduced that 5 minutes was the time required for 4 cm. of transport; hence the rate of transport is approximately 48 cm. per hour. Repetitions of this experiment gave results varying from 10 to 100 cm. per hour.

Several pieces of evidence show that while the movement of physiological amounts of auxin in stems is principally basipetal in its polarity, as in the *Avena* coleoptile, acropetal transport can occur. *Phaseolus* hypocotyls transport a fraction of their natural auxin acropetally, though the movement of applied auxin is polar (132). Transport through the apical "hook" may be very weak. There is also evidence of acropetal movement in the developing female flower of corn (43). Furthermore, there appear to be certain internal conditions under which a strict polarity may be modi-

fied.   With the advent of flower buds, the polar transport system in *Coleus*
stems is markedly weakened (163).   Consequently, while vegetative stem
tips show strict basipetal polarity, flowering stems do not.   In fact, the
phototropic stimulus has been shown to move upward in flowering stems,
whereas it can not move upward in vegetative stems.   Again, the strict
polarity of auxin movement in *Coleus* stems exists only in young tissue.
Stem sections taken at increasing distances from the tip show weaker and
weaker polar transport characteristics.   This weakening gradient is illustrated in Fig. 2, which shows that stem sections taken from vegetative apices

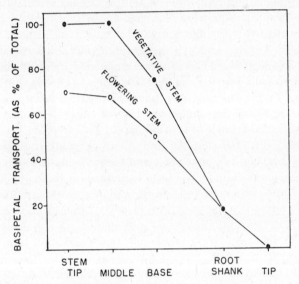

Fig. 2.   The polarity gradient in stem and root sections of *Coleus* plants.   From
Leopold and Guernsey, 1953 (163).

show only basipetal auxin transport, whereas root tip sections show only
acropetal transport.   Stem and root sections taken from intermediate positions show a declining gradient from one extreme to another.

There is also some evidence that environmental factors may modify the
polar transport of auxin.   High humidities retard the polar translocation
of the morphogenic effects of applied auxin in cuttings, and therefore presumably retard transport of the auxin itself (7).   Transpiration also exerts
an influence on lateral transport of auxins in roots (227).

There is one synthetic compound which can bring about the loss of
strict polarity of auxin transport in a manner very suggestive of the substance formed in *Coleus* flowers.   Niedergang and Skoog (215) have shown
that the application of 2,3,5 triiodobenzoic acid (TIBA) to tobacco stem

sections results in a loss of polarity such that callus tissues, which would be normally formed only at the base of the stem, are formed at random over the entire stem section. The same compound has been shown to prevent the transport of the phototropic stimulus down the plant, and to prevent the inhibition of bud growth by auxins applied higher on the stem (151). The interference of flowering with polarity in *Coleus*, discussed above, may be due to some kind of natural inhibitor, similar to TIBA, since a diffusible substance or substances from the flower buds can bring about the loss of strict polarity (163).

From studies on the diffusible auxin from the roots of lentils, Pilet (227, 228) suggested that there are actual currents of auxin transport. He conceives of a cyclic transport in the roots, with auxin first moving away from the tip, then being transported laterally some 6 to 16 mm. from the root tip, and returning to the tip by a basipetal movement. He also presents some evidence that such a cyclic flow of auxin is altered by the age of the root, by the presence of leaves on the stem, and of course by various tropistic stimuli.

The picture of the total transport of auxin thus appears to be one of transport in several directions occurring naturally and simultaneously, and by several independent systems. Whether it is correct to conceive of these as cyclic currents of auxins as visualized by Pilet is far from clear. Auxin carried upwards in stems in the transpiration stream is continually diffusing into the living tissue and being retransported downwards therein (269). This constitutes a kind of cycle, though only for auxin applied externally. Most indigenous auxin moves in a polar manner down the aerial parts, and transport toward the plant apex occurs naturally only in limited places and circumstances.

In an effort to arrive at a physiological explanation of the polar transport of auxin, a great deal of work has been carried out on bioelectric potentials in the *Avena* coleoptile. The existence of bioelectric gradients was recognized as early as 1907 by Bose, and the suggestion that such a gradient may be involved in the polar transport of auxins was made by Went in 1928, the electrical field being considered to move the auxin anion by electrophoresis. This concept is somewhat clouded by the more recent finding (259) that an electrical field imposed on a coleoptile results in an apparent movement of the auxin toward the negative charge, whereas one would expect an auxin anion to move toward the positive charge. However, the base of the coleoptile is positive to the apex, which means that the natural transport of auxin does take place toward the positive pole. Schrank has brought out strong evidence that stimuli which cause tropistic curvatures (light, gravity, and mechanical contact) bring about changes in the bioelectric gradient, which may be able to account for the lateral transport of auxins directly, causing the tropistic response. These bioelectric changes precede the redistribution of auxin (258), and in the case of stimulation by gravity, they persist for about as long a time interval as does the geotropic growth response (323). It is important to note that bioelectric changes alone will not cause curvature, a supply of auxin being essential (260). Limitations of the theory at present appear to be: (*1*) the bioelectric gradient in the coleoptile shows a peak in negative potential 5 to 8 mm. below the coleoptile tip, and no reflection of this has been found in auxin transport; and (*2*) imposing artificial electrical fields upon a coleoptile results in auxin movement opposite to that which would be predicted on the basis of simple electrophoretic movement (259).

VI. The Role of Auxin in Physiological Inhibitions

A. APICAL DOMINANCE AND THE INHIBITION OF BUDS[3]

It has been recognized for many years that auxin produced at the stem apex inhibits the growth of lateral buds—a phenomenon termed apical dominance. This is the classical case of correlative inhibition due to auxin. The concept that auxin brings about apical dominance by inhibiting bud development has been challenged in several ways in recent years.

In the first place, a number of instances have been described where growth-promoting rather than growth-inhibiting influences seem to control growth of lateral buds. In woody plants whose branches are growing with unusual vigor, lateral buds which normally would be inhibited may grow out (58, 62a). The diffusible auxin content of these branches is higher than that of controls (62a). In *Cicer arietinum*, certain laterals develop in the middle of the stem, where the diffusible auxin content should be near its peak (62, 62a). In these cases, bud development clearly parallels general growth vigor. Another type is that of seedlings of *Impatiens* and others, where the buds in the cotyledonary axils are usually inhibited by the cotyledons, or probably by auxin coming therefrom; the relationship is sometimes reversed and the bud becomes promoted by the cotyledon in whose axil it grows. In *Bidens pilosus* the cotyledon promotes its axillary bud at first, and then inhibits it (57). This may be explained by the observation that in daylight, where the cotyledons yield more auxin than in artificial light, the inhibition comes on sooner and is more complete. The inhibition is therefore probably still due to auxin, while the promotion is due to nutritive factors (59). Champagnat (60) has also shown that the inhibiting action of the cotyledons can be suppressed by the young leaves in the terminal bud, but not by the apical meristem. In general, it is the

[3] This section is based in part upon a review presented to the Section on Physiology at the International Botanical Congress (294a).

young leaves which inhibit lateral bud development, but their action appears here to be exerted on the auxin *production* from the cotyledons.

In the second place, an inhibition of a different type has come to light. In *Ginkgo biloba* the growing point does not inhibit the lateral buds from developing, but merely from elongating (105, 106). The resulting "short shoots" produce auxin for a very brief time only and exert no appreciable inhibiting influence on other buds. If the terminal bud is removed early in the season, from one to three laterals may develop into long shoots with many leaves and with greatly prolonged auxin production. Substitution of a little naphthaleneacetic acid for the terminal bud maintains the laterals in the "short-shoot" form. The transition from short to long shoots is thus clearly controlled by auxin. Yet the short and long shoots differ from one another in their auxin production; the long shoot forms auxin throughout its elongation. A characteristic of these shoots is that the auxin is not formed mainly in the young leaves, or even in the apex, but all through the stem. The leaves may contribute a precursor, but the stem, whether still elongating or having just ceased to do so, is the "auxin-forming center." This type of auxin production is probably general in woody plants.

Comparison between the auxin content of organs and their ability to inhibit buds has been made in tissue cultures of chicory (*Cichorium intybus*). Camus (55) showed that developing buds, whether arising spontaneously or grafted in from another culture, inhibited the growth of other buds in the tissue, and that the inhibition is exerted polarly in the direction shoot–root. He then determined the auxin content by extraction with ether for 6 hours. The basal end yielded more auxin than the apical end for the first few days, but by the ninth day, when the buds were beginning to develop and hence the auxin content beginning to increase, the difference became very small. The buds at the basal end, nevertheless, remained only one-half to one-third as long as those at the apical end. The auxin level was thus qualitatively correlated with bud development; nevertheless, because the rate of bud growth was not inversely proportional to the extracted auxin found, Camus concluded that auxin "plays no role" in the inhibition. Such a conclusion is too drastic, for three reasons: (*1*) although the auxin differences were admittedly small, the bud inhibition was also only partial; (*2*) there is no assurance that a 6-hour ether extraction measures the auxin available to the bud-forming tissue; and (*3*) in nearly all auxin actions, the presence of other substances in the tissue can greatly alter the effectiveness of the auxin action (Section VI,C below).

In experiments on growth, a close correlation with auxin content as determined by extraction has always been hard to establish. In addition to the older work, von Abrams recently (6) has found in dwarf and normal peas no parallelism between the growth type and either the production or inactivation of auxin. Yet one knows that auxin does control growth rapidly and precisely. The apparent deduction is, then, that the inhibition is due to auxin, as has been thoroughly established with many different plants, but that it can be enhanced or lessened by other factors.

These factors may be numerous. The influence of general growth vigor was mentioned above. Probably more important—certainly more concrete—are nutritional factors. High phosphate nutrition will partly overcome the inhibition by auxin. Added adenine specifically promotes the formation of buds in tobacco callus (272, 276), and other purines in the presence of adenine have similar effects; deoxyribose is also effective. Probably, therefore, bud differentiation depends on the synthesis of nucleic acids. In line with this conclusion, Silberger and Skoog (267) observed that concentrations of IAA too low to cause appreciable increase in growth cause a 40% to 50% increase in both ribonucleic acid (RNA) and deoxyribonucleic acid (DNA) within 7 days. There are other substances effective in promoting the growth and development of buds. Among synthetic substances, maleic hydrazide breaks apical dominance sharply (213, 14), as does triiodobenzoic acid (151). Eosin, which destroys auxin in light, causes rapid development of lateral buds in *Perilla* (183, 26). Some of these synthetic materials may well be similar in their action to natural antagonists of auxin or auxin-destroying systems. The many naturally occurring materials which lower auxin effectiveness are taken up in Section VI,C below.

Another fact which has led several workers to doubt the role of auxin is that inhibition is occasionally exerted in an "upward" or acropetal direction. To the older observations on this score may be added three new ones. Removal of lateral buds in *Coleus* stimulates elongation of the terminal bud and growth of its young leaves (133). Removal of adult leaves of lilac accelerates the development of lateral buds higher up on the stem (61). Removal of lateral buds of *Cercidiphyllum* enables the apical shoot, which would otherwise have regularly abscised, to remain on and to continue to grow (303). But in recent years the strictness of polarity of auxin transport has been shown to be subject to modification. The data in Section V show that the polarity may be modified by both internal and external factors. It follows that when an inhibition is exerted on organs situated morphologically "upward," this is not necessarily evidence that the inhibition is not mediated by auxin. Furthermore, acropetal inhibitions are in the majority of cases less marked than basipetal ones, so that only a small acropetal auxin transport would be needed.

It is still possible that auxin exerts inhibition indirectly, through being converted to an inhibitor in the basal tissue of the inhibited bud or other receptor organ. Several pieces of evidence point, though not conclusively, in this direction. Dormant potatoes and dormant ash buds, on extraction, yield a growth inhibitor, while later in the season when dormancy is over the inhibitor seems to disappear (121; see Section VI,C). Extracts from dormant maple buds inhibit carrot tissue cultures, and again the inhibition disappears with onset of the growing season (278). Chromatograms from extracts of *Vicia Faba* showed a strong inhibitor of coleoptile growth to be present in lateral inhibited buds and much less in the growing apex (139). Also in apple buds and leaves, chromatograms show that the amount of inhibitor (as measured by growth inhibition of *Avena* coleoptiles) roughly parallels the amount of auxin. Both materials are present in largest amount in the tip and are almost absent from mature leaves (114). If these data are taken at their face value, it could be deduced that many tissues form an inhibitor *from* auxin or under the influence of auxin. Further, it is possible that this substance inhibits a process leading to auxin *formation*.

B. Inhibition of Root Growth

The role of auxins in root inhibition has been discussed in Section IV, and little need be added here. The relation between inhibition by externally applied auxin and the mutual inhibitions exerted within the root has never been thoroughly explored. In the first place, a clear inhibition exerted by the main meristem and axis on the development of lateral roots has long been known. Some material has now been extracted from pea root tips which is apparently responsible for the inhibition by the tip of root growth and lateral root formation (129). The material is clearly not an auxin. In the second place, root decapitation almost always accelerates lateral root growth. Street and Roberts (283) have now shown that in tomato roots this is to some extent mutual, *i.e.*, that laterals inhibit the growth of the main axis. Red light inhibits growth of laterals (in pea roots), and, perhaps as a result, this too stimulates elongation of the main axis (304). Very low intensities of white light have a similar effect on tomato roots (282). In a comparable way, the nodules of legumes inhibit one another's development (220); the main root tip also inhibits the development of nodules. It is the meristem of the nodule, and not the bacterial tissue, which is effective. The inhibitors of nodule formation seem also to be secreted by the root into the external medium. In none of these cases does the inhibitor really behave like an auxin.

Inhibitions of root growth by different substances have very different morphological and anatomical bases. Torrey (305) finds that indoleacetic acid and enzyme poisons like iodoacetate or dinitrophenol all inhibit elongation, but the auxin accelerates at least one physiological process, and indeed one which it also accelerates in shoots, namely, the differentiation of xylem, whereas the enzyme poisons, by contrast, appear to inhibit much more generally. The action of auxin in promoting xylem differentiation is particularly marked in tissue cultures (55) and in wounded stems (132). Iodoacetate and other inhibitors are certainly not true auxin antagonists.

The geotropic responses of roots can be altered under conditions where elongation itself is not much affected. This results from treatment with some synthetic substances, such as the α- and β-naphthylphthalamic acids (199), 2,4,6-trichlorophenoxyacetic acid (46), or indoleisobutyric acid (255). In consequence, the phenomenon has been used (255) in the analysis of the geotropic reaction. It seems possible that these substances specifically affect auxin transport, just as TIBA (see above) does in stems. In any hormonal system, effects exerted on the movement or circulation of the hormone must be distinguished from those exerted on its production or action, though the distinction is not easy to make.

C. Agents Which Accentuate Auxin Action

For many years it has been known that various compounds which were not themselves auxins could increase the effectiveness of an auxin application. Sugars are of course necessary for the growth of many isolated plant parts and in their presence the effect of auxin may be greatly enhanced. Sugar phosphates cannot be substituted (299), though some organic acids are moderately effective.

Unsaturated lactones are a class of compounds with this synergistic character. Detailed studies of the effects of coumarin and protoanemonin have shown that these lactones can synergistically increase growth in the presence of auxins by some 20% to 60% (298). Some lactones, particularly coumarin and scopoletin, are known to be of common occurrence in plants, and the interesting possibility exists that this property may permit them to alter growth in the natural condition. At higher concentrations lactones act as growth inhibitors, and at least in one case their naturally occurring concentrations may be high enough to cause such an inhibition (97). The inhibition of the growth of stems and coleoptiles is reversed by BAL (2,3 dimercapto-1-propanol), suggesting that the effect of these compounds is through an attraction for sulfhydryl groups (298); such a characteristic of lactones was originally suggested by Cavallito and Haskell (56). Another effect of some unsaturated lactones relates to the enzymatic destruction of auxin. Scopoletin, for example, appears to spare auxin destruction (8). Another lactone, umbelliferone, stimulates the enzymatic oxidation of auxins (9); this, however, would result in a growth inhibition.

A synergistic compound which may be of even more general occurrence in plants is chelidonic acid. This compound has slightly less synergistic activity than coumarin, but its occurrence in large amounts in nearly two-thirds of the many plants which have been tested suggests that it may be important in influencing growth (170).

Synergism depends strongly on the growth process involved. Thus, indole was found to increase the effectiveness of a given auxin concentration when incorporated with root-inducing auxin treatments (237, 238). However, in the growth of pea stem and coleoptile sections its action was only inhibitory (u). Triiodobenzoic acid shows powerful synergism in the split pea stem test (297, 293) but only moderate synergism in the straight growth of *Avena* (5) and small synergism over a limited concentration range, or none at all, in the agar-block *Avena* test (297, 316). A number of compounds inactive or weakly active as auxins show synergism in the split pea stem test (see Section IV). These include indoleacetonitrile (221), which, as mentioned in Section III, is almost inactive in *this* test though active in other systems.

A variety of other compounds of physiological interest have been shown to promote growth in one or another test system in the presence of auxin; among these are several vitamins (256, 123), thiourea (225), giberellin (138), and some antibiotics (u). Mention must also be made of coconut milk and similar endosperm preparations; these greatly promote growth of young embryos in culture (239) and are used widely in tissue culture media. Their active constituents have not yet been identified.

Since synergistic effects are obtained with such a variety of compounds, it seems rather difficult to attempt to interpret them all as having effects on growth through the same specific system. It is entirely clear, however, that a wide variety of naturally occurring substances may be able to influence auxin effects. It follows that simple measurements of the quantity of auxins in a plant tissue do not necessarily describe its potential ability to respond to auxin.

D. Auxin Inhibitors

A great variety of compounds can inhibit the action of auxin on growth. In many cases, the identity of the inhibiting compounds has not been established, and in some cases it is not clear whether the inhibition is exerted on those growth reactions which are controlled by auxin or on some other part of metabolism. The widespread occurrence and diverse nature of these compounds is evident from the review of Evenari (80), and their importance in processes of growth and especially of dormancy is gradually becoming evident.

In ecological terms, growth inhibitors may play a limited role in the control of the distribution of plants. For example, toxic materials can be extracted from leaves of a variety of desert plants, and as the leaves accumulate under the parent plant and their toxic consituents are leached into the soil they may prevent the establishment of competing plants in the immediate area (19). One of these compounds is 3-acetyl-6-methoxy-benzaldehyde (101). Several other toxic substances which have been separated from plants may be of similar ecological significance, including juglone (73), absinthin (27), and *trans*-cinnamic acid (33).

Investigations of dormancy have revealed that in several instances the dormancy of buds and tubers can be correlated with the presence of inhibitors (120–122). These inhibitors may be assayed by their capacity to

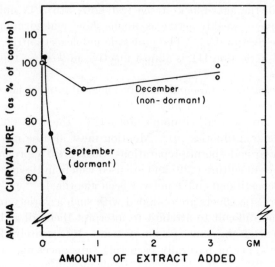

Fig. 3. Effect of extract of *Fraxinus* buds (made at two different seasons) on the curvature caused by a constant amount of IAA. From Hemberg, 1949 (121).

inhibit the auxin stimulation of growth in the *Avena* test. As dormancy is broken, the inhibitor content of the tissue falls drastically, as shown for ash buds in Figure 3. The similar inhibitors in dormant apple seeds also disappear as dormancy is broken, in this case by cold treatment (187, 188). However, because no absolute correlation was found between the breaking of dormancy and the disappearance of inhibitor, Luckwill could not conclude that the inhibitors were directly responsible for the dormant condition. Treatment of potato tubers with chemical agents which break dormancy results in a similar disappearance of inhibitor (122). Hemberg has pointed out that the effectiveness of the inhibitors may be lowered naturally by the increase in glutathione content which occurs in potatoes with the termination of dormancy. Although he did not specifically propose that these dormancy-inducing inhibitors may be sulfhydryl reagents, the fact that glutathione can protect against them suggests that they may in fact be sulfhydryl inhibitors. The possible importance of sulfhydryl compounds in dormancy is somewhat heightened by the suggestion that the mechanism of the auxin stimulation of growth may be through a direct reaction with a sulfhydryl group (see below).

An inhibitor of quite a different type is formed in *Datura* embryos (240). This material, which appears to be a nucleic acid, inhibits growth of the embryos both *in vivo* and in tissue culture. It does not appear to be the cause of the abortion of the ovules in incompatible crosses, as was at first hoped. However, its apparent multiplication or reproduction within the embryo sac makes this material of great interest.

The germination of seeds is another physiological phase which may be under the control of auxin inhibitors. The role of unsaturated lactones as germination inhibitors was discussed in Volume I, and their effects on growth in Section VI, C above. Their interaction with auxins in this function has been demonstrated by Mayer and Evenari (198), who found that the inhibition of germination could be reversed, at least in part, by compounds which protect sulfhydryl groups, such as thiourea and cysteine. Further evidence of the sulfhydryl-combining nature of germination inhibitors has been advanced by Elliott and Leopold (79), who assayed for the material by measuring inhibition of the enzyme amylase, which is very sensitive to sulfhydryl reagents. They correlated the extent of this inhibition by natural inhibitors with their effectiveness in inhibiting germination. The inhibition of germination by lactones can be reversed by light, as was first shown by Nutile (219), and indeed the germination of several types of seeds is known to require light. The effective wavelengths have been carefully determined on lettuce seeds by Borthwick *et al.* (36), who find that whereas red (*ca.* 6800 A.) erases the inhibition, allowing the seeds to germinate, far-red (*ca.* 7200 A.) reinstates it. The inhibition can be reversed and re-established an indefinite number of times by exposure to the appropriate wavelengths. Apparently, therefore, the effect of light may involve the conversion of a pigment reversibly from one form to another and back. Whether the pigment itself acts as a germination inhibitor, or whether it is only the first member of a chain of reactants, is not yet established.

VII. The Formation and Destruction of Auxin

It was shown in Section III that indoleacetic acid can be produced in plant tissue from indoleacetaldehyde, indoleacetonitrile, and indolepyruvic acid. It can probably be formed from tryptamine also. Strong, though essentially circumstantial, evidence points to tryptophane as the overall parent substance (158, 98, 295). Enzymes converting tryptophane to indoleacetic acid directly have not been much studied, but spinach leaf sections, infiltrated with tryptophane, or a preparation from the cytoplasm of the leaves, will form some auxin (333). Tryptophane applied to tissue cultures, under sterile conditions, causes formation of auxin (149a). Hot alkali treatment of various proteins will certainly produce auxin, though in small yield (257, 337). The evidence summarized in Volume I indicates that proteolysis of plant tissues yields auxin, and this doubtless derives from tryptophane, which is present in most proteins. The existence of an "auxin-protein" as an auxin precursor, for which evidence was earlier adduced, has not been confirmed, although a complex of this sort may well be involved in the functioning of auxin (see Section X). Since tryptophane may be synthesized by a condensation of indole with serine, as in *Neurospora*, the indole deriving from anthranilic acid, we can sketch at least a skeleton of the paths of biogenesis of auxin.

The disappearance of auxin from the plant is less well understood. This process is probably of critical importance in controlling growth rates, but it remains elusive. The destruction of auxin by light has been the most amenable to study. This reaction is catalyzed by various dyes, including eosin (268, 25), riboflavin (91), chlorophyll (38), and almost any fluorescent compound (82). Photodestruction with riboflavin involves disappearance of the acid group, with concomitant shift of pH (38, 40) and uptake of a mole of oxygen (91, 93). The initial product has been tentatively identified as indolealdehyde (77):

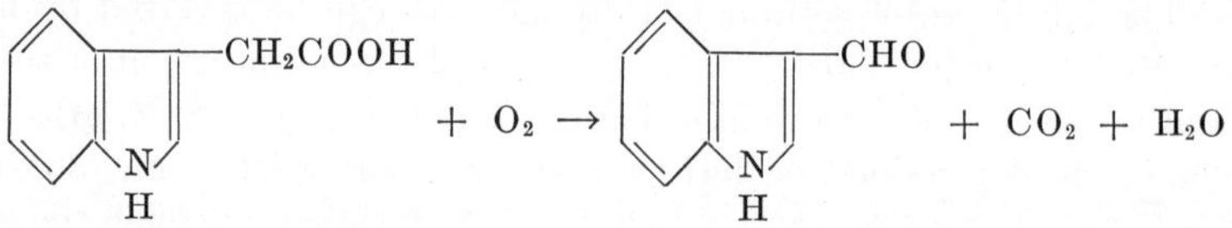

The identification rests on the R_f and color reactions in chromatographic and electrophoretic separations. It is probable that the destructive reactions do not terminate here, however. Brauner (39) has noted that the indole ring is ruptured soon after the acid group is removed. The later stages of the reaction, involving the ring, undoubtedly account for the divergent conclusions of earlier workers as to whether the ring was destroyed or not (90, 285).

Auxin is also destroyed in an enzymatic reaction, first demonstrated in *Helianthus* leaf brei in 1934 (289). The enzyme, later called "indoleacetic acid oxidase" (285), is apparently a peroxidase. Like tryptophane peroxidase (143, 144) it appears both to produce and to use peroxide. Pure peroxidase, plus H_2O_2, also destroys indoleacetic acid (96, 229). Indoleacetic acid can, of course, be chemically destroyed by H_2O_2, but for this more peroxide is required than exists in physiologically natural conditions. Catalase inhibits the enzyme reaction, and blue light reverses the inhibition (93). The enzyme is more or less specific for indoleacetic acid, though reports on this differ (318). It contains a heavy metal, probably Fe^{+++}; it is inhibited by Mn^{++} ions and the inhibition is apparently reversed by light. The reaction itself is promoted by light, but it is not excluded that this may perhaps merely be light-catalyzed oxidation of the type mentioned above, since a flavin is present. The product is certainly not indole-aldehyde, but apparently 3-methyl, 3-hydroxy-oxindole (279). Probably two reactions occur in sequence.

The enzyme is produced in numerous higher plant tissues and also by a fungus parasitic on leaves, where it is responsible for the resulting leaf-fall (263). It is well understood that leaf abscission occurs when the auxin supply from the blade ceases (see Section VII,C of 290; also ref. 264).

Finally it should be noted that several compounds can protect auxin from enzymatic oxidation. Cyanide acts, of course, by inhibiting the enzyme (285), and this makes possible the improved technique of "diffusing" auxin from cut surfaces described in Section II above (277). Scopoletin, a coumarin derivative, appears also to inhibit the enzyme (8), whereas ascorbic acid, which has been shown to increase auxin effectiveness in some circumstances, probably protects auxin by acting as a reducing agent (330, 39, 40). In artificial systems, peroxidase substrates such as proto-catechuic acid protect IAA, perhaps by acting as alternative substrates for the peroxidase enzyme (229).

It remains genuinely uncertain whether peroxidative auxin destruction actually occurs in intact cells, especially at the rapid rates characteristic of the usual experiments. Indeed, such destruction may be mainly a phenomenon of wounds and cut surfaces, and *in vivo* auxin destruction may proceed much more slowly (229). Further work is needed in this area.

VIII. Hormones and Reproduction

The physiological mechanism which controls reproduction in plants is a subject of great interest but not very complete understanding. The auxins, as *growth* hormones, strongly influence those phases of reproduction which involve growth, but their influence on the transition from vegetation to reproduction is less clear. It has been suggested in several different quarters that the growth hormones antagonize reproductive activity—a generalization which has been made improbable by the multitude of instances where auxin has been found to promote reproductive activity, especially floral initiation (see p. 31).

A. THE HUMORAL STIMULUS CONTROLLING FLOWERING

After the discovery that flowering is in many plants controlled by the length of day and night (photoperiodism), it was soon learned that the flowering stimulus originates primarily in leaves. And since the response must occur in the buds, it was deduced that flowering may be in fact controlled by a hormone (see discussion in Vol. 1, Chapter III). Attempts to extract such a hormone have never been successful, or the reported successes have not been repeatable. A substance, apparently a calcium soap, has been extracted from plants in the flowering state which is absent from the vegetative state (247). This material has been reported to have antagonistic effects on auxin and may have a slight effect in promoting the flowering of plants to which it is applied. However, it is not a "flowering hormone" in the usual sense. Nevertheless, in spite of the absence of an identifiable hormone, the flowering stimulus does move through plants, and some factors concerning its translocation have been identified.

Whatever the nature of the stimulus, there is good evidence for believing that it is the same in each of the photoperiodic classes of plants. By ingenious experiments in which plants of long-day type, short-day type, and intermediate type have been grafted together in various paired combinations, it has been shown that if one member of such a pair is induced to flower, the other can become induced by the translocation of the flowering stimulus across the graft (see ref. 154). Other evidence pointing in the same direction is found in the observations of Holdsworth and Nutman (127) that the parasitic *Orobanche* becomes reproductive only when the host plant upon which it is growing has been induced to flower. A somewhat weaker, though clear, response was obtained with the parasite *Cuscuta*, which was promoted in flowering by the flowering of its host plants (75).

In brief, then, it can be concluded that a flowering stimulus exists which is probably common to most plants and which can move about in the plant. It is quite clear too that the flowering stimulus is not identical with auxin, for it is nonpolar in movement and can not be substituted for by auxin except in the special case of pineapple.

B. Auxins and Flowering

The demonstration that auxins could induce flowering in the pineapple is the most dramatic influence of auxin on reproduction yet recorded (67). The application of small amounts of nearly any substance with auxin activity can induce flowering, whereas the application of relatively large amounts can completely prevent flowering (67, 222). An interesting complication has been observed in that indoleacetic acid is almost without effect in this regard, which has led to the suggestion that the application of synthetic auxins induces flowering by lowering the effective auxin level in the plant (31). A more probable explanation is that pineapple leaves are rich in enzymes which bring about the destruction of indoleacetic acid (99), resulting in the lack of effectiveness of that auxin. It seems quite likely that the ability of auxin to induce flowering in the pineapple may be through removing some secondary limitation to flowering when the primary flowering stimulus is already present. The arguments for such a point of view have been summarized elsewhere (160).

The effects of auxin in *modifying* flowering of plants generally follow an optimum curve, similar to that which describes the effects of auxin on growth and other physiological functions. Low concentrations of auxin can promote flowering in many plants (171, 66, 163, 182), whereas higher concentrations inhibit flowering. The promotive effects on reproduction begin at concentrations of auxin which are too low to bring about detectable vegetative responses (118). The promotion effect is generally not large, and auxin treatment cannot substitute for the requirement for a particular photoperiod or temperature cycle, although it can slightly modify the threshold photoperiodic treatment required for flowering (182). The inhibiting effect, however, can be virtually complete, and a number of instances of the auxin inhibition of flowering have been described in the last few years (33a, 171, 78, 262). The inhibiting effect on flowering is most pronounced in short-day species, but these species too can show promotion of flowering by auxin under special environmental conditions (163). This may be still another instance in which cofactors are involved in determining the net effect of a given auxin concentration in plants.

The modification of flowering by auxin is brought out also by the action of auxin antagonists. These compounds cannot in general *produce* flowering, although a small effect has been reported just at the threshold of photoinduction (29). The effect of the antiauxin was erased if auxin was added simultaneously. However, the antiauxins used included 2,4-dichloroanisole and 2,3,5-triiodobenzoic acid; the former of these is not necessarily a true auxin antagonist (12), while the latter sometimes exerts synergistic effects with auxins; this may account for the fact that other experiments attempting to use such compounds to increase flowering have not always been successful (117). Nevertheless, promotions of flowering have been recorded in various plants for triiodobenzoic acid (89, 171, 317).

Auxin has also been invoked to explain the need of a dark period for flowering (181). There are several instances in the older literature indicating that the auxin diffusing from leaves and stems decreases in the dark. Growth experiments on the effects of red and far-red light led to the proposal that the function of the dark period in photoperiodism is to permit the lowering of the active auxin content to a level at which the flowering stimulus can be formed. On this basis, light would counteract the effect of the dark period by causing the re-formation of auxin from some bound form or auxin complex. Although such a theory is certainly interesting, it is difficult to adapt it to the findings that: (*1*) auxins sometimes promote flowering, (2) auxins may increase in leaves during the night (328), and (*3*) some plants, especially of the rosette type, actually show greatly accelerated growth during flowering.

The fact that auxin cannot imitate the control of flowering exerted by photoperiodism, nor yet that exerted by vernalization (see below), strongly suggests that auxin plays some secondary role in flower initiation. The variable effects of auxin applications—sometimes promoting and sometimes inhibiting—bear out this relegation of auxins to a secondary role. They are able to modify flowering or sometimes even prevent it, but they do not seem to constitute the primary control of flower initiation.

Besides modifying flowering in a quantitative way, auxins can also exert an influence, though apparently only a small one, on the sexuality of flowers. The application of lanolin pastes of auxin to gherkin plants has been found to increase the proportion of female to male flowers (153). Similar results have been obtained with acorn squash (218), though only at one node. A much more far-reaching control of sexuality is exerted by cool nights or long photoperiods.

Quite another effect of auxins on flowering is the inhibition of development of flower buds (102), which is simply another case of bud inhibition. Some attempts have been made to utilize this property horticulturally by applying auxins to retard blooming of fruit trees.

C. Auxins and Vernalization

In those cases where temperature rather than light controls flower initiation, it is interesting to find that auxins also play a role. In the study of flower initiation by cold, or vernalization, extensive researches, principally by Gregory and Purvis, have been directed towards understanding why some plants require a cold period in order to flower. These workers have established that the influence of low temperatures is perceived mainly by the embryo of the grains (104). The cold reaction can be reversed by several environmental manipulations, including exposure to nitrogen gas or to high temperatures (103, 235). In order to vernalize excised embryos on agar, sugar or other organic nutrient must be supplied (232). In addition, the endosperm has a pronounced effect in facilitating the response of seeds to cold, and this effect cannot be replaced entirely by sugars (233). The endosperm is known to be a rich source of auxin to the seedling, and it seems possible at least that when it is present during vernalization, it might serve to supply auxin to the tissue. However, auxin alone will not cause vernalization, as has been shown in many earlier experiments on seed treatment (see Vol. I, Chapter III, Section VIII,C). After a period of eclipse, this subject was reopened in 1952 by the finding that the treatment of seeds with auxin before chilling could considerably increase the vernalization effect (234, 160). Some species of plants whose flowering is not promoted by vernalization became susceptible to vernalization after auxin treatment (163, 164). These include peas, teosinte, soybeans, and corn. Experiments with excised embryos of winter rye indicated that an improved vernalization effect could be brought about by pretreatment of the seed with auxin whether the endosperm was present or not. Analysis of the factors influencing the auxin response (166) has led to the suggestion that auxin may be specifically required for some metabolic reactions which go on at low temperature. After the auxin low-temperature step, there appears to be a requirement for CO_2, as indicated by the finding that very rapid devernalization can be brought about by exposing the seeds to CO_2-free air.

D. HORMONES IN FRUIT-SET AND FRUIT DEVELOPMENT

After flowers have been formed on a plant, an entirely different requirement for auxin sets in, namely, for setting of the fruit. This subject has been reviewed recently (218) and may be treated relatively briefly here.

At fertilization, auxin is carried to the ovule by the pollen. However, the supply of auxin from the pollen is considerably less than the amounts found in the ovary of tobacco flowers after pollination (207, 208). It appears, therefore, that the pollination causes a large increase in the enzymatic production of auxin by the ovary itself. This spurt of auxin production shortly after fertilization is probably the key factor in the commencement of fruit growth. If this is correct, then the phenomenon of fruit-set is in fact the release of an enzymatic system for the production of auxin.

Some biochemical studies of the responses of flower ovaries to pollination and to auxins indicate that several enzymatic changes are brought about by these agents. Large increases in the activity of catalase and in salt and water uptake have been observed upon pollination of orchid embryos (130). In several other types of ovaries either auxin or pollen brings about marked increases in the activity of phosphorylase and some dehydrogenases, and the apparent mobilization of considerable amounts of carbohydrates (287, 195). Starch is also synthesized (193, 130). These changes in enzymes and in carbohydrates are 1 or 2 days slower in appearance following pollination than they are following auxin treatment. The slower response is probably due to the time required for the release of the auxin-forming apparatus in the ovary, a process which requires from 48 to 60 hours (207).

For either auxins or pollen to be effective in bringing about fruit-set, there appears to be a strong requirement for the presence of mature leaves on the plant (169). By culturing excised flowers, the nature of this dependence has been studied, and a wide variety of materials has been found to substitute for leaves.   It is probable that the function of mature leaves is simply to supply substrates necessary for any of several metabolic pathways.   Ovary growth is promoted especially by malate, which is perhaps decarboxylated in the process (162).

The sources of auxin to the enlarging fruit have been studied by Nitsch (217) and Luckwill (187–189).   It appears that, at least in some fruits, the auxin source changes with the stage of development.   Upon fertilization, the initial auxin supply is apparently derived from the ovary itself, but as the endosperm enlarges, the auxin source shifts to that structure. By the time the endosperm has developed to the stage where it is clearly segmented, the embryo has developed sufficiently to take over the auxin-producing function.   The embryo then serves as the auxin source for the final stages of fruit growth, and when this supply ceases the fruit is abscised from the tree (189).   In the strawberry, the "seeds" or achenes are on the outside of the fruit and therefore readily accessible for experimentation (216–218).   If they are removed, the "fruit," or receptacle, at once stops growth; application of auxin reinstates it, causing the formation of a sort of parthenocarpic fruit.   The application of auxin cannot take the place of pollination in the strawberry but can take the place only of the young achenes on the enlarging fruit.   Fig. 4 presents the stages in the apple.

Auxins have particularly strong effects upon the young developing embryos in fruits.   The promotive and inhibitory effects of indole acetic acid upon the various parts of *Datura* embryos have been compared, and the

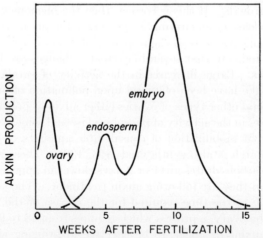

FIG. 4.   The production of auxin during the development of the apple fruit.   The curves for endosperm and embryo are averages of several experiments.   The relative values for the ovary in relation to the other two are highly uncertain.   Plotted from data of Luckwill, 1953 (189).

development of roots and cotyledons found to be particularly sensitive to high auxin levels (245). If the auxin supply is sufficiently high, the embryos may completely abort, and as a consequence fruit growth may be terminated (284). This abortion of young fruits by auxin is one of the bases for the agricultural use of auxins in thinning young apple fruits.

IX. Auxins and Pathological Growth

The various types of tumors induced in plants by bacteria and viruses show considerable similarity to the swellings induced by auxins. The suggestion that the pathogens act by causing an overproduction of auxin was therefore a natural one and some of the evidence for this idea was discussed in Volume I of *The Hormones*. There are several reasons for suspecting, however, that whereas auxin plays a part in the growth of tumors, it is not the initial causative agent. For one thing, swellings induced by excess auxin are usually accompanied by the formation of roots, whereas tumors very seldom differentiate any root primordia. More important is the fact that bacterially induced tumors of crown gall can give rise on transplantation, or even by heat treatment, to secondary tumors which are bacteria-free. This has led to the concept of a special tumor-inducing principle, T.I.P. Since tumors can be transmitted only through grafts, the principle must be nondiffusible and able to move only through living tissue (252, 253). Clearly this concept has much in common with that of the Rous Sarcoma virus and other virus-induced transplantable tumors of animals. The properties of T.I.P are discussed by Braun (in 44).

Avirulent strains of crown-gall bacteria have been made virulent by being cultured in a synthetic medium containing deoxyribonucleic acid (DNA) purified from the cells of a virulent strain (140). Klein has also found that within a short time after inoculation with crown gall the DNA content of host tissue increases rapidly (141). Crown gall which has been mildly heat-treated so as to lose all or most of its tumor-inducing potency has a much smaller effect on the DNA level (142). The significance of these observations, however, is weakened by the finding (267; see Section VI) that auxin alone can cause a marked increase in DNA content of stem tissue.

However, the facts are consistent with an interpretation that the crown-gall organism, *Pseudomonas* (or *Agrobacterium*) *tumefaciens*, carries a virus-like or DNA-like agent, perhaps similar to the *Pneumococcus* transforming substance; that this agent, in presence of sufficient auxin to stimulate at least initial growth of the tissues, can multiply therein; and that in so doing it affects the auxin relations of the plant in such a way as to cause continued further growth (see Kehr and Smith, and Klein, in ref. 44).

Similar to the bacteria-free secondary crown galls are the spontaneous tumors which arise in tissue cultures. These are distinguished from the original cultures by their ability to grow on the same medium but without added auxin (95, 206). They can be transplanted to healthy host tissue where they form smaller and slower growing tumors than crown gall; also they can be propagated indefinitely in tissue culture. Apparently these tumors represent mutations, perhaps in several steps, towards auxin-independence.

Whatever the initial tumor-inducing agent, the various tumor types will all characteristically grow in culture without added auxin. It follows, then, that their common character is the ability to produce auxin spontaneously (95) or else perhaps to destroy it less rapidly than normal tissue (24, 125). Ether extraction of such auxin-independent tissues does in fact show that their auxin content is higher than in normal tissue (148, 149). Attempts to find significant differences in enzymes which might be concerned with auxin metabolism were unsuccessful, however (125), perhaps because the tissues used had been lyophilized. In "model" auxin-destroying systems, using horseradish peroxidase, both gall and normal tissues were found to contain materials which protected indoleacetic acid from destruction (229). Paradoxically, though, it was the normal that contained the more protective agent, and this actually is the only real metabolic difference yet found between the two types. The possibility arises that perhaps these very "protective" agents, which appear to be phenolic in nature, may have growth-inhibiting properties, which account for the reduced growth of normal tissue (229).

In line with the concept that the *in vivo* growth of tumors is strictly a function of their effective auxin content is the observation that factors which destroy or reduce the auxin content of healthy tissues have generally been found to limit the growth of tumorous tissues. This is apparently not a prevention of the *inception* of tumorous activity, but rather an inhibition of the growth phase. The irradiation of tumors with X-rays greatly reduces their growth (319), and the effects of these radiations on auxin destruction are well known. Maleic hydrazide, which acts as an antiauxin in several ways (168, 8), has been found similarly to reduce tumor growth (320, 150). In addition a number of antivitamins, especially folic acid antagonists, inhibit tumor growth at quite low concentrations (254).

The action of auxin in tumorous growth appears not to be a simple one, for some types of galls are dependent for their growth upon yeast extract (252) or upon various amino acids (135). It is curious that the ammonium ion was also somewhat effective in the presence of an auxin. There is some evidence that the nitrogenous materials which facilitate the action of auxin in cabbage tumor growth may be synergistic with auxin (134).

The invasion of plants by pathogenic organisms appears to be strongly affected, though in different directions, by auxins and related compounds. On the one hand, nonpathogenic strains of crown-gall bacteria can be rendered gall-forming by simultaneous application of an auxin (302).   On the other hand, it has been reported that auxin treatments may actually reduce the severity of infection by potato virus (178), tobacco mosaic virus (152), and bean brown spot (71).   The ability of a substance to control virus does not seem to be dependent upon its auxin activity as we know it in growth reactions, since good control of the bean virus has been reported with antiauxins such as 2,4,6-trichlorophenoxyacetic acid (72).   The significance of these observations, as well as their potential value in agriculture, remains to be evaluated.

X. Mode of Action of Auxin

Our concept of the means by which auxin acts to cause growth developed considerably in the last few years.   Some of the advances in this field have sprung from the studies of molecular structure in relation to auxin activity, and some from studies on the metabolism which takes place during growth.

A. The Combination of Auxin with Its Substrate

It was first suggested by Skoog *et al.* (271) that auxin may function by serving to link an enzyme to its substrate, thus making possible some biochemical reaction essential for growth.   The molecule would essentially be one which can combine simultaneously with two different substances. This theory has received new support recently from kinetic studies, which have been interpreted as showing that auxin does react at the molecular level in two positions.

A study of the rate of growth of coleoptile sections in the first few hours, as distinguished from their total growth, led McRae and Bonner (191, 192) to the conclusion that the combination of auxin with its receptor in the coleoptile can be competitively inhibited by structurally related compounds (*cf.* Section IV,B).   Evidence was adduced that these compounds inhibit the reaction by combining at either of two positions on the molecule.   In agreement with the concept of Skoog and co-workers it was assumed that when auxin molecules are in excess they inhibit the growth reaction by interference with one another.   Thus if two separate auxin molecules, instead of one, combine at the two points of attachment, then the enzyme and substrate are held apart instead of being linked together, and growth inhibition will result.   Analysis of the growth performance of inhibitory levels of auxins (83) indicates that the inhibition obtained was precisely what would have been predicted from known enzyme kinetics, assuming two points of attachment.   These workers were able to estimate numerically the affinity of several different auxins for the positions of attachment.   It is interesting to note that indoleacetic acid was found to have the greatest estimated affinity for the receptor complex and also the greatest auxin activity of all the compounds tested (the nitrile not being included).

These kinetic analyses have been interpreted in terms of the view (*cf.* ref. 271) that auxins must have at least two characteristics for activity: (*1*) the proper configuration for attachment to the receptor materials, and (*2*) the reactivity to carry through the growth reaction. Any compound which will satisfy only one of these requirements will be an antiauxin. Consequently there could be three types of antiauxins: those which can combine only at the first position of attachment, those which can combine only at the second position, and those which can satisfactorily combine at both positions but are of such low reactivity that they fail to bring about growth. McRae and Bonner point out that if the two points of attachment are located in the ring and in the acid side chain, respectively, one would predict the existence of antiauxins with improper ring structures, such as the excessively substituted 2,4,6-trichlorophenoxyacetic acid, or anti-auxins with an insufficient side chain such as 2,4-dichloroanisole. Evidence for two such types of antiauxins was advanced, and the third type, that with low reactivity, may perhaps be fulfilled by phenylacetic acid (131) and γ-phenylbutyric acid (271).

Thus the kinetics of auxin stimulation of growth in shoots appear to be consistent with the assumption that auxin reacts at two different points of attachment. Whether two points of attachment are sufficient to explain all the observed phenomena is uncertain, and the role played by optical isomerism in the side chain (*cf.* Section IV) suggests strongly that the situation is more complex than this. The further fact that 2,4-dichloro-anisole does not show true antiauxin activity in some tests is disturbing. Skatole would be predicted to be a strong antiauxin on the basis of its structure, but unpublished experiments have not found it to be so either. No doubt further work will clear up some of these discrepancies.

In roots, unfortunately, these relatively simple considerations do not seem to apply. Burström has pointed out (53) that compounds which remove the auxin inhibition of growth (*i.e.*, antiauxins) do not necessarily promote root elongation (see also references 2, 3). Further, these presumed antagonists may actually antagonize each other. He concludes that antagonism is not necessarily exerted at the growth locus (*cf.* Section IV). If true, this would make antagonism studies of little value for elucidating the mechanism of auxin action.

B. Metabolic Functions of Auxin

The fact that the stimulation of growth by auxin is commonly associated with a stimulation of respiration has been reviewed in Volume I of *The*

Hormones. The problem of the relationship between the respiratory effects and the growth effects has received considerable attention since that time.

One fact which has emerged with new clarity is that the metabolic pathways by which auxin stimulates growth are strictly aerobic. Singularly small differences in oxygen availability to pea and *Avena* sections in auxin solutions have been found to alter the growth responses (265, 296). Experimental alteration of oxygen tension, with potato discs, has provided a direct demonstration of the linear dependence of auxin function upon aerobiosis (112a). The increases of respiration caused by auxin are usually smaller than the effects on growth, though parallel to them; in *Avena* coleoptiles, indeed, they have often been reported to be zero and appear to depend on the conditions used. In phosphate buffer the optimum rise in respiration is only 14%, but the curve does parallel that for growth (336). In *Pisum* stem sections the increase approximates 20% (64), and in potato tuber slices it is of somewhat larger magnitude but is delayed for about 48 hours in its onset, just as is the effect on growth (113). In artichoke sections, however, the increase is 400% and is immediate (112); the effect on growth is equally rapid and even larger.

Another aspect which has been established firmly is the significant role of sulfhydryl materials in auxin action. That sulfhydryl inhibitors such as iodoacetate, arsenite, organic mercurials, and the unsaturated lactones profoundly inhibit auxin functions has been established for the respiratory response to auxin (112, 113), for the uptake of water in response to auxin (111, 112a), and for growth by elongation (69, 297a). It is noteworthy that each of the current theories of the molecular functioning of auxins suggests a direct role of sulfhydryl compounds. The two-point attachment theory as originally proposed by Muir *et al.* (212) suggested that a sulfhydryl may be the point of attachment for the ring or nucleus of the auxin; Leopold and Guernsey (165) observed a measurable utilization of sulfhydryl groups in the presence of auxin (see below); and Siegel and Galston (266) have reported that the attachment of auxin to a pea root protein material could be severed by the addition of Coenzyme A, a sulfhydryl compound.

Some evidence concerning a relationship between auxin action and phosphorylation has been brought forward (88, 32). It has been pointed out that compounds with ring structures common to certain auxins (phenoxy series) but without the acidic side chain may often be uncoupling agents between oxidative metabolism and phosphorylation reactions (88). Both types of materials can elicit respiratory increases, auxins with an associated growth stimulation, and the uncoupling agents such as dinitrophenol with a growth inhibition. It has been suggested, as also by Bonner earlier (28), that both types of compounds may stimulate respiration by making phosphorus acceptors available—auxins doing so by catalyzing the utilization of high-energy phosphates in growth, and dinitrophenol by stripping off the high-energy phosphates in some less constructive manner. It would follow that the respiratory responses to auxin would be a consequence of the growth stimulation, rather than the first stage in its realization. There is a growing body of evidence suggesting that respiration rate may frequently be controlled by the abundance of phosphate acceptors—a suggestion originally attributed to Maskell (248) (see also refs. 28, 226, 201). If auxin serves to increase the rate of turnover of high-energy phosphate bonds, there will result an increase in available phosphate acceptors, and hence a secondary increase in respiration. The observation that alkaline pH causes an increase of respiration in *Avena* coleoptiles, but not of growth (336), would be worth study in this connection.

This concept of the indirect nature of auxin effects on respiration would require that tissues which are unable to increase in growth in response to auxin because of age, differentiation phenomena, or osmotic barriers would likewise not be stimulated in respiration. While this, indeed, is often true, unfortunately it is not always so. Pea stem sections which have ceased growing continue to show an undiminished respiration increase (63, 64). Similarly, growth increases of pea roots in response to auxin were not synchronized with respiratory increases, but the growth response was essentially terminated before the respiratory increase had reached its peak (11). It is to be noted, however, that dinitrophenol is more effective in stimulating respiration of older tissues than of growing ones (15), and that Bonner *et al.* (32) have indicated that osmotic barriers which prevent water uptake also prevent respiratory stimulations by auxin. However, these experiments have been criticized (51), and the evidence is thus somewhat conflicting at present.

If the ring or nucleus of the auxin molecule is directly related to high-energy phosphate utilization, then the possibility arises that the material with which the auxin nucleus reacts might be a phosphorylase or a phosphate bond itself. Both possibilities have been suggested earlier (331, 243) but it is only very recently that two pieces of evidence have emerged concerning the possible nature of such receptor material. The first is the observation that auxin can be enzymatically bound to some protein material from pea roots (266). This binding is facilitated by the presence of high-energy phosphate bonds. It is stated that the Salkowski reaction still gives a color with bound indoleacetic acid, which suggests that the strong acid of this reagent liberates the auxin. However, the auxin-protein complex is claimed to be stable to both acid and alkali.

The second finding is that in the presence of auxin there is an enzymatic disappearance of the free sulfhydryl of coenzyme A (165). An enzyme preparation from tomato ovaries was used.   This reaction also utilizes high-energy phosphate bonds, and it has been suggested that a thiol ester may be formed between auxin and coenzyme A.   Such an ester would be expected to be a high-energy bond in the same manner as are the esters of coenzyme A with the common organic acids.   It has been found that the relative activity of the enzyme which causes the utilization of coenzyme A is approximately correlated with growth rate of the plant part (167).   There is also a good correlation between the growth-promoting activity of the auxin used and its apparent reactivity with coenzyme A.   The presence of an excessive amount of auxin was found to inhibit the reaction with coenzyme A, and such an inhibition was more pronounced in the presence of enzymes from dicotyledonous plants than in the presence of enzymes from grasses.   The suggestion is made that the differential sensitivity of mono-cotyledons and dicotyledons to toxic concentrations of auxin may find its basis in this reaction of auxin with coenzyme A.

A large number of enzymes have been tested for possible stimulation by auxins *in vitro* but without success.   Only inhibitions are generally reported (see ref. 31).   However, analyses of the activities of various enzymes following auxin treatment *in vivo* have been generally more rewarding.   The number of enzymes which have been found to increase in activity following the application of auxin to tissues is so large that it would seem hasty to interpret any of them as being responsible for the action of auxin on respiration.   A compilation of some reported increases is presented in Table I.   To this should be added the effects reported in animal tissues (23a, 337a); indole-acetic acid is stated to increase the respiration of rat liver and kidney slices by 30–40 %, while higher concentrations lowered both respiration and anaerobic glycolysis.   Tissues of animals fed IAA (100 mg. per kg.) showed increased levels of glycogen and cocarboxylase.

The increase in ascorbic acid oxidase activity following auxin application to tobacco stem pith tissue (214) is a particularly interesting one.   Not only are the reported increases very large, and roughly parallel to the increases in growth, but the increases appear to precede the growth response. In the opposite direction, however, is the action of auxin in preventing the (oxidative) decrease of ascorbic acid in pea stems and coleoptiles (194a). Parallelisms between growth inhibition by several enzyme poisons and some specific metabolic reactions were found by Christiansen and Thimann (63–65).   The utilization of ether-soluble neutral material (fats) and the formation of asparagine both showed excellent parallelism with growth when inhibitors were used, although these reactions were only slightly promoted by auxin when growth was promoted.   With radioactive substrates, however, though only in short-term experiments, no particular metabolic pathway was found to be stimulated by auxin (35).   Instead,

TABLE I

ENZYMES REPORTED TO BE STIMULATED IN ACTIVITY *in Vivo* BY AUXIN
APPLICATIONS

(?) indicates no direct measures of enzyme activity made.

Enzyme	Species	Reference
α-Amylase	Wheat stems and leaves	335
Ascorbic acid oxidase	Barley leaves and stems	200
	Tobacco pith	214
Catalase	Bean stems and leaves	70
	Wheat stems and leaves	335
Dehydrogenases	Oat coleoptile	22
	Tomato fruit	287
Indoleacetic acid oxidase	Pea seedling	94
Pectin methylesterase	Bean stems and leaves	213a
	Tobacco pith	47
Phosphatase (?)	Bean leaves, stems and roots	185
Phosphorylase	Iris epidermis	196
	Wheat stems and leaves	335
Polypeptidase	Soybean leaves, stems, and roots	87
Proteinase	Soybean leaves, stems and roots	87

a number of processes showed slight stimulation; this did not suggest any close linkage between them and the growth process.

It must be concluded, therefore, that whereas the actual realization of growth involves a large number of processes, no one of them has yet been found to be causally related to its inception.

C. WATER UPTAKE

Since cell enlargement means irreversible increase in volume, and since some 90% of the volume of growing plant parts is contributed by water, it follows that water uptake is a major constituent of the growth process.

Burström (50a) has raised the question whether gravimetric measures of water uptake can be distinguished from the more conventional measurements of growth, or whether measures of weight and length are not simply two means to the same end. The two functions are not identical, for they are not strictly proportional. Thus, wheat roots in α-(p-chlorophenoxy)-isobutyric acid reach almost double the length of controls while gaining only 25 % in fresh weight (49). Furthermore, some compounds causing cell enlargement may stimulate growth in cell width (92), whereas others stimulate principally growth in length. Christiansen and Thimann (63) noted that increase in weight of pea stem sections is somewhat more sensitive to inhibition by iodoacetate than is increase in length. Whereas weight and length measurements are thus not interchangeable, either one can nevertheless be used as a measure of the growth process, providing the limitations of the measure are understood. It is clear that in many instances water uptake would be a much more intimate and precise measure of growth than cell length.

In measuring growth or water uptake it is important to distinguish between reversible and irreversible changes. When plasmolyzed cells are placed in water, the initial increase in volume will not represent growth; some elastic (*i.e.*, reversible) volume increase is necessarily included in all measurements of turgid tissue. Usually its influence is minimized by measuring the tissue sections both before and after treatment at full elastic turgidity, but if changes occur in the degree of elastic extension they are overlooked. Ideally all measurements should be made after rapid reduction to the state of incipient plasmolysis. This has been done on roots (50, 51) and in the early work on cell elongation, but only Brauner and Hasman (42) have applied the distinction to water uptake studies on tubers.

The first conclusion from studies of the auxin stimulation of water uptake is that it is under metabolic control. Since the first indications of this (242, *cf. The Hormones*, Vol. I) it has been shown *in extenso* that both in potato and artichoke slices the process is subject to exactly the same metabolic controls, quantitatively and qualitatively, as cell elongation in oat coleoptiles and stem sections (111, 112a). The use of a variety of inhibitors has shown the dependence of water uptake on a sulfhydryl enzyme system, a phosphorylation, the metabolism of acetate, and a heavy metal terminal oxidase. Similar deductions were made earlier for cell elongation (296, 297a, 34, 26).

Water uptake is linearly proportional to the oxygen content of the air up to about 20 % (112a). The elongation of coleoptile or stem sections (109) and the water uptake of potato slices (110) are both very largely inhibited by carbon monoxide in the dark and completely reinstated in the light. It is deduced that the terminal oxidase for growth and water uptake in all three tissues is cytochrome oxidase.

Another conclusion concerning water uptake is that its relation to respiration is an indirect one. This is shown in several ways. The decrease in respiration caused by several inhibitors is very much smaller than the decrease in water uptake (113), as was found earlier for cell elongation (*cf.* Vol. I, Chapter II, Section VII, and Section X, B above). With dinitro-phenol, respiration may be even increased while water uptake is reduced (32), and the same behavior has been noted for respiration and growth (88) and for respiration and salt uptake (249). Also, when potato slices are aged, the respiration loses its sensitivity to carbon monoxide, whereas water uptake remains sensitive (301). The differential sensitivity of res-piration and water uptake to inhibitors resembles that found in phos-phorylation with isolated enzyme preparations, where the differential effect is usually ascribed to "uncoupling" of the phosphorylation system from oxidative metabolism. In any event, the supply of energy for water uptake is clearly a number of steps away from the actual consumption of oxygen.

Changes in the cell wall were long ago detected following auxin treatment. Studies of Brauner and Hasman (41, 42) have demonstrated that the auxin-induced changes in cell walls of potato are dependent upon oxygen in a manner strikingly parallel to changes in water uptake. By attempting an experimental distinction between plastic and elastic cell wall changes, Burström (50a, 52) has recognized two stages in the growth process in cells of wheat roots. The first stage is an apparent increase in both plastic and elastic extensibility, which is interpreted as due to a softening or partial dissolution of the cell wall. As a result water is absorbed and the wall becomes stretched. In the second stage the elasticity remains constant while elongation continues; this is interpreted as due to the deposition of new wall material, presumably by intussusception. It was suggested (52) that the action of auxin in inhibiting root growth is due to its causing a shift from plasticity to elasticity of the cell wall, with no change in the total extensibility. The cell thus begins to elongate but becomes fixed in a partially elongated state when auxin is present. Pohl and Ochs (230) have suggested that auxin may have two effects on the cell wall of roots, one metabolic and one purely physical. Such behavior might help to reconcile the conflicting conclusions from the study of structure and ac-tivity (Section IV). One may also envisage the action of auxin in promot-ing elongation as due to a respiration-mediated promotion of the chemical reactions causing both dissolution and re-formation of the cell wall (*cf.* refs. 52, 295, and below). In this connection the report that pectin methyl-esterase activity is greatly increased in tobacco pith during the period of rapid enlargement in IAA (47) is interesting. The action might, of course, be only the result of the growth, but in view of the possibility that pectin may be the main continuous constituent of the wall, the site of auxin action could well be located here.

A possible alternative means by which metabolic activity could bring about water uptake would be through a direct water-accumulating process, which would cause a passive irreversible stretching of the cell wall and membrane. In this case the energy of respiration would be used in running a kind of protoplasmic force pump. Such a pumping action, involving forces other than osmotic ones, has been envisaged by several workers (see refs. 16 and 190) and evidence for and against the idea has been discussed by Thimann (292, 295). A possible role of electroosmotic, electrostatic, or van der Waals' forces in water movement has also been suggested (186). There is some evidence that mitochondria taken out of cytoplasm may carry on a metabolic secretion of water (231). This water secretion is dependent on added phosphate acceptors and is prevented by dinitrophenol in a manner strongly suggestive of the water-uptake mechanism in cells.

It is interesting to note that metabolic water secretion systems are known in animal physiology, notably for the reabsorption of water from the glomerular urine, the secretion of sweat and saliva (250), and the absorption of water from air by insects (159). However, the mechanism of these processes is not known.

The concept of active water uptake has been vigorously criticized by Levitt (175, 176), essentially on the grounds that insufficient energy is available for it. Evidence believed to show active water uptake in tuber tissues (32) has been criticized by Burström (51). Thus although active water transport systems in plants and animals have been suggested from a variety of evidence, the existence of such systems has been challenged and remains to be established.

An attractive means of analysis of the water-uptake process consists in reducing the osmotic gradient by adding an external solute, such as salts, sugars, or mannitol, in high concentration. Water uptake is then proportionately reduced (300). Mannitol is preferable to sugar, because it is not taken up appreciably by most tissues, though the osmotic value of artichoke cells is markedly raised by immersion in mannitol solutions (51). Using sucrose, Commoner et al. (68) produced some evidence that auxin can cause elongation in solutions which would otherwise cause the outflow of water from the tissue. This interesting experiment remains to be confirmed. When water uptake is prevented by mannitol, neither the conversion of fats to sugars nor the consumption of amino acids by pea stem sections is interfered with, indicating a clear separation between osmotic inhibitions and metabolic inhibitions (300).

If the cell wall is the site of the growth reaction, and water uptake simply follows the growth of the wall in a passive fashion, then one would expect that under some circumstances water uptake might be retarded temporarily without altering the final size attained. This has been shown in fact with potato discs (295). By placing the tissue in mannitol solution the uptake of water has been retarded osmotically, and when these sections were then placed in fresh auxin solution, growth proceeded very rapidly until a size was attained nearly identical with that of sections which had not experienced the mannitol.   This is certainly evidence that the changes in the cell walls were proceeding even in the mannitol solution when water uptake was retarded.   However, such an explanation must remain tentative, because pea tissues treated similarly are permanently retarded in growth by mannitol immersion (292).

Analysis of the effects of ions upon water uptake has introduced some interesting points with relation to the auxin effect.   The early suggestion (68) that growth may be a consequence of the active uptake of ions has been discussed previously.   The absence of any increase in the osmotic values of cell contents during growth and the vigorous enlargement of tuber tissues without any added ions indicate that the uptake of ions is not responsible for growth.   However, the presence of a variety of ions has been observed to increase growth or water uptake in several instances (242, 68, 300, 69a, 119a).   Potassium is particularly important, both in short-term experiments and in tissue cultures (119a).   Contrary to the popular impression, phosphate, at least in the external solution, is without effect (299).   Calcium and magnesium inhibit growth (300), while manganese (28) and cobalt promote it.   The water-uptake mechanism associated with root pressure is catalyzed by ions (190).   On the other hand, electrolytes in the ambient solution have sometimes been found to cause an osmotic loss of water by cells, greater in extent than the loss with nonelectrolytes of the same osmotic value.   This was observed by Bennet-Clark (16) and was taken as evidence that an electroosmotic mechanism might be involved in water uptake.   Somewhat similar water losses had been reported (41) with calcium and magnesium ions.   That these observations support the idea of an active water-uptake mechanism was criticized (175) on the basis that the water loss should have been immediate, and the report in question indicated that the water loss extended for 6 hours.   However, other observations have indicated that potassium ions were capable of bringing about such a water loss in a period as brief as 5 minutes (16). In roots calcium promotes growth—an effect ascribed by Burström (52) to its "helping to form the elastic component of the final wall."

One activity of the cytoplasm which may be intimately related to water uptake and which lends itself readily to measurement is the cytoplasmic streaming.   The older observation that auxin accelerates streaming (see Vol. I, Section VII) finds many homologies in the more recent observations on water uptake.   It is notable that Turner et al. (306) have very recently confirmed the cytoplasmic streaming phenomenon in almost all details. Their material, the staminal hairs of Tradescantia, was somewhat less auxin-sensitive than the Avena coleoptile epidermis, but the response to

different auxins, to pH, to sugar and malate and to inhibitors, closely re-
sembled that of *Avena*. The effect of oxygen in reducing the acceleration
by auxin was, however, found by them to be due to some kind of reversible
reaction between oxygen and IAA, and not to competition for respiratory
systems as earlier believed.

Of considerable significance to the problem of water uptake is the finding
of von Guttenberg and Beythien (107) that auxin strikingly promotes the
rate of deplasmolysis of plasmolyzed *Rhoeo* cells. Leaving out of account
the action of high concentrations, which probably damage the semiperme-
ability of the membrane (see the good discussion in ref. 42), it seems clear
that physiological auxin concentrations increase the rate of entry of water
into the protoplast. The acceleration of water uptake during deplasmolysis was attributed to an increase in water permeability. Similarly the
careful experiments of Ketellapper (139a), on the uptake of D_2O by coleoptile tissue, have been interpreted in terms of an alteration of water permeability by auxin. Tonzig and Trezzi, however, in confirming an increased
rate of deplasmolysis, and finding also a decreased rate of plasmolysis,
attribute these to changes in protoplasmic viscosity (303a). All these
experiments have established new and interesting means of following the
effects of growth substances on water uptake, but the means by which the
water entry is obtained is not yet attributable to a single characteristic of
either the cell wall or the cytoplasm.

Summarizing, we may say that, at least in some quarters, thought and
experiment have come nearly full circle to the ideas of 20 years ago, and
again the action of auxin may be found to be exerted on the cell wall or
perhaps the cell membrane. This time it is clear, however, that the auxin
action is metabolically controlled, and the rather crude physicochemical
notions of the past have been abandoned. How any auxin mechanism may
allow growth to be promoted in some tissues and inhibited in others, cell
division to be stimulated in cambium and fruits, flowering to be prevented,
and all the other varied effects of auxin to be exerted, remains to be seen.
Progress in this particular part of the field is slow, and probably some new
techniques will have to be brought to bear before it can be greatly accelerated.

With the multiplicity of actions of the so-called growth hormone in
plants, the picture has gradually emerged of this hormone system controlling or exerting a major influence on apparently all of the developmental
functions of the plant. That the influence of auxin is exerted on cell
division, on differentiation of tissues and organs, on each of the reproductive
phases (flower initiation, fruit-set, and development), on the gross form of
plants, and on the abscission or retention of the organs formed, leads to the
concept of an over-all hormonal control of plant growth and development

by the auxin system.   The concept of auxin as only a *growth* hormone is inadequate (161), and it appears to be a hormone both of growth and of development.

REFERENCES

1. Åberg, B.   *Arkiv Kemi* **3**, 549–555 (1951).
2. Åberg, B.   *Physiol. Plantarum* **6**, 277–291 (1953).
3. Åberg, B.   *Ann. Roy. Agr. Coll. Sweden* **20**, 241–295 (1953).
4. Åberg, B.   *Physiol. Plantarum* **7**, 241–252 (1954).
5. Åberg, B., and Khalil, A.   *Ann. Roy. Agr. Coll. Sweden* **20**, 81–103 (1953).
6. Abrams, G. J. von.   *Plant Physiol.* **28**, 443–456 (1953).
7. Almeida, C. R. M. de.   *Anais. inst. super. agron. Univ. téc. Lisboa* **19**, 25–34 (1952).
8. Andreae, W. A.   *Nature* **170**, 83 (1952).
9. Andreae, W. A., and Andreae, S. R.   *Can. J. Botany* **31**, 426–437 (1953).
10. Audus, L. J.   Plant Growth Substances.   Leonard Hill Ltd., London, 1953.
11. Audus, L. J., and Garrard, A.   *J. Exptl. Botany* **4**, 330–348 (1953).
12. Audus, L. J., and Shipton, M. C.   *Physiol. Plantarum* **5**, 430–455 (1952).
13. Audus, L. J., and Thresh, R.   *Physiol. Plantarum* **6**, 451–465 (1953).
14. Beach, R. G., and Leopold, A. C.   *Proc. Am. Soc. Hort. Sci.* **61**, 543–547 (1953).
15. Beevers, H.   *Am. J. Botany* **40**, 91–96 (1953).
16. Bennet-Clark, T. A.   *Discussion Faraday Soc.* **3**, 134–139 (1948).
17. Bennet-Clark, T. A., and Kefford, N. P.   *Nature* **171**, 645–647 (1953).
18. Bennet-Clark, T. A., Tambiah, M. S., and Kefford, N. P.   *Nature* **169**, 452–453 (1952).
19. Bennett, E. L., and Bonner J.   *Am. J. Botany* **40**, 29–33 (1953).
20. Bentley, J. A.   *Nature* **65**, 449 (1950).
21. Bentley, J. A., and Bickle, A. S.   *J. Exptl. Botany* **3**, 406–423 (1952).
22. Berger, J., and Avery, G. S., Jr.   *Am. J. Botany* **30**, 297–302 (1943).
23. Berger, J., Smith, P., and Avery, G. S., Jr.   *Am. J. Botany* **33**, 601–604 (1946).
23a. Bernard, B. de.   *Boll. soc. ital. biol. sper.* **27**, 803–805 (1951); **28**, 81–82 (1952); **30**, 457–459 (1954).
24. Bitancourt, A. A.   Segunda Semana de Genetica Piracicaba, Sao Paulo, Feb. 8–12 (1949).
25. Boas, F., and Merkenschlager, F.   *Ber. deut. botan. Ges.* **43**, 381–390 (1925).
26. Bocchi, A.   *Ateneo parmense* **24**, fasc. 3–4 (1953).
27. Bode, N. R.   *Planta* **30**, 567–589 (1939).
28. Bonner, J.   *Am. J. Botany* **36**, 323–332, 429–436 (1949).
29. Bonner, J.   *Botan. Gaz.* **110**, 625–627 (1949).
30. Bonner, J.   *Harvey Lectures Ser.* **48**, 1–34 (1954).
31. Bonner, J., and Bandurski, R. S.   *Ann. Rev. Plant Physiol.* **3**, 59–86 (1952).
32. Bonner, J., Bandurski, R. S., and Millerd, A.   *Physiol. Plantarum* **6**, 511–522 (1953).
33. Bonner, J., and Galston, A. W.   *Botan. Gaz.* **106**, 185–198 (1944).
33a. Bonner, J., and Thurlow, J.   *Botan. Gaz.* **110**, 613–624 (1949).
34. Bonner, W. D., Jr., and Thimann, K. V.   *Am. J. Botany* **37**, 66–75 (1950).
35. Boroughs, H., and Bonner, J.   *Arch. Biochem. and Biophys.* **46**, 279–290 (1953).
36. Borthwick, H. A., Hendricks, S. B., Parker, M. W., Toole, E. H., and Toole, V. K.   *Proc. Natl. Acad. Sci. U. S.* **38**, 662–666 (1952).

37. Bose, J. C. Comparative Electro-physiology. London, 1907.
38. Brauner, L. *Naturwissenschaften* **39**, 282–284 (1952).
39. Brauner, L. *Naturwissenschaften* **40**, 23 (1953).
40. Brauner, L., and Brauner, M. *Z. botan.* **42**, 83–124 (1954).
41. Brauner, L., and Hasman, M. *Rev. fac. sci. univ. Istanbul* **B12**, 210 (1947).
42. Brauner, L., and Hasman, M. *Protoplasma* **41**, 302–326 (1952).
43. Britten, E. J. *Am. J. Botany* **37**, 345–352 (1950).
44. Brookhaven Symposia in Biol. No. 6 (1954).
45. Brown, J. B., Henbest, H. B., and Jones, E. R. H. *J. Chem. Soc.*, pp. 3634–3638 (1950).
46. Brumfield, L. T. Paper presented at Am. Assoc. Advancement Sci. meeting, Boston, December, 1953.
47. Bryan, W. H., and Newcomb, E. H. *Physiol. Plantarum* **7**, 290–296 (1954).
48. Burström, H. *Physiol. Plantarum* **3**, 277–292 (1950).
49. Burström, H. *Physiol. Plantarum* **4**, 199–208 (1951).
50. Burström, H. *Physiol. Plantarum* **4**, 641–651 (1951).
50a. Burström, H. *Physiol. Plantarum* **6**, 262–276 (1953).
51. Burström, H. *Physiol. Plantarum* **6**, 685–691 (1953).
52. Burström, H. *Physiol. Plantarum* **7**, 548–559 (1954); *Rapp. Comm. 8th. Intern. Botan. Congr.* p. 161 (1954).
53. Burström, H. *Rapp. Comm. 8th Intern. Botan. Congr.*, pp. 167–173 (1954).
54. Burström, H. *Physiol. Plantarum* **7**, 332–342 (1954).
55. Camus, G. *Rev. cytol et biol. végétale* **11**, 1–199 (1949).
56. Cavallito, C. J., and Haskell, T. H. *J. Am. Chem. Soc.* **67**, 1991 (1945).
57. Champagnat, P. *Rev. gén. botan.* **56**, 333–352 (1949).
58. Champagnat, P. *Ann. Biol.* **26**, 763 (1950); Thèse Sc. Strasbourg (in Ms), 1952; also *Bull. assoc. phil. Alsace Lorr.* **9**, 36–38 (1950).
59. Champagnat, P. *Compt. rend. soc. biol.* **145**, 1371–1373 (1951).
60. Champagnat, P. *Compt. rend. soc. biol.* **145**, 1374–1376 (1951).
61. Champagnat, P. *Bull assoc. phil. Alsace Lorr.* **9**, 54–56 (1951).
62. Champagnat, P. *Compt. rend.* **235**, 389–391, 630–632 (1952).
62a. Champagnat, P. *Rev. cytol. et biol. végétale* **15**, 1–51 (1954).
63. Christiansen, G. S., and Thimann, K. V. *Arch. Biochem.* **26**, 230–247 (1950).
64. Christiansen, G. S., and Thimann, K. V. *Arch. Biochem.* **26**, 248–259 (1950).
65. Christiansen, G. S., and Thimann, K. V. *Arch. Biochem.* **28**, 117–129 (1950).
66. Claes, H. *Z. Naturforsch.* **7b**, 50–55 (1952).
67. Clark, H. E., and Kerns, K. R. *Science* **95**, 536–537 (1942).
68. Commoner, B., Fogel, S., and Muller, W. H. *Am. J. Botany* **30**, 23–28 (1943).
69. Commoner, B., and Thimann, K. V. *J. Gen. Physiol.* **24**, 279–296 (1941).
69a. Cooil, B. *Plant. Physiol.* **26**, 822–831 (1951).
70. Corns, W. G. *Can. J. Research* **28**, 393–405 (1950).
71. Crowdy, S. H. *Nature* **161**, 320 (1948).
72. Crowdy, S. H., and Wain, R. L. *Nature* **165**, 937–938 (1950).
73. Davis, R. F. *Am. J. Botany* **15**, 620 (1928).
74. Day, B. E. *Plant Physiol.* **27**, 143–152 (1952).
75. Denffer, D. von. *Nachr. Akad. Wiss. Göttingen* **7**, 24–26 (1947).
76. Denffer, D. von, Behrens, M., and Fischer, A. *Naturwissenschaften* **39**, 258–259 (1952).
77. Denffer, D. von, and Fischer, A. *Naturwissenschaften* **39**, 549–550 (1952).
78. Denffer, D. von, and Grunder, H. *Biol. Zentr.* **69**, 272–282 (1950).

79. Elliott, B. B., and Leopold, A. C.   *Physiol. Plantarum* **6**, 66–78 (1953).
80. Evenari, M.   *Botan. Rev.* **15**, 153–194 (1949).
81. Fawcett, C. H., Ingram, J. M. A., and Wain, R. L.   *Nature* **170**, 887 (1952).
82. Ferri, M. G.   *Arch. Biochem. and Biophys.* **31**, 127–131 (1951).
83. Foster, R. J., McRae, D. H., and Bonner, J.   *Proc. Natl. Acad. Sci. U. S.* **38**, 1014–1022 (1952).
84. Fredga, A., and Matell, M.   *Arkiv Kemi* **3**, 429–436 (1951).
85. Fredga, A., and Matell, M.   *Arkiv. Kemi* **4**, 325–330 (1952).
86. Freed, V. H.   *Science* **107**, 98–99 (1948).
87. Freiburg, S. R.   *Science* **115**, 674–675 (1952).
88. French, R. C., and Beevers, H.   *Am. J. Botany* **40**, 660–666 (1953).
89. Galston, A. W.   *Am. J. Botany* **34**, 356–360 (1947).
90. Galston, A. W.   *Science* **111**, 619–624 (1950).
91. Galston, A. W., and Baker, R. S.   *Am. J. Botany* **36**, 773–780 (1949).
92. Galston, A. W., Baker, R. S., and King, J. W.   *Physiol. Plantarum* **6**, 863–872 (1953).
93. Galston, A. W., Bonner, J., and Baker, R. S.   *Am. J. Botany* **40**, 534–538 (1953).
94. Galston, A. W., and Dalberg, L. Y.   *Am. J. Botany* **41**, 373–380 (1954).
95. Gautheret, R. J.   *Growth* **10** (Suppl. 5th Symposium Soc. Growth and Development) 21–43 (1946).
96. Goldacre, P. L., Galston, A. W., and Weintraub, R. L.   *Arch. Biochem. and Biophys.* **43**, 358–373 (1953).
97. Goodwin, R. H., and Kavanagh, F.   *Bull. Torrey Botan. Club* **76**, 255–265 (1949).
98. Gordon, S. A.   *In* W. E. Loomis, Growth and Differentiation.   The Iowa State College Press, Ames, 1953.
99. Gordon, S. A., and Nieva, F. S.   *Arch. Biochem.* **20**, 356–366 (1949).
100. Gordon, S. A., and Weber, R. P.   *Plant Physiol.* **26**, 192–195 (1951).
101. Gray, R., and Bonner, J.   *Am. J. Botany* **35**, 52–56 (1948).
102. Green, M., and Fuller, H. J.   *Science* **108**, 415–416 (1948).
103. Gregory, F. G., and Purvis, O. N.   *Nature* **140**, 547 (1937).
104. Gregory, F. G., and de Ropp, R. S.   *Nature* **142**, 481–482 (1938).
105. Gunckel, J. E., and Thimann, K. V.   *Am. J. Botany* **36**, 145–151 (1949).
106. Gunckel, J. E., Thimann, K. V., and Wetmore, R. H.   *Am. J. Botany* **36**, 309–318 (1949).
107. Guttenberg, H. von, and Beythien, A.   *Planta* **40**, 36–58 (1951).
108. Hackett, D. P.   *Plant Physiol.* **27**, 279–284 (1951).
109. Hackett, D. P., and Schneiderman, H. A.   *Arch. Biochem. and Biophys.* **47**, 190–204 (1953).
110. Hackett, D. P., Schneiderman, H. A., and Thimann, K. V.   *Arch. Biochem. and Biophys.* **47**, 205–214 (1953).
111. Hackett, D. P., and Thimann, K. V.   *Plant Physiol.* **25**, 648–652 (1950).
112. Hackett, D. P., and Thimann, K. V.   *Proc. Natl. Acad. Sci. U. S.* **38**, 770–775 (1952).
112a. Hackett, D. P., and Thimann, K. V.   *Am. J. Botany* **39**, 553–560 (1952).
113. Hackett, D. P., and Thimann, K. V.   *Am. J. Botany* **40**, 183–188 (1953).
114. Hancock, C. R., and Barlow, H. W. B.   *Ann. Rept. for 1952 East Malling Research Sta. Kent*, pp. 88–94 (1953).
115. Hansch, C., Muir, R. M., and Metzenberg, R. C.   *Plant Physiol.* **26**, 812–821 (1951).
116. Hansen, B. A. M.   *Botan. Notiser*, (Lund) pp. 230–268, 318–325 (1954).

117. Harder, R., and Oppermann, A. *Planta* **41,** 1–24 (1952).

118. Harder, R., and Senden, H. van. *Naturwissenschaften* **11,** 1–3 (1949).

119. Havinga, E., and Nivard, R. J. F. *Rec. trav. chim.* **67,** 846 (1948).

119a. Heller, R. Recherches sur la nutrition minérale des tissus végétaux. Thèse D.Sc., Paris.

120. Hemberg, T. *Acta Horti Bergiani* **14,** 134–220 (1947).

121. Hemberg, T. *Physiol. Plantarum* **2,** 37–44 (1949).

122. Hemberg, T. *Physiol. Plantarum* **3,** 17–21 (1950).

123. Hemberg, T. *Physiol. Plantarum* **6,** 17–20 (1953).

124. Henbest, H. B., Jones, E. R. H., and Smith, G. F. *J. Chem. Soc.,* pp. 3796–3801 (1953).

125. Henderson, J. H. M., and Bonner, J. *Am. J. Botany* **39,** 444–451 (1952).

126. Hesse, A. *Ber.* **32,** 2611–2620 (1899).

127. Holdsworth, M., and Nutman, P. S. *Nature* **160,** 223–4 (1947).

128. Holley, R. W., Boyle, F. P., Durfee, H. K., and Holley, A. D. *Arch. Biochem. and Biophys.* **32,** 192–199 (1951).

129. Howell, R. W. *Plant Physiol.* **29,** 100–102 (1954).

130. Hsiang, T. T. *Plant Physiol.* **26,** 708–721 (1951).

131. Ingestad, T. *Physiol. Plantarum* **6,** 796–803 (1953).

132. Jacobs, W. P. *Am. J. Botany* **39,** 301–309 (1952).

133. Jacobs, W. P., and Bullwinkel, B. *Am. J. Botany* **40,** 385–392 (1953).

134. Jagendorf, A. T. *Am. J. Botany* **39,** 546–552 (1952).

135. Jagendorf, A. T., Bonner, D., and Naylor, A. W. *Botan. Gaz.* **113,** 334–347 (1952).

136. Jerchel, D., and Muller, R. *Naturwissenschaften* **38,** 561–562 (1951).

137. Jonsson, A., Nilsson, G., and Burström, H. *Acta Chem. Scand.* **6,** 993–998 (1952).

137a. Julia, M., and Baillargé, M. *Bull soc. chim. France* **19,** 1065–1067 (1952).

137b. Julia, M., and Baillargé, M. *Bull soc. chim. France* **20,** 640–643 (1953).

137c. Julia, M., and Baillargé, M. *Bull soc. chim. France* **20,** 644–647 (1953).

137d. Julia, M., and Baillargé, M. *Bull soc. chim. France* **21,** 470–473 (1954).

137e. Julia, M., and Tchernoff, G. *Bull soc. chim. France* **20,** 479–483 (1953).

137f. Julia, M., and Tchernoff, G. *Bull soc. chim. France* **20,** 812–813 (1953).

138. Kato, J. *Mem. Coll. Sci. Univ. Kyoto* **B20,** 190–193 (1953); **B21,** 77–85 (1954).

139. Kefford, N. P. Dissertation, King's College, London, 1953.

139a. Ketellapper, H. Dissertation, Utrecht, 1952.

140. Klein, D. T., and Klein, R. M. *J. Bacteriol.* **66,** 220–228 (1953).

141. Klein, R. M. *Plant Physiol.* **27,** 335–354 (1952).

142. Klein, R. M. *Am. J. Botany* **40,** 597–599 (1953).

143. Knox, W. E., and Mehler, A. H. *J. Biol. Chem.* **187,** 419–430 (1950).

144. Knox, W. E., and Mehler, A. H. *J. Biol. Chem.* **187,** 431–438 (1950).

145. Kögl, F., and de Bruin, H. *Rec. trav. chim.* **69,** 729 (1950).

146. Kögl, F., and Verkaaik, B. *Z. physiol. Chem.* **280,** 167–176 (1944).

147. Kramer, M., and Went, F. W. *Plant Physiol.* **24,** 207–221 (1949).

148. Kulescha, Z. *Compt. rend. soc. biol.* **142,** 931–933 (1948).

149. Kulescha, Z. *Compt. rend. soc. biol.* **143,** 354–355 (1949).

149a. Kulescha, Z. Thèse sci. nat., Paris, 114 pp., 1951.

150. Kulescha, Z. *Compt. rend. soc. biol.* **236,** 958–959 (1953).

151. Kuse, G. *Mem. Coll. Sci. Univ. Kyoto* **B20,** 207–215 (1953).

152. Kutsky, R. J., and Rawlins, T. E. *J. Bacteriol.* **60,** 763–766 (1950).

153. Laibach, F., and Kribben, F. J. *Ber. deut. botan. Ges.* **63**, 119–120 (1950).
154. Lang, A. *Ann. Rev. Plant Physiol.* **3**, 265–307 (1952).
155. Larsen, P. Dissertation, Copenhagen University, 1944.
156. Larsen, P. *Nature* **159**, 842 (1947).
157. Larsen, P. *Am. J. Botany* **36**, 32–41 (1949).
158. Larsen, P. *Plant Physiol.* **26**, 697–707 (1951).
159. Lees, A. D. *Discussions Faraday Soc.* **3**, 187–193 (1948).
160. Leopold, A. C. *Proc. 6th Intern. Grassland Congr.*, pp. 683–691 (1952).
161. Leopold, A. C. *Auxins and Plant Growth.* University of California Press, Berkeley, 1955.
162. Leopold, A. C., and Guernsey, F. S. *Arch. Biochem. and Biophys.* **41**, 64–73 (1952).
163. Leopold, A. C., and Guernsey, F. S. *Am. J. Botany* **40**, 603–607 (1953).
164. Leopold, A. C., and Guernsey, F. S. *Botan. Gaz.* **115**, 147–154 (1953).
165. Leopold, A. C., and Guernsey, F. S. *Proc. Natl. Acad. Sci. U. S.* **39**, 1105–1111 (1953).
166. Leopold, A. C., and Guernsey, F. S. *Am. J. Botany* **41**, 181–185 (1954).
167. Leopold, A. C., and Guernsey, F. S. In press.
168. Leopold, A. C., and Klein, W. H. *Science* **114**, 9–10 (1951).
169. Leopold, A. C., and Scott, F. I. *Am. J. Botany* **39**, 310–317 (1952).
170. Leopold, A. C., Scott, F. I., Klein, W. H., and Ramstad, E. *Physiol. Plantarum* **5**, 85–90 (1952).
171. Leopold, A. C., and Thimann, K. V. *Am. J. Botany* **36**, 342–347 (1949).
172. Le Tourneau, D., and Krog, N. *Plant. Physiol.* **27**, 822–827 (1952).
173. Levitt, J. *Plant Physiol.* **22**, 514–525 (1947).
174. Levitt, J. *Plant Physiol.* **23**, 505–515 (1948).
175. Levitt, J. *Physiol. Plantarum* **6**, 240–252 (1953).
176. Levitt, J. *Physiol. Plantarum* **7**, 592–594 (1954)
177. Lexander, K. *Physiol. Plantarum* **6**, 406–411 (1953).
178. Limasset, P., Levieil, F., and Sechet, M. *Compt. rend.* **227**, 643–645 (1948).
179. Linder, P. J., Brown, J. W., and Mitchell, J. W. *Botan. Gaz.* **110**, 628–632 (1949).
180. Linser, H. *Planta* **39**, 377–401 (1951).
181. Liverman, J. L., and Bonner, J. *Proc. Natl. Acad. Sci. U. S.* **39**, 905–916 (1953).
182. Liverman, J. L., and Lang, A. *Abstr. Am. Inst. Biol. Sci., Madison, Wis.* (1953).
183. Lona, F., and Bocchi, A. *Soc. bot. italiana* **59**, 511–514 (1952).
184. Loomis, W. E. (*ed.*). Growth and Differentiation in Plants. The Iowa State College Press, Ames, 1953.
185. Loustalot, A. J., Morris, M. P., Garcia, J., and Pagan, C. *Science* **118**, 627–628 (1953).
186. Low, P. F., and Deming, J. M. *Soil Sci.* **75**, 187–202 (1953).
187. Luckwill, L. C. *J. Hort. Sci.* **27**, 53–67 (1952).
188. Luckwill, L. C. *Nature* **169**, 375 (1952).
189. Luckwill, L. C. *J. Hort. Sci.* **28**, 14–24, 25–40 (1953).
190. Lundegårdh, H. *Discussions Faraday Soc.* **3**, 139–146 (1948).
191. McRae, D. H., and Bonner, J. *Plant Physiol.* **27**, 834–838 (1952).
192. McRae, D. H., and Bonner, J. *Physiol. Plantarum* **6**, 485–510 (1953).
193. Marré, E. *Boll. soc. ital. biol. sper.* **25**, 334–337 (1949).
194. Marré, E. *Atti accad. ligure sci. e Lettere* **7**, 1–11 (1951).
194a. Marré, E. *Atti accad. nazl. Lincei Rend. classe sci. fis. mat. e nat.* **16**, 758–763 (1954).

195. Marré, E., and Murneek, A. E.   *Plant Physiol.* **28,** 255–266 (1953).
196. Marré, E., and Profumo, P.   *Accad. Nazl. Lincei Roma* **12,** 181–184 (1952).
197. Matell, M.   Stereochemical studies on plant growth substances.   Dissertation, Uppsala, 1953.
198. Mayer, A. M., and Evenari, M.   *Bull Research Council Israel* **1,** 125–129 (1951).
199. Mentzer, C., and Nétien, G.   *Bull. mens. soc. linnéenne Lyon* **19,** 102–104 (1950).
200. Miller, I. H., and Burris, R. H.   *Am. J. Botany* **38,** 547–549 (1951).
201. Millerd, A., Bonner, J., and Biale, J. B.   *Plant Physiol.* **28,** 521–531 (1953).
202. Mitchell, J. W., Duggar, W. M., and Gauch, H. G.   *Science* **118,** 354–355 (1953).
203. Mitsui, T.   *J. Agr. Chem. Soc. Japan* **25,** 186–194 (1951).
204. Mitsui, T.   *J. Agr. Chem. Soc. Japan* **25,** 526–527 (1952).
205. Moewus, F.   *Biol. Zentr.* **68,** 118–140 (1949).
206. Morel, G.   *Ann. épiphyt.* **24,** 1–234 (1948).
207. Muir, R. M.   *Am. J. Botany* **29,** 716–720 (1942).
208. Muir, R. M.   *In* F. Skoog, Plant Growth Substances.   University of Wisconsin Press, Madison, 1951, pp. 357–364.
209. Muir, R. M., and Hansch, C. L.   *Plant Physiol.* **25,** 389–393 (1950).
210. Muir, R. M., and Hansch, C. L.   *Plant Physiol.* **26,** 369–374 (1951).
211. Muir, R. M., and Hansch, C. L.   *Plant Physiol.* **28,** 218–232 (1953).
212. Muir, R. M., Hansch, C. L., and Gallup, A. H.   *Plant Physiol.* **24,** 359–366 (1949).
213. Naylor, A. W., and Davis, E. A.   *Botan. Gaz..* **112,** 112–126 (1950).
213a. Neely, W. B., Ball, C. D., Hamner, C. L., and Sell, H. M.   *Plant Physiol.* **25,** 525–530 (1950).
214. Newcomb, E. H.   *Proc. Soc. Exptl. Biol. Med.* **7,** 504–509 (1951).
215. Niedergang, E., and Skoog, F.   *Abstr. Am. Inst. Biol. Sci., Ithaca, N. Y.* (1952).
216. Nitsch, J. P.   *Compt. rend.* **228,** 120–122 (1949).
217. Nitsch, J. P.   *Am. J. Botany* **37,** 211–215 (1950).
218. Nitsch, J. P.   *Quart. Rev. Biol.* **27,** 33–57 (1952).
219. Nutile, G. E.   *Plant Physiol.* **20,** 433–442 (1945).
220. Nutman, P. S.   *Ann. Botany (London)* [N.S.] **16,** 79–101 (1952); *ibid.* **17,** 95–126 (1953).
221. Osborne, D. J.   *Nature* **170,** 210 (1952).
222. Overbeek, J. van.   *Science* **102,** 621 (1945).
223. Overbeek, J. van, Blondeau, R., and Horne, V.   *Am. J. Botany* **38,** 589–595 (1951).
224. Pacheco, H.   *Bull. soc. chim. biol.* **33,** 1915–1918 (1951).
225. Parry, D. W.   *Nature* **170,** 1074 (1952).
226. Pearson, J. A., and Robertson, R. N.   *Australian J. Sci.* **15,** 99–100 (1952).
227. Pilet, P. E.   *Bull soc. botan. Suisse* **61,** 410–424 (1951).
228. Pilet, P. E.   *Mem. soc. vaudoise sci. nat.* **10,** 137–244 (1951).
229. Platt, R. M.   *In* La Physiologie des Cultures de Tissus Végétaux.   Premior Colloq. International; R-J. Gautheret, Paris, 1954.
230. Pohl, R., and Ochs, G.   *Naturwissenschaften* **40,** 24–25 (1953).
231. Price, C. A., and Davies, R. E.   *Biochem. J.* **58,** 3 (1954).
232. Purvis, O. N.   *Ann. Botany (London)* [N.S.] **8,** 285–313 (1944).
233. Purvis, O. N.   *Ann. Botany (London)* [N.S.] **12,** 183–206 (1948).
234. Purvis, O. N.   *Proc. 6th Intern. Grassland Congr.,* pp. 661–666 (1952).
235. Purvis, O. N., and Gregory, F. G.   *Nature* **155,** 113 (1945).
236. Raadts, E.   *Planta* **40,** 419–430 (1952).

237. Raalte, M. H. van. *Koninkl. Ned. Akad. Wetenschap. Proc.* **C54,** 21–29 (1951).
238. Raalte, M. H. van. *Koninkl. Ned. Akad. Wetenschap. Proc.* **C54,** 117–125 (1951).
239. Rappaport, J. *Botan. Rev.* **20,** 201–225 (1954).
240. Rappaport, J., Satina, S., and Blakeslee, A. F. *Science* **111,** 276–277 (1950).
241. Redemann, C. T., Wittwer, S. H., and Sell, H. M. *Arch. Biochem. and Biophys.* **32,** 80–84 (1951).
241a. Resende, F., *Bol. soc. portug.-cienc. nat.* **4,** 157–158 (1952).
242. Reinders, D. E. *Rec. trav. botan. néerl.* **39,** 1–140 (1942).
243. Rhodes, A., and Ashworth, R. B. *Nature* **169,** 76 (1952).
244. Rice, E. L. *Botan. Gaz.* **109,** 301–314 (1948).
245. Rietsema, J., Satina, S., and Blakeslee, A. F. *Proc. Natl. Acad. Sci. U. S.* **39,** 924–933 (1953).
246. Roberts, R. H. *In* F. Skoog, Plant Growth Substances (270), pp. 347–350.
247. Roberts, R. H. *Science* **117,** 456–457 (1953).
248. Robertson, R. N., and Turner, J. F. *Australian J. Sci. Research* **B4,** 92–107 (1951).
249. Robertson, R. N., Wilkins, M. J., and Weeks, D. C. *Australian J. Sci. Research* **B4,** 248–260 (1951).
250. Robinson, J. R. *Biol. Revs.* **28,** 158–194 (1953).
251. Rohrbaugh, L. M., and Rice, E. L. *Botan. Gaz.* **111,** 85–89 (1949).
252. de Ropp, R. S. *Ann. Botany (London)* [N.S.] **11,** 439–447 (1947).
253. de Ropp, R. S. *Bull. Torrey Botan. Club* **75,** 45–50 (1948).
254. de Ropp, R. S. *In* F. Skoog, Plant Growth Substances. University of Wisconsin Press, Madison, 1951, pp. 381–390.
255. Rufelt, H. *Rapp. Comm. 8th. Intern. Botan. Congr.* Sect. 11, 130–131 (1954).
256. Scheuermann, R. *Planta* **40,** 265–300 (1952).
257. Schocken, V. *Arch. Biochem.* **23,** 198–204 (1949).
258. Schrank, A. R. *Plant Physiol.* **20,** 133 (1945).
259. Schrank, A. R. *In* F. Skoog, Plant Growth Substances. University of Wisconsin Press, Madison, 1951, pp. 123–140.
260. Schrank, A. R., and Backus, G. E. *J. Cellular Comp. Physiol.* **38,** 361–376 (1951).
261. Sen, S. P., and Leopold, A. C. *Physiol. Plantarum* **7,** 98–108 (1954).
262. Senden, H. van. *Biol. Zentr.* **70,** 537–565 (1951).
263. Sequeira, L., and Steeves, T. *Plant Physiol.* **29,** 11–16 (1954).
264. Shoji, K., Addicott, F. T., and Swett, W. A. *Plant Physiol.* **26,** 189–191 (1951).
265. Showacre, J. L., and duBuy, H. G. *Am. J. Botany* **34,** 175–181 (1947).
266. Siegel, S. M., and Galston, A. W. *Proc. Natl. Acad. Sci. U. S.* **39,** 1111–1118 (1953).
267. Silberger, J., and Skoog, F. *Science* **118,** 443–444 (1953).
268. Skoog, F. *J. Cellular Comp. Physiol.* **7,** 228–270 (1935).
269. Skoog, F. *Am. J. Botany* **25,** 361–372 (1938).
270. Skoog, F. (Ed.) Plant Growth Substances. University of Wisconsin Press, Madison, 1951.
271. Skoog, F., Schneider, C. L., and Malan, P. *Am. J. Botany* **29,** 568–576 (1942).
272. Skoog, F., and Tsui, C. *In* F. Skoog, Plant Growth Substances. University of Wisconsin Press, Madison, 1951, pp. 264–285.
273. Smith, M. S., Wain, R. L., and Wightman, F. *Ann. Appl. Biol.* **39,** 295–307 (1952).
274. Söding, H. G. Die Wuchsstofflehre. Thieme Verlag, Stuttgart, 304 pp., 1952.
275. Söding, H., and Raadts, E. *Planta* **43,** 25–36 (1953).

276. Steeves, F. A., Morel, G., and Wetmore, R. H. *Am. J. Botany* **40,** 534–538 (1953).
277. Sterling, C. *Am. J. Botany* **38,** 761–767 (1951).
278. Steward, F. C., and Caplin, S. M. *Science* **113,** 518–520 (1951).
279. Stowe, B. B., Ray, P. M., and Thimann, K. V. *Rapp. Comm. 8th Intern. Botan. Congr.* Sect. 11, 151–152 (1954); also Suppl. Vol., in press.
280. Stowe, B. B., and Thimann, K. V. *Nature* **172,** 764 (1953).
281. Stowe, B. B., and Thimann, K. V. *Arch. Biochem. and Biophys.* **51,** 499–516 (1954).
282. Street, H. E. *Physiol. Plantarum* **6,** 466–479 (1953).
283. Street, H. E., and Roberts, E. H. *Physiol. Plantarum* **5,** 498–509 (1952).
284. Swanson, C. P., LaVelle, G., and Goodgal, S. H. *Am. J. Botany* **36,** 170–175 (1949).
285. Tang, Y. W., and Bonner, J. *Arch. Biochem.* **13,** 11–25 (1947).
286. Terpstra, W. Extraction and identification of growth substance. Thesis; University of Utrecht, 1953.
287. Teubner, F. G., and Murneek, A. E. *Science* **116,** 39–41 (1952).
288. Teubner, F. G. *Science* **118,** 418 (1953).
289. Thimann, K. V. *J. Gen. Physiol.* **18,** 23–34 (1934).
290. Thimann, K. V. Chapters 2 and 3 *in* The Hormones, Vol. 1. Academic Press, New York, 1948; The Action of Hormones in Plants and Invertebrates, *ibid*, 1952.
291. Thimann, K. V. *In* F. Skoog, Plant Growth Substances. University of Wisconsin Press, Madison, 1951, pp. 21–36.
292. Thimann, K. V. *Growth* (Suppl., 10th Symposium Soc. Growth and Development) 5–22 (1951).
293. Thimann, K. V. *Plant Physiol.* **27,** 392–404 (1952).
294. Thimann, K. V. *Arch. Biochem. and Biophys.* **44,** 242–243 (1953).
294a. Thimann, K. V. *Rapp. Comm. 8th Intern. Botan. Congr., Paris*, Sect. 11, 114–128 (1954).
295. Thimann, K. V. *Am. Scientist* 589–606 (1954).
296. Thimann, K. V., and Bonner, W. D., Jr. *Am. J. Botany* **35,** 271–281 (1948a).
297. Thimann, K. V., and Bonner, W. D., Jr. *Plant Physiol.* **23,** 158–161 (1948b).
297a. Thimann, K. V., and Bonner, W. D., Jr. *Am. J. Botany* **36,** 214–221 (1949).
298. Thimann, K. V., and Bonner, W. D., Jr. *Proc. Natl. Acad. Sci. U. S.* **35,** 272–276 (1949).
299. Thimann, K. V., and Marré, E. *Am. J. Botany* **41,** 556–560 (1954).
300. Thimann, K. V., Slater, R. R., and Christiansen, G. S. *Arch. Biochem.* **28,** 130–137 (1950).
301. Thimann, K. V., Yocum, C. S., and Hackett, D. P. *Arch. Biochem. and Biophys.* **53,** 239–257 (1954).
302. Thomas, J. E., and Riker, A. J. *Phytopathology* **38,** 25 (1948).
303. Titman, L. C. (1952). Long and short shoot growth in Cercidiphyllum. Thesis, Harvard University.
303a. Tanzig, S., and Trezzi, F. *Atti accad. nazl. Lincei Rend. classe sci. fis. mat. e nat.* **16,** 603–610, 695–702 (1954).
304. Torrey, J. G. *Plant Physiol.* **27,** 591–602 (1952).
305. Torrey, J. G. *Am. J. Botany* **40,** 525–533 (1953).
306. Turner, J. S., MacRae, J., and Lipp, P. G. *Rapp. Comm. 8th Intern. Botan. Congr.*, Sect. 11, 152–155 (1954).
307. Veldstra, H. *Enzymologia* **11,** 97–136, 137–163 (1944).

308. Veldstra, H. *Proc. 2nd Intern. Congr. Crop Protection, London*, Sect. 3, 1–19 (1949a).
309. Veldstra, H. *Bull soc. chim. biol.* **31,** 1–29 (1949b).
310. Veldstra, H. *Ann. Rev. Plant Physiol.* **4,** 154–198 (1953).
311. Veldstra, H., and Booij, H. L. *Biochim. et Biophys. Acta* **3,** 278–312 (1949).
312. Veldstra, H., and Westeringh, C. van de. *Biochim. et Biophys. Acta* **7,** 1113–1126 (1951).
313. Veldstra, H., and Westeringh, C. van de. *Biochim. et Biophys. Acta* **7,** 1127–1135 (1951).
314. Vernon, L. P., and Aronoff, S. *Arch. Biochem. and Biophys.* **36,** 383–398 (1952).
315. Vlitos, A. J., and Meudt, W. *Contribs. Boyce Thompson Inst.* **17,** 197–202 (1953).
315a. Vlitos, A. J., and Meudt, W. *Contribs. Boyce Thompson Inst.* **17,** 413–417 (1954).
316. Waard, J. de, and Florschütz, P. A. *Proc. Koninkl. Ned. Akad. Wetenschap.* **51,** 1317–1321 (1948).
317. Waard, J. de, and Roodenburg, J. W. M. *Proc. Koninkl. Ned. Akad. Wetenschap.* **51,** 3–6 (1948).
318. Wagenknecht, A. C., and Burris, R. H. *Arch. Biochem.* **25,** 30–53 (1950).
319. Waggoner, P. E., and Dimond, A. E. *Am. J. Botany* **39,** 679–684 (1952).
320. Waggoner, P. E., and Dimond, A. E. *Science* **117,** 13 (1953).
321. Wain, R. L. *Roy. Inst. Chem. (London) Lecture* No. 2, 16 pp. (1953).
322. Wain, R. L., and Wightman, F. *Ann. Appl. Biol.* **40,** 244–249 (1953) and in press.
323. Webster, W. W., Jr., and Schrank, A. R. *Arch. Biochem. and Biophys.* **47,** 107–118 (1953).
324. Weintraub, R. L., and Brown, J. W. *Plant Physiol.* **25,** 140–149 (1950).
325. Weintraub, R. L., Brown, J. W., and Yeatman, J. N. *Science* **111,** 493–494 (1950).
326. Weller, L. E., Wittwer, S. H., and Sell, H. M. *J. Am. Chem. Soc.* **76,** 629–630 (1954).
327. Went, F. W. *Rec. trav. botan. néerl.* **25,** 1–116 (1928).
328. Went, F. W. *Am. J. Botany* **31,** 597–618 (1944).
329. Went, F. W. *Arch. Biochem. and Biophys.* **20,** 131–136 (1949).
330. Wetmore, R. H., and Morel, G. (Abstract) *Am. J. Botany* **36,** 830 (1949).
331. Wildman, S. G., and Bonner, J. *Arch. Biochem.* **14,** 381–413 (1947).
332. Wildman, S. G., and Bonner, J. *Am. J. Botany* **35,** 740–746 (1948).
333. Wildman, S. G., Ferri, M. G., and Bonner, J. *Arch. Biochem.* **13,** 131–144 (1947).
334. Wilske, C., and Burström, H. *Physiol. Plantarum* **3,** 58–67 (1950).
335. Wort, D. J., and Cowie, L. M. *Plant Physiol.* **28,** 135–139 (1953).
336. Yamaki, T. *Misc. Repts. Research Inst. Nat. Resources (Japan)* No. 11, 37–40 (1948).
337. Yamaki, T., and Nakamura, K. *Sci. Papers Coll. Gen. Educ. Univ. Tokyo* **2,** 81–98 (1952).
337a. Zambotti, V., and Bernard, B. de. *Boll. soc. ital. biol. sper.* **28,** 320–322, 928–929 (1952); **29,** 505–508 (1953).
338. Zimmerman, P. W., and Hitchcock, A. E. *Contribs. Boyce Thompson Inst.* **12,** 321–343 (1942).
339. Zimmerman, P. W., and Hitchcock, A. E. *Contribs. Boyce Thompson Inst.* **16,** 209–213 (1951).

CHAPTER II

Hormones in Invertebrates[1]

BY BERTA SCHARRER

CONTENTS

I. Introduction

Our knowledge of the anatomy and physiology of the organs of internal secretion in invertebrate animals, still so inadequate only 20 years ago that texts on endocrinology excluded reference to them altogether, has grown at an extraordinary rate in recent years. The great multitude of types of invertebrates, and the manifold ways in which their life processes depend on environmental influences, mediated through endocrine systems controlling reproduction, development, color change, metabolism, etc., provide challenging and novel problems of an infinite variety.

Groups of invertebrates in which some of these problems have been in-

[1] In the preparation of this review the writer was materially aided by grants from the American Cancer Society and The Anna Fuller Fund.

57

vestigated more thoroughly than in others are the insects and the crustaceans. The hormone actions in these forms have been discussed in the first volume of this treatise (66, 432; for other reviews see 67, 68, 70, 93, 135, 253, 312, 431, 434, 440, 507, 508). In the following chapter, an attempt is made to give an integrated survey of the present status of invertebrate endocrinology, including all groups in which organs of internal secretion have been investigated, *i.e.*, worms, arthropods, mollusks, and tunicates. However, complete coverage is impossible within the allotted space; such an undertaking would require a separate volume. The interested reader, therefore, should consult preceding reviews for the documentation of earlier data, in particular with respect to first discoveries of endocrine organs and their hormone actions in invertebrates.

In the following, it will become evident that the most important recent progress in invertebrate endocrinology is based on the understanding of neurosecretory organ systems (p. 82). The concept of the structural and functional analogy of these systems in invertebrates and vertebrates (reviews: 239, 255, 403, 445–449) has clarified many points which had hitherto been difficult to evaluate and has thus greatly benefited endocrinology in general.

II. Worms

In addition to the internephridial organs, and possibly the nephridia and gonads, the central nervous system plays an important role as a source of hormones in worms. Groups of neurosecretory cells are present in a variety of species (see 13, 234, 448, 449). Chromaffine cells occurring in the central nervous system of various annelids as well as in that of other invertebrates contain an adrenaline-like substance which, like the neurosecretory material, seems to pass along the axons to the periphery (see, for example, 24, 33, 34, 240).

The presence of hormones stimulating the development of sex organs in planarians is suggested by an observation in *Dugesia tigrina*, a species occurring in two physiological races, sexual and asexual. If the anterior third of a sexual animal is grafted to the posterior two-thirds of an asexual individual, testes and copulatory organs develop in the asexual part (293). A humoral ("clitellogenic") factor may also be responsible for the successive reappearance of somatic sex characters in certain *Lumbricidae* which are characterized by reversible development with intermittent stages of diapause (353). Whether or not this factor originates in the gonads seems uncertain (see 68, 431). Furthermore, there are indications that a hormone is involved in the metamorphosis of the actinotrocha larva to the adult sessile marine worm *Phoronis* (511).

While in these cases the hormone source is not definitely known, the following endocrine activities can be attributed to the *central nervous system*. The brain of oligochetes contains a chromatophorotropin (see 449). In the planarian, *Polycelis*, a substance originating in the brain is necessary for the regeneration of the eyes (326). Regeneration of the anterior segments of the body in several annelid species is controlled by a growth hormone present in the brain and anterior ventral ganglia (260, 261). From their localization and secretory activity, it appears that one type of neurosecretory cells (b-cells) are the source of the growth factor in question, and another (a-cells) may be concerned with reproduction (272). Furthermore, in earthworms, brain extracts increase the intensity and, under certain conditions, the frequency of intestinal movements, whereas extracts from subesophageal ganglia and ventral cord always result in a decrease of frequency. The frequency-increasing principle (also present in gut extracts) is not genus-specific, acts in great dilution, and resists boiling; it seems to be acetylcholine (195; for other data concerning the occurrence of acetylcholine in worms see 24, 94, 358, 364).

The brain of certain polychetes contains an inhibitory hormone which, like that operating in crustaceans, governs reproductive activity. Regardless of sex or age, brain removal leads to the precocious transformation of *Perinereis* into the sexually mature "epitokous" form (*Heteronereis*). Reimplantation of brain causes 50% of these animals to remain sexually immature or "atokous" (175–179). Again, it is assumed that neurosecretory cells which are present in the polychete brain in large numbers (42, 149, 445) are the site of origin of this inhibitory hormone. This view is supported by the close correlation between the cytological changes observed in the neurosecretory "cerebrovascular complex," which releases its product into the circulation, and the transformation of the animal into the epitokous form. At this time there occurs also a sudden release of neurosecretory material which can be traced from one specific type of neurosecretory cell along the "epidermal nerve" to the surface of the body. It is possible that the released substance is an "ectohormone" serving the attraction of the opposite sex (43). In view of this situation, the "cerebral organ" of the nemerteans (429) and the "subcerebral gland" of the rotifers (146) may perhaps be considered as forerunners of neuroendocrine organs of higher animals.

A similar relationship between the secretory activity of neurosecretory cells and the maturation of the gonocytes seems to exist in the sipunculid *Phascolion* (234).

In a related species (*Physcosoma japonicum*), extracts from *nephridia* as well as from certain other tissues of the body induce or increase the rate of rhythmic movements of isolated nephridia (309, 313). Attached to the nephridia of these worms is the *internephridial organ* whose extirpation

in *Physcosoma lanzarotae* (259), but not in *Physcosoma japonicum* (312),
leads to disturbances comparable to adrenocortical insufficiency in vertebrates.   Reimplantation of internephridial organs prevented the death of
the experimental animals and led to recovery.   The cytology of this organ,
which was discovered by Harms (259), is comparable to that of the adrenal
cortex.

III. Crustaceans

Known *sources of hormones* among crustaceans are the neurosecretory
organ systems, the molting gland, and the gonads.   As will be seen, the
interpretation of the gonads as endocrine organs, at least among females,
is based on physiological evidence only.   The molting gland or y organ,
recently discovered in 58 species of *Malacostraca* by Gabe (233) has the
same histological characteristics as the prothoracic (ventral) gland of
insects.

Neurosecretory cell groups are found in various parts of the central
nervous system including those in the eyestalk (10, 11, 254).   Their unique
morphological characteristics, only recently elucidated (36, 39–41, 114, 188,
191, 194, 227–229, 235, 255, 350, 376, 378, 379, 506), are important for the
understanding of functional relationships, but only certain essentials can
be discussed here (for details, compare 403, 448, 449).   The best known
neurosecretory center to date is the x organ which in certain groups (*Natantia*) consists of two parts, a pars ganglionaris and a pars distalis (102, 114).
It is reasonable to assume that the different cytological types of neurosecretory cells found among crustaceans give origin to distinct types of
hormones, but a detailed study of these relationships has only just been
started (113).   A characteristic feature of these and other neurosecretory
cells is the proximodistal transport of secretory material along axons (actually observed in living eyestalk preparations; 105, 108) and its storage in
organs at some distance from the cells of origin.   One of these storage
centers is the sinus gland, long thought to be the source of the various
hormones it contains (see 70).   Another is the pars distalis of the x organ.
Both organs receive neurosecretory material not only from the x organ,
but also from other neurosecretory cell groups.   Whether or not the sinus
gland and the pars distalis contain glandular products of nonneurosecretory
origin, as suggested by certain authors (114, 228), needs further investigation.   Removal of the sinus gland, or severance of its connection with the
neurosecretory cells, may lead to accumulation of neurosecretory material
at the proximal stump (379) and to the regeneration of a "substitute sinus
gland" (41, 194), comparable to the formation of a functioning posterior
lobe at the cut end of the pituitary stalk in vertebrates (32, 328, 478).

Also of interest are certain organs classified together with the sinus gland as "neurohemal organs" (4–7, 112, 304, 306–308). On further study some of these may turn out to be neurosecretory in nature. The pericardial organs seem to furnish 5-hydroxytryptamine (110). There are also indications for the presence of acetylcholine in crustaceans (310, 518).

A variety of physiological processes among crustaceans are conditioned by external factors such as temperature, illumination, and food (162, 163), as well as by internal factors such as hormones (reviews: 65, 66, 70, 165, 192, 299, 373). Some of these are cyclic in nature and consequently interrelated with each other. Thus, the molting behavior is correlated with changes in metabolism, with seasonal reproductive rhythms, etc. (164, 484, 515, 551). The identities of various hormones governing these activities are, therefore, not established in every case. It is possible that the molt-inhibiting hormone is identical with the metabolic principle (or principles); the ovarian-inhibiting hormone seems the same as that controlling sex reversal in *Lysmata* (104). On the other hand, the ovarian-inhibiting, the molt-inhibiting, and the molt-promoting hormones can be clearly differentiated from each other (108). At least five separate chromatophorotropins seem to exist aside from two principles controlling retinal pigment (70).

A. COLOR CHANGE

Numerous studies concerning physiological color adaptation in crustaceans have been reported in the past (see reviews: 70, 440). Among the more important newer contributions are those dealing with the site of origin of different chromatophorotropic principles. Although it has been known for some time that these hormones can be extracted from the sinus gland of the eyestalk and from several parts of the central nervous system (see 70, 186, 425, 520), the neurosecretory origin of the active principles has become evident mainly from the contributions by Enami (188, 190, 191, 193, 194; see also 351, 528). The distribution of the chromatophorotropins in the central nervous system can be correlated with the occurrence of neurosecretory cells; the high activity of sinus gland extracts is due to its content of neurosecretory material.

Different types of crustacean chromatophorotropins can be distinguished from each other by their specific effects on certain types of chromatophores (84, 88, 116, 185, 186, 302, 305), by their distribution in the organism (525), and, to some extent, by their chemical properties, for example, their solubility in alcohol (75).

Crustacean chromatophorotropins which are not genus-specific act in low concentrations. Their action is part of a neuroendocrine reflex chain. Following a light stimulus reaching the central nervous system via the compound eye, hormone is released into the circulation and causes either contraction or expansion of pigments in various types of chromatophores ("secondary response"; 133, 382). Not only the light intensity but also the nature of the background and the diurnal sequence of light and dark periods condition the outcome in any given pigmentary response. Superimposed on persistent diurnal rhythms of pigment distribution (78 79, 81, 85, 184, 521, 522) may be tidal rhythms (72, 83, 86), with the result that a semilunar rhythm of color change is established (80).

Another nonhormonal factor playing a role in crustacean color responses was found to be an enzyme whose action is pigment-dispersing; it either inhibits or destroys a concentrating hormone. The effect of this enzyme cannot be duplicated by other known enzymes (117, 119, 189).

B. Retinal Pigment Migration

The pigments present in the retina of the compound eye, similarly to those of the integumentary chromatophores, respond to changes in light intensity, temperature, etc. (422, 423). They also show a persistent diurnal rhythmicity (359, 360, 523, 524). Retinal pigment migration is governed by at least two principles, a dark-adapting and a light-adapting one (69, 76, 77, 82, 87, 300, 360, 424, 524). Weak light stimulation causes the production mainly of dark-adapting hormone, whereas strong light results exclusively in light-adapting hormone (89). The two principles are present in the central nervous system and in the sinus gland. In all probability they are not identical with any of the known chromatophorotropins (87, 303). The effect of illumination on retinal pigment seems to be mediated by a combination of nervous and hormonal mechanisms (524).

C. Molting and Growth

Some crustaceans, such as *Lysmata*, molt throughout the year, the intermolt periods being shorter in summer than in winter; others, for example, *Uca* or *Cambarus*, show a seasonal molting behavior, *i.e.*, there are long intervals of rest conditioned by environmental factors. Hormones are involved in the induction of molting (molt-promoting hormones) as well as in the control of quiescent periods (molt-inhibiting hormones).

As with insects (p. 72), molting in crustaceans seems to be the result of a two-step hormone reaction. The existence of a molt-promoting factor, originating in neurosecretory cells of the eyestalk (x organ), the brain, and the thoracic ganglia, has been postulated by Carlisle and Dohrn (103, 106, 111) on the basis of the following experiment. If, in *Lysmata*, eyestalk extracts prepared from summer animals are injected into less frequently molting winter animals, these show an increase in molting rate. The responsible factor is different from other known crustacean hormones; it can be administered orally. Its function seems to be the stimulation of another organ of internal secretion, the molting gland proper (233).   Its total extirpation in the crab, *Carcinus maenas*, prevents molting, provided that the operation is performed early enough during the intermolt period (180).

In animals with a seasonal molting behavior, the quiescent periods are the result of a molt-inhibiting hormone which seems to be lacking in continuously molting species (106).   The existence of this factor had been known long before that of the molt-promoting hormones (see 31, 137, 162–164), but its place of origin has been properly identified only recently. The molt-inhibiting hormone arises in the beta-neurosecretory cells of the x organ (191) and similar cell groups in the central nervous system (107, 475); it is stored in the sinus gland.   The conclusion that the sinus gland does not produce this hormone, was reached on the basis of the following observations.   Extirpation of the x organ, performed outside of the molting season, initiates the changes characteristic of the premolt period, such as increase in the content of body water and resorption of calcium from the exoskeleton.   Removal of the sinus gland does not cause precocious molting, but molting in eyestalk-less animals can be delayed or inhibited by the implantation of either x organs or sinus glands (36, 37, 41, 266, 376, 377, 379, 380).

A certain restraint on molting frequency can be demonstrated also during the molting season.   Since this effect is not abolished by eyestalk removal, the responsible factor must originate in another center, probably the beta-neurosecretory cells of the brain and commissural ganglia (107).

It is interesting to point out that the molt-inhibiting hormone and the molt-promoting hormone, although sharing their place of origin in the x organ, are transported along different routes to different storage and release centers.   The molt-promoting hormone is absent in the sinus gland, but reaches its storage center, the pars distalis of the x organ, via the x organ connective (102, 103).

The role of this organ system, which controls growth and molting, reflects itself in structural changes in different phases of the molting cycle.   Such changes were shown in the x organ and sinus gland of the isopod, *Sphaeroma* (229), and in the molting gland of various *Malacostraca* (233).   In *Lysmata*, the injection of an extract containing molt-promoting hormone results in a pronounced depletion of neurosecretory substance, which stains with Gomori's chrome hematoxylin, in the x organ and in the x organ connective (108).

D. Reproduction

The reproductive activity of crustaceans depends on seasonal and other extrinsic factors as well as on hormonal action.   The over-all picture is rather complex and is as yet only partially understood (477). The existence of *sex hormones* in crustaceans has been a controversial question for many years. Evidence has been sought in various directions, most of them concerned with the demonstration of a possible dependence of "secondary sex characters" on humoral agents produced by the gonads. As will be seen, the results differ with respect to permanent sex characters and cyclic (seasonal) characters, such as the special structures necessary for the care of the brood.

One approach consists in the analysis of castrated animals. (*1*) Studies of the results of "parasitic castration" did not solve the question, since the effects of the parasites on the permanent sex characters of the host appear to be due either to metabolic changes in the host, or possibly to damage to its thoracic ganglion (349, 350), but probably not to castration (512, 513; see also 411–413). Presumably, there is a genetically determined difference in the male and female internal environments which in the presence of the parasite undergoes a shift in the female direction. The result is feminization in the male and hyperfeminization in the female (136, 409). Regenerating organs respond more readily to the feminizing stimulus than normal intact control organs (138). A precise analysis of the chemical difference between these internal environments is still lacking, but there are indications that it concerns protein rather than lipid content (215, 513). (*2*) Irradiation by radium or X-rays, causing gonadal arrest or modification (485), does not seem to affect permanent secondary sex characters. The influence of this treatment on temporary sex characters, such as the oöstegites of certain species, could be explained in other ways, such as sensitivity to irradiation of these organs (128, 130, 485). The results of irradiation experiments are, therefore, inconclusive with regard to the mechanisms involved in the development of sexual dimorphism. (*3*) Surgical castration in crustaceans is difficult to accomplish, and negative results regarding its effects on secondary sex characters may, in certain cases, be due to incomplete extirpation of the gonads. In the isopod, *Armadillidium*, no influence of castration on either permanent or temporary sex characters was observed (486). On the other hand, Charniaux (126–128, 130) observed positive effects on secondary sex characters in the amphipod, *Orchestia*, results which are the more conclusive, because they could be reversed by the reimplantation of the gonads. If *Orchestia* females were gonadectomized at an appropriate time ("sensitive period") before an expected egg-laying stage, the oöstegites lacked a transitory secondary sex character, the long bristles, which normally serve the proper enclosure of the eggs in the brood chamber. Reimplantation of ovaries into gonadectomized females led to the formation of long bristles at the second postoperative molt, *i.e.*, at a time when vitellogenesis in the implants was completed. An active implant needed to remain in the host for only a few days to exert its effect which must be tentatively attributed to an ovarian hormone, presumably originating in "follicular cells." No humoral effect of gonads on either growth or regeneration of the permanent sex characters of male or female *Orchestia* has been observed.

These results are in agreement with observations regarding transitory sex characters in parasitized *Callinectes* (409; but see 550) and strongly suggest a hormonal activity, at least with respect to the female gonad of certain crustaceans.

A second approach to the problem is the study of the effects of gonadal implants in hosts of the opposite sex. In isopods, females with testicular implants develop male secondary sex characters. Furthermore, in young hosts, the ovary (in which eggs are missing) may develop a process resembling a vas deferens in form and pigmentation (321, 325). Ovaries, when implanted into males of the amphipod, *Orchestia*, become transformed into testes. The fact that this takes place not only in normal hosts but in males which have been castrated for three months suggests that the presumed humoral agent causing the gonadal change must be outside of the gonad. It is possible that it is identical with the sex-reversal hormone of the eyestalk (104). By contrast, testes that had been allowed to remain in female hosts for four months were unchanged. In contrast to *Oniscus*, the presence of a gonad of the opposite sex did not affect the secondary sex characters of either males or females in *Orchestia* (129).

In addition to the evidence given in the preceding paragraphs, there exist observations which demonstrate the occurrence of *hormone sources outside of the gonads* which control reproductive processes. Such hormones are furnished by the neurosecretory systems of the eyestalk and associated cell groups. Regarding gonadotropic effects, the inhibiting action on ovarian development has been confirmed: eyestalk removal causes an acceleration in the development of the ovaries (108, 159, 160, 348, 370, 374; see also 139). Conversely, the injection of eyestalk extracts inhibits ovarian growth (108, 348); brain extracts have the same result (108). There is a corresponding effect on the testis (158).

The neurosecretory cells furnishing these gonad-inhibiting hormones are located in the brain and in the x organ (pars ganglionaris of the x organ in the case of *Natantia*). Their storage and release center is the sinus gland (102, 104, 108). Unlike the molt-promoting hormone (103) also originating in the x organ, the ovarian-inhibiting hormone of *Lysmata* is ineffective on oral administration (104). This as well as the difference of its storage center indicates that it cannot be identical with the molt-promoting hormone. The gonad-inhibiting hormone also seems to be different from the molt-inhibiting hormone (104, 140, 159) and from known chromatophorotropins (486). On the other hand, the factor which inhibits sex reversal in *Lysmata* is probably identical with the ovarian-inhibiting hormone (104, 108). The relationship between gonad and sinus gland is evident also from the observation (279) that this organ of the eyestalk is enlarged in parasitized crabs with degenerated gonads.

Eyestalk hormones also control, besides the gonads, both permanent and cyclic sex characters (143, 160, 476, 514). Eyestalk removal inhibits the feminization of male parasitized crabs and of immature females (136, 137, 142, 143). Since there exists other evidence indicating an endocrine relationship between eyestalk and gonads (104, 279, 477), the influence of the "eyestalk" on the development of the female characters could take place by way of a humoral stimulation of the gonad (see 29). These data, therefore, do not necessarily speak against the postulation of an ovarian hormone. Such an effect of the neurosecretory cells of the eyestalk on the gonads would have to be visualized as directed specifically on those cells (follicular cells?) which presumably furnish gonadal hormones, and not on the germ cells, which, as has been stated, develop independently of the eyestalk. A search for the occurrence and cytological features of such follicular or interstitial cells in crustaceans, therefore, seems desirable.

E. METABOLISM

The x organ and perhaps additional groups of neurosecretory cells furnish a hormone (or hormones) controlling crustacean metabolism. This factor is present also in the sinus gland where it is stored. The stimulation of metabolic activity observed after eyestalk removal is comparable to that occurring in preparation for a molt. The relationships between various phases in the molting cycle and metabolism are also evident from the observation (140) that in sacculinized *Pachygrapsus* whose metabolism is depressed by the parasite, removal of the eyestalk does not raise the metabolic activity sufficiently to reach the level necessary for the initiation of molting.

In the absence of the metabolic hormone the rate of oxygen consumption rises and the respiratory quotient falls (30, 36–40, 181, 216; see also 451). The metabolic principle also controls calcium, phosphorus, and water metabolism (37, 38, 40, 250, 266, 298, 320, 379, 464, 505).

The role of hormone factors in the control of carbohydrate metabolism is demonstrated by the effect of eyestalk removal, *i.e.*, hypoglycemia (301, 359, 450) and glycogen increase in the hypodermis (461). Persistent diurnal, tidal, and semilunar rhythms in the metabolic rate of certain crustaceans (71, 73, 250, 359) indicate rhythmic variations in the available amount of metabolic hormone.

Such a hormone also plays a role in the metabolism of an astacine-protein complex, a carotenoid pigment contained in chromatophores of *Carcinus maenas* (327).

A possible correlation between gonads and metabolic processes is demonstrated by the increase in body fat after gonadectomy in the isopod *Armadillidium* (484).   There are also relationships between eyestalk hormones and certain enzyme systems (319, 451).

F. OTHER ACTIVITIES

Various authors have observed that the life span is shortened (see 70, 162, 164), and that certain organs such as the midgut-gland degenerate in eyestalk-less crustaceans (549).   The postulation of a hormone maintaining "viability" is, however, unnecessary; it seems preferable to attribute the observed deficiencies to specific causes such as the lack of metabolic hormone, but further work will be needed to clarify this point.

The situation is similarly unclear with respect to possible effects of an eyestalk hormone on locomotor activity (see 70).   It has been established, however, that the diurnal locomotor rhythms observed in many species are abolished after eyestalk removal and that this effect is not due to blinding (164).   Furthermore, humoral factors from various organs are known to act on the musculature of the heart, the intestine, etc.   The central nervous system of some species contains a heart-accelerating principle, in the anterior portion of central nervous system, and a heart rate-decreasing principle, in the tritocerebral commissure (256, 257).   Amplitude and frequency of the heart rate in certain crustaceans is also increased by a substance from the "pericardial organs" of decapods (7), and decreased by extracts from insect heads and vertebrate posterior pituitaries (209).   As to the nature of these active substances, an adrenaline-like principle and enteramine have been under discussion (7, 211, 212).   As in certain mollusks, enteramine seems to replace adrenaline as a nerve transmitter in decapod crustaceans (213).

IV. Insects

Among the known *organs of internal secretion* in insects, the key position is held by the neurosecretory centers.   These consist of groups of secreting nerve cells in the brain (medial groups—pars intercerebralis, and lateral group), in the subesophageal and ventral ganglia, and in the frontal ganglion.   Some of these neurosecretory cell groups are in intimate contact with other glands of internal secretion.   The morphological relationship between the neurosecretory cells of the brain and the corpora cardiaca and corpora allata has been known for some time (see 255, 437) and has become the basis for the functional understanding of these glands, as well as of corresponding organ systems in other phyla of invertebrates.   More recent work (21) offers morphological evidence that the prothoracic glands (and their "homologues") also must be included among the components of the neuroendocrine organ systems of insects. Morphological and histophysiological studies on these endocrine organs are numerous; recent data are found in the following publications: 15–17, 20, 56, 59, 131, 134, 147, 148, 151, 153, 156, 157, 172, 183, 235, 236, 244, 245, 322, 330, 332, 333, 336, 339, 346, 357, 361–363, 396, 397, 417, 426, 462, 479, 493, 499–502, 526, 531; see also 337, 338.

A feature peculiar to such neurosecretory systems is the proximodistal transport along nerve fibers of neurosecretory material, a microscopically visible substance with distinct staining properties (435, 437, 497, 498). As in the case of other neurosecretory centers, this material is presumed to contain active principles originating in neurosecretory cells. The transport to the corpora cardiaca (433) and in certain cases to the corpora allata and prothoracic glands (23, 63) has two results, directed discharge and storage. It looks as though the endocrine stimulation of the corpora cardiaca, the corpora allata, and the prothoracic glands by neurosecretory cells, postulated on the basis of physiological data, may be achieved by the active principles reaching the target glands not via the general circulation but along the connecting nerve fibers, i.e., in a "directed" fashion. This mechanism, although favored by certain data, such as the necessity for intactness of the glandular complex in transplantation experiments (401), is not definitely established and does not seem to apply to all species.

In the case where neurosecretory material appears in large quantities, as in the nerve terminals of the corpora cardiaca of certain species, it is interpreted as stored product (433, 436). It will be demonstrated that its physiological effects are the same as those of the material contained in the cells of origin.

It seems that the task of the active principles originating in neurosecretory cells of insects is twofold. These principles act directly, and they stimulate other organs of internal secretion. In some cases changes in histological appearance of the neurosecretory system go hand in hand with distinct phases in postembryonic development and egg maturation (14, 63, 64, 168, 170, 406, 407).

In addition to releasing "tropic" hormones, the neurosecretory cells seem to control the target glands by means of nervous stimuli. The interdependency of these organs is also evidenced by the observation of definite relationships between the neurosecretory activity of the cells of origin and the maximal development of the glands which they innervate (18, 19, 22).

It is still uncertain whether the gonads or the fat body of insects act as glands of internal secretion. For reviews on insect endocrinology see 154, 282, 352, 386, 431, 432, 434, 440.

A. REPRODUCTION

Reproductive processes in insects are controlled by several organs of internal secretion. Recent work in this field concerns mainly the situation in the female, but a number of questions regarding both sexes are still open. One of these concerns the existence of sex hormones for which no direct evidence has yet been found.

Among the hormone functions involved, the role of the corpora allata has been known for some time, whereas that of the neurosecretory cells of the brain and of the corpora cardiaca has been recognized only recently. Since these three organs form a neurosecretory system, one can assume a high degree of interaction between the hormones they furnish. Evidently one of these hormones originates in the medial neurosecretory cells of the protocerebrum (496). Extirpation of this brain area, but not of others, in the fly *Calliphora* prevents egg maturation. Reimplantation of neurosecretory cells in animals from which they have been previously removed, furthers egg development. Ovarian development in flies deprived of their medial neurosecretory cells can also be induced by implants of corpus cardiacum tissue from mature female donors. On the other hand, absence of the corpus cardiacum alone does not prevent egg development. This result indicates that the gonad-stimulating principle which is active in cardiacum implants does not originate there but is derived from the pars intercerebralis of the brain and is stored in the terminals of the neurosecretory neurons.

Whereas the action of the substance present in the corpus cardiacum is the same as that of the brain hormone, the active material furnished by the corpus allatum seems to be different. This is borne out by two observations: (1) Allatectomy interrupts egg development in animals whose medial neurosecretory cells and corpus cardiacum are left intact (see 434), and (2) this interruption of egg development takes place at a later stage than that caused by the removal of the medial neurosecretory cells of the brain (496). However, the endocrine action of the corpus allatum on the gonads is not entirely independent. It is under the control of the neurosecretory center of the brain, and this control may involve endocrine (allatotropic hormone?; 496) and nervous factors (372, 437).

With regard to a comparable relationship between protocerebrum and corpus cardiacum, it seems probable that the latter also is controlled by neurosecretory cells, as was suggested by Thomsen (496), but this control concerns most likely the production and release of the intrinsic hormone factor of the corpus cardiacum (p. 77), which must be differentiated from the gonad-stimulating hormone of neurosecretory origin.

An interesting recent contribution (280) concerns the mechanism by which in starving insects egg maturation is arrested. In starved as well as newly emerged females of the milkweed bug, *Oncopeltus*, the corpora allata are small, whereas they are distinctly larger in mature egg-laying specimens. Egg development in starved animals can be induced by the implantation of "mature" corpora allata. Thus the cessation of egg production under conditions of starvation seems to be due to insufficiency of the corpus allatum.

The activity of the corpora allata appears to be restricted not only by extraneous factors such as starvation or seasonal conditions (283) but also by the ovaries. The observation that in various insect species the corpora allata hypertrophy after gonadectomy may be taken as indirect evidence for the presence of sex hormones.

There are other indirect indications for the existence of *sex hormones* in insects (see 242, 434, 438, 439), and newer observations point in the same direction. Extracts from ovaries of queen bees injected into sterile workers induce their ovaries to produce eggs (8, 9). However, it is questionable whether the active substance involved should be classified as a true sex hormone, because comparable effects are obtained with extracts from other organs of the queen, such as the corpora allata.

Furthermore, the sex behavior (rejection of the male during certain phases of the reproductive cycle) in grasshoppers (*Euthystira*) is governed by the ovary (410).

Finally, egg deposition in *Bombyx* depends on fertilization; transfusion of blood from fertilized females is said to induce unfertilized females to deposit their eggs within a short time (355).

B. Embryonic Development

The factors controlling the rate of embryonic development in insects have been under investigation for some time. In addition to certain environmental (light, temperature) or experimental conditions (culture *in vitro*; 90), intrinsic mechanisms were postulated in order to explain the observed developmental rhythms. Such rhythms are particularly evident, for example, in the silkworm (*Bombyx mori*), for which periods of developmental arrest (diapause) are characteristic. Depending on the race, uninterrupted generations (nondiapausing summer eggs) may alternate with dormant generations (diapausing winter eggs). This behavior is called voltinism. Its control by an endocrine factor has been recently demonstrated. Hasegawa (263–265) found that this hormone originates in the subesophageal ganglion—an observation which was confirmed almost simultaneously by Fukuda (217–224). Implants of subesophageal ganglia in silkworm pupae which are destined to produce nonhibernating eggs, induce the deposition of hibernating eggs by the resulting moths.

The diapause factor is not species-specific. The effect of one subesophageal ganglion from a hibernating donor approximately equals that of two subesophageal ganglia from a nonhibernating donor (265). One can assume, although this has not been definitely proved, that the diapause factor originates in the neurosecretory cells of the subesophageal ganglion. The action of these cells must be distinctly different from that of the neurosecretory cells of either the brain or the prothoracic ganglia, because implants of the two latter organs do not furnish the diapause factor.

An extension of these studies to include univoltine, as well as bi- and multi-voltine, silkworm races (222–224) led to the conclusion that the release of the diapause factor from the subesophageal ganglion is under the control of the brain. This is demonstrated, for example, by the result of transplantation experiments in pupal hosts normally destined to lay nondiapausing eggs. Implants of subesophageal ganglia alone cause the production of only a certain proportion of diapausing eggs, but this proportion is considerably increased and may reach 100% in cases in which the implants consist of the intact complex of brain and subesophageal ganglion.

Histophysiological studies and ligation experiments in embryos of *Locustana* have demonstrated the existence of endocrine mechanisms similar to those controlling postembryonic development (288). Dormancy seems to be terminated by a humoral factor from the brain whose neurosecretory cells show a peak of activity before that of the prothoracic glands which probably represent the long known "differentiation center" in the presumptive prothorax (see 415).

C. POSTEMBRYONIC DEVELOPMENT

Since the discovery of the first invertebrate hormone in 1917, namely the brain factor controlling pupation (318; see also 57), a great deal has been learned regarding the endocrine control of molting, growth, and differentiation in insects (reviews: 52, 432, 434, 440, 448, 449, 471, 534, 539, 541). Although recent contributions in this field do not necessitate changes in the interpretation of the known basic data, they permit certain generalizations and fill specific gaps in our knowledge of the sequence of events leading from the immature larva to the adult insect, or imago.

In addition to extrinsic factors, such as temperature, light, and food (44, 50, 394, 543), four hormone centers are known to participate in the control of postembryonic development. These are the neurosecretory cells of the protocerebrum, the corpora cardiaca, the corpora allata, and the prothoracic glands. The prothoracic glands are the equivalents of the ventral glands of lower *Pterygota* (386), the thoracic glands of *Hemiptera* (538), and the peritracheal gland or lateral ring gland cells of *Diptera* (401).

There is now additional proof that in a variety of insect species belonging to several different orders, growth and differentiation depend on a hormone furnished by the prothoracic glands (273–277, 290, 291; see also 58, 60, 61, 241, 331, 366, 367, 389, 392, 483, 535, 536), and that these glands (or their equivalents) require for their proper function a hormonal stimulation by the neurosecretory cells of the protocerebrum. This two-step hormone action, first established for *Lepidoptera* (544–546), holds equally for *Hemiptera* (537, 538), *Diptera* (395, 398–402; see also 152, 404, 405), *Orthoptera* (466), and probably other groups (12). Interestingly, it seems to apply also to the endocrine control of molting in crustaceans (p. 62).

The corpora cardiaca act as storage and release center for the "prothoracotropic hormone" of the brain; the corpora allata furnish the juvenile hormone whose presence during larval life counterbalances the effect of the growth and differentiation hormone of the prothoracic gland. This hormone balance is the basis for the occurrence of larval molts, *i.e.*, developmental steps in which growth predominates and little or no adult differentiation occurs. During the last larval (nymphal) stage, a shift in hormone proportion, greatly favoring the growth and differentiation hormone over the juvenile hormone, makes metamorphosis possible. Evidence for such a shift in hormone balance was obtained not only from physiological (see 391) but also from morphological studies (289). In brief, the process of molting as well as the kind of molt (larval or imaginal) which an insect undergoes depends largely on the hormonal milieu. That this is the case was again demonstrated in recent experiments in which adults or adult cuticle were induced to undergo molts—a process not normally occurring in insects (see 46, 47, 49, 393). Molting in adult roaches (*Periplaneta americana*) occurred (*1*) when the newly emerged imago was allatectomized—an operation which in this species prevents the normally occurring regression of the prothoracic glands—(*2*) when allatectomized adults were joined in parabiosis to nymphs, and (*3*) when older adults deprived of their own corpora cardiaca and allata, received implants of corpora cardiaca and prothoracic glands from nymphal donors. Molting did not occur when, in a modification of experiment (*1*), the corpora cardiaca were removed together with the corpora allata—an operation which is followed by regression of the prothoracic glands. These experiments demonstrate that the presence of functional prothoracic glands is necessary for molting, that adult corpora allata counteract the stimulus for molting exerted by the prothoracic glands, and that the function of the prothoracic glands depends on the corpora cardiaca. In the opinion of the author, this dependency of the prothoracic glands on the corpora cardiaca is best explained by the latter's content of stored neurosecretory substance which may be presumed to be the carrier of the prothoracotropic hormone.

It is of further interest that certain transplantation experiments resulted in integumental structures with superimaginal characteristics (46). This observation as well as the induction of molting in adults demonstrates that the insect imago is the result of a balanced hormone milieu with a reserve of normally not realized developmental potentialities.

The spinning behavior of lepidopterans is controlled by the corpus allatum and the prothoracic gland (92, 390, 509, 510).

With increasing knowledge of the hormonal mechanisms governing postembryonic development, the mode of action of each participating hormone can be defined more precisely, with the result that certain adjustments in terminology become necessary. Thus the term "inhibitory hormone," originally suggested by Wigglesworth for the factor furnished by the corpus allatum, was changed by him to the more encompassing term "juvenile hormone" (533), when it became evident that the hormone favors "juvenile" characters and tendencies in the tissues rather than merely inhibits their differentiation in the adult direction. An illustration of this function is the observation that excessive amounts of juvenile hormone can induce adult tissues to revert to the juvenile type (62, 533).

Similarly, the hormone of the prothoracic glands which, in collaboration with the juvenile hormone, brings about larval molts was originally called "molting hormone" (see 538). At that time it was assumed that two additional hormones control pupation and metamorphosis in holometabolous insects. When it became known that, in holo- as well as hemi-metabolous insects, the "molting hormone" is active throughout postembryonic development and that its functional significance reaches beyond that assumed by earlier workers, the original designation became inadequate. For this reason the term "growth and differentiation hormone" was proposed (432) to replace the terms "molting, pupation, and metamorphosis hormones." This more comprehensive name implies that in the presence of this hormone growth and molting, as well as imaginal differentiation, take palce. Furthermore, under the conditions in which adult cuticle is experimentally induced to molt again, the growth and differentiation hormone seems to favor the maintenance of adult characters when these have once been acquired (see 46, 532). Whether, in the developing insect, the growth and differentiation hormone merely permits, or actually causes, adult development (540) is still a matter of debate. However, a variety of data clearly indicates that the function of the hormone in question is not restricted to the control of molting and that one of its additional functions is that of providing a milieu for differentiation. Among these data may be cited the observation (294, 454, 460) that isolated male sex cells from dormant pupae of *Platysamia* develop into spermatids when cultured in a medium containing growth and differentiation hormone, and that spermiogenesis is arrested at any stage by withdrawal of the hormone (296).

Another example is the regulation and differentiation within field-dis-

tricts in transplanted fragments of imaginal discs of *Drosophila*. The
regulatory process depends on the time available for the enlargement of
the field-district by mitosis. Thus, in younger hosts full regulation may
occur, whereas in older hosts (soon to undergo metamorphosis) "the disc
cells fall too soon under the influence of the metamorphosing hormones
which force the implant into immediate differentiation" (251).

D. METABOLISM

Metabolic processes in insects are controlled by the neurosecretory cells
of the brain, by the corpora cardiaca, and by the corpora allata. In the
fly *Calliphora* removal of the medial *neurosecretory cells* of the protocerebrum
leads to diminished fat and increased glycogen deposits in the fat body
(496). No clear-cut effect of brain removal on metabolism was observed
in the roach *Leucophaea* (442).

In the roach *Periplaneta*, absence of the *corpora cardiaca* results in the
disappearance of the urates normally occurring in the fat body—an observation which suggests a role in the regulation of protein metabolism (48).
It is not certain, but quite possible, that this effect is due to the metabolic
principle originating in the neurosecretory cells of the brain, since the
histologically demonstrable substance presumably containing this hormone
is abundantly stored in the corpora cardiaca of *Periplaneta*. That the
corpora allata play a role in the fat metabolism of at least certain insect
species, is indicated by the following data. The content of fatty acids
showed a pronounced rise after allatectomy in adult females of the grass-
hopper, *Melanoplus differentialis* (385). In *Calliphora*, removal of the
corpora allata led to a hypertrophy of the fat body (494, 496), in *Periplaneta* to an increased fat content of the fat body cells (48). By contrast,
no significant changes in the percentual content of fatty acids were observed
in allatectomized *Leucophaea* (442), and in *Carausius* (*Dixippus*; 334).

In the two last-named insects, however, the corpora allata seem to be
concerned with carbohydrate metabolism. Allatectomized *Leucophaea*
tend to have carbohydrate contents above normal (442). In *Carausius*
the blood:tissue ratio of carbohydrate values changed (334); in addition
there seemed to be a partial inhibition of protein synthesis (335).

There are a few data indicating a possible role of the *gonads* in the control of metabolic processes, and the results are not conclusive. Castration
resulted in decreased "lipid" content in *Melanoplus* females (385), but the
opposite effect seems to have been observed in *Bombyx* (252) and *Drosophila*
(45; see also 115). In *Leucophaea* no effect of gonadectomy on fat, carbohydrate, or protein metabolism could be observed (442).

Additional data concern the role of pericardial cells in intermediary

protein metabolism (463), and a possible hormonal control of water metabolism (311, 480).

Another question studied in recent years concerns possible relationships
between endocrine factors and *enzyme systems* important in intermediary
metabolism. Such studies aim at an understanding of the biochemical
events mediating between hormonal stimuli and target organs undergoing
metamorphosis. In the course of development, several biochemical systems
are in operation, and morphological events are closely paralleled by changes
in metabolism as evidenced by studies of the activities of oxidative enzymes.
The work of Williams and others (1–3, 53, 456, 458, 547) shows the participation of the glycolytic system, the tricarboxylic cycle, and oxidative
phosphorylation as energy sources in the differentiation of the whole insect
as well as of isolated cells (spermiogenesis). The terminal oxidase in the
morphogenesis of insect tissues in all developmental stages seems to be
cytochrome oxidase (420, 460). Several enzymes of the classical cytochrome system are absent in the diapausing pupa of *Platysamia*; they
reappear at the time when the presence of the growth and differentiation
hormone initiates adult development (421, 469, 543). During developmental arrest, metabolic processes are maintained by a different, carbon-
monoxide– and cyanide–insensitive respiratory system which seems to
suffice in the absence of morphogenesis but disappears at the onset of
imaginal differentiation (132, 262, 419, 457, 459; see also 341). There is
now good evidence that the terminal oxidase during diapause is cytochrome
b_5, which throughout this period is present in all tissues (375, 470). These
observations suggest that one of the functions of the growth and differentiation hormone is to bring about the resynthesis of the cytochrome oxidase
system and thus to effect a break in the state of presumed chemical deficiency existing during diapause (460; for additional data on relationships
between developmental hormones and enzymes, see 278, 365, 455). Changes
in the endocrine pattern during various physiological stages also seem to
reflect themselves in variations in the content of a number of blood proteins
studied with immunological techniques (488–492).

In adult insects (*Drosophila*) no significant difference was found between
cytochrome oxidase activity of males in which the corpora cardiaca and
allata were removed together with the head and that of control animals
in which only the head was removed. Similarly, the implantation of ring
glands (containing larval corpora cardiaca, corpora allata, and prothoracic
glands) into adult males did not alter their enzyme activity (53). Although
these results show no relationship between hormones and cytochrome system in adult *Drosophila*, the work of E. Thomsen (495; see also 249) demonstrating changes in oxygen consumption after the removal or implanta-

tion of corpus allatum may indicate an effect of allatum hormone on the cytochrome system of adult *Calliphora*.

E. COLOR CHANGE

A small number of insect species exhibit morphological and physiological color adaptation. Slow, *i.e.*, *morphological*, changes in body pigmentation occur, for example, in migratory locusts (284, 286, 287). If nymphs of the gregarious type (orange and black) receive implants of endocrine organs, they may show, after the following molt, the green pigmentation typical of the solitary type. This holds even if the donor, which may be a nymph or imago, belongs to the gregarious type. The hormone source responsible for this type of color change is the corpus allatum. Changes in body coloration preceding the pupal molt in the lepidopteran *Cerura* seem to be under the control of developmental hormones (91, 92).

Physiological color adaptation seems to be controlled exclusively or at least predominantly by hormones originating in neurosecretory cells—an observation which is in line with observations on other invertebrates such as crustaceans and xiphosurans. Chromatophorotropins of this kind can be extracted from the brain, the subesophageal and ventral ganglia, and the frontal ganglion (167), all of which in one species or another contain neurosecretory cells. They are also present in the corpus cardiacum. Since this organ, in addition to the neurosecretory material derived from the brain, contains a secretory product of its own (97, 542), the question arises which of the two substances is responsible for the action of cardiacum extracts on color adaptation. The following points speak in favor of the neurosecretory material: (*1*) Cardiacum extracts have an effect comparable to that of parts of the central nervous system which contain neurosecretory cells (171); (*2*) cardiacectomy does not disturb the mechanisms of color adaptation (169); (*3*) the chromatophorotropic effect of the corpus cardiacum disappears after the neurosecretory pathway (nervi corporis cardiaci), connecting it with the brain, has been severed (97)—an operation which results in a decrease of neurosecretory material in the corpus cardiacum (see 437).

There are, however, a number of points which need further study. For example, a chromatophorotropin present in the brain of *Carausius* does not seem to originate in the pars intercerebralis, but in an area comprising the deuto- and trito-cerebrum in which a fuchsinophilic material can be demonstrated (169, 173, 174). Various observations indicate that some neurosecretory products in insects as well as in other arthropods stain red, instead of blue, with Gomori's chrome hematoxylin phloxine method (281, 408, 442). It is interesting to note that this staining property also applies to vertebrate melanophore-expanding hormone (449).

F. Other Activities

Myotropic principles have been extracted from various organs of insects; they act in very low concentrations and they are not species-specific. A factor present in the brain either elicits rhythmic movements of isolated Malpighian tubules which, prior to the administration of the active substance, showed no motility, or increases the frequency of spontaneous rhythmic movements (314). Similar effects are obtained with extracts from corpora cardiaca which increase not only the frequency but also the amplitude of the muscular contractions in the Malpighian tubules, the intestine, and the heart. The responsible agent, probably an orthodiphenol (97; see also 248, 369), seems to be elaborated by the cellular elements of the corpus cardiacum and is thus different from the neurosecretory material stored in this organ (97, 542). Whether the latter is responsible for the myotropic effect of extracts prepared from central nervous tissue is not certain (see 449).

An increase in intestinal motility was observed in Tenebrio after the administration of extracts from insect brains. The same effect was obtained with extracts from crustacean brains and ventral ganglia, and from eyestalks of dark-adapted animals. On the other hand, eyestalks from light-adapted crustaceans contain a substance which decreases the frequency of muscular contraction (316; see also 256).

Insect muscles, corpora allata, etc., also yield extracts which act on musculature. The nature of the substances responsible for these effects is unknown. It may be added that, in addition to adrenaline-like principles, enteramine (369) and acetylcholine or related substances, such as mecholyl, seem to occur in insects (125, 270, 317, 329, 416, 473, 504).

Additional activities in which the participation of hormones is or may be involved are regeneration (see 51), midgut secretion (145), and diurnal rhythms of activity (258). Hormonal control of caste differentiation is suggested by the dimorphism of the prothoracic glands in queen bees and workers (342) as well as other data (8, 414, 427, 428). In normal termite colonies the development of "supplementary reproductives" seems to be prevented by a substance ("ectohormone"?) given off by the king and queen (246, 343–345).

V. Additional Arthropods

In contrast to the wealth of data on hormone actions in crustaceans and insects, the information regarding other groups of arthropods is still very scanty. Among two representatives of the *xiphosurans*, the existence of physiologically active substances originating in nervous structures has been demonstrated. These principles were tested on crustacean chromatophores. In *Limulus*, the potency of extracts prepared from various separate parts of the central nervous system (74) correlates well with the quantitative distribution of neurosecretory elements present in these areas (430)—a result which led to the conclusion that the neurosecretory cells of *Limulus* furnish hormones which act on crustacean chromatophores. Similarly, chromatophorotropins were found to be present in extracts from the secreting neurosensory cells of the so-called lateral rudimentary eye of *Tachypleus* (519).

Neurosecretory cells are also present in the central nervous system of certain *Onychophora* (144, 237) and of various species of *Chilopoda* (230). In the latter, there exists a neurosecretory system similar to those in insects and crustaceans. The so-called brain gland (155) acts as a storage organ for neurosecretory material which it receives from the brain. A similar neurosecretory system occurs in *Araneidae* (238, 323, 324). Although the functional significance of these glandular centers is still unknown, one should, in analogy with known neurosecretory systems, consider them as sources of hormones.

VI. Mollusks

Among the mollusks several organs must be mentioned as hormone sources (see 431, 552). The *posterior salivary glands* of certain cephalopods and the *hypobranchial body* of *Muricidae* (prosobranch snails) contain glandular cells belonging to the enterochromaffine system which occurs in invertebrates and vertebrates alike (516). The enterochromaffine cells are characterized by certain physicochemical properties (chromaffinity, argentaffinity, fluorescence in Wood's light, stainability with diazonium salts, etc.). They produce or store enteramine (5-hydroxytryptamine), which, according to Erspamer and his co-workers, who isolated and synthesized this substance (197–199, 202–204, 207), has the properties of a true hormone which increases oxygen consumption and heart action in mollusks (25, 27, 28, 206). Enteramine also seems to function as an excretory product in *Octopus* and as a nervous transmitter in *Venus* and *Buccinum* (529, 530). Besides the salivary glands, the central nervous system (212) and the hemolymph of cephalopods (205) also contain enteramine.

In addition to enteramine, the posterior salivary glands of cephalopods contain other physiologically active substances (468), one of whose actions seems to be the stimulation of the nervous elements which control the chromatophores (124). Hydroxyoctopamine, present in *Octopus vulgaris*, has been identified as *l*-noradrenaline (200, 201, 208). An indication for the occurrence of adrenaline-like substances in *Loligo* and *Sepia* is the presence of amine oxidase (35).

The *branchial glands*, whose destruction by electrocautery in *Octopus* causes decrease of muscular tone, anemia, respiratory impairment, etc., and finally leads to death, are considered by some authors to be an analogue of the adrenal medulla (354, 487).

Neuroglandular organs are the epistellar body (54, 123, 124, 552), the subpeduncular gland (54, 122, 124, 503), the juxtaganglionic secretory tissue (55) of cephalopods, and clusters of neurosecretory cells in a variety of groups of mollusks (see 225, 226, 231, 232, 448).   Their precise function is unknown, but in certain mollusks there is a relationship between neurosecretory activity and reproductive cycles (239); in others chromatophorotropic effects have been observed (see 449).

As in other invertebrates, acetylcholine occurs in mollusks, where it may act in capacities other than that of nervous transmitter (24, 95, 212, 530).

Certain indirect evidence seems to speak in favor of the production of sex hormones by the *gonads* of cephalopods (356, 467) and prosobranchs (340).   However, regeneration experiments in castrated *Octopus* males and females offered no evidence for the control of secondary sex characters, such as the hectocotylus, by gonadal hormones (96; see also 387).   In oysters the sex of the host has no influence on the sexual differentiation of gonadal grafts (182).

VII. Tunicates

The question of the endocrine role of the *neural gland* has been controversial for a long time.   The neural gland plus the ciliated pit of ascidians is now considered to be a homologue of the entire vertebrate pituitary (100).   The presence in this organ complex of an oxytocic principle is claimed by some investigators (26) and denied by others (383).   Several studies have demonstrated chromatophore expanding (26, 99) and gonadotropic activities (98, 100).

In *Ciona*, a hermaphrodite, ovariectomy or a seasonal state of ovarian inactivity causes testicular involution which can be prevented by ovarian implants or extracts.   This humoral influence of the *ovary* on the testis concerns mainly the maturation division (384).

Finally, the *intestinal mucosa* of certain ascidians contains enteramine which in chemical and biological respects is indistinguishable from that of mollusks and of vertebrates (196).

VIII. General Considerations

A survey of invertebrate hormones would be incomplete without a brief discussion of their position in general endocrinology.   In order to evaluate this position, one has to consider the nature and mode of action of invertebrate hormones against the background of established criteria for endocrine mechanisms.   In the study of invertebrate endocrinology, the difficulties

in defining hormone actions are accentuated by the occurrence of substances which exert their influence either outside of the organism or within
the cells in which they are produced.   These two modes of action are the
only ones possible in unicellular organisms, where a physiologically active
principle either influences the cells which manufacture it, or diffuses to
other cell individuals via the surrounding medium or by contact (472).
Substances of the second kind, referred to by some authors as ectohormones, are the "sex hormones" of certain protozoans (297).   In multi-
cellular invertebrates, i.e., in worms (p. 59), echinoderms (418), and
insects (p. 77), cases of the occurrence of "ectohormones" are also known.

"Hormone activities" within the cells in which the active substance is
produced, also seem to occur in protozoans (472) and metazoans alike.
An example of such local hormone action in mollusks is the control of the
rhythmic ciliary movements in the gill plates of *Mytilus* by acetylcholine,
whose presence in this tissue has been ascertained (95; see also 310, 347,
465).   This action of acetylcholine on nonnervous structures is of interest
in that it constitutes a function other than that of nervous transmitter—a
dual capacity which acetylcholine shares with adrenaline and enteramine.

It is for this reason that the occurrence of acetylcholine, adrenaline,
enteramine, and closely related substances in various groups of invertebrates has been recorded in this review, even though their endocrine
nature may not be definitely established in every case.   Future work
along these lines in invertebrates and vertebrates alike will probably
necessitate a redefinition and broadening of the hormone concept.

The majority of substances discussed in this chapter, however, are
"typical" hormones in that they are produced in specific glands of internal
secretion and are carried via the circulation to their target tissues (effector
organs or other endocrine glands).   The kind of hormone response elicited
is determined in some degree by differences in the sensitivity of the effector
organs (392, 483).   Invertebrate hormones, including those produced by
neurosecretory cells (169), act in exceedingly low concentrations.   They
are, as a rule, nonspecific with respect to genus, order, or sex (see 169, 219,
256, 276, 366, 367, 388, 450).

Certain physicochemical properties of a variety of invertebrate hormones are known.   Crustacean chromatophorotropins, for example, seem
to be substances with a relatively low molecular weight.   Various invertebrate hormones are known to be resistant to heat and desiccation and to
be soluble in water and ethyl alcohol, but not in ether or chloroform.
The growth and differentiation hormone of lepidopterans is either a protein
or a smaller molecule bound to a protein; it is stable when heated for 5
minutes to 75°C. (295, 452–454).

In an attempt to compare hormone actions in invertebrates to those of other organisms, especially vertebrates, it is important to know whether invertebrate hormones act on other organisms, and vice versa. Many attempts were made to exchange hormones between vertebrates and invertebrates, or even plants, but only a few seem to have yielded conclusive results (see 431). Some examples will demonstrate this point.

Concerning tests with vertebrate hormones in invertebrates, there are certain more or less unspecific effects of *adrenaline*, such as that on chromatophores (210), on the heart (481), and on the oxygen consumption of crustaceans (214), on the heart of cephalopods (24), or on the blood sugar of snails (482). Equally undefined is a reported case of growth stimulation of parasitic nematodes by bovine *ovarian material* (243). Mammalian *gonadotropin* as well as *lactogen* stimulates the ovaries of the ascidians *Ciona* and *Phallusia*, which cannot distinguish between the two factors (98, 100, 101, 109). Extracts from vertebrate *pituitaries* act on crustacean chromatophores (99, 187)—an observation not confirmed by some investigators (548). Negative results were obtained with a variety of vertebrate hormones tested to replace the growth and differentiation hormone of insects (452).

Certain alleged effects of invertebrate hormones on vertebrates also appear to be unspecific, such as the *estrogenic* actions of a variety of tested materials, including lobster eggs (161), insect tissues (474), etc. A substance (echinochrome) occurring in mature sea urchin eggs brings about "nuptial body coloration" in fishes in the manner of *sex hormones* (292). Invertebrate *chromatophorotropins*, besides being exchangeable among insects, crustaceans, and ascidians (99, 166, 171, 187, 381), also show effects on vertebrate chromatophores (187, 210, 247, 381), but the latter effects have been questioned (548). The neural gland complex of ascidians has a *gonadotropic* effect on mice (98), whereas crustacean eyestalk extracts do not (118). Concerning *neurohypophyseal* type actions, the eyestalk affects only water metabolism (pitressin-like effect on the water uptake of the frog; 247, 268, 269, 315).

Extracts from insect tissues containing neurosecretory substance (pars intercerebralis and corpus cardiacum-allatum of the roach *Blabera*) are said to have an *antidiuretic* effect in the rat. One milliliter of a solution corresponding to 1 mg. of acetone powder caused a retardation of urinary excretion of 45 minutes, *i.e.*, it contained an equivalent of about 2.5 milliunits of antidiuretic substance (480). By contrast, tests for possible oxytocic, vasopressor, or antidiuretic effects with corpora cardiaca from the roaches *Leucophaea* and *Periplaneta* were inconclusive (271, 517), and therefore further studies seem necessary to substantiate the positive results in *Blabera*.

As an example of an effect on protozoans, the control of the sexual cycles (gametogenesis) of flagellates living in the hindgut of the wood-feeding roach *Cryptocercus* by the growth and differentiation hormone of the insect host (134) may be cited. Finally, there appears to be a relationship between crustacean ovary-inhibiting hormone and growth hormone of plants (371).

It seems evident that few pertinent cases of hormone interchangeability between vertebrates and invertebrates can be cited. The lack of information on the chemical constitution of invertebrate hormones to some extent precludes a final decision on this point. To date, only one invertebrate hormone, enteramine (5-hydroxytryptamine), has been chemically isolated; it is identical with the corresponding vertebrate hormone (202).[2] A functional similarity seems to exist between the organ complex comprising neural gland plus ciliated pit of ascidians and its homologue, the vertebrate pituitary (see 100, 267).

It is interesting that ascidians, while being able to respond to vertebrate hormones, show less discrimination than higher chordates and, as has been stated above, cannot differentiate between some of them. Thus, hormone specificity seems to increase in the ascending phylogenetic line.

If one considers basic mechanisms of hormone action, invertebrates and vertebrates show remarkable parallelisms. In both groups, there exist neuroendocrine relationships, in which a nervous (for instance, optical) stimulus leads to an endocrine response mediated by a neurosecretory center (see 253, 285, 287, 368, 382, 436, 444). These activities reflect themselves in topographic relationships, in both vertebrates and invertebrates, between optic and neurosecretory centers, and in light sensitivity of central nervous organs (527) as well as in an intimate connection between neurosecretory centers and endocrine organs. The resulting *neurosecretory systems* in invertebrates (insects, crustaceans, chilopods, and spiders) resemble in almost every detail the corresponding hypothalamic-hypophyseal system of the vertebrates—a parallelism which to a varying degree has attracted the attention of a number of investigators (see 120, 121, 239, 255, 443).

Neurosecretory systems consist of groups of neurosecretory cells in distinct locations within the central nervous system. They are connected with endocrine organs, such as the corpora cardiaca and allata of insects, by nerves along which their glandular products are transported proximodistally. These substances are stored and eventually released from some of these organs, which thus may function as a reservoir. Depending on whether or not the organs in which the neurosecretory neurons terminate

[2] After this chapter went to press, the isolation of the growth and differentiation hormone from the prothoracic glands of silkworms has been announced (Butenandt, A., and Karlson, P. Z. *Naturforsch.* **9b,** 389, 1954).

are themselves hormone sources (see 239), one can assume that neurosecretory substances, reaching them in a "directed" fashion instead of via the general circulation, regulate the activity of these glands. The presence of neurosecretory material can be demonstrated in all parts of a neurosecretory system by means of its stainability with various techniques, among which Gomori's chrome hematoxylin phloxine method has proved particularly useful. In the majority of cases neurosecretory products take up the hematoxylin, but phloxinophilic substances have also been found. It should be emphasized that this stainability, although being highly selective, does not represent a histochemical reaction. Furthermore, it seems that the stainable component of the neurosecretory material is a cement substance rather than the hormone or hormones themselves whose presence it merely indicates.

Another point of similarity is the existence, in invertebrates as well as vertebrates, of two-step hormone reactions in which a given endocrine substance, instead of acting directly on the effector organ, does so by way of stimulating another gland of internal secretion. Thus a hormone of the insect brain controls postembryonic development via the prothoracic glands, as the hypophysis acts by means of stimulating the thyroid or gonads (see 58, 546 Chap. X sect. V and Chap. XII sect. VIII).

REFERENCES

1. Agrell, I. *Acta Physiol. Scand.* **28**, 306 (1953).
2. Agrell, I. *Trans. 9th Intern. Congr. Entomol., Amsterdam* **2**, 73 (1953).
3. Agrell, I. *J. Embryol. and Exptl. Morphol.* **1**, 279 (1953).
4. Alexandrowicz, J. S. *Pubbl. staz. zool. Napoli* **23**, 201 (1952).
5. Alexandrowicz, J. S. *Pubbl. staz. zool. Napoli* **24**, 29 (1953).
6. Alexandrowicz, J. S. *J. Marine Biol. Assoc. United Kingdom* **31**, 563 (1953).
7. Alexandrowicz, J. S., and Carlisle, D. B. *J. Marine Biol. Assoc. United Kingdom* **32**, 175 (1953).
8. Altmann, G. *Z. Bienenforsch.* **1**, 24 (1950).
9. Altmann, G. *Z. Bienenforsch.* **1**, 124 (1952).
10. Amar, R. *Compt. rend.* **230**, 407 (1950).
11. Amar, R. *Bull. soc. zool. France* **78**, 171 (1953).
12. Andrewartha, H. G. *Biol. Revs.* **27**, 50 (1952).
13. Arvy, L. *Compt. rend.* **238**, 511 (1954).
14. Arvy, L., Bounhiol, J. J., and Gabe, M. *Compt. rend.* **236**, 627 (1953).
15. Arvy, L., and Gabe, M. *Bull. soc. zool. France* **75**, 267 (1950).
16. Arvy, L., and Gabe, M. *Ann. sci. nat. Zool. et biol. animale* [11] **14**, 345 (1952).
17. Arvy, L., and Gabe, M. *Experientia* **8**, 12 (1952).
18. Arvy, L., and Gabe, M. *Arch. zool. exptl. et gén.* **90**, 105 (1953).
19. Arvy, L., and Gabe, M. *Z. Zellforsch.* **38**, 591 (1953).
20. Arvy, L., and Gabe, M. *Compt. rend.* **237**, 844 (1953).
21. Arvy, L., and Gabe, M. *Cellule* **55**, 203 (1953).
22. Arvy, L., and Gabe, M. *Pubbl. staz. zool. Napoli* **24**, Suppl., 54 (1954).
23. Arvy, L., and Gabe, M. *Biol. Bull.* **106**, 1 (1954).

24. Bacq, Z. M. *Biol. Revs.* **22**, 73 (1947).
25. Bacq, Z. M., Fischer, P., and Ghiretti, F. *Arch. intern. physiol.* **60**, 165 (1952).
26. Bacq, Z. M., and Florkin, M. *Experientia* **2**, 451 (1946).
27. Bacq, Z. M., and Ghiretti, F. *Arch. intern. physiol.* **59**, 288 (1951).
28. Bacq, Z. M., and Ghiretti, F. *Bull. classe sci.*, *Acad. Roy. Belg.* **37**, 79 (1951).
29. Balesdent-Marquet, M. L. *Compt. rend.* **236**, 1086 (1953).
30. Bauchau, A. G. *Ann. soc. roy. zool. Belg.* **79**, 73 (1948).
31. Bauchau, A. G. *Ann. soc. roy. zool. Belg.* **79**, 125 (1948).
32. Billenstien, D. C., and Leveque, T. F. Personal communication.
33. Blaschko, H. *In* G. Pincus and K. V. Thimann, The Hormones. Academic Press, New York, 1950, Vol. 2, p. 601.
34. Blaschko, H., and Himms, J. M. *J. Physiol.* **120**, 445 (1953).
35. Blaschko, H., and Himms, J. M. *J. Exptl. Biol.* **31**, 1 (1954).
36. Bliss, D. E. *Anat. Record* **111**, 502 (1951).
37. Bliss, D. E. *Biol. Bull.* **104**, 275 (1953).
38. Bliss, D. E. *Anat. Record* **117**, 599 (1953).
39. Bliss, D. E., Durand, J. B., and Welsh, J. H. *Z. Zellforsch.* **39**, 520 (1954).
40. Bliss, D. E., Durand, J. B., and Welsh, J. H. *Pubbl. staz. zool. Napoli* **24**, Suppl., 68 (1954).
41. Bliss, D. E., and Welsh, J. H. *Biol. Bull.* **103**, 157 (1952).
42. Bobin, G., and Durchon, M. *Arch. anat. microscop. et morphol. exptl.* **41**, 25 (1952).
43. Bobin, G., and Durchon, M. *Arch. anat. microscop. et morphol. exptl.* **42**, 112 (1953).
44. Bodenheimer, F. S. *Trans. 9th Intern. Congr. Entomol., Amsterdam* **1**, 21 (1952).
45. Bodenstein, D. *J. Exptl. Zool.* **104**, 101 (1947).
46. Bodenstein, D. *J. Exptl. Zool.* **123**, 189 (1953).
47. Bodenstein, D. *J. Exptl. Zool.* **123**, 413 (1953).
48. Bodenstein, D. *J. Exptl. Zool.* **124**, 105 (1953).
49. Bodenstein, D. *Trans. 9th Intern. Congr. Entomol., Amsterdam* **2**, 58 (1953).
50. Bodenstein, D. *In* K. D. Roeder, Insect Physiology. Wiley, New York, 1953, p. 821.
51. Bodenstein, D. *In* K. D. Roeder, Insect Physiology. Wiley, New York, 1953, p. 866.
52. Bodenstein, D. *In* K. D. Roeder, Insect Physiology. Wiley, New York, 1953, p. 879.
53. Bodenstein, D., and Sacktor, B. *Science* **116**, 299 (1952).
54. Bogoraze, D., and Cazal, P. *Arch. zool. exptl. et gén.* **83**, 413 (1944).
55. Bogoraze, D., and Cazal, P. *Arch. zool. exptl. et gén.* **84**, 115 (1946).
56. Boisson, C. J. *Bull. biol. France et Belg.* Suppl. 34, 1 (1949).
57. Bounhiol. J. J. *Compt. rend.* **203**, 1182 (1936).
58. Bounhiol, J. J. *Congr. Assoc. Franç. Avanc. Sci., Biarritz*, p. 1 (1947).
59. Bounhiol, J. J. *Congr. Assoc. Franç. Avanc. Sci., Clermont-Ferrand* p. 1 (1949).
60. Bounhiol, J. J. *Compt. rend.* **235**, 671 (1952).
61. Bounhiol, J. J. *Compt. rend.* **235**, 747 (1952).
62. Bounhiol, J. J. *Trans. 9th Intern. Congr. Entomol., Amsterdam* **2**, 63 (1953).
63. Bounhiol, J. J., Gabe, M., and Arvy, L. *Bull. biol. France et Belg.* **87**, 323 (1953).
64. Bounhiol, J. J., Gabe, M., and Arvy, L. *Pubbl. staz. zool. Napoli* **24**, Suppl., 52 (1954).
65. Brown, F. A. *Quart. Rev. Biol.* **19**, 32, 118 (1944).

66. Brown, F. A. *In* G. Pincus and K. V. Thimann, The Hormones. Academic Press, New York, 1948, Vol. 1, p. 159.
67. Brown, F. A. *In* C. L. Prosser, Comparative Animal Physiology. Saunders, Philadelphia, 1950, p. 675.
68. Brown, F. A. *In* C. L. Prosser, Comparative Animal Physiology. Saunders, Philadelphia, 1950, p. 725.
69. Brown, F. A. *Anat. Record* **111**, 442 (1951).
70. Brown, F. A. *In* K. V. Thimann, The Action of Hormones in Plants and Invertebrates. Academic Press, New York, 1952, p. 171.
71. Brown, F. A. *Biol. Bull.* **105**, 362 (1953).
72. Brown, F. A. *J. Natl. Cancer Inst.* **13**, 1384 (1953).
73. Brown, F. A., Bennett, M. F., and Webb, H. M. *Biol. Bull.* **105**, 371 (1953).
74. Brown, F. A., and Cunningham, O. *Biol. Bull.* **81**, 80 (1941).
75. Brown, F. A., and Fingerman M. *Federation Proc.* **10**, 20 (1951).
76. Brown, F. A., Fingerman, M., and Hines, M. N. *Biol. Bull.* **101**, 217 (1951).
77. Brown, F. A., Fingerman, M., and Hines, M. N. *Physiol. Zool.* **25**, 230 (1952).
78. Brown, F. A., Fingerman, M., and Hines, M. N. *Anat. Record* **117**, 634 (1953).
79. Brown, F. A., Fingerman, M., and Hines, M. N. *Biol. Bull.* **106**, 308 (1954).
80. Brown, F. A., Fingerman, M., Sandeen, M. I., and Webb, H. M. *J. Exptl. Zool.* **123**, 29 (1953).
81. Brown, F. A., and Hines, M. N. *Physiol. Zool.* **25**, 56 (1952).
82. Brown, F. A., Hines, M. N., and Fingerman, M. *Biol. Bull.* **102**, 212 (1952).
83. Brown, F. A., Sandeen, M. I., and Fingerman, M. *Biol. Bull.* **103**, 297 (1952).
84. Brown, F. A., Sandeen, M. I., and Webb, H. M. *Anat. Record* **111**, 569 (1951).
85. Brown, F. A., and Stephens, G. C. *Biol. Bull.* **101**, 71 (1951).
86. Brown, F. A., Webb, H. M., and Graves, R. C. *Biol. Bull.* **103**, 297 (1952).
87. Brown, F. A., Webb, H. M., and Sandeen, M. I. *Anat. Record* **111**, 569 (1951).
88. Brown, F. A., Webb, H. M., and Sandeen, M. I. *J. Exptl. Zool.* **120**, 391 (1952).
89. Brown, F. A., Webb, H. M., and Sandeen, M. I. *J. Cellular Comp. Physiol.* **41**, 123 (1953).
90. Bucklin, D. H. *Anat. Record* **117**, 539 (1953).
91. Bückmann, D. *Naturwissenschaften* **39**, 213 (1952).
92. Bückmann, D. *Biol. Zentr.* **72**, 276 (1953).
93. Von Buddenbrock, W. Vergleichende Physiologie. Birkhäuser Verlag, Basel (Switzerland), 1950, Vol. 4.
94. Bueding, E. *Brit. J. Pharmacol.* **7**, 563 (1952).
95. Bülbring, E., Burn, J. H., and Shelley, H. *Proc. Roy. Soc. (London)* **B141**, 445 (1953).
96. Callan, H. G. *Pubbl. staz. zool. Napoli* **18**, 15 (1940–41).
97. Cameron, M. L. *Nature* **172**, 349 (1953).
98. Carlisle, D. B. *Nature* **166**, 737 (1950).
99. Carlisle, D. B. *Pubbl. staz. zool. Napoli* **22**, 192 (1950).
100. Carlisle, D. B. *J. Exptl. Biol.* **28**, 463 (1951).
101. Carlisle, D. B. *Quart. J. Microscop. Sci.* **92**, 201 (1951).
102. Carlisle, D. B. *Compt. rend.* **236**, 2541 (1953).
103. Carlisle, D. B. *Pubbl. staz. zool. Napoli* **24**, 279 (1953).
104. Carlisle, D. B. *Pubbl. staz. zool. Napoli* **24**, 355 (1953).
105. Carlisle, D. B. *Pubbl. staz. zool. Napoli* **24**, 435 (1953).
106. Carlisle, D. B. *J. Marine Biol. Assoc. United Kingdom* **32**, 289 (1953).
107. Carlisle, D. B. *J. Marine Biol. Assoc. United Kingdom* **33**, 61 (1954).

108. Carlisle, D. B. *Pubbl. staz. zool. Napoli* **24,** Suppl, 79 (1954).
109. Carlisle, D. B. *J. Marine Biol. Assoc. United Kingdom* **33,** 65 (1954).
110. Carlisle, D. B. Personal Communication.
111. Carlisle, D. B., and Dohrn, P. F. R. *Pubbl. staz. zool. Napoli* **24,** 69 (1953).
112. Carlisle, D. B., and Knowles, F. G. W. *Nature* **172,** 404 (1953).
113. Carlisle, D. B., and Knowles, F. G. W. Personal communication.
114. Carlisle, D. B., and Passano, L. M. *Nature* **171,** 1070 (1953).
115. Carson, H. L., and Stalker, H. D. *Proc. Natl. Acad. Sci. U. S.* **34,** 124 (1948).
116. Carstam, S. P. *Bull. biol. France et Belg.* Suppl. 33, 139 (1949).
117. Carstam, S. P. *Nature* **167,** 321 (1951).
118. Carstam, S. P. *Kgl. Fysiogr. Sällskap. Lund Förhandl.* **22** (No. 2) 7, (1952).
119. Carstam, S. P., and Suneson, S. *Kgl. Fysiogr. Sällskap. Lund Förhandl.* **19** (No. 11) 1, (1949).
120. Cazal, P. *Biol. méd. (Paris)* **29,** 545 (1939).
121. Cazal, P. *Biol. Méd. (Paris)* **33,** 141 (1943).
122. Cazal, P., and Bogoraze, D. *Bull. inst. océanog.* (No. 847) 1 (1943).
123. Cazal, P., and Bogoraze, D. *Arch. zool. exptl. et gén.* **84,** 10 (1944).
124. Cazal, P., and Bogoraze, D. *Ann. biol.* [3] **25,** 225 (1949).
125. Chadwick, L. E., and Hill, D. L. *J. Neurophysiol.* **10,** 235 (1947).
126. Charniaux, H., *Compt. rend.* **234,** 2570 (1952).
127. Charniaux, H. *Compt. rend.* **236,** 141 (1953).
128. Charniaux, H. *Proc. 14th Intern. Congr. Zool., Copenhagen* 1953.
129. Charniaux-Cotton, H. *Compt. rend.* **238,** 953 (1954).
130. Charniaux-Cotton, H. Personal communication.
131. Chaudonneret, J. *Bull. soc. zool. France* **74,** 164 (1949).
132. Chefurka, W., and Williams, C. M. *Anat. Record* **113,** 562 (1952).
133. Chicewicz, Z. *Bull. internat. Acad. Sci. Cracovie* (B)II, 81 (1950).
134. Cleveland, L. R. *J. Morphol.* **85,** 197 (1949).
135. Colloques Internationaux du Centre National de la Recherche Scientifique. IV. Endocrinologie des Arthropodes. *Bull. biol. France et Belg.* Suppl. 33, 1–209 (1949).
136. Cornubert, G. *Compt. rend.* **234,** 1218 (1952).
137. Cornubert, G. *Compt. rend.* **236,** 1082 (1953).
138. Cornubert, G. *Compt. rend.* **236,** 1211 (1953).
139. Cornubert, G. *Compt. rend.* **238,** 952 (1954).
140. Cornubert, G. *Bull. inst. océanog.*, No. 1039, 1 (1954).
141. Cornubert, G. *Compt. rend.*, **238,** 952 (1954).
142. Cornubert, G., and Démeusy, N. *Compt. rend.*, in press (1954).
143. Cornubert, G., Démeusy, N., and Veillet, A. *Compt. rend.* **234,** 1405 (1952).
144. Day, M. F. Personal communication.
145. Day, M. F., and Powning, R. F. *Australian J. Sci. Research* B2, 175 (1949).
146. De Beauchamps, P. M. *Compt. rend.* **143,** 249 (1906).
147. De Buen, A. M. *Anal. inst. biol. (Univ. nac. Mexico)* **20,** 465 (1949).
148. De Buen, A. M. Doctoral Thesis, University of Mexico, 1950.
149. Defretin, R. *Compt. rend.* **235,** 100 (1952).
150. De Lattin, G., and Gross, F. J. *Experientia* **9,** 338 (1953).
151. De Lerma, B. *Arch. zool. ital.* **17,** 417 (1932).
152. De Lerma, B. *Boll. zool. (ital.)* **13,** 1 (1942).
153. De Lerma, B. *Arch. zool. ital.* **32,** 1 (1947).
154. De Lerma, B. *Boll. zool. (ital)* **17,** Suppl. (vol. Atti Convegno cinquant. U. Z. I.), 67 (1950).

155. De Lerma, B. *Ann. ist. e mus. zool. Univ. Napoli* **3**, 1 (1951).
156. De Lerma, B. *Boll. zool. (ital.)* **19**, 53 (1952).
157. De Lerma, B. *Pubbl. staz. zool. Napoli* **24**, Suppl., 56 (1954).
158. Démeusy, N. *Compt. rend.* **236**, 974 (1953).
159. Démeusy, N., and Lenel, M. R. *Compt. rend. soc. biol.*, **148**, 156 (1954).
160. Démeusy, N., and Veillet, A. *Compt. rend.* **234**, 1224 (1952).
161. Donahue, J. K. *Proc. Soc. Exptl. Biol. Med.* **69**, 179 (1948).
162. Drach, P. *Bull. biol. France et Belg.* **78**, 40 (1944).
163. Drach, P. *Compt. rend.* **225**, 1376 (1947).
164. Drach, P. *Bull. biol. France et Belg.* Suppl. 33, 164 (1949).
165. Drach, P. *Bull. biol. France et Belg.* Suppl. 33, 177 (1949).
166. Dupont-Raabe, M. *Compt. rend.* **228**, 130 (1949).
167. Dupont-Raabe, M. *Arch. zool. exptl. et gén.* **86**, 32 (1949).
168. Dupont-Raabe, M. *Bull. soc. zool. France* **76**, 386 (1951).
169. Dupont-Raabe, M. *Compt. rend.* **232**, 886 (1951).
170. Dupont-Raabe, M. *Arch. zool. exptl. et gén.* **89**, 128 (1952).
171. Dupont-Raabe, M. *Arch. zool. exptl. et gén.* **89**, 102 (1952).
172. Dupont-Raabe, M. *Bull. soc. zool. France* **77**, 235 (1952).
173. Dupont-Raabe, M. *Compt. rend.* **238**, 950 (1954).
174. Dupont-Raabe, M. *Pubbl. staz. zool. Napoli* **24**, Suppl., 63 (1954).
175. Durchon, M. *Compt. rend.* **227**, 157 (1948).
176. Durchon, M. *Compt. rend.* **229**, 81 (1949).
177. Durchon, M. *Compt. rend.* **232**, 442 (1951).
178. Durchon, M. *Ann. sci. nat. zool. et biol. animale* [11] **14**, 117 (1952).
179. Durchon, M. *Ann. biol.* [3] **29**, 31 (1953).
180. Echalier, G. *compt. rend.* **238**, 523 (1954).
181. Edwards, G. A. *Physiol. comp. et oecol.* **2**, 34 (1950–52).
182. Egami, N. *Annot. zool. japon.* **25**, 182 (1952).
183. Ehnbohm, K. *Opuscul. entomol. (Lund)* Suppl. 8, 1 (1948).
184. Enami, M. *Japan. J. Zool.* **9**, 497 (1941).
185. Enami, M. *Japan. J. Zool.* **9**, 515 (1941).
186. Enami, M. *Proc. Imp. Acad. Tokyo* **19**, 693 (1943).
187. Enami, M. *Proc. Imp. Acad. Tokyo* **19**, 698 (1943).
188. Enami, M. *Physiol. and Ecol. (Kyoto)* **3**, 23 (1949).
189. Enami, M. *Physiol. and Ecol. (Kyoto)* **4**, 1 (1950).
190. Enami, M. *Biol. Bull.* **100**, 28 (1951).
191. Enami, M. *Biol. Bull.* **101**, 241 (1951).
192. Enami, M. *J. Exptl. Morphol. (Japan)* **7**, 1 (1951), in Japanese.
193. Enami, M. *Kagaku (Monthly J. Sci., Tokyo)* **24**, 135 (1954), in Japanese.
194. Enami, M. *Pubbl. staz. zool. Napoli* **24**, Suppl., 70 (1954).
195. Enders, E. *Ann. Univ. Saraviensis* **4**, 294 (1952).
196. Erspamer, V. *Experientia* **2**, 369 (1946).
197. Erspamer, V. *Arch. intern. pharmacodynamie* **74**, 113 (1947).
198. Erspamer, V. *Arch. intern. pharmacodynamie* **76**, 308 (1948).
199. Erspamer, V. *Acta pharmacol. et toxicol.* **4**, 213 (1948).
200. Erspamer, V. *Acta pharmacol. et toxicol.* **4**, 228 (1948).
201. Erspamer, V. *Nature* **169**, 375 (1952).
202. Erspamer, V. *Rend. sci. Farmitalia* **1**, 1 (1954).
203. Erspamer, V., and Asero, B. *Nature* **169**, 800 (1952).
204. Erspamer, V., and Asero, B. *J. Biol. Chem.* **200**, 311 (1953).
205. Erspamer, V., and Faustini, R. *Naturwissenschaften* **40**, 317 (1953).

88 BERTA SCHARRER

206. Erspamer, V., and Ghiretti, F. *J. Physiol.* **115**, 470 (1951).
207. Erspamer, V., and Ottolenghi, A. *Arch. intern. Pharmacodynamie* **93**, 177 (1953).
208. Euler, U. S. v. *Acta. Physiol. Scand.* **28**, 297 (1953).
209. Florey, E. *Verhandl. deut. Zool. Wilhelmshaven*, p. 199 (1951).
210. Florey, E. *Biol. Zentr.* **71**, 499 (1952).
211. Florey, E. *Z. vergleich. Physiol.*, **36**, 1 (1954).
212. Florey, E., and Florey, E. *Naturwissenschaften* **40**, 413 (1953).
213. Florey, E. Personal communication.
214. Flückiger, E. *Acta Physiol. Scand.* **30**, 33 (1953).
215. Frentz, R., and Veillet, A. *Compt. rend.* **236**, 2168 (1953).
216. Frost, R., Saloum, R., and Kleinholz, L. H. *Anat. Record* **111**, 572 (1951).
217. Fukuda, S. *Zool. Mag. (Dobuts. Zasshi)* **60**, 119 (1951).
218. Fukuda, S. *Proc. Japan Acad.* **27**, 582 (1951).
219. Fukuda, S. *Proc. Japan Acad.* **27**, 672 (1951).
220. Fukuda, S. *Annot. zool. japon.* **25**, 149 (1952).
221. Fukuda, S. *Proc. Japan Acad.* **28**, (1952).
222. Fukuda, S. *Proc. Japan Acad.* **29**, 381 (1953).
223. Fukuda, S. *Proc. Japan Acad*. **29**, 385 (1953).
224. Fukuda, S. *Proc. Japan Acad*. **29**, 389 (1953).
225. Gabe, M. *Compt. rend.* **229**, 1172 (1949).
226. Gabe, M. *Rev. can. biol.* **10**, 391 (1951).
227. Gabe, M. *Compt. rend.* **235**, 90 (1952).
228. Gabe, M. *Compt. rend.* **235**, 900 (1952).
229. Gabe, N. *Compt. rend.* **235**, 973 (1952).
230. Gabe, M. *Compt. rend.* **235**, 1430 (1952).
231. Gabe, M. *Compt. rend.* **236**, 323 (1953).
232. Gabe, M. *Compt. rend.* **236**, 2166 (1953).
233. Gabe, M. *Compt. rend.* **237**, 1111 (1953).
234. Gabe, M. *Bull. Lab. Dinard* **38**, 3 (1953).
235. Gabe, M. *Experientia* **9**, 352 (1953).
236. Gabe, M. *Bull. soc. zool. France* **78**, 177 (1953).
237. Gabe, M. *Compt. rend.* **238**, 272 (1954).
238. Gabe, M. *Compt. rend.* **238**, 1265 (1954).
239. Gabe, M. *Ann. biol.* [3] **30**, 5 (1954).
240. Gaskell, W. H. The Involuntary Nervous System. Longmans Green & Co., London, 1916.
241. Geigy, R., and Rahm, U. *Rev. suisse zool.* **58**, 408 (1951).
242. Geyer, K. *Z. wiss. Zool.* **105**, 349 (1913).
243. Glaser, R. W. *J. Exptl. Zool.* **84**, 1 (1940).
244. Grandori, L., and Caré, E. *Ann. Fac. Agrar. Milano* **11**, 1 (1953).
245. Grandori, L., and Caré, E. *Pubbl. staz. zool. Napoli* **24**, Suppl., 50 (1954).
246. Grassé, P. P. *Trans. 9th Intern. Congr. Entomol., Amsterdam* **1**, 51 (1952).
247. Gray, S. W., and Ford, W. *Endocrinology* **26**, 160 (1940).
248. Gregerman, R. I., and Wald, G. *J. Gen. Physiol.* **35**, 489 (1952).
249. Gunn, D. L. *Nature* **135**, 434 (1935).
250. Guyselman, J. B. *Biol. Bull.* **104**, 115 (1953).
251. Hadorn, E. *J. Embryol. and Exptl. Morphol.* **1**, 213 (1953).
252. Hamasaki, S. *Proc. Imp. Acad. (Tokyo)* **8**, 267 (1932).
253. Hanström, B. Hormones in Invertebrates. Oxford University Press, 1939.
254. Hanström, B. *Bull. biol. France et Belg.* Suppl. 33, 98 (1949).

255. Hanström, B.　*Nature* **171**, 72 (1953).
256. Hara, J.　*Annot. zool. japon.* **25**, 162 (1952).
257. Hara, J.　*Annot. zool. japon.* **25**, 411 (1952).
258. Harker, J. E.　*Nature* **173**, 689 (1954).
259. Harms, W.　*Arch. Entwicklungsmech. Organ.* **47**, 307 (1921).
260. Harms, J. W.　*Biol. Zentr.* **64**, 1 (1944).
261. Harms, J. W.　*Arch. Entwicklungsmech. Organ.* **143**, 332 (1947).
262. Harvey, W. R., and Williams, C. M.　*Anat. Record* **117**, 544 (1953).
263. Hasegawa, K.　*Proc. Japan Acad.* **27**, 667 (1951).
264. Hasegawa, K.　*Nippon Sanshigaku Zasshi* **20**, 403 (1951), in Japanese.
265. Hasegawa, K.　*J. Fac. Agr. Tottori Univ.* **1**, 83 (1952).
266. Havel, V. J., and Kleinholz, L. H.　*Anat. Record* **111**, 571 (1951).
267. Heller, H.　*Experientia* **6**, 368 (1950).
268. Heller, H., and Smith, B.　*Nature* **159**, 544 (1947).
269. Heller, H., and Smith, B.　*J. Exptl. Biol.* **25**, 388 (1948).
270. Henschler, D.　*Naturwissenschaften* **41**, 142 (1954).
271. Hild W.　Personal communication.
272. Hubl, H.　*Arch. Entwicklungsmech. Organ.* **146**, 421 (1953).
273. Ichikawa, M.　*J. Exptl. Morphol.* (*Japan*) **7**, 23 (1951), in Japanese.
274. Ichikawa, M., and Kaji, S.　*Annot. zool. japon.* **24**, 1 (1950).
275. Ichikawa, M., Kaji, S., Yatsushika, K., and Nishiisutsuji, J.　*Zool. Mag.* (*Dobuts Zasshi*) **60**, 25 (1950), in Japanese.
276. Ichikawa, M., and Nishiisutsuji, J.　*Annot. zool. japon.* **24**, 205 (1951).
277. Ichikawa, M., and Nishiisutsuji, J.　*Annot. zool. japon.* **25**, 143 (1952).
278. Ito, T.　*Bull. Sericult. Expt. Sta.* (*Japan*) **13**, 585 (1951).
279. Iwakura, C.　*Publ. Tokyo Gakugei Univ.* **2**, 33 (1951).
280. Johansson, A. S.　*Nature*, **174**, 89 (1954).
281. Johansson, A. S.　Personal communication.
282. Joly, P.　*Ann. biol.* [3] **21**, 1(1945).
283. Joly, P.　*Compt. rend. soc. biol.* **144**, 1217 (1950).
284. Joly, P.　*Compt. rend. soc. biol.* **145**, 1362 (1951).
285. Joly, P.　*Compt. rend.* **235**, 1054 (1952).
286. Joly, P.　*Compt. rend.* **235**, 1555 (1952).
287. Joly, P., and Joly, L.　*Ann. sci. nat. zool. et biol. animale* [11] **15**, 331 (1953).
288. Jones, B. M.　*Nature* **172**, 551 (1953).
289. Kaiser, P.　*Arch. Entwicklungsmech. Organ.* **144**, 99 (1949).
290. Karlson, P., and Hanser, G.　*Z. Naturforsch.* **7b**, 80 (1952).
291. Karlson, P., and Hanser, G.　*Z. Naturforsch.* **8b**, 91 (1953).
292. Kawakami, A.　*J. Constitutional Med.* **10**, 611 (1942).
293. Kenk, R.　*J. Exptl. Zool.* **87**, 55 (1941).
294. Ketchel, M., Feder, N., and Schneiderman, H. A.　*Anat. Record* **111**, 518 (1951).
295. Ketchel, M., and Williams, C. M.　*Anat. Record* **113**, 57 (1952).
296. Ketchel, M., and Williams, C. M.　*Anat. Record* **117**, 542 (1953).
297. Kimball, R. F.　*Genetics* **27**, 269 (1942).
298. Kincaid, F. D., and Scheer, B. T.　*Physiol. Zool.* **25**, 372 (1952).
299. Kleinholz, L. H.　*Biol. Revs.* **17**, 91 (1942).
300. Kleinholz, L. H.　*Bull. biol. France et Belg.* Suppl. 33, 127 (1949).
301. Kleinholz, L. H.　*Biol. Bull.* **99**, 454 (1950).
302. Knowles, F. G. W.　*Bull. biol. France et Belg.* Suppl. 33, 149 (1949).
303. Knowles, F. G. W.　*Biol. Bull.* **98**, 66 (1950).

304. Knowles, F. G. W. *Nature* **167**, 564 (1951).
305. Knowles, F. G. W. *Physiol. comp. et oecol.* **2**, 289 (1950–52).
306. Knowles, F. G. W. *Proc. Roy. Soc. (London)* **B141**, 248 (1953).
307. Knowles, F. G. W. *Nature* **171**, 131 (1953).
308. Knowles, F. G. W. *Pubbl. staz. zool. Napoli* **24**, Suppl., 74 (1954).
309. Kobayashi, H., and Yoshida, M. *Zool. Mag. (Dobuts. Zasshi)* **60**, 132 (1951).
310. Koch, H. J. *Arch. intern. physiol.* **62**, 136 (1954).
311. Koidsumi, K. *Annot. zool. japon.* **25**, 156 (1952).
312. Koller, G. Hormone bei wirbellosen Tieren. Akad. Verlagsgesellschaft, Leipzig, 1938.
313. Koller, G. *Verhandl. deut. Zool.*, p. 440 (1939).
314. Koller, G. *Biol. Zentr.* **67**, 201 (1948).
315. Koller, G. *Ann. Univ. Saraviensis* **1**, 242 (1952).
316. Koller, G. *Pubbl. staz. zool. Napoli* **24**, Suppl., 67 (1954).
317. Kooistra, G. *Physiol. comp. et oecol.* **2**, 75 (1950).
318. Kopeć, S. *Bull. Acad. Sci., Cracovie, classe sci. math. nat. sér. B.*, p. 57 (1917).
319. Kuntz, E. *Biol. Bull.* **93**, 198 (1947).
320. Kuntz, E. *Federation Proc.* **10**, 77 (1951).
321. de Lattin, G., and Gross, F. J. *Experientia* **9**, 338 (1953).
322. Legay, J. M. *Compt. rend. soc. biol.* **144**, 512 (1950).
323. Legendre, R. *Compt. rend.* **237**, 1283 (1953).
324. Legendre, R. *Compt. rend.* **238**, 1267 (1954).
325. Legrand, J. J. *Compt. rend.* **238**, 2030 (1954).
326. Lender, T. *Compt. rend.* **238**, 1742 (1954).
327. Lenel, R., and Veillet, A. *Compt. rend.* **233**, 1064 (1951).
328. Leveque, T. F. *Anat. Record* **118**, 325 (1954).
329. Lewis, S. E. *Nature* **172**, 1004 (1953).
330. L'Hélias, C. *Bull. soc. zool. France* **75**, 70 (1950).
331. L'Hélias, C. *Compt. rend. soc. biol.* **145**, 233 (1951).
332. L'Hélias, C. *Bull. soc. zool. France* **77**, 106 (1952).
333. L'Hélias, C. *Bull. soc. zool. France* **77**, 191 (1952).
334. L'Hélias, C. *Compt. rend.* **236**, 2164 (1953).
335. L'Hélias, C. *Compt. rend.* **236**, 2489 (1953).
336. Lhoste, J. *Bull. soc. zool. France* **75**, 285 (1950).
337. Lhoste, J. *Compt. rend.* **232**, 264 (1951).
338. Lhoste, J. *Bull. soc. zool. France* **76**, 306 (1951).
339. Lhoste, J. *Arch. zool. exptl. et gén.* **89**, 169 (1953).
340. Linke, O. *Zool. Anz.*, Suppl. 7, 164 (1934).
341. Ludwig, D. *J. Gen. Physiol.* **36**, 751 (1953).
342. Lukoschus, F. *Naturwissenschaften* **39**, 116 (1952).
343. Lüscher, M. *Rev. suisse zool.* **58**, 404 (1951).
344. Lüscher, M. *Z. vergleich. Physiol.* **34**, 123 (1952).
345. Lüscher, M. *Trans. 9th Intern. Congr. Entomol., Amsterdam* **1**, 289 (1952).
346. Maher, A. Doctoral Thesis, University of London, 1953.
347. Maroney, S. P., and Ronkin, R. R. *Biol. Bull.* **105**, 378 (1953).
348. Matsumoto, F. *Zool. Mag. (Dobuts. Zasshi)* **60**, 13 (1951), in Japanese.
349. Matsumoto, K. *Biol. J. Okayama Univ.* **1**, 84 (1952).
350. Matsumoto, K. *Biol. Bull.* **106**, 60 (1954).
351. Mendes, E. G. *Proc. 8th Am. Sci. Congr.* **3**, 423 (1942).
352. Mendes, M. V. *Anais acad. brasil. cienc.* **19**, 259 (1947), in Portuguese.

353. Michon, J.   *Compt. rend.* **236**, 2545 (1953).
354. Mitolo, M.   *Arch. sci. biol.* **24**, 33 (1938).
355. Mokia, G. G.   *Compt. rend. acad. sci. U. R. S. S.* [N. S.] **30**, 371 (1941).
356. Montalenti, G., and Vitagliano, G.   *Pubbl. staz. zool. Napoli* **20**, 1 (1946).
357. Moretti, G. P., and Cianficconi, F.   *Boll. soc. ital. biol. sper.* **28**, 134 (1952).
358. Nachmansohn, D.   *In* G. Pincus and K. V. Thimann, The Hormones. Academic Press, New York, 1950, Vol. 2, p. 513.
359. Nagano, T.   *Science Repts. Tôhoku Univ.*, [*Ser. 4*] **19**, 118 (1951).
360. Nagano, T.   *Science Repts. Tôhoku Univ.* [*Ser. 4*] **19**, 219 (1952).
361. Nayar, K. K.   *Current Sci.* (*India*) **22**, 149 (1953).
362. Nayar, K. K.   *Nature* **172**, 768 (1953).
363. Nayar, K. K.   *Current Sci.* (*India*) **23**, 26 (1954).
364. Nicol, J. A. C.   *Physiol. comp. et oecol.* **2**, 339 (1950–52).
365. Nittono, Y.   *Japan. J. Sericult.* **20**, 100 (1951), in Japanese.
366. Novák, V. J. A.   *Nature* **167**, 132 (1951).
367. Novák, V. J. A.   *Věstník Čsl. zool. společnosti* **15**, 1 (1951).
368. Nowikoff, M.   *Z. Morphol. Ökol. Tiere* **29**, 374 (1934).
369. Östlund, E.   *Nature* **172**, 1042 (1953).
370. Otsu, T., and Hanaoka, K. I.   *J. Yamagata Univ.* **1**, 269 (1951).
371. Otsu, T., and Hanaoka, K. I.   *J. Yamagata Univ.* **2**, 219 (1953).
372. Ozeki, K.   *Sci. Papers Coll. Gen. Educ. Univ. Tokyo* **1**, 83 (1951).
373. Panouse, J. B.   *Ann. biol.* [3] **23**, 33 (1947).
374. Panouse, J. B.   *Bull. biol. France et Belg.* Suppl. 33, 160 (1949).
375. Pappenheimer, A. M., and Williams, C. M.   *Anat. Record* **117**, 543 (1953).
376. Passano, L. M.   *Anat. Record* **111**, 502 (1951).
377. Passano, L. M.   *Anat. Record* **111**, 559 (1951).
378. Passano, L. M.   *Anat. Record* **112**, 460 (1952).
379. Passano, L. M.   *Physiol. comp. et oecol.* **3**, 155 (1953).
380. Passano, L. M.   *Pubbl. staz. zool. Napoli* **24**, Suppl., 72 (1954).
381. Pautsch, F.   *Bull. intern. acad. polon. sci.* [*Sér. B.*] **2**, 17 (1951).
382. Pautsch, F.   *Experientia* **9**, 274 (1953).
383. Pérès, J. M.   *Experientia* **3**, 330 (1947).
384. Pérès, J. M.   *Compt. rend.* **233**, 274 (1951).
385. Pfeiffer, I. W.   *J. Exptl. Zool.* **99**, 183 (1945).
386. Pflugfelder, O.   Entwicklungsphysiologie der Insekten. Akad. Verlagsgesellschaft, Leipzig, 1952.
387. Pickford, G. E.   *Science* **105**, 522 (1947).
388. Piepho, H.   *Biol. Zentr.* **69**, 1 (1950).
389. Piepho, H.   *Biol. Zentr.* **69**, 261 (1950).
390. Piepho, H.   *Z. Tierpsychol.* **7**, 424 (1950).
391. Piepho, H.   *Zool. Anz.*, Suppl. 16, 62 (1952).
392. Piepho, H., and Heims, A.   *Z. Naturforsch.* **7b**, 231 (1952).
393. Piepho, H., and Meyer, H.   *Biol. Zentr.* **70**, 252 (1951).
394. Pittendrigh, C. S.   *Science* **118**, 768 (1953).
395. Possompès, B.   *Bull. soc. zool. France* **73**, 100 (1948).
396. Possompès, B.   *Bull. soc. zool. France* **73**, 201 (1948).
397. Possompès, B.   *Bull. soc. zool. France* **73**, 228 (1948).
398. Possompès, B.   *Compt. rend.* **228**, 1527 (1949).
399. Possompès, B.   *Compt. rend.* **231**, 594 (1950).
400. Possompès, B.   *Trans. 9th Intern. Congr. Entomol., Amsterdam* **1**, 216 (1952).

401. Possompès, B. *Arch. zool. exptl. et gén.* **89,** 203 (1953).
402. Possompès, B. *Pubbl. staz. zool. Napoli* **24,** Suppl., 59 (1954).
403. Proceedings of the Symposium on Neurosecretion, Naples 1953. *Pubbl. staz. zool. Napoli* **24,** Suppl., 1–98 (1954).
404. Rahm, U. *Experientia* **8,** 62 (1952).
405. Rahm, U. H. *Rev. suisse zool.* **59,** 173 (1952).
406. Rehm, M. *Z. Naturforsch.* **5b,** 167 (1950).
407. Rehm, M. *Arch. Entwicklungsmech. Organ.* **145,** 205 (1951).
408. Rehm, M. *Personal communication.*
409. Reinhard, E. G. *Biol. Bull.* **98,** 277 (1950).
410. Renner, M. *Z. Tierpsychol.* **9,** 122 (1952).
411. Reverberi, G. *Accad. nazl. Lincei,* quaderno no. 22, 38 (1950).
412. Reverberi, G. *Boll. zool. (ital.)* **17,** 89 (1950).
413. Reverberi, G. *Pubbl. staz. zool. Napoli* **23,** 285 (1952).
414. Rhein, W. v. *Verhandl. deut. Zool., Wilhelmshaven* **99,** (1952).
415. Richards, A. G. *J. N. Y. Entomol. Soc.* **45,** 1 (1937).
416. Richards, A. G., and Cutkomp, L. K. *J. Cellular Comp. Physiol.* **26,** 57 (1945).
417. Risler, H. *Zool. Jahrb. Anat. Ontog.* **71,** 325 (1951).
418. Rybak, B. *Bull. soc. chim. biol.* **31,** 464 (1949).
419. Sacktor, B. *Biol. Bull.* **100,** 229 (1951).
420. Sacktor, B. *J. Gen. Physiol.* **35,** 397 (1952).
421. Sanborn, R. C., and Williams, C. M. *Anat. Record* **108,** 558 (1950).
422. Sandeen, M. I., and Brown, F. A. *Biol. Bull.* **101,** 228 (1951).
423. Sandeen, M. I., and Brown, F. A. *Physiol. Zool.* **25,** 222 (1952).
424. Sandeen, M. I., Fingerman, M., and Brown, F. A. *Biol. Bull.* **103,** 307 (1952).
425. Sawaya, P. *Proc. 8th Am. Sci. Congr.* **3,** 487 (1942).
426. Schaller, F. *Compt. rend. soc. biol.* **144,** 1097 (1950).
427. Schaller, F. *Compt. rend. soc. biol.* **145,** 1351 (1951).
428. Schaller, F. *Bull. soc. zool. France* **77,** 195 (1952).
429. Scharrer, B. *J. Compt. Neurol.* **74,** 109 (1941).
430. Scharrer, B. *Biol. Bull.* **81,** 96 (1941).
431. Scharrer, B. *Physiol. Revs.* **21,** 383 (1941).
432. Scharrer, B. *In* G. Pincus and K. V. Thimann, The Hormones. Academic Press, New York, 1948, Vol. 1, p. 121.
433. Scharrer, B. *Anat. Record* **111,** 554 (1951).
434. Scharrer, B. *In* K. V. Thimann, The Action of Hormones in Plants and Invertebrates, Academic Press, New York, 1952, p. 125.
435. Scharrer, B. *Anat. Record* **112,** 386 (1952).
436. Scharrer, B. *Pflüger's Arch. ges. Physiol.* **255,** 154 (1952).
437. Scharrer, B. *Biol. Bull.* **102,** 261 (1952).
438. Scharrer, B. *Cancer Research* **13,** 73 (1953).
439. Scharrer, B. *J. Natl. Cancer Inst.* **13,** 951 (1953).
440. Scharrer, B. *Ann. Rev. Physiol.* **15,** 457 (1953).
441. Scharrer, B. *Pubbl. staz. zool. Napoli* **24,** Suppl., 38 (1954).
442. Scharrer, B. Unpublished data.
443. Scharrer, B., and Scharrer, E. *Biol. Bull.* **87,** 242 (1944).
444. Scharrer, E. *Scientia (Milano)* [6] **87,** 177 (1952).
445. Scharrer, E., and Scharrer, B. *Biol. Revs.* **12,** 185 (1937).
446. Scharrer, E., and Scharrer, B. *Physiol. Revs.* **25,** 171 (1945).
447. Scharrer, E., and Scharrer, B. *Science* **118,** 579 (1953).

448. Scharrer, E., and Scharrer, B. *Von Moellendorff's Handb. mikr. Anat. Menschen* **VI/5**, 953 (1954).
449. Scharrer, E., and Scharrer, B. *Recent Progr. Hormone Research* **10**, 183 (1954).
450. Scheer, B. T., and Scheer, M. A. R. *Physiol. comp. et oecol.* **2**, 198 (1950–52).
451. Scheer, B. T., Schwabe, C. W., and Scheer, M. A. R. *Physiol. comp. et oecol.* **2**, 327 (1950–52).
452. Schmidt, E. L. Doctoral Thesis, Harvard University, 1951.
453. Schmidt, E. L., and Williams, C. M. *Anat. Record* **111**, 517 (1951).
454. Schmidt, E. L., and Williams, C. M. *Biol. Bull.* **105**, 174 (1953).
455. Schneiderman, H. A., Feder, N., and Ketchel, M. *Anat. Record* **111**, 518 (1951).
456. Schneiderman, H. A., Ketchel, M., and Williams, C. M. *Biol. Bull.* **105**, 188 (1953).
457. Schneiderman, H. A., and Williams, C. M. *Anat. Record* **113**, 55 (1952).
458. Schneiderman, H. A., and Williams, C. M. *Biol. Bull.* **105**, 320 (1953).
459. Schneiderman, H. A., and Williams, C. M. *Biol. Bull.* **106**, 210 (1954).
460. Schneiderman, H. A., and Williams, C. M. *Biol. Bull.* **106**, 238 (1954).
461. Schwabe, C. W., Scheer, B. T., and Scheer, M. A. R. *Physiol. comp. et oecol.* **2**, 310 (1950–52).
462. Schwinck, I. *Arch. Entwicklungsmech. Organ.* **145**, 62 (1951).
463. Schwinck, I. *Naturwissenschaften* **39**, 160 (1952).
464. Scudamore, H. H. *Physiol. Zool.* **20**, 187 (1947).
465. Seaman, G. R. *Biol. Bull.* **99**, 347 (1950).
466. Sellier, R. *Arch. zool. exptl. et gén.* **88**, 61 (1951).
467. Sereni, E. *Am. J. Physiol.* **90**, 512 (1929).
468. Sereni, E. *Biol. Bull.* **59**, 247 (1930).
469. Shappirio, D. G., and Williams, C. M. *Anat. Record* **113**, 55 (1952).
470. Shappirio, D. G., and Williams, C. M. *Anat. Record* **117**, 542 (1953).
471. Snodgrass, R. E. *Smithsonian Inst. Publs. Misc. Collections* **122**, (No. 9) 1 (1954).
472. Sonneborn, T. M. *Cold Spring Harbor Symposia Quant. Biol.* **10**, 111 (1942).
473. Stegwee, D. *Physiol. comp. et oecol.* **2**, 241 (1950–52).
474. Steidle, H. *Endokrinologie* **28**, 134 (1951).
475. Stephens, G. C. *Anat. Record* **111**, 572 (1951).
476. Stephens, G. C. *Biol. Bull.* **103**, 242 (1952).
477. Stephens, G. J. *Physiol. Zool.* **25**, 70 (1952).
478. Stutinsky, F. *Compt. rend. soc. biol.* **145**, 367 (1951).
479. Stutinsky, F. *Bull. soc. zool. France* **77**, 61 (1952).
480. Stutinsky, F. *Bull. soc. zool. France* **78**, 202 (1953).
481. Suomalainen, P. *Ann. Zool. Soc., Zool.-Botan. Fennicae Vanamo* **7** (No. 3) 1 (1939).
482. Suomalainen, P. *Ann. Zool. Soc., Zool.-Botan. Fennicae Vanamo* **7** (No. 4) 1 (1939).
483. Takaoka, M. *Sci. Rept. Tôhoku Univ. [Ser. 4]* **19**, 88 (1951).
484. Takewaki, K. *Zool. Mag. (Dobuts. Zasshi)* **56**, 5 (1944).
485. Takewaki, K. *Zool. Mag. (Dobuts. Zasshi)* **57**, 6 (1947).
486. Takewaki, K. and Nakamura N. *J. Fac. Sci. Imp. Univ. Tokyo, Sect. IV,* **6**, 369 (1944).
487. Taki, I. *J. Sci. Hiroshima Univ., Sect. B1,* **10**, 131 (1943), in Japanese.
488. Telfer, W. H. *Anat. Record* **117**, 541 (1953).
489. Telfer, W. H. *Federation Proc.* **12**, 734 (1953).

490. Telfer, W. H., and Williams, C. M. *Anat. Record* **108,** 559 (1950).
491. Telfer, W. H., and Williams, C. M. *Anat. Record* **113,** 563 (1952).
492. Telfer, W. H., and Williams, C. M. *J. Gen. Physiol.* **36,** 389 (1953).
493. Thomsen, E. *Naturwissenschaften* **29,** 605 (1941).
494. Thomsen, E. *Vidensk. Medd. Dansk Nathist. Forening* **106,** 317 (1942).
495. Thomsen, E. *J. Exptl. Biol.* **26,** 137 (1949).
496. Thomsen, E. *J. Exptl. Biol.* **29,** 137 (1952).
497. Thomsen, E. *Pubbl. staz. zool. Napoli* **24,** Suppl., 48 (1954).
498. Thomsen, E. *J. Exptl. Biol.,* **31,** 322 (1954).
499. Thomsen, M. *Kgl. Danske Videnskab. Selskab. Biol. Skrifter* **6** (No. 5) 1 (1951).
500. Thomsen, M. *Pubbl. staz. zool. Napoli* **24,** Suppl., 46 (1954).
501. Thomsen, M. *Kgl. Danske Videnskab. Selskab. Biol. Skrifter* **7** (No. 5) 1 (1954).
502. Thomsen, E., and Thomsen, M. *Experientia* **10,** 206 (1954).
503. Thore, S. *Kgl. Fysiograf. Sällskap. Lund. Förhandl.* **6,** 147 (1936).
504. Tobias, J. M., Kollros, J. J., and Savit, J. *J. Cellular Comp. Physiol.* **28,** 159 (1946).
505. Travis, D. F. *Anat. Record* **111,** 503 (1951).
506. Turchini, J. *Acta Anat.* **19,** 383 (1953).
507. Turner, C. D. General Endocrinology. Saunders, Philadelphia, 1948.
508. Umeya, Y. Hormones in Invertebrates. Syokabo, Tokyo, 1953, in Japanese.
509. Van der Kloot, W., and Williams, C. M. *Anat. Record* **108,** 511 (1950).
510. Van der Kloot, W. G., and Williams, C. M. *Behaviour* **5,** 157 (1953).
511. Veillet, A. *Bull. inst. océanog.* (No. 810) 1 (1941).
512. Veillet, A. *Ann. inst. océanog.* **22,** 193 (1945).
513. Veillet, A. In press.
514. Veillet, A., Cornubert, G., and Démeusy, N. *Compt. rend. soc. biol.,* **147,** 1264 (1953).
515. Veillet, A., and Reynier, M. *Congr. Assoc. Franç. Avanc. Sci.,* Saarbrücken (1953).
516. Vialli, M., and Erspamer, V. *Mikrochemie* **24,** 253 (1938).
517. Vogt, Marthe. Personal communication.
518. Walop, J. N., and Boot, L. M. *Biochim. et Biophys. Acta* **4,** 566 (1950).
519. Waterman, T. H., and Enami, M. *Pubbl. staz. zool. Napoli* **24,** Suppl., 81 (1954).
520. Webb, H. M., Bennett, M. F., and Brown, F. A. *Anat. Record* **117,** 633 (1953).
521. Webb, H. M., Bennett, M. F., and Brown, F. A. *Biol. Bull.* **106,** 371 (1954).
522. Webb, H. M., Bennett, M. F., Graves, R. C., and Stephens, G. C. *Biol. Bull.* **105,** 386 (1953).
523. Webb, H. M., and Brown, F. A. *Biol. Bull.* **101,** 231 (1951).
524. Webb, H. M., and Brown, F. A. *J. Cellular Comp. Physiol.* **41,** 103 (1953).
525. Webb, H. M., Brown, F. A., Fingerman, M., and Hines, M. N. *Anat. Record* **111,** 569 (1951).
526. Weber, H. *Fortschr. Zool.* [N. F.] **9,** 18 (1952).
527. Wells, P. H. *Anat. Record* **113,** 613 (1952).
528. Welsh, J. H. *Anat. Record* **111,** 442 (1951).
529. Welsh, J. H. *Arch. exptl. Pathol. u. Pharmakol.* **219,** 23 (1953).
530. Welsh, J. H. *Anat. Record* **117,** 637 (1953).
531. Wenk, P. *Zool. Jahrb. Anat. Ontog.* **73,** 103 (1953).
532. Wiedbrauck, H. *Biol. Zentr.* **72,** 530 (1953).
533. Wigglesworth, V. B. *J. Exptl. Biol.* **17,** 201 (1940).
534. Wigglesworth, V. B. The Principles of Insect Physiology, 4th ed. Dutton, New York, 1950.

535. Wigglesworth, V. B.   *Endeavour* **10,** (No. 37), 22 (1951).
536. Wigglesworth, V. B.   *Proc. Roy. Entomol. Soc. (London)* **C15,** 78 (1951).
537. Wigglesworth, V. B.   *Nature* **168,** 558 (1951).
538. Wigglesworth, V. B.   *J. Exptl. Biol.* **29,** 561 (1952).
539. Wigglesworth, V. B.   *J. Exptl. Biol.* **29,** 620 (1952).
540. Wigglesworth, V. B.   *J. Embryol. and Exptl. Morphol.* **1,** 269 (1953).
541. Wigglesworth, V. B.   *Trans. 9th Intern. Congr. Entomol., Amsterdam* **2,** 51 (1953).
542. Wigglesworth, V. B.   *Pubbl. staz. zool. Napoli* **24,** Suppl., 41 (1954).
543. Williams, C. M.   *Federation Proc.* **10,** 546 (1951).
544. Williams, C. M.   *Anat. Record* **111,** 441 (1951).
545. Williams, C. M.   *Biol. Bull.* **103,** 120 (1952).
546. Williams, C. M.   *Harvey Lectures* **47,** 126 (1952).
547. Wolff, B., and Williams, C. M.   *Anat. Record* **117,** 542 (1953).
548. Wright, P. A., and Kohn, R. R.   *Biol. Bull.* **103,** 312 (1952).
549. Yamamoto, Y.   *J. Coll. Art. Sci., Chiba Univ., Japan* **1,** 115 (1953).
550. Yoshida, M.   *Annot. zool. japon.* **25,** 362 (1952).
551. Yoshida, M.   *Annot. zool. japon.* **25,** 366 (1952).
552. Young, J. Z.   *J. Endocrinol.* **7,** vii (1950–51).

CHAPTER III

Neurohormones

BY JOHN H. WELSH

CONTENTS

I. Introduction

During the past three decades, our view of the basic mode of operation of the nervous system has undergone considerable change. Earlier, and stemming largely from the work of Du Bois Reymond, had come the notion that the nervous system was a complex, ramifying system of cables and that the all-important sign of nervous activity was electrical. Biologists were prone even to forget that underlying the electrical change called the nerve impulse, or action potential, there must be complex chemical events. Perhaps a changing viewpoint can be said to have begun with Elliott (86, 87) in England. Certainly, there came a time when the pharmacologists and the physiologists, interested in the mechanism of action of drugs, began to wonder why certain drugs closely mimicked the action of some parts of the nervous system, whereas other drugs were equally effective in blocking nervous action.   Sir Henry Dale (76) was one of these.   However, it took the simple, but now classical, frog heart experiments of Loewi to start a new train of thought and to open a new avenue of approach to the intricacies of the nervous system.   There followed an outpouring of contributions from the laboratories of Loewi, Dale, Cannon, and others, which established a role for acetylcholine in the transmission process at some synapses and neuroeffector junctions, and for an adrenaline-like substance at others.   Gradually more and more persons came to hold the view that acetylcholine and adrenaline or related substances were important constituents of nerve cells.   Dale (75, 77) proposed the term "cholinergic" for neurons that produce and release acetylcholine and "adrenergic" for adrenaline-releasing neurons.   These substances were variously referred to as chemical transmitters, chemical mediators, and neurohumors.   In the minds of many, there was the thought that these substances were released at nerve endings and participated in the transmission of the nerve impulse. That the product of adrenergic neurons might be carried for some distance in the circulation was recognized, but the rapid destruction of acetylcholine in body fluids made it apparent that it must serve mainly as a short-range transmitter substance (cf. Burn, ref. 50).

Although the quantitative distribution of acetylcholine and active amines in different parts of the vertebrate nervous system and in nervous systems of some invertebrates is quite well known, little effort has been made to demonstrate visually their presence in nerve cells.   The chromaffin reaction helps to identify cells producing certain amines (142) and possibly methylene blue reacts selectively with proteins which combine with acetylcholine (p. 107).   However, certain nerve cells in a variety of animals, following appropriate histological procedures, do show striking cellular inclusions.   Ernst and Berta Scharrer (246) are responsible for the location and description of many of these neurons, which they refer to as neurosecretory cells.   Recently from many quarters has come striking confirmation of the significance and clarification of the functions of some neurosecretory cell systems.   Chief among these is the evidence that the neurohypophysis is, in part, an aggregate of nerve fiber endings with cell bodies located in the hypothalamus (28), that crustacean "sinus glands" are grouped endings of neurosecretory cells with cell bodies in many parts of the nervous system (26, 27), and that certain cells in the brains of insects end in the corpora cardiaca and contribute to the hormonal activity of these organs (p. 138).   Here are neurons, neither adrenergic nor cholinergic, whose chief function is the formation, storage, and release of physiologically active chemicals.   The view held by Cabanis (59) of a brain secreting thought much in the manner that liver secretes bile is, perhaps, not so far from the truth as it once might have seemed.   For, on the one hand, there are neurons synthesizing and releasing at their endings the "neurohumors" acetylcholine and certain amines, whereas, on the other, there are neurons producing and releasing "neurosecretory materials" such as oxytocin and vasopressin.

In this chapter an attempt will be made to see what all neurons have in common with respect to production, transport, storage, and release of regulator substances. It is proposed that the term "neurohormone" be used to designate these substances. We may well continue to speak of "neurohumors" and of "neurosecretory materials," but it appears highly desirable to have an inclusive term, and "neurohormone," previously used in this series without precise definition (*e.g.*, Parker, Chapter IX of *The Hormones*, Vol. II), seems highly appropriate.

A brief survey will also be made of the modes of action of the several neurohormones, to see whether any patterns of action may evolve. Obviously, with such a plan, it will be impossible to cover with any degree of completeness the literature on the neurohormones since the appearance of Volume II of *The Hormones*. It is to be hoped, however, that the more important developments will be touched upon.

II. The Diversity of Neurohormones and Their Distribution

The term neurohormone, as it will be used herein, may be defined as an organic compound produced by neurons and released at their endings to act as a chemical messenger or hormone, either locally or at a distance. According to this definition, the chemically defined neurohormones are acetylcholine, nor-adrenaline, adrenaline, 5-hydroxytryptamine, oxytocin, and vasopressin. Whether certain other amines such as tyramine, hydroxy-tyramine, and tryptamine act as neurohormones is not yet entirely clear. To these may be added such chemically undetermined substances as the crustacean chromatophore-activating principles; the products of neuro-secretory cells of insect brains and crustacean nervous systems, products which control glands or directly regulate metabolic processes; substance P; and probably a number of additional products of neurosecretory cells of invertebrates and lower vertebrates.

The chemically known neurohormones belong to three different classes of compounds. Acetylcholine is a quaternary ammonium base and is the acetic acid ester of choline. Nor-adrenaline, adrenaline, and 5-hydroxy-tryptamine are amines, but whereas the first two are phenolic compounds, the last is an indole derivative. Oxytocin and vasopressin are polypeptides with structures recently determined by du Vigneaud and co-workers (229, 279, 280). Clearly the neurohormones belong to several different classes of chemical compounds.

The number and identity of chromatophorotropic substances in crusta-

ceans is yet uncertain. The substance that concentrates the red chromatophores of some prawns, such as *Palaemonetes*, and disperses pigment in the
dark chromatophores of crabs, such as *Uca*, the fiddler crab, is a small,
heat-stable molecule that passes through cellophane. It is soluble in water
and the lower alcohols but is insoluble in fat solvents (2, 68). Whether the
hormone which plays an inhibitory role in suppressing crustacean growth,
molting, and development of gonads is chemically different from chromatophore-activating substance is not known.

Several additional neurohormones will probably be recognized and identified in the future. Propionylcholine has been found as a constituent of
ox spleen (16, 135) and urocanylcholine occurs in the hypobranchial gland of
Murex (90, 91). These or other choline esters may eventually be found in
nerve tissue. Among the several biologically active amines known to occur
in animals, such as tyramine, hydroxytyramine, tryptamine, and bufote-
nine, some may be found to play the role of neurohormones. It is only recently that evidence of the occurrence of 5-hydroxytryptamine in nerve
tissue (8, 276) and of its action as a chemical mediator has been presented
(122, 291, 293). This evidence will be referred to later.

In discussing the neurohumors responsible for the control of vertebrate
melanophores, Parker (213, 214) found it convenient to include intermedin
from the vertebrate pituitary because of the similarity of its action with
that of acetylcholine and because of its synergism with, or substitution for,
this nerve product. Our knowledge of intermedin is far from complete, and
its true source and physiological roles are poorly known. Since the pars
intermedia is dependent upon neural contact for initial differentiation, since
the infundibulum continues to exert a regulatory influence (94, 95, 154,
155), and since, in certain amphibians, the production of intermedin depends on intimate association of pars intermedia with some portion of the
brain (84), there appears to be some justification for continuing to class this
interesting substance with the neurohormones.

Substance P, present in all parts of the mammalian brain, in peripheral
nerves and ganglia, and in the intestine (nerve plexus?), appears to be a
polypeptide. Pernow (225) finds that it is stable at 100°C. in weak acid,
but labile in alkali and strong acid. It is soluble in alcohol and acetone containing small parts of water. Trypsin and chymotrypsin inactivate it. Its
physiological action (p. 137) will indicate why it is tentatively classed as a
neurohormone.

A. ACETYLCHOLINE

A brief review of the phylogenetic and tissue distribution of the several
neurohormones will be given. Acetylcholine would seem to be the most
widely distributed. It has been pharmacologically identified in nervous

tissues of most major groups of invertebrates (13, 72, 232) and in all vertebrates that have been examined (72, 114). It has been found in certain
protozoa (46). It is present in planaria (288), and the evidence suggests
that it is concentrated in their nervous systems. Annelids, molluscs, crustaceans, and insects have been shown to have acetylcholine in their nervous
systems (13, 232). The very large amounts reported to be present in some
insect nervous systems are believed by Lewis (190) to be due, in part, to
active synthesis during the extraction procedure.

Within the vertebrates the amount of acetylcholine per unit weight of
brain appears to be highest in the lower vertebrates (72). The quantitative
distribution between different parts of the nervous systems of some mammals
is well known (114, 197). Perhaps one of the more significant generalizations that may be made is that in going from newer to more primitive parts
of the nervous system there is a progressive increase in acetylcholine content. Cerebellum and cortex are lowest in acetylcholine. Brain stem and
medulla show increasing amounts, with spinal cord and spinal nerves still
higher. Autonomic ganglia are generally considered to have the highest
acetylcholine content of any vertebrate nerve tissues, but Welsh and Hyde
(298) suggested that the neurons of the myenteric plexus might contain
more acetylcholine than do autonomic ganglia. The physiological significance of this quantitative distribution of acetylcholine in the mammalian
nervous system is not known.

The general pattern of distribution of acetylcholine in the autonomic nervous system is the following. All preganglionic fibers are cholinergic, as
are postganglionic fibers of the cervical and sacral divisions (parasympathetic). Some postganglionic fibers of the sympathetic systems (those to
sweat glands and erector muscles of hairs) are cholinergic. Recently
Feldberg (117) has made the interesting suggestion that within the vertebrate central nervous system, cholinergic neurons may alternate with noncholinergic neurons.

The question of the occurrence of acetylcholine in sensory neurons is of
renewed interest in view of the results of Singer (p. 130). The evidence
indicates that sensory nerves contain small but measurable amounts of
acetylcholine (69, 193, 197). Chang et al. (69) found for the dog relative
values of acetylcholine in motor, mixed, and sensory nerves to be 50:25:1.
From the data given by MacIntosh (197) for motor, mixed, and sensory
nerves of the cat one derives relative values of 13:5:1. That sensory endings in the cornea may contain unusually large amounts of acetylcholine is
indicated by the results of von Brücke (39, 40), who found 20 to 25 μg.
acetylcholine per gram of cattle cornea and 25 μg. per gram of rabbit
cornea. Two days after sectioning the first branch of the trigeminal nerve
of the rabbit a 12 % to 83 % decline of corneal acetylcholine was observed.

B. Adrenaline and Nor-adrenaline

The results of the past few years have done much to banish the confusion that existed concerning the products of adrenergic neurons and the true nature of the "sympathins" of Cannon. Excellent reviews by von Euler (99, 100, 102) cover all but the most recent literature on adrenaline and nor-adrenaline, and the review by Blaschko (21) deals with amine oxidase and amine metabolism.

Chromatography (73, 105, 249) and the fluorescence spectra of certain derivatives (226, 284) have made it possible to distinguish adrenaline from nor-adrenaline in tissue extracts and biological fluids. With these procedures and with careful comparison of the effects of nerve stimulation with the application of adrenaline or nor-adrenaline, the important fact has emerged that *the principal product of adrenergic neurons is nor-adrenaline*. It is this finding that does so much to clarify the issue of the "sympathins."

The quantitative distribution of adrenaline and nor-adrenaline in adrenal medullas and sympathetic nerves (or organs with sympathetic innervation) has been summarized by von Euler (99, 100, 102). When estimated in micrograms per gram of tissue or volume of venous blood from a stimulated organ, adrenaline represents usually less than 10 % of the total adrenaline and nor-adrenaline present. Whether both substances occur together in a given neuron is not known.

In the adrenal medulla, which may be considered an aggregate of highly modified neurosecretory cells without processes, adrenaline is sometimes present in much larger quantities than nor-adrenaline (*e.g.*, rabbit, guinea pig, and rat). In other species (*e.g.*, cat, toad, pigeon) the amounts of adrenaline and nor-adrenaline in the suprarenal glands are nearly equal. See von Euler (102) for a summary of values. Hillarp and Hökfelt (157), using potassium iodate to produce pigment formation in cells containing nor-adrenaline but not adrenaline, conclude that all adrenal medullary cells can form nor-adrenaline but that only certain cells can methylate to adrenaline. They further suggest that by means of selective innervation either amine can be secreted from the medulla alone or they may be released together. In human suprarenals, an average adrenaline content of 0.49 mg. per gram and an average nor-adrenaline content of 0.090 mg. per gram were found (104). M. Vogt (281, 282) reports the presence of adrenaline and nor-adrenaline in the dog's brain that cannot be accounted for by the adrenergic vasomotor innervation. She finds the highest concentration (1 μg. nor-adrenaline per gram fresh tissue) in the hypothalamus, less (0.5 μg. per gram) in gray stratum around the aqueduct, and still less in the remaining midbrain. The nonnervous *area postrema* has a high content of nor-adrenaline.

Little recent information is available regarding the occurrence of adrenaline and nor-adrenaline in nervous tissue of the lower vertebrates. Both amines have been found in large amounts in the chromaffin bodies of a variety of dogfishes (101, 251). From 60 % to 80 % of the total amine content is nor-adrenaline.

Our knowledge of the occurrence of adrenaline and nor-adrenaline in the invertebrates is most incomplete. Chromaffin cells in leeches have long been known, and it has been supposed, since the publications of Gaskell (136, 137), that the chromaffin cells of the ventral nerve cord of the leech, *Hirudo medicinalis*, produce adrenaline. This is a matter that should be checked by newer methods of isolation and identification. Much confusion exists concerning the occurrence of amines in insects and especially in the mealworm, *Tenebrio molitor*. Wense (307) reported the isolation and crystallization of large amounts of adrenaline from larvae of the mealworm. Using chromatographic means of separation and identification, Gregerman and Wald (147) failed to find adrenaline in the same species but did obtain evidence for the presence of two other orthodiphenols. Östlund (209, 210) reports finding adrenaline, nor-adrenaline, and hydroxytyramine in extracts of *Tenebrio* and of *Apis mellifica*, the honeybee. The unsatisfactory state of our knowledge of the occurrence of adrenaline and nor-adrenaline in the invertebrates can be seen from these few examples. Evidence that amines other than these may occur as neurohormones will follow.

C. Hydroxytyramine (Dopamine)

This amine has been extracted from sheep adrenal glands and heart (143). Its occurrence in the adrenal medulla of the sheep was confirmed by Shepherd and West (250), who also found it in the adrenal medulla of cattle but not in pig, dog, cat, rabbit, or man. These authors say that the presence of hydroxytyramine bears no relation to the total or relative catechol amine content of the adrenal medulla. The occurrence of hydroxytyramine in certain insects has been referred to earlier (210).

D. 5-Hydroxytryptamine (Serotonin, Enteramine, Thrombotonin)

A great advance in our understanding of the biological amines was made when the substance variously known as enteramine, serotonin, or thrombotonin was chemically identified. The pioneering work of Erspamer, Vialli, and co-workers in Italy on enteramine, of Page, Rapport, and collaborators in the United States on serotonin, and of Reid and Rand in Australia on thrombotonin had demonstrated the presence of a highly active vasoconstrictor and smooth muscle-contracting substance in the enterochromaffin tissue of the intestine of a variety of vertebrates, in clotted blood, and elsewhere. On the basis of chemical and physical tests Rapport (235) deduced that serotonin was 5-hydroxytryptamine. A creatinine sulfate salt of 5-hydroxytryptamine was synthesized in 1951 (149, 256). In 1952 Erspamer and Asero reported the synthesis of enteramine and its identity with 5-hydroxytryptamine (11, 89). Reviews by Erspamer (88) and Page (210a) cover nearly all of the literature on 5-hydroxytryptamine up to the latter part of 1953.

TABLE I

QUANTITATIVE ESTIMATES OF 5-HYDROXYTRYPTAMINE IN VARIOUS TISSUES

Values for other tissues or species are to be found in certain of the references cited

Tissue	Animal	5-Hydroxytryptamine[a] μg./g. fresh tissue	Reference
Brain (entire)	Dog (2)	0.1 and 0.36	276
Brain (entire)	Rat	0.24	276
Cortex	Dog (2)	0.09 and 0.19	276
Cortex	Rabbit	0.13	276
Cortex (gray matter)	Dog	0.026–0.032	8a
Cortex (white matter)	Dog	0.013	8a
Thalamus	Dog	0.014–0.022	8a
Hypothalamus	Dog	0.220–0.330	8a
Mesencephalon	Dog	0.200–0.210	8a
Ganglia (pooled)	*Venus mercenaria*	15	295
Ganglia (pooled)	*Busycon canaliculatum*	17	295
Ganglia, optic	*Sepia officinalis*	21.2[b]	122
Ganglia, cerebral	*Sepia officinalis*	24[b]	122
Ganglia, ventral	*Dromia vulgaris*	26.5[b]	122
Leg nerves	*Dromia vulgaris*	30.4[b]	122
Platelets	Guinea pig	0.2 –0.4[c]	164
Platelets	Goat	4.3[c]	164
Platelets	Rabbit	7.5[c]	164
Platelets	Beef	2300[b]	317
Spleen	Guinea pig	0.25–1.65	92
Spleen	Goat	4.70–4.90	92
Spleen	Rabbit	16.40–22.50	92
Intestinal mucosa (different regions)	Dog	4 to 10	120
Posterior salivary glands	*Octopus vulgaris*	426–512	88
Posterior salivary glands	*Eledone moschata*	760	88
Hypobranchial gland (median zone)	*Murex trunculus*	80–290	88
Amphibian skin	*Rana esculenta*	13–25	88
Amphibian skin	*Bombinator*	700–1000	88
Venom	*Vespa vulgaris*	320	169
Venom	*Bufo marinus*	1000[b]	277

[a] Some values equivalent to 5-hydroxytryptamine (free base), others to 5-hydroxytryptamine creatinine sulfate.

[b] Per gram dry weight.

[c] Per 10[9] platelets.

The distribution of 5-hydroxytryptamine by phyla and by tissues is so unusual that it is not immediately obvious that it should be classed with the neurohormones. An effort will be made in this section and later to set forth the reasons for so doing.

This amine occurs in blood platelets of a variety of vertebrates, in the enterochromaffin cells of the intestine, in the skin of certain amphibia, in posterior salivary glands of *Octopus vulgaris*, and in the mammalian brain. Table I gives examples of the amounts found in representative tissues or organs. More complete data are to be found in the Erspamer review. Twarog and Page (276) reported the occurrence of 5-hydroxytryptamine in the brains of the rat, dog, and rabbit. An independent recognition of its occurrence in mammalian brain was made by Amin, Crawford, and Gaddum (8).

By maens of paper chromatography or bio-assay, 5-hydroxytryptamine has been identified in nerve tissue of several molluscs (122, 292, 293). Its role as a neurohormone in molluscs will be discussed in a later section of this chapter. By use of chemical tests and bio-assay, Florey and Florey (122) identified 5-hydroxytryptamine in the nervous system of certain crustaceans. We have evidence that tryptamine is present in considerable amounts in crustacean nervous tissue. Whether it is a mediator in this class of animals remains to be seen.

E. Oxytocin and Vasopressin

The evidence of Bargmann, Hild, Zetler, E. Scharrer, and others that oxytocin and vasopressin are products of neurosecretory cells of the hypothalamus has been summarized by the Scharrers (247). The reader is also referred to Chapter IX. The pituitary pars nervosa from representatives of several classes of vertebrates has yielded factors with physiological activities comparable to those of oxytocin and vasopressin. To date, however, these substances have been isolated in pure form only from certain mammals.

F. Neurosecretory Materials of Invertebrates

The distribution of neurosecretory materials of the invertebrates is thoroughly covered by Berta Scharrer in Chapter II. Additional reference is made to the neurosecretory systems of insects and crustaceans later in this chapter.

III. Production, Transport, Storage, and Release of Neurohormones

For the purpose of the present discussion all neurons may be looked upon as elongated cells that release specific chemical substances at one end, the termination of the axon. Since these endings are normally far removed from the cell body of the neuron, various questions arise. Where in nerve cells are neurohormones produced?   If produced near the metabolic center, the cell body, how are they transported over the very considerable distance from this point to points of release?   If storage occurs, in what form are these highly active substances held in reserve?   What mechanisms allow appropriate quantities of a given neurohormone to leave the nerve fiber ending at the time when needed?   These are questions to which thought should be given.

A. Production and Storage

1. *Acetylcholine*

Only in the case of acetylcholine is the biochemical synthesis of a neurohormone known in any considerable detail.   The literature on acetylcholine synthesis has been frequently reviewed (*e.g.*, 15, 114, 115, 153, 205, 206). Choline acetylase and Coenzyme A, given an adequate energy source (adenosinetriphosphate), can acetylate choline.   This process can take place, apparently, in any part of a neuron, but there are differences to be found between cell body and axon, more active synthesis occurring in regions containing masses of cell bodies.   Thus finely ground cholinergic nerves lose their ability to synthesize acetylcholine, but finely ground brain tissue does not (113).   Acetone powder preparations of rabbit brain synthesize more acetylcholine than do those from cholinergic nerves (153). Preparations of the retina are highly active, but those of the optic nerve are not (81, 153).

That most of the acetylcholine in a nerve cell (or at least in an homogenate) is bound to particles was indicated by the work of Corteggiani (72) and Trethewie (273).   That these particles have certain osmotic properties, such as characterize mitochondria, was shown by the following observations of Corteggiani.   When homogenized tissue was diluted with water in the absence of eserine, the acetylcholine rapidly disappeared.   If diluted either with isosmotic glucose or NaCl without eserine, the acetylcholine was preserved.   Other investigators have observed that freezing and thawing results in a rapid destruction of acetylcholine in brain tissue (299); that protein denaturants must be used to free the major portion of the acetylcholine in nerve tissue; and that nerve tissue, when incubated, will synthesize very limited amounts of acetylcholine, which appears to be chiefly "bound," except when the tissue is bathed in a medium with excess potassium (198, 297).   After confirming and extending certain of these earlier observations on the state of rat brain acetylcholine, Brodkin and Elliott (31) suggest that the acetylcholine in this organ may be located in mitochondria.

Three preliminary reports of electron microscope studies of neurons mention that clusters, collections, or agglomerations of mitochondria or of

mitochondria and small vesicles occur in axon terminations (211, 212, 237). Palade (211) comments that a greater number of mitochondria and small vesicles (diameter = 300 to 500 A.) are present in axon endings than occur in dendrites. Too little information is available to allow the final conclusion that acetylcholine is to be found in either mitochondria or these "vesicles." However, we shall see that there is further indirect evidence bearing on this question when bound catechol amines are discussed.

One of the criteria for the identification of neurosecretory cells used by the Scharrers is that they contain their specific products in aggregates, which, after suitable procedures, are visible at the usual magnifications of the light microscope. Little direct effort has been made to visualize acetylcholine in a neuron, but one may well ask what component is stained by vital methylene blue. The chemical structure of methylene blue is such that it can combine with a protein to which acetylcholine may also selectively adsorb (see p 120). Methylene blue has been reported to stain parasympathetic but not sympathetic nerve endings (178).

That acetylcholine may be concentrated (stored) in axonal terminations is suggested by the higher concentrations that occur in layers of terminals as compared with axonal regions. The vast amount of terminal branching of most cholinergic neurons provides added storage space for acetylcholine.

2. Adrenaline and Nor-adrenaline

The exact pathways in the synthesis of nor-adrenaline and adrenaline are not known. Some of the evidence and opinions are briefly reviewed by Blaschko (22). The finding of Dopa decarboxylase in the adrenal medulla (187) lends support to the view that this enzyme catalyzes one of the steps in the biosynthesis of adrenaline and nor-adrenaline.

Recently von Euler has made reference to the distribution of nor-adrenaline and adrenaline along the length of adrenergic nerves such as the splenic nerve. He presents reasons for believing that there is sufficient storage in nerve endings to give estimated concentrations of 3 to 30 mg. per gram of nerve terminals. These figures are in the same range as the catechol amine content of the adrenal medulla.

Little is known concerning the state in which the catechol amines exist within adrenergic nerves, but observations on adrenal medullary tissue are of the greatest interest (102, 148, 158, 159). Blaschko and Welch (23) find that cell-free homogenates of cattle adrenal medulla, prepared in ice-cold isotonic sucrose, contain at least two-thirds of their pressor activity in a granule fraction that has sedimentation properties similar to those of rat liver mitochondria. In a suspension of these granules in isotonic sucrose at 0°C., relatively little adrenaline is released. Blaschko and Welch refer to these particles as "pre-secretory granules." Here is further evidence

that neurohormones may be stored in organized particles with properties that relate them to mitochondria. Observations of a similar nature have been made by Hillarp and co-workers (158, 159).

3. 5-Hydroxytryptamine

Little direct information exists concerning the production and storage of 5-hydroxytryptamine in nervous tissue. In nonnervous tissues (enterochromaffin cells, posterior salivary gland cells of certain cephalopods, hypobranchial glands of *Murex*, skin of certain amphibia), characteristic granules are seen after appropriate histological procedures. These granules contain the 5-hydroxytryptamine. For a review of the literature see Erspamer (88).

4. Oxytocin and Vasopressin

A discussion of production and storage of these posterior pituitary neurohormones will be found in Chapter IX.

5. Neurosecretory Materials of Insects and Crustaceans

The chemical nature of the substances produced by the neurosecretory cells of insects and crustaceans is unknown. However, we know something of the state in which the material exists in the living cell. Neurosecretory cells of the insect brain (268) and crustacean nervous system contain a pale-blue, light-reflecting material that is best seen in dark-field illumination, with bright reflected light, or with phase contrast microscopy. The first detailed study of this material in living tissue was that of Passano (217, 218). In the marsh crab, *Sesarma reticulatum*, he described "spheres" or "spheroid systems" in living neurosecretory cells. They consisted of highly refractive granules about 0.3 μ in diameter arranged around an optically empty central droplet. Sometimes these "systems" coalesced to form large droplets. Spheroid systems or droplets were found in cell bodies, axons, and nerve terminations ("sinus gland"). In the brain of the blowfly, *Calliphora erythrocephala*, there are two medial groups of neurosecretory cells containing bluish-white granules. These have been examined with the dark-field microscope by Thomsen and Thomsen (268). With oil immersion the "granules" are seen to be aggregates of particles about 0.4 μ in diameter. The granules are most easily seen in the axons of these cells. The authors could not decide whether the granules were secretory material or whether some are mitochondria or other elements. For further discussion of the neurosecretory substances of invertebrates see Chapter II.

B. Axon Terminations and Storage of Neurohormones

It would appear from the above that neurohumors and neurosecretory materials are made and held by the producing cells in more or less organized

commissural organ of Knowles (172) belongs in the same category of structures. These clusters of fine axon terminations as well as the "sinus glands" are adjacent to or in blood sinuses, and they release their products directly into the circulation. For this reason it has been suggested that all be called "neurohaemal organs" (67).

The plexiform nerve structures associated with autonomic neuroeffector mechanisms lack discrete nerve endings (183). Perhaps the extensive branching here and in the neuropile of the brain is a device to facilitate storage and release of neurohormones.

C. Axonal Transport of Neurohormones

Some neurohormones occur throughout the length of their respective neurons, although evidence has been cited to indicate their storage in axon terminals. If synthesis takes place, in part, in the region of the cell body (for which there is evidence), how does the neurohormone reach axon endings far removed from the cell body? That there may be a proximodistal flow of axoplasm or of materials through the axoplasm has often been assumed or deduced from indirect evidence (*e.g.*, 215). From observations on the "damming" of axoplasm on the proximal side of a nerve constriction (Fig. 3), Weiss and Hiscoe (285) conclude that there is a distal "growth" or movement of the axon at a rate determined to be of the order of 1 mm. per day. Some figures, published by Carey (62), of motor nerve fibers and endplates, fixed after violent convulsions, appear to show a distal flow and

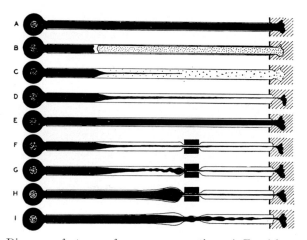

Fig. 3. Diagram of stages of nerve regeneration; *A–E*, without constriction; *F–I*, with constriction. *G* and *H* show the swelling that occurs proximal to a constriction. This is thought to result from interference with the normal proximodistal flow of axoplasm. From Weiss and Hiscoe (285).

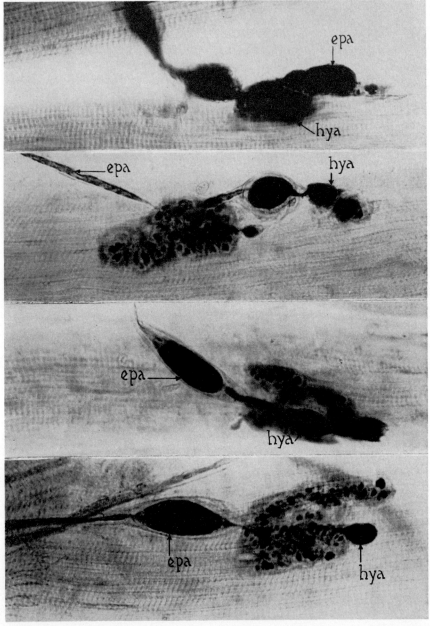

FIG. 4. Accumulations of aurophilic material in epilemmal (epa) and hypolem-
mal (hya) axons of motor end-plates in the biceps femoris muscle of the chameleon,
after subjection to treatment resulting in violent spasms. From Carey (62).

abnormal discharge of aurophilic material (Fig. 4).   Certain evidence for the proximodistal movement of neurosecretory materials will be reviewed.

No direct indication of the movement of acetylcholine along the axon of cholinergic neurons is known to the writer.   An early reference to the possible movement of adrenaline in a nerve is that of J. F. Gaskell (136), who, in referring to the chromaffin cells in the nerve cord of the leech and the observed action of adrenaline on their pulsating blood vessels, said ". . . it is just possible that in the case of the leech the adrenaline passes from the cell to the periphery by way of the motor nerve itself." Tainter (263) has frequently referred to the probable production of amines in the cell body of an adrenergic neuron, their transport through the axon, and release from the fiber endings.   This concept was based on deductions such as the following: cell bodies in the adrenal medulla synthesize adrenaline and nor-adrenaline; therefore, cell bodies of postganglionic sympathetic fibers, rather than nerve endings, are probable centers of formation.   Yet von Euler (102) feels that the high concentration of nor-adrenaline in the terminal portion of some adrenergic nerves indicates that it is synthesized here instead of being made in the cell body and conveyed to the terminals via the axoplasm.

Convincing evidence exists, however, for the axoplasmic transport of neurosecretory materials in the vertebrate hypothalamic-posterior pituitary system and in the analogous system of insects and crustaceans.   Hild (156) was one of the first to show that cutting the pituitary stalk in the frog resulted in an accumulation of neurosecretory substance in the fibers proximal to the cut.   This observation has since been extended to a variety of vertebrates (fishes, amphibia, birds, and mammals) by a number of investigators.   Their results have been summarized elsewhere (247). When the axons of neurosecretory cells of the insect, *Leucophaea*, are cut, there is a similar piling up of neurosecretory substance proximal to the cut (242).   Comparable observations have been made on a variety of crustaceans when their neurosecretory axons have been interrupted or their endings removed (27, 218).

D. The Release of Neurohormones from Nerve Endings

Although there were earlier hints that physiologically active substances might be released from nerve endings, the evidence that opened a new chapter in neurophysiology came from the frog heart experiment of Loewi. In the two following decades, and mainly from the laboratories of Loewi, Dale, Cannon, and their students, there came a series of studies that convinced most biologists that from endings of cholinergic and adrenergic neurons, small amounts of acetylcholine or "sympathin" were released at the arrival of the nerve impulse.   These acted in some manner to help bridge

the gap between neurons, or between neuron and effector. While acetylcholine appeared always to be quickly destroyed by cholinesterase, the
sympathin of Cannon was shown to be able to enter the circulation and act
at a distance from the point of release. The long controversy over the
importance of acetylcholine as a transmitting agent is well known, and the
literature has been extensively reviewed; hence reference concerning acetylcholine release will be made only to a few papers earlier than 1950. In this
section, however, it is not the intention to discuss in detail the release of any
one neurohormone but instead to look for features that may be common to
all neurons that relase physiologically active materials.

Thus far, a picture has been drawn of nerve cells synthesizing one or more
neurohormones in the vicinity of the nucleus and transporting them through
the axoplasm by proximodistal flow to the endings, which are often modified
in a manner that increases their storage capacity. The question now to be
considered is: Under what circumstances does a neurohormone leave the
neuron?

1. *Release from "Resting" Neurons*

When the action potential is used as a sole criterion of activity, it is
relatively easy to distinguish an "active" neuron from a "resting" neuron.
It is in this sense that the term "resting" is here used. It is important to
know whether there are extended periods when a neuron retains, completely,
its neurohormone or whether there may be a steady leakage from the endings in the absence of propagated nerve impulses. Aside from a little indirect evidence, such as that provided by the so-called trophic action of
nerves, the most direct evidence for an escape of acetylcholine from resting
neurons is provided by the work of Fatt and Katz on end-plate "noise."
These workers found (107, 109) that end-plates of resting muscle fibers of
a frog, lizard, and tortoise exhibit spontaneous subthreshold electrical activity. This consists of a random succession of miniature end-plate potentials with an amplitude 1/100 of the normal end-plate response to a
motor nerve impulse. The miniature potentials are reduced in size by a
small dose of tubocurarine and increased in size and duration by prostigmine. Denervation and nerve anesthetics abolish them. Fatt and Katz
believe that these miniature potentials result from the spontaneous release
of acetylcholine from restricted areas of the nerve terminals. In an interpretation of their results (110, 111) they suggest that the acetylcholine is
released in packets of molecules, perhaps bound to lipoid-soluble carrier
molecules. They further suggest that the carrier substance may be
anchored to the lipoid phase of the nerve membrane, but capable of changing position within it.

Although it appears probable that a similar "spontaneous" leakage of other neurohormones (such as chromatophorotropins from the crustacean sinus gland) does occur, there is no direct evidence to support the view. It would appear rather difficult to obtain such evidence except when working with isolated preparations, as were Fatt and Katz, because of the difficulty of maintaining untreated neurons, *in situ*, in an inactive state.

2. *Release from Active Neurons*

It is now quite generally accepted that the arrival of a nerve impulse at the terminals of a cholinergic or adrenergic neuron releases its characteristic neurohumor. Do some of the more highly modified secretory neurons conduct nerve impulses and is the accompanying shift in membrane permeability responsible for the release of such products as oxytocin and vasopressin? In an attempt to answer this question as it relates to the crustacean neurosecretory system, Nancy Milburn (unpublished) has recorded from intact and semi-isolated nerve endings in the "sinus glands." Whereas electrical activity could be recorded, it has not yet been possible to show an increase in this activity when appropriate centers, containing the cell bodies, were electrically stimulated. Stimulation of a crayfish eye by light, however, produces increased electrical activity in the nerve endings constituting the sinus glands.

That a neurohormone may escape along the axon or at regenerating endings is seen in the escape of the antidiuretic hormone after surgical removal of the posterior pituitary (228) and in the relatively normal condition of a decapod crustacean after removal of the sinus glands (218). However, several factors join to make the axon terminations the major site of release of a neurohormone. They are (*1*) increased surface area, (*2*) lack of myelin and perhaps a change in structure and chemical constitution of the nerve membrane, and (*3*) the high concentration of neurohormones at nerve endings relative to the remainder of the nerve cells.

3. *Reflex Release*

In a chain of neurons running, for example, from a sense organ through the central and autonomic nervous systems to the walls of certain blood vessels, some neurons would be cholinergic and one or possibly more adrenergic. Unfortunately, rather little is known of the details of chemical transmission in the central nervous system. Feldberg (117) has suggested that cholinergic neurons might alternate with noncholinergic neurons in the central nervous system. Here, as in the peripheral nervous system, in reflex action a chain of neurohormonal reactions may be involved. As Cannon (60) so clearly demonstrated, a variety of stimuli, giving rise to emotional reactions, result in an outpouring of an adrenaline-like substance from sympathetic nerves. In order to release these sympathetic amines, acetylcholine is released at several links of the neuron chain.

A good example of the complex reflex control of a neurohormone is that of the release of antidiuretic substance (ADH) from the neurohypophysis. This phenomenon was extensively studied long before the true nature of the neurohypophysis was known. In addition to direct electrical stimulation of supraoptic nuclei to release ADH, it is released by dehydration, pain, fainting, suckling, and a variety of emotional stresses (for references see refs. 208, 283).

In the higher Crustacea one or more neurohormones control the migration of retinal pigments (170). If the prawn, *Palaemonetes*, is kept in a darkroom until dark-adapted, a short period of illumination releases enough hormone to produce complete migration of distal retinal pigment to the light position (35). Anoxia, low temperature, and certain anesthetics cause a movement of eye pigments to the light position in crayfish maintained in darkness (287).

These are only a few selected instances illustrating nervous control of the release of neurohormones via complex reflex arcs.

4. *Cyclical Release*

Normally recurring changes in the environment (*e.g.*, seasonal, tidal, diurnal) may lead to the cyclical release of neurohormones. This is especially obvious in certain invertebrates, and crustaceans might again serve as examples. The molting cycle of adult decapod crustaceans (crabs, crayfish, lobster) is usually seasonal, at least in higher latitudes. A neurohormone from the sinus glands is important in the regulation of molting (p. 141, Chapter II). Apparently there is a seasonal fluctuation in blood level of this hormone.

Crustaceans often show diurnal changes in body color, positions of eye pigments, glucose and calcium metabolism, and motor activity. These processes are regulated, at least in part, by the 24-hour cycle in blood level of one or more neurohormones. Under normal day-night conditions this could result from reflex control of release originating in cycles of sensory activity. When, however, these 24-hour cycles persist under constant external conditions, one must postulate endogenous rhythms which have become "fixed" in each generation. It has been suggested that a sequence of events—metabolic—nervous—endocrine—metabolic, and so on—which requires 24 hours for one cycle, and which has become more or less independent of day and night changes in light, temperature, and humidity, can account for persisting diurnal rhythms (286). If some cyclical processes are *directly controlled by chemical products of neurons*, the postulated mechanism in such instances can be made much less complex. Cyclical activity of the nervous system of a crayfish directly controls the release of materials from some of its neurons and appears to account for its persistent diurnal rhythms. To what extent endogenous 24-hour cycles in the mammals (*e.g.*, running in the rat) are due to cyclical release of one or more neurohormones remains to be determined.

5. *Chemicals Affecting Release*

It may be assumed that any drug or chemical affecting the level of activity of a neuron, either increasing or decreasing its tendency to discharge, will affect the rate at which substances leave the neuron. For example, diisopropyl fluorophosphate (DFP) releases antidiuretic substance from the neurohypophysis (228). The DFP acting as an anticholinesterase might affect the neurosecretory cell directly, or it might allow the accumulation of acetylcholine at a junction one or more neurons removed from the neurosecretory cell. Since, in addition to affecting release, drugs may antagonize the actions of neurohormones or potentiate their action by slowing their destruction, it is difficult to determine what causes a change in blood level of a given neurohormone.

That potassium, when present in excess of normal blood levels, releases acetylcholine from nerve, is an old observation (*e.g.*, refs. 36, 37). This is probably due in part to the effects of increased external K^+ on resting potential and permeability of the neuron membrane. Any other substance acting directly to depolarize a nerve membrane might increase the rate of release of a neurohormone (*e.g.*, NH_4^+, H^+). Likewise there might be indirect actions of such substances as O_2 and glucose, required to furnish energy for normal maintenance of membrane polarity and permeability. An excess of magnesium ions reduces the output of acetylcholine from the superior cervical ganglion of the cat (166) and from the frog sciatic (80). In these same preparations an excess of calcium ions increases the amount of acetylcholine released and relieves a magnesium block.

Recent studies on the mode of action of botulinum toxin have suggested that certain agents affecting synaptic or neuromuscular transmissions may act specifically by regulating the release of transmitter agents. This extraordinarily active substance causes paralysis at junctions of nerve and voluntary muscles, but affects neither nerve conduction nor skeletal muscle excitability (32, 47, 261). It lacks significant action either on choline acetylase or cholinesterase. The evidence indicates that it prevents the release of acetylcholine from nerve endings.

The purpose of this section has been to show, by means of a few selected examples, that the basic processes of transport, storage, and release of neurohumors and neurosecretory substances are similar. Attention will now be paid to some of the recent advances in the physiology of the several neurohormones.

IV. Recent Advances in Understanding the Modes of Action of Neurohormones

Whereas electrical phenomena are a prominent feature of spread of excitation *within a cell*, in communication *between cells* chemical agents are usually employed by the organism. These chemical messengers often act by altering the physical properties (electrical charge, permeability) of the cell membrane; hence the transmission process consists of complex series of physicochemical events. In the regulation of the activities of a given organ or tissue, the effectiveness of a particular chemical messenger is determined mainly by the degree of specialization and the physiological state of the cells making up this organ or tissue. For, as a radio set is tuned to receive from only one broadcasting station, so may a given tissue or organ respond only to one or a few hormones or neurohormones.

As chemical messengers, how do the hormones and neurohormones differ from one another? Although no clear-cut distinctions can be made, the following differences may be pointed out. Hormones are the products of endocrine glands. Some are protein in nature and relatively stable in body fluids. They are employed for widespread, long-duration control of such processes as growth, reproduction, and general metabolism. Neurohormones, on the other hand, are products of nerve cells. None is yet known that is a protein, and some are rapidly destroyed when they reach the circulation. They are used in long- and short-range, brief-duration control of a great variety of physiological processes. That some groups of neurons have become so highly modified that they are essentially endocrine glands must be recognized. Thus the hypothalamic-neurohypophyseal system produces two relatively stable neurohormones, oxytocin and vasopressin. These may act at some distance from the point of release into the circulation. If we recognize the adrenal medulla as nervous in origin, we have the final step in the transformation of potential nerve cells into an endocrine organ. Most neurons, however, are elongated pipelines from one point to another within the body. They accumulate chemical messengers at their endings. These endings show varying degrees of specialization for storage and release. The usefulness of these neurons in fast, private communication resides, in large measure, in their ability to conduct propagated electrical changes from end to end. The arrival of the action potential at the nerve ending releases a specific chemical messenger that acts across the junction to excite or inhibit the adjacent unit, either neuron or effector cell.

In the sections to follow, each of the neurohormones will be considered. For each substance, a brief resumé of the present state of our knowledge will be given with only occasional reference to literature previous to 1950. Selected aspects of published work since 1950 will then be discussed. Major attention will be paid to mechanisms of action and correlated problems. Here, our present knowledge is most inadequate, but for future guidance, it seems worthwhile to summarize our scanty information and to speculate.

A. ACETYLCHOLINE

1. *Physiological Role*

The literature of the physiology and pharmacology of the acetylcholine system has been reviewed (12, 29, 114, 116, 121, 174, 205, 236, 264, 271). A recent and welcome historical addition is Sir Henry Dale's *Adventures in Physiology.* This consists of a selection of his scientific papers, together with comments made in the light of subsequent research. From these reviews, one learns the stepwise progress that has brought us to our present stage of knowledge of the role of acetylcholine. There was the early period when the pharmacologists such as Reid Hunt were dealing with acetylcholine as a new and highly active drug, unsuspecting that it was a normal constituent of the cat on which the tests were being made. Then came the studies of Loewi, Dale, and their students, showing that acetylcholine was a naturally occurring substance in a wide variety of animals. In the vertebrates, the role of acetylcholine in the actions of the autonomic nervous system was first studied. Following this, attention was paid the voluntary nervous system, and the importance of acetylcholine in transmission from nerve to skeletal muscle was established. Then came the question of the part played by acetylcholine in transmission in the central nervous system. Experimental approaches to this problem are peculiarly difficult, and much remains to be learned of the details of central nervous actions of acetylcholine.

During the past few years, although physiologists have continued to work with a variety of problems involving acetylcholine, probably more basic information has been contributed by the pharmacologists, looking for better acetylcholine antagonists, and by the many groups investigating the organophosphorus inhibitors of cholinesterase. Some aspects of this work will be referred to when discussing the mode of action of acetylcholine.

2. *Locus of Action*

Possibly some cells of all animals respond to acetylcholine. Certainly the enzymes involved in acetylcholine synthesis and destruction are very widespread, and new evidences of acetylcholine action appear not infrequently (*e.g.*, refs. 44, 177). However, certain tissues and even certain portions of cells are far more sensitive to acetylcholine than others. Whereas some smooth muscle may have a low threshold to acetylcholine, and a given cell may have equal sensitivity over its entire surface (275), in skeletal muscle the region of the motor end-plate is far more sensitive than the remainder of the fiber (41, 181). Similarly, perfusion of acetylcholine through an autonomic ganglion reaches sensitive dendrites or cell bodies, setting up a nerve impulse, whereas acetylcholine applied to a nerve trunk or to an axon has never been shown to have significant physiological action. According to the "receptive substance" hypothesis, sensitive areas would be places of concentration of a cellular component (receptors) with which acetylcholine reacts. They would also be areas readily accessible to acetylcholine *released from nerve endings* or released elsewhere in the normal physiology of the organism, but they might be areas quite inaccessible to acetylcholine applied by the experimenter. For example, arthropod skeletal muscle is peculiarly insensitive to acetylcholine and to drugs generally (300). This is in spite of the presence of relatively large amounts of acetylcholine in arthropod nerves (232). Motor fiber-endings in insect and crustacean muscle may penetrate the interior of the fiber or lie under the sarcolemma. Possibly, the receptor areas are inaccessible to substances applied at the muscle surface. This could be a modification brought about by the characteristic open circulation of the arthropods, to prevent the rapid washing away of mediators released at the nerve terminals.

The exact place of action of acetylcholine in any cell is unknown, but there are reasons for believing that the outer surface of the cell membrane contains the acetylcholine receptors. One of these reasons is that acetylcholine acts rapidly, even when applied experimentally to the surface of certain organs. For example, when applied to the outside of the isolated ventricle of the *Venus* heart, it begins to depress the beat in about 1 second.

Among the more effective acetylcholine antagonists are some large molecules which, as quaternary bases, may penetrate cells slowly. Therefore, they probably act at or near the surface of the cell. In this connection some little-known observations of Cook (71) are of much interest. Cook observed that methylene blue acted like atropine in antagonizing the effects of acetylcholine in the isolated frog's heart. In the heart cavity, slightly more than one molecule of methylene blue was required to block one molecule of acetylcholine. The dye penetrated the nerves and cells of the heart, turning them deep blue in color, its concentration within the cells being 20 to 200 times that of the fluid outside the cells. When the heart was deeply colored, if rinsed with Ringer's, its original sensitivity to acetylcholine was quickly restored. Both the methylene blue and acetylcholine had to be *outside* the cardiac tissue for the dye to exert a blocking action. Cook concluded: "This antagonism, therefore, is independent of the entrance of the dye into the nerve and muscle cells; the dye appears to produce its antagonism to acetylcholine by a freely reversible action on the surface of the cells."

Couteaux found Janus green B a good dye for supravital staining of parts of motor end-plates. The structures stained were oriented rodlike particles ("batonnets") on the muscle side of the junction, and in close proximity to the nerve terminals. Postulating that the batonnets should contain receptor substance with which Janus green B, a basic dye, might combine, Welsh and Zacks (306) tried to prevent staining by pretreatment with *d*-tubocurarine. The results were inconclusive because Janus green B also combines with, and inactivates, cholinesterase (30, 202, 315). That acetylcholine-receptive substance and cholinesterase exist in close proximity is probable. Since they both might specifically combine with such dyes as methylene blue and Janus green B, such attempts to visualize acetylcholine receptors will be fruitless, it seems, unless the combining groups of cholinesterase can be previously and selectively occupied by slowly reversible inhibitors.

3. Acetylcholine-Receptive Substance

Although many years have passed since Langley's (188, 189) speculation concerning "receptive substances" for nicotine and other drugs, little progress has been made in understanding the molecular interactions between most well-known drugs and cellular components. The same may be said for the hormones and neurohormones. However, if one examines the vast literature dealing with the acetylcholine system, and drugs or chemicals that react somewhere with components of the system, it becomes apparent that molecular structure and exactness of "fit" between reacting molecules is of great importance. From designed experiments, it has been possible to learn much concerning the interaction of acetylcholine and the cholinesterases (20, 206, 309, 310, 311, 312). This has been facilitated by the possibility of isolating cholinesterases and studying them in a cell-free system. Both the specific or acetylcholinesterase and the nonspecific or serum cholinesterase have now been shown to possess an "esteratic site" and a nearby anionic site. These allow two or more bonds to be formed between an acetylcholine molecule and the esterase. Although acetylcholine-receptive substance has not yet been isolated and studied in a similar manner, much can be indirectly deduced concerning it or, at least, concerning the distribution of charged groups within a cell which combine with acetylcholine. Either there are combining groups with a precise distribution and surrounded by a definite atom pattern within given species of large molecules, or a fixed pattern of distribution of smaller molecules to provide

properly spaced combining groups. Thus the cholinesterases and acetylcholine-receptive substances have some common properties.

Some of the literature bearing on the question of molecular fit between
acetylcholine and its receptors is referred to in several brief discussions of
this problem (167, 227, 248, 290). Certain recent reviews (236, 264) provide further sources of information on structure-activity relations of
acetylcholine and cell components.

To illustrate the manner in which the problem of the nature of acetylcholine receptors may be approached, our observations on the isolated heart
of the mollusc, *Venus mercenaria*, will be briefly summarized. This heart
is innervated by cholinergic neurons which, when active, inhibit the beat
(231, 301). The quantitative actions of a number of acetylcholine analogues have been determined on the *Venus* heart (302–305). Many of the
findings serve only to confirm the results of other workers using other test
preparations. Among these is the importance of size of the "cationic
head." On the *Venus* heart, acetylcholine and tetramethylammonium
ions have similar depressor actions, but acetylcholine is more than 10,000
times as active as tetramethylammonium. The triethyl analogue of acetylcholine and tetraethylammonium ions, however, excite the *Venus* heart by
blocking endogenous acetylcholine that normally keeps the heart from beat-
ing at a maximal frequency and amplitude. By the substitution of ethyl
or other alkyl groups for the methyl groups of tetramethylammonium, it

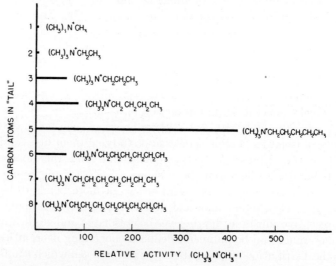

Fig. 5. Relative inhibitory actions on the *Venus* heart of the alkyltrimethyl-
ammonium ion series. An illustration of the "5-carbon rule." Based on data from
Welsh and Taub (303).

was found that a minimum of two methyl groups was required for any acetylcholine-like activity and that three methyl groups provided maximal activity (303).

Changes in over-all length of acetylcholine analogues clearly demonstrated that the equivalent of a five-carbon chain was required for maximal activity (302, 303).   This is seen in Fig. 5, where the relative activities of the n-alkyltrimethylammonium series are shown.   The amyl member with the five-carbon chain, which is closest in length to the long chain of acetylcholine, is by far the most active on the *Venus* heart.

Amyltrimethylammonium is approximately $\frac{1}{70}$ as active as acetylcholine on the *Venus* heart.   The difference must reside in the OC group.

$$\overset{\text{OC}}{\underset{\text{O}}{\|}}$$

By synthesizing a new series of ketone analogues of acetylcholine, Welsh and Taub (304) were able to show the importance of the presence and position of the carbonyl group (see Table II).   It is apparent that the carbonyl group serves as a combining group, as earlier suggested by Pfeiffer (227). When tested on a variety of vertebrate preparations the ketone with the oxygen in the 4-position was always the most active member of the series (168).   If the ketone oxygen of the 4-ketoamyltrimethylammonium compound is reduced or a methyl or acetoxy group substituted (Table II), there is great loss of activity when tested on the *Venus* heart (304).

These studies on the *Venus* heart have yielded results which support earlier views of the nature of the linkage between acetylcholine and its receptive substance.   It would seem that in *Venus* heart muscle a bond is formed between the cationic nitrogen and a negatively charged group in the receptor molecule.   If groups other than methyl surround the nitrogen, the two molecules do not come in close enough contact for this to occur. However, van der Waals' forces may, as in the case of tetraethylammonium or the triethyl analogue of acetylcholine, hold these molecules at the receptor site, thereby excluding acetylcholine and, at times, producing an opposing response if the normal action of acetylcholine is inhibitory.   A second bond must form between the carbonyl group of acetylcholine and the receptive substance in the *Venus* heart.   This might be a hydrogen bond between the ketone oxygen and a group such as NH in the receptor molecule. Clearly, from the results at hand the over-all dimensions and precise atomic arrangement in the acetylcholine molecule are important in its reaction. This indicates the importance of short-range attractive forces between acetylcholine atoms and receptor atoms, which are dependent on exactness of "fit."   With the *Venus* heart, no acetylcholine analogue has been found with greater physiological activity than acetylcholine itself.   The smallest molecular alteration has resulted in a loss of activity.   With other test

TABLE II

EQUIACTIVE MOLAR RATIOS OF CERTAIN ACETYLCHOLINE ANALOGUES SELECTED TO
SHOW THE SIGNIFICANCE OF THE POSITION OF THE CARBONYL GROUP

Compound	Cat's blood pressure[a]	Rabbit auricles[a]	Guinea pig ileum[a]	Frog heart[a]	Frog rectus[a]	Venus heart[b]	LD50 miceS.C.[b] mg./kg.
Acetylcholine iodide or bromide [$(CH_3)_3NCH_2CH_2OCCH_3$] I or Br, $\overset{\|}{O}$	1	1	1	1	1	1	170
4-Keto-amyltrimethylammonium iodide [$(CH_3)_3NCH_2CH_2CH_2CCH_3$] I, $\overset{\|}{O}$	Purely pressor	50	80	416	1.1	12	16
3-Keto-amyltrimethylammonium iodide [$(CH_3)_3NCH_2CH_2CCH_2CH_3$] I, $\overset{\|}{O}$	Purely pressor	250	670	1670	1.3	160	34
2-Keto-amyltrimethylammonium iodide [$(CH_3)_3NCH_2CCH_2CH_2CH_3$] I, $\overset{\|}{O}$	84 pressor after atropine	1660	330	5010	153	620	200
n-Amyltrimethylammonium iodide [$(CH_3)_3NCH_2CH_2CH_2CH_2CH_3$] I	66	44	8	325	13	70	—

[a] Reference 168.
[b] Reference 304.

animals or organs this has not been true because of the interference of cholinesterase hydrolysis, certain stable analogues being much more active than acetylcholine. The *Venus* heart has a very low level of cholinesterase activity; hence the advantage of precise fit between acetylcholine and receptor more than offsets the disadvantage of instability compared with a nonhydrolyzable compound such as the 4-ketone analogue.

At certain points in the vertebrate (*e.g.*, heart and intestine) the action of acetylcholine is mimicked by pilocarpine or muscarine, and atropine is one of the most effective blocking agents. At such places the action of acetylcholine is said to be muscarine-like, or muscarinic. At other points (*e.g.*, autonomic ganglia and neuromuscular junctions) nicotine mimics acetylcholine in low concentrations and blocks it in high concentrations. Here the action of acetylcholine is said to be nicotine-like or nicotinic. However, an important difference exists between autonomic ganglia and vertebrate neuromuscular junctions. At the former, tetraethylammonium salts are effective blocking agents and d-tubocurarine is not, whereas at the latter the reverse is true. Among the newer junctional blocking agents the compounds pentamethonium, or C_5, and hexamethonium, or C_6, are highly effective at autonomic ganglia but not at neuromuscular junctions; the reverse is true of decamethonium or C_{10} (58, 219–221, 223, 236). One may conclude from such observations that acetylcholine-receptive substance is not the same wherever it occurs or, at least, that the pattern of combining groups differs. If acetylcholine-receptive substance is protein in nature, small differences in a family of related molecules could account for the observed pharmacological patterns.

Up to a certain stage in the study of the *Venus* heart the actions of a variety of drugs suggested that its acetylcholine-receptive substance was most like that of vertebrate autonomic ganglia. It was then found that neither C_5 nor C_{10} significantly antagonized the action of acetylcholine; instead mytolon, a blocking agent at vertebrate neuromuscular junctions, was shown to be a highly effective acetylcholine antagonist (195, 305). These observations suggest that the receptive substance of the *Venus* heart has configurations or other properties intermediate between those found at vertebrate autonomic ganglia and skeletal muscles. This is not be be taken as an indication that there are many different types of acetylcholine receptors among the lower animals. On the contrary, from such evidence as exists for other invertebrates where cholinergic systems are known, the patterns of drug action are surprisingly like those found in the vertebrates. Whatever the true nature of the acetylcholine-receptive substance or substances, there is a basic pattern throughout animals from protozoa to man.

Some drugs commonly used in the treatment of central nervous disorders, such as certain of the antiepileptics and anticonvulsants, have in the active portion of their molecules two or more carbonyl groups (270, 272). It has been suggested (305) that these compounds may combine with acetylcholine-receptive substance and form relatively stable linkages by virtue of two properly spaced carbonyl groups. An analogy with the bis-quaternary ammonium blocking agents is obvious.

4. Concerning the Mechanism of Action of Acetylcholine

Evidence is accumulating to show that cells which are excited by acetylcholine (*e.g.*, skeletal muscle and some smooth muscle) undergo depolarization when acetylcholine is externally applied (41, 106, 180, 182, 274, 275). In the case of cardiac muscle, whose activity is normally inhibited by acetylcholine, the application of this neurohumor results in an increase in resting potential (*e.g.*, 48).

Fatt and Katz have examined in detail the depolarizing action of acetylcholine at motor end-plates in the frog. They conclude (108, 111) that relatively few molecules of acetylcholine are released per nerve impulse. These act to produce an increase in permeability that allows a general exchange of free cations and anions and not alone K^+ and Na^+, as seems to be true for the axon (161, 162). A "short circuit" of the muscle fiber at the end-plate results and so reduces the active-membrane potential. The end-plate region does not respond to local currents of the muscle impulse set up by direct electrical stimulation of the muscle. Fatt and Katz (108) say, "Thus, it appears that the end-plate, i.e. the neuroreceptive area of the muscle fibre, differs from the surrounding fibre surface not only in its specific sensitivity to chemical stimulants, but in its lack of sensitivity to electric currents." Nastuk (207) holds the view that the depolarization at the end-plate produced by acetylcholine is due primarily to changes in permeability to sodium ions and not to cations generally.

There is the remaining question of the number and nature of the events intervening between the arrival of the few acetylcholine molecules and the postulated general breakdown in ion barriers of the end-plate region. What happens when acetylcholine reaches the largely hypothetical receptive substance? As a working hypothesis, Welsh (289) suggested the following: Acetylcholine-receptive substance is an enzyme requiring acetylcholine for its activation. The activated enzyme reacts with a substrate in the cell membrane to split off polar-nonpolar ions whose changing orientation (*cf.* Höber, 160) might then account for the observed permeability change in the cell membrane. No direct test of the hypothesis has been made. As an alternative, it is possible to conceive of acetylcholine displacing, by competition, a few key molecules in a region where molecular orientation might be of peculiar importance. Specifically, lecithin (or certain other phospholipids) might be bound to protein molecules in the cell membrane, as shown in Fig. 6. If a sufficient number of lecithin molecules were displaced, the selective permeability might be so altered that local polarization changes or short-circuiting would lead to a propagated impulse.[1] Danielli (79) suggests that, provided the cell membrane has molecules that specifically adsorb a given agent such as adrenaline or acetylcholine, there might be an

---

[1] If some phospholipid molecules are linked by calcium through phosphate bonds, they might similarly be liable to disorientation if the calcium were removed by chelation or otherwise. Any theory of excitation must take into account the stabilizing action of calcium in the cell membrane (*cf.* 144, 296).

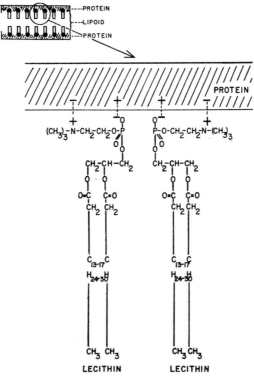

FIG. 6.   Illustrating a possible structural relationship between lecithin and a protein component of a cell surface.   Specific adsorption of acetylcholine at the cell surface might displace oriented lipids leading to surface disorganization (*cf.* Danielli, ref. 79).

accumulation of a considerable amount of such a substance in the membrane relative to the concentration in the surrounding fluid.   Thus one need not consider the oftentimes very low concentration outside the cell (*e.g.*, $10^{-10}M$ or less) to be the acting concentration in the cell membrane.

5. *Excitation and Inhibition by Acetylcholine*

That stimulation of the vagus nerve slows the heart while it increases the activity of intestinal smooth muscle has long been recognized.   Acetylcholine experimentally applied has the same actions.   This has raised the important question: Are there basic differences in the mechanism of action of acetylcholine on these two organs?   That acetylcholine may, on some structures, have a stimulating action in low concentrations and a depressing action in high concentrations is seen from studies on skeletal muscle and autonomic ganglia.   Some of the earlier literature has been reviewed by

Rosenblueth (239). If, at a junction where acetylcholine normally excites, an anticholinesterase is applied, repeated stimulation of the prejunctional unit allows acetylcholine to accumulate. Eventually, as with experimentally applied acetylcholine, block appears. A recent and interesting example of this is found in the work of Barnes and Duff (18). Using large doses of diisopropyl p-nitrophenyl phosphate (isopropyl paraoxon), they produced complete or very nearly complete inhibition of the cholinesterases present in the rat diaphragm. Single, indirect stimuli still produced a response of the diaphragm muscle, but stimuli repeated at rates higher than one per second failed to stimulate. In the latter case, repeated stimulation, even at a very slow rate, must permit the accumulation of paralyzing amounts of acetylcholine. Why should excess acetylcholine prevent junctional transmission? One likely explanation arises from an earlier interpretation of the inhibition of red cell cholinesterase by excess acetylcholine. Zeller and Bissegger (316) suggested that a two-point attachment must occur between acetylcholine and acetylcholinesterase: one between the positively charged nitrogen and a negatively charged group in the enzyme and one between the ester group and a group in the enzyme. Excess substrate might then result in a single linkage to each molecule. Since we now have evidence that there is a two-point attachment between acetylcholine and its receptors, a similar explanation could account for junctional block produced by excess acetylcholine.

One might now ask: Is it possible that the vertebrate heart normally operates at a level of endogenous acetylcholine that is already slightly over into the inhibitory range? From results with the *Venus* heart, where acetylcholine in very low concentrations is sometimes excitatory, this interpretation was applied (289). Evidence has now been presented showing that vertebrate hearts are excited by acetylcholine (*1*) when washed for long periods until the residual level of acetylcholine and the rate of synthesis are low (43, 203, 255); (*2*) after exposure to an excess of cholinesterase (138); (*3*) when treated with certain drugs (52, 57, 163, 204). The excitation of the isolated frog's heart produced by atropine and the excitation of the *Venus* heart produced by various substances known to antagonize the action of acetylcholine on this organ, provide supporting evidence for the view that levels of acetylcholine in certain organs may normally be inhibitory. As a parallel to this it was once thought that shoot growth in plants was stimulated by auxin, whereas the growth of roots was inhibited. Thimann (265) was able to show that this was a concentration phenomenon. Low concentrations of auxin stimulate root growth. Intermediate concentrations inhibit root growth but stimulate shoot growth. High concentrations have only an inhibitory action on both roots and shoots. This led to a similar suggestion to account for the different actions of acetylcholine

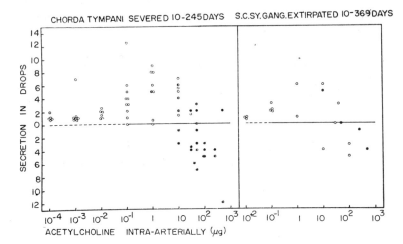

Fig. 7. The vasomotor and secretory effects of different quantities of acetylcholine (intraarterial) as observed in the chronically and acutely denervated submaxillary gland of the cat. The difference between the volume of secretion of the chronically denervated gland and that of the acutely denervated gland is plotted relative to the secretion of the acutely denervated gland which is represented by the horizontal "O" line.

○ = Vasodilatation in both glands.

◐ = Vasoconstriction in the chronically denervated gland and vasodilatation in the acutely denervated gland.

● = Vasoconstriction in both glands.

(Figure from Graham and Stavraky, 146.)

on vertebrate heart and intestine (289). A good example of the reversal of action of acetylcholine as a function of concentration is seen in Fig. 7 from a study on the response of the chronically denervated submaxillary gland of the cat to acetylcholine (146). Many drugs and other neurohormones (51) have biphasic actions, depending on the concentration applied, on cellular accumulation from previous exposure of the tissue to the drug or hormone, and on normal endogenous tissue levels in the case of the neurohormones.

6. Trophic Action of Acetylcholine

Acetylcholine is found in certain places where it can not be acting as a transmitter agent, and, in fact, is not of obvious nervous origin (e.g., certain protozoa; ciliated epithelium; spleen; placenta). It has been suggested (e.g., refs. 1, 50, 289) that acetylcholine might have a basic role in the regulation of cellular metabolism and secondarily have assumed a prominent part in the actions of the nervous system. That denervation of a cholinergically innervated organ usually results in increased sensitivity to acetylcholine is well known (61).   In his study of the regeneration of urodele limbs Singer has described his methods and made a preliminary report on the effect of infused drugs (252, 253).   Atropine infused in the regenerating limb bud will stop or delay regeneration.   Cholinesterase solutions of high concentration generally interrupt growth for a few days after infusion. These and other results obtained by Singer suggest that acetylcholine may be the nerve substance necessary for regeneration of amputated amphibian (*Triturus*) limbs.   Somewhat similar effects of atropine and certain acetylcholine-like substances, especially pilocarpine, had been found earlier on regenerating planaria (288).   Further work (Welsh and Travis, unpublished) has substantiated the view that acetylcholine in planaria is involved in growth and tissue maintenance.   If acetylcholine released from cholinergic neurons normally effects changes in membrane polarization and permeability, acetylcholine, whether originating in nervous or nonnervous tissue, may exert important actions on cellular metabolism by way of alterations in the properties of the cell membrane.

B. ADRENALINE AND NOR-ADRENALINE

Progress in understanding the physiology and pharmacology of the sympathetic division of the autonomic nervous system has been slow for a number of reasons.   Among them are (*1*) the presence of extranervous chromaffin tissue that also gives rise to active amines, (*2*) earlier belief that only one catechol amine is released by adrenergic neurons, (*3*) twofold action of sympathetic nerves—excitation and inhibition, (*4*) reversal of action of applied adrenaline by several means, (*5*) different basic methods of action of sympathomimetic drugs (*e.g.*, by imitating adrenaline, by protecting adrenaline from destruction, by blocking acetylcholine).

In this section some of the more recent contributions toward a fuller understanding of the physiological actions of adrenaline and nor-adrenaline will be briefly considered.   Among these has been the establishment of nor-adrenaline as the principal neurohumor of adrenergic neurons (97, 98). Much of the recent work dealing with the differences in physiological actions of adrenaline and nor-adrenaline has been reviewed by von Euler (99, 100, 102).   Table III shows some of these differences.

How do adrenaline and nor-adrenaline produce such manifold effects, and why should such closely related compounds so often have opposing actions? Similar questions may be asked of other pairs of related molecules among the hormones, such as vasopressin and oxytocin, or estrogen and progesterone.   The answers are far from complete, for our knowledge of the mechanisms of action of the hormones at cellular and molecular levels is growing with extraordinary slowness.

TABLE III

Physiological Actions of Adrenaline and Nor-adrenaline

[Based on reviews by von Euler (99, 100, 102)]

Adrenaline	Nor-adrenaline
Net peripheral vascular effect = vasodilatation	Limited vasodilator actions; over-all vasoconstriction
Marked action on metabolism, e.g., increases O_2 consumption and increases glucose output from liver	Metabolic actions only $\frac{1}{5}$ to $\frac{1}{10}$ those of adrenaline
Central excitation pronounced	Weak central excitation
Multifarious action and emergency function	Regulator of normal homeostasis in respect to blood pressure

1. Acetylcholine and Adrenaline Antagonisms and Synergisms

Discussions of the interactions of acetylcholine and adrenaline are to be found elsewhere (49, 60, 70). It has long been recognized that acetylcholine and adrenaline customarily have opposing actions on organs innervated by the autonomic nervous system. Marrazzi has contended that acetylcholine and adrenaline have opposing actions in autonomic ganglia and in parts of the central nervous system (199, 200, 201). Recent studies of transmission in sympathetic ganglia support Marrazzi in showing that adrenaline and nor-adrenaline interfere with transmission (196, 222). The finding of adrenaline and nor-adrenaline in the central nervous system and their release by appropriate drug action (282) should encourage further study of the central nervous actions of these two amines.

Within the invertebrates the observation that acetylcholine and adrenaline have synergistic, or similar, excitatory actions on the decapod crustacean heart has frequently been made (see refs. 124, 179). Since there is no indication that adrenaline or nor-adrenaline occur in the Crustacea (210), these observations are without full significance.

A potentiation of the indirect maximal twitch of mammalian skeletal muscle by adrenaline and nor-adrenaline has been extensively reinvestigated by Goffart (139, 140).

Whether the actions of acetylcholine and adrenaline are similar or opposing sometimes depends on the level of endogenous neurohumor, on the concentration applied, or on both. This leads to the interesting question of reversal of action of adrenaline.

2. Reversal of action of Adrenaline and Nor-adrenaline

The reversal of the vasomotor action of adrenaline by extracts of ergot was first described by Dale (74). Since then, a reversal of action produced

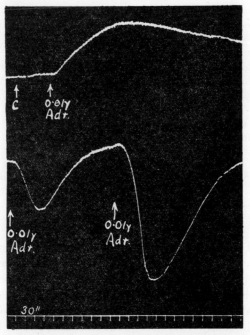

FIG. 8. Upper tracing shows dilator effect on the perfused rabbit's ear of an injection of adrenaline at the beginning of perfusion. Lower tracing shows effects of two later injections of the same dose. An example of reversal from a dilator response to a constrictor response with repeated doses. From Burn and Robinson (53).

by a variety of drugs, by changes in concentration, by denervation, and in other ways has been observed. A few recent studies will be mentioned. When the ear vessels of the rabbit are perfused with adrenaline, occasional preparations respond initially by vasodilatation. After perfusion has continued for an hour or more, the response changes spontaneously to vasoconstriction (53). An example of this reversal is seen in Fig. 8.

Small quantities of adrenaline (10^{-8} to 10^{-2} μg.), injected intraarterially, cause vasodilatation in the submaxillary salivary glands of the cat, whereas large quantities of adrenaline (10^{-1} to 5μg.) cause vasoconstriction and diminished secretion (145). After chronic denervation of this gland there is increased sensitivity to adrenaline and nor-adrenaline. A lowered secretory threshold and greater volume of secretion are seen with small and moderate doses of these amines, whereas greater vasoconstriction and reduction of secretion result when they are introduced in large amounts (146).

An invertebrate smooth muscle, the anterior byssus retractor of the edible mussel, *Mytilus*, shows a reversal in response to repeated applications of a given concentration of adrenaline. When adrenaline of about 10^{-5} M concentration is first applied, it produces a contraction similar to that produced by acetylcholine. After washing the muscle and allowing time for relaxation, a second application of 10^{-5} M adrenaline produces a smaller contraction. A third application may be without effect, while a fourth or later applications will relax a muscle that is not in a state of complete relaxation (275). One way to interpret such a reversal is to assume that repeated applications of adrenaline, in spite of washing, leave behind some adrenaline firmly bound to receptors in the muscle. The number of occupied receptors would then determine whether the muscle responded to adrenaline by contraction or by relaxation. Such an interpretation was suggested by Burn and Robinson (53) to account for their observations on the perfused rabbit's ear. However, these same authors (54, 55) suggest that the increased sensitivity of the denervated nictitating membrane of the cat to adrenaline and nor-adrenaline may be due to the observed decrease in amine oxidase content (*cf.* ref. 56). That the denervated nictitating membrane shows increased sensitivity as the result of the uncovering of amine receptors would seem an equally attractive explanation of the observations.

3. *Concerning the Mechanism of Action of Adrenaline and Nor-adrenaline*

The mode of action of the catechol amines at cellular and molecular levels is largely unknown. Loewi (194) states that it is his opinion that both acetylcholine and adrenaline act exclusively at the cell surface. The evidence for this is indirect but rather convincing. That which concerns acetylcholine has been discussed earlier. Adrenaline produces changes in membrane polarization, as does acetylcholine. On the tibialis muscle of the cat, Brown *et al.* (38) found that adrenaline, nor-adrenaline, and stimulation of the sympathetic supply to the lower limb produced a small increase of the demarcation potential. After denervation, d-tubocurarine, and decamethonium (C_{10}), there was hyperpolarization followed by depolarization. Lundberg (196) has found hyperpolarization of ganglion cells sometimes associated with adrenaline inhibition of ganglionic transmission. Using internal electrodes, Bülbring (42) observed the membrane potential of cells of the taenia coli of the guinea pig to fall after application of acetylcholine (which increases muscle tension) and to rise after adrenaline (which decreases muscle tension). As might be expected, changes in permeability accompany the changes in membrane polarization produced by adrenaline and nor-adrenaline. Brown *et al.* (38) found some evidence of a diminished exchange of K during hyperpolarization of the tibialis muscle with adrenaline and nor-adrenaline. After equilibration of diaphragm muscle of the rat with K^{42}, subsequent application of adrenaline or nor-adrenaline in K-free Tyrode's solution slowed the loss of K for about 10 minutes, after which the rate of loss increased above that preceding the application of one of these amines (139, 141). After injection of adrenaline into the cat's heart, Robertson and Peyser (238) observed an increase in intracellular Na and a decrease in intracellular K.

Ussing and his colleagues have studied the effects of adrenaline on active transport of ions in isolated frog skin. Ussing and Zerahn (278) found that in short-circuited frog skin the electric current came largely from the active transport inward of Na. This held when Na transport was increased by posterior-lobe hormone or decreased by added CO_2. There was uncertainty, however, concerning the effects produced by adrenaline. Whereas this amine only moderately increased the current and the influx of Na, it brought about a great increase in outflux of Na. On further exploration of this problem with Na^{22}, Na^{24}, Cl^{36}, and Cl^{38} as tracers, it was found that the nonsodium current evoked by adrenaline is due to the active transport outward of Cl by mucous glands of the skin (173). These significant studies strongly suggest that the effects of adrenaline on frog's skin are produced by specific reactions regulating the active transport of Na and Cl ions.

4. Adrenaline and Nor-adrenaline Receptors

The literature on the structural requirements for sympathomimetic drug action (184, 185) show the same importance of "fit" between drug molecule and cell receptor as is seen in the case of acetylcholine and related compounds. Ahlquist (3) suggested that there were two types of adrenaline receptors—*alpha* receptors associated with most of the excitatory functions, and *beta* receptors associated with most of the inhibitory functions as well as with excitation of the heart. Lands (186), after comparing the actions of a wider variety of sympathomimetic amines than were available to Ahlquist, likewise concludes that there are two main types of receptors. For combining with the excitor type an *m*-hydroxyl group is important, whereas for combining with the inhibitor type an alcoholic hydroxyl in the side chain has special significance. Lands concluded that the sympathetic receptor of the heart is undifferentiated and stimulated by substances with a strong affinity for either receptor. Burn (51, 53) has suggested that the amount of adrenaline combined with cell receptors at a given moment may determine whether the effect of added adrenaline is excitatory or inhibitory. With the recognition of the biological importance of nor-adrenaline and 5-hydroxytryptamine, and with the prospect of other amines serving in place of adrenaline in certain invertebrates, it is obvious that the question of the number and nature of specific cellular components reacting with these amines will be with us for some time to come.

C. 5-HYDROXYTRYPTAMINE

At the time this is written, few biologists are convinced that 5-hydroxy-tryptamine (serotonin or enteramine) should be classed as a neurohormone. This is due, in part, to its unusual distribution, to the earlier attention paid to its occurrence in blood platelets and the intestinal mucosa, and to its occurrence as a component of toxic or protective substances in several widely separated animal groups.   The literature on this new and interesting indole amine is covered by the reviews of Erspamer (88) and Page (210a).   In this brief consideration of the physiological actions of 5-hydroxytryptamine, discussion will be restricted to some of the arguments for classing it as a neurohormone and to its functional significance.

1. A Neurohumor in Molluscs

5-Hydroxytryptamine has been identified by chromatographic and pharmacological procedures in nerve tissue of three of the five classes of molluscs that have been examined (122, 292, 293).   We were led to look for 5-hydroxytryptamine in the molluscan nervous system because of the observation that enteramine (93) and 5-hydroxytryptamine (14) had powerful excitor actions on the molluscan heart and because of our interest in the nature of the excitor substance produced by nerves innervating the *Venus* heart (291).   Certain of the ergot alkaloids and lysergic acid diethylamide (LSD) have strong excitor actions on the *Venus* heart.   These actions resemble closely that of 5-hydroxytryptamine (291), but they are far more persistent.   A heart treated with extremely low doses of dihydroergotamine or LSD and then washed repeatedly fails to respond to high doses of 5-hydroxytryptamine because it is already maximally excited.

Twarog (275) finds that 5-hydroxytryptamine is the most effective agent for relaxing the tonically contracted anterior byssus retractor muscle of *Mytilus*.   Her evidence strongly suggests that it is the mediator of inhibitor nerves to this muscle.

Florey and Florey (122) have presented evidence that leads them to consider 5-hydroxytryptamine as a nerve "aktionssubstanz" in cephalopod molluscs and decapod Crustacea.

2. 5-Hydroxytryptamine in the Brain

Reference was made in an earlier section to the discovery of 5-hydroxy-tryptamine in the vertebrate brain.   Pharmacological evidence suggests that it plays an important physiological role there.   Among the alkaloids having a central action are certain indole derivatives such as the ergot alkaloids and yohimbine.   Far more striking, however, is the action of the diethylamide derivative of lysergic acid (which constitutes the central ring structure of the ergot alkaloids).   This was synthesized by A. Stoll and

Hofmann (258), and its profound central action in minute doses was accidentally discovered by Hofmann. W. A. Stoll (259, 260) first reported the central effects of minute oral doses of LSD, and these effects have been confirmed and observations extended by many investigators. Great interest resides in the fact that as little as 30 μg. of LSD taken orally can produce, in a normal person, the symptoms of schizophrenia. Gaddum (131, 132) appears to have been the first to demonstrate an antagonism between LSD and 5-hydroxytryptamine on certain isolated tissues and to suggest that the action of LSD on the brain might be due to the blocking of normally required 5-hydroxytryptamine.

Woolley and Shaw (313, 314) have suggested that alkaloids that contain the 5-hydroxytryptamine structure (yohimbine and certain ergot and harmala alkaloids), as well as the synthetic analogue "medmain," may have central actions due to their interference with the normal functions of 5-hydroxytryptamine. They suggest that certain mental aberrations might arise from too little or too much 5-hydroxytryptamine. The observations of Feldberg and Sherwood (119) on the effect of introducing 5-hydroxytryptamine into one of the lateral ventricles of the cat bear on this problem.

Although the heart of a clam is far removed from the human brain, biologically speaking, it shows a pattern of response to LSD and 5-hydroxytryptamine that suggests that the action of LSD on the human brain is not necessarily due to its antagonism of 5-hydroxytryptamine. When an isolated *Venus* heart is bathed with LSD in a concentration as low as 10^{-16} M it adsorbs, within 1 to 2 hours, a sufficient amount of the drug to produce a maximal increase in frequency and amplitude of heart beat. Washing the heart for hours fails to return it to normal. At the time of maximal excitation with LSD, high concentrations of 5-hydroxytryptamine fail to have any further effect on the heart. The author earlier spoke of this as an antagonism between the two substances (293, 294). However, it should be recognized that on the *Venus* heart LSD acts as an essentially irreversible analogue of 5-hydroxytryptamine. The same might be true in the human brain.

3. *Peripheral Actions of 5-Hydroxytryptamine*

From the extensive studies of Erspamer, Page, Reid, and others (88, 210a), the peripheral actions of 5-hydroxytryptamine, in a variety of mammals, are quite well known. In relatively low doses this indole amine has pronounced effects on blood pressure, respiration, water excretion, and the activity of the intestine and certain other smooth muscles. Whether there are peripheral neurons in the vertebrates that use 5-hydroxytryptamine as a mediator is not yet known. Possibly the enterochromaffin tissue of the intestinal mucosa (78, 120) that contains 5-hydroxytryptamine represents highly modified neurons, comparable with chromaffin tissue that produces the catechol amines. Although the studies of Gaddum (133, 134) indicate that there are specific cell receptors for 5-hydroxytryptamine located in various peripheral structures, the normal sources of the material that reacts with them are not yet well understood. The 5-hydroxytryptamine might come from blood platelets, from enterochormaffin tissue, or, possibly, from peripheral neurons of a type yet to be discovered in the vertebrates but quite certainly present in some invertebrates.

D. Polypeptide Neurohormones

Several physiologically active substances, known or thought to be polypeptides, are produced by nerve cells, or, in the case of vertebrate intermedin, by cells that are dependent on the nervous system in an intimate way. The best known are oxytocin and vasopressin, two closely related polypeptides and the only ones with known structure. The first of these contracts uterine muscle and releases milk from mammary glands, whereas the second acts mainly on the smooth muscle of blood vessels. Their physiological actions overlap, however, and both appear to play some part in "water balance" in amphibia and as antidiuretic substances in the higher vertebrates (240).

Intermedin, or the melanophore-expanding hormone, has long been known for its control of color changes in the lower vertebrates (213). Intermedin is now thought to be closely related to adrenocorticotropic hormone (ACTH) (see Chapter IX; also refs. 19, 257, 266), and the latter substance is considered to be a polypeptide (191, 192). Vertebrate melanophores have certain features in common with smooth muscle cells, and intermedin acts on melanophores as though it were a stable, long-acting substitute for acetylcholine.

Insects and crustaceans also make use of intermedin-like substances as controlling agents for certain chromatophores and eye pigment.

Substance P, considered to be a polypeptide (96, 225), occurs in various parts of the brain (8, 225) and has also been extracted from the intestine (82). Pernow believes that substance P of the intestine may come from the nerve plexus. This substance has a stimulating action on a variety of smooth muscle, both *in vitro* and *in vivo*. Whereas that of the intestine may play a part in regulating intestinal motility, the role of substance P in the central nervous system appears to be unknown.

E. Neurosecretory Materials of Crustaceans and Insects[2]

Berta Scharrer has presented, in a comprehensive review, the functions of invertebrate hormones and neurosecretory substances (Chapter II).

[2] This section was written by Dr. Dorothy E. Bliss.

The present discussion, therefore, will be limited to a brief survey of neuro-secretion in insects and crustaceans and to an analysis of certain controversial aspects.

1. Development of the Concept of Neurosecretory Systems in Crustaceans and Insects

The presence of physiologically active substances in the nervous system of crustaceans was first indicated with the discovery by Perkins (224) that a chromatophorotropic factor, already shown by Koller (176) to be blood-borne, could be localized in the eyestalks of *Palaemonetes*. After Hanström (150, 151) had described in each eyestalk two structures, the sinus gland and the x organ, which appeared histologically to be of a secretory nature, it was concluded that the sinus glands were responsible for the production of chromatophorotropically active materials, since the regions of the eyestalks containing the sinus glands had the highest or, in some cases, the entire activity.

Further experimental work, relating the sinus glands to molting, retinal pigment migration, and other physiological processes in crustaceans, suggested that the morphologically simple sinus glands were synthesizing either one hormone with several functions or several hormones (33, 34, 171, 241). This conclusion was based on experiments with eyestalk removal and with sinus gland implants or extracts. Recent investigators, employing various techniques of sinus gland removal, have shown beyond doubt that the sinus glands are not producing physiologically active materials but are storing and releasing them. Hormones or their precursors are being formed in the bodies of secretory nerve cells distributed throughout the central nervous system. They are being transported along axons to the swollen nerve fiber endings (the sinus glands) which constitute the storage-release organs. (For references see Chapter II; see also refs. 26, 65, 130, 218, 233, 243, 246, 247.)

Neurosecretory cells were first recognized in the central nervous system of an insect by Weyer (308), who described them in the brain of the honey-bee, *Apis mellifica*. After the discovery of similar cells in other insects, there appeared reports that the corpora cardiaca and the corpora allata were innervated by fiber tracts from medial and lateral groups of brain neurosecretory cells and that secretory material could be seen along portions of the fiber tracts anterior to the corpora cardiaca. Some time elapsed before it could be determined whether the secretory material was originating within the brain or the corpora cardiaca. The recent experiments of B. Scharrer (242) have shown conclusively that in *Leucophaea* neurosecretory products are formed in the brain and travel to the corpora cardiaca for storage and release into the blood. Her observations have been ex-

tended to *Calliphora* by E. Thomsen (267; see also ref. 233). Thus, first
in insects and later in crustaceans, there appeared support for the hypothesis proposed by Scharrer and Scharrer (244) that secretory products are
produced in nerve cell bodies, migrate along axons, and are collected in
common storage-release sites composed of nerve fiber endings. In this
way, neurosecretory systems of insects and crustaceans have been shown
to be analogous to the hypothalamic–posterior-lobe neurosecretory system
of vertebrates.

2. *Significance of Differences in Storage-Release Organs*

A comparison of physiological processes controlled by various components
of insect and crustacean neurosecretory systems is complicated by recent
observations (9, 10, 262, 269) that secretory material, originating in the
pars intercerebralis of the brain of certain insects, can be traced not only
along the nervi corpori cardiaci into the corpora cardiaca but also along
the nervi corpori allati into the corpora allata. There appear to be two
neurosecretory storage organs in insects, but these two storage centers
seem to have functional glandular portions as well. On the contrary, with
one exception (65) the only neurosecretory storage organs thus far reported
in crustaceans are aggregates of nerve endings, apparently with no associated glandular elements (6, 26, 27, 65, 172, 216, 217). The complicated
nature of an insect's response to extirpation and implantation of corpora
cardiaca and corpora allata may well be related to the dual role, storing-
releasing and secreting, of these two organs. The clear-cut experimental
results which follow removal of the crustacean sinus glands, on the other
hand, are probably related to the one function, that of storage-release,
fulfilled by these structures.

Gabe (130), nevertheless, has concluded from the presence within the
sinus glands of two histochemically distinguishable secretory materials,
only one of which is visible in x organ cells, that the sinus glands are producing one component and are thus completely analogous to the corpora
cardiaca. Two possibilities preclude at this time such a conclusion. The
first, recognized by Gabe (130), is that the material found in the sinus glands
but not in x organ cells may have been transformed from products arriving
in the sinus glands from the x organs. According to J. B. Durand (83) in
early summer there is a marked increase in secretory material visible within
cell bodies (Group El; see ref. 26) of the crayfish eyestalk. A corresponding
observed increase in secretory content within fiber endings composing the
sinus glands is understandable, since secretory products migrate from their
places of synthesis (cell bodies) to storage depots (fiber endings). For this
demonstration of seasonal correlation in amount of secretory material
within cell bodies and endings, two staining modifications, employing differ-

ent preparations of aldehyde fuchsin and different treatments of the tissues, must be used. One modification shows seasonal changes in cell bodies. The other modification is required to demonstrate corresponding changes in the fiber endings. This suggests that a chemical transformation occurs either while the secretory material is traveling to the fiber endings or very soon after it arrives there. The ability of a structure to transform its stored materials must be distinguished from the ability to produce substances *in situ*. The corpora cardiaca, histologically and physiologically, appear able to produce secretory materials *in situ*. So far there is no convincing evidence that the sinus glands can do so.

The presence of more than one component in the sinus glands can be explained in another way. Neurosecretory cells not only of the x organs but also of other parts of the central nervous system transmit their products to the sinus glands. The products of various groups of cells may be histochemically and physiologically different. Some recent observations bearing on this may be mentioned. Using Heidenhain's Azan and modifications of Gomori's aldehyde-fuchsin technique, Potter (230) has found five tinctorially separable materials in the sinus glands of the blue crab, *Callinectes sapidus*, and of the land crab, *Gecarcinus lateralis*. These differentially stained materials are visible in axons leading to the sinus glands. Cell bodies of various groups of eyestalk neurosecretory cells also react differentially to the dyes employed. In these animals no evidence has been found for the production of material within the sinus glands themselves. Present indications favor the concept that the sinus glands are exclusively storage-release organs for one or several neurosecretory products, which may be activated or otherwise transformed during transport or storage.

3. *Role of Neurosecretory Materials in the Control of Growth*

With the fact in mind that their storage organs are not entirely analogous, an attempt, summarized in Table IV, has been made to compare control of growth in crustaceans and insects.[3] During growth of crustaceans, metabolic changes, which are reflected in respiratory rate and quotient and in fat, protein, calcium, and water metabolism, are triggered by the neurosecretory system. Among insects, on the contrary, the glandular character of their neurosecretory storage organs poses the following question: Are respiratory, fat, and protein metabolism controlled by the corpora cardiaca and corpora allata through stored neurosecretory materials, through their own intrinsic glandular products, or through both? Owing to the complicated nature of the evidence available, this question will not be discussed here.

[3] The term "growth" is used here in its broadest sense, not with the restricted connotation of increase in total nitrogen.

TABLE IV

CONTROL OF GROWTH IN CRUSTACEANS AND INSECTS

Effect of hormone	Process affected	Neurosecretory products				Nonneurosecretory products	
		Crustaceans		Insects		Crustaceans	Insects
		Production	Storage	Production	Storage		
Inhibition	Growth and/or differentiation	Eyestalk; brain (supraesophageal ganglion)	Sinus glands	Subesophageal ganglion (diapause factor)			Corpora allata (juvenile and adult hormones)
Promotion	Growth and/or differentiation	x organ?	x organ?	Pars intercerebralis of the brain	Corpora cardiaca	y organ	Prothoracic glands (ventral, pericardial, peritracheal glands)

Growth in insects and crustaceans is controlled directly by secretory products of the central nervous system (Table IV).   Furthermore, neurosecretory materials from the insect brain govern one of two nonneurosecretory endocrine organs, the prothoracic glands being triggered by the activity of cells of the pars intercerebralis.   Comparable nonneurosecretory organs in crustaceans, the recently discovered y organs (85, 129), have not yet been shown to be under neurosecretory control, but possibly such control exists.

Analogues of glandular corpora allata have not appeared in crustaceans. Insects require throughout life the control of differentiation, a role performed by hormones of the corpora allata.   Since crustaceans undergo growth and molt but not metamorphosis once the embryonic stages have been completed, corpora allata analogues may be unnecessary in older crustaceans.   They may be present in crustacean larvae.

On the basis of certain experiments with the prawns, *Lysmata* and *Leander*, Carlisle (63, 64, 66) has postulated a "moult-accelerating principle." Yet its presence, clear enough in insects, has not been generally and conclusively demonstrated in crustaceans.   Nor, with the exception of the "egg-diapause factor" in *Bombyx mori* (125–128, 152), has a growth-inhibiting principle, comparable to that synthesized by crustaceans, been found in insects.   However, Hasegawa (152) has suggested that the subesophageal ganglion, source of the "egg-diapause factor," may determine the onset of hibernation, regardless of whether the insect hibernates in egg or pupal stage. The "egg-diapause factor" may prove eventually to have more general growth-inhibiting properties.

Although the eyestalks seem to be primary sources of crustacean neurosecretory hormones, other parts of the central nervous system have not been adequately tested. Preliminary experiments with *Gecarcinus* (25) have shown that the brain (supraesophageal ganglion) may be a source of growth-inhibiting hormone in concentrations comparable to those yielded by eyestalks. These experiments have indicated that response to a central nervous system implant is governed both by the physiological states of donor and recipient and by the type of implant. There is a strong suggestion that the response, growth promotion or growth inhibition, may depend upon the resulting concentration of an active material in the blood and tissues of the recipient. Perhaps we are dealing not with separate neurosecretory growth promotor and inhibitor substances but with one neurosecretory product, which may either promote or inhibit growth according to its blood and tissue concentration.

E. Scharrer (245) has proposed that the significance of the neurosecretory cell lies in its ability to transform nervous impulses into hormonal activity. The control of crustacean and insect metabolism requires that the organism receive internal or external stimuli of sufficient intensity to activate receptor neurons and bring into action the neurosecretory system. When eggs of *Bombyx mori* are reared in light and at high temperature, the pupal brain stimulates the subesophageal ganglion to release the inhibiting "egg-diapause factor," the effects of which are visible in the following generation (125–128). Light and temperature also affect the production of silkworm larvae, which molt three rather than four times (175).

Growth responses of crustaceans are regulated by certain combinations of environmental factors. When *Gecarcinus* is maintained at a favorable temperature and a high relative humidity, growth and molt are promoted by constant darkness. In light, however, by release of an inhibitory neurosecretory product, growth and its associated processes, including regeneration, water uptake, calcium resorption, and molt, are halted (24).

These examples indicate that hormones of the central nervous system, released into the blood by appropriate environmental stimuli, control growth in crustaceans and insects. In these forms the central nervous system serves as a chemical integrating mechanism of great importance.

V. Summary

It has been suggested in this chapter that the most characteristic physiological feature of neurons is their production and release of substances of high biological activity used for the integration of bodily functions. These neurohormones are of two main types (*1*) the neurohumors (*e.g.*, acetylcholine and nor-adrenaline) which act mainly at short range, and (*2*) the neurosecretory materials (*e.g.*, oxytocin and vasopressin) which may be carried via the circulation to act at points far removed from the place of release. This distinction between neurohumors and neurosecretory materials is none too clear but, for the present, seems worth retaining. Likewise there is no sharp boundary between the neurohormones and the classical hormones except as to source—nervous or nonnervous tissue. Neurohormones may be produced in any part of the neuron, but the principal regions of release are the axon terminations, except in those neurons so modified that axons have disappeared. Release may then be directly from the cell body. There is convincing evidence that neurohormones are transported via an axon to its terminations, where they often occur in greater concentration than elsewhere in the neuron. Acetylcholine and adrenaline appear to be synthesized and stored in granules with properties relating them to mitochondria. While neurohormones may "leak" from resting neurons at a low rate, the arrival of a nerve impulse at the nerve fiber endings is the occasion for an increase in rate of output. Much of the anatomical modification seen in nerve cell endings (branching or swelling) is attributable to the role of these endings in storage and release of neurohormones.

The neurohormones may be classified chemically in the following scheme (*1*) quaternary ammonium derivatives, of which acetylcholine is the only well-known representative; (*2*) amines, both phenolic and indolic, represented by adrenaline, nor-adrenaline, and 5-hydroxytryptamine; (*3*) polypeptides, with oxytocin and vasopressin chemically identified but with several other possible members, such as invertebrate "intermedin" and substance P.

The chemically known neurohormones function by exciting or inhibiting certain normal processes in cells, such as contraction or secretion. A given cell may be under the influence of two substances, one of which excites the cell while the other inhibits. There is much to suggest that they act at the cell surface and initiate processes leading to alterations in membrane polarization and permeability. The neurohumors are known to react in a specific manner with molecules or parts of molecules referred to as receptors. These receptor molecules might be enzyme-like, requiring the neurohumors as activators or coenzymes.

Polypeptide neurohormones appear at times to be acting as relatively stable substitutes for acetylcholine and the amines. This could account for the fact that a given cell (*e.g.*, smooth muscle) is often excited by two neurohormones (*e.g.*, adrenaline and oxytocin or 5-hydroxytryptamine and substance P). The brief dispersion of pigment in melanophores can be brought about by release of acetylcholine from adjacent nerve endings,

whereas its long-time dispersion is occasioned by circulating intermedin.
One amino acid in a polypeptide neurohormone might determine the physiological property of the molecule and might react with a receptor group
with which a chemically simpler neurohumor also combined.   Thus tryptophane in a polypeptide and the tryptophane derivative, 5-hydroxytrypta-
mine, might, through structural resemblance, enter into the same chemical
reaction at the cell surface.   Solubility and other properties of the two
molecules might then determine which will be the longer acting and therefore which will be released under a given set of circumstances.

Neurosecretory materials of unknown chemical nature play an important
role in regulating growth and a variety of associated physiological processes
in crustaceans and insects.   Their modes of action are largely unknown.

REFERENCES

1. Abdon, N. O.   *Acta Pharmacol. Toxicol.* **1**, 169 (1945).
2. Abramowicz, A. A.   *Biol. Bull.* **72**, 344 (1937).
3. Ahlquist, R. P.   *Am. J. Physiol.* **153**, 586 (1948).
4. Alexandrowicz, J. S.   *Pubbl. staz. zool. Napoli* **23**, 201 (1952).
5. Alexandrowicz, J. S.   *Pubbl. staz. zool. Napoli* **24**, 29 (1953).
6. Alexandrowicz, J. S.   *J. Marine Biol. Assoc. United Kingdom* **31**, 563 (1953).
7. Alexandrowicz, J. S., and Carlisle, D. B.   *J. Marine Biol. Assoc. United Kingdom* **32**, 175 (1953).
8. Amin, A. H., Crawford, T. B. B., and Gaddum, J. H.   *Abstr. 19th Intern. Physiol.
   Congr.* p. 165 (1953).
8a. Amin, A. H., Crawford, T. B. B., and Gaddum, J. H.   *J. Physiol. (London).*
    126, 596 (1954).
9. Arvy, L., Bounhiol, J. J., and Gabe, M.   *Compt. rend.* **236**, 627 (1953).
10. Arvy, L., and Gabe, M.   *Biol. Bull.* **106**, 1 (1954).
11. Asero, B., Colò, V., Erspamer, V., and Vercellone, A.   *Ann.* **576**, 69 (1952).
12. Augustinsson, K. B.   *Acta Physiol. Scand.* **15**, Suppl. 52 (1948).
13. Bacq, Z. M.   *Biol. Revs.* **22**, 73 (1947).
14. Bacq, Z. M., Fischer, P., and Ghiretti, F.   *Arch. intern. physiol.* **60**, 165 (1952).
15. Balfour, W., and Hebb, C. O.   *J. Physiol. (London)* **118**, 94 (1952).
16. Bannister, J., Whittaker, V. P., and Wijesundera, S.   *J. Physiol. (London)*
    121, 55 (1953).
17. Bargmann, W.   *Z. Zellforsch. u. mikroskop. Anat.* **34**, 610 (1947).
18. Barnes, J. M., and Duff, J. I.   *Brit. J. Pharmacol.* **8**, 334 (1953).
19. Benfey, B. G.   *Brit. J. Pharmacol.* **8**, 435 (1953).
20. Bergmann, F., and Wurzel, M.   *Biochim. et. Biophys. Acta* **13**, 251 (1954).
21. Blaschko, H.   *Pharmacol. Revs.* **4**, 415 (1952).
22. Blaschko, H.   *Pharmacol. Revs.* **6**, 23 (1954).
23. Blaschko, H., and Welch, A. D.   *Arch. exptl. Pathol. Pharmakol.* **219**, 17 (1953).
24. Bliss, D. E.   *Anat. Record* **120**, 742 (1954).
25. Bliss, D. E.   Unpublished data.
26. Bliss, D. E., Durand, J. B., and Welsh, J. H.   *Z. Zellforsch. u. mikroskop. Anat.*
    39, 520 (1954).
27. Bliss, D. E., and Welsh, J. H.   *Biol. Bull.* **103**, 157 (1952).
28. Bodian, D.   *Bull. Johns Hopkins Hosp.* **89**, 354 (1951).

29. Bovet, D., and Bovet-Nitti, F. Structure et activité pharmacodynamique des médicaments du système nerveux végétatif. S. Karger, Bâle and New York, 1948.
30. Brenner, S. *Biochim. et Biophys. Acta* **11**, 480 (1953).
31. Brodkin, E., and Elliott, K. A. C. *Am. J. Physiol.* **173**, 437 (1953).
32. Brooks, V. B. *J. Physiol. (London)* **123**, 501 (1954).
33. Brown, F. A., Jr. *Quart. Rev. Biol.* **19**, 32, 118 (1944).
34. Brown, F. A., Jr. The Hormones, Vol. 1. Academic Press, New York, 1948, p. 159.
35. Brown, F. A., Jr., Fingerman, M., and Hines, M. M. *Physiol. Zoöl.* **25**, 230 (1952).
36. Brown, G. L., and Feldberg, W. *J. Physiol. (London)* **86**, 290 (1936).
37. Brown, G. L., and Feldberg, W. *J. Physiol. (London)* **88**, 265 (1936).
38. Brown, G. L., Goffart, M., and Vianna Dias, M. *J. Physiol. (London)* **111**, 184 (1950).
39. Brücke, H. v. *Klin. Wochschr.* **17**, 420 (1938).
40. Brücke, H. v., Hellauer, H. F., and Umrath, K. *Intern. J. Ophthalmol.* **117**, 19 (1949).
41. Buchtal, F., and Lindhard, J. *Acta Physiol. Scand.* **4**, 136 (1942).
42. Bülbring, E. *J. Physiol. (London)* **125**, 302 (1954).
43. Bülbring, E., and Burn, J. H. *J. Physiol. (London)* **108**, 508 (1949).
44. Bülbring, E., Burn, J. H., and Shelley, H. *Proc. Roy. Soc. (London)* **B141**, 445 (1953).
45. Bülbring, E., and Hooton, I. N. *J. Physiol. (London)* **125**, 292 (1954).
46. Bülbring, E., Lourie, E. M., and Pardoe, U. *Brit. J. Pharmacol.* **4**, 290 (1949).
47. Burgen, A. S. V., Dickens, F., and Zatman, L. J. *J. Physiol. (London)* **109**, 10 (1949).
48. Burgen, A. S. V., and Terroux, K. G. *J. Physiol. (London)* **120**, 449 (1953).
49. Burn, J. H. *Physiol. Revs.* **25**, 377 (1945).
50. Burn, J. H. *Proc. Roy. Soc. (London)* **B137**, 281 (1950).
51. Burn, J. H. *Physiol. Revs.* **30**, 177 (1950).
52. Burn, J. H. *Pharmacol. Revs.* **6**, 107 (1954).
53. Burn, J. H., and Robinson, J. *Brit. J. Pharmacol.* **6**, 110 (1951).
54. Burn, J. H., and Robinson, J. *Brit. J. Pharmacol.* **7**, 304 (1952).
55. Burn, J. H., and Robinson, J. *J. Physiol. (London)* **120**, 224 (1953).
56. Burn, J. H., and Trendelenburg, U. *Brit. J. Pharmacol.* **9**, 202 (1954).
57. Burn, J. H., and Vane, J. R. *J. Physiol. (London)* **108**, 104 (1949).
58. Burns, B. D., and Paton, W. D. M. *J. Physiol. (London)* **115**, 41 (1951).
59. Cabanis, P. J. G. Rapports du physique et du moral de l'homme. Paris, 1802.
60. Cannon, W. B., and Rosenblueth, A. Autonomic Neuro-effector Systems. Macmillan, New York, 1937.
61. Cannon, W. B., and Rosenblueth, A. The Supersensitivity of Denervated Structures. A Law of Denervation. Macmillan, New York, 1949.
62. Carey, E. J. *Am. J. Pathol.* **20**, 341 (1944).
63. Carlisle, D. B. *Pubbl. staz. zool. Napoli* **24**, 69 (1953).
64. Carlisle, D. B. *Pubbl. staz. zool. Napoli* **24**, 279 (1953).
65. Carlisle, D. B. *Pubbl. staz. zool. Napoli* **24**, 435 (1953).
66. Carlisle, D. B. *J. Marine Biol. Assoc. United Kingdom* **32**, 289 (1953).
67. Carlisle, D. B., and Knowles, F. G. W. *Nature* **172**, 404 (1953).
68. Carlson, S. P. *Kgl. Fysiograf. Sällskap. Lund Förh.* **6**, 1 (1936).

69. Chang, H. C., Hsieh, W. M., Lee, L. Y., Li, T. H., and Lim, R. K. S. *Chinese J. Physiol.* **14**, 27 (1939).
70. Clark, A. J. *In* Heffter's Handbuch der experimentellen Pharmakologie. Springer, Berlin, 1937, Vol. 4.
71. Cook, R. P. *J. Physiol. (London)* **62**, 160 (1926).
72. Corteggiani, E. Contribution à l'étude de l'acétylcholine libre et dissimulée sous forme d'un complexe dans le cerveau. Theses, Universitè de Paris, Doullens, Paris, 1938.
73. Crawford, T. B. B., and Outschoorn, A. J. *Brit. J. Pharmacol.* **6**, 8 (1951).
74. Dale, H. H. *J. Physiol. (London)* **34**, 163 (1906).
75. Dale, H. H. *J. Physiol. (London)* **80**, 10 (1933).
76. Dale, H. H. Adventures in Physiology. Pergamon Press, London, 1953.
77. Dale, H. H. *Pharmacol. Revs.* **6**, 7 (1954).
78. Dalgliesh, C. E., Toh, C. C., and Work, T. S. *J. Physiol. (London)* **120**, 298 (1953).
79. Danielli, J. F. Cell Physiology and Pharmacology. Elsevier Publishing Co., Houston, Texas, 1950.
80. del Castillo, J., and Engbaek, L. *J. Physiol. (London)* **124**, 370 (1954).
81. De Roeth, A. *J. Neurophysiol.* **14**, 55 (1951).
82. Douglas, W. W., Feldberg, W., Paton, W. D. M., and Schachter, M. *J. Physiol. (London)* **115**, 163 (1951).
83. Durand, J. B. Personal communication.
84. Eakin, R. M. *Anat. Record* **117**, 613 (1953).
85. Echalier, G. *Compt. rend.* **238**, 523 (1954).
86. Elliott, T. R. *J. Physiol. (London)* **31**, xx (1940).
87. Elliott, T. R. *J. Physiol. (London)* **32**, 401 (1905).
88. Erspamer, V. *Rend. sci. farm.* **1**, 5 (1954).
89. Erspamer, V., and Asero, B. *Nature* **169**, 800 (1952).
90. Erspamer, V., and Benati, O. *Science* **117**, 161 (1953).
91. Erspamer, V., and Benati, O. *Biochem. Z.* **324**, 66 (1953).
92. Erspamer, V., and Faustini, R. *Naturwissenschaften* **40**, 317 (1953).
93. Erspamer, V., and Ghiretti, F. *J. Physiol. (London)* **115**, 470 (1951).
94. Etkin, W. *J. Exptl. Zool* **86**, 113 (1941).
95. Etkin, W. *J. Exptl. Zool.* **92**, 31 (1943).
96. Euler, U. S. von. *Arch. exptl. Pathol. u. Pharmakol.* **181**, 181 (1936).
97. Euler, U. S. von. *Acta Physiol. Scand.* **12**, 73 (1946).
98. Euler, U. S. von. *Acta Physiol. Scand.* **16**, 93 (1948).
99. Euler, U. S. von. *Ergeb. Physiol. biol. Chem. u. exptl. Pharmakol.* **46**, 261 (1950).
100. Euler, U. S. von. *Pharmacol. Revs.* **3**, 247 (1951).
101. Euler, U. S. von. *Acta Physiol. Scand.* **28**, 297 (1953).
102. Euler, U. S. von. *Pharmacol. Revs.* **6**, 15 (1954).
103. Euler, U. S. von, Franksson, C., and Hellström, J. *Acta Physiol. Scand.* **31**, 1 (1954).
104. Euler, U. S., von, Franksson, C., and Hellström, J. *Acta Physiol. Scand.* **31**, 6 (1954).
105. Euler, U. S. von, and Hamberg, U. *Acta Physiol. Scand.* **19**, 74 (1949).
106. Fatt, P. *J. Physiol. (London)* **111**, 408 (1950).
107. Fatt, P., and Katz, B. *Nature* **166**, 597 (1950).
108. Fatt, P., and Katz, B. *J. Physiol. (London)* **115**, 320 (1951).
109. Fatt, P., and Katz, B. *J. Physiol. (London)* **117**, 109 (1952).
110. Fatt, P., and Katz, B. *Cold Spring Harbor Symposia Quant. Biol.* **17**, 275 (1952).

111. Fatt, P., and Katz, B. *Acta Physiol. Scand.* **29**, 117 (1953).
113. Feldberg, W. *J. Physiol. (London)* **101**, 432 (1943).
114. Feldberg, W. *Physiol. Revs.* **25**, 596 (1945).
115. Feldberg, W. *In* R. W. Gerard, Methods in Medical Research. Year Book Publishers, Chicago, 1950, Vol. 3.
116. Feldberg, W. *Arch. intern. Physiol.* **59**, 544 (1951).
117. Feldberg, W. *Pharmacol. Revs.* **6**, 85 (1954).
118. Feldberg, W., Harris, G. W., and Lin, R. C. Y. *J. Physiol. (London)* **112**, 400 (1951).
119. Feldberg, W., and Sherwood, S. L. *J. Physiol. (London)* **123**, 148 (1954).
120. Feldberg, W., and Toh, C. C. *J. Physiol. (London)* **119**, 352 (1953).
121. Fessard, A., and Posternak, J. *J. Physiol. (Paris)* **42**, 319 (1950).
122. Florey, E., and Florey, Elisabeth. *Z. Naturforsch.* **9b**, 58 (1954).
123. Folkow, B., and Euler, U. S. von. *Circulation Research.* **2**, 191 (1954).
124. Frédéricq, H. *Biol. Revs.* **22**, 297 (1947).
125. Fukuda, S. *Proc. Japan Acad.* **27**, 582 (1951).
126. Fukuda, S. *Proc. Japan Acad.* **27**, 672 (1951).
127. Fukuda, S. *Annot. zool. japon.* **25**, 149 (1952).
128. Fukuda, S. *Proc. Japan Acad.* **29**, 389 (1953).
129. Gabe, M. *Compt. rend.* **237**, 1111 (1953).
130. Gabe, M. *Ann. biol. (Paris)* **30**, 6 (1954).
131. Gaddum, J. H. *J. Physiol. (London)* **121**, 15P (1953).
132. Gaddum, J. H. *Ciba Foundation Symposium, London* (1953).
133. Gaddum, J. H. *J. Physiol. (London)* **119**, 363 (1953).
134. Gaddum, J. H., and Hameed, K. A. *Brit. J. Pharmacol.* **9**, 240 (1954).
135. Gardiner, J. E., and Whittaker, V. P. *Biochem. J.* **58**, 24 (1954).
136. Gaskell, J. F. *Phil. Trans. Roy. Soc.* **B205**, 153 (1914).
137. Gaskell, J. F. *J. Gen. Physiol.* **2**, 73 (1919–1920).
138. Giachetti, A., Peruzzi, P., and Spadolini, I. *Abstr. 19th Intern. Physiol. Congr.*, p. 391 (1953).
139. Goffart, M. *Arch. Intern. physiol.* **60**, 367 (1952).
140. Goffart, M. *Pharmacol. Revs.* **6**, 33 (1954).
141. Goffart, M., and Perry, W. L. M. *J. Physiol. (London)* **112**, 95 (1951).
142. Gomori, G. *J. Histochem. and Cytochem.* **2**, 50 (1954).
143. Goodall, McC. *Acta Physiol. Scand.* **24**, Suppl. 85 (1951).
144. Gordon, H. T., and Welsh, J. H. *J. Cellular Comp. Physiol.* **51**, 395 (1948).
145. Graham, A. R., and Stavraky, G. W. *Rev. can. biol.* **11**, 446 (1953).
146. Graham, A. R., and Stavraky, G. W. *Rev. can. biol.* **13**, 120 (1954).
147. Gregerman, R. I., and Wald, G. *J. Gen. Physiol.* **35**, 489 (1952).
148. Hagen, P. *J. Physiol. (London)* **123**, 53P (1954).
149. Hamlin, E., and Fischer, F. E. *J. Am. Chem. Soc.* **73**, 5007 (1951).
150. Hanström, B. *Z. Morphol. Ökol. Tiere* **23**, 80 (1931).
151. Hanström, B. *Zool. Jahrb. Abt. Anat. Ont. Tiere* **56**, 387 (1933).
152. Hasegawa, K. *J. Fac. Agr., Tottori Univ.* **1**, 83 (1952).
153. Hebb, C. O. *Pharmacol. Revs.* **6**, 39 (1954).
154. Hegre, E. S. *J. Exptl. Zool.* **101**, 65 (1946).
155. Hegre, E. S. *J. Exptl. Zool.* **103**, 321 (1946).
156. Hild, W. *Arch. pathol. Anat. u. Physiol.* **319**, 526 (1951).
157. Hillarp, N-A., and Hökfelt, B. *Acta Physiol. Scand.* **30**, 55 (1953).
158. Hillarp, N-A., and Hökfelt, B. *Kgl. Fysiograf. Sällskp. Lund Förh.* **23**, (4) (1953).

159. Hillarp, N.-A., and Nilson, B. *Acta Physiol. Scand.* **31,** Suppl. 113, 79 (1954).
160. Höber, R. *Ann. N. Y. Acad. Sci.* **47,** 381 (1946).
161. Hodgkin, A. L. *Biol. Revs.* **26,** 339 (1951).
162. Hodgkin, A. L., and Huxley, A. F. *Proc. Roy. Soc. (London)* **B140,** 177 (1952).
163. Hoffmann, F., Hoffmann, E. J., Middleton, S., and Talesnik, J. *Am. J. Physiol.* **101,** 460 (1945).
164. Humphrey, J. H., and Jacques, R. *J. Physiol. (London)* **124,** 305 (1954).
165. Humphrey, J. H., and Toh, C. C. *J. Physiol. (London)* **124,** 300 (1954).
166. Hutter, O. F., and Kostial, K. *J. Physiol. (London)* **124,** 234 (1954).
167. Ing, H. R. *Science* **109,** 264 (1949).
168. Ing, H. R., Kordik, P., and Tudor Williams, D. P. H. *Brit. J. Pharmacol.* **7,** 103 (1952).
169. Jaques, R., and Schachter, M. *Brit. J. Pharmacol.* **9,** 53 (1954).
170. Kleinholz, L. H. *Biol. Bull.* **70,** 159 (1936).
171. Kleinholz, L. H. *Biol. Revs.* **17,** 91 (1942).
172. Knowles, F. G. W. *Proc. Roy. Soc. (London)* **B141,** 248 (1953).
173. Koefoed-Johnsen, V., Ussing, H. H., and Zerahn, K. *Acta Physiol. Scand.* **27** 38 (1952).
174. Koelle, G. B., and Gilman, A. *J. Pharmacol. Exptl. Therap.* **95** (part 2), 166 (1949).
175. Kogure, M. *J. Dept. Agr. Kyushu Imp. Univ.* **4,** 1 (1933).
176. Koller, G. *Z. vergleich. Physiol.* **5,** 191 (1927).
177. Kordik, P., Bülbring, E., and Burn, J. H. *Brit. J. Pharmacol.* **7,** 67 (1952).
178. Koskowski, W., and Maigre, E. *Compt. rend.* **173,** 397 (1921).
179. Krijgsman, B. J. *Biol. Revs.* **27,** 320 (1952).
180. Kuffler, S. W. *J. Neurophysiol.* **6,** 99 (1943).
181. Kuffler, S. W. *J. Neurophysiol.* **9,** 367 (1946).
182. Kuffler, S. W., and Vaughn Williams, E. M. *J. Physiol. (London)* **121,** 318 (1953).
183. Kuntz, A. *Anat. Record* **118,** 322 (1954).
184. Lands, A. M. *Pharmacol. Revs.,* **1,** 279 (1949).
185. Lands, A. M. Symposium on Chemical-Biological Correlation. National Academy of Science, National Research Council, Washington, D. C., 1951.
186. Lands, A. M. *Am. J. Physiol.* **169,** 11 (1952).
187. Langemann, H. *Brit. J. Pharmacol.* **6,** 318 (1951).
188. Langley, J. N. *J. Physiol. (London)* **33,** 374 (1905).
189. Langley, J. N. *J. Physiol. (London)* **36,** 347 (1907).
190. Lewis, S. E. *Nature* **172,** 1004 (1953).
191. Li, C. H. *Acta Endocrinol.* **10,** 255 (1952).
192. Li, C. H. *J. Am. Chem. Soc.* **74,** 2124 (1952).
193. Lissák, L., and Pásztor. *Pflügers Arch. ges. Physiol.* **244,** 120 (1940).
194. Loewi, O. *In* E. S. G. Barron, Modern Trends in Physiology and Biochemistry. Academic Press, New York, 1952.
195. Luduena, F. P., and Brown, R. G., Jr. *J. Pharmacol. Exptl. Therap.* **105,** 232 (1952).
196. Lundberg, A. *Acta Physiol. Scand.* **26,** 252 (1952).
197. MacIntosh, F. C. *J. Physiol. (London)* **44,** 436 (1941).
198. Mann, P. J. F., Tennenbaum, M., and Quastel, J. H. *Biochem. J.* **33,** 822 (1939).
199. Marrazzi, A. S. *Science* **118,** 367 (1953).
200. Marrazzi, A. S., and Hart, E. R. *Progr. Neurol. and Psychiat.* **7,** 84 (1952).
201. Marrazzi, A. S., and Hart, E. R. *Progr. Neurol. and Psychiat.* **8,** 69 (1953).
202. Massart, L., and Dufait, R. P. *Enzymologia* **9,** 364 (1941).

203. McDowell, R. J. S. *J. Physiol. (London)* **104,** 392 (1946).
204. Middleton, S., Hoffmann, F., Oberti, C., Prager, R., and Middleton, H. H. *Abstr. 19th Intern. Physiol. Congr.,* p. 615 (1953).
205. Nachmansohn, D. *In* The Hormones. Academic Press, New York, 1950, Vol. 2.
206. Nachmansohn, D., and Wilson, I. B. *Advances in Enzymol.* **12,** 259 (1951).
207. Nastuk, W. L. *J. Cellular Comp. Physiol.* **42,** 249 (1953).
208. Noble, R. L., and Taylor, N. B. G. *J. Physiol. (London)* **122,** 220 (1953).
209. Östlund, E. *Nature* **172,** 1042 (1953).
210. Östlund, E. *Acta Physiol. Scand.* **31,** Suppl. 112 (1954).
210a. Page, I. H. *Physiol. Revs.* **34,** 563 (1954).
211. Palade, G. E. *Anat. Record* **118,** 335 (1954).
212. Palay, S. L. *Anat. Record* **118,** 336 (1954).
213. Parker, G. H. Animal Color Changes and their Neurohumors. Macmillan, New York, 1948.
214. Parker, G. H. *in* The Hormones. Academic Press, New York, 1950, Vol. 2.
215. Parker, G. H., and Paine, V. L. *Am. J. Anat.* **54,** 1 (1934).
216. Passano, L. M. *Anat. Record* **111,** 86 (1951).
217. Passano, L. M. *Anat. Record* **112,** 460 (1952).
218. Passano, L. M. *Physiol. Comparata et Oecol.* **3,** 155 (1953).
219. Paton, W. D. M. *Ann. N. Y. Acad. Sci.* **54,** 347 (1951).
220. Paton, W. D. M. *Pharmacol. Revs.* **6,** 59 (1954).
221. Paton, W. D. M., and Perry, W. L. M. *J. Physiol. (London)* **119,** 43 (1953).
222. Paton, W. D. M., and Thompson, J. W. *Abstr. 19th Intern. Physiol. Congr.,* p. 664 (1953).
223. Paton, W. D. M., and Zaimis, E. J. *Brit. J. Pharmacol.* **4,** 381 (1949).
224. Perkins, E. B. *J. Exptl. Zool.* **50,** 71 (1928).
225. Pernow, B. *Acta Physiol. Scand.* **29,** Suppl. 105 (1953).
226. Persky, H., and Roston, J. *Science* **118,** 381 (1953).
227. Pfeiffer, C. C. *Science* **107,** 94 (1948).
228. Pickford, M. *Physiol. Revs.* **25,** 573 (1945).
229. Popenoe, E. A., and du Vigneaud, V. *J. Biol. Chem.* **206,** 353 (1954).
230. Potter, D. D. *Anat. Record* **120,** 716 (1954).
231. Prosser, C. L. *Biol. Bull.* **78,** 92 (1940).
232. Prosser, C. L. *Physiol. Revs.* **26,** 337 (1946).
233. *Pubbl. staz. zool. Napoli* **24,** Suppl. (1954).
234. Raab, W., and Humphreys, R. J. *Am. J. Physiol.* **148,** 460 (1947).
235. Rapport, M. M. *J. Biol. Chem.* **180,** 961 (1949).
236. Riker, W. J., Jr. *Pharmacol. Revs.* **5,** 1 (1953).
237. Robertson, J. D. *Anat. Record* **118,** 346 (1954).
238. Robertson, W. B., and Peyser, P. *Am. J. Physiol.* **166,** 277 (1951).
239. Rosenblueth, A. The Transmission of Nerve Impulses at Neuroeffector Junctions and Peripheral Synapses. Technology Press of Mass. Inst. Technol. and Wiley, New York, 1950.
240. Sawyer, W. H., and Sawyer, M. K. *Physiol. Zoöl.* **25,** 84 (1952).
241. Scharrer, B. *In* The Hormones. Academic Press, N. Y., 1948, Vol. 1, p. 121.
242. Scharrer, B. *Biol. Bull.* **102,** 261 (1952).
243. Scharrer, B. *Ann. Rev. Physiol.* **15,** 457 (1953).
244. Scharrer, B., and Scharrer, E. *Biol. Bull.* **87,** 242 (1944).
245. Scharrer, E. *Scientia (Milan)* [6] **46,** 177 (1952).

246. Scharrer, E., and Scharrer, B.   *In* Handbuch der mikroskopischen Anatomie des Menschen.   Springer, Berlin, 1954, Vol. 6, p. 953.
247. Scharrer, E., and Scharrer, B., *Recent Progr. Hormone Research* **10**, 183 (1954).
248. Schueler, F. W., Keasling, H. H., and Featherstone, R. M.   *Science* **113**, 512 (1951).
249. Shepherd, D. M., and West, G. B.   *Brit. J. Pharmacol.* **6**, 665 (1951).
250. Shepherd, D. M., and West, G. B.   *J. Physiol. (London)* **120**, 15 (1953).
251. Shepherd, D. M., West, G. B., and Erspamer, V.   *Nature* **172**, 509 (1953).
252. Singer, M.   *Proc. Soc. Exptl. Biol. Med.* **86**, 378 (1954).
253. Singer, M., Scheuing, M., and Hall, M.   *Anat. Record* **117**, 576 (1953).
254. Smith, S. W.   *Anat. Record* **112**, 390 (1952).
255. Spadolini, I., and Domini, G.   *Arch. fisiol.* **40**, 147 (1940).
256. Speeter, M. E., Heinzelman, R. V., and Weisblat, D. I.   *J. Am. Chem. Soc.* **73**, 5514 (1951).
257. Stack-Dunne, M. P., and Young, F. G.   *Ann. Rev. Biochem.* **23**, 405 (1954).
258. Stoll, A., and Hofmann, A.   *Helv. Chim. Acta* **26**, 944 (1943).
259. Stoll, W. A.   *Schweiz. Arch. Neurol. Psychiat.* **60**, 279 (1947).
260. Stoll, W. A.   *Schweiz. med. Wochschr.* **79**, 110 (1949).
261. Stover, J. H., Jr., Fingerman, M., and Forester, R. H.   *Proc. Soc. Exptl. Biol. Med.* **84**, 146 (1953).
262. Stutinsky, F.   *Bull. soc. zool. France* **76**, 307 (1951).
263. Tainter, M. L., and Luduena, F. P.   *Recent Progr. Hormone Research* **5**, 3 (1950).
264. Taylor, D. B.   *Pharmacol. Revs.* **3**, 412 (1951).
265. Thimann, K. V.   *Am. J. Botany* **24**, 407 (1937).
266. Thing, E.   *Acta Endocrinol.* **16**, 179 (1954).
267. Thomsen, E.   *J. Exptl. Biol.* **31**, 322 (1954).
268. Thomsen, E., and Thomsen, M.   *Experientia* **10**, 206 (1954).
269. Thomsen, M.   *Kgl. Danske Videnskab. Selskab, Biol. Skrifter* **7**(5), 1 (1954).
270. Toman, J. E. P.   *Electroencephalog. and Clin. Neurophysiol.* **1**, 33 (1949).
271. Toman, J. E. P.   *Pharmacol. Revs.* **4**, 168 (1952).
272. Toman, J. E. P., and Davis, J. P.   *Pharmacol. Revs.* **1**, 425 (1949).
273. Trethewie, E. R.   *Australian J. Exptl. Biol. Med. Sci.* **16**, 225 (1938).
274. Twarog, B. M.   *Federation Proc.* **11**, 164 (1952).
275. Twarog, B. M.   *J. Cellular Comp. Physiol.* **44**, 141 (1954).
276. Twarog, B. M., and Page, I. H.   *Am. J. Physiol.* **175**, 157 (1953).
277. Udenfriend, S., Clark, C. T., and Titus, E.   *Experientia* **8**, 379 (1952).
278. Ussing, H. H., and Zerahn, K.   *Acta Physiol. Scand.* **23**, 110 (1951).
279. du Vigneaud, V., Lawler, H. C., and Popenoe, E. A.   *J. Am. Chem. Soc.* **75**, 4880 (1953).
280. du Vigneaud, V., Ressler, C., Swan, J. M., Roberts, C. W., and Katsoyannis, P. G.   *J. Am. Chem. Soc.* **76**, 3115 (1954).
281. Vogt, M.   *Pharmacol. Revs.* **6**, 31 (1954).
282. Vogt, M.   *J. Physiol. (London)* **123**, 451 (1954).
283. Waring, H., and Landgrebe, F. W.   *In* The Hormones.   Academic Press, New York, 1950, Vol. 2, p. 427.
284. Weil-Malherbe, H., and Bone, A. D.   *Biochem. J.* **58**, 132 (1954).
285. Weiss, P., and Hiscoe, H. B.   *J. Exptl. Zool.* **107**, 315 (1948).
286. Welsh, J. H.   *Quart. Rev. Biol.* **13**, 123 (1938).
287. Welsh, J. H.   *J. Exptl. Zool.* **86**, 35 (1941).
288. Welsh, J. H.   *Anat. Record* **94**, 79 (1946).
289. Welsh, J. H.   *Bull. Johns Hopkins Hosp.* **83**, 568 (1948).

290. Welsh, J. H. *Science* **112**, 467 (1950).
291. Welsh, J. H. *Arch. Exptl. Pathol. Pharmakol.* **219**, 23 (1953).
292. Welsh, J. H. *Anat. Record* **117**, 637 (1953).
293. Welsh, J. H. *Federation Proc.* **13**, 162 (1954).
294. Welsh, J. H. *Nature* **193**, 955 (1954).
295. Welsh, J. H. Unpublished data.
296. Welsh, J. H., and Gordon, H. T. *J. Cellular Comp. Physiol.* **30**, 147 (1947).
297. Welsh, J. H., and Hyde, J. E. *Am. J. Physiol.* **142**, 512 (1944).
298. Welsh, J. H., and Hyde, J. E. *Proc. Soc. Exptl. Biol. Med.* **55**, 256 (1944).
299. Welsh, J. H., and Prajmovsky, M. *J. Biol. Chem.* **171**, 829 (1947).
300. Welsh, J. H., and Schallek, W. *Physiol. Revs.* **26**, 447 (1946).
301. Welsh, J. H., and Slocombe, A. G. *Biol. Bull.* **102**, 48 (1952).
302. Welsh, J. H., and Taub, R. *Biol. Bull.* **95**, 346 (1948).
303. Welsh, J. H., and Taub, R. *J. Pharmacol. Exptl. Therap.* **99**, 334 (1950).
304. Welsh, J. H., and Taub, R. *J. Pharmacol. Exptl. Therap.* **103**, 62 (1951).
305. Welsh, J. H., and Taub, R. *Brit. J. Pharmacol.* **8**, 327 (1953).
306. Welsh, J. H., and Zacks, S. I. *Anat. Record* **105**, 46 (1949).
307. Wense, T. *Pflügers Arch. ges. Physiol.* **241**, 284 (1938).
308. Weyer, F. *Zool. Anz.* **112**, 137 (1935).
309. Whittaker, V. P. *Physiol. Revs.* **31**, 312 (1951).
310. Wilson, I. B. *J. Biol. Chem.* **208**, 123 (1954).
311. Wilson, I. B., and Bergmann, F. *J. Biol. Chem.* **185**, 479 (1950).
312. Wilson, I. B., and Bergmann, F. *J. Biol. Chem.* **186**, 683 (1950).
313. Woolley, D. W., and Shaw, E. *Proc. Natl. Acad. Sci. U. S.* **40**, 228 (1954).
314. Woolley, D. W., and Shaw, E. *Brit. Med. J.* **4880**, 122 (1954).
315. Zacks, S. I., and Welsh, J. H. *Am. J. Physiol.* **165**, 620 (1951).
316. Zeller, E. A., and Bissegger, A. *Helv. Chim. Acta* **26**, 1619 (1943).
317. Zucker, M. B., Friedman, B. K., and Rapport, M. M. *Proc. Soc. Exptl. Biol. Med.* **85**, 282 (1954).

Chapter IV

Physiology and Chemistry of the Parathyroids

By ROY O. GREEP and ALEXANDER D. KENNY

The recent literature dealing with the physiological activity of the parathyroids has been reviewed in a thorough manner by Bartter (10). The effects of the parathyroids are principally concerned with kidney and bone and as such are often described as the phosphaturic and calcium-mobilizing actions, respectively. It must be remembered that these effects are interrelated, inasmuch as any action on the glomerular filtration rate, for example, will affect both calcium and P excretion, and similarly any bone resorption will involve the liberation of P as well as of calcium. In addition, there have been hints in recent years of at least two other physiological effects which are neither renal nor skeletal. One of these, suggested in the work of Munson et al. (112), is the possibility of parathyroid control over the calcium-concentrating mechanism of the mammary gland. The other, a shift of P between the extracellular (ECF) and intracellular (ICF) fluids, is still not substantiated by any direct evidence but is alluded to by some investigators, among whom may be mentioned Milne (105), Bartter (11), and Howard et al. (77, 78).

A. The Effects of the Parathyroid on the Kidney

Much of the work on the renal contribution to the phosphaturic effect is based on the assumption that the P is not secreted into the renal tubules. Although the possibility exists that this assumption is invalid (86), there is no satisfactory evidence of this. Another basic assumption is that all the P in the serum is ultrafilterable except under extreme conditions of hypercalcemia and hyperphosphatemia. In vitro and in vivo studies of recent years have substantiated such an assumption (43, 63, 65, 73, 74, 76, 95). Govaerts (56) in an in vivo study produced evidence to the contrary, concluding that but a small fraction of the inorganic P was able to filter through the glomerulus. Jacobs and associates (71, 82) have refuted this finding in papers describing their own work with P clearance in dogs. They found that the clearances of the injected labeled inorganic P and that of the acid-soluble inorganic P differed by less than 8%. They were thus in agreement with the many in vitro studies (43, 63, 73, 74). The difference between the two clearances proved significant, but the authors felt that it was not important. Parathyroid extract increased both clearance rates but did not affect the ratio between them.

Although the decrease in urinary P excretion after parathyroidectomy is no longer a subject for controversy, the evidence for an increase after injection of parathyroid extract is still equivocal. Most of the recent studies confirm the earlier observations of a P diuresis following parathyroid injection, first made by Greenwald and Gross (57, 58) in dogs and later confirmed by Albright and associates (1, 2) in man, and include work in rats (32, 36, 85, 90, 122, 136, 141, 148, 150), mice (37), dogs (11, 64, 66, 68, 72, 73, 134), and man (32, 81, 86, 87, 97, 104). However, Jahan and Pitts (83) found no P diuresis in normal dogs 12 to 16 hours after injection of extract during P infusions. In addition several clinical investigators, although eliciting some phosphaturia in hypoparathyroid patients, have failed to obtain the marked increase in urinary P in normal subjects observed by Ellsworth and Howard (44). These include Dent (39, 40), who has tried 20 tests on 15 subjects, Milne (105), Martin et al. (103), and Albright et al. (3). The latter investigators' explanation that the extract used may have been inactive is only partly correct, as some of their samples of extract, when assayed for calcium-mobilizing activity by the method of Munson et al. (110), proved to be of standard potency. In addition there have been at least two reports of the failure of the Ellsworth-Howard test to give the expected response in patients with hypoparathyroidism (39, 92). In connection with this test, Dent (40), citing the work of Ollayos and Winkler (115), warns that diurnal variations alone could account for increases in urinary P excretion, even without injection of extract. Kenny et al. (85) have shown that when a current commercial preparation of parathyroid extract was compared with a crude hot acid extract by assaying them for both calcium-mobilizing and phosphaturic activities by the rat bio-assay methods of Munson et al. (110) and Kenny et al. (85), respectively, the ratio of phosphaturic to calcium-mobilizing activity in the crude extract was found to be more than three times that of the commercial preparation. This finding was confirmed by Davies, Gordon, and Mussett (37). It is quite possible that because the U.S.P. requires an assay of calcium-mobilizing activity only, the process of manufacture could have been slightly changed over the years, resulting in an undetected change in phosphaturic potency.

Although there is considerable agreement concerning the number of the various renal effects contributing to the phosphaturic response, investigators differ as to their relative importance. Those favoring an effect on renal hemodynamics as the major contributing cause include Hogben and Bollman (72), Michie and Shorey (104), and Handler and associates (64, 66, 67, 68). Those favoring an effect on tubular reabsorption of P include Klein and Gow (87), McCrory et al. (97), Bartter (11), Kleeman and

Cooke (86), Cargill and Witham (25), Jacobs and Verbanck (81), Sirota (130), and Crawford *et al.* (32).

Crawford *et al.* (32) suggest that the ratio TRP:GFP[1] be used as an index of parathyroid activity. Although this ratio proves to be a good index of parathyroid function, it is not intended to distinguish between mechanisms, as such a ratio would reflect changes in either GFP or TRP. However, they point out that in their data there is no evidence that elevation of glomerular filtration rate as a mechanism for increasing urinary P excretion is ordinarily a factor of importance.

The role of the parathyroids in controlling renal calcium excretion and the mechanism of the latter are discussed by Talbot *et al.* (138). These authors suggest that a renal tubule threshold mechanism exists for calcium excretion, and that parathyroid extract administration raises this threshold (Tm). In support of this they present data recalculated from Albright and Ellsworth (2), who had shown that in a patient with hypoparathyroidism injection of parathyroid extract immediately raised the serum ionized calcium concentration but decreased the urine calcium excretion. The urine calcium did not rise until over 24 hours later when the serum ionized calcium had risen above what was assumed to be a threshold value. Recently Talmage and associates (139, 142) have obtained similar findings in rats. They found that in the period 2 to 4 hours after parathyroidectomy there was an increase in urinary excretion of both total and labeled calcium, whereas after injection of parathyroid extract into intact rats there was a decrease in the calcium excretion in the same period. However in the period 25 to 27 hours after parathyroidectomy the situation was reversed, there being a decrease after parathyroidectomy and an increase after injection. These results are understandable if one assumes that the parathyroids control the Tm for Ca, such an effect being immediate and more pronounced until the serum level of calcium becomes the more prominent feature. The renal effect on calcium contributes towards maintaining calcium homeostasis and is thus complementary with bone resorption in this regard. In connection with the renal excretion of calcium Berliner (13) found no evidence for tubular secretion of this element. Tweedy *et al.* (151) injected parathyroid extract into intact rats and studied the Ca^{45} excretion during periods not less than 18 hours after injection of the radiocalcium. Under these conditions the treated animals showed an increased urinary calcium excretion over the controls.

B. The Effect of the Parathyroids on Bone

Efforts to demonstrate an independent control over bone metabolism by the parathyroids have been directed along several lines of approach.

---

[1] TRP: phosphorus reabsorbed by renal tubules; GFP: glomerular filtrate phosphorus.

These include effects on: bone histology with and without nephrectomy; calcium mobilization, as reflected in the serum calcium, in the absence of the kidneys; calcium and P mobilization as indicated by the removal of Ca^{45} and P^{32} from bone; direct resorption of bone by parathyroid transplants. Studies involving nephrectomy have always been plagued with the resulting uremic conditions of the plasma; and, as Grollman (60) points out, in an excellent paper which should help to close a chapter of controversy, this is the probable reason for the apparently conflicting results obtained in this field.

Direct effects of parathyroid extract administration on bone as reflected in bone histology have been studied by Engel (45, 47), Carnes (26), and Heller and associates (70). The latter group were able to show that in young rats administration of single toxic doses of parathyroid extract was followed by rapid resorption of bone and by a slower phase of regeneration; in both phases cellular transformations were demonstrable. As the kidneys of these animals were intact, complete independence of action could not be claimed, unless, of course, the extract administered was devoid of phosphaturic activity. Carnes (26) injected parathyroid extract intraperitoneally into rachitic rats and obtained histological evidence of resorption of uncalcified matrix and concluded that the action of parathyroid extract on bone is mediated through an effect primarily on the bone matrix. In a more controversial paper Engel (45) describes depolymerization and solution of the glycoprotein ground substance of bones and of the cartilage spicules at the epiphysis as a result of injection of parathyroid extract into intact rats. An associated rise in serum mucoprotein level was observed. No effects were observed in controls receiving injections of dilute bovine γ-globulin. In a later paper Engel and Catchpole (46) found an increased urinary excretion of mucoprotein following parathyroid extract administration. Shetlar et al. (129) suggest that the elevation of serum mucoprotein obtained by Engel is a nonspecific effect caused by foreign proteins. This suggestion is based on experiments which showed that both active parathyroid extract and extract inactivated by formaldehyde (as indicated by the absence of effect on serum calcium and P) caused significant increases in serum mucoprotein levels. However, Baker et al. (6, 7), in studying experimental nephrocalcinosis induced by parathyroid extract administration in the rat, found that the state of the connective tissue is vitally concerned with calcifiability, thus supporting Engel's theory. By altering the connective tissue ground substance in vivo with agents such as toluidine blue, DCA, and compensatory renal hypertrophy, they were able to increase, decrease, and increase, respectively, the induced calcification. They further showed, and this is an important observation, that merely increasing the serum calcium, by calcium salts administration, to the same level as that produced by parathyroid extract did not produce nephrocalcinosis in untreated rats in the same period of time. One may ask, if calcification and resorption are solely the result of effects on ground substance, why it is that under conditions of hyperparathyroidism bone matrix is resorbed and connective tissue ground substance is calcified.

Studies on the calcium-mobilizing effect of parathyroid extract in nephrectomized animals continue to accumulate, and the weight of the evidence tends to favor a positive effect, in contrast to the earlier work of Tweedy and associates (152, 153) and Neufeld and Collip (113). Stewart and Bowen (133) were able to produce elevations of serum calcium with 500 and 1000 U.S.P. units of parathyroid extract in both nephrectomized and nephrectomized-parathyroidectomized dogs. Moreover by intravenous injection of sodium oxalate in nephrectomized dogs they were able to depress the serum calcium, which, in absence of the parathyroids, failed to return to normal levels unless parathyroid extract was administered. In a later study (134) the same authors found that in nephrectomized dogs reducing the serum ionized calcium by intravenous injection of sodium citrate resulted in a hypercalcemia in dogs both nephrectomized and parathyroidectomized. Working with rats Talmage et al. (143) were able to show that parathyroidectomy caused a decrease in serum calcium in the nephrectomized animal and that as little as 200 U.S.P. units of parathyroid extract administered subcutaneously over a period of 24 hours could cause a significant elevation in serum calcium in spite of concomitantly elevated serum P values. These elevated levels of serum P are but part of the general abnormal conditions existing in the plasma following nephrectomy. However, using the technique of peritoneal lavage, Grollman (60) was able to maintain nephrectomized dogs for long periods without attendant abnormal levels of blood constituents, particularly P. In the bilaterally nephrectomized, but otherwise intact, dog not maintained by lavage, he was able to show that 6 days after nephrectomy when the serum P had reached 19.6 mg. %, injection of 50 U.S.P. units per kilogram failed to obtain any marked rise in serum calcium 18 hours after the injection. Significant rises had been obtained in the first 4 days immediately following the operation when the serum P level had not risen above 11 mg. %. On the 10th and 15th day after nephrectomy with the serum P reduced to 7.4 and 8.2 mg. %, respectively, by peritoneal lavage, injection of the extract as before elicited a significant rise in serum calcium. Grollman suggests that hyperphosphatemia was the cause of the failure of some investigators (113, 152, 153) to obtain a rise in serum calcium. Although the number of animals used by Grollman leaves something to be desired (it is not clear how many animals were used in the crucial experiment described above), the work is an important step forward in the field, and,

158   ROY O. GREEP AND ALEXANDER D. KENNY

as a result, it is to be expected that in the future studies involving nephrec-tomized animals with uremic conditions will receive less attention.

Using the technique of radioautography Talmage and associates (145) have been able to show the effects of parathyroid extract administration on the removal of radiocalcium and radiophosphorus from rat femurs. Although significant amounts of both radio elements were removed by in-jecting 300 and 600 U.S.P. units of parathyroid extract into rats of less than 200-g., the interesting finding was that comparatively greater amounts of radiophosphorus were removed than of calcium. Another intriguing facet of this work is the demonstration that the extract increased the ex-cretion of inorganic P by a factor of 20, whereas the increase in radiophos-phorus excreted was by a factor of 40. In a further study (96) the effect of parathyroid extract administration on the removal of radiocalcium and radiophosphorus from sheep long bones was investigated. Daily doses of 30 to 90 U.S.P. units per kilogram for 7 days removed observable amounts of radiophosphorus but failed to cause any detectable removal of radio-calcium. Engfeldt and Zetterstrom (50a, 160) point out the importance of age in studies comparing the renewal rate of bone phosphate in normal and parathyroid treated rats. These authors found that there was a de-crease in renewal rate in young rats treated with parathyroid extract whereas old rats showed an increase.

One of the more spectacular and clear-cut contributions to the skeletal parameter in parathyroid physiology has been the demonstration of a direct resorptive effect on parietal bone by parathyroid transplants, first described by Barnicot (9) and later confirmed and extended by Chang (28, 29). Barnicot transplanted pieces of parietal bone together with para-thyroid tissue to the cranial cavity of mice. The parietal bone proximal to the parathyroid tissue underwent resorption while deposition occurred on the distal side. Chang placed autogenous and homogenous grafts of para-thyroid tissue against the parietal bones of mice and rats (see Fig. 1). He was able to demonstrate the specificity of the resorptive effect of the para-thyroid tissue as compared with controls consisting of pieces of compact bone, cartilage, urinary bladder mucosa, testis, gastric mucosa, lymph node, blood clot, pancreas, spleen, bone marrow, anterior lobe of the pitui-tary, adrenal cortex, thyroid, silk thread, soft paraffin, tincture of iodine, and alcohol.

Although the relationships between calcium and citrate in both serum and urine have been studied to a considerable extent, particularly by Free-man and Chang (30, 52, 53), the effect of the parathyroids on bone citrate has received less attention than it deserves. The administration of "mas-sive and prolonged dosage" of parathyroid extract into puppies had been shown by Dickens (41) to increase bone citrate relative to the inorganic

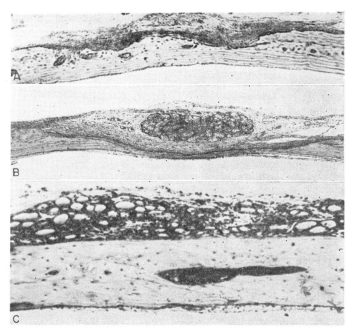

FIG. 1.   *A*. Parietal bone of rat 8 days after autogenous transplantation of parathyroid gland, showing bone resorption especially at the periphery of the graft. × 58.

B. Parietal bone of rat 14 days after autogenous transplantation of parathyroid gland. Most of the bone beneath the graft has been resorbed.   × 58.

C. Parietal bone of rat 14 days after homogenous transplantation of thyroid. There has not been any resorption of bone beneath the graft, although there was a little at its margins beyond the area photographed.   × 112.   (From originals of figs. 1, 2 and 8, H. Chang, *Anat. Record* **111**, 23–47.)

constituents.   More recently Dixon and Perkins (42) have observed that the ratio of citrogenase or aconitase to isocitric dehydrogenase activity is greater in bone than in the kidney or liver of the rabbit.   They suggested that in bone there is a mechanism for producing a local high concentration of citric acid, and that bone deposition and resorption may be related to this.   In a later paper the same authors (118) studied the effect of parathyroidectomy and injection of parathyroid extract on rat bone citrogenase. They found that parathyroidectomy lowered the bone citrogenase four to six weeks after the operation.   However, they found no effect in 4 days. Intraperitoneal injection of parathyroid extract (150 U.S.P. units) into intact rats resulted in no change in bone citrogenase 20 hours later.   Similarly, injection of 300 U.S.P. units 4 days after parathyroidectomy produced no change.   Unfortunately the interesting experiment of injecting the extract into rats four to six weeks after parathyroidectomy when the bone citrogenase was markedly decreased in contrast to the effect after 4 days, was not performed. However, the authors point out that as the serum calcium, but not the bone citrogenase, has fallen within 4 days following parathyroidectomy, the former effect cannot be due to changes in bone citrogenase.

A beginning has been made in the important matter of determining the effect of parathyroid extract on bone metabolism *in vitro*. Laskin and Engel (91) found that the respiration of epiphyseal bone slices was depressed in rabbits receiving 1000 U.S.P. units in 42 hours but that anaerobic glycolysis was unaffected. They found evidence for the presence of succinic dehydrogenase and on measurement found that the enzyme activity was decreased by one-half in the extract-treated animals. The suggestion was made that bone resorption may be related to this change in dehydrogenase activity. Prolonged treatment of puppies, maintained at different levels of calcium intake, with parathyroid extract, was observed to have no chemical effect on bone growth and calcification, as judged by inorganic analysis (22).

Two studies which show that the parathyroid effect on the serum calcium does not have to be preceded by any opposite change in the serum P, as suggested by Albright and Reifenstein (4) and Reifenstein and Howard (120), are represented in the work of Munson et al. (106, 108) and Jacobs (80). Munson and associates (106) have found that following parathyroidectomy in calcium-depleted rats the serum calcium falls before the P rises (see Fig. 2). A similar effect is obtained in rats maintained on a normal diet (111). Jacobs prevented the drop in serum P following parathyroid extract injection into intact dogs by repeated oral administration of inorganic P. Under such conditions there still was a rise in serum calcium.

C. The Effect of the Parathyroids on Soft Tissues

The probability that a P shift between the ECF and the ICF is a contributory factor in the phosphaturic action of parathyroid extract, although inherent in the data of several investigators, has received more attention in recent years. Milne (105), in studying the effect of parathyroid administration in patients, observed that the total amount of P lost in the urine was well below that lost from the extracellular fluid and concluded that some P must have entered the cells in response to the extract. Howard et al. (77, 78), investigating the effects of hypoparathyroidism induced by infusion of calcium salts into patients, found the opposite effect. The total increase of extracellular P (estimated from the serum value) was greater than could be accounted for by the concomitant decrease in urine

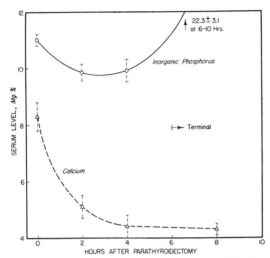

Fig. 2. Serum calcium and inorganic phosphate values following parathyroidectomy (at 0 time) in rats maintained on a diet low in calcium for 15 days prior to the experiment. The point at the 8-hour interval is the mean value of rats in terminal tetany 6 to 10 hours after parathyroidectomy. The vertical dashed lines represent the standard errors.

P. The suggestion was made that elevation of the serum calcium per se causes this shift of P from the intracellular to the extracellular fluid. Whether this shift is a direct effect of the hormone, or in the latter case, of an absence of it, is not known. This whole field needs further study on its own merits. One approach to the problem is that made by Tweedy and associates (149, 150), who observed the effect of parathyroid extract and parathyroidectomy on the uptake of P^{32} by some of the soft tissues. Although the results were not especially clear-cut, in the earlier work (149) in which intact rats received 500 U.S.P. units subcutaneously there was a consistently higher P^{32} content in the liver as compared with the controls at periods varying from 2 to 49 hours after injection of the extract. However, in the later paper (150) they failed to obtain any consistent effects in thyroparathyroidectomized rats with and without administration of extract. The uptake of radiocalcium by several soft tissues of the rat before and after parathyroidectomy was studied by Talmage et al. (144), but no definite effect was observed.

D. The Stimulation of Parathyroid Activity

The original concept that the parathyroids are controlled by the level of serum calcium, based on the earlier work of Ham et al. (61), Patt and Luckhardt (117), and Carnes and associates (27, 135), has not been seriously challenged in recent years. In fact, it has been further substantiated by the work of Wolf and Ball (159) and Howard *et al.* (75, 77, 78). The latter group found that by increasing the serum calcium by infusion of calcium gluconate-glucoheptonate into normal human subjects the serum P increased and the urinary excretion of P decreased. They interpreted this as indicative of decreased parathyroid activity caused by the hypercalcemia. The failure to obtain this response in patients with hyperparathyroidism was not unexpected owing to the excessive activity of the adenoma. They were at a loss to explain the reverse response in patients with both surgical and idiopathic hypoparathyroidism. Earlier Wolf and Ball (159) had found that intravenous infusion of calcium chloride or gluconate into intact dogs was followed by a small rise in serum calcium and a depression of P excretion in the urine.

More recently the effect of the blood P level on parathyroid activity has received greater attention, as evidenced by the work of Tornblom (148) and Crawford *et al.* (32, 138). The latter authors found that, in human beings, a hyperphosphatemia produced by increasing the dietary P will result in stimulation of parathyroid activity as reflected in the TRP:GFP ratio within 12 hours despite no change in serum ionized calcium. They concluded that hyperphosphatemia per se appears to stimulate increased parathyroid activity. In addition the interesting suggestion is made that under physiological conditions of changing dietary P intake the parathyroids may be stimulated to produce a hormone which would decrease tubular P reabsorption specifically without affecting tubular calcium reabsorption (138). Tornblom (148) administered P over a 48-hour period by means of continuous intravenous infusion to intact rabbits and also to parathyroidectomized rabbits maintained by continuous intravenous infusion of parathyroid extract (26.7, 40, and 60 U.S.P. units/kg./24 hours). The infusion of P in intact animals caused a considerable increase in urinary P excretion, but no change in plasma P or calcium. In the operated animals maintained with extract there was no corresponding increase in urinary P excretion, though there was an increase in plasma P and a decrease in plasma calcium. On the basis of these findings Tornblom maintains that administration of P induces parathyroid hyperfunction.

These observations on the effect of the blood P level on the control of parathyroid activity are important, for not only do they show that the serum calcium level does not alone control parathyroid activity, but they open up a means of explaining the action of diverse agents, such as growth hormone, ACTH, and factors relating to carbohydrate metabolism, which have been reported to have effects on parathyroid activity. In particular the question of the existence of a pituitary parathyrotropic hormone has been raised by several groups of investigators. Tornblom (148) and Engfeldt (48) (both papers contain excellent reviews of the literature appertaining to a parathyrotropic factor) re-examined this question and found the parathyroid glands of hypophysectomized animals to be smaller than those of control animals. Tornblom working with rabbits and Engfeldt with rats obtained similar findings, although they gave different interpretations. Both investigators found that hypophysectomy decreased the serum P in intact animals and modified the changes following simultaneous parathyroidectomy. Tornblom observed that either pituitary extract or ACTH administered to hypophysectomized and hypophysectomized-parathyroidectomized rabbits tended to restore the serum P to normal. However, in rats Engfeldt found that neither ACTH nor ACE increased the low blood P. Both authors maintained that the anterior, and not the posterior, lobe of the pituitary was responsible for the P-increasing action. Engfeldt presented evidence to suggest that this action is not mediated through the adrenals. Although both Tornblom and Engfeldt maintained that the pituitary affects the parathyroids indirectly via the effect on blood chemistry, they differed as to whether the effect is mediated through the blood calcium or P. As mentioned above, Tornblom suggested that parathyroid function is influenced by the blood P. Engfeldt, on the other hand, did not commit himself in this study (48). In a later paper Engfeldt et al. (50) studied parathyroid function in long-term dietary experiments and proposed that the primary factor in regulating the parathyroids was the blood calcium or some fraction of it. This conculsion was based on studies in which they found that a diet rich in P fed to rats for more than a year led to hyperfunction and hyperplasia of the parathyroids. The blood P, after an initial fall, remained at a low level. A diet rich in calcium caused atrophy of the parathyroids with a blood calcium, initially high, falling to below normal. The blood P was found to increase during the latter part of the experiment. The lack of direct pituitary control over the parathyroids is also suggested by the work of Brolin (20), who found no significant increase in pituitary weights after parathyroidectomy in rats. It was shown by Sen et al. (128) that the increase in serum calcium in rabbits following intravenous administration of glucose, although probably mediated through the parathyroids, was not due to the stimulation of the glands by insulin. The relationship between the thyroid and the parathyroids has recently received attention. Engfeldt and Hjertquist (49) noted that in dogs an increase in thyroid function produced with thyrotropic hormone resulted in changes in calcium and P metabolism, which in turn led to increased parathyroid function. Thyroidectomy had no effect on the blood P, however. Malcolm et al. (99) treated rats for 56 to 122 weeks with thiourea and related compounds and found hyperplasia of the parathyroids. It was not prevented by the simultaneous administration of thyroxine.

164 ROY O. GREEP AND ALEXANDER D. KENNY

E. MISCELLANEOUS EFFECTS OF THE PARATHYROIDS

From time to time investigators report various parathyroid effects which appear unrelated to the effects on calcium and P metabolism. Many of these actions could be secondary; some could be artifacts. Any such reports based solely on injection of parathyroid extract, because of the crudity of such extracts, must be accepted with reservations until opposite effects are observed in parathyroidectomized animals and the *status quo* restored by extract administration.

The arginine and histidine contents of serum and urine have been shown to be decreased in parathyroidectomized dogs (132); however, injection of parathyroid extract into human beings decreases the blood amino acid content and the blood glucose level (23). Caccialanza (24) found that parathyroidectomy in dogs caused a lowering of blood glutathione, which could be raised to normal levels by injection of parathyroid extract. However, Vacirca (154) found that parathyroid extract seldom produced a rise in blood glutathione in intact dogs. Malmejac and associates (100, 101) found that parathyroidectomy in dogs caused an increase in blood fibrinogen which could be returned to normal by injection of parathyroid extract. An increase in serum proteases after administration of parathyroid extract in puppies was observed by Majno and associates (98, 125), who later showed that this was due to the increase in circulating pepsinogen caused by metastatic calcification in the fundic glands of the gastric mucosa. On the other hand, Striganova (137) found that injection of parathyroid extract raised the proteolytic activity of bone tissue in both rats and rabbits. Contrary to the work of Bonelli and Sala (19), who found parathyroid extract to increase rat kidney alkaline phosphatase, Kochakian and Terepka (88, 90) found no effect. The latter finding was confirmed in a subsequent paper in which the two groups of investigators combined in a joint experiment (89). Injection of parathyroid extract into rats has been shown to decrease their resistance to potassium poisoning (147). Vancea *et al.* (155) showed that parathyroid extract administration usually caused an increase of sodium chloride excretion in tears. The effect of parathyroid extract on the regulation of hemopoiesis has been reported (157), and Venzmer (156) has studied the psychological effects of parathyroid extract administration. The reaction time necessary to elicit a response to painful stimuli in parathyroidectomized rats was studied by Smith and Stoerk (131), who found it significantly prolonged 10 days after the operation. Barnicot (8) found that the grey-lethal mouse could tolerate chronic treatment with parathyroid extract better than normal controls. Several studies on the anatomy and histology of the parathyroids have been made (12, 33, 34, 54, 69, 119, 123, 124, 126), but they do not represent any important contribution to the field.   The relation of the parathyroids to calcium absorption has been covered adequately in a recent review by Nicolaysen *et al.* (114).

F. EXTRACTION, PURIFICATION, AND NATURE OF PARATHYROID HORMONES

It is now 30 years since Collip and Hanson first prepared active parathyroid extracts, and yet it is still not known whether the parathyroid secretes one or more hormones.   In the opinion of the reviewers the purification of the various activities associated with the parathyroids would be the most important step forward in the parathyroid field.   Without the pure hormone further major contributions to the understanding of parathyroid physiology are not likely to be made.

In recent years more effort has been spent on attempts to separate the various activities attributed to parathyroid extracts rather than to obtain more highly purified extracts.   One of the leaders in this field has been Handler (62, 64, 67), who, with his group, has been attempting to separate the factors in crude extract responsible for raising the blood pressure, for mobilizing the calcium, and for increasing the glomerular filtration rate and renal plasma flow.   He was able to remove the blood pressure factor by dialysis and show that it was unaffected by incubation with pepsin for 24 to 48 hours, whereas the remaining factors were completely destroyed. One of the more controversial papers of recent years has been that of Stewart and Bowen (134).   These authors claimed to have effected a separation of the calcium-mobilizing and phosphaturic activities of parathyroid extract by formaldehyde inactivation of the former, leaving the latter intact.   In addition they prepared extracts of thymus and spleen with phosphaturic activity and deduced that such activity must be a "pharmacologically active tissue degradation product" and therefore of an artifactitious nature in parathyroid extract.   It is quite possible, indeed very probable, that some of the phosphaturic activity in parathyroid extracts is nonhormonal, but it is difficult to believe that all of it is.   Davies and Gordon (35), in a paper in which they take issue with Stewart and Bowen's claim, were able to dialyze some of the phosphaturic activity unaccompanied by calcium-mobilizing activity.   Both activities were found in the nondialyzable fraction.   Kenny and Munson (84), using 0.37 % and 2.0 % formaldehyde and under conditions admittedly different from those of Stewart and Bowen, were unable to inactivate the calcium-mobilizing activity without also destroying the phosphaturic activity to approximately the same extent.   Talmage *et al.* (140) have also reported inability to duplicate Stewart and Bowen's claim, by failing to obtain the immediate rise in radiophosphorus excretion in the urine of dogs following injection with either (*1*) commercial parathyroid extract inactivated with formaldehyde, (*2*) spleen extract prepared according to the method of

L'Heureux *et al.* (93), or (*3*) serum albumin solution adjusted to pH 3.5. They did, however, obtain the usual immediate increase in urine P excretion with untreated commercial extract. In view of the reports in the literature of the calcium-mobilizing effect of both spleen and thymus extracts (as an example of each, the work of Brougher (21) and Schwarz *et et al.* (127), respectively, may be cited), it would be of interest to know what effects, if any, Stewart and Bowen's extracts would have on serum calcium. One further piece of evidence which supports the concept that the calcium-mobilizing and phosphaturic activities are separable is that reported by Kenny *et al.* (85).

Although there have been several attempts to separate the various activities, there has been little published work in the field of purification. Opienska-Blauth (116) reported some unsuccessful attempts, but no experimental details were given.   Handler and associates (62, 67) have attempted purification with the aid of countercurrent distribution, ultracentrifugation, and partition chromatography from several absorbants, but have met with little success.   With the aid of Dowex 50 chromatography and by gradient elution with citrate, lactate, phosphate, borate, and carbonate buffers ranging from pH 2.8 to 11.0, they were able to separate crude extracts into several protein fractions. However, no purification resulted as all fractions, when assayed by the U.S.P. dog method, were found to contain similar potencies in terms of units per milligram nitrogen. In Greep's laboratory Kenny and Munson (84) using Amberlite IRC-50 chromatography have so far been unsuccessful in effecting purification. Thus the preparations of Ross and Wood (121) and those of L'Heureux *et al.* (93), each containing approximately 300 units per milligram N (although, owing to the different assay methods used, their estimates of potency cannot strictly be compared), still remain the purest to date.   In connection with the electrophoretic mobilities of the components of the preparation of L'Heureux *et al.* (93), Wilhelmi and Sayers (158) have since published corrected values, as the original data were subject to an instrumental error.   Gordon (55) has conducted an electrophoretic investigation of parathyroid preparations both in the Tiselius apparatus and in a medium of potato starch.   Using 0.1 M calcium acetate buffer at pH 5.8 he found that both the calcium-mobilizing and phosphaturic activities traveled together towards the cathode in a broad band with a mobility of approximately 3×10^{-5} cm^2 v^{-1} sec^{-1}.   Considerable differences of mobility were obtained on varying the conditions of extraction from acetone powders of the glands.

G. Assay Methods

The dog assay method for parathyroid preparations has held its own for 30 years, despite the statistical assault it received from Bliss and Rose

(18) and the inconvenience in many laboratories of maintaining a dog colony. In the course of its history many rival methods have been devised, but so far none has succeeded in displacing it from the U.S.P. Biering (16, 17) gives a brief review of the many methods published up to 1950 in the first of two papers describing his own method. Since Biering's work there have been several further attempts, which is undoubtedly but a reflection of the more general revival of interest in the parathyroid. Now that the independence of action of the calcium-mobilizing and phosphaturic effects is being more widely recognized (5, 106), the necessity for a phosphaturic assay method is becoming important. Hence, four attempts to develop phosphaturic assay methods (36, 37, 85, 122) have been made in recent years. Attempts to develop a calcium-mobilizing assay method have been described by Biering (16, 17), Munson et al. (110), and Davies et al. (38). Biering (16, 17) used approximately 150-g. intact rats and measured the increment of serum calcium increase 18 hours after injection of the parathyroid preparation. Although the precision he claimed is good (calculations from his data yield a λ of 0.16), the sensitivity of his method requires doses ranging from 150 to 1000 U.S.P. units per rat, and leaves much to be desired. In addition each rat requires two bleedings and calcium determinations. On the other hand, Munson et al. (110) describe a method based on the maintenance of serum calcium in calcium-depleted, parathyroidectomized rats in the 6 hours immediately after operation and injection of the preparation. Sensitivity is good, requiring in a two-dose factorial assay design two dose levels of only 5 and 20 U.S.P. units per 100 g. body weight, and in 50 assays involving over 1400 rats an average λ of 0.28 was obtained (107). Davies et al. (38) have described a method in rats which had been parathyroidectomized 10 days previously and maintained on a stock diet. Serum calcium was determined before, and 21 hours after, injection of the extract. With the aid of a three-dose crossover design, in which the rats were injected twice at an interval of from 2 to 4 days, and a correction made for the dependence of the response on the initial calcium and magnesium plasma level, an average λ of 0.49 was obtained in four assays. The sensitivity, requiring only 20, 50, and 125 U.S.P. units per rat, is similar to that of Munson et al. (110). However, on the basis of precision and simplicity of design and execution, the method of Munson et al., requiring half the number of bleedings and calcium determinations and able to be completed in 1 day, appears somewhat better than that of Davies and associates.

Of the three attempts to develop phosphaturic assay methods in rats, that of Kenny et al. (85), though not so sensitive as that of Rubin and Dorfman (122), is the most precise. Kenny et al. (85) based their method on the total urinary P excretion in rats during the 6 hours immediately following parathyroidectomy and injection of the parathyroid preparation. The two-dose factorial assay design was used at levels of 8 and 32 units per 100 g. body weight and yielded an average λ of 0.27 in four assays. As the conditions for the phosphaturic assay are identical with those for the calcium-mobilizing assay of Munson *et al.* (110), with the exception of the 4 days calcium depletion period in the latter, the possibility of being able to run the two assays simultaneously appeared attractive. This was not possible without the sacrifice of some precision in one of the methods, as running both assay methods with and without calcium depletion has shown (84). However, in practice urine is collected during the routine calcium-mobilizing assay, thus affording simultaneous, if not so precise, phosphaturic information. The method of Rubin and Dorfman (122) is based on the measurement of P^{32} excreted in the urine after the simultaneous intraperitoneal injection of 1.2 mg. P^{32} labeled Na_2HPO_4 per 100 g. and the parathyroid preparation in rats which had been parathyroidectomized at least 24 hours previously. Three-hour urine collections were made. In addition tracer doses of P^{32} and variations in the injection time relative to parathyroidectomy were tried. They obtained a regression line equation $y = 8.3 + 8.6 \log x$ over the range 0.5 to 3.0 U.S.P. units, giving a λ of 0.6. Davies and Gordon (36) were unable to produce a satisfactory assay method in rats, recording a λ of 0.84. It appears that the only major difference between their method and that of Kenny *et al.* (85) is that the latter used rats immediately after parathyroidectomy in contrast to the 2 to 21 days postoperative period of Davies and Gordon (36). The latter authors also re-examined the rat serum P assay method of Tepperman *et al.* (146) but used parathyroidectomized rats instead of intact ones. By this means they increased the sensitivity. Intact mice have been the tools of a new phosphaturic assay method developed by Davies, Gordon, and Musset (37). The method, based on the increase in rate of P excretion during the 3½ hours following injection of a parathyroid preparation into saline-loaded intact mice, used a two-dose crossover design. The mice were injected twice at an interval of not less than 2 and not more than 7 days. The sensitivity was excellent, requiring dose levels of only 0.2 and 1.0 U.S.P. units per mouse of a commercial preparation, and in spite of the fact that the design used 3 cages of 16 mice each (a total of 48 mice per group), this still required a total of only 9.6 and 48 units per dose level, respectively. In order to improve the method a correction for the dependence of the rate of urine P excretion on the urine volume was applied, and in one assay reduced the λ from 0.41 to 0.25. No average values of λ were quoted, but the precision was similar to that obtained in the calcium-mobilizing assay of Davies *et al.* (38) discussed above.

The response of serum citric acid to injection of parathyroid extract in the parathyroidectomized rat was explored by L'Heureux and Roth (94) as a possible basis for a bio-assay method. Young adult female rats were thyroparathyroidectomized and 24 hours later were injected subcutaneously with 25, 50, and 100 U.S.P. units. The serum citric acid level was determined 18 hours after the injection. Although there was an increase in serum citric acid, the authors conclude from their rather scanty data that the use of such a response as a basis would offer no advantage over existent methods. '

H. Lactation

The role of the parathyroids in lactation had long been alleged, but it was not confirmed until the work of Folley and associates (31, 51) showed that parathyroidectomy definitely impaired lactation in rats as reflected in the growth of the young. In addition an effect of these glands on the calcium-concentrating mechanism of the mammary gland is suspected in the work of Munson, Toverud, and Kenny (112). These investigators showed that imposition of a low-calcium diet, but not parathyroidectomy, decreased the milk calcium concentration of lactating rats. By placing the lactating mothers on a low-calcium diet it was possible to decrease the dry weight and ash content of the femurs of the weanling young as compared with those from young raised from both intact and parathyroidectomized mothers maintained on a stock diet. It would thus appear that the parathyroids, when stimulated by the imposition of a low-calcium diet, may cause a decrease in the milk calcium concentration. However, this hypothesis is at variance with the work of Manunta and Mureddu (102), who found parathyroid extract to increase the milk calcium concentration of the ewe.

I. Relation of the Parathyroids to Dental Defects

The recent contributions to this field have been made mainly by Schour and his associates (14, 79). Irving et al. (79) studied the effect of parathyroid extract on the dentin and pulp of the incisor in normal and nephrectomized rats and found that the formation of dentin was decreased by parathyroid extract and increased by nephrectomy. Parathyroid extract tended to counteract the increase resulting from nephrectomy. Working with a strain of rats in which the teeth fail to erupt as a genetic anomaly (15, 59), Bhaskar, Schour, Greep, and Weinmann (14) found that parathyroid extract exerted a corrective action. By promoting physiological resorption of the alveolar crypt the teeth were permitted to erupt from the bony encasement in which they are otherwise sealed in this strain.

REFERENCES

1. Albright, F., Bauer, W., Ropes, M., and Aub, J. C.   *J. Clin. Invest.* **7,** 139–181 (1929).

170   ROY O. GREEP AND ALEXANDER D. KENNY

 2. Albright, F., and Ellsworth, R.   *J. Clin. Invest.* **7**, 183–201 (1929).
 3. Albright, F., Forbes, A. P., and Hennemann, P. H.   *Trans. Assoc. Am. Physicians* **65**, 337–350 (1952).
 4. Albright, F., and Reifenstein, E. C.,   The Parathyroid Glands and Metabolic Bone Disease.   Williams and Wilkins Co., Baltimore, 1948.
 5. Aub, J. C.   *In* W. D. McElroy and B. Glass, Phosphorus Metabolism.   Johns Hopkins Press, Baltimore, 1952, Vol. 2, pp. 622–631.
 6. Baker, R., Reaven, G., and Sawyer, J.   *Proc. Soc. Exptl. Biol. Med.* **83**, 281–284 (1953).
 7. Baker, R., Reaven, G., and Sawyer, J.   *J. Urol.* **71**, 511–522 (1954).
 8. Barnicot, N. A.   *J. Anat.* **79**, 83–91 (1945).
 9. Barnicot, N. A.   *J. Anat.* **82**, 233–248 (1948).
10. Bartter, F. C.   *Ann. Rev. Physiol.* **16**, 429–444 (1954).
11. Bartter, F. C.   *J. Clin. Endocrinol. and Metabolism* **14**, 826 (1954).
12. Bensley, S. H.   *Anat. Record* **98**, 361–381 (1947).
13. Berliner, R. W.   *Am. J. Med.* **9**, 541–559 (1950).
14. Bhaskar, S. N., Schour, I., Greep, R. O., and Weinmann, J. P.   *J. Dental Research* **31**, 257–270 (1952).
15. Bhaskar, S. N., Weinmann, J. P., Schour, I., and Greep, R. O.   *Am. J. Anat.* **86**, 439–478 (1950).
16. Biering, A.   *Acta Pharmacol. Toxicol.* **6**, 40–58 (1950).
17. Biering, A.   *Acta Pharmacol. Toxicol.* **6**, 59–73 (1950).
18. Bliss, C. I., and Rose, C. L.   *Am. J. Hyg.* **31**, 79–98 (1940).
19. Bonelli, M., and Sala, G.   *Arch. intern. pharmacodynamie* **80**, 457–463 (1949).
20. Brolin, S.   *Acta Endocrinol.* **1**, 304–318 (1949).
21. Brougher, J. C.   *Am. J. Physiol.* **92**, 648–650 (1930).
22. Burns, C. M., and Henderson, N.   *Biochem. J.* **40**, 501–507 (1946).
23. Buttaro, C. A.   *Arch. studio fisiopatol. e clin. ricambio.* **14**, 105–113 (1950).
24. Caccialanza, P.   *Klin. Wochschr.* **21**, 922–924 (1942).
25. Cargill, W. H., and Witham, A. C.   *Federation Proc.* **8**, 21–22 (1949).
26. Carnes, W. H.   *Am. J. Pathol.* **26**, 736 (1950).
27. Carnes, W. H., Pappenheimer, A. M., and Stoerk, H. C.   *Proc. Soc. Exptl. Biol. Med.* **51**, 314–316 (1942).
28. Chang, H.   *Anat. Record* **106**, 100 (1950).
29. Chang, H.   *Anat. Record* **111**, 23–47 (1951).
30. Chang, T. S., and Freeman, S.   *Am. J. Physiol.* **160**, 330–334 (1950).
31. Cowie, A. T., and Folley, S. J.   *Nature* **156**, 719–720 (1945).
32. Crawford, J. D., Osborne, M. M., Jr., Talbot, N. B., Terry, M. L., and Merril, M. F.   *J. Clin. Invest.* **29**, 1448–1461 (1950).
33. Czerski, P.   *Polski Tygodnik Lekarski* **7**, 258–263 (1952).
34. Czerski, P.   *Fol. Morph. Warsz.* **3**, 407–414 (1952).
35. Davies, B. M. A., and Gordon, A. H.   *Nature* **171**, 1122–1123 (1953).
36. Davies, B. M. A., and Gordon, A. H.   *J. Endocrinol.* **9**, 292–300 (1953).
37. Davies, B. M. A., Gordon, A. H., and Mussett, M. V.   Personal communication.
38. Davies, B. M. A., Gordon, A. H., and Mussett, M. V.   *J. Physiol.* **125**, 383–395 (1954).
39. Dent, C. E.   *Proc. Roy. Soc. Med.* **46**, 291–294 (1953).
40. Dent, C. E.   *In* A. A. G. Lewis and G. E. W. Wolstenholme, Ciba Foundation Symposium on The Kidney.   Little, Brown, Boston, 1954, pp. 242–254.
41. Dickens, F.   *Biochem. J.* **35**, 1011–1023 (1941).
42. Dixon, T. F., and Perkins, H. R.   *Biochem. J.* **52**, 260–265 (1952).

43. Elliott, G. C., Hahn, L., and Hevesy, G.   *Acta Physiol. Scand.* **16,** 20–25 (1948).
44. Ellsworth, R., and Howard, J. E.   *Bull. Johns Hopkins Hosp.* **55,** 296–308 (1934).
45. Engel, M. B.   *Arch. Pathol.* **53,** 339–351 (1952).
46. Engel, M. B., and Catchpole, H. R.   *Proc. Soc. Exptl. Biol. Med.* **84,** 336–338 (1953).
47. Engel, M. B., Catchpole, H. R., and Joseph, N. R.   *Trans. 5th Josiah Macy, Jr., Conf. on Metabolic Interrelations,* 105–129 (1954).
48. Engfeldt, B.   *Acta Endocrinol.,* Suppl. No. 6 (1950).
49. Engfeldt, B., and Hjertquist, S. O.   *Acta Endocrinol.* **15,** 109–118 (1954).
50. Engfeldt, B., Hjertquist, S. O., and Strandh, J. R. E.   *Acta Endocrinol.* **15,** 119–128 (1954).
50a. Engfeldt, B., and Zetterstrom, R.   *Endocrinology* **54,** 506–515 (1954).
51. Folley, S. J., Scott-Watson, H. M., and Amoroso, E. C.   *J. Endocrinol.* **3,** 178–191 (1942).
52. Freeman, S., and Chang, T. S.   *Am. J. Physiol.* **160,** 335–340 (1950).
53. Freeman, S., and Chang, T. S.   *Am J. Physiol.* **160,** 341–347 (1950).
54. Geurrier, Y., and Bolony, F.   *Compt. rend. assoc. anat.* **47,** 234–238 (1947).
55. Gordon, A. H.   Personal communication.
56. Govaerts, J.   *Arch. intern. pharmacodynamie* **75,** 261–287 (1948).
57. Greenwald, I., and Gross, J.   *J. Biol. Chem.* **66,** 217–227 (1925).
58. Greenwald, I., and Gross, J.   *J. Biol. Chem.* **68,** 325–333 (1926).
59. Greep, R. O.   *J. Heredity* **32,** 397–398 (1941).
60. Grollman, A.   *Endocrinology* **55,** 166–172 (1954).
61. Ham, A. W., Littner N., Drake, T. G., Robertson, E. C., and Tisdall, F. F.   *Am. J. Pathol.* **16,** 277–286 (1940).
62. Handler, P.   *In* W. D. McElroy and B. Glass, Phosphorus Metabolism.   Johns Hopkins Press, Baltimore, 1952, Vol. 2, pp. 631–632..
63. Handler, P., and Cohn, D. V.   *Am. J. Physiol.* **164,** 646–653 (1951).
64. Handler, P., and Cohn, D. V.   *Am. J. Physiol.* **169,** 188–193 (1952).
65. Handler, P., and Cohn, D. V.   *Trans. 5th Josiah Macy, Jr., Conf. on Metabolic Interrelations* 339–343 (1954).
66. Handler, P., Cohn, D. V., and De Maria, W. J. A.   *Am. J. Physiol.* **165,** 434–441 (1951).
67. Handler, P., Cohn, D. V., and Dratz, A. F.   *Trans. 5th Josiah Macy, Jr., Conf. on Metabolic Interrelations* 320–330 (1954).
68. Handler, P., De Maria, W. J. A., and Cohn, D. V.   *Federation Proc.* **8,** 204 (1949).
69. Hanssler, H.   *Monatschr. Kinderheilk.* **101,** 178–179 (1953).
70. Heller, M., McLean, F. C., and Bloom, F. C.   *Am. J. Anat.* **87,** 315–348 (1950).
71. Henry, J. A., Jacobs, E., and Verbanck, M.   *Arch. intern. pharmacodynamie* **94,** 235–247 (1953).
72. Hogben, C. A. M., and Bollman, J. L.   *Federation Proc.* **8,** 357 (1949).
73. Hogben, C. A. M., and Bollman, J. L.   *Am. J. Physiol.* **164,** 670–681 (1951).
74. Hopkins, T. R., Howard, J. E., and Eisenberg, H.   *Bull. Johns Hopkins Hosp.* **91,** 1–21 (1952).
75. Howard, J. E.   *Trans. 4th Josiah Macy, Jr., Conf. on Metabolic Interrelations* 140–153 (1952).
76. Howard, J. E.   *Trans. 5th Josiah Macy, Jr., Conf. on Metabolic Interrelations* 11–42(1954).
77. Howard, J. E., Hopkins, T. R., and Connor, T. B.   *Trans. Assoc. Am. Physicians* **65,** 351–358 (1952).

78. Howard, J. E., Hopkins, T. R., and Connor, T. B. *J. Clin. Endocrinol. and Metabolism* **13**, 1–19 (1953).

79. Irving, J. T., Weinmann, J. P., Schour, I., and Tweedy, W. R. *J. Dental Research* **28**, 369–378 (1949).

80. Jacobs, E. *Arch. intern. pharmacodynamie* **95**, 225–233 (1953).

81. Jacobs, E., and Verbanck, M. *Acta Med. Scand.* **145**, 143–154 (1953).

82. Jacobs, E., Verbanck, M., and Henry, J. A. *Arch. intern. pharmacodynamie* **95**, 321–332 (1953).

83. Jahan, I., and Pitts, R. F. *Am. J. Physiol.* **155**, 42–49 (1948).

84. Kenny, A. D., and Munson, P. L. Unpublished (1953).

85. Kenny, A. D., Vine, B. G., and Munson, P. L. *Federation Proc.* **13**, 241 (1954).

86. Kleeman, C. R., and Cooke, R. E. *J. Lab. Clin. Med.* **38**, 112–127 (1951).

87. Klein, R., and Gow, R. C. *J. Clin. Endocrinol. and Metabolism* **13**, 271–282 (1953).

88. Kochakian, C. D. *Trans. 4th Josiah Macy, Jr., Conf. on Metabolic Interrelations* 130–139 (1952).

89. Kochakian, C. D., Reed, B. A., Bonelli, M., and Sala, G. *Proc. Soc. Exptl. Biol. Med.* **82**, 495–496 (1953).

90. Kochakian, C. D., and Terepka, A. R. *Am. J. Physiol.* **165**, 142–148 (1951).

91. Laskin, D. M., and Engel, M. B. *Federation Proc.* **13**, 521 (1954).

92. Leiffer, E., and Hollander, W. *J. Clin. Endocrinol. and Metabolism* **13**, 1264–1269 (1953).

93. L'Heureux, M. V., Tepperman, H. M., and Wilhelmi, A. E. *J. Biol. Chem.* **168**, 167–176 (1947).

94. L'Heureux, M. V., and Roth, G. J. *Proc. Soc. Exptl. Biol. Med.* **84**, 7–9 (1953).

95. Liljestrand, A., and Swedin, B. *Acta Physiol. Scand.* **25**, 168–173 (1952).

96. Lotz, W. E., Talmage, R. V., and Comar, C. L. *Proc. Soc. Exptl. Biol. Med.* **85**, 292–295 (1954).

97. McCrory, W. W., Forman, C. W., McNamara, H., and Barnett, H. L. *J. Clin. Invest.* **31**, 357–366 (1952).

98. Majno, G., Perrottet, E., Rutishauser, E., and Schupback, S. *Arch. Sci Geneva* **4**, 400–407 (1951).

99. Malcolm, J., Griesback, W. E., Bielschowsky, F., and Hall, W. H. *Brit. J. Exptl. Pathol.* **30**, 17–23 (1949).

100. Malmejac, J., Cruck, S., Neverre, G., and Naurais, E. *Compt. rend. soc. biol.* **142**, 505–507 (1948).

101. Malmejac, J., Cruck, S., and Enrich, S. *Compt. rend. soc. biol.* **142**, 1528 (1948).

102. Manunta, G., and Mureddu, F. *Arch. fisiol.* **51**, 1–11 (1951).

103. Martin, P. G., Babel, J., and Courvoisier, B. *Ann. endocrinol. (Paris)* **13**, 943–946 (1952).

104. Michie, A. J., and Shorey, J. M. *Federation Proc.* **9**, 88–89 (1950).

105. Milne, M. D. *Clin. Sci.* **10**, 471–486 (1951).

106. Munson, P. L. *Ann. N. Y. Acad. Sci.*, in press.

107. Munson, P. L., Iseri, O. A., Kenny, A. D., and Greep, R. O. Unpublished (1954).

108. Munson, P. L., Iseri, O. A., Parker, L. W., and Greep, R. O. *J. Dental Research* **31**, 463 (1952).

110. Munson, P. L., Kenny, A. D., and Iseri, O. A. *Federation Proc.* **12**, 249 (1953).

111. Munson, P. L., Kenny, A. D., Iseri, O. A., and Greep, R. O. *J. Dental Research* **32**, 670 (1953).

112. Munson, P. L., Toverud, S. U., and Kenny, A. D.   *J. Dental Research* **33**, 676–677 (1954)
113. Neufeld, A. H., and Collip, J. B.   *Endocrinology* **30**, 135–141 (1942).
114. Nicolaysen, R., Eeg-Larsen, N., and Malm, O. J.   *Physiol. Revs.* **33**, 424–444 (1953).
115. Ollayos, R. W., and Winkler, A. W.   *J. Clin. Invest.* **22**, 147–154 (1943).
116. Opienska-Blauth, J.   *Ann. Univ. Mariae Curie-Sklodowska, Lublin, Polonia, Sect. D.*, **2**, 13–38 (1947).
117. Patt, H. M., and Luckhardt, A. B.   *Endocrinology* **31**, 384–392 (1942).
118. Perkins, H. R., and Dixon, T. F.   *Science* **118**, 139–140 (1953).
119. Raybuck, H. E.   *Anat. Record* **112**, 117–123 (1952).
120. Reifenstein, E. C., and Howard, R. P.   Glandular Physiology and Therapy, 5th ed.   Lippincott, Philadelphia, 1954.
121. Ross, W. F., and Wood, T. R.   *J. Biol. Chem.* **146**, 49–58 (1942).
122. Rubin, B. L., and Dorfman, R. I.   *Proc. Soc. Exptl. Biol. Med.* **83**, 223–225 (1953).
123. Rucart, G.   *Arch. anat. microscop. morphol. exptl.* **38**, 1–37 (1949).
124. Rucart, G.   *Compt. rend. soc. biol.* **145**, 342–344 (1951).
125. Rutishauser, E., and Majno, G.   *Presse méd.* **14**, 286–288 (1953).
126. Schneider, R.   *Z. mikroskop.-anat. Forsch.* **57**, 104–114 (1951).
127. Schwarz, H., Price, M., and Odell, C. A.   *Metabolism* **2**, 261–267 (1953).
128. Sen, S. C., Gupta, P. S., and Sarcar, U.   *Indian J. Med. Research* **39**, 391–396 (1951).
129. Shetlar, M. R., Howard, R. P., and Reifenstein, E. C.   *Federation Proc.* **13**, 296 (1954).
130. Sirota, J. H.   *Federation Proc.* **12**, 133 (1953).
131. Smith, C. C., and Stoerk, H. C.   *Federation Proc.* **8**, 369 (1949).
132. Spisni, D., and Bogogna, G.   *Atti. soc. ital. sci. vet.* **3**, 221–231 (1949).
133. Stewart, G. S., and Bowen, H. F.   *Endocrinology* **48**, 568–575 (1951).
134. Stewart, G. S., and Bowen, H. F.   *Endocrinology* **51**, 80–86 (1952).
135. Stoerk, H. C., and Carnes, W. H.   *J. Nutrition* **29**, 43–50 (1945).
136. Stoerk, H. C., and Silber, R. H.   *Federation Proc.* **8**, 371 (1949).
137. Striganova, A. R.   *Arkh. Patol.* **11** (No. 2) 50–56 (1949).
138. Talbot, N. B., Sobel, E. H., McArthur, J. W., and Crawford, J. D.   Functional Endocrinology.   Harvard University Press, Cambridge, 1952.
139. Talmage, R. V.   *Federation Proc.* **13**, 150 (1954).
140. Talmage, R. V., Buchanan, G. D., and Kraintz, F. W.   *Abstr. 19th Intern. Physiol. Congr.*, pp. 820–821 (1953).
141. Talmage, R. V., and Kraintz, F. W.   *Proc. Soc. Exptl. Biol. Med.* **85**, 416–419 (1954).
142. Talmage, R. V., and Kraintz, F. W.   *Proc. Soc. Exptl. Biol. Med.*, **87**, 263–267 (1954).
143. Talmage, R. V., Kraintz, F. W., Frost, R. C., and Kraintz, L.   *Endocrinology* **52**, 318–323 (1953).
144. Talmage, R. V., Kraintz, F. W., and Kraintz, L.   *Proc. Soc. Exptl. Biol. Med.* **80**, 553–557 (1952).
145. Talmage, R. V., Lotz, W. E., and Comar, C. L.   *Proc. Soc. Exptl. Biol. Med.* **84**, 578–582 (1953).
146. Tepperman, H. M., L'Heureux, M. V., and Wilhelmi, A. E.   *J. Biol. Chem.* **168**, 151–165 (1947).
147. Thatcher, J. S., and Radike, A. W.   *Am. J. Physiol.* **151**, 138–146 (1947).

174   ROY O. GREEP AND ALEXANDER D. KENNY

148. Tornblom, N.   *Acta Endocrinol.*, Suppl. No. 4 (1949).
149. Tweedy, W. R., and Campbell, W. W.   *J. Biol. Chem.* **154,** 339–347 (1944).
150. Tweedy, W. R., Chilcote, M. E., and Patras, M. C.   *J. Biol. Chem.* **168,** 597–610 (1947).
151. Tweedy, W. R., L'Heureux, M. V., and Zorn, E. M.   *Endocrinology* **47,** 219–227 (1950).
152. Tweedy, W. R., Templeton, R. D., and McJunkin, F. A.   *Am. J. Phsyiol.* **115,** 514–519 (1936).
153. Tweedy, W. R., Templeton, R. D., and McJunkin, F. A.   *Endocrinology* **21,** 55–59 (1937).
154. Vacirca, F.   *Sperimentale* **93,** 168–190 (1939).
155. Vancea, P., Lazarescu, D., and Micsa, M.   *Klin. Monatsbl. Augenheilk.* **110,** 119 (1944).
156. Venzmer, G.   *Hippokrates* **24,** 225–230 (1953).
157. Verrotti, M.   *Clin. Pediat.* **34,** 719–728 (1952).
158. Wilhelmi, A. E., and Sayers, G.   *J. Biol. Chem.* **176,** 175–176 (1948).
159. Wolf, A. D., and Ball, S. M.   *Am. J. Physiol.* **158,** 205–217 (1949).
160. Zetterstrom, R., and Engfeldt, B.   *Nature* **168,** 81–82 (1951).

Chapter V

The Hormones of the Islets of Langerhans

By DeWITT STETTEN, JR., and BEN BLOOM

CONTENTS

Since 1922 it has been known that insulin arises in the islets of Langerhans. A year later evidence pointing to the existence of a second hormone of the islets was adduced. Whereas the investigation of insulin has flourished during the ensuing years, the study of glucagon has been largely neglected, and this neglect is reflected in the fact that reference to glucagon, or hyperglycemic-glycogenolytic factor, is not to be found in the indexes of Volumes I and II of the present series. A recent resurgence of interest in glucagon has dictated to the present reviewers that it be included in this chapter. The material to be discussed has therefore been divided into two main sections, one treating with insulin, the hormone of the β-cells, and the other with glucagon, presumably secreted by the α-cells of the islets of Langerhans.

I. Insulin

A. Introduction

Since the last review treating of insulin in the present series of volumes, great advances in our understanding of the chemistry of this hormone have occurred. Also many important observations relating to the function and mode of action of insulin have been recorded. In the present discussion these recent advances will be stressed. For background material the reader is referred to earlier articles and reviews (7, 12, 69, 70, 90, 127).

B. CHEMISTRY

1. *Molecular Weight*

Observations of the sedimentation and diffusion rates of insulin in neutral solution have yielded molecular weights of approximately 36,000 and 48,000. More recent studies based on sedimentation and diffusion measurements in acid solution (88, 93, 148), measurements of light scattering (28, 147), and measurements of osmotic pressure (54, 56), favor a molecular weight of 12,000. Micelles weighing 2, 3, and 4 times the unit weight of 12,000 appear to exist in solution, and this polymerization seems to be dependent upon pH as well as upon ionic strength (55). X-ray studies of crystalline insulin by Crowfoot indicate that the molecule possesses trigonal symmetry, apparently owing to the presence of the trimeric (molecular weight = 36,000) variety (27).

Evidence has also been presented that 6000 rather than 12,000 represents the minimum molecular weight of insulin. One of several studies of light scattering by insulin in various salt solutions resulted in a calculated molecular weight of 6000 (42). Subsequent determinations from the same laboratory, using a more precise technique, have, however, yielded a value of 12,000 (148). Harfenist and Craig, by a method of partial substitution of insulin with 2,4-dinitrofluorobenzene, separation of the several reaction products by countercurrent distribution, and comparison of extinction coefficient with weight of that component which they presumed to contain 1 mole of reagent per mole of insulin, have computed a minimal combining weight of 6500 for insulin (59). In contrast, Udenfriend and Velick (152), employing the pipsyl derivative method, detected the presence of only one N-terminal[1] glycine and one N-terminal phenylalanine residue per molecule of molecular weight = 12,000. It may be pointed out that the most reliable analytical data to date, namely those of Sanger, to be discussed subsequently, can be fitted to a molecular weight of 6000 or any multiple thereof. In the remainder of this discussion a molecular weight of 12,000 will be assumed to describe the unit molecule of insulin.

2. *Analytical Studies*

There have been several carefully conducted analyses of purified insulin for its constituent amino acids. In Table I are summarized the results of these studies. The data are presented as the number of amino acid residues per unit molecular weight of 12,000, and in general good agreement is observed. Differences may have arisen from selection of analytical methods, impurities in the insulin employed, and species variations in

---

[1] The N-terminal amino acid of a polypeptide chain is the one bearing a free α-amino group. The C-terminal amino acid has a free carboxyl group on the α-carbon.

TABLE I

AMINO ACID COMPOSITION OF INSULIN AND SANGER CHAINS A AND B

(Number of amino acid residues in columns 4, 5, 6, and 7 have been calculated per molecular weight 12,000.)

	1 A Sanger (118)	2 B Sanger (120)	3 2(A + B)	4 Fromageot (46)	5 Velick and Ronzoni (154)	6 Cambridge workers (84, 102, 150)	7 Brand (15)
% N			15.88	15.3	—	15.54	16.04
Mol. Weight	2333	3394	11,454	—	—	—	—
Alanine	1	2	6	6.2	—	6.8	—
Arginine	0	1	2	2.0	2.3	2.1	2.4
Aspartic	2	1	6	5.0	—	—	6.1
Cystine/2	4	2	12	12.5	11.7	12.5	11.0
Glutamic acid	4	3	14	15.7	16.2	15.0	16.4
Glycine	1	3	8	7.2	7.2	6.9	7.4
Histidine	0	2	4	3.8	4.1	3.8	4.1
Isoleucine	1	0	2	1.4	2.6	2.6	2.7
Leucine	2	4	12	13.4	11.9	12.0	12.3
Lysine	0	1	2	2.2	2.0	2.1	2.1
Phenylalanine	0	3	6	6.0	5.8	5.9	5.7
Proline	0	1	2	2.1	3.0	2.7	3.1
Serine	2	1	6	5.9	7.5	6.0	6.6
Threonine	0	1	2	2.4	3.5	2.1	3.2
Tyrosine	2	2	8	8.0	8.1	8.7	8.2
Valine	2	3	10	7.6	9.3	8.0	9.1
Amide N	4	2	12	12.1	—	11.6	15.1

composition. The absence of tryptophan and methionine is to be noted. The abundant sulfur of native insulin is entirely accounted for as cystine. The protein is also unusually rich in leucine and glutamic acid. It is a "simple" protein in that it yields, upon hydrolysis, only amino acids.

A sample of beef insulin, repeatedly recrystallized and apparently homogeneous when tested by the solubility method, centrifugation, and electrophoresis (42), proved resolvable into two components after numerous transfers in the countercurrent distribution apparatus (58). Certain quantitative differences in amino acid composition have been observed when insulin samples from different species have been compared (60, 79, 115). The major components of beef, pork, and sheep insulins yield identical partition coefficients upon countercurrent distribution. Despite this fact, differences in amino acid composition of these samples have been noted (see Table II).

TABLE II

AMINO ACID RESIDUES IN BEEF, PORK, AND SHEEP INSULIN

The number of residues of each amino acid per molecule of insulin (molecular weight = 12,000) has been calculated from data of Harfenist and Craig (60).

Amino acid	Beef	Pork	Sheep
Serine	5.78	5.58	4.14
Threonine	1.94	3.54	1.92
Glycine	7.88	7.88	9.40
Alanine	5.82	4.34	5.98
Valine	9.36	7.36	9.60
Isoleucine	1.32	3.08	1.38

3. Structural Formula

The brilliant success of Sanger and his colleagues in their studies of the sequence of amino acids in the peptide chains of insulin permits today the virtually complete formulation of a structure for insulin. As a result of these studies insulin is the first protein to which a structure, albeit incomplete in certain details, can be assigned. This historic accomplishment has rested upon: (1) The finding that insulin may be oxidatively split into two readily separable species of unbranched polypeptide chains; (2) the development of a new reagent, 2,4-dinitrofluorobenzene, which reacts under mild conditions with primary amino groups to yield stable colored products; (3) the development of chromatographic techniques permitting separation of peptides and of amino acids; (4) a combination of happy characteristics of the insulin molecule.

When performic acid acts upon the amino acid cystine, the molecule is oxidatively cleaved to give two molecules of cysteic acid:

$$CH_2—S—S—CH_2 \qquad\qquad CH_2—SO_3H$$
$$| \qquad\qquad | \qquad \xrightarrow{HCOOOH} \qquad |$$
$$CHNH_2 \qquad CHNH_2 \qquad\qquad 2\ CHNH_2 \qquad (1)$$
$$| \qquad\qquad | \qquad\qquad\qquad |$$
$$COOH \qquad COOH \qquad\qquad COOH$$

Cystine   Cysteic Acid

Whereas this reagent also attacks tryptophan and methionine, both fortunately absent in insulin, it has little effect upon other amino acids (149). When insulin is treated with performic acid, it splits to yield only two species of polypeptides. These have been separated and have been designated as the A-(acidic) chain and the B-(basic) chain (111). The only expected alteration beyond this fracture of the molecule was the generation of cysteic acid at sites which, in native insulin, were occupied by half-cystine residues.

Prior to the use of performic acid, Sanger (112) had introduced 2,4-dinitrofluorobenzene as a reagent for primary amino groups.

$$O_2N-\bigcirc\!\!\!\!\!\overset{NO_2}{-}\!\!\!\!-F \ + \ H_2N-R \ \rightarrow \ O_2N-\bigcirc\!\!\!\!\!\overset{NO_2}{-}\!\!\!\!-\underset{H}{N}-R \tag{2}$$

This reaction proceeds in mild alkali, and the dinitrophenylamine bond which is formed is stable under the conditions of acid digestion necessary to hydrolyze peptide bonds. If a linear polypeptide is first treated with dinitrofluorobenzene, the product then hydrolyzed with acid, and the α-dinitrophenylamino acid, yellow in color, isolated and identified, the N-terminal amino acid of the polypeptide chain may be determined. Sanger has applied this technique to native insulin and has shown that per unit weight of 12,000 there are four N-terminal amino acids, two glycine and two phenylalanine. After the oxidative disruption of insulin into A- and B-chains had been accomplished, Sanger identified the A-chain as the one bearing an N-terminal glycine and the B-chain as terminating in a phenylalanine residue. From these facts it was clear that insulin, molecular weight = 12,000, contained two A-chains and two B-chains per molecule, the chains linked to each other by disulfide bridges between half-cystine residues. If the molecular weight of 6000 is assumed, one of each species of chain occurs per molecule.

The further study of the sequence of amino acids was first pursued in the B-chain. The sequence immediately adjacent to the N-terminal phenylalanine was elucidated by partial acid hydrolysis of the N-dinitrophenyl substituted derivative (113). Several yellow peptides were isolated and identified, including DNP-phenylalanine, DNP-phenylalanylvaline, DNP-phenylalanylvalyl-aspartic acid, etc. From such findings, the sequence of the terminal four amino acids was established as: Phe-Val-Asp-Glu. To secure information relating to the remaining amino acids in the B-chain, the polypeptide was subjected to partial hydrolysis, fragments were isolated and purified, and these in turn were studied by the method of DNP substitution. Fifty such peptide fragments were characterized after partial acid hydrolysis (119) and ten more after digestion of the B-chain with pepsin, chymotrypsin, and trypsin (120). The array of short amino acid sequences which resulted from all these studies permitted a unique formulation for the sequence of amino acid residues in this fraction of the insulin molecule (Fig. 1).

The application of similar methods to the A-chain of insulin led to the identification of 34 short sequences of amino acids after initial partial hydrolysis with acid (116) and 16 more after enzymatic hydrolysis (117).

Phe-Val-Asp(—NH₂)-Glu(—NH₂)-His-Leu-CySO₃H-Gly-Ser-His-Leu-Val-Glu-Ala-
1 2   3   4   5 6   7   8   9 10 11 12 13 14

Leu-Tyr-Leu-Val-CySO₃H-Gly-Glu-Arg-Gly-Phe-Phe-Tyr-Thr-Pro-Lys-Ala
15 16 17 18   19   20 21 22 23 24 25 26 27 28 29 30

FIG. 1. The amino acid sequence of the B-chain of insulin. (After Sanger and Tuppy (120).)

Gly-Ileu-Val-Glu-Glu(—NH₂)-CySO₃H-CySO₃H-Ala-Ser-Val-CySO₃H-Ser-Leu-Tyr-
1 2   3   4   5   6   7   8 9 10   11   12 13 14

Glu(—NH₂)-Leu-Glu-Asp(—NH₂)-Tyr-CySO₃H-Asp(—NH₂)
15   16 17   18   19   20   21

FIG. 2. The amino acid sequence of the A-chain of insulin. (After Sanger et al. (118).)

From these results a single possible sequence of amino acids in the A-chain was obtained (Fig. 2).

There is considerable evidence that the β-carboxyl group of the C-terminal aspartic acid bears an amide substituent, asparagine being split off the A-chain by the action of carboxypeptidase (61). The other amide groups, as tentatively indicated by Sanger, Thompson, and Tuppy (118), reside on the β-carboxyl and γ-carboxyl groups of aspartic and glutamic acids, respectively, as indicated in Figs. 1 and 2.

From the foregoing discussion it will be seen that essentially complete structural formulas may be now written for the A-chain and the B-chain of insulin. Remaining to be considered is the question of the nature of the linkages between these chains in the native insulin molecule. That these linkages are disulfide bonds of cystine is apparent from the fact that in native insulin all the sulfur is present as cystine (disulfide) and that performic acid, used to split insulin into A- and B-fragments, reacts preferentially with these disulfide bridges. Counting from the N-terminus, half-cystine residues occur in the A-chain at the 6th, 7th, 11th, and 20th positions, and in the B-chain at the 7th and 19th positions. Hundreds of

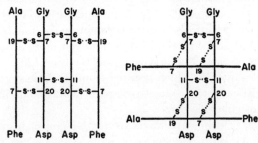

FIG. 3. Two of the possible structures of the insulin molecule. (Redrawn from Sanger (114).)

possibilities exist whereby these half-cystine residues may be coupled one to another to yield molecules containing two A-chains and two B-chains (molecular weight = 12,000) or one of each species of chain (molecular weight = 6000). Some of these are indicated in Fig. 3. Whereas certain of these possibilities can be eliminated on the basis of crystallographic data, molecular models, and considerations of steric hindrance (3, 82, 106), a definitive answer is not presently available.

C. PHYSIOLOGY

1. *Comment*

Now that complete knowledge of the chemical structure of insulin is being approached, it would be gratifying if this structural information could be applied toward an elucidation of its physiological actions. Unfortunately, at the present time, there is no fusion between the structural chemical approach and the physiological approach to the study of this important compound. Perhaps it is as a consequence of lack of comparable information regarding other proteins that it is not possible to attribute the functions of insulin to any unique or characteristic structural feature.

2. *Site of Action*

The current conflicting views on the probable primary site of action of insulin have recently been reviewed (63, 128). For purposes of the present discussion it will be assumed that in mammalian systems an obligatory phosphorylation of glucose by adenosine triphosphate precedes all the known routes of glucose utilization.

$$\text{Glucose} + \text{ATP} \xrightarrow{\text{hexokinase}} \text{glucose-6-phosphate} + \text{ADP} \qquad (3)$$

The glucose-6-phosphate formed by this reaction may engage in at least four different processes (Fig. 4).

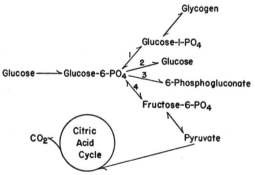

FIG. 4. The metabolic fates of glucose-6-phosphate.

1. It may be transformed into glucose-1-phosphate, which is at one and the same time the precursor and the major product of glycogen.

2. Glucose-6-phosphate is subject to irreversible hydrolysis in liver, but not in muscle, to yield glucose and inorganic phosphate.

3. Glucose-6-phosphate may be oxidized in certain tissues to 6-phosphogluconic acid, and this product, upon oxidative decarboxylation, yields CO_2 and pentose phosphate (66, 67).

4. It may be isomerized to fructose-6-phosphate, which may then yield pyruvic and lactic acids by the reactions of glycolysis. Pyruvic acid, oxidatively decarboxylated to acetyl-coenzyme A, serves as a precursor of fatty acids, CO_2, and a host of other products.

In the diabetic organism, the production of lactate, CO_2, glycogen, and fatty acids from glucose is decreased, whereas the administration of insulin enhances all of these fates of glucose. From the fact that the several pathways diverge at glucose-6-phosphate (Fig. 4) it is an attractive hypothesis to assign to insulin some action at, or prior to, glucose-6-phosphate production. This hypothesis has the advantage of simplicity in that a single site of action can be assigned which will account for many if not all of the observed effects of hypo- and hyper-insulinism.

At least three factors can govern the rate of formation of glucose-6-phosphate (Equation 3). These are: (*1*) the supply of glucose *within the cell*; (*2*) the activity of the enzyme hexokinase; (*3*) the availability of adenosine triphosphate. The primary action of insulin has been attributed, by various workers, to an effect on each of these three variables.

a. Translocating Effect. Whereas it generally has been held that the common sugars are capable of free diffusion across cell membranes, studies originating from Levine's laboratory indicate that this is not necessarily the case. These workers have measured the volume of distribution of galactose, injected intravenously into the eviscerated-nephrectomized dog, and have found this volume to be approximately 40 % of body weight, in contrast to a volume of about 70 % throughout which urea was distributed. The injection of insulin, either at the outset or during the course of a galactose-space measurement, resulted in a prompt enlargement of the galactose-space to equal the urea-space (Fig. 5). These results were interpreted to mean that galactose, in the absence of insulin, was excluded from a large portion of the intracellular space, presumably, in this preparation, the intramuscular space. The action of insulin was considered to be one of favoring transport across the cell membrane. Further extension of the argument rested upon observations that galactose underwent no chemical transformations in the eviscerated preparation (81). In the main these results have been confirmed by Wick and Drury (162), who studied the fate of galactose-C^{14} in eviscerated rabbits. Whereas $C^{14}O_2$ was generated

EVISCERATED-NEPHRECTOMIZED DOG

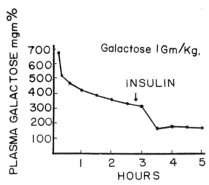

FIG. 5. Galactose was injected at 0 time. The injection of insulin was begun 2 hours later and continued for the remainder of the experiment. Note the blood galactose level fell sharply, reached an approximately 70% body weight distribution, and was then maintained. (From Levine *et al.* (81).)

to a small extent, the calculated rate of entry of galactose into the intra-cellular compartment was markedly enhanced by insulin.

Levine and his collaborators (50, 80) have studied various sugars other than galactose to ascertain whether or not their distributions were influenced by insulin. Of the eight sugars studied, only three were found to be insulin-sensitive (Fig. 6).

It was pointed out that the configuration about carbon atoms 1, 2, and 3 of the responsive sugars was identical with that of glucose. Any change from this configuration appeared to render the sugar nonresponsive to insulin. It was further noted that muscle work in the eviscerated-nephrec-tomized dog has an effect similar to that of insulin in increasing the volume of distribution of certain sugars (51). Haft *et al.* (57) have studied the influence of insulin on the uptake of several sugars by diaphragm sections *in vitro* and have reported that the uptake of galactose and arabinose is enhanced by insulin. In their system D-xylose was not responsive to insulin, whereas fructose was.

Experiments by Park (95) have shed some light upon the manner in which insulin influences the distribution of glucose. Park has measured the free glucose of the intracellular space of diaphragm and has shown, both *in vivo* and *in vitro*, that at various levels of extracellular glucose concentration the addition of insulin results in a rise in intracellular glucose concentration. This result is the one anticipated on the assumption that insulin acts by favoring entry of glucose, and is contrary to expectations based on the view that insulin favors the phosphorylation of glucose.

Further support of the view that insulin favors the passage of certain sugars across certain membranes comes from the work of Ross (107), who

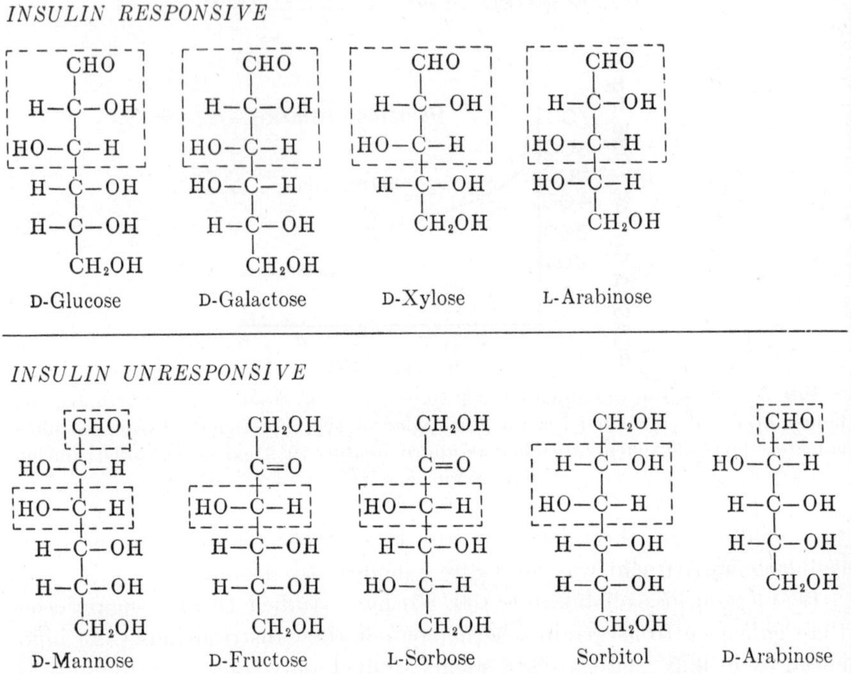

INSULIN RESPONSIVE

D-Glucose   D-Galactose   D-Xylose   L-Arabinose

INSULIN UNRESPONSIVE

D-Mannose   D-Fructose   L-Sorbose   Sorbitol   D-Arabinose

FIG. 6.   Structure of sugars and response to insulin.   (After Levine and Goldstein (80).)

measured the concentrations of glucose in blood and in aqueous humor of rabbits and computed, from these data, velocity constants for the process of transport of glucose across the ciliary body.   During the hypoglycemic phase of alloxanization, when the concentration of circulating insulin was believed to be high, the rate of entry of glucose into the aqueous humor was found to be enhanced.   In other studies the same author reported an increased uptake of both glucose and galactose by the isolated lens *in vitro*, in response to added insulin (108).

The above-described experiments have been interpreted to support the view that the role of insulin in carbohydrate metabolism is to favor the *translocation* of glucose and certain other sugars from extra- to intra-cellular compartments.   In contrast, there are many experimental results which favor the conclusion that the role of insulin is to augment a chemical *transformation*, phosphorylation of glucose, to glucose-6-phosphate.

b. Transforming Effect. Price *et al.* (101) have described an inhibition of mammalian hexokinases in cell-free extracts by crude APE (anterior pituitary extracts) both *in vivo* and *in vitro*.   Muscle hexokinase activity was also found to be depressed when the enzyme was measured in cell-free extracts obtained from alloxan-diabetic rats.   In either case, insulin, which was without effect upon purified hexokinase, served to abolish the observed inhibition. Crude ACE (adrenocortical extract) markedly enhanced the inhibition of hexokinase by APE and prolonged the inhibition occurring spontaneously in muscle extracts of diabetic animals (25, 26). When muscle extracts of alloxanized rats were treated with ACE and the rate of glucose disappearance was compared with that in similar extracts treated with ACE + insulin, it was found that in about half of the experiments an inhibition of glucose utilization, reversible by insulin, was produced by adrenocortical substances. No single crystalline adrenocortical hormone was found to cause such inhibition.

Some confirmation of these findings occurs in a report by Weil-Malherbe (160), who detected a factor in the serum of untreated human diabetics which had an inhibitory influence upon rat brain hexokinase. Injection of insulin into the patient abolished this inhibition, but addition of insulin to the *in vitro* system did not. The inhibitor was unstable, especially at low temperatures. Normal serum was noted to augment the activity of hexokinase.

The reports of the St. Louis workers provoked similar studies in various laboratories. Broh-Kahn and Mirsky (16) found no differences in hexokinase activities of extracts derived from diabetic and normal rats, and whereas occasional inhibition with APE, reversible by insulin, was noted, this inhibition bore no relation to the diabetogenic activity of the extract. Occasional inhibition of hexokinase in tissue extracts by APE has also been reported by other workers (103, 126). The hexokinase of erythrocytes was insensitive to all hormones tested but was subject to an inhibitor in plasma (23).

Stadie and collaborators (129, 130) have been unable to confirm the finding of Cori's group. No difference in hexokinase activity could be elicited *in vitro* with APE, ACE, or insulin. Neither insulin, nor ACE, nor a combination of these two had any significant effect upon the activity of hexokinase in muscle extracts from diabetic cats.

3. *In Vitro Effects*

Since the classical studies of Houssay it has been recognized that an antagonism exists between some secretion of the anterior pituitary gland and insulin. There are numerous observations in the literature re-establishing this antagonism with respect to glucose utilization, glycogen synthesis, etc., in tissue slices, diaphragm sections, and other tissue preparations containing intact cells. Some of these studies have been interpreted as supporting specifically the concept that insulin releases hexokinase from a hypophyseal inhibition. It should be pointed out that the demonstration of an altered glucose utilization by any preparation of which cell membranes are a part does not discriminate between the *translocation* mechanism of insulin action proposed by Levine and the *transformation* mechanism suggested by Cori.

Among the first studies of an effect of insulin *in vitro* was the demonstration by Gemmill (49) that the uptake of glucose and the synthesis of glycogen by rat diaphragms were enhanced by addition of insulin. With various modifications this experiment has been repeated and extended in other laboratories. (See reviews by Krahl (74), Park (94), and Haugaard and Marsh (63).) The results of Hastings and collaborators (104, 145, 155), in addition to confirming Gemmill's conclusions, reveal an enhanced insulin response by tissues derived from hypophysectomized and/or adrenalectomized animals. Conversely, preinjection with APE (91) and more recently with purified growth hormone (94) were shown to decrease the insulin response of isolated diaphragms. The insulin sensitivity of the hypophysectomized-adrenalectomized animal or its tissues is sufficient to indicate that the action of insulin is something more than mere antagonism to pituitary and adrenal materials.

The presence of a humoral factor which inhibits glucose utilization and glycogenesis has been detected in sera from diabetic rats and human diabetic patients (10, 151). Inhibitory effects were abolished if the diabetic rats were subjected to hypophysectomy or to adrenalectomy but could be restored by the simultaneous administration of pituitary somatotropic hormone and cortisone (10). The inhibitory activity has been associated with the β-lipoprotein fraction of diabetic serum and has been found to be unstable at low temperatures (9).

4. *Binding*

Light has been cast upon the intimate nature of the reaction between insulin and target tissues by the studies of Stadie and his group (128). It was noted that the effect of insulin upon the metabolism of diaphragm (131), mammary gland (65), and adipose tissue (62) was demonstrable after a short immersion of each tissue in insulin solution, even when followed by exhaustive washing. These findings were interpreted to mean that insulin was firmly bound to certain tissues, and this binding has received additional confirmation from studies in which insulin tagged with I^{131} or S^{35} was employed (133). The quantity of insulin bound, measured isotopically, bore a linear relationship to the extra glycogen synthesized by diaphragm sections. It was found that, per gram muscle, 1 μg. of insulin yielded an increased synthesis of 3 to 4 mg. of glycogen per hour. The antiinsulin effect of anterior pituitary materials, orginally attributed to interference with insulin binding (132), was later found not to impede binding (133). Its action was therefore assigned to a peripheral antagonism between pituitary and pancreatic hormones. Insulin labeled with I^{131} has been further shown by Lee and Williams (78) to pass through cell membranes and distribute in a characteristic pattern among the cytoplasmic structures. That insulin is bound by muscle is also indicated from experiments in intact human beings (6).

5. In Vivo Effects

The availability of labeled sugars has provoked a reinvestigation in the intact animal of metabolic defects relating to insulin. Most investigators have recorded a diminution in formation of $C^{14}O_2$ from glucose-C^{14} in diabetic animals (34, 139). The disposition of glucose carbon atoms in various fractions of extrahepatic tissues of rabbits has been measured by Wick et al. (163), and in general each fraction studied was found to contain larger amounts of carbon derived from glucose when insulin was injected.

6. Other Insulin Effects

a. Phosphorus Metabolism. In addition to its postulated effects upon the translocation of glucose from extra- to intra-cellular fluids and upon the release of hexokinase from the action of inhibitors, various other functions have been attributed to insulin. It has been pointed out that ATP is required for the operation of the hexokinase reaction (Equation 3), and various workers have suggested that a deficit in ATP may be the primary consequence of insulin lack. The incorporation of P^{32} from inorganic phosphate into various intracellular organic compounds of phosphorus: the terminal position of ATP (72), phosphocreatine (52, 109), thiamine pyrophosphate (41, 124), glucose-1-phosphate (110), and glucose-6-phosphate (109), is favored by insulin and is inhibited in the diabetic state. This has been variously ascribed to an insulin effect upon phosphate transport or to an influence upon the efficiency of coupled oxidative phosphorylation. The latter explanation appears unlikely in view of the dissimilarity between diabetes and dinitrophenol intoxication, in which oxidative phosphorylation is known to be diminished. In the latter condition, it is an increase, not a decrease, in glucose utilization that would be anticipated.

b. Oxygen Uptake. There are other lines of evidence suggesting that oxidative reactions, including those of the citric acid cycle, are subject to influence by insulin. In minced pigeon breast muscle, Krebs and Eggleston (76) found that oxygen uptake, in the presence of various members of the citric acid cycle, was better sustained when insulin was added. Other laboratories have failed to find an analogous effect with mammalian muscle (123, 134). A decrease in concentration of the several members of the citric acid cycle has been reported in rat muscle after alloxanization (45).

c. Lipogenesis. The loss in weight in uncontrolled diabetes and the gain in weight following insulin administration to normal or diabetic subjects, are well-documented clinical findings. Drury (29) suggested that insulin might participate in fatty acid synthesis, and Stetten and Boxer (137) measured the uptake of deuterium in the fatty acids of rats and found a depression of lipogenesis in diabetes to about 5 % of the normal rate. In rabbits the injection of insulin resulted in a fourfold exaltation of hepatic lipogenesis (138). Synthesis of fatty acids from acetate has been studied with liver slices from diabetic animals (14, 22) and with normal liver slices to which insulin was added (8, 13). Most of the reported results are in accord with the view that the absence of insulin inhibits the formation of long-chain fatty acids from acetate, whereas under the same conditions the synthesis of cholesterol is either unaffected (14) or favored (68). This defect in diabetic tissues is also demonstrable in a water-soluble enzyme system from lysed mitochondria (121). If derived from a diabetic animal, this extract is depressed with regard to its capacity to synthesize fatty acids, but normal activity is largely restored by the addition of glycogen, fructose, glucose-6-phosphate, and hexose-diphosphate, but not of glucose.

Baker *et al.* (5), reinvestigating fatty acid synthesis by liver slices, found that the marked depression of lipogenesis after alloxanization could be overcome, and lipogenesis from acetate could be restored to normal, if the diabetic rats were fed for four days prior to sacrifice a diet containing 58 % of fructose. This normal fatty acid synthesis could be observed in tissues of animals essentially devoid of insulin, establishing that insulin, as such, is not an essential component of lipogenesis. Striking similarities in the metabolic defects have been observed when the livers of fasted and of diabetic animals have been compared (20, 85, 164). Whereas fructose utilization by liver slices from either type of animal is normal, glucose utilization and fatty acid synthesis are defective.

d. Proteogenesis. The relation of protein metabolism to diabetes stems from the old clinical observation of negative nitrogen balance in this disease. Several recent observations indicate that this negative nitrogen balance results from an impairment of protein synthesis from amino acids. Krahl (75) has found that glycine enters the protein of diaphragm sections, and the glutathione and protein of liver slices, more slowly than normal when tissues from diabetic animals are used. Sinex *et al.* (125) find that addition of insulin accelerates the incorporation of alanine into diaphragm protein *in vitro*.

The several effects of insulin which have been discussed that do not relate directly to glucose utilization include impaired phosphorylation of various substrates, impaired fatty acid synthesis from acetate, and impaired protein synthesis from amino acids. Many additional effects might have been discussed, including an impairment in acetylation of p-aminobenzoic acid (21) and the clinically cardinal defect of ketosis. It is possible that all of these defects are secondary to the interference with glucose utilization which appears to be the most striking biochemical manifestation of hypoinsulinism.

D. Production of Experimental Diabetes

In recent years several compounds have been discovered which produce a fairly specific necrosis of β-cells in the islets of Langerhans. Over and above their usefulness in the laboratory, these agents, because of their structural similarity to compounds of biological importance, have provoked speculation regarding the etiology of spontaneous human diabetes. Foremost among these compounds is alloxan, first announced by Dunn *et al.* (31). It lies beyond the scope of this article to review the large literature in this area. Good reviews are readily available (4, 83). Certain derivatives of alloxan exhibit a similar diabetogenic action (17, 64). Possibly related to alloxan poisoning is the report of Griffiths (53) that large doses of uric acid injected into rabbits are diabetogenic. The structural similarities between alloxan and uric acid are very suggestive. In addition, three

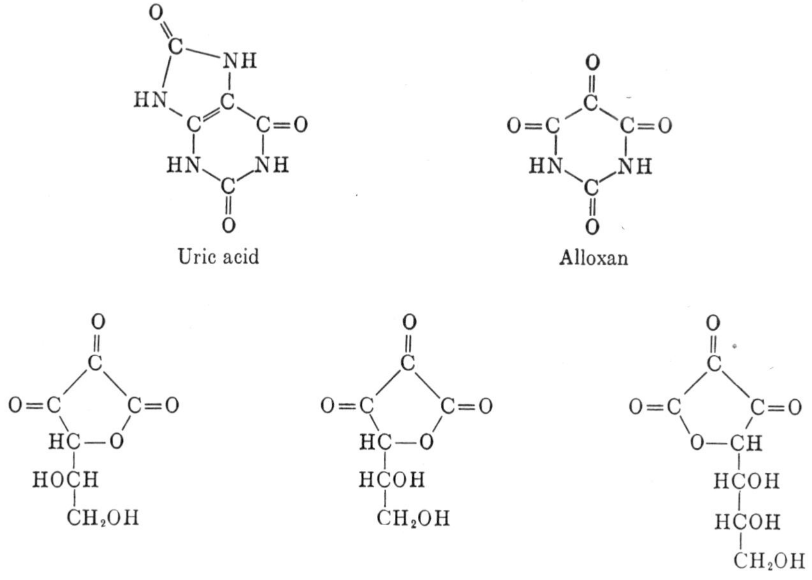

Uric acid   Alloxan

Dehydroascorbic acid   Dehydroisoascorbic acid   Dehydroglucoascorbic acid
(Dehydro-L-   (Dehydro-D-   (Dehydro-D-
xyloascorbic acid)   riboascorbic acid)   glucoascorbic acid)

Fig. 7. Structural relationships of certain diabetogenic compounds.

compounds, dehydroascorbic, dehydro*iso*ascorbic, and dehydrogluco-ascorbic acids (96, 97), have been shown to be diabetogenic. Although superficially unrelated to alloxan, a structural similarity is apparent in that each compound exhibits three adjacent carbonyl groups (Fig. 7). Similarities in chemical reactivity between alloxan and dehydroascorbic acid have been recorded. It is of interest that dehydroascorbic acid elicits symptoms of parasympathetic stimulation, and that its diabetogenic activity can be blocked by atropine (98).

II. Glucagon

A. HISTORICAL

In the year following the discovery of insulin, Murlin *et al.* (89) proposed the existence of a second physiologically active factor in aqueous acid extracts of pancreas. The activity of this material, which was named glucagon (73), was measured by a rise in glucose level in the blood of normal rabbits and of pancreatectomized dogs. Reports of a "transient hyperglycemia" following intravenous injection of crude insulin were compatible with the possibility that insulin might contain a contaminating hyperglycemic principle. The demonstration by Geiling and de Lawder (48) that insulin crystallized according to the procedure of Abel (1) did not exhibit a hyperglycemic activity clearly established the existence of a physiologically active contaminant of crude insulin preparations. With increasing information concerning the mode of action of this agent, the name hyperglycemic-glycogenolytic, or H-G, factor has been used, but in accord with current convention, we shall revert to the earlier name of glucagon in the present review.

Whereas some investigators have cautioned against the premature acceptance of the hormonal nature of glucagon (77, 87, 156), most students of this problem seem to believe that glucagon is a second hormone of the islets of Langerhans. Several criteria indicating its endocrine nature have been fulfilled, and these will be discussed in the succeeding sections.

B. CHEMICAL PROPERTIES

The purification and crystallization of glucagon have been achieved by Staub *et al.* (135). Commencing with an amorphous fraction obtained in the commercial preparation of insulin, they effected purification by pre-cipitation at pH 6.7, fractional precipitation from aqueous acetone and from buffers, and final crystallization from a chilled alkaline solution (Fig. 8). This material, injected intravenously into cats at a dosage level of 0.1 μg. per kilogram, causes a rise in blood glucose of 25 mg. per 100 ml. in 15 minutes. It gives a positive biuret test, contains 0.6 % sulfur cor-responding to a minimal molecular weight of about 5000, and is virtually

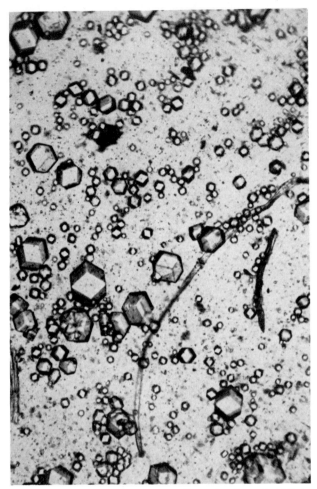

FIG. 8. Crystalline glucagon. (From Staub *et al.* (135).)

devoid of cystine and zinc. The following amino acids have been detected to date: lysine, alanine, histidine, methionine, valine, phenylalanine, leucine, glycine, tyrosine, threonine, serine, glutamate, arginine, aspartate, and tryptophan (136). The presence of methionine and tryptophan and the virtual lack of cystine distinguish this protein from insulin and indicate its independent origin. It is of interest that methionine, previously found lacking in crystalline insulin but present in crude amorphous insulin (43), occurs as the major or sole sulfur amino acid in glucagon. The absence of cystine in this molecule may account for its stability toward alkali or cysteine, reagents which inactivate insulin (18, 142).

C. ORIGIN

It has been proposed that the α-cells of the islets of Langerhans generate glucagon. In support of this contention it has been shown that the tail of the pancreas, richer in islets, is likewise richer in glucagon than is the head. Per unit of weight, the sclerosed pancreas incident to duct ligation is richer in hyperglycemic activity than is the normal pancreas. Normal amounts of glucagon persist in the pancreas after damage to β-cells has been effected by alloxan (39, 99, 144). Glucagon has also been extracted from the pancreas of a dog subjected to both pancreatic duct ligation and alloxanization (47). Hyperglycemic activity has been demonstrated in extracts of the mucosa of the gastric fundus in the dog and has been correlated with the presence in this tissue of cells which, like the α-cells, can be stained with silver (36, 144).

Cobaltous chloride has been shown to damage selectively the α-cells of the pancreatic islets. Administration of this material to guinea pigs is followed by a transient hyperglycemia and a reduction in the residual glucagon activity of the pancreas (153, 157). The attribution of the hyperglycemic phase to α-cell "irritation" is rendered questionable by the observation that in the dog cobalt chloride administration is followed by hyperglycemia even after resection of both pancreas and upper gastrointestinal tract (77, 156). No direct correlation has been observed between prolonged damage to α-cells by cobalt chloride and a lowering of the blood sugar, and these findings have introduced doubt into the interpretation that glucagon normally arises in α-cells. Diethyldithiocarbamate has been shown to damage α-cells and, when administered to rabbits, results in death in hypoglycemia (71). Possibly related to this situation is the clinical report of two members of a family, both exhibiting hypoglycemia and the absence of demonstrable α-cells in the pancreatic islets (86; see also 44).

The demonstration of hyperglycemic activity in the blood draining the pancreas has been accomplished in cross-circulation experiments by Foà et al. (35, 38). When blood from the pancreatico-duodenal vein of a donor dog was introduced into the femoral vein of a recipient dog, the injection of insulin into the donor was followed by a rise in blood glucose in the recipient. Conversely, the injection either of glucose or of glucagon into the donor provoked a fall in blood glucose in the recipient dog. Hyperglycemic activity was also detected in the venous drainage of the pancreas of an alloxanized dog (40). Similarly when the isolated dog pancreas is perfused with solutions poor in glucose (40 to 50 mg. per 100 ml.) hyperglycemic activity is demonstrable in the perfusate (33), whereas when solutions rich in glucose are used (240 to 360 mg. per 100 ml.), the perfusate contains insulin in excess (2).

D. Interhormonal Relations

From the foregoing discussion it will be apparent that evidence is accumulating indicative of a relationship between insulin, arising in the β-cells, and glucagon, presumably formed in the α-cells of the islets. An early evidence of this relationship stems from the observations of Thorogood and Zimmerman (146), who found that the insulin requirement of alloxan-diabetic dogs was reduced by subsequent pancreatectomy. Pancreatectomized dogs were more prone to ketosis and, when untreated, died earlier than did untreated dogs rendered diabetic either with alloxan or with pituitary diabetogenic hormone. In view of the finding that ligation of the pancreatic duct had no effect on the course of alloxan-diabetes, it was proposed that a material antagonistic to insulin normally arises in the islets of Langerhans. This suggestion is in accord with the fact that totally pancreatectomized human subjects require less insulin for regulation than do many patients with spontaneous diabetes (30, 100).

With respect to the concentration of glucose in the blood, there are other experiments indicating an antagonism between insulin and glucagon. Among these are the findings that a far greater rise in blood glucose level in response to glucagon and a far greater fall in response to insulin ensue in the regulated pancreatectomized than in the normal dog (99).

Whereas glucagon and insulin may appear to exert antagonistic actions when the level of blood glucose alone is considered, these two pancreatic substances may be regarded as synergists from the point of view of the peripheral tissues. Glucagon, by favoring a contribution to blood glucose at the expense of liver glycogen, is providing the very substrate to muscle the utilization of which is enhanced by insulin. In the same sense an infusion of glucose can be considered either antagonistic or synergistic to administered insulin.

The regulation of glucagon production appears to be influenced by STH (pituitary somatotropic hormone). Bornstein *et al.* (11) noted the appearance of hyperglycemic activity in the blood of the portal vein, but not of the femoral vein, of the alloxan-diabetic-hypophysectomized-adrenalectomized rat after protracted STH administration. Confirmatory data were also secured from cats made diabetic with STH. Foǎ *et al.*, from cross-circulation experiments with dogs, detected a hyperglycemic response in the recipient dog when transfused with pancreatico-duodenal vein blood from an STH-treated donor (37).

E. Site and Mechanism of Action

From the evidence now available, the liver appears to be the sole target organ of glucagon. It was shown by Collens and Murlin (24) and again by Bürger and Kramer (19) that the intraportal administration of glucagon results in a greater hyperglycemia than does its injection into a peripheral vein. In order of decreasing effectiveness were the intraportal, intravenous, intraperitoneal, intramuscular, and subcutaneous routes of administration (92, 99, 161). Whereas earlier studies had failed to demonstrate any effect of subcutaneously injected glucagon, Vulysteke and de Duve (158) have reported that subcutaneously injected glucagon decreases the hypoglycemic response resulting from simultaneously injected insulin.

Pincus has found that in the eviscerated-hepatectomized dog glucagon is without effect upon the blood glucose level (99). Much earlier, Bürger and Kramer had suggested that the rise in blood glucose after glucagon injection was a consequence of breakdown of glycogen in the liver (19). In support of this view was the observation by Shipley and Humel (122) of a decline in glycogen content of liver slices upon addition of glucagon-contaminated insulin. Sutherland and Cori (142) subsequently showed that this fall in glycogen of liver slices was clearly not due to the action of insulin *per se* but rather to a frequently encountered contaminant, *i.e.*, glucagon, and this fact has served as a basis for the quantitative assay of glucagon as devised by Sutherland and de Duve (144).

There is an obvious similarity between the apparent effect of glucagon and that of epinephrine upon the breakdown of liver glycogen. An enzymatic basis for this similarity has been brought to light by studies of Sutherland and Cori (140, 143). The three enzymatic steps intervening between liver glycogen and blood glucose can be summarized as follows:

$$\text{Glycogen} + \text{inorg. phosphate} \underset{\xleftarrow{\hspace{2cm}}}{\xrightarrow[\text{Phosphorylase}]{\hspace{2cm}}} \text{glucose-1-phosphate} \qquad (4)$$

$$\text{Glucose-1-phosphate} \underset{\xleftarrow{\hspace{2cm}}}{\xrightarrow[\text{Phosphoglucomutase}]{\hspace{2cm}}} \text{glucose-6-phosphate} \qquad (5)$$

$$\text{Glucose-6-phosphate} \xrightarrow{\text{Glucose-6-phosphatase}} \text{glucose} + \text{inorg. phosphate} \qquad (6)$$

Sutherland and Cori (143) have shown that the rate-determining step in liver slices is the reaction catalyzed by phosphorylase (Equation 4). The mutase as well as the phosphatase (Equations 5 and 6) are present in large excess, and therefore an acceleration of the over-all process of conversion of glycogen to glucose would most logically be assigned to augmentation of the phosphorylase reaction. The intracellular concentrations of both glucose-1-phosphate and glucose-6-phosphate increase in liver slices in response to added glucagon. Preincubation of liver slices with glucagon results in an enhancement of phosphorylase activity as assayed on homogenates prepared from such slices. Glucagon protects liver phosphorylase against the inactivation which otherwise supervenes on incubation and serves to reactivate such inactivated preparations (141). In all these regards epinephrine and glucagon exert identical actions, and indeed the estimated effective molarities of these two agents are of similar orders of magnitude. That these two agents do not necessarily produce their effects by the same mechanism has been suggested by studies *in vivo* and *in vitro* showing that dihydroergotamine interferes with the action of epinephrine without affecting that of glucagon (32). In addition epinephrine has been shown to favor the conversion of inactive *muscle* phosphorylase *b* into active phosphorylase *a*. Thus far glucagon has not been shown to influence *muscle* phosphorylase.

It should be pointed out that activation of phosphorylase of itself is an incomplete explanation of the effects attributed to glucagon or epinephrine in the intact animal. The phosphorylase reaction is freely reversible, and acceleration in both directions would be anticipated to follow activation of its catalyst. The fact that glucagon has never been observed to favor glycogenesis in the intact animal and the fact that epinephrine reverses the accumulation of glycogen in isolated diaphragm (105, 159) indicate the operation of an as yet unexplained directional influence.

REFERENCES

1. Abel, J. J. *Proc. Natl. Acad. Sci. U. S.* **12**, 132 (1926).
2. Anderson, E., and Long, J. A. *Endocrinology* **40**, 92 (1947).
3. Arndt, U. W., and Riley, D. P. *Nature* **172**, 245 (1953).
4. Bailey, C. C. *Vitamins and Hormones* **7**, 365 (1949).
5. Baker, N., Chaikoff, I. L., and Schusdek, A. *J. Biol. Chem.* **194**, 435 (1952).
6. Bell, D. M., and Burns, T. W. *J. Clin. Invest.* **31**, 717 (1952).
7. Bennett, L. L., and Evans, H. M. *In* G. Pincus and K. V. Thimann, The Hormones. Academic Press, New York, 1950, Vol. 2, p. 405.
8. Bloch, K., and Kramer, W. *J. Biol. Chem.* **173**, 811 (1948).
9. Bornstein, J. *J. Biol. Chem.* **205**, 513 (1953).
10. Bornstein, J., and Park, C. R. *J. Biol. Chem.* **205**, 503 (1953).
11. Bornstein, J., Reid, E., and Young, F. G. *Nature* **168**, 903 (1951).
12. Bouckaert, J. P., and deDuve, C. *Physiol. Revs.* **27**, 39 (1947).
13. Brady, R. O., and Gurin, S. *J. Biol. Chem.* **186**, 461 (1950).
14. Brady, R. O., and Gurin, S. *J. Biol. Chem.* **187**, 589 (1950).
15. Brand, E. *Ann. N. Y. Acad. Sci.* **47**, 187 (1946).
16. Broh-Kahn, R. H., and Mirsky, I. A. *Science* **106**, 148 (1947).
17. Brückmann, G., and Wertheimer, E. *J. Biol. Chem.* **168**, 241 (1947).
18. Bürger, M., and Brandt, W. *Z. ges. Exptl. Med.* **96**, 375 (1935).
19. Bürger, M., and Kramer, H. *Z. ges. Exptl. Med.* **67**, 441 (1929).
20. Chaikoff, I. L. *Harvey Lectures* **47**, 99 (1951–1952).
21. Charalampous, F. C., and Hegsted, M. D. *J. Biol. Chem.* **180**, 623 (1949).
22. Chernick, S. S., Chaikoff, I. L., Masoro, E. J., and Isaeff, E. *J. Biol. Chem.* **186**, 527 (1950).
23. Christensen, W. R., Plimpton, C. H., and Ball, E. G. *J. Biol. Chem.* **180**, 791 (1949).
24. Collens, W. S., and Murlin, J. R. *Proc. Soc. Exptl. Biol. Med.* **26**, 485 (1929).
25. Colowick, S. P., Cori, G. T., and Slein, M. W. *J. Biol. Chem.* **168**, 583 (1947).
26. Cori, C. F. *Harvey Lectures* **41**, 253 (1945–1946).

27. Crowfoot, D. *Proc. Roy. Soc. (London)* **A164,** 580 (1938).
28. Doty, P., Gellert, M., and Rabinovitch, B. *J. Am. Chem. Soc.* **74,** 2065 (1952).
29. Drury, D. R. *Am. J. Physiol.* **131,** 536 (1940).
30. Duncan, G. G. *In* G. G. Duncan, Diseases of Metabolism, 3rd ed. Saunders, Philadelphia, 1952.
31. Dunn, J. S., Sheehan, H. L., and McLetchie, N. G. B. *Lancet* **i,** 484 (1943).
32. Ellis, S., Anderson, H. L., Jr., and Collins, M. C. *Proc. Soc. Exptl. Biol. Med.* **84,** 383 (1953).
33. Eser, S. *Bull. faculte méd. Istanbul* **14,** 242 (1951).
34. Feller, D. D., Chaikoff, I. L., Strisower, E. H., and Searle, G. L. *J. Biol. Chem.* **188,** 865 (1951).
35. Foǎ, P. P. *Chicago Med. School Quart.* **14,** 145 (1953).
36. Foǎ, P. P., Berger, S., Santamaria, L., Smith, J. A., and Weinstein, H. R. *Science* **117,** 82 (1953).
37. Foǎ, P. P., Magid, E. B., Glassman, M. D., and Weinstein, H. R. *Proc. Soc. Exptl. Biol. Med.* **83,** 758 (1953).
38. Foǎ, P. P., Santamaria, L., Weinstein, H. R., Berger, S., and Smith, J. A. *Am. J. Physiol.* **171,** 32 (1952).
39. Foǎ, P. P., and Weinstein, H. R. *Am. J. Physiol.* **163,** 711 (1950).
40. Foǎ, P. P., Weinstein, H. R., and Smith, J. A. *Am. J. Physiol.* **157,** 197 (1949).
41. Foǎ, P. P., Weinstein, H. R., Smith, J. A., and Greenberg, M. *Arch. Biochem. and Biophys.* **40,** 323 (1952).
42. Fredericq, E., and Neurath, H. *J. Am. Chem. Soc.* **72,** 2684 (1950).
43. Freudenberg, K., Dirscherl, W., and Eyer, H. *Z. physiol. Chem.* **187,** 89 (1930).
44. Froelich, A. L., Tverdy, G., and Vanderberghe, G. *Acta Gastro-Enterol. Belg.* **14,** 179 (1951).
45. Frohman, C. E., Orten, J. M., and Smith, A. H. *J. Biol. Chem.* **193,** 803 (1951).
46. Fromageot, C. *Cold Spring Harbor Symposia Quant. Biol.* **14,** 49 (1950).
47. Gaede, K., Ferner, H., and Kastrup, H. *Klin. Wochschr.* **28,** 388 (1950).
48. Geiling, E. M. K., and deLawder, A. M. *J. Pharmacol.* **39,** 369 (1930).
49. Gemmill, C. L. *Bull. Johns Hopkins Hosp.* **66,** 232 (1940).
50. Goldstein, M. S., Henry, W. L., Huddlestun, B., and Levine, R. *Am. J. Physiol.* **173,** 207 (1953).
51. Goldstein, M. S., Mullick, V., Huddlestun, B., and Levine, R. *Am. J. Physiol.* **173,** 212 (1953).
52. Goranson, E. S., and Erulkar, S. D. *Arch. Biochem.* **24,** 40 (1949).
53. Griffiths, M. *J. Biol. Chem.* **184,** 289 (1950).
54. Gutfreund, H. *Biochem. J.* **42,** 156 (1948).
55. Gutfreund, H. *Biochem. J.* **42,** 544 (1948).
56. Gutfreund, H. *Biochem. J.* **50,** 564 (1952).
57. Haft, D., Mirsky, I. A., and Perisutti, G. *Proc. Soc. Exptl. Biol. Med.* **82,** 60 (1953).
58. Harfenist, E. J., and Craig, L. C. *J. Am. Chem. Soc.* **74,** 3083 (1952).
59. Harfenist, E. J., and Craig, L. C. *J. Am. Chem. Soc.* **74,** 3087 (1952).
60. Harfenist, E. J., and Craig, L. C. *J. Am. Chem. Soc.* **74,** 4216 (1952).
61. Harris, J. I. *J. Am. Chem. Soc.* **74,** 2944 (1952).
62. Haugaard, N., and Marsh, J. B. *J. Biol. Chem.* **194,** 33 (1952).
63. Haugaard, N., and Marsh, J. B. The Action of Insulin. Charles C Thomas, Springfield, Ill., 1953.
64. Hidy, P. H. *J. Biol. Chem.* **163,** 307 (1946).

65. Hills, A. G., and Stadie, W. C.   *J. Biol. Chem.* **194**, 25 (1952).
66. Horecker, B. L.   *In* W. D. McElroy and B. Glass, Phosphorus Metabolism. Johns Hopkins Press, Baltimore, 1951, Vol. 1, p. 117.
67. Horecker, B. L.   *Brewers Dig.* **28**, 214 (1953).
68. Hotta, S., and Chaikoff, I. L.   *J. Biol. Chem.* **198**, 895 (1952).
69. Jensen, H. F.   "Insulin."   The Commonwealth Fund, New York, 1938.
70. Jensen, H.   *In* G. Pincus and K. V. Thimann, The Hormones.   Academic Press, New York, 1948, Vol. 1, p. 301.
71. Kadota, I., and Midorikawa, O.   *J. Lab. Clin. Med.* **38**, 671 (1951).
72. Kaplan, N. O., and Greenberg, D. M.   *J. Biol. Chem.* **156**, 553 (1944).
73. Kimball, C. P., and Murlin, J. R.   *J. Biol. Chem.* **58**, 337 (1923).
74. Krahl, M. E.   *Ann. N. Y. Acad. Sci.* **54**, 649 (1951).
75. Krahl, M. E.   *J. Biol. Chem.* **200**, 99 (1953).
76. Krebs, H. A., and Eggleston, L. V.   *Biochem. J.* **32**, 913 (1938).
77. Lazarus, S. S., Goldner, M. G., and Volk, B. W.   *Metabolism Clin. and Exptl.* **2**, 513 (1953).
78. Lee, N. D., and Williams, R. H.   *Endocrinology* **54**, 5 (1954).
79. Lens, J., and Evertzen, A.   *Biochim. et Biophys. Acta* **8**, 332 (1952).
80. Levine, R., and Goldstein, M. S.   *Brookhaven Symposia in Biol.* **5**, 73 (1952).
81. Levine, R., Goldstein, M. S., Huddlestun, B., and Klein, S. P.   *Am. J. Physiol.* **163**, 70 (1950).
82. Low, B. W.   *Nature* **172**, 1146 (1953).
83. Lukens, F. D. W.   *Physiol. Revs.* **28**, 304 (1948).
84. Macpherson, H. T.   *Biochem. J.* **40**, 470 (1946).
85. Masoro, E. J., Chaikoff, I. L., Chernick, S. S., and Felts, J. M.   *J. Biol. Chem.* **185**, 845 (1950).
86. McQuarrie, I., Bell, E. T., Zimmermann, B., and Wright, W. S.   *Federation Proc.* **9**, 337 (1950).
87. Mirsky, I. A., Futterman, P., Wachman, J., and Perisutti, G.   *Endocrinology* **49**, 73 (1951).
88. Moody, L. S.   Thesis, University of Wisconsin, 1944, cited by Williams, J. W. *Ann. Rev. Phys. Chem.* **2**, 412 (1951).
89. Murlin, J. R., Clough, H. D., Gibbs, C. B. F., and Stokes, A. M.   *J. Biol. Chem.* **56**, 253 (1923).
90. Najjar, V. A. (ed.)   Carbohydrate Metabolism.   Johns Hopkins Press, Baltimore, 1952.
91. Nelson, J. F.   *Australian J. Exptl. Biol. Med. Sci.* **22**, 131 (1944).
92. Olsen, N. S., and Klein, J. R.   *Proc. Soc. Exptl. Biol. Med.* **66**, 86 (1947).
93. Oncley, J. L., Ellenbogen, E., Gitlin, D., and Gurd, F. R. N.   *J. Phys. Chem.* **56**, 85 (1952).
94. Park, C. R.   *In* V. A. Najjar, Carbohydrate Metabolism.   Johns Hopkins Press, Baltimore, 1952, p. 43.
95. Park, C. R.   *J. Clin. Invest.* **32**, 593 (1953).
96. Patterson, J. W.   *J. Biol. Chem.* **183**, 81 (1950).
97. Patterson, J. W.   *Science* **111**, 724 (1950).
98. Patterson, J. W.   *Proc. Soc. Exptl. Biol. Med.* **83**, 850 (1953).
99. Pincus, I. J.   *J. Clin. Endocrinol.* **10**, 556 (1950).
100. Pincus, I. J.   *Trans. N. Y. Acad. Sci.* **14**, 319 (1952).
101. Price, W. H., Cori, C. F., and Colowick, S. P.   *J. Biol. Chem.* **160**, 633 (1945).
102. Rees, M. W.   *Biochem. J.* **40**, 632 (1946).

103. Reid, E., Smith, R. H., and Young, F. G. *Biochem. J.* **42,** xix (1948).
104. Renold, A. E., Teng, C. T., Nesbett, F. B., and Hastings, A. B. *J. Biol. Chem.* **204,** 533 (1953).
105. Riesser, O. *Biochim. et Biophys. Acta* **1,** 208 (1947).
106. Robinson, C. *Nature* **172,** 27 (1953).
107. Ross, E. J. *J. Physiol.* **116,** 414 (1952).
108. Ross, E. J. *Nature* **171,** 125 (1953).
109. Sacks, J. *Cold Spring Harbor Symposia Quant. Biol.* **13,** 180 (1948).
110. Sacks, J. *Am. J. Physiol.* **172,** 93 (1953).
111. Sanger, F. *Biochem. J.* **39,** 507 (1945).
112. Sanger, F. *Biochem. J.* **44,** 126 (1949).
113. Sanger, F. *Biochem. J.* **45,** 563 (1949).
114. Sanger, F. *Cold Spring Harbor Symposia Quant. Biol.* **14,** 153 (1949).
115. Sanger, F. *Nature* **164,** 529 (1949).
116. Sanger, F., and Thompson, E. O. P. *Biochem. J.* **53,** 353 (1953).
117. Sanger, F., and Thompson, E. O. P. *Biochem. J.* **53,** 366 (1953).
118. Sanger, F., Thompson, E. O. P., and Tuppy, H. *2nd Intern. Congr. Biochem.,* Paris, p. 26 (1952).
119. Sanger, F., and Tuppy, H. *Biochem. J.* **49,** 463 (1951).
120. Sanger, F., and Tuppy, H. *Biochem. J.* **49,** 481 (1951).
121. Shaw, W., and Gurin, S. *Arch. Biochem. and Biophys.* **47,** 220 (1953).
122. Shipley, R. A., and Humel, E. J., Jr. *Am. J. Physiol.* **144,** 51 (1945).
123. Shorr, E., and Barker, S. B. *Biochem. J.* **33,** 1798 (1939).
124. Siliprandi, D., and Siliprandi, N. *Nature* **169,** 329 (1952).
125. Sinex, F. M., MacMullen, J., and Hastings, A. B. *J. Biol. Chem.* **198,** 615 (1952).
126. Smith, R. H. *Biochem. J.* **44,** xlii (1949).
127. Soskin, S., and Levine, R. *Carbohydrate Metabolism,* 2nd ed. Univ. Chicago Press, Chicago, 1952.
128. Stadie, W. C. *Physiol. Revs.* **34,** 52 (1954).
129. Stadie, W. C., and Haugaard, N. *J. Biol. Chem.* **177,** 311 (1949).
130. Stadie, W. C., Haugaard, N., and Hills, A. G. *J. Biol. Chem.* **184,** 617 (1950).
131. Stadie, W. C., Haugaard, N., and Marsh, J. B. *J. Biol. Chem.* **189,** 53 (1951).
132. Stadie, W. C., Haugaard, N., and Marsh, J. B. *J. Biol. Chem.* **198,** 785 (1952).
133. Stadie, W. C., Haugaard, N., and Vaughan, M. *J. Biol. Chem.* **200,** 745 (1953).
134. Stare, F. J., and Baumann, C. A. *J. Biol. Chem.* **133,** 453 (1940).
135. Staub, A., Sinn, L., and Behrens, O. K. *Science* **117,** 628 (1953).
136. Staub, A., Sinn, L., and Behrens, O. K. Personal communication.
137. Stetten, D., Jr., and Boxer, G. E. *J. Biol. Chem.* **156,** 271 (1944).
138. Stetten, D., Jr., and Klein, B. V. *J. Biol. Chem.* **162,** 377 (1946).
139. Stetten, D., Jr., Welt, I. D., Ingle, D. J., and Morley, E. H. *J. Biol. Chem.* **192,** 817 (1951).
140. Sutherland, E. W. *In* W. D. McElroy and B. Glass, Phosphorus Metabolism. Johns Hopkins Press, Baltimore, 1951, Vol. 1, p. 53.
141. Sutherland, E. W. *In* W. D. McElroy and B. Glass, Phosphorus Metabolism. Johns Hopkins Press, Baltimore, 1952, Vol. 2, p. 577.
142. Sutherland, E. W., and Cori, C. F. *J. Biol. Chem.* **172,** 737 (1948).
143. Sutherland, E. W., and Cori, C. F. *J. Biol. Chem.* **188,** 531 (1951).
144. Sutherland, E. W., and deDuve, C. *J. Biol. Chem.* **175,** 663 (1948).
145. Teng, C., Sinex, F. M., Deane, H. W., and Hastings, A. B. *J. Cellular Comp. Physiol.* **39,** 73 (1952).

146. Thorogood, E., and Zimmermann, B. *Endocrinology* **37,** 191 (1945).
147. Tietze, F., and Neurath, H. *J. Biol. Chem.* **194,** 1 (1952).
148. Tietze, F., and Neurath, H. *J. Am. Chem. Soc.* **75,** 1758 (1953).
149. Toennies, G., and Homiller, R. P. *J. Am. Chem. Soc.* **64,** 3054 (1942).
150. Tristram, G. R. *Biochem. J.* **40,** 721 (1946).
151. Tuerkischer, E., and Wertheimer, E. *Biochem. J.* **42,** 603 (1948).
152. Udenfriend, S., and Velick, S. F. *J. Biol. Chem.* **190,** 733 (1951).
153. Van Campenhout, E., and Cornelis, G. *Bull. acad. roy. méd. Belg.* **16,** 382 (1951).
154. Velick, S. F., and Ronzoni, E. *J. Biol. Chem.* **173,** 627 (1948).
155. Villee, C. A., and Hastings, A. B. *J. Biol. Chem.* **179,** 673 (1949).
156. Volk, B. W., Lazarus, S. S., and Goldner, M. G. *Proc. Soc. Exptl. Biol. Med.*
     82, 406 (1953).
157. Vuylsteke, C. A., Cornelis, G., and deDuve, C. *Arch. intern. physiol.* **60,** 128
     (1952).
158. Vuylsteke, C. A., and deDuve, C. *Arch. intern. physiol.* **61,** 275 (1953).
159. Walaas, O., and Walaas, E. *J. Biol. Chem.* **187,** 769 (1950).
160. Weil-Malherbe, H. *Nature* **165,** 155 (1950).
161. Weisberg, H. F., Caren, R., Huddlestun, B., and Levine, R. *Am. J. Physiol.*
     159, 98 (1949).
162. Wick, A. N., and Drury, D. R. *Am. J. Physiol.* **173,** 229 (1953).
163. Wick, A. N., Drury, D. R., Bancroft, R. W., and MacKay, E. M. *J. Biol. Chem.*
     188, 241 (1951).
164. Wyshak, G. H., and Chaikoff, I. L. *J. Biol. Chem.* **200,** 851 (1952).

CHAPTER VI

Chemistry of the Anterior Pituitary Hormones

By EDWIN E. HAYS and SANFORD L. STEELMAN

CONTENTS

I. Introduction

It has been interesting to note the ebb and flow of the tide of research activity concerning the chemistry of the anterior pituitary hormones over the past 30 years. Periods of intense activity are followed by relative quiescence usually timed with the development and application of a new chemical laboratory technique or an improvement in biological assay.

The technique of experimental hypophysectomy, the development of protein fractionation procedures, the radiotracer methods, the observation that tissue constituents such as iodine, ascorbic acid, and cholesterol can be altered by humoral mechanisms have all served to stimulate progress in the understanding of the chemistry of these complex substances.

II. Growth Hormone (GH, STH, PGH)

In recent years growth hormone has been studied extensively from both chemical and physiological standpoints. Li et al. (60) isolated a preparation which was homogeneous by the present-day criteria for protein purity. Wilhelmi et al. (115), with their simplified method of preparation of the crystalline hormone in good yield, have made possible its extensive use for physiological studies. Until the work of Raben and Westermeyer (83), who devised a method for the preparation of pork growth hormone concentrates, the hormone from beef glands was used almost entirely for both chemical and physiological studies.

A. Standardization

In addition to the classical tibia and body weight methods (37, 60, 71) two other methods may be potentially employed for assays. Since there is good evidence that growth hormone is diabetogenic, the urinary glucose excretion of cats as described by Reid (84) may be useful. Mayer and Silides (72) found that hereditary obese mice showed an elevation of blood glucose levels when growth hormone was administered, whereas ACTH and TSH had essentially no effect.

The Expert Committee on Biological Standardization of the World Health Organization has authorized the establishment of an International Standard for growth hormone. This will consist of highly purified hormone from beef pituitaries. Much confusion should be eliminated by the use of such a standard, since workers will have, for the first time, a common basis for comparison of the activities of various preparations. The authors have found that highly purified growth hormone samples from a large number of laboratories have as much as fivefold differences in activities. As a rule, beef growth hormone samples prepared by the general methods of Li et al. (60) and Wilhelmi et al. (115) do not vary widely in their activities, as determined by the tibia or the body weight methods. However, it is difficult to prepare highly active, reasonably pure growth hormone by methods which include an exposure to acids such as glacial acetic.

B. Isolation

1. Method of Wilhelmi, Fishman, and Russell (115)

Fresh-frozen, ground beef anterior pituitary glands are stirred with $Ca(OH)_2$ solution at pH 11.5 for 24 hours. Carbon dioxide is then bubbled

into the mixture until a pH of 8.5 to 8.7 is reached. The supernatant solution is brought to an ethanol concentration of 12 % and the precipitate is designated Fraction A.

The supernatant liquid from Fraction A is adjusted to 24 % ethanol. The resulting precipitate, Fraction B, is set aside for reworking. The 24 % ethanol supernatant solution is brought to pH 6.8 with HCl and the insoluble Fraction C removed.

Fractions A, B, and C are reworked individually as follows: A 0.5 % solution in $0.1N$ KCl is made at pH 11.0. The pH is then readjusted to 5.0, and the resulting precipitate is suspended in one-half the original volume of $0.1N$ KCl and saved. The supernatant solution is brought to pH 8.5 to 8.7 and ethanol added slowly to a 5 % concentration. The resulting precipitate exhibits some crystals upon microscopic examination. The 5 % ethanol supernatant solution is slowly brought to 20 % ethanol with vigorous stirring. The resulting precipitate is crystalline growth hormone. The pH 5.0 precipitate together with the 5 % ethanol precipitate are put through the above procedure. The yield of purified growth hormone from Fractions A, B, and C is equivalent to 2.5 to 3.0 g. per kilogram of fresh tissue. All fractionation is carried out between 0° and 5°C.

2. Method of Campbell et al. (12)

Anterior pituitary glands are extracted in dilute salt solution at an alkaline pH and the extract dialyzed to precipitate the growth hormone. The hormone is soluble in 4 % and is precipitated by 15 % K_2HPO_4. Further purification is accomplished by the rework method of Wilhelmi et al. (115). The final product has a low TSH contamination.

3. Method of Raben and Westermeyer (83)

Crude hog corticotropin prepared by the method of Payne et al. (79) is dissolved in $0.1N$ acetic acid and stirred with a large excess of powdered oxidized cellulose (10.4 % carboxyl content) at room temperature. The supernatant solution is then brought to pH 8.5 and centrifuged. The precipitate is discarded and ethanol added to effect a 47.5 % to 60 % concentration. The yield amounts to 10 % to 13 % of the starting material, and the final fraction has good growth hormone activity.

C. PHYSICOCHEMICAL PROPERTIES

Li (63) has conducted studies on the stability of beef growth hormone in aqueous and acetic acid solutions. Maximal stability was observed at slightly alkaline solutions. Treatment with $0.1N$ acetic acid as well as glacial acetic acid was shown to reduce the activity. This loss of activity apparently was associated with the electrophoretic appearance of a fast-moving component which had an isoelectric point of approximately pH

TABLE I

CHEMICAL AND PHYSICAL PROPERTIES OF BEEF GROWTH HORMONE

	Smith et al. (92)	Li et al. (60, 62, 65)
Crystalline structure		
S_{20}	$3.6 \pm 0.1 \times 10^{-13}$	3.1×10^{-13}
D_{20}	7.36×10^{-7}	
Molecular weight		
Ultracentrifuge	49,200	44,000
Osmotic pressure		44,250
Amino acid comp.		47,300
Partial specific volume		0.76
Relative viscosity		7.64
Dissymmetric constant f/f_0		1.31
Nitrogen		15.65%
Sulfur		1.3%
Isoelectric point, pH		6.85

7.3. As a consequence of these studies, it was recommended that the hormone be isolated at low temperature and by techniques which could be performed as rapidly as possible.

The work of Raben and Westermeyer (83) using their hog growth hormone preparation suggests that it is stable for several weeks in 0.1N acetic acid at refrigerator temperatures. No doubt more definitive assays on both beef and hog preparations in acid solutions will establish whether the difference in stability is a real one or whether there is a species difference.

Li and Pederson (65) have investigated the sedimentation behavior of growth hormone in the ultracentrifuge. At pH's of 9.93 and 2.32 it has the same molecular weight, whereas at pH 4.0 it does not behave as a single substance but has a tendency to aggregate into a variety of particles of different molecular weights. Table I records some of the physical properties. Table II gives the amino acid composition of growth hormone as reported by Li and Evans (59).

In an attempt to separate growth hormone from its diabetogenic properties Reid (85) employed a variety of chemical modifications which throw some light on the relationship between chemical structure and physiological activity. Selective acetylation in which the ϵ-amino groups of lysine remained largely free and the α-amino groups became acetylated resulted in little or no loss in activity. Treatment with an enzyme from B. subtilis did not affect the activity nor did iodination at pH 7.6. Confirming the observations of Condliffe and Li (18), Reid found that carboxypeptidase did not destroy the biological potency even though alanine, phenylalanine, serine, leucine, and lysine were liberated.

Condliffe and Li (18) have reported that chymotrypsin can partially

TABLE II
Amino Acid Composition of Beef Growth Hormone

	Grams per 100 g. protein	Assumed number of residues
Amide	1.2	30
Arginine	9.1	25
Aspartic acid	9.0	32
Cystine	2.25	4
Glutamic acid	13.0	42
Glycine	3.8	24
Histidine	2.65	8
Isoleucine	4.0	14
Leucine	12.1	44
Lysine	7.1	23
Methionine	2.9	9
Phenylalanine	9.0	23
Threonine	0.84	36
Tryptophan	0.84	2
Tyrosine	4.30	11
Valine	3.9	16
Total		343

degrade purified growth hormone without appreciable loss of activity. After a 16 % digestion, as indicated by the increase in 5 % trichloracetic-acid–soluble nitrogen, there was no change in activity, but further hydrolysis to 25 % resulted in a 50 % loss. Further digestion to 39 % inactivated the hormone completely. Electrophoretic examination of the digested samples confirmed the presence of a new major component, indicating a protein having an electrical charge different from that of the starting material. Confirmatory observations have not yet appeared. There apparently are no low molecular weight fragments which are physiologically active.

D. Immunochemistry

A basic problem in the use of heterologous pituitary hormones in animals is the question of the possible formation of antihormones or neutralizing antibodies. Several pituitary hormones have been shown to be nonspecies specific, *i.e.*, they neutralize not only the hormone from one species but that from several species, and, since clinical studies with the preparations of growth hormone available to date have not been particularly encouraging, this subject becomes of considerable importance.

Elberg and Li (27) have injected growth hormone into rabbits in an effort to produce antisera as studied by the precipitin test. They also attempted to sensitize guinea pigs and challenged them with growth hormone in an effort to demonstrate antigenicity. Both attempts have been unsuccessful. These authors conclude that growth hormone is nonantigenic or very weakly so.

Morrison *et al.* (76, 77) produced precipitating antibodies to beef growth hormone and concluded that in the rabbit it was either antigenic or had a carrier protein that produced this effect.

Shorr *et al.* (90) have demonstrated that growth hormone has a metabolic effect in man. Patients given several series of prolonged intramuscular injections show no visible evidence that neutralizing antibodies are formed, since a metabolic response is obtained after each course of treatment.

There are no data in the literature to show conclusively that growth hormone is antigenic. Antihormone assays in which serum is administered to animals in an effort to demonstrate a blocking of the physiological response should be carefully studied in an effort to secure such proof.

III. Thyrotropic Hormone (TSH)

The thyrotropic hormone has been extensively investigated but, to the best of our knowledge, has never been isolated in pure form. Ciereszko (17) reported the preparation of a highly active TSH which showed some degree of homogeneity, but as yet no confirming data have appeared.

A. STANDARD PREPARATION

The U. S. Pharmacopoeia in 1952 established a Thyrotropin Reference Substance and a USP unit. This unit is defined as that amount of activity contained in 20 mg. of the Reference Substance. It was prepared by mixing lactose with a purified beef TSH preparation of known activity and content of physiologically active contaminants.

Identical International and USP Standards have been prepared by the Expert Committee on Biological Standardization of the World Health Organization and the U. S. Pharmacopoeia. Biological assays are presently being conducted in several collaborating laboratories prior to official acceptance. The USP unit will remain the same and it is anticipated that the International Unit and the USP unit will be readily convertible one to another. For reference purposes, it has been determined that 10 to 12 Junkmann-Schoeller units are equivalent to 1 USP unit.

B. ASSAY METHODS

1. *General*

Many methods based on gland weight increases in the thyroid have been published. The present trend is toward the measurement of the increased uptake or depletion of iodine or other chemical constituent of the thyroid gland as a result of the administration of TSH. The radioactive iodine or phosphorus methods may prove to be simple and accurate means of determining thyrotropic activity.

2. Iodine Assay Methods

a. Radioactive Iodine Uptake. Ghosh *et al.* (35) have studied the uptake of radioactive iodine by the thyroid of the hypophysectomized rat and shown that it is reduced. Thyrotropin restores the iodine-trapping capacity. These authors devised a method of assay which involves administering TSH and I^{131} to hypophysectomized rats and measuring the total radioactive iodine uptake. The thyrotropin is given to hypophysectomized rats in eight divided doses at 8-hour intervals. The injections begin three days after hypophysectomy. When the seventh dose of TSH is administered 20 microcuries of I^{131} is also given. Twenty-four hours later the animals are sacrificed and uptake measured. The workable dose range is 0.1 to 0.5 mg. of TSH. A lambda value of 0.149 was obtained for a three-level assay.

Querido *et al.* (82) investigated the effect of TSH on the radioactive iodine uptake of the thyroids of mice. A method was devised to detect small quantities of TSH with the use of an iodocasein diet to depress endogenous TSH production. Four injections of TSH are given at 12-hour intervals. The radioactive iodine is administered at the same time as the last TSH dose. Twenty-four hours later the animals are sacrificed, and the thyroids removed and digested with KOH, and the I^{131} concentration determined. The dose response curve is best at doses of TSH between 0.01 and 0.25 USP unit.

b. Iodine Depletion. Piotrowski, Steelman, and Koch (80) have published an assay method based on the depletion of iodine from the thyroids of one-day-old white leghorn cockerels. Using the USP Thyrotropin Reference Substance it was found that doses of 0.0125, 0.025, and 0.050 unit per animal gave a satisfactory dose response curve. The Armour Standard (2R3), on which much recent clinical data are based, was shown to have an activity of approximately 0.4 USP unit per milligram. Table III lists some comparative assay values for various species of pituitary glands.

The depletion of radioactive iodine from the chick thyroid has been

TABLE III
TSH CONTENT OF PITUITARY TISSUES

Fresh beef anterior pituitary	3 USP units/g.
Beef anterior pituitary, acetone powder	20 USP units/g.
Sheep pituitary, acetone powder	7 USP units/g.
Fresh swine pituitary (whole)	4 USP units/g.

proposed by Gilliland and Fraser (36) as a method of assay. One-day-old chicks are given 10 microcuries of I^{131} together with l-thyroxine to assure maximum thyroid iodine retention. When the I^{131} in the thyroid is at a maximum, TSH is administered and 24 hours later the radioactivity in the thyroid region of the neck is determined. A bird holder with a built-in radioactivity counter makes it possible to obtain direct measurements without sacrificing the animal. The minimal amount of TSH detectable is approximately 0.0025 USP unit.

3. Radioactive Phosphorus Assay Methods

Borell and Holmgren (6) have recommended the determination of the increase of radioactive phosphorus in the TSH-stimulated guinea pig thyroid as a means of bio-assay. The amount of radioactive phosphorus in the thyroid increases progressively with increasing doses of TSH.

Crooke and Matthews (21) employ the radioactive phosphorus (P^{32}) uptake in the thyroid gland of the two-day-old chick as a means of assay for TSH. The chicks are given TSH intraperitoneally, followed in 4 hours by 10 microcuries of P^{32}. Two hours later the animals are sacrificed, the thyroids dissected out and weighed, and the radioactivity ascertained. The number of counts of P^{32} per milligram of thyroid tissue is proportional to the log dose of TSH between the range of 2 μg. and 12 μg. This corresponds to a sensitivity of approximately 0.002 USP unit. The method has been used to detect TSH in the urine of a patient with exophthalmic ophthalmoplegia.

4. Histological Assay Methods

Tala (101) has published an excellent article on the assay of TSH in which he proposes the use of the percentage of epithelium, determined histologically, as the index of functional activity of the thyroid gland. The change in the percentage of epithelium ($\Delta E\%$) is a function of TSH dosage in the guinea pig.

D'Angelo and Gordon (22) have employed the stasis tadpole as a means of assaying small quantities of TSH in blood. By using a combination of thyroid cell heights and hind limb length, thyrotropic and thyroid hormones can be simultaneously assayed. As little as approximately 0.00005 USP unit of TSH and 0.025 μg. of d l-thyroxine can be detected. This method or its modification is now being used to measure TSH blood levels in various endocrine disturbances.

C. ISOLATION

Using fractional electrical transport methods as described by Spies et al. (94) and Williams and Waterman (116), Steelman, Giffee, and Hawrylewicz (98) have prepared small quantities of highly purified TSH. The apparent

TABLE IV

FRACTIONAL ELECTRICAL TRANSPORT EXPERIMENT ON BOVINE THYROTROPIN

Tube no.	Final pH	Potency USP units/mg.[a]
1	11.6	—
2	11.5	—
3	11.2	0.12
4	9.8	2.20
5	8.8	4.10
6	6.3	2.00
7	5.1	0.20
8	4.6	0.20
9	3.8	0.20
10	2.9	—
11	2.4	—
Starting matl. (BT-299-38A)		0.70

[a] Based on lyophilized contents of tube.
Conditions: 7000 v.
10 milliamperes
25 hours.

isoelectric point of TSH using this salt-free system of 11 tubes in series is approximately pH 8.0 at 2° to 3°C.   Table IV illustrates the results of a typical preparation by this method.   Submitting the contents of the tubes containing the most activity (Tubes 4, 5, and 6) to electrophoresis again yields preparations having potencies of approximately 10 USP units per milligram.

Heideman (40) has demonstrated that highly active TSH may be prepared by adsorption on the ion-exchange resin IRC-50.   Crude thyrotropin prepared by a combination of acetone and ammonium sulfate fractionation is used as the starting material.   Amberlite IRC-50 in a column is treated with successive portions of 0.25N NaOH, water, 0.5M sodium phosphate buffer (pH 8.0), and water.   The crude TSH solution (5 mg./ml.) is passed through the column and followed with water until the UV absorbing material is washed through.   The material is then eluted with M sodium chloride, collecting the eluate in small portions.   The inactive eluates are discarded.   To the cold active eluate, saturated picric acid is added dropwise until precipitation is complete.   The activity is not precipitated and the picric acid may be removed by dialysis, or Amberlite IR-4B and the solution lyophilized.   A total dose of 0.004 to 0.007 mg. of this preparation given to a day-old chick for three days produced a statistically significant increase in thyroid weight.

Fels et al. (29) prepared active TSH preparations by the following method: Anterior lobes of fresh beef pituitaries are ground with solid CO_2 and extracted twice with 0.25% acetic acid containing 1% NaCl.   The supernatant solutions are combined and adjusted to 3 molal with $(NH_4)_2$-SO_4 and the precipitate centrifuged. The solid material is taken up in 1 % NaCl and the solution made successively to 0.6 molal and 1.2 molal with $(NH_4)_2SO_4$ and the precipitates discarded. The supernatant solution is then made to 39 % acetone concentration by addition of cold ($-10°C$) acetone. The inert precipitate is discarded and the supernatant liquid is poured into 10 volumes of acetone. The precipitate is collected and washed with acetone three times and once with ether. The yield is 1.5 g. per kilogram of fresh pituitaries. The resultant product has a minimal effective dose of 25 μg. in the hypophysectomized rat and contains no growth hormone, ACTH, FSH, Prolactin, or LH when tested for these contaminants at the 1 mg. level.

D. Physicochemical Properties

The isoelectric point of thyrotropin has not been conclusively proved. The work of Steelman et al. (98) and that of Heideman (40) indicate that it may be more basic than some of the other anterior lobe hormones with the exception of Corticotropin B. TSH contamination encountered in the preparation of other pituitary hormones has been a serious problem especially in the cases of growth hormone and the gonadotropins. The fact that it apparently has a molecular weight of about 10,000 (103) and an alkaline isoelectric point might well account for its tendency to form complexes with the other hormones. Fels et al. (29) have pursued the original observations of Chow, Greep, and Van Dyke (15) with respect to the effects of papain on TSH. Using beef TSH and commercial papain they have demonstrated that not only is the activity not destroyed after treatment with papain but the molecule appears to be capable of passing through a dialysis membrane. The papain-digested TSH is not precipitated by 20 % trichloracetic acid, and, since it is dialyzable, may well have a molecular weight less than 10,000.

The highly active preparations of Steelman et al. (98) showed high concentrations of both acidic and basic amino acids, with small amounts of carbohydrates which were not identified. Preliminary investigations resulted in a failure to obtain N-terminal amino acids of TSH using the dinitrofluorobenzene method (96). It is possible that the N-terminal amino acid(s) are combined with the carbohydrate moiety and thus do not appear by the dinitrofluorobenzene method. The final answer to this and other interesting questions awaits the isolation of pure TSH.

IV. Exophthalmos-Producing Substance (EPS)

There has been speculation for some time that possibly clinical exophthalmos is not the result of TSH per se. Jefferies (44) showed that thyro-

VI. CHEMISTRY OF THE ANTERIOR PITUITARY HORMONES 211

tropin preparations treated with iodine largely lost their thyrotropic activity but some exophthalmos-producing activity remained. Using the *Fundulus*, the common Atlantic "minnow," as an assay animal, Dobyns and Steelman (25) tested a variety of pituitary preparations of known thyrotropin content and noticed that thyrotropic activity did not always parallel exophthalmic activity. One fraction was prepared having high TSH content and almost no exophthalmos-producing quality. This material is soluble in 8% trichloracetic acid. TSH may be largely separated from EPS by this means. Since the resultant products are either high in TSH and low in EPS or high in EPS and low in TSH, it has been postulated that TSH per se is not exophthalmic. The fact that the EPS fraction still retains some TSH activity makes it difficult to assign the activity to a separate and distinct hormone. It has not yet been ascertained whether TSH is necessary for the production of exophthalmos or whether a combination of known pituitary hormones is responsible for the physiological action tentatively assigned to EPS.

V. Prolactin (Luteotropin)

Since the summary published by White (104) in 1949, there has appeared in the literature very little concerning the chemistry of prolactin. Li (55) has published the amino acid composition of sheep prolactin. Table V summarizes the data. The molecular weight, calculated from the quantitative data on five different amino acids, is estimated by this author to be 33,300.

Koenig and King (46) have shown that highly active prolactin can be extracted at low temperatures from acetone-desiccated sheep pituitary powders with an acetate buffer having an ionic strength of 0.5 and containing 40% ethanol. Precipitation is accomplished by increasing the ethanol concentration to 80% and adding acetone to a concentration of 30%. The precipitate when dried contains approximately 20 I.U. of prolactin per milligram.

Coppedge and Segaloff (19) have demonstrated the presence of prolactin in human urine. At acid pH's it can be precipitated with approximately 80% ethanol. The material thus prepared is not dialyzable.

VI. Follicle-Stimulating Hormone (FSH)

A. STANDARDIZATION

In the quantitative assay of FSH the problem of interference of other hormones, especially LH (ICSH), is a constant complicating factor. The use of histological methods is often useful in circumventing this difficulty, but the methods are frequently tedious and require highly skilled personnel.

As a result of the work of Bates and Schooley (4) and others, Steelman

TABLE V

COMPOSITION OF SHEEP LACTOGENIC HORMONE

(Molecular Weight 33,300)

Constituent	G./100 g. protein	N as per cent of protein N	Estimated no. of residues
Nitrogen	15.86		
Sulfur	1.99		
Amide N	1.0	6.3	24
Arginine	8.6	17.4	17
Aspartic acid	11.6	7.6	28
Cystine	3.1	2.3	4
Glutamic acid	14.1	8.5	32
Glycine	4.0	4.7	18
Histidine	4.5	7.7	10
Isoleucine	7.2	4.8	18
Leucine	12.5	8.4	32
Lysine	5.3	6.4	12
Methionine	3.6	2.1	8
Phenylalanine	4.1	2.2	8
Proline	6.2	4.8	18
Serine	6.5	5.5	21
Threonine	4.8	3.5	13
Tyrosine	4.7	2.3	9
Tryptophan	1.2	1.0	2
Valine	5.9	4.4	17
Total		99.9	291

and Pohley (100) standardized the augmentation response of FSH with human chorionic gonadotropin (HCG) into a simple and accurate assay which is not affected by substantial quantities of five of the anterior pituitary hormones. Intact immature Sprague-Dawley female rats are injected subcutaneously three times a day for three days with a mixture of 20 I.U. of HCG and the appropriate quantity of FSH. On the fourth day the animals are sacrificed and the ovaries removed and weighed. Increasing amounts of FSH produce a linear dose response curve. With a standard preparation used as a reference substance, the slope-ratio method of Finney (30) can be used to calculated the relative activity. Two level assays give activities with a standard error of 15 % to 30 %.

Figure 1 shows a typical dose response curve employing 20 I.U. of HCG per animal and graded doses of the Armour FSH Standard (264-151-X). Table VI contains statistical data on two consecutive assays illustrating the duplicability of the method.

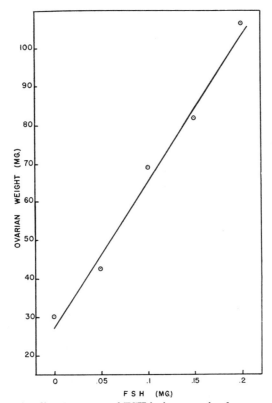

FIG. 1.   Regression line for assay of FSH in intact animals.

TABLE VI

RESPONSES OF INTACT IMMATURE FEMALE RATS TO 20 I.U. OF HCG AND GRADED
DOSES OF FSH

	Experiment 92	Experiment 93
Number of animals	40	40
b	382.08	368.97
s_b	42.50	36.83
$t = b/s_b$	8.99	10.02
Deviation from regression	151.29	287.37
Error mean square	379.32	550.78
F Ratio[a]	0.40	0.52

[a] An F Ratio of greater than 3.0 would indicate a nonlinear function.

B. Isolation

1. Sheep FSH

Li *et al.* (67) have succeeded in the isolation of sheep FSH in highly purified form by the following method:

Frozen sheep pituitaries are finely ground and extracted with $Ca(OH)_2$.
After the removal of the precipitate obtained by adding saturated $(NH_4)_2$-
SO_4 to half saturation, the supernatant solution is brought to 0.75 saturation by addition of solid $(NH_4)_2SO_4$. This precipitate is dissolved in water
and dialyzed. The slight precipitate formed during dialysis is discarded.
The clear reddish supernatant solution is adjusted to pH 6.0 and then to
pH 4.7. The precipitate formed at these two pH's is removed by centrifugation. The supernatant solution is brought to 0.5 saturation by the
slow addition of an equal volume of saturated $(NH_4)_2SO_4$ solution at pH
4.7. The precipitate formed is removed and the supernatant solution
again brought to 0.75 saturation by further addition of saturated $(NH_4)_2SO_4$
solution at the same pH. The precipitate is dissolved and dialyzed. The
procedure, beginning with the adjustment to pH 6.0, is repeated once more;
the final dialyzed solution is vacuum dried from the frozen state. The
resulting product is designated "crude FSH."

The "crude FSH" powder is next extracted with 0.10 M K_2HPO_4 in 40 %
ethanol. After the removal of the residue, the alcohol concentration in
the supernatant solution is increased to 80 % by slowly adding cold 95 %
ethanol at $-5°C$. The precipitate is dissolved in water and dialyzed.

The dialyzed solution is adjusted to pH 4.7 and clarified by centrifugation if precipitation occurs. A saturated $(NH_4)_2SO_4$ solution at pH 4.7 is
added until the concentration of 0.55 saturation is reached. This precipitate, which is devoid of FSH activity, is removed by centrifugation. The
supernatant solution is brought to 0.70 saturation with more saturated
$(NH_4)_2SO_4$ solution at pH 4.7; the precipitate formed is dissolved in water
and dialyzed. This fractionation between 0.55 and 0.70 saturation with
$(NH_4)_2SO_4$ is repeated twice.

Table VII summarizes the yields and biological activities of the various
fractions obtained.

2. Swine FSH

a. Method of Steelman et al. (99). The 70 % to 80 % acid-acetone–insoluble fraction obtained from frozen whole swine pituitaries by the method
of Lyons (69) is suspended in water at a pH of 8.5 to 9.0 and extracted at
$0°$ to $10°C$. The soluble fraction is adjusted to pH 4.5 and zinc acetate added
to 0.02 M. Crude FSH (Step I) is precipitated by bringing the ethanol
concentration of the supernatant solution to 50 % while maintaining a

TABLE VII
YIELD AND POTENCY OF FSH FRACTIONS OBTAINED IN THE PURIFICATION PROCEDURE
FROM SHEEP GLANDS

Fraction	Weight, g.	FSH[a], R.U./g.
Fresh sheep gland	1,000.0	67
"Crude FSH"	3.0	2,500
40% ethanol extract	1.2	6,700
Purified FSH	0.5	20,000

[a] One Rat Unit (R.U.) of FSH is the minimal amount which, given subcutaneously in three daily doses, followed by autopsy 72 hours after first injection, causes resorption of follicular growth in hypophysectomized female rats (26 to 28 days at operation, 6 to 8 days postoperative onset of injections

temperature of $-5°C$.   The Step I FSH is suspended in 40% ethanol at $-5°C$. containing $0.2M$ phosphate at a pH 7.4 to 7.5 and stirred for 4 hours. After centrifuging, the supernatant solution is adjusted to 75% ethanol at $-5°C$., whereupon the FSH precipitates (Step II).   Further purification of Step II FSH can be accomplished by extracting with 0.5 saturated ammonium sulfate solution at pH 7.4 to 7.5 and precipitating the FSH from the extract by increasing the solution to 0.8 saturation with $(NH_4)_2SO_4$ at a pH of 4.8 to 5.0.   Table VIII summarizes the biological data of the various fractions as well as yields obtained by this method.

b. Method of Van Dyke et al. (118).   The final crude ammonium sulfate precipitate described by Chow *et al.* (16) is dialyzed and lyophilized.   A 2.5% aqueous solution is brought to 0.33 saturation with saturated $(NH_4)_2$-SO_4 solution and the pH is adjusted to 7.35.   The supernatant solution is brought to pH 4.8 and $(NH_4)_2SO_4$ is added to 0.5 saturation and centrifuged

TABLE VIII
BIOLOGICAL ACTIVITIES AND YIELDS OF SWINE FSH FRACTIONS

	Step I	Step II	Step III
FSH[a]	20–40%	50–90%	100%
LH[b]	3–5%	3–4%	<2%
TSH (U.S.P. unit/mg.)	0.05–0.08	0.05–0.10	<0.05
ACTH (U.S.P. unit/mg.)	0.01	0.01	<0.01
Growth Hormone (%)	<3	<3	<3
Prolactin (I.U./mg.)	<0.5	<0.5	<0.5
Oxytocin (U.S.P. unit/mg.)	0.1–0.15	0.1–0.15	<0.02
Vasopressin (unit/mg.)	0.05–0.10	0.05–0.10	<0.02
Yield (g./kg.[c])	12–20	5–8	1.5–3.0

[a] Expressed as per cent of Armour FSH Standard (264-151-X).
[b] Expressed as per cent of Armour LH Standard (227-80) which is greater than 80% homogeneous as indicated by electrophoretic and ultracentrifugal analysis.
[c] Wet acid acetone residue (30%–40% solids).

to remove contaminants. Saturated $(NH_4)_2SO_4$ solution is then added to bring the concentration of the hormone solution to 0.6 saturation. The resulting precipitate is FSH. It is reprecipitated seven times with $(NH_4)_2$-SO_4. The final dialyzed, lyophilized product is 80% to 85% "pure" swine FSH.

Steelman and Pohley (100) have studied the comparative FSH activities of preparations made by the above three methods. Table IX summarizes the data. The swine preparation of Steelman et al. (99) and the sheep preparation of Li et al. (67) compare favorably in FSH activity.[1]

TABLE IX

COMPARATIVE ACTIVITIES OF SHEEP AND SWINE FSH PREPARATIONS

Sample	Species	Number of assay levels[a]	Potency (% of 264-151-X)[b]
Li	Sheep	2	134 ± 21
		2	137 ± 23
Li (11631)	Sheep	2	87 ± 14
		2	99 ± 15
Van Dyke (446-CC)	Swine	2	60 ± 12
		2	52 ± 12

[a] Eight animals per level.
[b] Prepared by method of Steelman et al. (99).

3. Equine Pituitary Gonadotropin[2]

A method for the preparation of equine pituitary gonadotropin has been described by Haley (38). Whole equine pituitaries are extracted at an alkaline pH (8.5) followed by an isoelectric precipitation of inert proteins at pH 5.5. The pH 5.5 soluble material is treated with chloroform and centrifuged. The aqueous phase is then gradually brought to a 71.5% acetone concentration by the step-wise addition of acetone. The precipitate resulting is collected by centrifugation. A yield of 12.5 g. per kilogram of fresh tissue is obtained. This material has an activity of approximately 1 Cartland-Nelson unit per milligram and is contaminated with posterior pituitary in the amount of 0.08 U.S.P. unit per milligram. It did not produce anaphylaxis in sensitized guinea pigs. No attempts were made to as-

[1] Steelman, Lamont, and Baltes [Endocrinology, in press (1955)] have recently reported that swine FSH can be made which is 8 to 10 times as active as that reported by Steelman et al. (99). Materials of this higher potency are still electrophoretically heterogeneous and, thus, the homogeneity of existing pituitary FSH preparations is questionable.

[2] We have chosen to place these two hormones under the FSH section of this review because they are both rich in FSH. It has not been demonstrated as yet that the FSH is separable from LH in these species.

certain whether it would form antihormones upon prolonged administration to animals or human beings.

4. Human Gonadotropin[2]

Donini and Marchetti (26) have from the urine of human menopausal women purified the gonadotropin which is assumed to be identical with pituitary gonadotropin.   The method of Katzman et al. (45) which employs permutit adsorption is used in making the concentrate.   The product obtained is a white, amorphous powder which is soluble in water and dilute solutions of alcohol and acetone but insoluble in ether.   It contains 0.77 % ash and 12 % nitrogen and gives a positive reaction in the Molisch, biuret, Millon and Elson and Morgan tests.   Carbohydrates found are galactose, mannose, hexosamine, and acetyl hexosamine.

TABLE X

PHYSICOCHEMICAL CHARACTERISTICS OF PITUITARY FOLLICLE-STIMULATING HORMONE (SHEEP)

N (%)	15.10
S (%)	1.50
Hexose (%)	1.23
Hexosamine (%)	1.51
Isoelectric point, pH	4.5
Sedimentation constant, S	4.70
Diffusion constant, D_A	6.0×10^{-7}
Specific volume, V_{20}	0.718
Molecular weight	67,000
Frictional ratio, f/f_0	1.33

In 26- to 28-day-old rats, the preparation produced an increase in uterine weight, an increase in ovarian weight accompanied by mature follicles and corpora lutea, opening of the vagina, and vaginal cornification.   Defining their rat unit as that amount of hormone which causes a 100 % increase in uterine weight under standard conditions, the authors estimate that each gram of purified material contains 8300 units.

Butt and Crooke (11) have studied by means of paper chromatography the urinary gonadotropins present during the various phases of the menstrual cycle.   There is some evidence that two gonadotropins ("A" and "B") appear, but it is possible that these could be the same active moiety attached to different proteins.   Gonadotropin "B" was found only during a brief part of the luteal phase of the cycles of some women.

C. PHYSICOCHEMICAL PROPERTIES

The physicochemical properties of the sheep preparation of Li et al. (67) have been investigated by Li and Pederson (66).   Table X summarizes the data. Amino acid analysis of the homogeneous preparation gave the following values in grams per 100 g. of protein: arginine, 5.3; aspartic acid, 9.3; cystine, 4.3; glutamic acid, 13.4; histidine, 3.7; isoleucine, 9.2; lysine, 11.1; methionine, 1.0; phenylalanine, 5.8; proline, 5.2; threonine, 4.7; tyrosine, 3.8; and valine, 5.8.

The stability of sheep FSH in aqueous solution was studied (66); it was shown to be unstable in 0.01 MHCl at 31°C. for 30 minutes, whereas at pH 4.0 in an acetate buffer of 0.1 ionic strength it was stable for 6 hours. Temperatures above 60°C. were found to destroy the activity rapidly.

Van Dyke et al. (118) indicate that at approximately pH 1.0 swine FSH is quickly destroyed at room temperature, whereas it is reasonably stable between pH 3.15 and 10.9.   Steelman (96) has found that dialysis of swine FSH at pH 10.5 to 11.0 for 48 hours at 5°C. does not destroy the FSH activity or cause it to pass through the membrane.

Li (54) reported that digestion of sheep FSH with crystalline pepsin at pH 4.0 in acetate buffer did not destroy the activity even after 65% hydrolysis as measured by the amount of nitrogen soluble in 5% trichloracetic acid.   This is in contrast with earlier reports of Evans et al. (28) that pepsin destroys gonadotropic activity.   Chow, Greep, and Van Dyke (15) have shown that extensive digestion of swine FSH with pepsin at pH 4.2 leads to inactivation.   Unpublished data of Steelman (96) using swine FSH supports the findings of Chow et al. (15).

The isoelectric point of swine FSH has not been definitely established. Van Dyke et al. (118) report that the major component found in their FSH has an isoelectric point of pH 4.8.   Steelman and Pohley (100) show that the swine FSH made by the method of Steelman et al. (99) has a major component whose isoelectric point is also 4.8.   Conclusive evidence as to the exact isoelectric point must await the isolation of the pure hormone.

D. Immunochemistry

When biologically active heterologous proteins are to be administered to animals over prolonged periods, the problem of antigenicity and antihormone formation becomes important.   Van Dyke et al. (118) have shown that purified sheep FSH and swine FSH produce precipitating antibodies in rabbits after administration for as short a period as two weeks.   Interestingly enough, the precipitating antibodies obtained were species-specific, indicating two immunologically distinct proteins.   Maddock et al. (70) have recently reported that neutralizing antibodies (antihormones) are formed in the serum of patients receiving purified swine FSH.   These neutralizing antibodies are active against human gonadotropin as well as human chorionic gonadotropin, thus indicating that they are not species specific. Leathem (50) and others have shown that antihormones formed in man

following the administration of sheep gonadotropins and equine gonadotropins are not species specific. These varied results pose the interesting
problem of the relationship between the precipitating antibodies and the
neutralizing antibodies, the latter being measured by the blocking of a physiological response of an animal to an exogenous hormone. That there can
be species differences is shown by the data of Steelman and Bunding (97),
in which purified swine FSH was administered to sheep in doses of up to
500 to 600 mg. per week, over four months, without either precipitating
antibodies or antihormones being detected. No doubt there are many
contributing factors to the formation of antibodies to protein hormones.
The species and endocrine state of the animal, the route and form of administration of the hormone, etc., are undoubtedly all important. Unfortunately our present state of knowledge does not allow us to understand
all of the factors which contribute to this problem.

VII. Luteinizing Hormone (ICSH)

Data on the chemistry of LH since 1949 are almost nonexistent. McArthur (73) demonstrated its presence in human urine, but this author gave
no information regarding its isolation. Koenig and King (46) reported
that purified sheep gonadotropins, containing high concentrations of LH,
could be extracted from acetone-dried sheep pituitary powder. Control
of temperatures, ionic strengths, pH, and alcohol concentrations resulted
in the preparation of LH with high activity; however, the quantity of FSH
present has not been ascertained.

VIII. The Chemistry of the Corticotropins (or the Adrenocorticotropins)

A. INTRODUCTION

For many years, it has been known that substances in the anterior pituitary gland stimulate the adrenal cortex. Reviews of Li and Evans (58),
Li and Harris (61), and others refer to these earlier aspects. The current
review of Stack-Dunne and Young (95) refers, in addition, to a number of
the physiological and pharmacological aspects. However, since a great
deal of work upon the chemical structure has been reported during the past
few years, this phase of the corticotropin problem will receive the most
attention here.

The physiology and biochemistry of the various corticotropins will be
discussed in another chapter of this volume. Since the correlation between
the adrenal cortical steroid output in animals and man and the depletion
of ascorbic acid or cholesterol in the adrenal cortices of animals resulting
from the administration of the corticotropins appears to be reasonably well
established, this review will be concerned primarily with those anterior
pituitary fractions which produce these effects. In general, for purposes of

presenting the material in this chapter, only references will be made to pituitary fractions active either by the intravenous assay procedure of Sayers *et al.* (88) (or its modification by Munson *et al.* (78)) or by one of the subcutaneous methods of assay depending either upon the involution of the thymus gland as described by Bruce *et al.* (10) or upon the adrenal ascorbic acid depression as summarized by Thompson and Fisher (102). In this manner, some of the less well-defined materials referred to in the literature which are based solely upon a physiological response will not be included in this review.

Some of the general relationships between the method of preparation and the physiological activity have been discussed by Hays and White (39) and Wolfson (117).

TABLE XI

THE PREPARATIVE TYPES OF CORTICOTROPIN

Preparative types	Treatments during isolation
I	Subjected to little or no hydrolysis
II	Subjected to pepsin hydrolysis
III	Subjected to pepsin and acid hydrolysis
IV	Subjected to acid hydrolysis

B. Isolation

1. *General Considerations*

Since 1948 when this subject was reviewed by Li and Evans (58), an appreciable amount of work has been published on the isolation and the chemistry of the corticotropins. In an endeavor to decrease the general confusion which arises from a field where one is dealing with a family of very closely related substances having slightly different physiological activities, Thompson and Fisher (102) classified the corticotropins by preparative types, as shown in Table XI. It is obvious that such a classification, although generally satisfactory, does not necessarily insure that a single active substance will be found in each type or group. In any event, however, such a classification is of assistance in referring to the chemical interrelationships between the various corticotropins insofar as they are known today.

2. *Methods of Concentrating Corticotropin Activity*

As might be expected, the methods employed recently for concentrating the corticotropins utilize all of the newer techniques for separating materials possessing the properties of peptides having molecular weights from

2000 to 10,000.   The method utilizing ultrafiltration has been carried on largely by Dedman and his co-workers (23) and Cortis-Jones and his co-workers (20).   Dedman *et al.* (23) have studied the effect of formic and acetic acids at different temperatures upon the dialyzability of corticotropin.   Heating in the presence of acetic acid appears to increase the stability of the resulting preparation.   It is possible that such treatment destroys the proteolytic enzyme which has been demonstrated to be present in crude extracts by Adams and Smith (1).

The use of chromatography has been applied by Lesh *et al.* (51) and Astwood *et al.* (3, 79), using cellulose and oxycellulose, and Dixon *et al.* (24) and White and Fierce (110), using ion-exchange columns.   Richter *et al.* (87), White (106), Payne *et al.* (79), and Carpenter *et al.* (13) have reported the use of countercurrent distribution techniques, usually in the system of secondary butyl alcohol versus aqueous trichloracetic acid.   Li *et al.* (57), Li and Pederson (64), and Li *et al.* (68) used carrier displacement chromatography, and MacDonald and Marbrack (74) and others used paper electrophoresis.   All the above have succeeded in substantially concentrating the active material.   Undoubtedly, the yields and potency obtained are related to the method of assay and to the degree of hydrolysis to which the material is subjected during the fractionation process.

To the best of our knowledge corticotropins satisfying the accepted criteria for homogeneity have thus far been isolated only from pork pituitaries, but the possibility that different species may yield adrenal-stimulating substances having a different chemical configuration certainly exists.   Li and his co-workers (31–33, 41, 42, 56, 68, 75) have reported studies on hydrolyzed and nonhydrolyzed sheep pituitary preparations and have obtained highly potent materials.   No publications have appeared, however, concerning the chemistry of these fractions.   The observation that corticotropin activity is not destroyed by treatment with pepsin was made in this same laboratory using crude concentrates from sheep pituitaries.   The observation (54) that acid treatment increases the corticotropin potency has not been confirmed (34).

Reiss and Halkerston (86) have summarized a simple procedure for preparing low-potency concentrates.   On the other hand, the procedure of Smith *et al.* (93) taking advantage of the solubility of lithium salts in various solvents yields a moderately active material.

3. *Isolation of Corticotropin B*

Corticotropin B was first isolated by the research team at the Merck Laboratories.   This apparently pure material was designated corticotropin B in order to differentiate it from the highly purified corticotropin as prepared by Astwood utilizing the oxycellulose adsorption technique of non-

hydrolyzed materials. The procedure used as reported in the series of publications from this laboratory (5, 8, 9, 87) involved the methanol-acetic acid extraction of acetone-dried and defatted hog pituitaries, adsorption on oxycellulose and elution with HCl as recommended in the procedure described by Astwood et al. (3), digestion with pepsin at pH 2.5 for 24 hours at 37°C., precipipitation of inert materials with 5% trichloracetic acid, countercurrent distribution between sec-butyl alcohol and 0.5% aqueous trichloracetic acid, and conversion to the acetate by means of ion-exchange with the exchange resin IRA-400. According to the data submitted, the resulting preparation is reported to be 300 I.U. per milligram.[3] More recently, corticotropin B has been isolated by digesting highly purified corticotropin A with pepsin followed by separation from among the hydrolytic products by means of ion-exchange column (109).

4. Isolation of Corticotropin A

In 1953, White (106) reported the isolation of an apparently pure material having a biological activity whose behavior was qualitatively equivalent to that found in the less pure preparations of Astwood (2). This material was designated corticotropin A because of these similarities. The procedure used consisted of adsorption on oxycellulose, acid elution, fractionation on the ion-exchange resin XE-97, and countercurrent distribution in the system secondary butanol/0.2% aqueous trichloracetic acid. The degree of homogeneity achieved was demonstrated by nearly theoretical behavior in a 6C0 tube countercurrent system. The presence of a reducing agent was maintained throughout the countercurrent distribution, as recommended by White et al. (112) and Dixon (24).

C. RELATIONSHIP BETWEEN CORTICOTROPIN A AND CORTICOTROPIN B

Since differences in physiological behavior of corticotropins prepared by different procedures are striking (102), it might be anticipated that they would differ chemically; yet, on the other hand, the difficulty encountered in their isolation indicates that they very likely have common structural

---

[3] A few words should be stated regarding the wide differences in values for the physiological activities of these and other preparations referred to in the literature. In our laboratories, the highest values for corticotropin A have been 100 to 125 units per milligram and for corticotropin B 150 units per milligram, whereas other groups report twice this value. Without pretending to know the reasons for these discrepancies, we would like to state that the same ratios seem to hold at lower levels of purity on types of material which have been assayed by all groups. For instance, our values for commercial acid-acetone powders are invariably in the range of 1.2 to 1.6 units per milligram, whereas the Merck group (5) has reported a value of 3.5 units per milligram for such a fraction obtained from The Armour Laboratories. Again, our oxycellulose eluates are in the range of 25 to 40 units per milligram, whereas Astwood et al. (2) report a value of about 80 units per milligram.

properties. As stated elsewhere, there appears to be a relationship between the degree of hydrolysis of crude corticotropin concentrates and the material isolated in the pure form. If pepsin treatment is included during the course of the isolation, corticotropin B is obtained as the resultant pure product. If it or other hydrolytic procedures are not included, corticotropin A is obtained. In early 1953, White and Fierce (111) showed that hydrolyzed and unhydrolyzed materials behave differently on XE-97 ion-exchange resin columns. When a pepsin and acid hydrolyzed material having an activity of approximately 65 I.U. per milligram is placed in a pH 8.5 buffer column of this resin, the activity remains on the column at this pH and can be eluted only at higher pH's, as shown in Fig. 1 of this

TABLE XII

EFFECT OF VARIOUS HYDROLYTIC TREATMENTS ON THE PERFORMANCE OF AN
OXYCELLULOSE ELUATE ON XE-97 RESIN

Type of hydrolytic treatment	pH 8.5 O.D.[a]	Type I activity	pH 9.25 O.D.[a]	Type II activity	pH 11.25 O.D.[a]	Type III activity
None	31	70	5	5	17	5
Pepsin 2 hours[b]	None	5	21	100	17	5
Pepsin 24 hours[b]	None	5	44	80	12	5
Pepsin 4 hours[b] Followed by 0.01 N HCl 1 hour 100°C.	None	5	27	75	21	25

[a] As per cent of total optical density recovered in all fractions. Inert front accounts for most of remaining absorption.
[b] In 0.01N HCl at 37°C.

reference. On the other hand, if an unhydrolyzed preparation of similar activity is put through such a column in a buffer at pH 8.5, it slowly passes through. This is illustrated in Fig. 2 of this same reference. As a result, it was predicted that the corticotropin A obtained from unhydrolyzed concentrates could be converted to corticotropin B. Table XII records the experimental results of such a conversion. Since purified corticotropin A can be altered by hydrolysis and corticotropin B obtained utilizing the XE-97 ion-exchange column, these two substances must have common molecular amino acid sequences. It is very likely, however, that a family of corticotropin B's may exist different one from another by one or more amino acids, depending upon the degree of hydrolysis and the conditions employed. It is expected that a more uniform product will result from the hydrolysis of a highly purified corticotropin A under controlled conditions of hydrolysis than would be obtained from the hydrolysis of a crude corticotropin mixture.   However, Dixon *et al.* (24) feel that there may likewise by a family of corticotropin A's which would complicate the picture further.

D. Physical and Chemical Properties of Corticotropins A and B

Information concerning the physical and chemical properties of these highly purified substances is indeed limited, since the only reports are those from the two laboratories which have reported their isolation.   In general, both corticotropins appear to be protein in nature, and although the possibility that they may contain a prosthetic group exists, it is not likely. Both are water-soluble white amorphous materials usually isolated as the acetate or trichloracetate.

The amino acid composition as reported is shown in Table XIII.   It will be noted that neither contains cystine.   The absence of this amino acid leaves unexplained the reversible oxidation-reduction of corticotropin B noted by Kuehl *et al.* (47).   In this connection, White in 1951 (105) re-

TABLE XIII

Amino Acid Composition of the Corticotropins (Per Cent by Weight)

Amino acid	Corticotropin A[a]	Corticotropin B[b]
Glycine	2.7	4.4
Alanine	3.5	1.9
Valine	4.0	6.7
Leucine	4.0	None
Isoleucine	None	None
Proline	4.1	5.8
Serine	3.1	4.5
Threonine	None	None
Phenylalanine	6.6	4.7
Tyrosine	3.5	6.9
Cystine	None	None
Methionine	1.7	2.5
Aspartic acid	4.3	5.3
Glutamic acid	11.2	8.1
Histidine	2.5	3.1
Lysine	7.2	11.4
Arginine	6.6	13.4
Ammonia	Not run	0.5
Tryptophane	4.0	7.3

[a] Armour Laboratories data (as the trichloroacetate).
[b] Brink *et al.* (as the acetate). (7)

ported a number of controlled experiments designed to study the instability of the corticotropin molecule during the usual laboratory manipulation. It was observed that neither oxygen nor heavy metals destroyed activity. Peroxide-bearing solvents do, however, destroy the activity with a corresponding disappearance of the ultraviolet absorption curve in the tyrosine-tryptophane absorbing region.   Later studies (39) with purified tyrosinase indicate that the decrease in activity resulting from such treatment is correlated with the destruction of tyrosine.   It is concluded that tyrosine is therefore necessary for the biological activity.   Other causes of instability may contribute to the problem.   It appears, for example, that in addition to the unusual instability of the tyrosine, the methionine present is also quite labile.   Attempts to quantitatively estimate this normally stable amino acid yield nearly zero values unless care is taken to remove oxygen during the course of hydrolysis.   Even when such care is taken, the analytical values for this amino acid appear low.   The similar behavior for amino acids which normally are considered stable toward hydrolysis has been reported (91), and there is some evidence that peptides having unusually stable bonds require hydrolytic procedures which will destroy amino acids considered stable to the ordinary methods of hydrolysis.

It will be noted from Table XIII that isoleucine and threonine are absent from both corticotropin A and B, while the conversion of corticotropin A to corticotropin B eliminates all of the leucine.   Li (53) first reported and then denied (52) that serine and histidine are also missing in his sheep preparations.

Both corticotropins absorb ultraviolet light at 2770 Å, as might be predicted from the presence of tyrosine and tryptophane in the molecules. Infrared absorption data show nothing that would not be predicted from the amino acid composition.

The matter of the exact molecular weight of corticotropin A and B has not been resolved.   Published work reports values of from 2300 to 7000, depending upon whether actual measurement is made in the ultracentrifuge or whether the value is calculated from the amino acid analyses.   It is safe to state that accurate estimations using the ultracentrifuge of the molecular weights of polyelectrolytes such as these in this range of molecular weights are difficult.   Likewise, as stated above, the unpredicted instability behavior of some of the amino acids during hydrolysis makes it difficult to arrive at a fully reliable value for molecular weights calculated on amino acid analyses.

In an early publication, White (106) reported the following empirical formula for corticotropin A:

$$Ala_2Arg_2Asp_1Glu_4Gly_2His_1Leu_2Lys_3Phe_2Pro_3Ser_1Tryp_1Val_2$$

Methionine was subsequently discovered under conditions stated above, and tyrosine was omitted as a printer's error. The analytical values upon which this empirical formula was based were obtained by quantitative paper chromatography. It is felt that it may be necessary to revise this empirical formula in order to account for all of the amino acids identified in the sequence studies. A revision toward a higher total molecular weight would also better correlate with the approximate 25% increase in ultraviolet absorption coefficient in converting corticotropin A to corticotropin B. Since approximately 11 amino acids are removed in such a conversion, corticotropin A must consist of approximately 40 to 45 individual amino acids.

The isoelectric point obtained by means of paper microelectrophoresis technique is reported (39) as pH 7 to 8 for corticotropin A and pH 10 for corticotropin B. The shift towards a more alkaline value in converting A to B confirms the observation that predominantly acidic amino acids are split off during this hydrolysis. It is conceivable that the higher isoelectric point of corticotropin B may be correlated with the metal binding effect (14, 43) through the formation of chelates or other complexes. Table XIV summarizes the properties of the purified corticotropins.

E. Structural Chemistry of Corticotropin A

Since little information has been published regarding the chemistry and structure of corticotropin B, this review will be confined largely to the work

TABLE XIV

Properties of the Corticotropins

	Corticotropin A	Corticotropin B
Molecular weight (ultracentrifuge)		2300 at pH 1–2 (39) 5200 at unknown pH (7)
Molecular weight (minimum) (Molar amino acid ratios)	3500 (106) 4500 (39)	6000–7000 (7)
Isoelectric point	7–8 (39)	4.6 (87) 10 (39)
Ultraviolet absorption[a] $E_{1\,cm.}^{1\%}$ at 2770 Å.	18 (39)	23 (39)
Physiological activity	125 unit/mg. (106)	300 unit/mg. (9) 150 unit/mg. (39)

[a] On basis of free peptide.
Literature references in parenthesis.

thus far accomplished on corticotropin A.   In general, the techniques utilized are those employed by Sanger on insulin, with modifications to meet
the need for methods using semi-micro quantities of this costly starting
material.   These methods include the dinitrofluorobenzene method of
Sanger and Thompson (89) and modifications (48) of the thiohydantoin
technique of Edman for the specific study of the N terminus, together with
enzymic hydrolysis with pepsin, trypsin, chymotrypsin, or carboxypeptidase followed by separation of the fragments by means of paper chromatography.   The peptide fragments thus obtained are then analyzed for their
amino acid composition, their N and C termini determined, and if necessary
subjected to further hydrolysis (cf. sect. I B of Chap. V).

1.   The Amino Acids Found at the Amino and Carboxyl Ends of Corticotropin A

Corticotropin A appears to have a single amino and a single carboxyl
terminus.   The amino acid serine is reported to be the N-terminal amino
acid by White (49), using the thiohydantoin derivative technique.   A
second application of this reaction to the residual peptide yielded the thiohydantoin of tyrosine.   It is concluded, therefore, that the N-terminus of
corticotropin A, when recorded by the conventional nomenclature utilized
by Sanger for insulin, is:

Ser. Tyr. . . .

White (107), using a time study of the rate of liberation of free amino acids
from corticotropin A upon treatment with the enzyme carboxypeptidase
has shown the carboxyl terminus to be:

. . . Leu. Glu. Phe

2.   The Amino Acid Sequence of the Central Portion of the Corticotropin A Molecule

a. Fragments Obtained by Hydrolysis with Pepsin.   It has been observed in
our laboratory (113) that several peptide fragments are produced when
highly purified corticotropin A is treated with crystalline pepsin at 37°C.
and pH 2 for 2 hours and for 24 hours.   Separation of these fragments by
two-dimensional paper chromatography with the use of the Partridge solvent system (secondary butanol:water:acetic acid: 4:5:1) and a secondary
butanol:ammonia 3:1 system yields four components, as shown in Table
XV.   For the balance of this review, the fragments are arranged in the
tables in the order of their postulated sequential position, starting with the
N-terminus at the top and ending with those nearest the carboxyl terminus
at the bottom.   It is felt that all of the peptides except the first are obtained
from the conversion of corticotropin A to corticotropin B, and Fragment 2

TABLE XV

Peptides Obtained from Peptic Hydrolysis of Corticotropin A

Fragment	Composition
1	Ser. Tyr. Met. Glu
2	Large basic peptide
3	(Asp) (Glu). Leu
4	Ala. Leu. Ala. Phe
5	Pro. Leu. Glu. Phe

TABLE XVI

Products of Tryptic Hydrolysis Following Peptic Digestion of Corticotropin A

Fragment	Composition
1	Ser. Tyr. Met. Glu. His. Phe. Arg
2	His. Phe. Arg
3	Gly. Lys
4	Arg. [(Lys)(Val)(Phe)]

represents corticotropin B whenever the exposure to pepsin is kept within a relatively short period of time. It is also felt that Fragments Numbers 5, 4, and 3 represent the sequence of the amino acids toward the carboxyl end, with phenylalanine actually the C-terminal amino acid.

b. *Fragments Obtained by Hydrolysis with Pepsin Followed by Trypsin.* Treatment of the large peptide (Fragment 2, Table XV) obtained from among the hydrolytic products produced by a short exposure of corticotropin A to pepsin followed by trypsin at pH 7.5 for 2 hours at 37°C. yields among others the peptides listed in Table XVI. These may likewise be separated by two-dimensional paper chromatography. It will be noted that Fragment 1 represents the heptapeptide at the N-terminus of both corticotropin A and corticotropin B.[4]

c. *Fragments Obtained by Hydrolysis with Chymotrypsin.* The treatment of corticotropin A with chymotrypsin at pH 7.7 for 20 hours at 37°C. followed by separation of the resulting peptide fragments yields (114) a number of peptides. Those thus far identified are listed in Table XVII. The first three fragments probably represent the sequence of the octapeptide at the N-terminus of corticotropin A, while Fragment 4 represents the dipeptide at the carboxyl end. The other as yet unidentified peptides

[4] As referred to earlier in the text, these peptides exhibit abnormal behavior during hydrolysis. In the early studies of the N-terminus, the problem of the presence and location of the second serine molecule was a major one. It is now agreed that the sequence Ser.Tyr.Ser.Met.Glu—is the correct one for this end of the molecule.

TABLE XVII

PEPTIDES OBTAINED FROM CORTICOTROPIN A RESULTING FROM CHYMOTRYPSIN
HYDROLYSIS

Fragment	Composition
1	Ser. Tyr
2	Met. Glu. His. Phe
3	Arg. Try
4	Glu. Phe

are primarily composed of basic amino acids and appear to occur in combinations not ordinarily found in proteins.   Whole new fields of analytical and synthetic peptide chemistry must be evolved to cope with the many problems presented by these basic materials.

d. Hydrolysis with Acid.   Treatment of a highly purified sample of corticotropin A with concentrated HCl at 37°C. for two days has yielded (114) among other fragments the peptide: Ala.Phe.Pro.Leu.

3. *Summary of the Structure Work to Date*

Although it is obvious from the foregoing that the structure for corticotropin A is far from being completely elucidated, certain conclusions can be postulated.   It is fair to state that the N-terminal amino acid sequence appears to be common to both corticotropin A and B, and modification at this end of the chain appears to destroy the physiological activity.   It may be postulated that corticotropin A has 40 to 45 amino acid residues.   Figure 2 summarizes in diagrammatic form the present-day knowledge of the structure of corticotropin A.

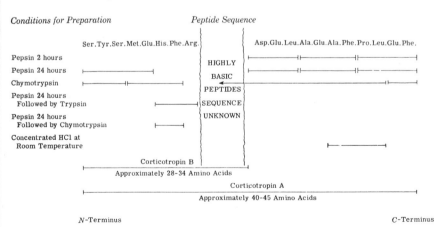

FIG. 2.   The known peptides of corticotropin A.

F. Destruction of Corticotropin by Blood and Plasma

Pincus *et al.* (81) have studied the inactivation of corticotropin preparations upon incubation with bovine, rat, or human blood or plasma. This inactivation may be prevented by heating the plasma prior to incubation. Not all preparations of corticotropin are inactivated; however, the addition of one which is destroyed to one which is not permits the destruction of the resulting mixture. These workers therefore postulate the presence of a heat-labile blood protein and a co-factor present in certain corticotropin concentrates the interaction of which is responsible for the observed destruction of the corticotropin activity.

IX. Summary

It is obvious that we have moved into the new frontiers of the science of peptides and proteins, and the techniques of chromatography, ionophoresis, countercurrent distribution, and low-temperature fractionation have contributed substantially toward the day when the relationship of chemical structure to physiological activity will be fully understood. During the six years that have passed since the chapter of Li and Evans appeared in Volume I of this monograph substantial progress has been made in the purification of several of the hormones of the anterior pituitary gland and a start made toward the unraveling of the chemical structure of one of these.

Addendum

Since this review was written, three papers have appeared concerning the chemical structure of the corticotropins. Members of the research team at the University of California [*J. Am. Chem. Soc.* **76**, 3607 (1954)] have reported the N-terminal sequence for sheep corticotropin as Ser.Tyr.-Ser.Met.Glu.His.Phe—which is in excellent agreement with that reported for swine corticotropin as recorded in this review. White reported [*J. Am. Chem. Soc.* **76**, 4194 (1954)] the C-terminus structure of 11 amino acids plus information on some additional peptides. It would appear that the 11 amino acid chain reported represents the peptide liberated in the conversion of corticotropin A to corticotropin B. And finally, Dr. Paul H. Bell and associates have proposed [*J. Am. Chem. Soc.* **76**, 5565 (1954)] a structure for the entire corticotropin B molecule. This, too, is identical with and extends the data thus far reported from The Armour Laboratories.

REFERENCES

1. Adams, A., and Smith, E. L.   *J. Biol. Chem.* **191**, 651 (1951).
2. Astwood, E. B., Raben, M S.., Payne, R. W., and Grady, A. B.   *J. Am. Chem. Soc.* **73**, 2969 (1951).

3. Astwood, E. B., Raben, M. S., and Payne, R. W.   *Recent Progr. Hormone Research* **7**, 1 (1952).
4. Bates, R. W., and Schooley, J. P.   *Endocrinology* **31**, 390 (1942).
5. Bazemore, A. W., Richter, J. W., Ayer, D. E., Finnerty, J., Brink, N. G., and Folkers, K.   *J. Am. Chem. Soc.* **75**, 1949 (1953).
6. Borell, U., and Holmgren, H.   *Acta Endocrinol.* **3**, 331 (1949).
7. Brink, N. G., Boxer, G. E., Jelinek, J. C., Kuehl, F. A., Jr., Richter, J. W., and Folkers, K.   *J. Am. Chem. Soc.* **75**, 1960 (1953).
8. Brink, N. G., Kuehl, F. A., Meisinger, M. A. P., Bishop, M. N., and Folkers, K.   *J. Am. Chem. Soc.* **74**, 480 (1952).
9. Brink, N. G., Kuehl, F. A., Richter, J. W., Bazemore, A. W., Meisinger, M. A. P., Ayer, D. E., and Folkers, K.   *J. Am. Chem. Soc.* **74**, 2120 (1952).
10. Bruce, H. M., Parkes, A. S., and Perry, W. L. M.   *Lancet* **i**, 790 (1952).
11. Butt, W. R., and Crooke, A. C.   Bioassay of Anterior Pituitary and Adrenocortical Hormones.   Little, Brown and Co., Boston 1953, Vol. 5, p. 44.
12. Campbell, J., and Davidson, I. W. F.   *Abstr. 19th Intern. Physiol. Congr.*, p. 257 (1953).
13. Carpenter, F. H., Hess, G. P., and Li, C. H.   *J. Biol. Chem.* **197**, 7 (1952).
14. Carr, J. E., Conn, J. B., and Wartman, T. G.   *Science* **116**, 566 (1952).
15. Chow, B. F., Greep, R. O., and Van Dyke, H. B.   *J. Endocrinol.* **1**, 440 (1939).
16. Chow, B. F., Van Dyke, H. B., Greep, R. O., Rothen, A., and Shedlovsky, T.   *Endocrinology* **30**, 650 (1942).
17. Ciereszko, L. S.   *J. Biol. Chem.* **160**, 585 (1945).
18. Condliffe, P. G., and Li, C. H.   *Federation Proc.* **11**, 198 (1952).
19. Coppedge, R. L., and Segaloff, A.   *J. Clin. Endocrinol.* **11**, 465 (1951).
20. Cortis-Jones, B., Crooke, A. C., Henly, A. A., Morris, P., and Morris, C. J. O. R.   *Biochem. J.* **46**, 173 (1950).
21. Crooke, A. C., and Matthews, J. D.   Bioassay of Anterior Pituitary and Adrenocortical Hormones.   Little, Brown and Co., Boston 1953, Vol. 5, p. 25.
22. D'Angelo, S. A., and Gordon, A. S.   *Endocrinology* **46**, 39 (1950).
23. Dedman, M. L., Farmer, T. H., Morris, P., and Morris, C. J. O. R.   *Recent Progr. Hormone Research* **7**, 59 (1950).
24. Dixon, H. B. F., Moore, S., Stack-Dunne, M. P., and Young, F. G.   *Nature* **168**, 1044 (1951).
25. Dobyns, B. M., and Steelman, S. L.   *Endocrinology* **52**, 705 (1953).
26. Donini, P., and Marchetti, E.   *Edizione Sci. (Pavia)* **7**, 418 (1952).
27. Elberg, S. S., and Li, C. H.   *Endocrinology* **47**, 143 (1950).
28. Evans, H. M., Simpson, M. E., and Austin, P. R.   *J. Exptl. Med.* **58**, 545 (1933).
29. Fels, G., Simpson, M. E., Sverdrup, A., and Evans, H. M.   *Endocrinology* **51**, 349 (1952).
30. Finney, D. J., Burn, J. H., and Goodwin, L. G.   Biological Standardization, 2nd ed.   Oxford University Press, 1950, p. 94.
31. Geschwind, I. I., Hess, G. P., Condliffe, P. G., Evans, H. M., and Simpson, M. E.   *Science* **112**, 436 (1950).
32. Geschwind, I. I., Hess, G. P., Condliffe, P. G., and Williams, B. S.   *Science* **111**, 625 (1950).
33. Geschwind, I. I., Porath, J. O., and Li, C. H.   *J. Am. Chem. Soc.* **74**, 2121 (1952).
34. Ghosh, B. N., Smith, E. L., and Sayers, G.   *Proc. Soc. Exptl. Biol. Med.* **79**, 23 (1952).
35. Ghosh, B. N., Woodbury, D. M., and Sayers, G.   *Endocrinology* **48**, 631 (1951).

36. Gilliland, I. C., and Fraser, R.   Bioassay of Anterior Pituitary and Adrenocortical Hormones.   Little, Brown and Co., Boston, 1953, Vol. 5, p. 20.
37. Greenspan, F. S., Li, C. H., Simpson, M. E., and Evans, H. M.   *Endocrinology* **45,** 455 (1949).
38. Haley, T. J.   *J. Am. Pharm. Assoc.* **39,** 136 (1950).
39. Hays, E. E., and White, W. F.   *Recent Progr. Hormone Research* **10,** 265 (1954).
40. Heideman, L. M.   *Endocrinology* **53,** 640 (1953).
41. Hess, G. P., and Carpenter, F. H.   *J. Am. Chem. Soc.* **74,** 4971 (1952).
42. Hess, G. P., Carpenter, F. H., and Li, C. H.   *J. Am. Chem. Soc.* **74,** 4956 (1952).
43. Holtermann, H., Heier, A., and Bergh, K.   *Lancet* **262,** 1308 (1952).
44. Jefferies, W. McK.   *J. Clin. Endocrinol.* **9,** 927 (1949).
45. Katzman, P. A., Godfrid, M., Cain, C. K., Doisy, E. A.   *J. Biol. Chem.* **148,** 501 (1943).
46. Koenig, V., and King, E.   *Arch. Biochem.* **26,** 219 (1950).
47. Kuehl, F. A., Jr., Meisinger, M. A. P., Brink, N. G., and Folkers, K.   *J. Am. Chem. Soc.* **75,** 1955 (1953).
48. Landmann, W. A., Drake, M. P., and Dillaha, J.   *J. Am. Chem. Soc.* **75,** 3638 (1953).
49. Landmann, W. A., Drake, M. P., and White, W. F.   *J. Am. Chem. Soc.* **75,** 4370 (1953).
50. Leathem, J. H.   *Recent Progr. Hormone Research* **4,** 115 (1949).
51. Lesh, J. B., Fisher, J. D., Bunding, I. M., Kocsis, J. J., Walaszek, L. J., White, W. F., and Hays, E. E.   *Science* **112,** 43 (1950).
52. Li, C. H.   Cited in Reference 39.
53. Li, C. H.   *Acta Endocrinol.* **10,** 255 (1952).
54. Li, C. H.   *J. Am. Chem. Soc.* **72,** 2815 (1950).
55. Li, C. H.   *J. Biol. Chem.* **178,** 459 (1949).
56. Li, C. H.   *J. Am. Chem. Soc.* **74,** 2124 (1952).
57. Li, C. H., Ash, L., and Papkoff, H.   *J. Am. Chem. Soc.* **74,** 1923 (1952).
58. Li, C. H., and Evans, H. M.   *In* G. Pincus and K. V. Thimann, The Hormones. Academic Press, New York, 1948, Vol. 1, p. 631.
59. Li, C. H., and Evans, H. M.   *Recent Progr. Hormone Research* **3,** 7 (1948).
60. Li, C. H. Evans, H. M., and Simpson, M. E.   *J. Biol. Chem.* **159,** 353 (1945).
61. Li, C. H., and Harris, J. I.   *Ann. Rev. Biochem.* **21,** 607 (1952).
62. Li, C. H., and Moskowitz, M.   *J. Biol. Chem.* **178,** 203 (1949).
63. Li, C. H., and Papkoff, H.   *J. Biol. Chem.* **204,** 391 (1953).
64. Li, C. H., and Pedersen, K. O.   *Arch. Biochem. and Biophys.* **36,** 462 (1952).
65. Li, C. H., and Pedersen, K. O.   *J. Biol. Chem.* **201,** 595 (1953).
66. Li, C. H., and Pedersen, K. O.   *J. Gen. Physiol.* **35** (No. 4), 629 (1952).
67. Li, C. H., Simpson, M. E., and Evans, H. M.   *Science* **109,** 445 (1949).
68. Li, C. H., Tiselius, A., Pedersen, K. O., Hagdahl, L., and Carstensen, L.   *J. Biol. Chem.* **190,** 317 (1951).
69. Lyons, W. R.   *Proc. Soc. Exptl. Biol. Med.* **35,** 645 (1937).
70. Maddock, W. O., Tokuyama, I., Leach, R. B., and Roy, W. R.   *J. Clin. Endocrinol.* **13,** 834 (1953).
71. Marx, W., Simpson, M. E., and Evans, H. M.   *Endocrinology* **30,** 1 (1942).
72. Mayer, J., and Silides, D. N.   *Endocrinology* **52,** 54 (1953).
73. McArthur, J. W.   *Endocrinology* **50,** 304 (1952).
74. McDonald, H. J., and Marbarek, E. P.   *J. Am. Chem. Soc.* **74,** 1619 (1950).
75. Mendenhall, R., and Li, C. H.   *Proc. Soc. Exptl. Biol. Med.* **78,** 668 (1951).

76. Morrison, J. F., Bazeley, P. L., and Ennor, A. H.   *Brit. J. Exptl. Pathol.* **33,** 48 (1952).
77. Morrison, J. F., Ennor, A. H., and Bazeley, P. L.   *Nature* **169,** 28 (1952).
78. Munson, P. L., Barry, A. G., and Koch, F. C.   *J. Clin. Endocrinol.* **8,** 586 (1948).
79. Payne, R. W., Raben, M. S., and Astwood, E. B.   *J. Biol. Chem.* **187,** 719 (1950).
80. Piotrowski, L. J., Steelman, S. L., and Koch, F. C.   *Endocrinology* **52** (No. 5), 489 (1953).
81. Pincus, G., Hopkins, T. F., and Hechter, O.   *Arch. Biochem. and Biophys.* **37,** 408 (1952).
82. Querido, A., Kassenaar, A. A. H., and Lamayer, L. B. F.   *Acta Endocrinol.* **12,** 335 (1953).
83. Raben, M. S., and Westermeyer, V. W.   *Proc. Soc. Exptl. Biol. Med.* **78,** 550 (1951).
84. Reid, E.   *J. Endocrinol.* **8,** 50 (1951–52).
85. Reid, E.   *Nature* **168,** 955 (1951).
86. Reiss, M., and Halkerston, I. D. K.   *J. Pharm. Pharmacol.* **2,** 236 (1950).
87. Richter, J., Ayer, D. E., Bazemore, A. W., Brink, N. G., and Folkers, K.   *J. Am. Chem. Soc.* **75,** 1952 (1953).
88. Sayers, G., Sayers, M. A., and Woodbury, L. A.   *Endocrinology* **43,** 379 (1948).
89. Sanger, F., and Thompson, E. O. P.   *Biochem. J.* **53,** 353 (1953).
90. Shorr, E., Carter, A. C., Kennedy, B. J., and Smith, R. W., Jr.   *Trans. Assoc. Am. Physicians* **66,** 114 (1953).
91. Smith, E.   Personal communication.
92. Smith, E. L., Brown, D. M., Fishman, J. B., and Wilhelmi, A.   *J. Biol. Chem.* **177,** 305 (1949).
93. Smith, E. L., Sayers, G., Ghosh, B. N., and Woodbury, D. M.   *Proc. Soc. Exptl. Biol. Med.* **79,** 27 (1952).
94. Spies, J. R., Bernton, H. S., and Stevens, H.   *J. Am. Chem. Soc.* **63,** 2163 (1951).
95. Stack-Dunne, M. P., and Young, F. G.   *Ann. Rev. Biochem.* **23,** in press (1954).
96. Steelman, S. L.   Unpublished data.
97. Steelman, S. L., and Bunding, I. M.   Unpublished data.
98. Steelman, S. L., Giffee, J. W., and Hawrylewicz, E. J.   *Federation Proc.* **11,** 292 (1952).
99. Steelman, S. L., Lamont, W. A., Dittman, W. A., and Hawrylewicz, E. J.   *Proc. Soc. Exptl. Biol. Med.* **82,** 645 (1953).
100. Steelman, S. L., and Pohley, F. M.   *Endocrinology* **53,** 604 (1953).
101. Tala, P.   *Acta Endocrinol., Suppl.* **9** (1952).
102. Thompson, R. E., and Fisher, J. D.   *Endocrinology* **52,** 496 (1953).
103. White, A.   Chemistry and Physiology of Hormones.   Science Press, Lancaster, Pa., 1945, p. 1.
104. White, A.   *Vitamins and Hormones* **7,** 253 (1949).
105. White, W. F.   *Proc. Armour Conf. on ACTH*, p. 69 (1951).
106. White, W. F.   *J. Am. Chem. Soc.* **75,** 503 (1953).
107. White, W. F.   *J. Am. Chem. Soc.* **75,** 4877 (1953).
108. White, W. F.   To be published.
109. White, W. F.   Reported in Hays, E. E., and White, W. F.   *Recent Progr. Hormone Research* **10,** 265 (1954).
110. White, W. F., and Fierce, W. L.   *J. Am. Chem. Soc.* **74,** 1923 (1952).
111. White, W. F., and Fierce, W. L.   *J. Am. Chem. Soc.* **75,** 245 (1953).
112. White, W. F., Fierce, W. L., and Lesh, J. B.   *Proc. Soc. Exptl. Biol. Med.* **78,** 616 (1951).

234 EDWIN E. HAYS AND SANFORD L. STEELMAN

113. White, W. F., and Landmann, W. A.   To be published.
144. White, W. F.   *J. Am. Chem. Soc.* **76,** 4194 (1954).
115. Wilhelmi, A. E., Fishman, J. B., and Russell, J. A.   *J. Biol. Chem.* **176** (1948).
116. Williams, R. R., and Waterman, R. E.   *Proc. Soc. Exptl. Biol. Med.* **27,** 56 (1929–30).
117. Wolfson, W. Q.   *Arch. Internal Med.* **92,** 108 (1953).
118. Van Dyke, H. B., P'an, S. Y., and Shedlovsky, T.   *Endocrinology* **46,** 563 (1950).

CHAPTER VII

Growth Hormone and Corticotropin

By E. B. ASTWOOD

CONTENTS

I. Introduction

Since the completion of the first two volumes of *The Hormones* the discovery of the remarkable and unexpected therapeutic properties of corticotropin has prompted extensive investigation of this hormone. The processing of large quantities of pituitary tissue to obtain corticotropic concentrates for clinical purposes and for research has made available to investigators larger quantities of pituitary material than had ever been obtainable before, and as a consequence studies on other pituitary hormones, and especially growth hormone, have been furthered. It is perhaps appropriate that an attempt be made to consider corticotropin and growth hormone together. Both hormones influence directly or indirectly a variety of metabolic processes throughout the body. In some actions their effects seem to be similar, whereas in many others they are antagonistic. The diverse physiological effects of growth hormone preparations have led many to speculate on possible clinical uses and on the part the hormone might play in the pathogenesis of disease. Less is known about growth hormone than about corticotropin, though the growth effects of pituitary extracts have been recognized for a much longer time. Corticotropic extracts are highly effective in man, whereas growth hormone preparations have usually failed to cause positive effects.

II. Growth Hormone

The concept of a growth hormone secreted by the anterior pituitary derived from the observations of (1) human acromegalic gigantism in association with pituitary tumors, (2) retardation of growth in animals following hypophysectomy, and (3) acceleration of growth in normal and hypophysectomized animals treated with pituitary gland tissue or extracts. It is currently believed that a single substance can account for these phenomena, and the term "growth hormone" has been applied to it. A more precise definition of this term is not yet possible; it is not known whether such a substance is secreted at all times or intermittently, whether it is essential to all phases of growth or only to some, or whether it is of more physiological importance during phases of rapid growth or during periods when conditions unfavorable to growth prevail, and finally it is still uncertain which metabolic effects of purified preparations of the hormone are to be regarded as physiologically important actions of the hormone and which as incidental side effects or effects of contaminants.

Much early work on the physiologic effects of growth hormone was carried out using crude pituitary preparations made by acid, alkaline, or saline extraction (34, 42, 103, 386, 399, 422) or globulin fractions derived therefrom. Much of this work has been repeated with purified preparations. For a decade or more the purified protein of Li, Evans, and Simpson (227) has been studied, and for a somewhat shorter time that of Wilhelmi, Fishman, and Russell (414). The latter has probably been used more widely than any other because it was made available from a commercial source. Recently the preparations of Raben and Westermeyer (290) and of Campbell and Davidson (50) have been investigated. Three of these preparations (227, 414, 50) have in common similar methods of extraction and in part somewhat similar steps in purification. Their biological activities also appear to be alike in so far as comparisons have been possible. The fourth preparation, derived from a hot glacial acetic acid extract, appears to differ somewhat in its biological effects from the others and is not regarded as a pure substance (287).

A. FACTORS INFLUENCING GROWTH AFTER HYPOPHYSECTOMY AND THE RESPONSE TO GROWTH HORMONE PREPARATIONS

In all species investigated, including fish, amphibia, reptiles, birds, and mammals, including man, absence or extensive destruction of the anterior pituitary has been noted to cause retardation of growth. In most species growth does not cease completely after hypophysectomy but proceeds at a much slower pace. Very young animals seem to be less dependent on the pituitary for growth than older ones. A rat hypophysectomized when a young adult weighing 150 g. or more loses weight and seldom regains it completely, whereas a weanling rat weighing 40 g. will slowly gain after the operation and reach a weight of 80 to 100 g. without any treatment.

In man a congenital absence of the anterior pituitary is not inconsistent with a normal birth weight and a rate of growth during the first two to four years of life that is not below the normal range. Thereafter growth is greatly slowed, and though the dwarfism thus becomes progressively more conspicuous until young adult life, growth apparently never completely stops. A final height of about 5 feet may be reached in the male and perhaps 4 feet 9 inches in the female, and even at ages beyond 50 years growth may still be measurable. The epiphyses of the long bones presumably never completely unite, though it may be difficult to tell with certainty, from skiagrams alone, whether the epiphyseal line is fused. In the rat hypophysectomy at the early age of 6 days had only a moderate effect on growth and development at first, but eventually growth was arrested. By the 60th day skeletal development had advanced to the stage normally seen at 24 to 25 days (405). Survival was not possible beyond 75 days of age because of the failure of the stunted cranium to accommodate the growing brain. Injection of a growth hormone preparation restored a normal rate of weight gain, accelerated growth and development of bone, including that of the base of the skull, and permitted survival (8).

1. Diet

Hypophysectomized rats provided with an excess of nutritious food by means of forced feeding exhibit distinct growth (326). Rats weighing about 100 g. at the time of operation gained 30 g. in 22 days and 50 g. in 54 days, or about 1 g. per day. This amount of weight gain in otherwise untreated animals would require 10 μg. or more of the most active growth hormone preparation daily. Normal rats given the same amount of food as the force-fed hypophysectomized animals gained more weight because they deposited about three times as much protein, whereas the hypophysectomized animals deposited many of the excess calories as fat. Bone growth in the operated animals was distinct but only about 10 % of that of the controls.

Provision of a nutritious diet without forced feeding also favors better gains in weight and length after hypophysectomy (348). Rats 28 days old at the time of operation and weighing an average of 50 to 60 g. gained to above 100 g. in 88 days, an average of 0.6 g. gain per day; one rat reached 133 g. in 140 days. The tail vertebrae grew in proportion to the weight

238 E. B. ASTWOOD

gain, and there was no evidence of closure of the epiphyseal lines, as noted formerly (119). Again excess fat was deposited and less protein was formed than in normal animals.

It has been a common experience that provision of a good diet favors the growth response to pituitary extracts. In the hypophysectomized rat food intake increases when growth-promoting preparations are given, but even when the quantity of diet is held constant, increased weight and length can still occur (335, 250).

Both the quality (64) and the quantity (139) of protein in the diet influence the growth response to pituitary extracts. When casein was fed maximal growth was observed when the diet contained 24 % (139) (Fig. 1). Growth can be stimulated even when certain deficient diets are fed (101);

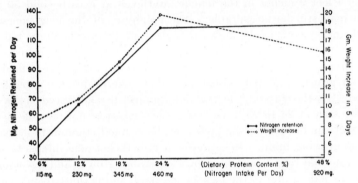

FIG. 1. Effects of the dietary protein concentration on nitrogen retention and weight increase produced by the daily injection of a growth hormone preparation for 5 days in adult female rats (from reference 139).

in choline-deficient rats weight loss was not prevented and large doses actually accelerated loss of weight (158).

2. Insulin

The great sensitivity of the hypophysectomized animal to the hypoglycemic effect of insulin has hindered studies on the effects of prolonged administration of insulin in the absence of the pituitary. Recently, by careful attention to diet and to dose it has been possible to show a pronounced growth effect of insulin in hypophysectomized rats (324, 325, 212, 26). A nutritious, high-carbohydrate diet was available at all times, and once-daily injections of protamine zinc insulin in doses of 0.4 to 0.5 unit increasing gradually to 2.4 to 3 units were given subcutaneously. The rate of weight gain, nearly 3 g. per day, approached that of normal animals, the viscera grew proportionately, the width of the epiphyseal cartilage nearly doubled in 15 days, and protein was deposited. It was further shown that as the dose of insulin increased there was progressive increase in positive nitrogen balance (212, 325). To induce a similar rate of weight gain, daily doses of a purified growth hormone preparation of 10 μg. increasing to 200 μg. were required. The insulin-treated animals ate more food, deposited more fat and less protein, and showed less widening of the tibial epiphyseal discs than did the animals treated with the pituitary preparation. The positive growth effects of concentrates of glucagon upon epiphyseal cartilage in hypophysectomized rats (97) have been explained on the basis of the insulin which contaminates impure glucagon preparations (134) (*cf.* sect. II D of Chap. V).

3. *Thyroid*

Though the activity of the thyroid gland is greatly depressed by hypophysectomy, a significant functional activity continues. Under a variety of circumstances the administration of thyroid has had little effect in inducing growth in the absence of the pituitary, though there have been numerous clinical reports of its benefit in human pituitary dwarfs, especially when given in conjunction with androgen therapy. In hypophysectomized animals thyrotropic preparations have exerted anabolic effects, such as a widening of the tibial epiphyseal cartilage (151, 152), nitrogen retention (247), and lowering of the concentration of circulating amino acids (117), but sometimes these effects were not clearly mediated by the thyroid and the purity of the preparations can properly be questioned.

The original observation of Smith, Greenwood, and Foster (367) that growth cannot be restored in hypophysectomized rats by the administration of thyroid has been amply confirmed. However, certain aspects of growth and anabolism have been induced. Thyroxine reduces the high concentration of urea in the blood of hypophysectomized rats (117) and restores the capacity of liver slices to form ketone bodies (33). In the rat thyroidectomized at birth growth may be induced by pituitary extracts (22). The growth response is greatly reduced, however, in the absence of the thyroid, and larger doses are required (107). The cretinous rats in the experiments of Salmon (323) failed completely to respond by growth or development to either pituitary extracts or implants. The administration of thyroid or thyroxine not only restores the growth response to pituitary extracts but actually potentiates it, especially in the hypophysectomized animal (203, 366, 107, 133, 211).

Probably the most striking growth effects of thyroxine in the hypophysectomized rat were those obtained by Geschwind and Li (133). The daily administration of 2 μg. to rats 28 days old at the time of operation induced a weight gain of 13 g. in 11 days and a widening of the tibial epiphyseal cartilage from a control width of 166 μ to 231 μ in 15 days; the latter effect equalled that from 25 μg. daily of a growth hormone preparation given for 4 days.

4. *Sex Hormones*

The growth spurt that occurs at puberty, and which is as well expressed in man as in any other animal, is dependent upon the secretion of sex hormones. In the absence of gonadal secretions the prepubertal rate of growth continues well into adult age and as the epiphyses of the long bones remain disunited gigantism in mild form results; the long bones become disproportionately long and the hands and feet large.

The pituitary dwarf does not, of course, exhibit an increased rate of growth at the age of normal puberty, but the administration of the appropriate sex hormone does cause a spurt in growth in the presumed absence of the pituitary. This has been more striking in the instance of androgen therapy in the male than of estrogen therapy in the female, though it must be pointed out that the latter has not been as carefully studied. After two to four years of growth induced by the administration of androgen, the epiphyses unite and further increase in height becomes impossible. The time of epiphyseal union is variable and seems to depend upon the quantity of sex hormone given. Small and perhaps slowly increased doses may favor a greater total growth than larger doses, and from experience thus far reported estrogen seems to cause a more prompt union of epiphyses than androgen. Many human "experiments" of this type have been complicated by the concomitant administration of thyroid.

Testosterone given to the weanling rat immediately after hypophysectomy accelerates growth, and a final weight of about 100 g. is reached in a few weeks instead of in several months. Like pituitary growth preparations, androgens can also cause a positive nitrogen balance (208), an increased growth of muscle and bone, a slight widening of the tibial epiphysial line (362, 151), and a maintenance of muscle glycogen on fasting (38). Excessive doses of androgen can inhibit growth in the normal animal.

Given with growth hormone preparation in hypophysectomized rats, androgen potentiates the growth effect as measured by increased weight or length or by widening of the epiphyseal cartilage. Given alone, however, androgen is less effective as an anabolic hormone than growth extracts in the absence of the pituitary (362).

In experimental animals estrogen exhibits little or no somatic growth-promoting effect, and large doses have been uniformly inhibitory. Doses which inhibit growth give evidence of being toxic; food intake is reduced, the adrenals enlarge, and the thymus atrophies. Hypophysectomized animals are more sensitive to the deleterious effects of estrogen, and large doses reduce survival. It is not unexpected, therefore, that estrogen would be found to inhibit the actions of growth hormone preparations (204). This inhibition can be overcome, however, and use can be made of the normal rat in growth stasis from the administration of stilbestrol to test growth hormone extracts (156).

5. Adrenal Cortex

A normal rate of growth appears to require a normally functioning adrenal cortex.   Adrenalectomy in young rats inhibits growth, but this can be restored at least in part by the administration of salt, deoxycorticosterone, or adrenal cortical extract.   Excessive quantities of adrenal hormones, especially cortisone and hydrocortisone, or of corticotropin (104), inhibit growth, but whether or not an optimal amount of cortical steroid can restore a normal rate of growth after adrenalectomy in the rat seems not to have been determined.

A mutual antagonism between the adrenal cortical secretions and growth hormone has been shown in many systems.   It has been repeatedly observed that corticotropin and adrenal steroids inhibit the weight-increasing effects of growth hormone preparations (21, 249) and also their effects upon bone growth (14, 21).

Following adrenalectomy it has been noted (184) that the arrested growth of the rat is associated with changes in the epiphyseal cartilage similar to those seen after hypophysectomy.   It has been pointed out, however, that these changes are probably caused by a decreased food intake and are correctable by the administration of salt.   It has also been observed that two or more weeks after adrenalectomy there is an actual widening of the epiphyseal cartilage (418), suggesting that the normally functioning adrenal cortex may exercise some measure of restraint upon the chondrotropic action of growth hormone.   When tested in hypophysectomized-adrenalectomized rats, however, this possibility was not borne out (223, 361); no increase in sensitivity to growth hormone could be detected after removal of the adrenals.

B. Secretion and Fate of the Growth Hormone

Methods have not yet been devised to measure the quantity of growth hormone in blood or urine; indeed the hormone has not even been detected in the body fluids of normal animals or man (149).   There are therefore no data bearing directly upon the rate or time of secretion of growth hormone from the pituitary or upon the factors which influence the secretion.   Estimates of the quantity of a growth hormone preparation needed to repair the growth deficit after hypophysectomy can be arrived at, but so many other factors influence growth processes under these circumstances that the quantitative validity of such estimates may be open to question.

Van Dyke *et al.* (398) have carried out ingenious experiments in parabiotic rats and estimated that the pituitary of the normal young rat may
secrete an amount of growth hormone equivalent to 210 to 220 μg. of
purified extract. They further estimated that after injection the growth-
promoting activity of the plasma decreased slowly with a half life of 9 hours,
and that the hormone distributed itself into 28 % of the body weight. The
slow rate of degradation is in keeping with earlier findings (151) that single
daily injections of growth-promoting extracts are just as effective as divided
daily doses and that daily intravenous injections are equally as effective as
subcutaneous or intraperitoneal injections. Similarly, the subcutaneous
administration of growth preparations combined with media designed to
slow absorption has not been found to enhance effectiveness. No information is available as to the sites of inactivation or as to the mode of degradation or elimination of growth hormone.

C. Biological Effects of Growth Hormone Preparations

1. *Growth*

Growth effects have been observed from relatively crude growth-
promoting preparations from pituitary glands in normal and hypophysectomized vertebrates of a number of species and classes. Detailed investigations, and especially those with the purer preparations, have been limited
to a very few species, and of these the rat takes first place; it has received
more attention than all other animals combined. It is probably true to
say that the growth effects of pituitary extracts in the rat are more impressive and consistent than those seen in any other species yet investigated.

a. Rat. The male rat continues to increase in weight and in length
throughout most of its life span, and though the rate of growth can be
accelerated by pituitary extract (103, 248), the effect is not as great as it is
in the normal adult female. After the age of five or six months the female
rat, having attained a weight of 250 to 300 g., grows at a very slow rate if
pregnancy is not permitted and the growth effects of pituitary preparations
are more easily observed. The rate of gain in weight is rapid during the
first week or so of injections and decreases steadily as treatment is continued; subsequent courses of treatment are also progressively less effective
and the response tends to become less with advancing age (63, 248). Over
a dose range of from 0.25 to 4.0 mg. per day of a growth-promoting globulin
fraction the weight gain in 20 days increased in direct proportion to the
log of the dose, and the weight gained amounted to from 22 to 58 g., *i.e.*,
1 to 3 g. per day (248). This has formed the basis of one assay method for
growth hormone (248, 216, 152).

Prolonged treatment with active preparations has resulted in a continued
increase of the growth rate, and animals weighing 550 g.—compared with

TABLE I

QUANTITIES OF RECENT GROWTH HORMONE PREPARATIONS FOUND TO BE REQUIRED
FOR VARIOUS RESPONSES IN EXPERIMENTAL ANIMALS; ARRANGED
APPROXIMATELY IN ORDER OF INCREASING DOSE ON A BODY
WEIGHT BASIS

Effect	Animal	Single or Daily Dose		References
		Per animal, mg.	mg./kg.	
Widening of tibial epiphyseal cartilage	Hypophysectomized rat	0.001–0.03	0.01–0.3	(151, 152, 52)
Restoration of insulin responsiveness	Hypophysectomized dog	—	0.02–0.3	
Increased milk yield	Cow	30	0.1	(70)
Growth	Hypophysectomized rat	0.01–0.03	0.1–0.3	(227, 152)
Growth and nitrogen retention	Dog	2.5–10.	0.1–0.5	(122)
Exacerbation of diabetes	Diabetic dog		0.25	(54)
Hypoglycemia	Hypophysectomized dog	—	0.3–1.0	(210)
Hypoglycemia	Hypophysectomized rat	0.01	0.5	(278)
Diabetes	Partially depancreatized cat	—	0.2–5.0	(180)
Diabetes	Hypophysectomized dog	—	1.0	(82)
Diabetes	Cat	3–5	1.0	(71)
Diabetes	Dog	—	1–3	(51, 52)
Growth	Adult female rat	0.2–1.0	0.8–4.0	(152)
Growth and nitrogen retention	Cat	3–10	1.0–2.0	(256)
Ketosis	Fasting rat	0.5–3.0	1.5–10.0 5.0	(24) (404, 236)
Glycostatic effect	Hypophysectomized rat	—	1.0–20.0	(320, 183)
Fat mobilization	Rat	0.5	2.0	(146)
Use of amino acids	Nephrectomized rat	—	10.0	(319)
Glycotropic effect	Rat	—	30.0	(257)
Vascular damage	Rat	3.0 & 6.0	15.0–30.0	(342)
Growth	Mouse	0.6–2.4	30.0–120.0	(365, 262)
Fat mobilization	Mouse	0.1–5.0	5.0–250.0	(407, 279, 222, 383)
Enlargement of spleen	Mouse	1–6	50.0–300.0	(209)

244 E. B. ASTWOOD

the normal of 310 g.—have been produced in 437 days (105). The liver, stomach, intestine, kidney, and heart increased in weight in proportion to the body. The dose required was large. The preparation used was found to cause a gain of 1 g. per day when given to hypophysectomized rats in a dose of 20 μg. per day for 10 days. The "plateaued" female rats received 0.4 mg. increasing to 2.0 mg. daily, and still the rate of gain declined toward the end (105).

Hypophysectomized young rats are consistently more sensitive to the growth effects of pituitary extracts, less than one-half (63) or even one-tenth (248) the dose or less (152) being sufficient to cause a gain in weight equal to that induced in "plateaued" normal females. The most active preparations of growth hormone in doses of 10 μg. per day will induce weight gains averaging 1 g. per day, whereas 30 μg. to 100 μg. per day may be required to double this rate of growth.

The most sensitive indicator of growth activity thus far encountered is the epiphyseal cartilage plate of the proximal end of the tibia. As little as 5 μg. of the more active extracts given over a 4-day period produces a measurable thickening of the cartilage (106, 151, 152).

The weight gain in the hypophysectomized rat is paralleled by an increase in body length, in bone length and weight, and in the weights of the muscles and most of the viscera (360). Thymus, spleen, and lymph nodes may increase in size disproportionately, whereas the thyroid, gonads, and adrenals may grow only slightly. The liver increases in size in proportion to the body, but the kidney, stomach, intestine, and heart lag behind. Though measurement is difficult, observation shows that there is also a growth of hair, an increase in area and thickness of skin, and presumably a proportional increase of connective tissue, blood vessels, and nerves throughout the body. Only the brain and eyeballs escape the stunting effects of hypophysectomy (405) and the growth effects of replacement therapy.

The following description by Simpson, Evans, and Li (360) of hypophysectomized rats which had been treated with a growth hormone preparation for 437 days illustrates the extent to which deficiency of the entire anterior pituitary is corrected by the growth preparation: "The injected rats were sluggish, although their muscle tone was good. Their noses and paws were pinker than in controls. The hair was long, soft and lusterless; the guard hairs were poorly developed . . . . The skin was redundant—large folds could be plucked up. Abnormalities of the pelvic girdle and the thoracic cage were noted ('pigeon breast,' 'shelf-like' pelvis). The wrists and ankles were thick, as were the digits. The paws were, however, not elongated as much as would have been anticipated from the general body growth. The head was not long and slender as in normal animals but thick laterally and dorso-ventrally.   The nose was coarse, the cheeks could properly be called 'jowls.' . . .   The eyes were less prominent than normal. The phallus was enlarged and there was a fullness between anus and vaginal orifice suggesting a scrotum.   The nipples were long . . . ."

"At autopsy the injected animals showed large amounts of subcutaneous and intraperitoneal fat.   Muscular hypertrophy was evident. . . .   The adrenals were observed to be larger than in the control animals (shown to be due to medullary and not to cortical enlargement). . . .   In spite of the atrophy of the ovaries, the vaginas of the injected animals were open whereas in controls all vaginal membranes were intact.   The thymus, though reduced in size, was semi-translucent and glistening as in the normal, whereas only a tag of tissue scarcely recognizable as thymus remained in the hypophysectomized controls."

b. Mouse.   From the limited published data it would appear that the mouse is much less sensitive than the rat to the growth effects of pituitary extracts.   Thus normal mice given daily doses of 0.04 mg. increasing to 2.0 mg. for 194 days showed little added growth (262).   The females gained somewhat more rapidly than controls, but the males showed no increased rate of growth, though the viscera were somewhat enlarged.   A crude alkaline extract in a dose of 0.02 ml. daily to mice beginning at the age of 28 days and continued for 105 days induced growth from an original weight of 12.5 g. to a final weight of 41 g., whereas the controls gained to 29.5 g. (95).   Tumor-bearing mice required 0.6, 1.2, and 2.4 mg. daily over successive 9-day periods in order to exhibit growth stimulation (365).   The untreated mice gained 4 g. in 27 days, the injected ones 12 to 15 g.   With the initial dose of 0.6 mg. (about 30 mg. per kilogram) growth was accelerated for only a few days.   Unlike the rat (261), the normal mouse exhibited no tendency to develop tumors with prolonged treatment (262). Normal male mice injected with a growth preparation for 4 days exhibited an enlargement of the spleen, the degree of which was proportional to the dose in the range of from 1 to 6 mg. daily (about 50 to 300 mg. per kilogram) (209).

It is difficult to conceive of the secretion of such quantities of a hormone from the hypophysis of a normal intact mouse.

c. Guinea Pig.   Apparently the guinea pig may sometimes continue to grow at an appreciable rate after hypophysectomy.   Growth stasis is the rule, however, and growth can proceed at a normal rate if transplants of pituitary tissue be made in the anterior chamber of the eye (336).   In one experiment of this type four hypophysectomized animals grew even though the ocular transplants failed to take (337).   In neither the normal nor the hypophysectomized animal have growth hormone preparations been effective in accelerating weight gain, although in the normal animal crude pituitary extract effects growth changes in cartilage and bone and premature union of the epiphyses (356, 357). Doses of 0.25 to 3.0 mg. daily sub-cutaneously in two daily doses for 10 days in normal young guinea pigs did not accelerate growth. The largest dose in hypophysectomized animals seemed actually to cause weight loss (260). The guinea pig is known to be highly sensitive to thyrotropin and to the development of hypersensitivity, and it is tentatively suggested that contamination of the preparation used with thyrotropin or with a toxic or allergenic impurity may account for the failure to obtain growth.

d. Monkey. Like the guinea pig, the monkey appears to derive no anabolic stimulus from the injection of purified growth hormone prepara-tions. Doses of 5 mg. per kilogram daily in normal immature *M. rhesus* caused no gain in weight and no changes in the blood concentrations of glucose, nonprotein nitrogen, or inorganic phosphorus. In the hypophys-ectomized animal, weight was not affected, and, except for a decrease in the concentration of nonprotein nitrogen in the blood, no positive effects were observed (207). Further studies on the guinea pig and monkey will be awaited with interest for they may lead to a better understanding of the factors which limit the effectiveness of growth hormone preparations in man.

Other animals have been caused to grow at an increased rate by the ad-ministration of pituitary extracts. Growth, acromegalic changes, and lac-tation have been induced in the normal and hypophysectomized *dog* by crude extracts (387, 103, 422); increased growth and positive nitrogen balances have been seen in the *cat* (422, 256) and *ferret* (94) following the injection of crude and more purified preparations. In the *pigeon* prolactin preparations were more effective in increasing the body weight and the size of the viscera than any other type of extract (312), and the capacity of pituitary extracts to prevent weight loss following hypophysectomy was correlated with their prolactin contents. The growth of the regenerating feather in the *chicken* was uninfluenced by a growth hormone preparation (198), but a slight growth stimulation was obtained in the developing chick embryo (181).

2. Effects on Protein Metabolism

A true increase of protoplasm and its constituents, implying an increase in the body stores of protein, requires a positive nitrogen balance. Meas-urements of nitrogen excretion on a constant diet or of excretion versus intake have been made in many species and under a variety of experimental conditions. Nitrogen retention following the administration of pituitary extract was first noted in the dog (387, 388). It has been clearly shown in the rat that growth-promoting extracts induce the retention of nitrogen and increase the quantity of protein in the body (335, 247, 422, 139, 76, 161, 232).   It has been estimated that, if tissue contains an average of 20 % of protein and protein 16 % of nitrogen, a gain of 1 kg. would be associated with a retention of 32 g. of nitrogen.   A purified growth preparation given to normal adult female rats induced nitrogen retention and growth which correlated almost exactly with this theoretical value (139) (see Fig. 2).

In response to a crude preparation of growth hormone the added weight in paired fed rats was found to contain 48 g. of nitrogen per kilogram (335), the high value possibly being accounted for by the loss in fat.   The carcass of the normal rat was found to contain 31.8 g. of nitrogen per kilogram, whereas after dietary restriction with depletion of depot fat the value was 35.1 g., and conversely that of hypophysectomized animals was 27.3 g.

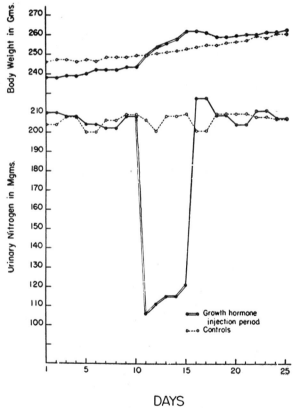

DAYS

FIG. 2.   Effects of a growth hormone preparation on body weight and nitrogen excretion of rats given a constant daily ration containing 18% casein (from reference 139).

During fasting growth hormone preparations do not cause nitrogen retention in the normal rat (24, 404).

Dogs given a single large injection of crude growth hormone preparations exhibited wide variations in the amount of nitrogen stored for a gain of 1 kg. (16, 17). In one series of experiments the values varied from 17.4 to 23.2 g., whereas in others as much as 9.7 g. of nitrogen was stored with no increase in weight. Greater and more constant effects were obtained when the dogs were treated for 10 days; 2.5 to 10 mg. of extract daily caused weight gains of 113 to 1500 g. and nitrogen storage of from 9.6 to 21.17 g. in 10 days (122).

The quantity of amino acids, urea, and total nonprotein nitrogen in tissues and entire carcass was found to be reduced following treatment of rats with a crude growth hormone preparation during 10 to 14 hours (335). Hypophysectomy induced changes in the opposite direction. In 4 hours after a single injection the amino acid content of the blood was reduced by preparations of growth hormone or of thyrotropin; the latter extract also reduced the concentration of urea, whereas the growth preparation was ineffectual, and the effects seemed not to be mediated by the thyroid (117). These same preparations induced nitrogen retention in normal adult female rats (247). The progressive rise in the amino acid content which follows evisceration in the rat was unaffected by the injection of pituitary extract (118).

The extra nitrogen stored in the bodies of normal rats in response to a growth hormone preparation was found to be accounted for chiefly by an increase in muscle, but different muscles were affected to widely different degrees (142). There was little change in the nitrogen content of spleen, kidney, liver, or heart, but there was an increase of as much as 60% in that of the acromiotrapezius. The nitrogen content of most other muscles increased 10% to 30%. The muscles enlarged in proportion to the nitrogen stored (142), and there was little change in the concentration of muscle proteins (148).

a. *Influence of Insulin.* Insulin is known to be essential for normal growth, and it has often been noted that growth cannot be induced by pituitary extracts in severely diabetic animals unless insulin is given (237). Pituitary extract increases protein catabolism in the Houssay dog (175). In the depancreatized dog given constant amounts of insulin a single injection of a crude growth hormone preparation caused an intensification of the diabetic state and negative nitrogen balance (123). The daily administration of 0.25 mg. per kilogram of a purified preparation, though greatly aggravating the diabetic state, had no effect on the excretion of nitrogen in dogs rendered diabetic by pancreatectomy or by prior treatment with pituitary extract (54).   Only when added amounts of insulin were provided did the extract induce nitrogen retention (123).

The rate of accumulation of nonprotein nitrogen of the blood of dogs after nephrectomy is slowed by pituitary extract, but if the pancreas is also removed the reverse effect was observed (258).   A partially purified growth hormone preparation retarded urea formation in nephrectomized rats given a protein hydrolyzate, but under these conditions injected insulin was without effect (319), indicating that increased secretion of insulin by the pancreas could not alone be responsible, though in the absence of insulin pituitary extract failed to retard the accumulation of amino acids in the blood (118).   In the diabetic rat, growth hormone preparations, while augmenting the glycosuria (318), caused a fall in the amino acid content of the blood, nitrogen retention, and growth (401), and reduced the excretion of sodium and potassium (137).   In the diabetic cat, however, insulin proved to be essential to nitrogen retention (256).

b. Effects on Nucleoproteins and Nucleic Acids.   Growth of tissue, associated with an increase of all cellular constituents, might be expected to require an increased synthesis of nucleoproteins and related compounds. Growth hormone preparations have been shown to restore the decreased concentration of liver ribonucleic acid (RNA) consequent to hypophysectomy in the rat (226), whereas under similar circumstances deoxyribonucleic acid (DNA) is little affected if at all (226, 90).   There is a comparable loss of protein from both cytoplasm and nucleus of liver cells after hypophysectomy, and these, too, are restored by growth hormone.   As RNA is thought to be of importance in protein synthesis, whereas DNA may be largely a structural element, these findings might suggest a specific effect of growth hormone on the former.   In the hen's egg with virtually no nucleic acid prior to incubation both DNA and RNA are synthesized by the embryo during development, and the injection of growth hormone augments somewhat the rate of synthesis of DNA but not of RNA (406).   The changes here are small in comparison with other effects of growth preparations on tissues and do not suggest a primacy of action on this nucleic acid.

3. *Effects on Metabolism of Inorganic Substances*

a. Phosphorus.   It is well established that the concentration of inorganic phosphorus in the serum is higher in young growing individuals than in the adult, is higher than normal in human beings with acromegaly, and is reduced following hypophysectomy in the rat.   Injection of crude pituitary extract in the dog has been noted to increase the concentration of inorganic phosphorus in the blood (388) and to reduce phosphate excretion (16).   In the young growing rat the concentration of phosphate in the plasma was found to be about 11 mg. per 100 ml., and in the adult about 7.5 mg. (228). Following hypophysectomy in the young animal the concentration fell from 10.7 mg. to 8.1 mg. in a week, to 6.6 mg. in two weeks, and to 2.7 mg. in 449 days; the initial concentration was maintained by a daily dose of 100 μg. of a growth hormone preparation for 15 days, and following prolonged injection for longer than a year the normal concentration was nearly but not quite maintained (228, 226).

Somewhat similar relationships have been noted in the case of the alkaline phosphatase of plasma. The concentration is high in growing rats, is reduced by hypophysectomy or by treatment with corticotropic extracts, and is increased by injection of growth hormone preparations (226). The concentration of phosphatase in bone is likewise increased by growth-promoting extracts (251).

Two hours after the injection of rats with phosphate labeled with P^{32} the specific activity of the plasma indicated a slower rate of removal of phosphate after hypophysectomy and a partial restoration by a growth hormone preparation. Similarly hypophysectomy reduced, and the pituitary preparation increased, the rate of turnover of nucleic acids and phospholipids of the thymus and liver.

b. *Calcium.* The growth of bone induced by pituitary extract would be expected to require a positive balance of calcium. Following removal of the pituitary of the rat the calcium balance becomes negative and a positive balance is restored by the injection of crude pituitary extract (286). Positive balances have been noted only on isolated occasions in man, and negative calcium balance was observed with crude extract in the dog (387). Using Ca^{45} as a tracer, a growth hormone preparation was found to have no effect on the uptake of Ca^{45} by bone in the normal rat but served to restore the diminished uptake of the hypophysectomized rat to normal (396, 395). It was further noted that 1 hour after the injection of Ca^{45} the hypophysectomized rat deposited more of the element in the region of the epiphyseal plate than did the normal animal, and the rate of removal of the radiocalcium from the blood was accelerated.

c. *Sulfur.* Because of its content of chondroitin sulfate, cartilage selectively accumulates radioactive sulfur following the administration of inorganic sulfate labeled with S^{35}. The rate at which the radioactive sulfate was removed from the plasma of rats after intravenous injection was greatly slowed following hypophysectomy, but nearly normal if the hypophysectomized animals were treated with 25 μg. of a growth hormone preparation for 3 days (96). Conversely the specific activity of the sulfate in cartilage 13 to 25 hours after injection was only one-fourth or one-fifth as great in the hypophysectomized rat as in the normal. Injection of the growth extract increased the incorporation of sulfate into cartilage but did

not restore it to normal (96).   The great change in the rate of disappearance of radiosulfate from the blood suggests that incorporation into other
substances such as protein is influenced by the pituitary, and is in keeping
with the reduction in total sulfate excretion noted in dogs following the
injection of pituitary extract (125), and the increased rate of incorporation
of methionine labeled with S^{35} into muscle protein in normal mice and
hypophysectomized rats induced by injections of a growth hormone preparation (120).

Positive balances of other elements resulting from the injection of growth
hormone have included sodium (137, 375, 413), potassium (137, 375, 413),
and chloride (375).

4. Effects of Growth Hormone Preparations on Carbohydrate and Fat Metabolism

Loss of the anterior pituitary leads to a tendency to hypoglycemia and
loss of hepatic and muscle glycogen on fasting, an increased sensitivity to
insulin, and an increased rate of utilization of carbohydrate; glycosuria and
ketosis from pancreatic or alloxan diabetes or from the administration of
phlorizin are attenuated by removal of the anterior lobe.   Crude anterior
pituitary extracts can reverse these effects and exert effects which are of
the opposite sense in normal animals; the several seemingly diverse actions
have sometimes been ascribed to individual metabolic factors.   Intensification of the diabetes of the hypophysectomized diabetic dog has been
ascribed to a *diabetogenic factor* (175), an immediate increase in the blood
sugar in normal animals to a *hyperglycemic factor*, an inhibitory action
against insulin to a *glycotropic factor* (419), an intensification of ketosis of
the fasting state to a *ketogenic factor* (43), and a preservation of muscle
glycogen of the hypophysectomized rat during fasting to a *glycostatic factor*
(316).   Mobilization of depot fat to the liver has been ascribed to a *fat-
mobilizing factor* (27) or *adipokinin* and a lowering of the respiratory quotient and increased oxygen consumption to a *specific metabolic principle*
(270).   It has further been noted that pituitary extracts may cause an
initial lowering of the blood sugar, and a *hypoglycemic factor* or *pancreatropic factor* (increasing insulin secretion) has been suggested (6, 170); the
induction of temporary and finally permanent diabetes in normal animals
by pituitary extracts implies a diabetogenic factor in the true sense.

During the past decade all of these effects have been obtained with
growth hormone preparations, and the concept that growth hormone is
inherently possessed with this diversity of potentialities is now current.
The relationship of the pituitary to diabetes mellitus has already been
thoroughly reviewed by Bennett and Evans (23).   The further investigations since then using purified growth hormone fractions have served to

show the close association of growth hormone with a number of phases of carbohydrate and fat metabolism.

a. *Glycostatic Effect.* The stores of glycogen not only in the liver but also in skeletal muscle are depleted in the hypophysectomized rat during fasting. Russell (316) found that certain pituitary extracts would preserve muscle glycogen under these conditions and suggested the term glycostatic factor for the active principle. A number of crude and partially purified extracts were tested, and the glycostatic effect did not seem to correlate well with any other activity. It was present in some thyrotropic, corticotropic, and growth preparations but was also present in extracts of low thyrotropic, lactogenic, corticotropic, and gonadotropic activity. Crude unfractionated extracts proved to be the most active, the minimal effective dose being about 10 mg. per kilogram. Partially purified growth hormone was later found to be active in doses of from 1 to 5 mg. per kilogram (167) and the purified preparation of Wilhelmi *et al.* (414) in doses of 1 to 2 mg. per kilogram (320).

The preservation of glycogen stores under these circumstances is considered to be the result of decreased carbohydrate utilization brought about by the extract (318), because either crude extracts (110) or purified growth preparations promoted the storage of glycogen and depressed the respiratory quotient of fasted rats or rats given glucose (257, 183). The glycogen content of the heart is of particular interest; it increases progressively with fasting in the normal rat but not after removal of the pituitary (3). The injection of growth hormone preparations greatly accelerates the accumulation of glycogen in the normal rat, as well as increasing it in the hypophysectomized animal from about 400 mg. per 100 g. to over 1000 mg. per 100 g. These findings led to the interesting suggestion, in line with that of Young (425), that with the stress of fasting increased amounts of growth hormone are secreted from the pituitary. It was also suggested that this response might serve as a simple method for the assay of growth hormone in the intact rat (3). Unfortunately, the effect does not appear to be specific. Corticotropic concentrates prepared by the glacial acetic acid-oxycellulose process are also myoglycostatic in the rat (276) and are considerably more active in this respect than growth hormone preparations. In the fasting mouse the activity of preparations of corticotropin is at least 10 times that of growth hormone in increasing the glycogen content of the heart (9).

b. *Ketogenesis and Depression of Respiratory Quotient.* The administration of pituitary extract to rats causes an intensification of the ketonuria of fasting (43, 30, 353, 144) and a fall in the respiratory quotient (110, 145)—effects which are the reverse of those which follow hypophysectomy

(175, 110). A search for the active principle involved has led in two directions, one leading to the conclusion that the factor is an unusually labile protein which tends to be associated with growth hormone (352, 353, 144, 295), the other suggesting that the active principle is a remarkably stable substance of small molecular proportions with properties not unlike current preparations of corticotropin. Greaves, Freiberg, and Johns (144) prepared concentrates of the factor by methods similar to those used for purifying growth hormone; activity was quickly lost in neutral or acid solutions but could be preserved in solutions at about pH 10. Even the dried powder lost activity *in vacuo* at 0°C.

Collip and collaborators (270, 86) have studied a very different type of preparation termed by them the specific metabolic principle. The extracts were stable to boiling temperatures over a wide range of pH and were resistant to alkali and to peptic digestion. They were found to have the properties of (*1*) increasing the oxygen consumption of normal or thyroidectomized rabbits, (*2*) decreasing the respiratory quotient, (*3*) increasing the ketonemia of normal or adrenalectomized rats, (*4*) increasing the glycosuria and ketonuria of the Houssay dog, (*5*) inhibiting the hypoglycemic action of insulin, (*6*) inhibiting the hyperglycemic action of adrenalin, (*7*) maintaining muscle glycogen, and (*8*) suppressing the utilization of carbohydrate. The physical properties and most of the biological activities of the "specific metabolic factor" resemble those of current preparations of purified corticotropin (314, 12).

The ketosis induced by crude pituitary extracts and by growth and corticotropic concentrates is believed to be due to an increased rate of ketone body production by the liver (24). Liver slices removed from rats 24 hours after the injection of pituitary extract exhibited increased rates of oxygen consumption and acetoacetate production, suggesting that the extract had promoted an increased rate of oxidation of fatty acids (49). A purified growth hormone preparation was found to have no effect on acetoacetate production when injected 2 hours before the slices were taken (33) and was even inhibitory at 6 hours (147); acetoacetate production and fatty acid oxidase activity were greatly augmented at 12 and 24 hours (147). Under similar conditions another study (236) showed that a large dose (5 mg.) of a growth hormone preparation caused ketosis in the rat within 2 hours and augmented acetoacetate production by liver slices.

The great lability of the ketogenic factor in the growth-hormone type of extract and its relatively great stability in the corticotropic preparation would certainly seem to indicate that two factors are involved here. However, the possibility must be considered that enzymatic destruction is involved; like corticotropin, the substance responsible for ketosis might be destroyed by enzymes contained in the growth-type of extract, while the deliberately vigorous extraction methods used for corticotropin might be expected to destroy such enzymes.

c. *Fat-Mobilizing Effect.* In the absence of the pituitary the use of depot fat for fuel is impaired. Lee and Ayres (214) found that hypophysectomized adult rats lost weight more rapidly than paired fed unoperated partners. The normal rats made use of 60 % of their depot fat during the 33 days of restricted diet, whereas the hypophysectomized animals consumed only 28 % during the same period. The greater weight loss in the absence of the pituitary was accounted for, therefore, by the utilization of 18.6 % of their initial nitrogen; the normal rats suffered no loss in tissue protein. Growth hormone preparations exerted a reverse effect. The animals injected with the pituitary extract gained weight more rapidly than the uninjected controls, even though they were not allowed more food; depot fat was used for energy, and a larger proportion of dietary material was thus available for growth.

Within a few hours of the injection of crude pituitary extracts into mice there is a pronounced increase of fat in the liver (27). It was clearly shown that this fat is derived from depot fat (15, 376) but that it accounts for only a fraction of the total fat mobilized in response to the injection (53).

When purified growth hormone was found to exert this adipokinetic effect (383, 407, 222, 232), it was widely accepted that fat mobilization was one of the intrinsic properties of this hormone. It is of interest therefore to note that other types of pituitary extract also have this property (279, 263, 314), and some of them are far more potent than growth preparations in this respect. The doses of purified growth preparation required to increase the concentration of liver lipid in the mouse are large, and have varied between 0.1 to 10 mg. per mouse or about 5 to 500 mg. per kilogram (383, 407, 221, 222, 279, 146). It has also been noted that some preparations of purified growth hormone were much weaker than others (Fig. 3), and some were inactive in this respect in doses as high as 5 mg per mouse, or about 250 mg. per kilogram (222).

Concentrates of thyrotropin have also been found to cause fat mobilization. In the guinea pig this is associated with the infiltration of fat into many tissues besides the liver and accompanied by lipemia (364, 91, 194). In the mouse some preparations of thyrotropin are more active than growth preparations (279). The most potent preparations of adipokinin thus far encountered are the corticotropin concentrates prepared by the glacial acetic acid-oxycellulose procedure (11) (Fig. 4). Doses of 3 to 10 μg. per mouse, *i.e.*, 0.150 to 0.5 mg. per kilogram, induce a proportional increase in the concentration of lipid in the liver (314). This preparation appears to

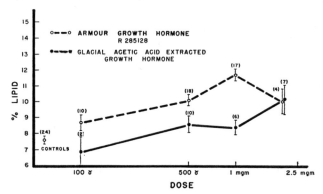

FIG. 3.   Comparison of adipokinetic activity of an Armour growth hormone preparation with one derived from a hot glacial acetic acid extract (from reference 314).

act more quickly and the maximal effect is seen in 3 hours instead of the 6 or 7 hours required for the maximal accumulation of fat in the liver after giving growth hormone preparations.   Further purification of this type of extract to yield corticotropin B and corticotropin A does not appreciably influence the adipokinetic potency.   It is apparent therefore that current growth hormone preparations contain only a very small fraction of the total fat-mobilizing potency of the pituitary, and the possibility must be

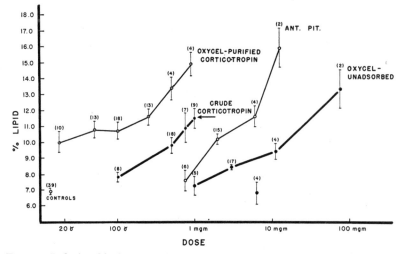

FIG. 4.   Relationship between dose and adipokinetic response (per cent hepatic lipid 7 hours after injection) for four pituitary preparations.   The numbers of animals used and the standard errors of the means are shown.   Crude corticotropin made by the glacial acetic acid method was about 4 times as active as the anterior pituitary powder, whereas the oxycel-purified corticotropin was roughly 1000 times as potent as the residual, unadsorbed fraction (from reference 314).

considered that the weak adipokinetic activity of growth extracts represents a contaminant.

It would, of course, be reasonable on teleologic grounds for growth hormone itself to promote the mobilization and oxidation of fat. If growth is to occur and protein be laid down in tissue, a source of calories is essential, and, if these are not supplied by excess food, body fat would have to be used. On a restricted diet fat is lost after hypophysectomy, whereas on a full diet more fat is laid down. So even in the absence of the pituitary, fat can be mobilized and burned though at a reduced rate. Perhaps then growth-promoting extracts by diverting more dietary protein and calories toward anabolic processes create a relative dietary insufficiency and fat is mobilized as a consequence. Viewed this way fat mobilization from growth hormone would be a secondary phenomenon. The potent adipokinetic activity of corticotropic preparations strongly favors the view that the pituitary may secrete a specific substance which favors the utilization of depot fat. The corticotropin concentrates also have the properties of lowering the respiratory quotient (314, 9), increasing ketosis (314, 98), and inhibiting insulin (410), suggesting that the utilization of carbohydrate is inhibited. Thus, upon fasting, the secretion of such a principle would favor the transfer of the source of energy for the body from carbohydrate to fat.

d. *Glycotropic Effect.* The factor in crude pituitary extracts which inhibits insulin has been termed the "glycotropic substance" by Young (419), who showed that extracts rich in this factor were not themselves diabetogenic. It was also pointed out that animals rendered highly insensitive to insulin by injection of these extracts exhibited normal concentrations of blood sugar. Glycotropic activity did not seem to be a property of prolactin, thyrotropin, gonadotropin, or the ketogenic factor but did appear to parallel glycostatic activity (420). A prolactin preparation had some glycotropic activity in the dog (363).

The antiinsulin effect has usually not been seen immediately after the injection of the pituitary extract but only several hours later (257) or following repeated injections over several days (213, 268, 175). In the mouse, however, a corticotropic preparation, although lowering the blood sugar when given alone, also inhibited insulin acutely. Given to adrenalectomized mice immediately before 0.5 to 1.0 unit of insulin, 100 μg. of the corticotropic extract inhibited convulsions, and with 5 units of insulin the blood sugar fell only to the extent expected from the extract alone (410).

The inhibitory influence of pituitary extracts and specifically of growth hormone preparations upon the action of insulin has been shown in several ways. The great sensitivity of the hypophysectomized dog to insulin can be corrected by pretreatment for several days with pituitary extract (179) or with purified growth hormone preparations (80).   To refer to pituitary extracts as glycotropic or insulin-inhibiting may be descriptively correct under the particular circumstances of the appropriate experiments, but it is probable that there is not a direct antagonism between insulin and the pituitary secretion.   Furthermore, it is most difficult in any given experiment to make a distinction between an antiinsulin effect and a diabetogenic effect, but it is possible to show that growth hormone preparations are both glycotropic and diabetogenic (425, 257), whereas corticotropic extracts are glycotropic but will not produce permanent diabetes in the dog (292).

In the depancreatized animal, and thus in the presumed absence of insulin, pituitary extracts can still further intensify the diabetic state (256, 54)—an effect most clearly shown in the Houssay dog (175).   This effect cannot be classed as glycotropic, but whether the effect is caused by the same principle which in the normal dog can lead to diabetes is still uncertain.

The inhibitory action of pituitary extracts on carbohydrate metabolism would be readily explained if it could be established that the action of hexokinase were inhibited (285).   The finding that certain pituitary preparations were inhibitory to hexokinase in vitro, the inhibition being reversed by insulin, has not been widely confirmed.   The inhibitory factor seemed to be associated with growth hormone, but, unlike the growth factor, it proved to be extremely unstable (285) and was even inactivated by freezing.   The glycotropic effect of such preparations was not readily lost, and this fact gave rise to the interesting hypothesis that the antihexokinase activity of growth hormone preparations so readily lost in vitro was regenerated when the inactivated preparation was injected in vivo (301).   There is recent evidence to suggest that the antihexokinase activity of fresh pituitary extracts may have been an effect of lipoproteins upon the enzyme system.   The serum of diabetic rats was found to inhibit the uptake of glucose by rat diaphragms in vitro (36); the inhibitory factor was associated with the lipoprotein fraction of such serum and appeared in the serum of normal rats injected with growth hormone preparations (35).   In most experiments involving tissue in vitro it has been found that pituitary extracts inhibit insulin only if injected into the ainmal before the tissue is taken and are ineffective when added in vitro (372, 373, 36).

e. "Pancreatropic" Effect.   It was suggested early (6, 170) on the basis of a lowering of the blood glucose that pituitary extracts exert a "pancreatropic" effect, and a proliferation of islet tissue was noted in the rat (6, 311, 79), dog (311), and rabbit (271) after the injection of certain extracts including purified growth preparations.   Recent investigations of the pancreatropic effect (in the histological sense) suggest that growth hormone may not be the factor mainly concerned with the changes seen.   By the

use of colchicine the mitotic activity of the cells of the pancreatic islets of
the rat was studied following the injection of corticotropic and of growth
preparations. Both of these extracts increased the mitotic count; of the
two, the growth preparation was the more effective and stimulated mitosis
mainly in the α-cells, whereas the β-cells were stimulated by the corticotropic preparation (58). Continuous subcutaneous infusion of a growth
hormone preparation into normal rats for a period of 10 days resulted in no
consistent change in the β-cells or in the size of the islets (1). Under the
same circumstances a corticotropic preparation caused great islet enlargement and cellular proliferation (Fig. 5). Both preparations seemed to
cause an increase in the size of the α-cells. The fact that increased nitrogen
retention and gain in body weight were induced by the growth perparation
without any visible effect upon the β-cells suggests that the growth effects
were not mediated by an increased insulin secretion. The extent of the
growth and proliferation of the islets and β-cells from corticotropin was
correlated with the degree of glycosuria, suggesting that it was the elevated
concentration of circulating glucose which affected the β-cells rather than
a direct action thereon of the pituitary extract (1).

Evidence from several sources has been adduced to show that the injection of pituitary extracts, and particularly of growth preparations, is
followed by an increased rate of secretion of insulin. In the diabetic dog
growth-promoting extracts intensify the diabetes and greatly increase the
quantity of insulin necessary for control. The fact that the same extract
may be tolerated for several days by the normal animal without producing
glycosuria suggests that the normal pancreas is stimulated by the injections
(123, 421, 256, 257). The quantity of extra insulin secreted under these
circumstances has been estimated to be 10 to 20 times the normal (421).
Various pituitary extracts were found to increase the insulin content of the
pancreas of the rat (246) but to cause a reduction in the pancreatic insulin
of the dog (see 425).

It is probable that these are not direct effects upon the pancreas but
rather changes secondary to alterations in the concentration of glucose in
the blood. Direct measurements on blood perfused through the pancreas
of the rat failed to show a stimulation of insulin secretion by a growth-
promoting extract (5). Indeed the extract inhibited insulin secretion in
response to hyperglycemia. It is of interest to note that perfusion blood
often induced a rise in the blood sugar of the test animals, especially when
the glucose content was low or when the growth preparation was added.
The presence of a hyperglycemic substance in the venous blood draining
the pancreas was detected in the rat and cat after the injection of a growth-
promoting preparation, suggesting that the pituitary extract had stimulated the pancreas to liberate glucagon (37). A similar conclusion was

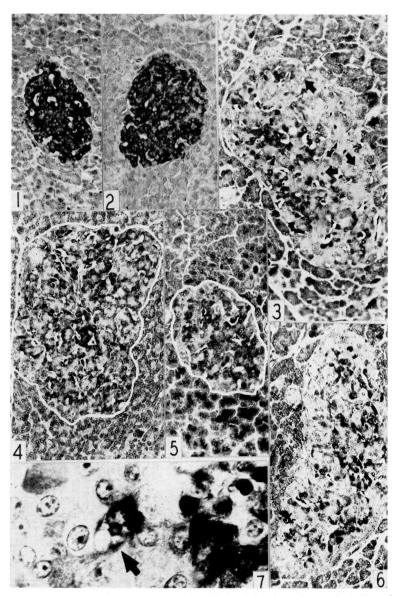

Fig. 5. Influence of continuous subcutaneous injection of growth and corticotropic preparations on the islets of Langerhans of normal adult female rats. (1)
Control; (2) 1 mg. growth hormone preparation daily. (3) and (5) 0.5 mg. corticotropin daily; (4), (6), and (7) both preparations in the same doses (from reference 1).

reached on the basis of the finding that blood draining the pancreas of the dog raised the blood sugar when infused into another dog if the donor dog was injected with a growth hormone preparation (111, 113).

f. Hypoglycemic Effect. It has been noted that shortly after the injection of various pituitary extracts, including growth hormone preparations, normal rats and dogs exhibit a fall in the concentration of glucose in the blood (170, 354, 408, 161, 339, 257). In the hypophysectomized and in adrenalectomized fasted rats the injection may be followed by actual symptoms of hypoglycemia, and the animals may die in convulsions (161, 257). Such effects immediately suggest that the extract may cause an increased rate of secretion of insulin. In most experiments hypolgycemic effects have not been seen in diabetic animals (257); in fact, a prompt increase in blood sugar has been observed even when the diabetes was mild (257), suggesting that the intact pancreas or else the presence of normal quantities of insulin is essential to the phenomenon. In the dog purified growth hormone has been noted to exert a hypoglycemic effect only for a short period of time after the first injection. Later the blood sugar may rise and with repeated injections hyperglycemia ensue (175, 425).

Some experiments with growth-promoting extracts have shown a continuing hypoglycemic action. Once-weekly injections of "Antuitrin G" into normal dogs induced hypoglycemia for 24 hours, and the fasting blood sugar progressively fell with succeeding weeks (408). In the mouse daily injections of a growth hormone preparation for 8 days did not diminish the immediate hypoglycemic response (410). A crude pituitary extract, capable of inducing diabetes in dogs, when given daily to two patients with hyperinsulinism caused a further and sustained lowering of the blood sugar (68). Under similar circumstances a growth hormone preparation was without effect in one patient (243), and slightly effective in relieving hypoglycemia in two others (29, 141). Hypophysectomized rats treated daily with a growth hormone preparation exhibited a smaller rise in blood sugar when given glucose than untreated controls (121). The hypoglycemic effect of growth preparations in hypophysectomized rats has been correlated with an increased *in vitro* uptake of glucose by diaphragm (278). Increased uptake of glucose was also seen when the hormone preparation was added *in vitro*. These effects, seen to some degree in normal rats (275), were transient and gave way to an inhibition of uptake. It would appear that the increased assimilation of glucose by the diaphragm in these experiments is insufficient to account for the hypoglycemic effect of pituitary extracts *in vivo*. It is further anomalous that the same extract should at first promote and later inhibit uptake. The specificity of the increased uptake of glucose by the diaphragm requires further investigation. Factors other than insulin and pituitary extract can accelerate uptake; the blood of an acromegalic patient was noted to exert a remarkable "insulin-like" activity of such a magnitude that, were it due to insulin, the blood would have had to contain about one-half of a unit in each milliliter (294).

The hypoglycemic effect of growth hormone preparations seems not be be mediated via the pancreas, for shortly after pancreatectomy in dogs the preparation was still clearly hypoglycemic (210). It would thus appear that the fall in blood sugar is caused by some action of the pituitary extract upon the tissues, and, as the action can be seen in the eviscerated rat, the effect is independent of the liver.

Evidence has been adduced that pituitary growth preparations cause an increased secretion of insulin and of glucagon by the pancreas. Entirely similar effects can result from alterations in the concentration of circulating glucose, hypoglycemia evoking a release of glucagon from the pancreas (112) and hyperglycemia calling forth a secretion of insulin (112).

The hypoglycemic response to purified corticotropic extracts occurs at the very time when the animal can be shown to be insensitive to large doses of exogenous insulin, and it therefore seems unlikely that the hypoglycemic effect is mediated by increased insulin secretion. Furthermore, the effect, unlike that of insulin, is strictly limited, and very large doses fail to induce hypoglycemic convulsions or very low concentrations of glucose in the blood.   Over a dose range of 3 to 100 μg. to the fed mouse there was a proportional lowering of the blood sugar; with the largest dose the fall was 55 % (Fig. 6). Growth hormone preparations were much weaker, a dose of 5 mg. producing a maximal fall of 40 % (410).

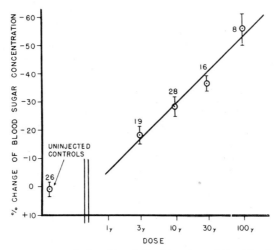

Fig. 6.   Dose-response relationship of the lowering of the blood sugar of mice 1 hour after injection of oxycel-purified corticotropin (from reference 410).

g. *Induction of Diabetes.* Extensive investigation has sought to define the relationship between the seemingly unrelated properties of growth promotion and diabetogenesis from pituitary extracts. The capacity of pituitary preparations to cause diabetes in cats and dogs has paralleled the growth activity of these extracts more closely than any other known hormonal property. Early experiments showed clearly that there was a poor correlation between diabetogenic potency and gonadotropic, thyrotropic, corticotropic, and lactogenic activities (420) but that correlation with growth-promoting potency was often good. It was noted, however, that the diabetogenic activity seemed to be lost more readily than growth potency, especially in crude extracts (245, 246, 301, 302).

When it was found that purified growth preparations exerted diabetogenic effects in cats (71, 255) and in dogs (51), further effort was devoted to the problem of whether growth hormone is itself diabetogenic or whether a contaminant in the growth hormone preparations is involved. The latter possibility was suggested by the finding (291) that a growth hormone preparation derived from a hot glacial acetic acid extract of pig pituitary glands was much less diabetogenic than a preparation made by the method of Wilhelmi *et al.* (Fig. 7). An amount of this extract as much as eight times greater than the diabetogenic dose of the commercial preparation was ineffectual in inducing diabetes. A slight diabetogenic activity was noted in one experiment with the largest dose. These findings suggested that the diabetogenic factor could be differentiated from the growth principle.

The extensive studies of Reid (297–302) have led to the reverse conclusion, namely, that growth hormone itself is inherently diabetogenic. Careful assays were performed for growth activity using "plateaued" female rats, and for diabetogenic activity using cats, and the ratio of these activities expressed as a diabetogenic to growth-promoting potency (D:G) ratio. With various purified growth preparations the ratio was nearly constant and was not altered significantly by further purification or by partial inactivation by enzymatic action, acid treatment, iodination, and acetylation, even though considerable chemical alteration of the preparations occurred (297). It was noted, however, that corticotropic preparations potentiated the diabetogenic effect of growth extracts, some being more effective in this regard than others. It was further observed that cruder growth preparations were often potentiated to a greater extent than more purified ones (298). The cat had been found to differ from the dog in requiring intact adrenals for the development of diabetes in response to growth hormone preparations (234). The fact that the potentiating action of various corticotropic extracts did not correlate with corticotropic potency suggested that some contaminant in the corticotropin was responsible. And it was further suggested that crude growth extracts contain a "co-

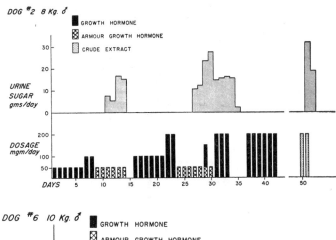

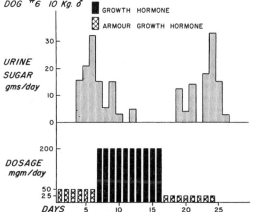

Fig. 7.   Comparison of growth hormone preparation made from hot glacial acetic acid extract of pig anterior lobes (black bars), an Armour preparation (cross-hatched bars), and a crude extract in the production of glycosuria in two normal dogs (from reference 291).

factor" which enables or helps the factor in corticotropic preparations to potentiate growth hormone (300).

A reinvestigation of crude preparations lent some support to the original findings (246) that diabetogenic potency may be lost more rapidly than growth potency upon incubation at 37°C. (300).   It was further noted that there were wide differences in the D:G ratio between extracts prepared in the same way.   At the one extreme an incubated extract showed a D:G ratio of less than 0.3, whereas with two others the ratio was 1.2 to 1.5. The D:G ratios found with sterile extracts varied from a minimum of 0.3 to 0.6 to a maximum of 3.3 to 3.6 (300).   These differences were of the same order of magnitude as those reported by Raben and Westermeyer

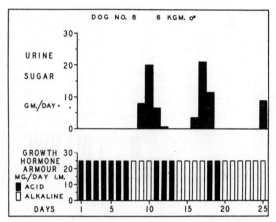

FIG. 8.   Influence of pH upon apparent diabetogenic potency.   The same growth
hormone preparation was used throughout and dissolved in water by the addition of
hydrochloric acid (black bars) or sodium hydroxide (open bars) just before daily
intramuscular injection (from reference 292).

(291).   Some factors which seemed to lower the relative diabetogenic activity were the use of frozen glands, extraction at a slightly acidic pH,
aeration, or the addition of thiodiglycol.

An example of the difficulties in reaching a final decision on this controversial question was the simultaneous and independent finding that the
injection of pituitary extracts in weakly acid solution is far less effective
in inducing diabetes than the administration of the same preparations in
mildly alkaline solution (300, 287) (Fig. 8).

This effect of pH upon diabetogenicity is not due to *in vitro* instability
in acid solutions but is related to the pH of the material at the moment of
injection.   Although no satisfactory explanation of the phenomenon is yet
forthcoming, it is possible that the acid solutions precipitate to a greater
extent at the site of injection and suffer destruction by the tissue before
much absorption can take place.   Alternatively, the diabetogenic activity
may be destroyed by an enzyme in tissue which is optimally effective in an
acid solution.   The fact that growth potency is unimpaired when injections
are made in acid solutions may be related to rapid absorption of the very
small doses which are given in growth assays.   Conversely, it may be
argued that these findings support the view that growth and diabetes are
caused by different factors.   Although Reid (300) has interpreted the
findings of Raben and Westermeyer (291) as entirely to be explained on
the basis of injections given in acid solutions, the latter workers feel that
there is a true difference in diabetogenic activity of different preparations
of comparable growth-promoting potency (292).

From the data currently available it would appear that the growth preparations of Li (227), Wilhelmi (414), and Campbell (50) and their respective associates are about equally diabetogenic (71, 297, 50, 52). Houssay
and Rodriguez (180) could find no difference in diabetogenic activity between the Raben-Westermeyer preparation and the commercial preparation. Subtotally depancreatized dogs were used in this comparison, and,
under similar experimental conditions, preparations of corticotropin,
growth hormone, and prolactin were all found to be active in large doses
(177, 178). Although oxycel-purified corticotropin is more potent than
growth preparations in causing fat mobilization, depression of respiratory
quotient, and lowering of the blood sugar, it is not diabetogenic in the dog
when tested in the usual way, i.e., with single daily intramuscular injections
of 2 mg. per kilogram (292).

Experiments on the hypophysectomized-depancreatized dog by DeBodo
and co-workers (80, 82) showed that purified growth hormone would relieve
the hypersensitivity to insulin (Fig. 9). If the growth preparation was
continued in a dose of about 1 mg. per kilogram, a diabetic state was induced and evidence of "toxicity" in the form of anorexia, vomiting, leth-
argy, and sometimes death would be observed. Even the smallest dose
(0.02 mg. per kilogram daily) which would restore insulin sensitivity to
normal caused a diabetic type of glucose tolerance to develop. The diabetogenic and "toxic" effects of the pituitary preparation were completely
prevented by the administration of cortisone or hydrocortisone (83). The
"toxic" effects of their own purified growth preparation have also been
studied by Campbell et al. (52, 54). In addition to the above-mentioned
symptoms, there were noted an increase in the plasma volume, an increase
in the concentrations of fibrinogen and globulin in the plasma, a lowered
albumin:globulin ratio, an increased rate of erythrocyte sedimentation,
and decreased clotting and prothrombin times (Fig. 10). In normal dogs
these changes were induced by 3.5 mg. per kilogram per day and concur-
rently diabetes developed (52). The diabetic dog was much more sensitive and as small a dose as 0.5 mg. per kilogram per day had to be
reduced by half to permit survival, and even so the symptoms were severe
and glycosuria was greatly increased (54). When insulin was withheld
from the diabetic dog the animals became ill, but there was no increase in
the sedimentation rate or fibrinogen concentration (54). Thus, it would
appear that growth hormone preparations exert deleterious effects in addition to causing diabetes, and one wonders if the two types of effect are
causally related. If both are prevented by cortisone, some form of allergic
response to the extracts is suggested.

In species other than the cat (93, 71, 255) and the dog (420, 175, 51) it
is difficult to elicit a diabetogenic response to pituitary extract. Tempo-

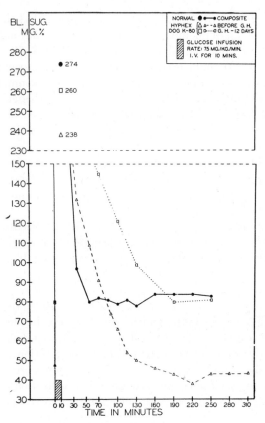

FIG. 9. Blood sugar curve produced by intravenous glucose (0.75 g./kg.) in normal dogs compared with those of hypophysectomized (Hyphex) dog K-80 before and during growth hormone regimen. Growth hormone Armour, 1 mg. per kilogram per day, given for 12 days (from reference 82).

rary but not permanent diabetes has been induced in the rabbit (271, 272), and following alloxan or partial pancreatectomy in the rat (400, 318, 177), frog (177), and toad (176, 177) diabetes has been induced or intensified. The rat is particularly insensitive, and even after the induction of diabetes by partial pancreatectomy or by the injection of alloxan, doses in excess of 30 mg. per kilogram of a purified growth hormone were required to increase the glycosuria (318).   Hyperglycemia and glycosuria can be induced in rats by forced feeding of a high-carbohydrate diet (185) and by the administration of adrenal cortical steroids or corticotropin (190, 187).   Addition of growth hormone has a further diabetogenic effect (99).   Preparations of growth hormone have thus far failed to cause diabetes in otherwise

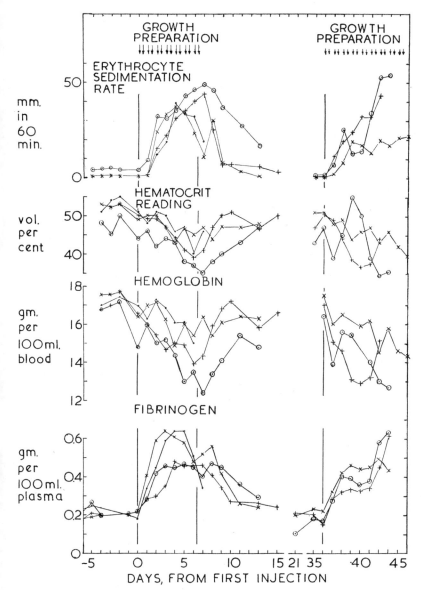

Fig. 10. Effects of twice daily injections of a growth hormone preparation in normal dogs. Each arrow indicates the injection of 1.75 mg. per kilogram from days 0 to 6 inclusive and 1 mg. per kilogram from days 36 to 44 (from reference 52).

untreated rats (422), guinea pigs (422), mice, and ferrets (94), furthermore during pregnancy and lactation and during the phase of rapid growth young cats and dogs are less sensitive to the diabetogenic action of pituitary extract (423, 424, 425).

h. *Comparison of effects of Growth and Corticotropic Preparations on Carbohydrate and Fat Metabolism.* It has been noted that current preparations of growth hormone and of corticotropin have in common actions on the metabolism of fat and carbohydrate which are not clearly related either to growth or to adrenal cortical activation. Some of these properties are shared by the two preparations, others not, and in addition there are quantitative differences. A single factor contaminating both types of preparation cannot explain all of the facts, and it seems likely that at least two substances are involved. Corticotropin concentrates are far more potent than growth preparations in causing: fat mobilization, increased oxygen consumption, lowering of the respiratory quotient, maintenance of muscle glycogen and lowering of the blood sugar. Growth hormone preparations, unlike purified corticotropic extracts, cause hyperglycemia in the absence of the adrenals and temporary or permanent diabetes in dogs and cats, and intensify pre-existing diabetes (without adrenal cortical mediation). Both types of preparation can be shown under appropriate circumstances to inhibit the action of insulin and to evoke or intensify ketosis.

The active principle in corticotropic preparations has not been separated from corticotropin, and it is comparable to corticotropin in stability to a variety of chemical manipulations and enzymatic actions. The factor in growth hormone concentrates has not been chemically separated from growth hormone; it seems to be less stable than the other factor, resembling growth hormone in this respect. Whether these phenomena are to be explained on the basis of extra-adrenal actions of corticotropin itself and of nongrowth effects of growth hormone, or on the existence of one or two additional factors contaminating these hormone extracts, cannot be decided on the basis of published data. The possibility of overlapping activities between the several hormones involved further complicates interpretation at present.

5. *"Toxic" Effects*

The administration of large doses of growth hormone preparations to the rat, although causing an initial acceleration of growth, resulted after a few weeks in weight loss. In young rats growth was actually inhibited by the "growth hormone," only to be resumed when the injections were discontinued (341). Chronic treatment with purified preparations was found to cause a variety of pathologic changes similar to those induced by large doses of deoxycorticosterone and interpreted to represent experimental replicas of hypertensive and rheumatic diseases (342).   Selye was thus led to the hypothesis that growth hormone is a "prophlogistic" substance acting either directly upon tissue in a manner similar to "mineralo-corti-coids" or "prophlogistic corticoids" or upon the adrenal cortex to cause the secretion of such corticoids.   A decision between these two modes of action has not yet been possible, because hypophysectomy prevents the patho-logical changes resulting from overdosage with either deoxycorticosterone or pituitary extracts, whereas adrenalectomy makes the animal so sensitive to the growth preparation that death results from the large doses needed before there is time for lesions to develop.

Selye's further observation (340, 341, 345) that the catabolic effects of stress and of overdosage with cortisone could be counteracted at least in part by growth hormone preparations, coupled with the idea that growth hormone is itself prophlogistic, has formed the basis for the far-reaching hypothesis that a great variety of diseases, and especially those that respond favorably to cortisone and corticotropin therapy, result from an overaction of growth hormone or "mineralo-corticoids" or both.   Conversely those disorders which are aggravated by adrenal "gluco-corticoids," such as in-fections, peptic ulceration, osteoporosis, and delayed healing of wounds, should be amenable to therapy with growth hormone.

It seems hardly likely that the pathological changes of hypertensive cardiovascular renal disease and those of the rheumatic, allergic, and collagen diseases are all due to an action of growth hormone.   A great variety of unfavorable or stressful conditions have been shown to favor the development of such lesions in animals, and this would imply an increased secretion of growth hormone in response to those very conditions which are most unfavorable for growth.

It is of great interest, however, that current growth hormone prepara-tions exhibit these "toxic" effects, because of the indication that they, like other foreign proteins, are capable of giving rise to reactions of hypersensi-tivity.   As hormones which are known to be pure do not do this, it seems quite likely that growth hormone will yield to further attempts at purifica-tion.

6. Other Effects of Growth Hormone Preparations

The numerous and diverse effects that have been noted following the administration of growth-promoting extracts of the pituitary cannot all be detailed in a brief review; some are effects which might be considered to be associated with growth processes, others not.

a. Wounds, Trauma, and Infections.   Contrary to expectation, no effect was noted from a crude growth hormone preparation upon the rate of heal-ing of skin wounds in rats (74); the extract did, however, prevent the increased loss of nitrogen and the weight loss which normally follow the fracture of a bone (75). An acid extract of cattle anterior pituitary was found to accelerate the rate of healing following fractures in the guinea pig (358). The claim (343) that growth hormone preparations can counteract the action of cortisone in increasing the susceptibility to infection (313, 202) has been denied (200, 202, 369). Protection was noted in rats against the catabolic effects of Roentgen irradiation (347), but not against a nitrogen mustard (347, 259); indeed the growth preparation seemed to increase the toxic effect of the catabolic agent.

b. *"Renotropic" Effect.* The increased weight of the kidney induced in hypophysectomized rats injected with growth hormone preparations has already been noted. In the dog two of four preparations were found to increase the renal clearances of para-aminohippuric acid and inulin when given in doses of 0.5 mg. per kilogram per day (411). In the hypophysectomized dog growth hormone preparations restored the state of diabetes insipidus, which otherwise largely subsided a few days or weeks after the operation; the water load test was improved, and, although the glomerular filtration rate and renal plasma flow were increased, they were not restored to normal (81). In the rat large doses damage the kidney and lead to nephrosclerosis, but only in the presence of intact adrenals (341); they also increase the renal damage resulting from choline deficiency (158).

c. *Galactopoietic Effect.* Of a number of pituitary extracts tested, growth preparations proved to be the most effective in increasing the milk production of cows in declining lactation (70). The galactopoietic effect of crude pituitary extract was found to be attributable entirely to its growth hormone content. However, another preparation (290) was found ineffectual in stimulating milk production in the cow and pig (164). A growth preparation was also found to be essential to the induction of milk secretion in hypophysectomized rats (238). The concept that milk secretion may normally be controlled by the secretion of growth hormone raises a number of questions. Can this be taken as proof that growth hormone is normally secreted in the adult individual? Does the quantity of growth hormone secreted increase after parturition and thereby sustain lactation, and, if so, does the lactating individual exhibit any other manifestations of excessive growth?

7. *Effects of Growth Hormone Preparations in Man*

Growth hormone preparations of proved potency in rat assays have been extensively investigated in the human being. Earlier studies using relatively crude extracts made by the methods of Teel (386), Van Dyke and Wallen-Lawrence (399), Bugbee, Simond, and Grimes (42), and Evans, Myer, and Simpson (103) indicated that substantial gains in height and in weight could be induced in human dwarfs (100, 333, 334, 174, 87, 393, 349, 350, 351). Currently it is difficult to evaluate these reports; the exact nature of the dwarfism is difficult to assess, and as some of the stunted children achieved sexual maturation, it is possible that many of the subjects were undersized because of malnutrition or chronic illness. Compared with more recent careful studies, however, some of the earlier responses were impressive. The preparation which has been most carefully tested of late is that described by Wilhelmi et al. (414), but materials made by the procedure of Li et al. (227) and by that of Raben and Westermeyer (290) have also been employed. In most instances these purified growth preparations have failed to induce weight gain, nitrogen or phosphorus retention, or an increased concentration of phosphorus in the serum. Instead they have often exhibited a catabolic effect with weight loss and negative nitrogen balance. Often the experimental subject has suffered malaise, anorexia, listlessness, and nausea and sometimes fever, vomiting, and an increased erythrocyte sedimentation rate. Contaminating thyrotropin has sometimes caused frank hyperthyroidism, but catabolic effects have also been observed in individuals lacking functional thyroid glands (219). A fall in serum cholesterol has also been observed in a cretinous subject (219). Water retention and even edema have sometimes been seen (72, 206).

Large doses of purified growth hormone preparations have been used in an attempt to induce growth in human beings. Escamilla and Bennett (102) gave increasing doses over a six-month period to a 16-year-old girl of 70 pounds who was only 4 feet 2 inches tall; although the dose finally reached 160 mg. daily (5 mg. per kilogram), growth was not stimulated, and there was no effect on the calcium, phosphorus, or nitrogen balances (25). That this individual was able to grow was later proved by the observation that she gained a total of 6-3/4 inches in height over the course of the next two years while receiving thyroid and methyltestosterone.

Some distinct anabolic effects of growth hormone preparations in man have been reported. Thus, Raben et al. (293) noted a retention of nitrogen and phosphorus in a case of hypopituitarism from as little as 30 mg. of their preparation daily (Fig. 11). Using the same preparation injected in acid solution, Conn et al. (67) obtained a positive nitrogen balance in a young male patient with hypopituitarism and diabetes mellitus (a "Houssay boy"). Shorr et al. (355) and Kinsell et al. (206) after numerous unsuccessful attempts finally were able to induce slight positive balances in three subjects. Current preparations still induce unfavorable systemic reactions in some individuals. Local reactions at the site of injections, as well as systemic reactions, may be noted with the first injection or may develop later in the course of therapy. Preparations made by the procedures of Li et al. (227) or of Wilhelmi et al. (414) often contain sufficient thyrotropin

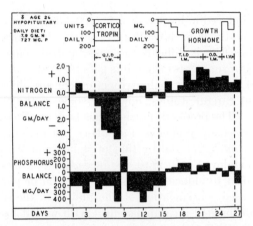

Fig. 11. Effects of oxycel-purified corticotropin and of a growth hormone preparation made from a hot glacial acetic acid extract upon balances of nitrogen and phosphorus in a young woman with hypopituitarism (from reference 292).

to cause hyperthyroidism, whereas the concentrate of Raben and Westermeyer (290), though free of thyrotropin, may contain significant amounts of corticotropin.

Clear-cut metabolic effects have been obtained in man following a single intravenous infusion of 1 to 3 mg. per kilogram of a growth hormone preparation together with an amino acid mixture (55). There was a lowering of blood amino nitrogen, a decreased amino nitrogen excretion, an increased ketonemia, and an increase in the urinary excretion of material which would induce sodium retention in adrenalectomized animals. No effect was observed in blood or urine phosphorus or serum alkaline phosphatase (55). Measurements of the urea and amino acid pools and the rate of protein synthesis using N^{15}-labeled urea and glycine (73) have shown that a growth hormone preparation (290) greatly enlarged the amino acid space and accelerated protein synthesis when given for 6 days to a human dwarf. It is to be noted that the reduced amino acid pool in this subject and the increase induced therein by the injections are the reverse of the changes found in experimental animals following hypophysectomy and the injection of pituitary extracts (335, 117).

Diabetogenic effects have usually not been seen in man, though large doses have been given. In one patient with a pancreatic islet cell tumor a transient improvement was observed during the administration of a growth hormone preparation (29). In a similar case distinct but transient inhibition of the hypoglycemia resulted from the injection of crude pituitary extract (141). The dose had to be repeatedly increased to sustain the effect, and finally 80 ml. were given daily. A total of 2695 ml., equivalent

to 673.75 g. of fresh ox pituitary, were given without producing any lasting effect upon the hypoglycemia.

Intravenous infusion of a growth preparation in nondiabetic subjects caused a transient hyperglycemia without glycosuria (55). Slightly increased glycosuria without change in the blood sugar was noted in a diabetic (72), 100 mg. daily by intravenous infusion intensified the manifestations of diabetes in one patient (205), and frank glycosuria developed for the first time in one patient given 9.375 g. over a period of 11 weeks (355); as much as 12 mg. per kilogram in a 6½-year-old dwarfed male with spontaneous hypoglycemic episodes did not elevate the serum sugar (219). The preparation of Raben and Westermeyer (290) failed to alter the intensity of the diabetes or to increase the insulin requirement in a 17-year-old boy (67).

D.   What Is the Normal Physiologic Role of Growth Hormone?

From this summary examination of the actions of growth-promoting extracts it should be possible to draw certain inferences concerning the secretion of growth hormone from the hypophysis and its normal action in regulating processes related to growth. It must be recalled, however, that a direct demonstration of the secretion of this hormone is still lacking, and there is no direct evidence bearing on the questions of when it may be secreted and of what regulates the rate of secretion.

Were it possible to conclude that the human diseases acromegaly and gigantism represented the consequences of a pure overproduction of growth hormone, one could arrive at a clear picture of the action of this hormone in excess. Unfortunately, there is evidence to suggest that other tropic hormones may also be excreted in excess in these disorders. The high incidence of goiter in acromegaly, variously estimated to amount to 30 % to 70 % of cases, and the higher than normal incidence of hyperthyroidism of an unusually difficult type to control suggest that thyrotropin may often be secreted in excess. Indeed the finding (78) of excessive quantities of thyrotropin in the blood in all cases studied suggests that excessive thyrotropin secretion may be a common feature of this disorder.

That corticotropin may sometimes be secreted in excess is suggested by the finding that the adrenal cortices are commonly enlarged in acromegaly and that cortical adenomas are common. Some observers have suggested that some of the clinical features such as hirsutism, weakness, and osteoporosis may sometimes be due to adrenal cortical overactivity. The high rate of metabolism, not attributable to hyperthyroidism, may be taken as suggestive evidence for the oversecretion of a metabolic factor similar to that encountered in corticotropin concentrates.

In view of these considerations, it is not possible to decide whether or not the high incidence of diabetes mellitus (about 17 %) (65) and the hypertrophy of the islets of Langerhans are caused by the excessive secretion of growth hormone.

It has already been noted that in very young animals and in human beings under the age of two to four years the pituitary seems unessential to normal growth. Thereafter and until adult life hypophysectomy exerts its greatest growth-retarding effect. If this kind of evidence has any weight, it might be supposed that the secretion of growth hormone is greatest in late childhood and during adolescence.

The question of continued secretion of growth hormone during adult life is one which has intrigued many investigators. Though the adult may not be growing in the usual sense—he is not increasing in length or in lean bulk —many tissues are growing. The entire epidermis is continually being renewed, the hair and nails grow, the intestinal epithelium is being replaced constantly and at a rapid rate. Following injury repair occurs with the formation of new connective tissue, bone, nerve fibers, blood vessels, and skin, and following partial hepatectomy or nephrectomy there is compensatory growth. It is tempting, therefore, to conclude that growth hormone may be secreted in physiologically important amounts during adult life.

On the other hand, recent observations on replacement therapy in adult human beings who have suffered a loss of anterior pituitary function through infarction, tumor growth, or hypophysectomy have failed to reveal an essential role for growth hormone in the adult. The administration of cortisone plus the appropriate sex hormone and thyroid restores the individual to an apparently normal state of health. Body hair sometimes regrows completely, the skin loses its fine wrinkled thinness, pigmentation returns, pallor disappears, and no clear-cut deficits can be established. Weight gain may be excessive, however, the eyes may remain sunken, and sometimes the body hair is sparse. In some individuals, however, the changes toward normal may not be complete, owing to improper doses.

In view of the diverse actions of growth-promoting extracts, one wonders whether the purest currently available growth hormone preparation represents an entity—growth hormone—or whether it is in fact a mixture of hormones. Currently the hormone is regarded as a protein of moderately large molecular weight (45,000) (50) with properties of a globulin and of limited solubility over a variably wide pH range near neutral. It is said to be electrophoretically homogeneous and to behave as a single substance by solubility measurements and upon sedimentation and diffusion. In a number of ways this substance exhibits peculiar behavior for a protein hormone of such molecular proportions. Judged by solubility behavior it

is readily denatured by the mildest conditions; in fact, different lots prepared in the same way may differ widely; some will dissolve readily at pH
5 or pH 8, whereas others are nearly insoluble over a much wider range.
Vigorous physical or chemical treatment, although greatly modifying the
protein, may not destroy the activity (230).   Potency remains after heating in glacial acetic acid at 70°C. (290, 292), boiling in acid at pH 2 for short
periods (352), heating in 0.1 N HCl for several hours at 50°C., and treatment at pH 11 to 12 at room temperature for 12 to 24 hours (103).   Extensive acetylation of amino groups can be carried out without much
change in potency (297), and manipulations designed to split off amino
acids from either carboxyl or amino termini need not decrease activity
(299).   Activity survives brief treatment with chymotrypsin and considerable degradation of the protein by carboxypeptidase.

The extraction methods which have been successfully applied to the
isolation of this protein have not differed greatly.   Extraction has been
effected by media which dissolve a large proportion of the pituitary tissue,
and from such extracts one of the less soluble components is reserved after
discarding a still more insoluble fraction.   Extensive fractionations, such
as those applied to corticotropic preparations, have not been successfully
used.   One cannot help but wonder whether the current status of the
growth hormone may not be similar to that of corticotropin 10 years ago,
when a supposedly pure protein was thought to be the hormone.

If the current protein is the growth hormone, the pituitary gland must
contain a sizable proportion of this substance.   If all of the growth activity
of whole anterior lobe powder were attributable to its content of this protein, the gland would have to contain some 5 % to 15 % of this hormone.
This might be compared with corticotropin, which in its present state of
purification would make up about 0.3 % of the dry weight of pig anterior
lobes.   Unfortunately, there are no exact figures for the growth activity of
whole anterior lobe powder.   Aside from the problem of solubility, there
are the potentiating effect of thyrotropin and the inhibitory effects of
corticotropin, the posterior lobe principles, and the toxic effects of this
crude material to render assays unreliable.

III. Corticotropin

A separate pituitary factor concerned with activation of the adrenal cortex was first generally recognized in the early 1930's.   It has been more
intensively investigated than any other pituitary hormone, and more is
known of its properties and actions than those of any other hormone of the
anterior lobe.   Corticotropin, by virtue of its well-known effects upon the
adrenal cortex, can be more precisely defined than can growth hormone,
but it is still not possible to be sure that it has no actions other than those

to be seen in the adrenal. Concentrates of corticotropin have been prepared which are nearly 500 times as active as dry anterior lobe tissue, and yet the degree of purity so far achieved is still in doubt.

In other chapters the chemical properties (p. 219) and clinical applications (p. 840) of corticotropin are described, and some of its properties relating to growth hormone have been considered above. What follows is a brief review of the nature of corticotropin, its secretion from the pituitary, some of its actions on the adrenal cortex, and some of the effects of corticotropic extracts which are not with certainty properties of corticotropin per se.

A. The Question of Multiple Corticotropins

There are two questions, neither yet satisfactorily answered, to be considered in defining the term corticotropin: (1) Does the pituitary secrete more than one substance affecting the adrenal cortex? (2) Can corticotropic activity reside in more than one molecular species? The first question was raised by the finding that changes in the weight and structure of the adrenal could be induced by extracts which were very weak in "corticotropin" in the usual sense of that term, and the second because of the widely different physical and chemical properties of concentrates of corticotropin, and because changes in these properties could be brought about by hydrolytic means without greatly affecting biological activity.

1. Corticotropin and Adrenal Size

Prior to the introduction of the ascorbic acid depletion method (332), most assay methods for corticotropin were based upon the maintenance of, or increase in, the weight of the adrenal or upon changes in its microscopic appearance, using intact or hypophysectomized rats (359, 85, 331, 10). For optimal effectiveness in tests requiring chronic administration provision for a continuous steady action of the hormone was found to be essential, and frequent injections or the use of materials to retard absorption were of importance. Certain types of extract were peculiarly ineffectual in tests of this type, presumably because of inactivation at the site of injection (see p. 293). Despite these limitations, tests based upon adrenal size and structure were applied successfully in the development of methods of extraction and purification of corticotropin.

When the purest preparations of corticotropin now available are administered in retarding media to hypophysectomized rats, the increase in adrenal weight is proportional to the logarithm of the dose over a wide range. With large doses given over a period of one to two weeks the adrenals grow to enormous proportions. In so far as comparisons have been made, the extracts which are the most active in enlarging the adrenal

beyond normal size are those which are most active by the ascorbic acid depletion method.   However, it has been noted that other types of pituitary extract which are not appreciably corticotropic by other criteria are capable of causing enlargement of the adrenal of hypophysectomized rats (370, 371) and of augmenting the weight increase when given with corticotropin.   On the basis of comparative assays by two methods, the Sayers' test and one based upon adrenal size, it was suggested (89) that there are two factors in pituitary extracts—an "ascorbic acid depleting factor" and a "weight factor."   The ratio of the two activities was found to differ in different extracts by a factor of several thousand fold.

The use of the term "weight factor" is apt to be confusing unless it is clearly understood what is meant by this, because, as mentioned above, purified corticotropin (ascorbic acid factor according to this terminology) is the most active substance in causing enlargement of the adrenal beyond normal size.   The assay used to measure "weight factor" is performed in hypophysectomized rats one to three weeks after the operation, with injections given for 3 days.   The response to the "weight factor," provided the "ascorbic acid" activity of the extract be low, is apparently a limited one, consisting of a slight increase in weight which partially restores the adrenal to normal size.   With increasing dose the adrenals are not caused to enlarge further.   Thus, 180 mg. of crude beef pituitary extract or 22 mg. of a purified growth hormone preparation, both weak in the Sayers' test, enlarged the adrenal from a control weight of 9 mg. to 12 to 15 mg. As little as 5 mg. of a crude "ascorbic acid" preparation was more effective in causing enlargement (371).

The factor responsible for this weight change has not been determined; it is associated with growth hormone preparations but has not been clearly identified therewith.   Most preparations of growth hormone were found to increase the size of the adrenal in proportion to the growth of the whole animal, but two purified preparations exerted a greater effect upon the adrenal than this.   Hydrolytic procedures which do not reduce corticotropic potency reduce the adrenal weight effect (264, 390, 225, 303, 304).

The increased weight is accompanied by increased mitotic activity and a deposition of lipid in the sudanophobic zone (57); the microscopic appearance of such adrenals is normal, whereas stimulation of the adrenal of hypophysectomized rats with corticotropin results in lipid depletion and a picture resembling that induced in normal animals by stress (57).

A variety of substances have been found to induce minor alterations in the adrenal of hypophysectomized animals; some of these have been brought together in Table II.   Of particular interest is the effect of certain steroids on the atrophy of the adrenal following hypophysectomy or after treatment with cortisone.   Testosterone as well as other androgens and

278 E. B. ASTWOOD

TABLE II

SOME FACTORS OTHER THAN CORTICOTROPIN SHOWN TO AFFECT THE ADRENAL
CORTEX OF HYPOPHYSECTOMIZED ANIMALS

Factor	Effect described	Species	References
Serum of pregnant mares	Increased size	Rat	(138)
Pregnant mares' serum gonadotropin	Increased size	Ground squirrel	(426)
Chorionic gonadotropin	Increased size	Ground squirrel	(426)
	Increased size	Pigeon	(254)
	Increased size	Rat	(273, 274)
	Reduced X-zone	Mouse	(197, 155)
Gonadotropin from human urine	Increased size	Ground squirrel	(426)
Pituitary gonadotropic preparations	Enlarged X-zone	Mouse	(197, 155)
Pituitary prolactin preparation	Increased size	Rat	(153)
Pituitary growth hormone preparations	Increased size and mitotic activity	Rat	(57)
Posterior pituitary extract	Increased size	Rat	(252)
Placental extracts	Increased size and reduced ascorbic acid	Rat	(273, 274, 370)
Insulin, thyroxin, or toxins	Increased size	Pigeon	(254)
Adrenalin	Increased size	Rat	(253)
Deoxycorticosterone and dietary Na, K, and Cl	Changes in zona glomerulosa	Rat	(154)
Androgens and related steroids	Increased size	Rat	(77, 217, 427, 416, 127, 128)
Intravenous saline	Reduced ascorbic acid	Rat	(266)
Bacterial extracts	Reduced ascorbic acid	Rat	(266)
Severe trauma	Cellular changes	Rat	(166)

related steroids causes partial maintenance of the weight of the adrenal and promotes mitotic activity following hypophysectomy (77, 217, 427, 214). Testosterone in a dose of 2.5 mg. daily for 15 days maintained adrenals weighing 19.6 mg., whereas the adrenals of the uninjected animals decreased to 8.8 mg. after the operation (416). The cortisone-induced atrophy of the adrenal cortex can be completely prevented in the rat by testosterone propionate, methylandrostenediol, and a large number of related steroids (416, 127, 128), and treatment with these steroids in combination with cortisone can maintain normal adrenal size after hypophysectomy (416, 127, 128). Thus it would appear that a number of substances in addition to pituitary extracts might be entitled to the term "weight factor."

The significance of the structural alterations brought about by these diverse agents must await further exploration, and it is not yet clear whether any of them exert an influence on the function of the adrenal cortex or upon the action thereon of corticotropin. It is clear, however, that purified preparations of corticotropin which can be regarded as weak in "adrenal weight factor" can induce the most intense degree of cortical activation, as judged by size and structure of the organ as well as by the effects brought about by the excessive secretion of corticoids. It seems likely, furthermore, that corticotropin is the chief controlling factor in the physiological regulation of adrenal size, mediating compensatory hypertrophy and atrophy.

2. Corticotropins of Differing Composition

Highly active corticotropic preparations made by somewhat different methods and subjected to different degrees of hydrolytic treatment have been found to possess quite dissimilar physical and chemical properties. Does this mean that corticotropic activity can reside in molecules of differing composition, or are the altered properties reflections of changes in the nature of associated contaminants? An answer to this question is intimately connected with the problem of the extra-adrenal activities of these same preparations (see below), and with the differences between them when they are used in man and when they are administered by subcutaneous injection in animals. The preparation of these concentrates has been described elsewhere (p. 201), and only some of their properties need be considered here. "Corticotropin A" (412, 165), a major component of the oxycellulose concentrate separated by the ion-exchange method of Dixon et al. (88), is described as a large, weakly basic polypeptide, which upon treatment with pepsin (165) yields the strongly basic "Corticotropin B" (40) through the loss of an acidic undecapeptide (165). A substance referred to as "α-Corticotropin," derived from sheep pituitaries (229), appears to resemble Corticotropin A. These have been described as "pure" compounds of roughly equal biological activity in the Sayers' test, but, as noted below, they still possess intermedin activity and the diverse metabolic effects referred to above (415, 12, 315). When oxycellulose-purified corticotropin is fractionated on carboxylic cation-exchange columns (88), intermedin and weakly corticotropic impurities emerge first, followed by the major corticotropic activity in the form of two distinct peaks (370, 315). It was noted that the material in the slower of these two corticotropic components could be converted quantitatively into material identical with that of the faster by mild treatment with alkali (370, 315). Paper electrophoresis confirmed that with care to avoid exposure to alkali, the major proteinaceous material of the oxycel concentrate behaves as a single component, and that upon exposure to 0.1 N NaOH at room temperature for 20 to 30 minutes this was transformed into a less basic substance. Presumably the substance with the slower chromatographic mobility, before transformation in alkali corresponds to Corticotropin A, but thus far no difference in biological properties between the original and the alkali-treated materials has been detected. Pepsin treatment of the chromatographically slower moving (more basic) original material yields a highly basic (cationic) substance, presumably corresponding to Corticotropin B, and whereas a similar increase in basic properties follows digestion of the alkali-transformed material, the product now is not as strongly basic as Corticotropin B (315). Thus two types of transformation, yielding four differing products, are possible without loss of corticotropic potency. Two further very basic materials resulting from acid hydrolysis of Corticotropin A and B, respectively, have been described but not yet further characterized (165). The retention of the extra-adrenal activities of these preparations through such diverse manipulations suggests either that the extra-adrenal activities are properties of corticotropin itself or of a remarkably similar substance associated with corticotropin, or else that these corticotropic preparations are grossly contaminated and that the alterations observed involve a major inert carrier for the hormones.

The findings to date are not inconsistent with the concept that the pituitary exerts its influence upon structure and function of the adrenal cortex by means of a single substance, corticotropin, and that the chemical nature of this normal secretory product has not yet been determined.

B. CONTROL OF CORTICOTROPIN SECRETION

The secretory activity of the adrenal cortex is capable of wide fluctuations, and the chief controlling influence on this activity is the quantity of corticotropin secreted by the anterior pituitary. Under normal circumstances the adrenal is thought to secrete at a fairly constant rate but with a regular diurnal rhythm; with severe trauma or stress the secretory rate increases greatly. By inference there is a basal rate of corticotropin release from the hypophysis which is quickly augmented in response to damage. Several theories have been proposed to define the mechanism whereby the rate of secretion of corticotropin is controlled. Chief among these are: (1) Regulation by the concentration of circulating adrenal steroids; (2) neurohumoral influences from the hypothalamus; (3) stimulation of corticotropin secretion by a circulating mediator such as epinephrine.

It is now clear that no one of these three proposed mechanisms can alone explain all of the accumulated observations, and it seems most likely that more than one factor is capable of altering the rate of secretion of corticotropin.

1. *Concentration of Circulating Adrenal Steroids*

There can be no doubt that the adrenal hormones and related compounds exert a suppressive effect upon the secretion of corticotropin and that a deficiency in these compounds provides a strong stimulus to corticotropin release. Adrenal atrophy, comparable in every way to that observed after hypophysectomy, follows the administration of adrenal cortical extract, cortisone, or hydrocortisone (331, 127, 416, 200, 131). Deoxycorticosterone (59, 60, 131) is also effective in this regard, but it is less effective for a given dose and very much less effective if considered in terms of relative "physiological" dose. The relative effectiveness of the naturally secreted mineralo-corticoid aldosterone will doubtless be known when this is read. A number of related steroids, including progesterone and androgens (218), have been shown to reduce adrenal size in normal rats.

The increased release of corticotropin consequent upon the application of a variety of damaging agents or conditions can also be inhibited by adrenal steroids and related compounds (168, 169). The degree of inhibition observed depends upon the dose of adrenal hormone provided and upon the severity of the damaging influence (341). As the stressful situation is made more intense the dose of adrenal hormone needed becomes larger and larger, until with the most severe damage no dose is able to abolish the release of excess corticotropin. The most extreme example of this is provided by the case when cortisone itself is the stressful agent. Administration of cortisone in daily doses which will eventually prove fatal at first causes the expected adrenal atrophy, but terminally, as the animal is about to succumb from the consequences of cortisone overdosage, the adrenal cortex becomes activated and enlarges (346), implying a release of corticotropin from the maximally suppressed anterior pituitary.

Sayers (328) has reviewed the evidence in favor of the concept that the secretion of corticotropin is controlled entirely by the concentration of adrenal cortical hormones in the blood. This theory depends heavily upon the concept that stressful situations and trauma increase the rate of "utilization" of adrenal steroids. The increased utilization would be reflected in an initial decrease in circulating corticoids, and this would be the stimulus to corticotropin secretion. There is little convincing evidence in favor of the view that damage increases the rate of utilization of the adrenal hormones. A good case can be made for the concept that damage increases the "need" for larger quantities of adrenal hormone, and there is good evidence to show that the concentration of adrenal hormones in the blood and the quantity excreted in the urine are increased rather than decreased in response to damage. Some additional stimulus must come into operation to provide for the excess adrenal cortical stimulation which follows the application of a damaging influence.

It would seem reasonable to suppose that the concentration of circulating adrenal cortical hormone exerts an important regulatory influence on the rate of secretion of corticotropin. It is probably a delicately adjusted mechanism capable of maintaining a "normal" adrenal cortex and a constant concentration of cortical hormones in the blood under circumstances which may be described as "normal" or "basal." It is probably operative at all times, and if there is such a thing as a changing rate of "utilization" or degradation of cortical hormones, it would nicely compensate. To it, also, may be ascribed the regrowth of adrenal tissue following partial adrenalectomy and the atrophy of the adrenal cortices during the administration of exogenous cortical steroids.

2. *Hypothalamic Control*

It is now generally agreed that the anterior lobe of the pituitary is not controlled by nerve fibers from the hypothalamus. Interruption of the nerve fibers entering the posterior lobe by transection of the stalk is compatible with complete recovery of all of the endocrine functions of the anterior lobe, provided that regeneration of the special blood supply from the tuberal region is re-established (160, 384, 61). Transplantation of the anterior lobe to sites distant from the normal position causes a profound disturbance of function in the rat and mouse (160, 62) but not in the guinea pig (336, 338), but transplantation in the region of the tuber cinereum of hypophysectomized rats restores normal hypophyseal activities (152a, 160).

Electrolytic lesions in the posterior part of the tuber cinereum and in the region of the mammillary bodies abolished the adrenal response of rabbits to noxious stimuli, whereas lesions elsewhere in the hypothalamus did not (84). In the dog a different region of the hypothalamus seemed to be involved (182). Electrical stimulation of various regions by means of precisely placed electrodes activated by remote control without otherwise disturbing the animals showed that evidence of adrenal cortical activation could be obtained only when the stimulus was applied to areas in the posterior hypothalamus. Stimuli applied elsewhere in the hypothalamus or anywhere in the pituitary gland itself were entirely ineffective. It was concluded from experiments of this type that there is a dual pathway concerned with the stimulus to corticotropin secretion—a neural path from the posterior hypothalamus to the tuber cinereum and a vascular path from the region of the median eminence through the zona tuberalis to the anterior lobe via the hypophyseal portal system of blood vessels (84).

The hypothalamic system seems to be of importance in the regulation of

corticotropin secretion in response to noxious stimuli, but it is still unknown how the nervous system is activated by damaging and stressful
stimuli applied at a distance.   When pain or emotion are involved, direct
nervous transmission might be envisioned, but other types of stress such
as those of a chemical or metabolic nature must influence the system in
some other way.   Although the adrenal fails to respond to stressful stimuli
after the placement of lesions in the posterior hypothalamus (84) or median
eminence (240), such lesions do not cause adrenal atrophy (240), suggesting
that corticotropin secretion in the normal, unstressed individual is not
regulated by the central nervous system.   On the other hand, it has been
claimed that transection of the spinal cord in the upper dorsal region
abolishes the response of the remaining adrenal to unilateral adrenalectomy
(409).

3. Stimulation of Corticotropin Secretion by Epinephrine

On the basis of extensive experiments Long (131, 235) evolved an attractive hypothesis built upon epinephrine as the mediator of corticotropin
secretion in response to stress.   In line with Cannon's concept of the primacy of the adrenal medulla and sympathetic nervous system in permitting
adjustment to a changed environment, it can be reasoned that those conditions which are now known to evoke an increased secretion of corticotropin also activate the sympathico-adrenal system.   Since the latter
response is a rapid one, epinephrine could well be the common mediator
activating the pituitary-adrenal cortical system in response to the variety
of noxious stimuli known to affect it.   In support of the concept that
epinephrine mediates corticotropin secretion, it was shown that adrenal
demedullation partially inhibited adrenal activation in response to various
stressful situations (242), that direct application of small amounts of
epinephrine to the anterior pituitary either in its normal location or after
transplantation into the anterior chamber of the eye caused a fall in circulating eosinophils (241), and that painful stimuli applied to the scalp failed
to activate the adrenal cortex after high spinal cord transection which
prevented reflex secretion of epinephrine (131, 242).

The primacy of epinephrine in the control of corticotropin secretion has
been brought into question by a number of investigators.   Were it the
final mediator, it should act more quickly than any other agent, but that
this is not the case was demonstrated by Gray and Munson (143), who
showed that histamine given intravenously caused a discharge of corticotropin within 10 seconds, whereas epinephrine under the same experimental
conditions was completely ineffective.   It was originally believed that a
decrease in the number of circulating eosinophils following the injection of
epinephrine required an increased secretion of adrenal corticoids (296, 392);

it was later shown that epinephrine can cause a pronounced eosinopenia in the adrenalectomized animal or man, provided that maintenance therapy with cortical steroids be given (195, 199). Reinterpretation of the early data on the effects of epinephrine on corticotropin secretion, using the eosinophil as an indicator, weakens the case for a primary role of epinephrine in this process.

Infusion of epinephrine intravenously was found to be completely ineffective in causing a lowering of the ascorbic acid content of the adrenal unless the infusion were continued for 15 minutes; rapid injection of sublethal amounts had no effect. Continuous intravenous infusion or repeated subcutaneous injections of epinephrine in normal human subjects in quantities which induced great discomfort failed to cause any increase in the concentration of cortical hormones in the blood or in the excretion of corticoids or 17-ketosteroids in the urine. However, the doses given caused a decrease in the number of circulating eosinophils, lymphocytopenia, and a polymorphonuclear leukocytosis (196). Given with corticotropin, epinephrine, surprisingly, reduced the corticotropic response in man, as measured by the quantities of steroids in the blood and urine (327). In the adrenalectomized rat epinephrine has been found to decrease the corticotropin content of both the pituitary and the blood, seeming to indicate an actual inhibition of corticotropin synthesis by epinephrine (129).

Despite the negative results in man, it has been clearly shown that epinephrine can activate the pituitary-adrenal system in the rat and dog, as judged by depletion of adrenal ascorbic acid, increase in the corticotropic content of the blood (108), and increase in the corticoids of adrenal vein blood. The discrepant results in man are probably to be explained on a quantitative basis, man requiring a much more severe noxious stimulus to evoke increased corticotropic secretion than laboratory animals. Exhausting exercise, exposure to cold, and other stressful conditions more rigorous than those required to activate the adrenals of animals were without effect in human subjects, as judged by the excretion of steroidal material in the urine (196). Major surgical procedures were uniformly effective in greatly increasing urinary corticoids (196) and increasing the concentration of corticoids in the blood.

It would seem unlikely, therefore, that epinephrine is the mediator of increased corticotropic secretion in response to stress. Many toxic substances are more rapid in eliciting this response than epinephrine (39), but there is no experimental evidence that either histamine, acetylcholine, or any of the other effective substances serves as the common mediator for pituitary stimulation. Noxious stimuli which give rise to pain may be relayed to the brain via sensory nerves and thence to the hypothalamus by neural pathways, and emotional responses may be similarly evoked through the hypothalamic system, but there is as yet no satisfactory theory to account for the release of corticotropin in response to those types of stress unassociated with pain or emotion.

C.   Rate of Release of Corticotropin from the Anterior Pituitary

On physiologic grounds it might be properly reasoned that corticotropin is normally secreted from the pituitary at all times and at a rate sufficient to maintain the structure and functional activity of the adrenal cortex within normal limits.   This rate of secretion has not yet been measured directly, but indirect estimates would suggest that the quantity is small, amounting to a few units per day in man and a few milliunits daily in the rat.

Many efforts have been made to estimate the quantity of corticotropin in body fluids.   The most recent tests using improved methods of concentration (381) indicate that there is less than 0.5 milliunit in 100 ml. of normal human blood (380).   Following an appropriate stimulus the anterior pituitary can greatly increase the rate of secretion of corticotropin in a very short period of time.   The rates of reduction in the concentrations of ascorbic acid and of cholesterol in the adrenal following hemorrhage in the rat are just as rapid as after the intravenous injection of corticotropin (331, 330), implying that corticotropin is released in increased amounts almost immediately.   Normal rats killed without prior disturbance by swift decapitation were found to have less than 0.5 milliunit of corticotropin per 100 ml. in the blood obtained from the headless body, whereas exsanguination of intact animals under ether anesthesia yielded blood containing more than 2 milliunits per 100 ml.   As the secreted corticotropin disappears from the blood at a rapid rate, the quantity secreted by the pituitary in the space of a few minutes time must have constituted a large fraction of the quantity stored therein.   Sayers (328) has estimated that a single rat hypophysis contains sufficient corticotropin to induce a half-maximal depletion in the ascorbic acid of the adrenals of 200 rats, but even under conditions of severe trauma the corticotropin content of the hypophysis is not reduced below one-half the normal value (330).   Some values for the corticotropin content of the pituitary are listed in Table III.   This must mean that a sudden release of corticotropin is quickly followed by an increased rate of synthesis.   Following adrenalectomy the corticotropin content of the pituitary falls from a normal value of 0.058 unit per gland (0.076 unit per milligram dry tissue) to as low as 0.03 unit per milligram in 6 hours; later the content rises to a value of about twice the normal (130).   The blood content increases progressively from undetectable amounts to about 10 milliunits per 100 ml. in a week following the opera-

TABLE III
CORTICOTROPIN CONTENT OF PITUITARY GLANDS

Species	Material assayed	Units/mg.	Reference
Pig	Acetone-dried whole gland	0.2	(280)
		0.25	(85)
		0.5	(20)
	Lyophilized anterior lobe	0.2	(44)
	Acetone-dried anterior lobe	0.4	(280)
Ox	Acetone-dried anterior lobe	0.06	(85)
Whale	Acetone-dried anterior lobe	0.2, 0.28	(172)
Rat	Lyophilized whole gland	0.08	(44)
		0.076	(130)
Man			
Adult	Lyophilized anterior lobe	0.2	(44)
	Lyophilized whole gland	0.22–0.59	(385)
Infant	Lyophilized anterior lobe	0.24	(44)
	Lyophilized whole gland	0.05–0.35	(385)
Fetus	Lyophilized whole gland	0.008–0.02	(385)

tion. It was estimated that the pituitary of the normal rat secreted corticotropin at a rate of about 5 milliunits per hour and that adrenalectomy increased this rate 30-fold (130).

The pronounced diurnal variation in the concentration of adrenal corticoids in human blood (32, 394, 267) and in the rate of their secretion in the urine (92) suggests that under normal circumstances the rate of secretion of corticotropin varies widely. The rate of cortical secretion, maximal in the early morning, slowly declines during the day and is minimal during the night (394, 92). The rhythm is not quickly altered by a reversal of the normal diurnal pattern of sleep and activity. The magnitude of these changes is such as to suggest that they are of major physiologic importance; the normal human being appears to pass from a state of hyperadrenocorticism in the early morning to a state approaching adrenal insufficiency during sleep. During sleep, conditions are optimal for processes of anabolism, and it would be of great interest to know whether growth hormone is secreted from the pituitary with a similar but reverse rhythm.

Several estimates have been made of the rate at which corticotropin disappears from the blood. A true value for this rate should also be the rate of corticotropin secretion under the conditions of the experiments and on the assumption that a steady state was maintained. The activity of relatively crude preparations of corticotropin injected into normal rats was found to disappear from the blood with a half time of 5.5 minutes (150) and 5 minutes (130), and the activity of dried rat pituitary given to rats, with a half time of 2 minutes (310, 382).   The rate at which corticotropin disappeared from the blood of adrenalectomized rats after hypophysectomy indicated half times of 1.25 and 0.95 minutes, respectively, in two experiments (382).   Under these conditions the quantity of corticotropin in the blood is much higher than normal, and the rate of disappearance may also have been higher than normal.   On the basis of indirect evidence in parabiotic rats a half time of 17 minutes has been calculated for endogenously secreted corticotropin (398).

D. FATE OF CORTICOTROPIN

Though corticotropin rapidly disappears from the body fluids, the sites of its degradation and the mode of its elimination are unknown.   Very little or none appears in the urine (310, 329), though it concentrates in the kidney to a higher degree than in any other tissue including the adrenal cortex (310).

The increased content of corticotropin in the blood following adrenalectomy is thought to disappear from shed blood at such a rapid rate that rigorous precautions are essential to prevent this if assays are to be made. Blood has sometimes been noted to cause rapid inactivation of corticotropin added *in vitro*, but here the rate varies widely with different preparations of corticotropin, purer preparations surviving better than crude ones; the blood from different species also appears to differ (310, 283).   Relatively crude preparations were rapidly inactivated upon incubation with slices or homogenates of rat liver, kidney, adrenal, and muscle (132); a pepsin-digested preparation seemed to be more labile than an unhydrolyzed extract; little inactivation occurred upon incubation in rat plasma (132). Destruction in blood or plasma has been attributed, at least in part, to accompanying enzymes contained in some cruder preparations of corticotropin (2, 283).   In any case, the fact that some preparations can survive incubation with blood, coupled with the finding that most preparations are highly effective when infused intravenously at very slow rates, suggests that the major site of degradation is probably tissue and, in particular, renal or hepatic tissue.   Although corticotropin concentrates in the kidney after injection and is inactivated *in vitro* upon incubation with renal or hepatic tissue, removal of both kidneys and most of the liver did not render a corticotropic preparation more effective in reducing the ascorbic acid content of the adrenal (159).

E. EFFECTS OF CORTICOTROPIN UPON THE ADRENAL CORTEX

Detailed studies have been made of the chemical and structural changes in the adrenal in response to various doses of corticotropin given for differ-

ent lengths of time.   In brief, the usual sequence of obseivable effects are:
increased secretion of corticoids, depletion of ascorbic acid and lipids
(cholesterol), and growth.

1. *Increased Secretion*

An increased rate of secretion of cortical hormone has been noted after
the addition of corticotropic extracts to the blood perfusing the adrenal
gland of the dog (403) and of the ox (282, 239).   Measurements on the
rate of secretion of adrenal corticoids into the blood leaving the gland via
the adrenal veins show that corticotropin increases the rate of release in a
remarkably short period of time.   During the first 10 to 20 minutes after
the intravenous injection of corticotropin into rats the quantity of cortical
steroid appearing in the venous effluent was increased (47).   An increased
rate of secretion was detected within seconds after the addition of corticotropin to the blood perfusing the ox adrenal (282).   In the human being an
increase in the concentration of adrenal corticoids in the blood has been
noted in 15 to 30 minutes (19) or even less (31) after the intravenous infusion of corticotropin.

The duration of enhanced secretion after a single corticotropic stimulus
has not been accurately determined, but it appears that activation outlasts
the stimulus by an appreciable period of time.   After a single intravenous
injection of corticotropin in man the concentration of corticoids in the blood
rose to a maximum in 1 hour (31) and then returned to normal values
within 3 hours (31).   In the dog an intravenous injection of 2.5 to 15 milliunits caused an increased concentration of corticosteroids in adrenal vein
blood for no longer than 15 minutes (265).   Following hypophysectomy,
secretion of hydrocortisone and corticosterone into the blood leaving the
adrenal fell to one-half in 1 hour and to one-third to one-tenth in 2 hours
(379).

2. *In Vitro Effects*

Corticotropin is one of the few hormones the actions of which have been
studied successfully *in vitro*.   When added to adrenal slices it has been
found to increase respiration, reduce the concentration of ascorbic acid,
and enhance the rate of steroidogenesis.   An increase in the rate of oxygen
consumption *in vitro* by adrenal slices has been observed in dogs (389, 307),
rats (56, 322), cattle (109, 307), sheep (307), and pigs (307).   Over a range
of from 4 to 32 milliunits the increased respiration was proportional to the
log dose (307), suggesting that a method for assay could be based upon this
measurement.   With all but the crudest extracts the capacity to increase
the oxygen consumption of cattle adrenal slices paralleled corticotropic
potency in the Sayers' test.   Large amounts of other proteins and extracts

also caused some increase in the rate of respiration (227, 307). It was found that glucose and pyruvate were suitable substrates, and in their absence no increase in respiration was observed when corticotropic extracts were added (307).

Stimulation of cortical steroid synthesis by corticotropin can be observed in adrenal slices or whole rat adrenals *in vitro* (322) and by slices from bovine glands (163), but not by slices of adrenals derived from the guinea pig, rabbit, cat, or dog (276). The reason for the failure of the glands of some species to respond is unknown, but in the case of the rat the rate of corticoid synthesis is greatly modified by alterations in the composition of the medium. Increased synthesis requires calcium (28), and the rate of synthesis without corticotropin is augmented by the addition of aceto-acetate, glycerol, or acetate, but in the presence of these agents corticotropin actually decreased synthesis (171). It is of interest that all of the steroid synthesized by whole or sliced adrenals of the rat appeared in the fluid medium, and none accumulated in the tissue (322), implying that secretion occurred in the absence of circulation of blood.

Preincubation of rat adrenals for an hour before adding them to the corticotropin-containing medium increased their sensitivity to corticotropin 20- to 25-fold, and doses of 0.1 unit per 100 mg. of adrenal or less were effective in enhancing steroid synthesis. Comparison of the effectiveness of several corticotropic preparations varying in potency from 2 to 80 units per milligram showed that the method could be used as a satisfactory assay for corticotropic activity (321).

Why corticotropin should be more effective following a period of incubation in unfortified medium (321) or prior perfusion (163), and yet ineffectual or even inhibitory in the presence of substrates which favor steroidogenesis (171), is not clear. It is possible that some substrates favor the action of corticotropin on the general cellular metabolism of the adrenal cortex, whereas, under conditions which might be regarded as unfavorable, steroidogenesis is more greatly influenced. It is of great interest that adrenal glands from hypophysectomized animals were found to respond to corticotropin in the short space of less than 2-$\frac{1}{2}$ hours (171), whereas in their normal location a much longer period would probably have been required. The stimulus applied *in vitro* seems also to have been effective for a longer period of time than one would have anticipated. An enhanced rate of steroid synthesis was still measurable 2 hours after removal from the corticotropin solution and after two washings in plain medium (321).

Most experiments have indicated that the materials secreted in increased amounts following stimulation with corticotropin *in vivo* and *in vitro* are qualitatively similar to the mixture of steroids normally secreted (45–48). Following prolonged injections, however, it has been noted in the rabbit that hydrocortisone became the major secretory product, whereas without stimulation corticosterone was the chief steroid produced (201). There is indirect evidence, furthermore, that the secretion of aldosterone is not stimulated by corticotropin. The quantity of sodium-retaining substance excreted in human urine was increased by the injection of a growth hormone preparation (55, 402), but not by corticotropin (13). These experiments provide support for the theory of Greep and Deane (154) that secretion of the salt-retaining hormone, not mediated by corticotropin, arises from special cells of the cortex which, in the rat, make up the zona glomerulosa. Though the injection of growth hormone preparations in man caused an increased secretion of sodium-retaining factor in the urine (55, 402), the effect may not imply an action of the pituitary extract upon the adrenal. The findings of Bennett and co-workers that growth preparations in rats induce retention of sodium, potassium, and chloride have been extended to show that the adrenal is not involved (137, 413).

3. *Depletion of Ascorbic Acid and Lipid*

Almost as rapid as enhanced secretion is the decrease in concentration of cholesterol, stainable lipid, and ascorbic acid of the adrenal from endogenous or exogenous corticotropin (331). The sequence of changes in these constituents and in the size of the gland following brief or prolonged stimulation have been thoroughly investigated (331, 328), and the conclusion reached that all of the changes noted to occur under natural conditions and under situations of brief or prolonged application of noxious stimuli can be duplicated by the administration of suitable quantities of corticotropin for proper lengths of time. In some animals such as the dog and the chick, adrenal enlargement in response to damage or to corticotropin is limited. Ascorbic acid depletion fails to occur in the chick (193) and hamster (4), and the adrenals of very young animals may be less responsive than those of older ones (192).

The adrenal of the rat responds quickly and greatly to corticotropin by an increase in size. Enlargement which may be detectable in a few hours can proceed rapidly until the adrenal size rivals that of the kidney after a few weeks. The human adrenal apparently exhibits pronounced enlargement during corticotropin therapy and atrophies profoundly when endogenous corticotropin is suppressed by the administration of cortical steroids.

F. Responsiveness of the Adrenal to Corticotropic Stimulation

The secretory response of the adrenal cortex to corticotropin is greatly modified by the state of the gland at the time of stimulation. The atrophic gland resulting from prolonged therapy with cortical steroids fails to re-

pond promptly to endogenous or exogenous corticotropin. This is a
triking accompaniment of cortisone therapy in man. The sudden cessa-
ion of cortisone given orally leaves the individual in a state of adrenal
nsufficiency which can lead to collapse and death. Stress in the form of
ι surgical operation, acute infection, or exposure can be particularly haz-
ιrdous under these circumstances, and a number of deaths have been a
ɩonsequence. If corticotropin is given after prolonged cortisone therapy,
ιarge doses may be completely ineffectual for several days, and sometimes
ι week of therapy is needed before a full corticoid response is seen (391).
Similarly, the first day of therapy with corticotropin in a previously un-
ιreated subject induces a limited response, as measured by the quantity of
ιteroids in blood or urine. Increasing doses up to 10 to 20 units by con-
ιinuous infusion over 8 hours cause an increasing response, but larger doses
ιave no greater effect (309, 31). If the therapy is repeated on successive
ιlays, however, the response to a given dose increases progressively (309).
Whether this conditioning effect is purely one of increased adrenal size
ιeems unlikely, and other effects upon the cortical cells are probably in-
ɼolved. It was tempting to assume that the so-called "weight factor" of
ιhe pituitary was important in this conditioning process, and indeed it was
ound that an extract of horse pituitary low in corticotropic activity could
ιimilarly enhance the response of the human adrenal to corticotropin if
ǥiven over a 5-day preparative period (233). However, extensive experi-
nents by Bush and Stack-Dunne (see Bush (47)) in hypophysectomized
ɾats failed to reveal any influence of extracts containing "weight factor";
ɩhe extracts caused no increased secretion of corticoids into the adrenal
ɼein, nor were they effective in priming the gland to respond more vigor-
ɔusly to corticotropin. These experiments also showed that the adrenal
ɔortex of the rat, like that of man, responded poorly to corticotropin if it
ɯas allowed to atrophy following hypophysectomy, even for as short a pe-
ɾiod as 24 hours, but that it secreted well if maintained by corticotropin
ιfter the operation.

G. Systemic Effects of Adrenal Stimulation

The systemic effects of adrenocortical stimulation might be expected to
resemble closely those resulting from the administration of cortisone or
hydrocortisone. In many respects the effects are indeed very similar, but
ɩn others there are differences (202, 284). In man the main secretory prod-
ɯct of the adrenal is considered to be hydrocortisone (69, 47), and the
ιdministration of this steroid produces effects which mimic closely those
which follow corticotropin therapy (69). It would appear, however, that
corticotropin tends to cause a greater degree of salt and water retention
ιnd is more apt to cause an increase in blood pressure than hydrocortisone

or cortisone, suggesting an increased output of a compound with properties similar to those of both deoxycorticosterone and hydrocortisone. This possibility has not received experimental support, however; large doses of aldosterone have failed to cause excess retention of water and salt (157), and corticotropin causes no increase in the quantity of sodium-retaining hormone excreted in the urine (13). Corticotropin is capable of inducing a greater effect in man than steroid therapy given in the doses thus far employed. Some unusually severe diseases, which fail to respond to cortisone, can be controlled by corticotropin, and some of the features of Cushing's syndrome can be more intense. Some believe, on the other hand, that such complications as osteoporosis are more apt to follow steroid therapy. A higher incidence of excess hair growth and of acne is interpreted by some as manifestations of androgen secretion by the adrenal in response to corticotropin, but experiments on castrated rats failed to show any indication of an androgenic influence from corticotropin given in doses which induced the growth of huge adrenal glands (397).

In animals such as the rat, cortisone acetate, in doses of 5 mg. or more daily, exerts a more strikingly deleterious effect than does corticotropin in the doses thus far employed. Weight loss is greater, and the susceptibility to infections is enhanced to a greater degree. As the major secretory product of the rat adrenal is corticosterone (46), these differences are perhaps understandable. However, a more important consideration in many animal experiments, some of which show corticotropin to be less effective than cortisone on one or another process, is the matter of constancy of effect. Cortisone, injected usually as a suspension, exerts a steady and relatively constant action, whereas corticotropin has often been given in the form of crude extracts in aqueous solution—a notably ineffective method of achieving cortical activation.

H. FACTORS INFLUENCING THE ACTIVITY OF CORTICOTROPIC PREPARATIONS

When corticotropic preparations are administered intravenously as in the Sayers' test, the responses obtained seem to reflect the actual quantity of corticotropin in the extracts more accurately than when tests are carried out by any other means. When corticotropin preparations are given subcutaneously or intramuscularly, wide differences in apparent potency are manifest (18, 390). The crude corticotropic extracts which were initially used for extensive investigations in man seemed to vary widely in potency, though they had been carefully standardized by the Sayers' test. Furthermore, certain individuals developed an apparent refractoriness (115, 19), and very large increases in dose failed to be effective in overcoming it. It was noted, however, that when these preparations were given by continuous

4. Alpert, M. *Endocrinology* **46,** 166 (1950).
5. Anderson, E., and Long, J. A. *Endocrinology* **40,** 92, 98 (1947).
6. Anselmino, K. J., Herold, L., and Hoffmann, F. *Klin. Wochschr.* **12,** 1245 (1933).
7. Asling, C. W., Simpson, M. E., Li, C. H., and Evans, H. M. *Anat. Record* **107,** 399 (1950).
8. Asling, C. W., Walker, D. G., Simpson, M. E., Li, C. H., and Evans, H. M. *Anat. Record* **114,** 49 (1952).
9. Astwood, E. B. Unpublished observations.
10. Astwood, E. B., Raben, M. S., and Payne, R. W. *Recent Progr. Hormone Research* **7,** 1 (1952).
11. Astwood, E. B., Raben, M. S., Payne, R. W., and Grady, A. B. *J. Am. Chem. Soc.* **73,** 2969 (1951).
12. Astwood, E. B., Raben, M. S., Rosenberg, I. N., and Westermeyer, V. W. *Science* **118,** 567 (1953).
13. Axelrad, B. J., Johnson, B. B., and Luetscher, J. A., Jr. *J. Clin. Endocrinol. and Metabolism* **14,** 783 (1954).
14. Baker, B. L., and Ingle, D. J. *Endocrinology* **43,** 422 (1948).
15. Barrett, H. W., Best, C. H., and Ridout, J. H. *J. Physiol.* **93,** 367 (1938).
16. Bartlett, P. D., and Gaebler, O. H. *Endocrinology* **43,** 329 (1948).
17. Bartlett, P. D., Gaebler, O. H., and Harmon, A. *J. Biol. Chem.* **180,** 1021 (1949).
18. Bates, R. W. *Endocrinology* **52,** 266 (1953).
19. Bayliss, R. I. S., and Steinbeck, A. W. *Brit. Med. J.* **i,** 486 (1954).
20. Bazemore, A. W., Richter, J. W., Ayer, D. E., Finnerty, J., Brink, N. G., and Folkers, K. *J. Am. Chem. Soc.* **75,** 1949 (1953).
21. Becks, H., Simpson, M. E., Marx, W., Li, C. H., and Evans, H. M. *Endocrinology* **34,** 311 (1944).
22. Becks, H., Scow, R. O., Simpson, M. E., Asling, C. W., Li, C. H., and Evans, H. M. *Anat. Record* **107,** 299 (1950).
23. Bennett, L. L., and Evans, H. M. *In* G. Pincus and K. V. Thimann, The Hormones Academic Press, New York, 1950, p. 405.
24. Bennett, L. L., Kreiss, R. E., Li, C. H., and Evans, H. M. *Am. J. Physiol.* **152,** 210 (1948).
25. Bennett, L. L., Weinberger, H., Escamilla, R., Margen, S., Li, C. H., and Evans, H. M. *J. Clin. Endocrinol.* **10,** 492 (1950).
26. Best, C. H. *Diabetes* **1,** 257 (1952).
27. Best, C. H., and Campbell, J. *J. Physiol.* **86,** 190 (1936).
28. Birmingham, M. K., Elliott, F. H., and Valere, P. H. L. *Endocrinology* **53,** 687 (1953).
29. Black, K. O., Macdougall, I., Reid, I., and Young, F. G. *Lancet* **262,** 19 (1952).
30. Black, P. T., Collip, J. B., and Thomson, D. L. *J. Physiol.* **82,** 385 (1934).
31. Bliss, E. L., Nelson, D. H., and Samuels, L. T. *J. Clin. Endocrinol. and Metabolism* **14,** 423 (1954).
32. Bliss, E. L., Sandberg, A. A., Nelson, D. H., and Eik-Nes, K. *J. Clin. Invest.* **32,** 818 (1953).
33. Bondy, P. K., and Wilhelmi, A. E. *J. Biol. Chem.* **186,** 245 (1950).
34. Bonsnes, R. W., and White, A. *Endocrinology* **26,** 990 (1940).
35. Bornstein, J. *J. Biol. Chem.* **205,** 513 (1953).
36. Bornstein, J., and Park, C. R. *J. Biol. Chem.* **205,** 503 (1953).
37. Bornstein, J., Reid, E., and Young, F. G. *Nature* **168,** 903 (1951).
38. Bowman, R. H. *Am. J. Physiol.* **172,** 157 (1953).

39. Briggs, F. N., and Munson, P. L. *J. Pharmacol. Exptl. Therap.* **110**, 7 (1954).
40. Brink, N. G., Boxer, G. E., Jelinek, V. C., Kuehl, F. A., Jr., Richter, J. W., and Folkers, K. *J. Am. Chem. Soc.* **75**, 1960 (1953).
41. Bruce, H. M., Parkes, A. S., and Perry, W. L. M. *Lancet* **262**, 790 (1952).
42. Bugbee, E. P., Simond, A. E., and Grimes, H. M. *Endocrinology* **15**, 41 (1931).
43. Burn, J. H., and Ling, H. W. *Quart. J. Pharm. and Pharmacol.* **6**, 31 (1933).
44. Burns, T. W., Merkin, M., Sayers, M. A., and Sayers, G. *Endocrinology* **44**, 439 (1949).
45. Bush, I. E. *Biochem. J.* **50**, 370 (1951).
46. Bush, I. E. *J. Endocrinol.* **9**, 95 (1953).
47. Bush, I. E. *Trans 4th Josiah Macy, Jr., Conf. on Adrenal Cortex, New York*, p. 68 (1953).
48. Bush, I. E., and Ferguson, K. A. *J. Endocrinol.* **10**, 1 (1953).
49. Campbell, J., and Davidson, I. W. F. *J. Biol. Chem.* **189**, 35 (1951).
50. Campbell, J., and Davidson, I. W. F. *Abstr. 19th Intern. Physiol. Congr., Montreal*, p. 257 (1953).
51. Campbell, J., Davidson, I. W. F., Snair, W. D., and Lei, H. P. *Endocrinology* **46**, 273 (1950).
52. Campbell, J., Hausler, H. R., Munroe, J. S., and Davidson, I. W. F. *Endocrinology* **53**, 134 (1953).
53. Campbell, J., and Lucas, C. C. *Biochem. J.* **48**, 241 (1951).
54. Campbell, J., Munroe, J. S., Hausler, H. R., and Davidson, I. W. F. *Endocrinology* **53**, 549 (1953).
55. Carballeira, A., Elrick, H., Mackenzie, K. R., and Browne, J. S. L. *Proc. Soc. Exptl. Biol. Med.* **81**, 15 (1952).
56. Carpenter, R. K., MacLeod, L. D., and Reiss, M. *J. Physiol.* **105**, 231 (1946).
57. Cater, D. B., and Stack-Dunne, M. P. *J. Pathol. Bacteriol.* **66**, 119 (1953).
58. Cavallero, C., and Mosca, L. *J. Pathol. Bacteriol.* **66**, 147 (1953).
59. Cheng, C.-P., and Sayers, G. *Endocrinology* **44**, 400 (1949).
60. Cheng, C.-P., and Sayers, G. *Proc. Soc. Exptl. Biol. Med.* **74**, 674 (1950).
61. Cheng, C.-P., Sayers, G., Goodman, L. S., and Swinyard, C. A. *Am. J. Physiol.* **158**, 45 (1949).
62. Cheng, C.-P., Sayers, G., Goodman, L. S., and Swinyard, C. A. *Am. J. Physiol.* **159**, 426 (1949).
63. Chou, C., Chang, C., Chen, G., and Van Dyke, H. B. *Endocrinology* **22**, 322 (1938).
64. Chow, B. F., and Greep, R. O. *Proc. Soc. Exptl. Biol. Med.* **69**, 191 (1948).
65. Coggeshall, C., and Root, H. F. *Endocrinology* **26**, 1 (1940).
66. Cohen, H., Freedman, H. H., Kleinberg, W., Eisler, N., and Martin, G. J. *Proc. Soc. Exptl. Biol. Med.* **82**, 749 (1953).
67. Conn, J. W., Fajans, S. S., Louis, L. H., and Seltzer, H. S. *J. Lab. Clin. Med.* **40**, 788 (1952).
68. Conn, J. W., and Louis, L. *J. Clin. Endocrinol.* **5**, 247 (1945).
69. Conn, J. W., Louis, L. H., and Fajans, S. S. *Science* **113**, 713 (1951).
70. Cotes, P. M., Crochton, J. A., Folley, S. J., and Young, F. G. *Nature* **164**, 992 (1949).
71. Cotes, P. M., Reid, E., and Young, F. G. *Nature* **164**, 209 (1949).
72. Crispell, K. R., and Parson, W. *J. Clin. Endocrinol. and Metabolism* **12**, 881 (1952).

73. Crispell, K. R., Parson, W., and Hollifield, G. *J. Clin. Invest.* **33,** 924 (1954).
74. Cuthbertson, D. P., Shaw, G. B., and Young, F. G. *J. Endocrinol.* **2,** 475 (1941).
75. Cuthbertson, D. P., Shaw, G. B., and Young, F. G. *J. Endocrinol.* **2,** 468 (1941).
76. Cuthbertson, D. P., Webster, T. A., and Young, F. G. *J. Endocrinol.* **2,** 459 (1941).
77. Cutuly, E., Cutuly, E. C., and McCullagh, R. D. *Proc. Soc. Exptl. Biol. Med.* **38,** 818 (1938).
78. D'Angelo, S. A., Paschkis, K. E., Gordon, A. S., and Cantarow, A. *J. Clin. Endocrinol. and Metabolism* **11,** 1237 (1951).
79. De Bastiani, G., Granata, L., and Sperti, L. *Boll. soc. ital. biol. sper.* **29,** 227 (1953).
80. De Bodo, R. C., Kurtz, M., Ancowitz, A., and Kiang, S. P. *Am. J. Physiol.* **163,** 310 (1950).
81. De Bodo, R. C., Schwartz, I. L., Greenberg, J., Kurtz, M., Earle, D. P., Jr., and Farber, S. J. *Proc. Soc. Exptl. Biol. Med.* **76,** 612 (1951).
82. De Bodo, R. C., and Sinkoff, M. W. *Ann. N. Y. Acad. Sci.* **57,** 23 (1953).
83. De Bodo, R. C., Sinkoff, M. W., Kiang, S. P., and Den, H. *Proc. Soc. Exptl. Biol. Med.* **81,** 425 (1952).
84. De Groot, J., and Harris, G. W. *J. Physiol.* **111,** 335 (1950).
85. Dedman, M. L., Farmer, T. H., Morris, P., and Morris, C. J. O. R. *Recent Progr. Hormone Research* **7,** 59 (1952).
86. Derrick, J. B., and Collip, J. B. *Can. J. Research* **E31,** 117 (1953).
87. Dingemanse, E., Freud, J., and Uyldert, I. E. *Acta Endocrinol.* **1,** 71 (1948).
88. Dixon, H. B. F., Moore, S., Stack-Dunne, M. P., and Young, F. G. *Nature* **168,** 1044 (1951).
89. Dixon, H. B. F., Stack-Dunne, M. P., Young, F. G., and Cater, D. B. *Nature* **168,** 1084 (1951).
90. Di Stefano, H. S., Bass, A. D., Diermeier, H. F., and Tepperman, J. *Endocrinology* **51,** 386 (1952).
91. Dobyns, B. M. *Surg. Gynecol. Obstet.* **82,** 717 (1946).
92. Doe, R. P., Flink, E. B., and Flink, M. G. *J. Clin. Endocrinol. and Metabolism* **14,** 774 (1954).
93. Dohan, F. C., Fish, C. A., and Lukens, F. D. W. *Endocrinology* **28,** 341 (1941).
94. Dolin, G., Joseph, S., and Gaunt, R. *Endocrinology* **28,** 840 (1941).
95. Downs, W. G., Jr. *J. Dental Research* **10,** 601 (1930).
96. Ellis, S., Huble, J., and Simpson, M. E. *Proc. Soc. Exptl. Biol. Med.* **84,** 603 (1953).
97. Elrick, H. *Proc. Soc. Exptl. Biol. Med.* **82,** 76 (1953).
98. Engel, F. L., and Engel, M. G. *J. Clin. Endocrinol. and Metabolism* **14,** 792 (1954).
99. Engel, F. L., Viau, A., Coggins, W., and Lynn, W. S., Jr. *Endocrinology* **50,** 100 (1952).
100. Engelbach, W. *Endocrinology* **16,** 1 (1932).
101. Ershoff, B. H. *Vitamins and Hormones* **10,** 79 (1952).
102. Escamilla, R. F., and Bennett, L. L. *J. Clin. Endocrinol.* **11,** 221 (1951).
103. Evans, H. M., Meyer, K., and Simpson, M. E. *Mem. Univ. Calif.* **11** (1933).
104. Evans, H. M., Simpson, M. E., and Li, C. H. *Endocrinology* **33,** 237 (1943).
105. Evans, H. M., Simpson, M. E., and Li, C. H. *Growth* **12,** 15 (1948).
106. Evans, H. M., Simpson, M. E., Marx, W., and Kibrick, E. *Endocrinology* **32,** 13 (1943).

107. Evans, H. M., Simpson, M. E., and Pencharz, R. I. *Endocrinology* **25**, 175 (1939).
108. Farrell, G. L., and McCann, S. M. *Endocrinology* **50**, 274 (1952).
109. Ferstl, A. E., Heppich, E., and Schmid, J. *Wien. Klin. Wochschr.* **63**, 28 (1951).
110. Fisher, R. E., Russell, J. A., and Cori, C. F. *J. Biol. Chem.* **115**, 627 (1936).
111. Foa, P. P., Magid, E. B., Glassman, M. D., and Weinstein, H. R. *Proc. Soc. Exptl. Biol. Med.* **83**, 758 (1953).
112. Foa, P. P., Santamaria, L., Weinstein, H. R., Berger, S., and Smith, J. A. *Proc. Soc. Exptl. Biol. Med.* **171**, 32 (1952).
113. Foa, P. P., Weinstein, H. R., Magid, E. B., Glassman, M. D., and Smith, J. A. *Abstr. 19th Intern. Physiol. Congr., Montreal*, p. 352 (1953).
114. Forsham, P. H., Liddle, G. W., and Bleifer, D. *J. Clin. Endocrinol. and Metabolism* **13**, 870 (1953).
115. Forsham, P. H., Renold, A. E., and Frawley, T. F. *J. Clin. Endocrinol.* **11**, 757 (1951).
116. Forsham, P. H., Renold, A., and Lesh, J. B. *Proc. 2nd Clin. ACTH Conf.* **1**, 7 (1951).
117. Fraenkel-Conrat, J., Fraenkel-Conrat, H., and Evans, H. M. *Am. J. Physiol.* **137**, 200 (1942).
118. Frame, E. G., and Russell, J. A. *Endocrinology* **39**, 420 (1946).
119. Freud, J., Levie, L. H., and Kroon, D. B. *J. Endocrinol.* **1**, 56 (1939).
120. Friedberg, F., and Greenberg, D. M. *Arch. Biochem.* **17**, 193 (1948).
121. Gaarenstroom, J. H., Huble, J., and De Jongh, S. E. *Acta Endocrinol.* **2**, 317 (1949).
122. Gaebler, O. H., Bartlett, P. D., and Sweeney, M. J. *Am. J. Physiol.* **165**, 486 (1951).
123. Gaebler, O. H., and Galbraith, H. W. *Endocrinology* **28**, 171 (1941).
124. Gaebler, O. H., and Mathies, J. C. *J. Clin. Endocrinol. and Metabolism* **12**, 939 (1952).
125. Gaebler, O. H., and Price, W. H. *J. Biol. Chem.* **121**, 497 (1937).
126. Garcia, J. F., Van Dyke, D. C., Huff, R. L., Elmlinger, P. J., and Oda, J. M. *Proc. Soc. Exptl. Biol. Med.* **76**, 707 (1951).
127. Gaunt, R., Tuthill, C. H., Antonchak, N., and Leathem, J. H. *Endocrinology* **52**, 407 (1953).
128. Gaunt, R., Tuthill, C. H., Antonchak, N., and Oppenheimer, E. *Arch. exptl. Pathol. u. Pharmakol.* **219**, 91 (1953).
129. Gemzell, C. A. *Endocrinology* **50**, 399 (1952).
130. Gemzell, C. A., Van Dyke, D. C., Tobias, C. A., and Evans, H. M. *Endocrinology* **49**, 325 (1951).
131. Gershberg, H., Fry, E. G., Brobeck, J. R., and Long, C. N. H. *Yale J. Biol. and Med.* **23**, 32 (1950).
132. Geschwind, I. I., and Li, C. H. *Endocrinology* **50**, 226 (1952).
133. Geschwind, I. I., and Li, C. H. *J. Clin. Endocrinol. and Metabolism* **12**, 937 (1953).
134. Geschwind, I. I., and Staub, A. *Proc. Soc. Exptl. Biol. Med.* **84**, 244 (1953).
135. Ghosh, B. N., Richards, J. H., Merkin, M., Burns, T. W., Brown, D. M., Sayers, G., and Smith, E. L. *Federation Proc.* **9**, 176 (1950).
136. Ghosh, B. N., Smith, E. L., and Sayers, G. *Proc. Soc. Exptl. Biol. Med.* **79**, 23 (1952).
137. Glafkides, C. M., and Bennett, L. L. *Proc. Soc. Exptl. Biol. Med.* **77**, 524 (1951).
138. Golla, Y. M. L., and Reiss, M. *J. Endocrinol.* **3**, 5 (1942).

139. Gordan, G. S., Bennett, L. L., Li, C. H., and Evans, H. M. *Endocrinology* **42,** 153 (1948).
140. Gordon, E. S. *J. Lab. Clin. Med.* **36,** 827 (1950).
141. Graham, G., and Oakley, W. G. *Quart. J. Med.* **19,** 21 (1950).
142. Gray, B. J., and Young, F. G. *J. Endocrinol.* **10,** 179 (1954).
143. Gray, W. D., and Munson, P. L. *Endocrinology* **48,** 471 (1951).
144. Greaves, J. D., Freiberg, I. K., and Johns, H. E. *J. Biol. Chem.* **133,** 243 (1940).
145. Greenbaum, A. L. *Biochem. J.* **54,** 400 (1953).
146. Greenbaum, A. L., and McLean, P. *Biochem. J.* **54,** 407 (1953).
147. Greenbaum, A. L., and McLean, P. *Biochem. J.* **54,** 413 (1953).
148. Greenbaum, A. L., and Young, F. G. *J. Endocrinol.* **9,** 127 (1953).
149. Greenspan, F. S. *J. Clin. Endocrinol.* **10,** 829 (1950).
150. Greenspan, F. S., Li, C. H., and Evans, H. M. *Endocrinology* **46,** 261 (1950).
151. Greenspan, F. S., Li, C. H., Simpson, M. E., and Evans, H. M. *Endocrinology* **45,** 455 (1949).
152. Greenspan, F. S., Li, C. H., Simpson, M. E., and Evans, H. M. *In* C. W. Emmens, Hormone Assay. Academic Press, New York, 1950, p. 273.
152a. Greep, R. O. *Proc. Soc. Exptl. Biol. Med.* **44,** 214 (1940).
153. Greep, R. O., Chow, B. F., and Van Dyke, H. B. *Federation Proc.* **1,** 33 (1942).
154. Greep, R. O., and Deane, H. W. *Ann. N. Y. Acad. Sci.* **50,** 596 (1949).
155. Greep, R. O., and Jones, I. C. *In* E. S. Gordon, A Symposium on Steroid Hormones. Univ. Wisconsin Press, Madison, 1950, p. 331.
156. Griffiths, M., and Young, F. G. *J. Endocrinol.* **3,** 96 (1942).
157. Gross, F., and Gysel, H. *Acta Endocrinol.* **15,** 199 (1954).
158. Hall, C. E., and Bieri, J. G. *Endocrinology* **53,** 661 (1953).
159. Hall, C. E., Hall, O., Finerty, J. C., Hess, M., and Binhammer, R. T. *Proc. Soc. Exptl. Biol. Med.* **79,** 690 (1952).
160. Harris, G. W., and Jacobson, D. *Proc. Roy. Soc. (London)* **B139,** 263 (1952).
161. Harrison, H. C., and Long, C. N. H. *Endocrinology* **26,** 971 (1940).
162. Hayashida, T., and Li, C. H. *Endocrinology* **50,** 187 (1952).
163. Haynes, R., Savard, K., and Dorfman, R. I. *Science* **116,** 690 (1952).
164. Hays, E. E. Personal communication.
165. Hays, E. E., and White, W. F. *Recent Progr. Hormone Research* **10,** 265 (1954).
166. Heni, F., Gruner, P., and Mast, H. *Acta Endocrinol.* **11,** 229 (1952).
167. Herring, V. V., and Evans, H. M. *Am. J. Physiol.* **140,** 452 (1943).
168. Hodges, J. R. *J. Endocrinol.* **9,** 343 (1953).
169. Hodges, J. R. *J. Endocrinol.* **10,** 173 (1954).
170. Hoffmann, F., and Anselmino, K. J. *Klin. Wochschr.* **12,** 1436 (1933).
171. Hoffmann, F. G., and Davison, C. *J. Clin. Endocrinol. and Metabolism.* **13,** 848 (1953).
172. Holtermann, H. *Farmakotherapi* **7,** 4 (1951).
173. Homan, J. D. H., Overbeek, G. A., Neutelings, J. P. J., Booij, C. J., and Van Der Vies, J. *Lancet* **266,** 541 (1954).
174. Horstmann, P. M. *Acta Endocrinol. Suppl.* **3,** 9 (1949).
175. Houssay, B. A. *Endocrinology* **30,** 884 (1942).
176. Houssay, B. A. *Quart. Rev. Biol.* **24,** 1 (1949).
177. Houssay, B. A., and Anderson, E. *Rev. soc. argentina biol.* **25,** 91 (1949).
178. Houssay, B. A., and Anderson, E. *Endocrinology* **45,** 627 (1949).
179. Houssay, B. A., and Potick, D. *Rev. soc. argentina biol.* **5,** 66 (1929).
180. Houssay, B. A., and Rodriguez, R. R. *Endocrinology* **53,** 114 (1953).
181. Hsieh, K. M., Wang, T. Y., and Blumenthal, H. T. *Endocrinology* **51,** 298 (1952).

182. Hume, D. M. *Ciba Colloquia Endocrinol.* **4,** 87 (1952).
183. Illingworth, B. A., and Russell, J. A. *Endocrinology* **48,** 423 (1951).
184. Ingalls, T. H., and Hayes, D. R. *Endocrinology* **29,** 720 (1941).
185. Ingle, D. J. *Endocrinology* **39,** 43 (1946).
186. Ingle, D. J. *J. Clin. Endocrinol. and Metabolism* **12,** 1601 (1952).
187. Ingle, D. J., and Li, C. H. *Proc. Soc. Exptl. Biol. Med.* **79,** 128 (1952).
188. Ingle, D. J., Nezamis, J. E., and Morley, E. H. *Am. J. Physiol.* **171,** 378 (1952).
189. Ingle, D. J., Nezamis, J. E., and Morley, E. H. *Endocrinology* **53,** 24 (1953).
190. Ingle, D., Prestrud, M. C., and Nezamis, J. E. *Am. J. Physiol.* **166,** 171 (1951).
191. Jacot, B., and Selye, H. *Proc. Soc. Exptl. Biol. Med.* **78,** 46 (1951).
192. Jailer, J. W. *Endocrinology* **46,** 420 (1950).
193. Jailer, J. W., and Boas, N. F. *Endocrinology* **46,** 314 (1950).
194. Jefferies, W. McK. *J. Clin. Endocrinol.* **9,** 913, 927, 937 (1949).
195. Jefferies, W. McK., Levy, R. P., and Kelley, L. W. *J. Clin. Endocrinol. and Metabolism* **13,** 873 (1953).
196. Jenkins, D., Laidlaw, J. C., Reddy, W. J., Mills, L. C., and Thorn, J. W. *J. Clin. Endocrinol. and Metabolism* **13,** 843 (1953).
197. Jones, I. C. *Endocrinology* **45,** 514 (1949).
198. Juhn, M. *Proc. Soc. Exptl. Biol. Med.* **76,** 118 (1951).
199. Kark, R. M., and Muehrcke, R. C. *Lancet* **262,** 1189 (1952).
200. Kass, E. H., and Finland, M. *Ann. Rev. Microbiol.* **7,** 361 (1953).
201. Kass, E. H., Hechter, O., Macchi, I. A., and Mou, T. W. *Proc. Soc. Exptl. Biol. Med.* **85,** 583 (1954).
202. Kass, E. H., Lundgren, M. M., and Finland, M. *J. Exptl. Med.* **99,** 89 (1954).
203. Kemp, T., and Marx, L. *Acta Pathol. Microbiol. Scand.* **14,** 197 (1937).
204. Kibrick, E. A., Simpson, M. E., Becks, H., and Evans, H. M. *Endocrinology* **31,** 93 (1942).
205. Kinsell, L. W., Balch, H. E., and Michaels, G. D. *Proc. Soc. Exptl. Biol. Med.* **83,** 683 (1953).
206. Kinsell, L. W., Margen, S., Partridge, J. W., Michaels, G. D., Balch, H. E., and Jahn, J. P. *J. Clin. Endocrinol. and Metabolism* **14,** 110 (1954).
207. Knobil, E., Ganong, W. F., and Greep, R. O. *J. Clin. Endocrinol. and Metabolism* **14,** 787 (1954).
208. Kochakian, C. D. *In* S. Soskin, Progress in Clinical Endocrinology. Grune & Stratton, New York, 1950, p. 429.
209. Kumagai, L. F., Brill, B. A., and Dougherty, T. F. *J. Clin. Endocrinol. and Metabolism* **14,** 786 (1954).
210. Kurtz, M., De Bodo, R. C., Kiang, S. P., and Ancowitz, A. *Proc. Soc. Exptl. Biol. Med.* **76,** 21 (1951).
211. Laqueur, E., Dingemanse, E., and Freud, J. *Acta Brevia Neerl. Physiol. Pharmacol. Microbiol.* **11,** 46 (1941).
212. Lawrence, R. T. B., Salter, J. M., and Best, C. H. *Abstr. 19th Intern. Physiol. Congr., Montreal*, p. 547 (1953).
213. Lazarus, S. S., and Volk, B. W. *Metabolism* **1,** 355 (1952).
214. Lee, M. O., and Ayres, G. B. *Endocrinology* **20,** 489 (1936).
215. Lee, M. O., and Schaffer, N. K. *J. Nutrition* **7,** 337 (1934).
216. Lee, M. O., (Personal communication).
217. Leonard, S. L. *Endocrinology* **35,** 83 (1944).
218. Lewis, R. A., Demajo, S., and Rosemberg, E. *Endocrinology* **45,** 564 (1949).
219. Lewis, R. A., Klein, R., and Wilkins, L. *J. Clin. Invest.* **29,** 460 (1950).
220. Lewis, R. A., Rosemberg, E., and Wilkins, L. *Endocrinology* **47,** 414 (1950).

221. Levin, L. *Am. J. Physiol.* **141,** 143 (1944).
222. Levin, L., and Farber, R. K. *Recent Progr. Hormone Research* **7,** 399 (1952).
223. Levie, L. H., and Uyldert, I. E. *Acta Brevia Neer. Physiol. Pharmacol. Microbiol.* **9,** 121 (1939).
224. Lewis, R. A., Klein, R., and Wilkins. *J. Clin. Invest.* **29,** 460 (1950).
225. Li, C. H. *Acta Endocrinol.* **10,** 255 (1952).
226. Li, C. H., and Evans, H. M. *Recent Progr. Hormone Research* **3,** 1 (1948).
227. Li, C. H., Evans, H. M., and Simpson, M. E. *J. Biol. Chem.* **159,** 353 (1945).
228. Li, C. H., Geschwind, I., and Evans, H. M. *Endocrinology* **44,** 67 (1949).
229. Li, C. H., Geschwind, I. I., Levy, A. L., Harris, J. I., Dixon, J. S., Pon, N. G., and Porath, J. O. *Nature* **173,** 251 (1954).
230. Li, C. H., and Papkoff, H. *J. Biol. Chem.* **204,** 391 (1953).
231. Li, C. H., Simpson, M. E., and Evans, H. M. *Growth* **12,** 39 (1948).
232. Li, C. H., Simpson, M. E., and Evans, H. M. *Arch. Biochem.* **23,** 51 (1949).
233. Liddle, G. W., Rinfret, A. P., Richard, J., and Forsham, P. H. *J. Clin. Endocrinol. and Metabolism* **13,** 842 (1953).
234. Lockett, M. F., Reid, E., and Young, F. G. *J. Physiol.* **121,** 28 (1953).
235. Long, C. N. H. *Recent Progr. Hormone Research* **7,** 75 (1952).
236. Lotspiech, W. D., and Petersen, V. P. *Am. J. Physiol.* **176,** 232 (1954).
237. Lukens, F. D. W. *Abstr. 19th Intern. Congr. Physiol., Montreal,* pp. 12–16 (1953).
238. Lyons, W. R., Li, C. H., Cole, R. D., and Johnson, R. E. *J. Clin. Endocrinol. and Metabolism* **13,** 836 (1953).
239. Macchi, I. A,. Hechter, O., and Pincus, G. *J. Clin. Endocrinol.* **11,** 756 (1951).
240. McCann, S. M. *Am. J. Physiol.* **175,** 13 (1953).
241. McDermott, W., Fry, E. G., Brobeck, J. R., and Long, C. N. H. *Proc. Soc. Exptl. Biol. Med.* **73,** 609 (1950).
242. McDermott, W., Fry, E. G., Brobeck, J. R., and Long, C. N. H. *Yale J. Biol. and Med.* **23,** 52 (1950).
243. McIntosh, H. W., and Carruthers, E. P. *Can. Med. Assoc. J.* **67,** 428 (1952).
244. Mandel, W., Singer, M. J., Gudmundson, H. R., Meister, L., and Modern, F. W. S. *J. Am. Med. Assoc.* **146,** 546 (1951).
245. Marks, H. P., and Young, F. G. *Chem. Ind.* **58,** 652 (1939).
246. Marks, H. P., and Young, F. G. *Lancet* **238,** 493 (1940).
247. Marx, W., Magy, D. B., Simpson, M. E., and Evans, H. M. *Am. J. Physiol.* **137,** 544 (1942).
248. Marx, W., Simpson, M. E., and Evans, H. M. *Endocrinology* **30,** 1 (1942).
249. Marx, W., Simpson, M. E., Li, C. H., and Evans, H. M. *Endocrinology* **33,** 102 (1943).
250. Marx, W., Simpson, M. E., Reinhardt, W. O., and Evans, H. M. *Am. J. Physiol.* **135,** 614 (1942).
251. Mathiew, J. C., and Gaebler, O. H. *Endocrinology* **45,** 129 (1949).
252. Miahle-Veloss, C. *J. physiol. (Paris)* **45,** 189 (1953).
253. Miller, R. A., and Dockrell, A. W. *Anat. Record* **115,** 404 (1953).
254. Miller, R. A., and Riddle, O. *Proc. Soc. Exptl. Biol. Med.* **41,** 518 (1939).
255. Milman, A. E., and De Moor, P. *Federation Proc.* **9,** 90 (1950).
256. Milman, A. E., De Moor, P., and Lukens, F. D. W. *Am. J. Physiol.* **166,** 354 (1951).
257. Milman, A. E., and Russell, J. A. *Endocrinology* **47,** 114 (1950).
258. Mirsky, I. A. *Endocrinology* **25,** 52 (1939).
259. Mitchell, M. L., and Girerd, R. J. *Proc. Soc. Exptl. Biol. Med.* **83,** 615 (1953).
260. Mitchell, M. L., Guillemin, R., and Selye, H. *Endocrinology* **54,** 111 (1954).

261. Moon, H. D., Simpson, M. E., Li, C. H., and Evans, H. M. *Cancer Research* **10**, 364, 297, 549 (1950).
262. Moon, H. D., Simpson, M. E., Li, C. H., and Evans, H. M. *Cancer Research* **12**, 448 (1952).
263. Morrison, J. F. *Australian J. Exptl. Biol. Med. Sci.* **30**, 313 (1952).
264. Moyer, A. W., Van Der Scheer, J., Ritter, H., Tesar, W. C., Logan, J. B., Oleson, J. J., and Cox, H. R. *Proc. Soc. Exptl. Biol. Med.* **79**, 1 (1952).
265. Nelson, D. H., and Hume, D. M. *J. Clin. Endocrinol. and Metabolism* **14**, 781 (1954).
266. Nelson, J. W., O'Connell, P. W., and Haines, W. J. *Science* **119**, 379 (1954).
267. Nelson, D. H., Samuels, L. T., Willardson, D. G., and Tyler, F. H. *J. Clin. Endocrinol.* **11**, 1021 (1951).
268. Newton, W. H., and Young, F. G. *J. Physiol.* **94**, 40 (1938).
269. Noble, R. L., and Collip, J. B. *Endocrinology* **29**, 934 (1941).
270. O'Donovan, D. K., and Collip, J. B. *Endocrinology* **23**, 718 (1938).
271. Ogilvie, R. F. *J. Pathol. Bacteriol.* **56**, 225 (1944).
272. Ogilvie, R. F. *Vitamins and Hormones* **10**, 183 (1952).
273. Opsahl, J. C., and Long, C. N. H. *Yale J. Biol. and Med.* **24**, 199 (1951).
274. Opsahl, J. C., Long, C. N. H., and Fry, E. G. *Yale J. Biol. and Med.* **23**, 399 (1951).
275. Ottaway, J. H. *Brit. Med. J* ii, 357 (1953).
276. Otto, J. F. Unpublished observations.
277. Overbeek, J. A., and Van Der Vies, J. *Acta Endocrinol.* **9**, 309 (1952).
278. Park, C. R., Brown, D. H., Cornblath, M., Doughaday, W. H., and Krahl, M. E. *J. Biol. Chem.* **197**, 151 (1952).
279. Payne, R. W. *Endocrinology* **45**, 305 (1949).
280. Payne, R. W., Raben, M. S., and Astwood, E. B. *J. Biol. Chem.* **187**, 719 (1950).
281. Payne, R. W., Rosenberg, I. N., Raben, M. S., Cleroux, A. P., and Astwood, E. B. *J. Clin. Invest.* **30**, 665 (1951).
282. Pincus, G., Hechter, O., and Zaffaroni, A. *Proc. 2nd Clin. ACTH Conf.* **1**, 40 (1951).
283. Pincus, G., Hopkins, T. F., and Hechter, O. *Arch. Biochem. and Biophys.* **37**, 408 (1952).
284. Pincus, J. B., Natelson, S., and Lugovoy, J. K. *Proc. Soc. Exptl. Biol. Med.* **78**, 24 (1951).
285. Price, W. H., Cori, C. F., and Colowick, S. P. *J. Biol. Chem.* **160**, 633 (1945).
286. Pugsley, L. I., and Anderson, E. M. *Am. J. Physiol.* **109**, 85 (1934).
287. Raben, M. S. *Recent Progr. Hormone Research* **8**, 497 (1953).
288. Raben, M. S., Rosenberg, I. N., and Astwood, E. B. *Federation Proc.* **11**, 126 (1952).
289. Raben, M. S., Rosenberg, I. N., Westermeyer, V. W., and Astwood, E. B. *J. Am. Med. Assoc.* **148**, 844 (1952).
290. Raben, M. S., and Westermeyer, V. W. *Proc. Soc. Exptl. Biol. Med.* **78**, 550 (1951).
291. Raben, M. S., and Westermeyer, V. W. *Proc. Soc. Exptl. Biol. Med.* **80**, 83 (1952).
292. Raben, M. S., and Westermeyer, V. W. Unpublished observations.
293. Raben, M. S., Westermeyer, V. W., and Leaf, A. *J. Clin. Invest.* **31**, 655 (1953).
294. Randle, P. J. *Lancet.* **266**, 441 (1954).
295. Recant, L. *J. Clin. Invest.* **31**, 656 (1952).

296. Recant, L., Hume, D. M., Forsham, P. H., and Thorn, G. W. *J. Clin. Endocrinol.* **10**, 187 (1950).
297. Reid, E. *J. Endocrinol.* **8**, 50 (1952).
298. Reid, E. *J. Endocrinol.* **9**, 185 (1953).
299. Reid, E. *J. Endocrinol.* **9**, 210 (1953).
300. Reid, E. *J. Endocrinol.* **9**, 323, 329 (1953).
301. Reid, E., Smith, R. H., and Young, F. G. *Biochem. J.* **42**, 19 (1948).
302. Reid, E., and Young, F. G. *Biochem. J.* **42**, 54 (1948).
303. Reinhardt, W. O., Geschwind, I. I., and Li, C. H. *Acta Endocrinol.* **8**, 393 (1951).
304. Reinhardt, W. O., and Li, C. H. *Proc. Soc. Exptl. Biol. Med.* **77**, 229 (1951).
305. Reinhardt, W. O., Geschwind, I. I., Porath, J. O., and Li, C. H. *Proc. Soc. Exptl. Biol. Med.* **80**, 439 (1952).
306. Reiss, M. *Endocrinology* **40**, 294 (1947).
307. Reiss, M., Brummel, E., Halkerston, I. D. K., Badrick, F. E., and Fenwick, M. *J. Endocrinol.* **9**, 379 (1953).
308. Renold, A. E., Forsham, P. H., Maisterrena, J., and Thorn, G. W. *New Engl. J. Med.* **244**, 796 (1951).
309. Renold, A. E., Jenkins, D., Forsham, P. H., and Thorn, G. W. *J. Clin. Endocrinol. and Metabolism* **12**, 763 (1952).
310. Richards, J. B., and Sayers, G. *Proc. Soc. Exptl. Biol. Med.* **77**, 87 (1951).
311. Richardson, K. C., and Young, F. G. *J. Physiol.* **91**, 352 (1937).
312. Riddle, O., Opdyke, D. F., and Bates, R. W. *Carnegie Inst. Wash. Publ.* **569**, 17 (1947).
313. Robinson, H. J. *Proc. 5th Symposium Colston Research Soc. Univ. Bristol.*, p. 105 (1953).
314. Rosenberg, I. N. *Proc. Soc. Exptl. Biol. Med.* **82**, 701 (1953).
315. Rosenberg, I. N., and Astwood, E. B. Unpublished.
316. Russell, J. A. *Endocrinology* **22**, 80 (1938).
317. Russell, J. A. *Am. J. Physiol.* **124**, 774 (1938).
318. Russell, J. A. *Endocrinology* **48**, 462 (1951).
319. Russell, J. A., and Cappiello, M. *Endocrinology* **44**, 333 (1949).
320. Russell, J. A., and Wilhelmi, A. E. *Endocrinology* **47**, 26 (1950).
321. Saffran, M., and Bayliss, M. J. *Endocrinology* **52**, 140 (1953).
322. Saffran, M., Grad, B., and Bayliss, M. J. *Endocrinology* **50**, 629 (1952).
323. Salmon, T. N. *Endocrinology* **29**, 291 (1941).
324. Salter, J. M., and Best, C. H. *Federation Proc.* **12**, 122 (1953).
325. Salter, J., and Best, C. H. *Brit. Med. J.* **ii**, 353 (1953).
326. Samuels, L. T., Reinecke, R. M., and Bauman, K. L. *Endocrinology* **33**, 87 (1943).
327. Sandberg, A. A., Nelson, D. H., Palmer, J. G., Samuels, L. T., and Tyler, F. H. *J. Clin. Endocrinol. and Metabolism* **13**, 629 (1953).
328. Sayers, G. *Physiol. Revs.* **30**, 241 (1950).
329. Sayers, G., Burns, T. W., Tyler, F. H., Jager, B. V., Schwartz, T. B., Smith, E. L., Samuels, L. T., and Davenport, H. W. *J. Clin. Endocrinol.* **9**, 593 (1949).
330. Sayers, G., Kerkin, M., and Tortoreto, J. N. *J. Clin. Endocrinol.* **8**, 587 (1948).
331. Sayers, G., and Sayers, M. A. *Recent Progr. Hormone Research* **2**, 81 (1948).
332. Sayers, M. A., Sayers, G., and Woodbury, L. A. *Endocrinology* **42**, 279 (1948).
333. Schaeffer, R. L. *Endocrinology* **20**, 64 (1936).
334. Schaeffer, R. L., and Strickroot, F. L. *Endocrinology* **26**, 599 (1940).
335. Schaffer, N. K., and Lee, M. *J. Biol. Chem.* **108**, 355 (1935).

306   E. B. ASTWOOD

336. Schweizer, M., Charipper, H. A., and Haterius, H. O.   *Endocrinology* **21**, 30 (1937).
337. Schweizer, M., Charipper, H. A., and Kleinberg, W.   *Endocrinology* **26**, 979 (1940).
338. Schweizer, M., and Long, M. E.   *Endocrinology* **46**, 191 (1950).
339. Scott, J. L., Jr., and Engel, F. L.   *Endocrinology* **46**, 582 (1950).
340. Selye, H.   *Endocrinology* **49**, 197 (1951).
341. Selye, H.   First Annual Report on Stress.   Acta, Inc., Montreal, 1951.
342. Selye, H.   *Brit. Med. J.* **i**, 263 (1951).
343. Selye, H.   *Can. Med. Assoc. J.* **64**, 489 (1951).
344. Selye, H.   *Nature* **168**, 149 (1951).
345. Selye, H.   *Am. J. Physiol.* **171**, 381 (1952).
346. Selye, H.   Personal communication.
347. Selye, H., Salgado, E., and Procopio, J.   *Acta Endocrinol.* **9**, 337 (1952).
348. Shaw, J. H., and Greep, R. O.   *Endocrinology* **44**, 520 (1949).
349. Shelton, E. K.   *Calif and Western Med.* **45**, 20 (1936).
350. Shelton, E. K., Cavanaugh, L. A., and Evans, H. M.   *Am. J. Diseases Children* **52**, 100 (1936).
351. Shelton, E. K., Cavanaugh, L. A., and Patek, P. R.   *Endocrinology* **20**, 846 (1936).
352. Shipley, R. A.   *Endocrinology* **31**, 629 (1942).
353. Shipley, R. A., and Long, C. N. H.   *Biochem. J.* **32**, 2242 (1938).
354. Shipner, L. B., and Soskin, S.   *Am. J. Physiol.* **109**, 97 (1934).
355. Shorr, E., Carter, A. C., Kennedy, B. J., and Smith, R. W., Jr.   *Trans. Assoc. Am. Physicians* **66**, 114 (1953).
356. Silberberg, M.   *Proc. Soc. Exptl. Biol. Med.* **32**, 1423 (1935).
357. Silberberg, M.   *Proc. Soc. Exptl. Biol. Med.* **34**, 333 (1936).
358. Silberberg, M., and Silberberg, R.   *Proc. Soc. Exptl. Biol. Med.* **34**, 108 (1936).
359. Simpson, M. E., Evans, H. M., and Li, C. H.   *Endocrinology* **33**, 261 (1943).
360. Simpson, M. E., Evans, H. M., and Li, C. H.   *Growth* **13**, 151 (1949).
361. Simpson, M. E., Marx, W., Becks, H., and Evans, H. M.   *Endocrinology* **35**, 234 (1944).
362. Simpson, M. E., Marx, W., Becks, H., and Evans, H. M.   *Endocrinology* **35**, 309 (1944).
363. Sinkoff, M. W., and De Bodo, R. C.   *Arch. exptl. Pathol. u. Pharmakol.* **219**, 100 (1953).
364. Smelser, G. K.   *Am. J. Pathol.* **15**, 341 (1939).
365. Smith, M. C., Slattery, P. A., Shimkin, M. B., Li, C. H., Lee, R., Clarke, J. C., and Lyons, W. R.   *Cancer Research* **12**, 59 (1952).
366. Smith, P. E.   *Proc. Soc. Exptl. Biol. Med.* **30**, 1252 (1933).
367. Smith, P. E., Greenwood, C. F., and Foster, G. L.   *Am. J. Pathol.* **3**, 669 (1927).
368. Solem, J. H., and Holtermann, H.   *Lancet* **262**, 468 (1952).
369. Spain, D. M., and Molomut, N.   *Proc. Soc. Exptl. Biol. Med.* **83**, 326 (1953).
370. Stack-Dunne, M. P.   *Ciba Colloquia Endocrinol.* **5**, 133 (1953).
371. Stack-Dunne, M. P., and Young, F. G.   *J. Endocrinol.* **7**, 66 (1951).
372. Stadie, W. C., Haugaard, N., Hills, A. G., and Marsh, J. B.   *Am. J. Med. Sci.* **218**, 275 (1949).
373. Stadie, W. C., Haugaard, N., and Marsh, J. B.   *J. Biol. Chem.* **198**, 785 (1952).
374. Stebbins, R. B., and Thomas, G. B.   *Proc. Soc. Exptl. Biol. Med.* **84**, 44 (1953).
375. Stein, J. D., Jr., Bennett, L. L., Batts, A. A., and Li, C. H.   *Am. J. Physiol.* **171**, 587 (1952).

376. Stetten, D., Jr., and Salcedo, J., Jr. *J. Biol. Chem.* **156,** 27 (1944).
377. Stormont, R. T. *J. Am. Med. Assoc.* **151,** 474 (1953).
378. Sulman, F. G. *Fefuah Veterinarith* **9,** 31 (1952).
379. Sweat, M. L., and Farrell, G. L. *J. Clin. Endocrinol. and Metabolism* **14,** 782 (1954).
380. Sydnor, K. L., Kelley, V. C., Raile, R. B., Ely, R. S., and Sayers, G. *Proc. Soc. Exptl. Biol. Med.* **82,** 695 (1953).
381. Sydnor, K. L., and Sayers, G. *Proc. Soc. Exptl. Biol. Med.* **79,** 432 (1952).
382. Sydnor, K. L., and Sayers, G. *Proc. Soc. Exptl. Biol. Med.* **83,** 729 (1953).
383. Szego, C. M., and White, A. *Endocrinology* **44,** 150 (1949).
384. Tang, P. C., and Patton, H. D. *Endocrinology* **49,** 86 (1951).
385. Taylor, N. R. W., Loraine, J. A., and Robertson, H. A. *J. Endocrinol.* **9,** 334 (1953).
386. Teel, H. M. *Science* **69,** 405 (1929).
387. Teel, H. M., and Cushing, H. *Endocrinology* **14,** 157 (1930).
388. Teel, H. M., and Watkins, O. *Am. J. Physiol.* **89,** 662 (1929).
389. Tepperman, J. *Endocrinology* **47,** 384 (1950).
390. Thompson, R. E., and Fisher, J. D. *Endocrinology* **52,** 496 (1953).
391. Thorn, G. W., Forsham, P. H., Frawley, T. F.,, Hill, S. R., Jr., Roche, M., Staehelin, D., and Wilson, D. L. *New Engl. J. Med.* **242,** 783, 824, 865 (1950).
392. Thorn, G. W., Forsham, P. H., Prunty, F. T. G., and Hills, A. G. *J. Am. Med. Assoc.* **137,** 1005 (1948).
393. Turner, H. H. *Southern. Med. J.* **28,** 309 (1935).
394. Tyler, F. H., Migeon, C., Florentin, A. A., and Samuels, L. T. *J. Clin. Endocrinol. and Metabolism* **14,** 774 (1954).
395. Ulrich, F., Copp, D. H., Asling, C. W., Li, C. H., and Reinhardt, W. O. *Endocrinology* **48,** 245 (1951).
396. Ulrich, F., Reinhardt, W. O., and Li, C. H. *Acta Endocrinol.* **10,** 117 (1952).
397. Vanderlaan, W. P. *J. Clin. Invest.* **32,** 609 (1953).
398. Van Dyke, D. C., Simpson, M. E., Li, C. H., and Evans, H. M. *Am. J. Physiol.* **163,** 297 (1950).
399. Van Dyke, H. B., and Wallen-Lawrence, *J. Pharmacol. Exptl. Therap.* **40,** 413 (1930).
400. Van Wieringen, G., and De Jongh, S. E. *Proceedings, Amsterdam.* **52,** 832 (1949).
401. Van Wieringen, G., and De Jongh, S. E. *Proceedings, Amsterdam* **52,** 835 (1949).
402. Venning, E. H., Carballeira, A., and Dyrenfurth, I. *J. Clin. Endocrinol. and Metabolism* **14,** 784 (1954).
403. Vogt, M. *J. Physiol.* **113,** 129 (1951).
404. Volk, B. W., and Lazarus, S. S. *Proc. Soc. Exptl. Biol. Med.* **83,** 151 (1953).
405. Walker, D. G., Asling, C. W., Simpson, M. E., Li, C. H., and Evans, H. M. *Anat. Record* **114,** 19 (1952).
406. Wang, T.-Y., Hsieh, K.-M., and Blumenthal, H. T. *Endocrinology* **53,** 520 (1953).
407. Weil, R., and Ross, S. *Endocrinology* **45,** 207 (1949).
407a. Weil, R., and Stetten, D. *J. Biol. Chem.* **168,** 129 (1947).
408. Weinstein, R. C. *Proc. Soc. Exptl. Biol. Med.* **40,** 667 (1939).
409. Weisz, P., Gláz, E., Vaseszky, Sz., and Gáti, T. *Acta Med. Acad. Sci. Hung.* **4,** 201 (1953).
410. Westermeyer, V. W., and Raben, M. S. *Endocrinology* **54,** 173 (1954).
411. White, H. L., Heinbecker, P., and Rolf, D. *Am. J. Physiol.* **165,** 442 (1951).
412. White, W. F. *J. Am. Chem. Soc.* **75,** 503 (1953).

413. Whitney, J. E., Bennett, L. L., and Li, C. H. *Proc. Soc. Exptl. Biol. Med.* **79,** 584 (1952).
414. Wilhelmi, A. E., Fishman, J. B., and Russell, J. A. *J. Biol. Chem.* **176,** 737 (1948).
415. Winter, C. A., Brink, N. G., and Folkers, K. *Proc. Soc. Exptl. Biol. Med.* **82,** 365 (1953).
416. Winter, C. A., Hollings, H. L., and Stebbins, R. B. *Endocrinology* **52,** 123 (1953).
417. Wolfson, W. Q. *Arch. Internal Med.* **92,** 108 (1953).
418. Wyman, L. C., and Tum-Suden, C. *Endocrinology* **36,** 340 (1945).
419. Young, F. G. *Lancet* **231,** 297, (1936).
420. Young, F. G. *J. Endocrinol.* **1,** 339 (1939).
421. Young, F. G. *Endocrinology* **26,** 345 (1940).
422. Young, F. G. *Biochem. J.* **39,** 515 (1945).
423. Young, F. G. *J. Clin. Endocrinol.* **11,** 531 (1951).
424. Young, F. G. *Abstr. 19th Internat. Physiol. Congr., Montreal,* p. 18 (1953).
425. Young, F. G. *Recent Progr. Hormone Research* **8,** 471 (1953).
426. Zalesky, M., Wells, L. J., Overholser, M. D., and Gomez, E. T. *Endocrinology* **28,** 521 (1941).
427. Zizine, L. *Compt. rend. Soc. Biol.* **147,** 1050 (1953).

CHAPTER VIII

Physiology of the Gonadotropins and the Lactogenic Hormone*

BY A. T. COWIE AND S. J. FOLLEY

CONTENTS

I. Introductory

In writing this chapter our aim has been to give an account of the progress in the physiology of the lactogenic hormone (prolactin) and the gonadotropins which has occurred since these topics were reviewed in Volumes I and II, respectively, of *The Hormones* and also to give historically more complete accounts of those aspects not previously dealt with. It is therefore hoped that within the covers of the three volumes of this treatise the reader will have access to a reasonably complete and up-to-date picture of the subject as it is at present. The two chapters on the mammary gland in Volume I in which the physiology of prolactin was dealt with, though published in 1948, were actually written in 1946; we therefore in the main cite papers about prolactin from 1946 onwards except where the development of the argument necessitates reference to earlier work. Since the publication of the chapter on the physiology of the gonadotropins

* In conformity with editorial practice the spellings "gonadotropin" and "hypophyseal" have been used in this Chapter although the authors prefer the forms "gonadotrophin" and "hypophysial."

in 1950 the mechanism of the control of pituitary function has become a subject of major interest and much debate. Consequently we have felt it desirable to describe the development of this aspect of the subject from as far back as seemed necessary to provide the reader with the background against which the recent and to some extent still controversial findings and hypotheses can be properly appreciated. On topics relating to the gonadotropins which were included in Volume II we have in general contented ourselves with discussing work done since that volume appeared.

The cellular origin of the pituitary hormones is a field in which recently there has been much activity. The development and application of newer cytological and cytochemical techniques has in some respects revolutionized previous ideas in this field. In guiding us along these hazardous paths we have been fortunate in being able to enlist the help of Mr. K. C. Richardson of University College London, who has kindly placed his expert knowledge and experience at our disposal. For reading and criticizing this portion of our manuscript we owe him our heartfelt thanks.

The lactogenic hormone has been given various names—prolactin, mammotropin, luteotropin—of which the first has been used in Europe almost to the exclusion of the others and quite extensively also in the United States. We therefore propose to retain it here, particularly as it was used in Volume I of *The Hormones*. As will be seen later in this chapter, prolactin has been shown with any certainty to have luteotropic properties in one species only, the rat, consequently, we feel it is premature at this stage to follow White (255) and Voss (253a) in adopting the name luteotropin.

II. The Gonadotropic Hormones

A. Cellular Origin of Gonadotropins

To determine the cellular origin of the hormones of the anterior pituitary two main methods of study have been used. The first attempts to correlate the changes in the proportional number of different types of cell with various physiological states; the second attempts to discover directly the secretory activity of the hypophysis by an analysis of the morphological changes within the cells. Severinghaus (237a) reviewing the position in 1937 showed that both these methods of approach had been used in studying the origin of the gonadotropins, and he considered that the view most in line with the somewhat inconclusive evidence was that the basophils produced the follicle-stimulating hormone (FSH) and the acidophils, the luteinizing hormone (LH).

Before discussing more recent cytological studies it is perhaps advisable to review briefly the present situation about the classification of the cell types of the adenohypophysis. Prior to about 1935 the cells were generally classified on the basis of their reactions to Mallory's triple stain, Mann's methyl blue-eosin, or Giemsa's blood stain. Three cell-types were recognized, the acidophil (sometimes called the alpha cell), basophil (beta cell) and the nongranular chromophobe. Since 1935 evidence has been forthcoming from modified staining procedures that there are two varieties of basophil and two sorts of acidophil. Thus Romeis (228) distinguished alpha, beta, gamma, delta, and epsilon cells; the alpha and epsilon cells belong to the acidophil class, the beta and delta to the basophil class. A zeta cell has since been added (113). The literature is, however, confused, as different workers, using different techniques and studying different species, have not always been in agreement as to which cell types the Greek letters should be applied.

Although there is as yet no general agreement on the exact identity of some of the cell types, considerable progress is being made in determining the functions of some of them, and this is particularly true in the case of gonadotropic function. The introduction of histochemical techniques, which reveal something of the biochemistry of the cell constituents, and carefully controlled studies with the more classical staining procedures have both contributed to the recent advances. Evidence is appearing that at least some of the cell types undergo secretory cycles and that their staining characteristics may change considerably during the cycles, thus making identification difficult. Already suggestions have been put forward for a classification scheme based on cytochemical and functional characteristics, and there can be little doubt that some such classification will completely displace the present system of borrowings from the Greek alphabet.

Early in the cytochemical field of investigation came the studies of Herlant (138-140). On the grounds that gonadotropins are glycoproteins and that such substances produce metachromasia with dyes like toluidine blue, he claimed that the basophils contained glycoproteins. Pearse (210) has confirmed that the granules of the basophils give a violet metachromatic reaction with toluidine blue but believes that "this is less likely to indicate that they are composed of mucoprotein than that they are composed of some substance in a state of polymerization" (see also Pearse, 213).

The use of periodic acid in histochemistry was described by McManus in 1946 for the demonstration of mucin, and later elaborated by Hotchkiss (147). The reaction is not now considered to be specific for mucin, but it will demonstrate a variety of polysaccharide-containing substances, as it depends on the presence of the 1,2-glycol grouping. In the reaction, periodic acid breaks the C—C bonds present as 1,2-glycol groups, converting them into dialdehydes which react with Schiff's reagent (decolorized basic fuchsin) to give a magenta red color. When this periodic acid-

Schiff (PAS) reaction is applied with suitable counterstains to the anterior pituitary, the basophils stain deeply red owing to the color of the beta granules, the chromophobes being, at the most, pale pink. The alpha granules are free from any trace of redness and will stain yellow with orange G counterstain. Further details of the cytochemistry of this reaction are given by Pearse (213).

The application of the PAS procedure to the anterior pituitary has been studied by Catchpole (44, 45), by Pearse (207, 210-212, and 214), Purves and Griesbach (219), and Siperstein et al. (242). Catchpole believed that the reaction demonstrated a glycoprotein constituent in the basophil cells of the rat pituitary, and he considered part of this material to be FSH. Studies on human and animal pituitaries (sheep, goat, and rat) by Pearse (207, 208, 210-212, 214) confirmed Catchpole's findings, but Pearse further concluded that LH was also derived from the basophils.

The application of the trichrome periodic acid-Schiff procedure (208) to the anterior pituitary has led Pearse to propose some modifications to the usual terminology, which, as we have seen, was evolved from studies using Mallory's stain or various modifications thereof. Three main cell types are recognized by Pearse: (1) mucoid cells, (2) acidophils, and (3) chromophobes. The "mucoid" cells include all cells which contain glyco- or muco-protein in diffuse, granular, or vesiculate form. Pearse has shown by comparative staining procedures that all basophils of the older terminology and up to 30 % of the chromophobes belong to the mucoid cell series. All of these cells may reasonably be assumed to be associated with the production of gonadotropie or thyrotropic hormones (glycoproteins). The glycoprotein granules can be divided on the basis of further staining reactions into beta and gamma granules. Both types are PAS-positive, the latter to a lesser degree. Pearse considers these gamma granules to be the same as the delta granules of Halmi (see p. 314) and that they represent mucoprotein in a lower state of polymerization than that of the beta granules. Pearse has classified the mucoid cells into eight types and has described a secretory cycle. He claims that the trichrome PAS procedures permit estimations to be made of the degree of mucoprotein storage, production, and secretion.

Pearse's claim that LH is derived from the mucoid cells is primarily based on the fact that the PAS reaction can easily detect 1 % of reacting polysaccharide. As the granules of the acidophils fail to stain by the PAS method, they therefore contain less than 1 % reacting material and possibly none at all. If the acidophils are the source of a glycoprotein gonadotropic hormone, it must either pass out of the cells as soon as it is formed or the cells must produce a carbohydrate-free precursor of the hormone. Pearse considers these explanations to be unlikely, and in the light of his experiments it is necessary to review the evidence on which the acidophilic origin of LH was originally based.

Subsequent to the studies reviewed by Severinghaus, the main evidence in favor of the acidophils as the source of LH was based on the experiments of Friedgood and Dawson (109, 110). They observed in the anterior pituitary of the rabbit and the cat (both animals which ovulate only after mating) the presence of a modified acidophil whose granules had a great affinity for azocarmine. These cells, present in small numbers in the anterior pituitary of the estrous animal, increased in number after coitus and reached a maximum number some 3 to 6 hours after mating. Degranulation in these "carminophil" cells began about the 4th hour, was well marked by the 6th hour, and was virtually completed by the 14th hour. Friedgood and Dawson concluded that these carminophil cells were responsible for the production of a luteinizing hormone, degranulation representing the secretory phase. Since these cells were also present in considerable numbers during late pregnancy and early lactation, it was considered that they had other functions. Subsequently Dawson (58) considered that prolactin was derived from these carminophil cells (see p. 346). Pearse (209, 212) has repeated these studies in the rabbit and has confirmed the occurrence of the degranulation changes in the carminophils. He also investigated the possibility that these carminophils might contain glycoprotein, but none was found. Degranulation changes were, however, noted in the mucoid cells. These were apparent within half an hour of coitus and were maximal at 1 hour. Six hours after coitus degranulated mucoid cells were still apparent, although the majority were refilling with beta granules. It is well established that within half an hour of coitus, 20 % of the gonadotropin in the rabbit pituitary has been discharged, and within an hour sufficient has passed into the blood stream to cause ovulation. The secretory changes in the mucoid cells are therefore much more closely correlated with the known time of liberation of the gonadotropic hormones than are the changes in the carminophils. In view of these findings it is clear that the experiments of Friedgood and Dawson can no longer be held as providing strong evidence in favor of the acidophilic origin of LH.

Desclin (68) has, moreover, described experiments which are in agreement with Pearse's claim that LH is a basophilic secretion. Gonadectomized rats were grafted with ovarian tissue in the ear or spleen. The implant in the spleen was susceptible to, and therefore an indicator of, pituitary gonadotropic secretion but could not itself affect pituitary function since its estrogens were inactivated in the liver. Ovarian grafts in the ear, on the other hand, could influence pituitary function and be influenced by the pituitary. Clear evidence was obtained of LH secretion by the pituitary of the gonadectomized rat with ovarian grafts in the spleen, but the only difference in the cytological picture of the anterior pituitary as between those rats with ear grafts and spleen grafts lay in the appearance of the basophil cells, there being castration changes in the basophils of the spleen-grafted animals. The acidophils were unchanged. Desclin concluded that both FSH and LH were produced in the basophils.

To date there is no evidence to indicate that the glycoprotein in the granules in fact represents the gonadotropic hormones. Pearse (214) believes it more probable that the hormone is present in the form of a precursor which is released by enzymic or other action.

Before considering the work of Purves and Griesbach it is necessary to refer to the interesting study by Halmi (124). Using a modification of an aldehyde-fuschin stain in combination with a modified azan technique described by Gomori for elastic tissue, Halmi studied the staining reactions of the basophil cells in the pituitaries of rats which had been subjected to influences likely to affect the secretion of FSH as well as thyrotropin and adrenocorticotropin. Halmi considered that two types of basophil (beta and delta) could be distinguished and that the evidence was in favor of the delta cells being the source of both FSH and thyrotropin. Subsequent research with this staining procedure, or modifications of it, has extended these observations, and an attempt has been made to correlate these findings with those obtained by cytochemical procedures.

In an intensive study of the cytology of the rat pituitary using both the PAS procedure and a modified Mallory stain, Purves and Griesbach (219) have concluded that the PAS-positive cells in the rat pituitary are identical with the basophils as determined by the Mallory-type stain. These basophils, however, could be differentiated into two functional groups. In one group of cells, localized mainly on the lower surface of the anterior pituitary and on the upper surface adjacent to the pars intermedia with the greatest concentration at the anterior border of the pituitary, the intensity of the glycoprotein reaction followed closely the gonadotropic-hormone content of the gland. It was concluded that these cells were the source of gonadotropin and they were termed "gonadotrophs." The second group of cells were localized mainly in the central region of the anterior lobe. They were considered to be concerned with thyrotropic function and were termed "thyrotrophs." In further studies involving the Halmi aldehyde-fuchsin stain, Purves and Griesbach (220) concluded that their gonadotrophs were identical with Halmi's delta cells, the thyrotrophs, with his beta cells. They disagreed, therefore, with Halmi's view that thyrotropin was produced in the delta cells, and they believed that Halmi's aldehyde-fuchsin stain was specific for thyrotropic hormone and differentiated it from gonadotropin. Halmi (125) has reinterpreted somewhat his conclusions, and there is now close agreement between the findings of Purves and Griesbach and those of Halmi; both groups consider the gonadotrophs to be the source of FSH and possibly of LH.[1]

Recently Siperstein *et al.* (242) have reported on a cytological study of the anterior pituitary of the male and female rat from birth to maturity using the PAS technique, an aldehyde-fuchsin stain, and a modified Mallory stain. They confirmed the localized concentration of gonadotrophs on the lower surface and anterior border of the anterior pituitary, but in addition, they noted the occurrence of gonadotrophs lying in the central areas among the thyrotrophs. Degranulation of all the gonadotrophs was observed in the pituitary of the female rat at about the age of 35 days. This was taken to indicate a release of gonadotropin associated with the onset of estrous cycles. From the 42nd day degranulation of the gonadotrophs was complete. In contrast, there was no evidence of a diminished glycoprotein content of the gonadotrophs in the male rat. In some cases in the female, it was observed that the peripheral gonadotrophs had degranulated prior to the central ones, and the possibility that the former are responsible for FSH production, the latter for LH, is touched upon.[2] That two types of gonadotrophs can be recognized appears to be confirmed by the very recent and interesting study of pituitary cytology by Farquhar and Rinehart (86), who examined ultra thin sections of rat pituitary by electron microscopic techniques.

Ladman and Runner (162) using a complex trichrome staining method studied the cytology of mouse pituitaries at various stages of pregnancy. They concluded that differential cell counts gave less information about the gonadotropic content than did suitable bioassays. These authors observed, however, that it would be of great interest to repeat their study using the trichrome periodic acid-Schiff procedure of Pearse.[3]

A histochemical technique said to be specific for detecting protein-bound sulfhydryl and disulfide groups has recently been applied to the pituitary of the mouse, rat, dog, cat, and monkey by Ladman and Barrnett (161).

[1] Recent electron microscope studies of the pituitary cytology in the rat have supported the view that gonadotrophs and thyrotrophs are separate cell types (Farquhar and Rinehart, 86a).

[2] Further experimental evidence has now been presented by Purves and Griesbach (220a) in support of the contention that the peripheral gonadotrophs are associated with the secretion of FSH, and the central gonadotrophs with LH formation.

[3] Burt and Velardo (38a) have carried out bioassays for gonadotropin, ACTH, and thyrotropin in conjunction with cytological studies of 18 human pituitaries (sections stained with PAS-Orange G). Although no specific cytological feature could be correlated with the thyrotropic or adrenocorticotropic activity, high gonadotropic activity was associated with the presence of large numbers of intermediate-type mucoid cells.

Acidophils were found to contain a significant amount of sulfhydryl and/ or disulfide groups, whereas basophils and chromophobes contained little or no reactive material.   On this basis the authors conclude that since both LH and prolactin contain disulfide groups one or both of these hormones might arise in the acidophils.   At present these tentative deductions are not reconcilable with the conclusions of Pearse on the source of LH.   Further work on both the specificity of this reaction and its application under conditions known to alter the gonadotropic content of the pituitary is necessary before any evaluation can be made of the results obtained by this procedure.

In addition to extension of our understanding of the cellular distribution of gonadotropins afforded by cytochemical procedures, recent studies on the various fractions of pituitary homogenates isolated by differential centrifugation are providing further information.   McShan and Meyer (190) and McShan, Rozich, and Meyer (191) have investigated the gonadotropic activity of nuclear, large-granule, and supernatant fractions of rat-pituitary homogenates and have found that some 70 % to 75 % of the gonadotropic activity was associated with the small-granule fraction.   The authors, however, point out that it is not clear whether the gonadotropin was produced by the particles with which it was associated or was concentrated in those particles after production at some other point in the cell.

Herlant (141) has used cytochemical staining procedures to identify the granule fractions obtained by differential centrifugation.   Sucrose homogenates of sheep, swine, and ox anterior pituitaries were centrifuged for a few minutes (500 to 1000 g) to remove intact or partially disintegrated cells, nuclei, and erythrocytes.   The supernatant was then further centrifuged for half an hour (2000 to 2500 g), when a sediment was obtained which, after fixation, had staining properties identical with those of the granules of the acidophil cells.   Further centrifugation of the supernatant for 1 hour (10,000 to 12,000 r.p.m.) threw down a fine sediment which stained with aniline blue and was McManus-positive.   The supernatant liquor, or the McManus-positive sediment obtainable from it, when injected into immature rats, guinea pigs, or rabbits gave marked gonadotropic effects.   Slight gonadotropic effects were observed on injection of the acidophilic granules, these effects being diminished on further washing of the granules.   The acidophilic granule fraction obtained from sheep and ox anterior pituitaries gave a positive crop test when injected into pigeons, but its supernatant fraction did not.   Herlant concluded that the fine McManus-positive sediment represented at least part of the disintegrated gonadotropin-containing granules of the basophils and that the slight gonadotropic effect of the prolactin-containing acidophilic granules was due to contamination of these granules with the smaller basophilic particles.

B. CONTROL OF PITUITARY GONADOTROPIC FUNCTION

1. *Effect of Light on Gonadotropic Activity of Anterior Pituitary*

Zuckerman (269, 270) in discussing the influence of environmental changes on the endocrine organs has classified these into (*1*) physical changes such as alterations in hours of daylight, temperature, humidity, and nutritional environment and (*2*) social factors in the sense of stimuli derived from the group of which an animal is part. So far as the environmental influence on the anterior pituitary is concerned the chain of events is likely to be (*a*) the stimulation of one or more sets of receptors, (*b*) the transmission of afferent impulses to the thalamus, hypothalamus, and cortex, (*c*) the initiation or modification of hypothalamic activity by the thalamus and cerebral cortex, and (*d*) the excitation of the adenohypophysis. In recent years considerable study has been devoted to the effect of light on the reproductive functions of animals, and these investigations will now be briefly discussed. The earlier work in this field has been extensively reviewed by Marshall (176) and Burrows (38).[4]

The experiments of Rowan (229, 230) were among the first to demonstrate conclusively that in some species of birds seasonal changes in length of day were responsible for the rhythm of gonadal function. It was later demonstrated by Bissonnette (26) and confirmed by others that changes in the hours of daylight could influence the breeding season in mammals. Different species are affected in differing ways. During the fall and winter the ferret is normally anestrous, but estrus can be induced by exposure to 6 hours of artificial light in addition to normal daylight. Conversely in the goat and sheep, species which are anestrous during spring and summer, estrus can be induced by decreasing the daily amount of light (28, 263).

In view of the possible economic importance of controlling the breeding season in sheep by modifications of the light environment, considerable study has been devoted to this question in recent years. Yeates (263) demonstrated that the onset of the sexual season in sheep in England was a response to decreasing daily amounts of daylight and occurred some 13 to 16 weeks after the change from increasing to decreasing length of day. Similarly the cessation of the breeding season was found to be a response to increasing daily amounts of light and occurred some 14 to 19 weeks after the change from decreasing to increasing length of day.

Whereas the gradual seasonal changes in length of day appear to be involved in the natural control of the breeding season in sheep, other types of light stimuli can be used to induce estrus (135). A standard and regularly maintained rhythm of short periods of light and long periods of

[4] The effect of light on the breeding season of the domestic animals is the subject of a recent review by Yeates (263a). The wider aspects of light regulation of hormone secretion have been extensively reviewed by Hammond (126a).

darkness—4 hours light and 8 hours darkness—repeated throughout the 24 hours effectively induced estrous cycles.   Other rhythms of periods of short light and long dark were also effective.   It was later shown that the ferret, which comes into estrus in the spring, could be brought into estrus by using an opposite ratio of light to dark, *i. e.*, 2 parts light to 1 part darkness (136).

Hafez (123) has made a detailed analysis of the relationship between environment, particularly variations in the length of daylight, and the breeding season of sheep throughout the world.   In general he found that sheep living in equatorial or tropical conditions (*i.e.*, located between latitude 35°N. and 35°S.) generally bred all the year round, whereas outside these latitudes the breeding season was restricted and was shortest nearest the poles.   Hafez concluded that the duration of the breeding season, which differs between breeds and strains of sheep, is dependent on the geographical origin of the breed or that of its ancestors, both latitude and altitude being factors involved.

Although in some mammals seasonal changes in the length of day may play an important role in the regulation of the breeding season, it cannot be assumed with certainty that, because the sex cycle can be induced experimentally by manipulation of the hours of light, the onset of the natural breeding season is entirely due to the gradual lengthening or shortening of the hours of daylight.   It has been shown that ferrets kept in the dark or blinded ferrets come into estrus in the spring at much the same time as normal animals (142, 248).   Thus although light stimulation can precipitate the onset of estrus in the anestrous ferret, other factors must be participating in the control of the breeding season.   Factors such as temperature and humidity may well have subsidiary roles, but at present little is known about them (see review by Andrews, 1a).

It should be carefully noted that whereas the changing hours of daylight may affect the onset and duration of the period of sexual activity, there is no evidence that light influences the rhythm of the sex cycle within the period of sexual activity.   Of the mechanism of control of this rhythm practically nothing is known.

2. *Receptor-Pituitary Connections*

Environmental factors influence the reproductive processes by effecting alterations in the gonadotropic function of the anterior pituitary (see Marshall, 176).   In recent years some research has been devoted to the nature of the receptors and the paths traversed by the stimuli from the receptors to the adenohypophysis.

The eye would appear to be an obvious receptor organ for light stimuli, and there is experimental evidence in favor of this choice.   For example, the ferret (27) and the mare (37) when hooded are unresponsive to additional light.   The role played by the eye has recently been more carefully investigated by Thomson (247) in experiments designed to determine whether the stimulus for light-induced estrus was carried along the optic nerve fibers themselves or by way of the retinal blood vessels or by the ciliary nerves.   Neither ferrets with sectioned optic nerves nor those with the blood supply to the retina interrupted came into estrus in response to added illumination.   The feature common to both these procedures was degeneration of the ganglion cell layer of the retina.   It would therefore appear that the initial mechanism in the transference of light stimuli to the pituitary in the ferret is situated in the retina and is a nervous one.

In birds, however, there is evidence that receptors other than the retina may receive and transmit light stimuli to the pituitary.   Of particular interest in this field are the studies of Benoit and his colleagues on the male duck (see reviews by Benoit and Assenmacher, 23, 23a).   The immature drake if exposed to 15 hours of light per day for three weeks will show considerable testicular development at the end of this period.   Neither section of the optic nerves nor enucleation of the eyeballs will prevent photostimulation of the testes, although the degree of maturation is reduced.   The presence of the pituitary, however, is absolutely essential.   To explain these observations Benoit and his colleagues have postulated the presence of photoreceptors in the orbital region in the duck.   They have shown that direct illumination of the hypophyseal region by means of a quartz rod will produce testicular growth, as will illumination of the hypothalamus, in the region of the supraoptic nuclei, or of the rhinencephalon.   No effect was noted after illumination of the optokinetic region.   It is believed that in the duck, because of the translucent nature of the skull and adjacent tissues, considerable quantities of light reach these deep areas of the brain even under conditions of diffuse lighting.   Photographic studies made of the light-transmitting properties of the head tissues of the orbital region of the duck showed that red radiations were the most penetrating, followed in order by orange, yellow, green, and blue.   There may be a fundamental difference between the photosensitive mechanism of the retina and that of the deeper structures, as the latter is sensitive to the whole of the visible light spectrum but the former is responsive only to the red and orange end.

Benoit and Assenmacher consider that the possibility of deep photosensitive areas in the brain of mammals should not be entirely discounted, as despite the denser nature of the skull and tissues they were able to demonstrate an encephalic penetration of light in the rat, guinea pig, rabbit, and macaque.   The failure of the ferret, however, to respond to light following section of the optic nerves (247) would appear to rule out this method of stimulation in that species.

Few experiments have been devoted to the relative importance and effectiveness of different light intensities and wavelengths in inducing sexual activity in mammals. These have recently been reviewed by Yeates (263), who concludes that, with the possible exception of ultraviolet, the use of particular wavelengths has no definite advantage over ordinary white light.

a. *Pathways of Stimulus from Retina to Pituitary.* It has already been noted that in the ferret, at least, the initial receptor mechanism for light stimuli resides in the retina and is a nervous one. Few attempts have been made to study further links in the neural chain. Clark, McKeown, and Zuckerman (46) attempted to track the impulses from the retina of the ferret. They interrupted the visual pathways at various levels in anestrous ferrets which were then submitted to additional daily illumination. It was found that sexual activity could be induced in the absence of the superior colliculi or when all retinal impulses to the dorsal nucleus of the lateral geniculate body and the visual cortex had been completely interrupted. Attempts to divide the optic tract at the level of the ventral border of the lateral geniculate body were only partly successful, but it was concluded that neither the integrity of the visual cortex nor that of the midbrain was essential for the response, and it was suggested that the response depended on impulses passing either to the ventral nucleus of the lateral geniculate body or to the subthalamus by way of the accessory optic tracts. Further study of the material from these experiments by Jefferson (155), however, failed to demonstrate the existence either of accessory optic tracts or of any connection between the main optic pathways and the hypothalamus. This lack of any apparent pathway led Jefferson to suggest that the light response might be an indirect one depending on changes of total activity on the part of the animal. In view of the subsequent experiments of Yeates and others on sheep it would appear that light has a specific effect, and it would follow that pathways must exist between retina and hypothalamus. Recently, indeed, evidence for the existence of an opticohypothalamic tract and an optic hypothalamic center in the guinea pig has been presented by Frey (106). There is considerable reason for believing that control of the pituitary gonadotropic function by the central nervous system is exercised via the hypothalamus, but before considering the role of the hypothalamus two other possible routes of control must be mentioned.

b. *Sympathetic Innervation.* Numerous claims, many on rather scant evidence, have been put forward that stimulation or removal of the cervical sympathetic system affects the secretion of the gonadotropic hormones by the anterior pituitary. Harris (130) has critically examined the literature on the subject and found that "the large mass of negative evidence forces the conclusion that the sympathetic sytem plays little part in the control of secretion of the gonadotropic hormones."[5]

c. Parasympathetic Innervation.   Claims have been made that control over the anterior-pituitary gonadotropic activity is exercised through the parasympathetic system *via* the sphenopalatine ganglion or petrosal nerves. Consideration of the data leads to the conclusion that the parasympathetic system cannot be of more than subsidiary importance in controlling the gonadotropic activity of the pituitary (see review by Harris, 130).

3. *Hypothalamic "Centers" Controlling Hypophyseal Gonadotropic Function*

Evidence has long existed that damage to, or disease of, the hypothalamus leads to disturbance in the reproductive function (see review by Harris, 130).   The studies on female guinea pigs by Dey and his colleagues (70, 71) showed that the anterior hypothalamus and the median eminence were concerned in the regulation of pituitary gonadotropic function, as destruction of these areas by electrolytic lesions upset the normal sex cycles.   Lesions placed in the anterior hypothalamus at the caudal end of the optic chiasma apparently interfered with the liberation of luteinizing hormone. Destruction of the median eminence, however, resulted in genital atrophy. Hillarp (143) has recently attempted to locate more precisely the hypothalamic areas controlling the sex cycle in the rat.   Confirming the observations of Dey, he described an area controlling LH secretion in the anterior hypothalamus immediately anterior and ventral to the paraventricular nucleus.   Fairly large bilateral lesions in this area produced a state of persistent estrus.   The same disturbance was produced by smaller lesions basal and caudal to the paraventricular nucleus.   These results were taken to indicate that the stimulus traversed fibers which passed from

[5] Two papers on the possible sympathetic control of the anterior pituitary have recently appeared.   After bilateral superior cervical sympathetic ganglionectomy at 21 days of age, 14 rats along with unoperated controls were placed in one of three groups and kept in either (a) constant light, (b) constant darkness, or (c) normally alternating light and darkness, for a period of 85 days.   Estrous cycles were normal in all animals of the dark and normal light groups, but both the operated and control animals kept in constant light were in continuous estrus.   On autopsy, differential cell counts made on PAS-stained sections of the anterior pituitary showed no marked differences in the pituitary cytology as between operated and control rats except a higher percentage of chromophobes in the control animals of the constant light groups (Ifft, 151a).   In contrast to this largely negative effect of superior sympathetic ganglionectomy on the gonadotropic activity of the pituitary in the rat, Abrams *et al.* (1) have found that 16 ferrets failed to respond to exposure to additional light by precocious estrus after bilateral superior sympathetic ganglionectomy.   They suggest that the cervical sympathetic chains are in some way concerned with the mechanism whereby exposure to light accelerates the onset of estrus in the ferret.

the anterior hypothalamic area and ran superficially on both sides of the median eminence. Total destruction of these areas, however, did not completely suppress LH secretion. Greer (122) has confirmed Hillarp's localization of the areas whose destruction results in persistent estrus. He found moreover that lesions in the posterior hypothalamus did not affect the reproductive cycle. Neither Hillarp nor Greer observed genital atrophy, but none of their lesions were placed in the median eminence. Greer further found that the daily administration of 0.5 mg. progesterone to rats showing persistent estrus following hypothalamic lesions, resulted in fairly normal vaginal cycles and corpus luteum formation. Progesterone, in the above dosage, had no effect on lesioned animals with prolonged diestrus. This observation will be referred to again on page 333. In male rats, testicular atrophy occurred after complete destruction of the median eminence (187). Atrophy was also observed in several rats with lesions of the infundibular hypothalamus which left the median eminence intact. In these cases, the arcuate nucleus was consistently at least partially destroyed by the lesions (187).

Using the production of ovulation in the rabbit as a criterion for successful activation of the adenohypophysis, Markee, Sawyer, and Hollinshead (174) studied activation following electrical stimulation of the hypothalamus and the pituitary. Direct unipolar stimulation of the pituitary caused ovulation only when there was evidence of spread of the stimulation to the central nervous system. Bipolar stimulation of the pituitary with voltage and current of the same magnitude never caused ovulation, nor were there any signs of spread to the central nervous system. Bipolar stimulation of the hypothalamus, under conditions found ineffective on the hypophysis, induced ovulation in three out of four rabbits. More precise studies by Harris (131) showed that stimulation of the tuber cinereum for as short a period as 3 minutes might be followed by a free ovulating response. The most active area appeared to be in the anterior wall of the tuber cinereum just above the anterior part of the median eminence. Direct stimulation of the anterior lobe itself, pars intermedia, or the infundibular stem was ineffective.

Observations derived from the effect of hypothalamic lesions and hypothalamic stimulation are therefore fully in line with the view that the gonadotropic activity of the anterior pituitary is under hypothalamic control, although many of the details of this mechanism remain to be elucidated.

4. Pathways from Hypothalamus to Anterior Pituitary

Two pathways at least may be involved in the transmission of stimuli from the hypothalamus to anterior pituitary. Transmission may be en-

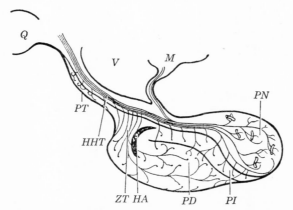

FIG. 1. Diagram of a sagittal section through the hypothalamus and pituitary gland to illustrate the distribution of nerve fibres in the pituitary body.

HHT	= hypothalamo-hypophyseal tract	PN	= posterior lobe
PD	= anterior lobe	HA	= anterior hypophyseal artery
PT	= pars tuberalis	V	= third ventricle
ZT	= zona tuberalis	M	= mammillary body
PI	= intermediate lobe	Q	= optic chiasma

(From Vazquez-Lopez, 252.)

tirely nervous by way of the hypothalamo-hypophyseal tract or there may be a neurovascular pathway involving the hypophyseal portal system.

    a. Hypothalamo-Hypophyseal Tract. The origin of the hypothalamo-hypophyseal tract is complex (see Green, 114) and although composed of nerves fibers which arise mainly from the supraoptic nuclei, it also contains fibers from the anterior hypothalamic area and possibly from the lateral tuberal nuclei, mammillary bodies, and paraventricular nuclei. The tract ends in the posterior pituitary. There has been in recent years some controversy as to whether secretomotor fibers pass from this tract into the anterior pituitary. As a result of a detailed study of the rabbit adenohypophysis, Vazquez-Lopez (252) (Fig. 1) concluded that (*1*) many nerve fibers cross from several regions of the neurohypophysis to the adenohypophysis, (*2*) at the level of the zona tuberalis there is a concentration of such fibers which is probably related to the anatomical disposition in the early stages of development, (*3*) the number of nerve fibers visible in the gland depends upon the conditions of impregnation, and (*4*) a knoblike formation is an almost universal type of nerve ending in relation to the glandular cells.[6] Vazquez-Lopez considered that many of the negative

    [6] Results which appear to support Vazquez-Lopez's findings have recently been published by Metuzals (199b).

results obtained by other investigators might be due to their lack of experience with the difficult histological techniques for studying nervous tissue. On the other hand, evidence and cogent arguments have been put forward by Green and Harris (116), Harris (130), and Green (114, 115) against the validity of claims for a nerve supply to the adenohypophysis. They hold that as yet there is no stain specific for nerve tissue and that the differentiation of nerve fibers from reticulum is often impossible. Moreover, in some species, *e.g.*, porpoise, a connective tissue septum intervenes between the posterior and anterior lobes, thus limiting the route for transference of nerve fibers from one lobe to the other.

At the present time the existence of a nerve supply to the anterior lobe based on histological evidence must be regarded as an unresolved question, and other experimental results on pituitary function must be considered in relation to the problem.   Before discussing these, it is convenient to consider evidence in favor of a neurovascular pathway.

b. Neurovascular Transmission of Hypothalamic Stimuli. Popa and Fielding (216, 217) were the first to describe accurately a true portal system of blood vessels in the pituitary stalk.   They referred to these as a system of vessels collecting blood from all parts of the pituitary gland and uniting into larger trunks traceable up the stalk into the hypothalamus, where they broke up into a capillary net. Wislocki and King (262) and Wislocki (260, 261) confirmed the description of these vessels but considered that the flow of blood was from the upper limit in the median eminence downward into the anterior lobe.   That Wislocki and King were correct in their views has been demonstrated by several methods (see De Groot, 59), including direct observation experiments by Houssay, Biasotti, and Sammartino (148), Green and Harris (117), and Barrnett and Greep (19).

Green and Harris (116) have described this neurovascular link in the rabbit in detail (see Fig. 2).   The blood supply of the pars tuberalis is derived from branches from the internal carotid artery.   These branches break up into small twigs that penetrate the pars tuberalis to form a rich vascular plexus between the pars tuberalis and the median eminence. From this plexus arise vessels in the form of sinusoidal loops that enter the median eminence and infundibular stem and pass towards the infundibular recess of the third ventricle.   These capillary loops then pass into large trunks which run down the hypophyseal stalk, finally draining into the large sinusoids in the anterior pituitary.   In the median eminence the sinusoidal loops are in intimate relationship with the fibers of the hypothalamo-hypophyseal tract.

The general pattern of the hypophyseal portal system is similar in all mammals, the small differences being variations in loop pattern. The comparative aspects of the hypophyseal portal system in some 76 species

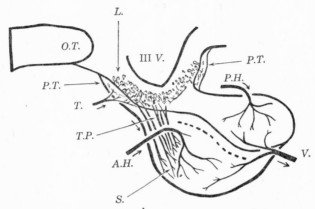

Fig. 2. Diagram of a sagittal section through the hypothalamus and pituitary gland to illustrate the hypophyseal vascular system. Small twigs (T.) from the internal carotid arteries supply a vascular plexus situated between the pars tuberalis (P.T.) and the median eminence. From this plexus sinusoidal loops (L.) penetrate the tissue of the median eminence. The blood from these loops is drained by the portal trunks (T.P.), which eventually break up into the sinusoids of the pars distalis (S.). Both anterior and posterior lobes receive a systemic arterial supply (A.H. and P.H.) from the internal carotid artery. The venous drainage is by wide short veins into the surrounding venous sinuses (V.). O.T. = optic tract; III V. = third ventricle. (From Harris, 132.)

ranging from amphioxus to man have been studied. A hypophyseal portal circulation appeared to be always present from anura to the primates, and similar vessels occur in the cyclostomes, fishes, and salamanders. In none of the vertebrates examined did the adenohypophysis receive *only* a direct vascular supply (114, 115).[7]

The possibility that the hypophyseal portal system might be the route by which humorally transmitted stimuli reached the anterior hypophysis has been put forward tentatively by several investigators (see review by Harris, 130). Green and Harris (116), however, brought very cogent arguments for the view that nervous stimuli from the hypothalamus caused the liberation of a chemotransmitter into the hypophyseal portal system which on reaching the adenohypophysis excited or depressed the activity of that gland. It has already been noted that the capillary loops in the median eminence are in close association with the fibers of the hypothal-

[7] A detailed description of the hypophyseal portal system in man has been given by Xuereb *et al.* (262b) who found that the hypophyseal portal vessels are the only afferent blood vessels to the epithelial tissue of the human anterior lobe. Moreover, in addition to the capillary formations in the hypophyseal stalk, similar formations were found in the lower infundibular stem which also communicated with the sinusoids of the anterior lobe by way of portal vessels.

amo-hypophyseal tract. As we have seen, these fibers are derived from
several hypothalamic nuclei which in turn are connected with thalamic
and subthalamic centers and so with the cerebral cortex and other regions
of the nervous system.

Evidence, derived from functional studies, concerning the nature of the
hypothalamo-pituitary pathways can now be considered.

c. *Stalk Section.* Various upsets of gonadotropic function—lengthening
of the estrous cycle, cessation of estrus, gonadal atrophy—have been observed after stalk section. Others, however, have seen no ill effects on the
reproductive cycle (see review by Harris, 130). A satisfactory explanation
of these discordant results would appear to have been given by Harris
(133), who was able to show in the rat that the effect of stalk section on
pituitary function was dependent on the varying degrees of regeneration of
the portal system. Harris found that vascular connections between the
median eminence and the anterior pituitary were necessary for the occurrence of estrous cycles. Regeneration of the portal system could begin
within a day of section of the stalk. If regeneration was prevented by
insertion of a foreign body (*e.g.*, disc of waxed paper) between the cut ends
of the stalk, then such a rat would remain anestrous for months (Table I).
The rapid restoration of the estrous cycle which may follow stalk section if
steps are not taken to separate the cut ends of the stalk would appear to
exclude the possibility of nervous pathways playing an important part in
the control of the secretory function of the anterior pituitary, since nerve
regeneration could not occur in the short space of time.

Further evidence of great interest has been produced by Harris and Jacobsohn (134) from a study of the function of pituitary grafts. Grafts
were placed into hypophysectomized adult rats either under the median
eminence of the tuber cinereum or under the temporal lobe of the brain or
into the hypophyseal capsule. Good union was obtained in all three sites,
the grafts becoming richly vascularized. Those placed under the median

TABLE I

EFFECT OF STALK SECTION ON THE ESTROUS CYCLE OF THE RAT

(Adapted from Harris, 133)

Operation	No. of rats	Estrous cycles		
		Regular	Irregular	Nil
Control, stalk exposed	15	15	0	0
Simple stalk section	23	14	8	1
Stalk section with plate of paper placed between cut ends of stalk	19	1	7	11

TABLE II
Anterior Pituitary Grafts in Hypophysectomized Rats
(Adapted from Harris and Jacobsohn, 134)

No. of obser- vations	Site of graft	Origin of graft	Gonadotro- pic function of graft	Mean wt. (mg.) of recipients'	
				Ovaries	Adrenals
12	Median eminence	Rat's own young	+	53.0 ± 3.5	41.7 ± 1.2
5	Median eminence	Adult rats	+	35.8 ± 4.7	39.4 ± 2.6
5	Median eminence	Adult rats	−	19.4 ± 4.0	38.4 ± 4.1
10	Temporal lobe	Rat's own young	−	27.3 ± 2.1	20.7 ± 1.4
12	Temporal lobe	Adult rats	−	21.9 ± 2.4	17.5 ± 1.2
12	Pituitary capsule	Rat's own young	−	16.7 ± 2.1	14.7 ± 1.0
2	Pituitary capsule	Rat's own young	+[a]	48.0	39.5
19 Normal adult female rats				63.8 ± 4.1	53.4 ± 2.5
6 Hypophysectomized adult female rats				13.2 ± 1.3	14.5 ± 1.0

[a] In these two rats pituitary tissue was in contact with pituitary stalk and was vascularized by the portal vessels of the stalk.

eminence established contact with the hypophyseal portal system, whereas those in the other two sites did not.   In most cases the functional activity of the grafts under the median eminence appeared normal.   Estrous cycles, pregnancy, and delivery of living young were observed in eight completely hypophysectomized rats so grafted.   Animals with grafts under the temporal lobe or in the hypophyseal capsule, on the other hand, had no estrous cycles, and the reproductive organs became atrophic.   Any gonadotropic function of these grafts was slight or absent (see Table II).

Experiments on the duck by Benoit and his colleagues (see reviews by Benoit and Assenmacher, 23, 23a) are of interest in the analysis of the role of the hypophyseal portal system.   In birds the portal vessels collect the blood from the median eminence and pass downwards to the anterior lobe through an opening in the dura.   They do not form part of the infundibular stalk as they do in mammals (114, 22).   The effect of section of the portal system and the infundibular stalk could thus be studied separately in young male ducks.   If the infundibular stalk was cut (mischotomy) before submitting the bird to additional illumination, the response of the testes to light was normal.   Section of the median eminence at the level of the hypothalamo-hypophyseal tract or of the portal tract prevented the response to light (see Fig. 3).   Histological study of the median eminence revealed unusual nervous structures.   Nerve fibers pass from the hypothalamo-hypophyseal tract towards the surface of the median eminence, where they form fine loops in close association with the capillaries (Fig. 4).

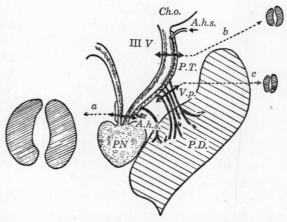

FIG. 3.   Diagram of hypothalamus and pituitary gland of the duck showing level of section of: *a*. Infundibular stalk (mischotomy), *b*. Median eminence (eminentiotomy), *c*. Hypophyseal-portal tract (tractotomy).   (From Benoit and Assenmacher, 23.)

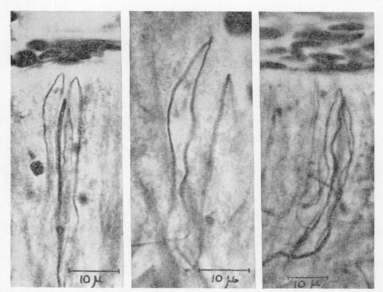

FIG. 4.   Nerve loops from the superficial layer of the median eminence of the duck. (From Benoit and Assenmacher, 23.)

In this area, moreover, there was a concentration of neurosecretory material, which stained with the Gomori chrome alum-hematoxylin-phloxine stain and which appeared to be identical with the material found in the cells of the supraoptic nuclei, in the length of the tract, and in the posterior lobe itself.   Benoit and Assenmacher suggest that the chemotransmitter substance responsible for controlling the gonadotropic function of the pituitary may be contained in this Gomori-staining material and that it passes from this material into the portal vessels.   There is now considerable evidence (see review by Zuckerman, 271) that this neurosecretory material found in the neurons of the supraoptic and paraventricular nuclei and their axons, and in the posterior lobe, is a carrier substance for at least some of the posterior-lobe hormones which, it now seems, may only be stored in that lobe, having been actually secreted in the hypothalamus. From their experiments, Benoit and Assenmacher conclude that the anterior lobe in the duck no longer exerts a gonadotropic response to additional illumination if it is deprived of blood coming from this specialized region of the median eminence, even though, as in many of their experiments, the blood supply from other sources can be considered to be adequate to maintain a considerable part of the gland in a normal condition. Lack of function following mischotomy was not therefore due to ischemia or infarction.   These experiments on the duck are in harmony with the concept that the gonadotropic functioning of the adenohypophysis is dependent on the presence of vascular connections between it and the median eminence.

Other experimental evidence has, however, been obtained which would appear to indicate that gonadotropic activity of the anterior pituitary is not always necessarily dependent on an intact hypophyseal portal system. Greep and Barrnett (119) put forward the view that stalk section entails considerable damage to the general blood supply of the anterior pituitary and that loss of gonadotropic function is due to a general ischemia and infarction of the gland, subsequent recovery of function being due to revascularization.   This view is difficult to reconcile with the above-mentioned study of Harris and Jacobsohn (134) of the behavior of pituitary grafts which, although they became well vascularized, showed gonadotropic function only when vascular contact was established with the median eminence.   Barrnett and Greep (20) as a result of further work on male rats concluded that stalk section greatly reduced the gonadotropic activity of the pituitary but did not inhibit it completely.   Recent experiments by Thomson and Zuckerman (249)[8] on ferrets have also been cited as evidence that the pituitary may show gonadotropic activity after interruption of the portal system.   These workers observed that 16 of 23 ferrets came into estrus following exposure to additional light after stalk section. On autopsy, it was found that in most cases section had been incomplete or that there was regeneration of the portal vessels.   In two animals, however, there appeared to be complete vascular separation of the pituitary

[8] See also Thomson and Zuckerman (249b).

from the hypothalamus.   They also noted that some ferrets, in which the
vascular connections had become re-established, did not react to light.

Zuckerman (270) has pointed out other problems bearing on this question which concern the site of production of the presumed chemotransmitter.   If produced in the hypothalamus, it is outside the area in the median
eminence drained by the portal system.   If this is the case, then it is difficult to see why the chemotransmitter is not swept into the general circulation.   If the chemotransmitter is produced in the median eminence, which
is part of the neurohypophysis, it then becomes necessary to postulate a
highly specialized function of the hypothalamo-hypophyseal tract in this
area.   In the above connection it is of interest to note that the release of a
hypothalamic chemotransmitter into the general circulation has been
postulated by Hume (149, 150) to account for the control of the adrenocorticotropic function of the adenohypophysis.   So far as a specialized
function of the hypothalamo-hypophyseal tract in the median eminence is
concerned, the experiments of Benoit and his colleagues referred to above
have provided some evidence of this in the duck.   In mammals, however,
such evidence is lacking.   There is thus strong evidence for the view that
the hypophyseal portal system plays an important role in the passage of
stimuli from hypothalamus to anterior pituitary, but there are several gaps
in our knowledge which must be filled before the concept is generally sustained.[9]

5. Nature of the Chemotransmitter

In 1946 Markee, Sawyer, and Hollinshead (174) reported on experiments
on rabbits which indicated that the hormone link between hypothalamus
and pituitary was of an adrenergic nature.   Subsequent work by Markee,
Everett, and Sawyer (173) showed that the adrenergic mediator was preceded by a cholinergic link.   Cholinergic and adrenergic links were also
found to be involved in the control of the gonadotropic activity of the rat
adenohypophysis.   Markee and his colleagues demonstrated that the in-
stillation of epinephrine (1 in 1000 dilution) into the anterior pituitary
resulted in ovulation in 5 of 10 estrous rabbits; also, under suitable conditions of "atropine protection" the intravascular injection of epinephrine
(1 mg. per kilogram) induced ovulation in 5 of 7 estrous rabbits.   Epinephrine is believed to be involved in the normal release of gonadotropin
from the pituitary in the rabbit, since an adrenergic blocking agent (Dibenamine) injected intravascularly within 1 minute after the end of copula-

[9] Vigorous arguments for and against the view that the hypophyseal portal system
is an essential pathway for a chemotransmitter substance between hypothalamus and
anterior pituitary have recently been propounded by Donovan and Harris (74a) and
Thomson and Zuckerman (249a), respectively.

tion inhibited ovulation. The same dose of Dibenamine given 3 or more minutes after copulation was ineffective. Whereas the intrahypophyseal injection of acetylcholine was ineffective in inducing ovulation, the intravenous injection of atropine or Banthine (drugs possessing powerful anticholinergic properties) within 15 seconds of mating did inhibit ovulation. It may thus be inferred that in the rabbit the link between the central nervous system and the pituitary involves both adrenergic and cholinergic components. Markee and colleagues concluded from their experiments on rabbits that during the first minute after mating an adrenergic substance is liberated in the median eminence which is carried in the hypophyseal portal system to the anterior pituitary, where it activates the gland to release gonadotropin. Preceding this adrenergic phase there appeared to be a cholinergic mediator which stimulated the secretion of the adrenergic component. In the rat the release of luteinizing gonadotropin would also appear to be mediated through cholinergic and adrenergic links. Recent experiments by Hansel and Trimberger (128) show that a cholinergic link is present in the neural pathways controlling LH release in the cow. There is also evidence that a neurohormonal mechanism, having cholinergic and adrenergic components, is part of the mechanism controlling ovulation in the hen (266). Certain aspects of the interpretation of the results of experiments involving blocking agents and their specificity have been criticized both by Green (114) and Zuckerman (270), who are of the opinion that it is too soon to concede that either an adrenergic or cholinergic link exists.

The interesting suggestion put forward by Benoit and Assenmacher (23, 23a) that the chemotransmitter substance may be carried in the neurosecretion of the hypothalamic nuclei is one perhaps worthy of further investigation, implying as it does an integration to some extent of anterior- and posterior-lobe functions.[10]

Many questions remain to be answered concerning the mechanisms by which the hypothalamus controls pituitary functions. As Zuckerman (271) has recently emphasized in a detailed and critical examination of the relations of the hypothalamus to the pituitary, "the anterior lobe of the pituitary controls many functions; and we have either to suppose that the gland is differentially activated by different kinds of chemotransmitter, or that, once activated by a single stimulus, the gland of itself adjusts its secretions according to the needs of the body. If it is the former which is implied, we are well beyond the area of fact. If it is the latter, the hy-

[10] The possibility that the hypothalamus may exert some control on the functioning of the anterior pituitary by way of the neurohypophysis has recently been discussed at some length by the Scharrers (223a, b), Mirsky *et al.* (200a), and Barrnett (18a).

332   A. T. COWIE AND S. J. FOLLEY

pothesis merely transfers the critical problem we are trying to understand—
how the reflex functions of the pituitary are controlled—from the hypothalamus to the pituitary itself."

6. Neurogenic and Hormonal Stimuli from Reproductive Organs Affecting the Gonadotropic Activity of the Anterior Pituitary

It has long been known that the stimulus of coitus is responsible for
ovulation in the rabbit as also in many Sciuridae, Felidae, Mustelidae, and
some Soricidae (2). In other species, however, where ovulation occurs
spontaneously, copulation may influence the time of ovulation. Sterile
copulation has been shown to reduce the interval between the onset of
estrus and ovulation in heifers from 9.9 to 7.7 hours, the difference being a
significant one (172).

Stimuli arising from afferent nerve endings in regions of the genital tract
other than the uterine cervix or vagina may influence the gonadotropic
functions of the anterior pituitary. In the sheep, Moore and Nalbandov
(201) have shown that distension of the uterine horn by the insertion of
plastic balls produced a marked shortening of the estrous cycle; removal of
the balls or denervation of the uterine segment containing them restored
the cycles to their normal length, whereas denervation of the normal uterus
did not affect the length of the cycle. It was not ascertained whether the
continuous stimulation of the uterine nerves affected the secretion and
release of total pituitary gonadotropins or merely of one of the gonadotropins (FSH or LH), but prolactin production (see later) may also have
been increased. That neurogenic stimuli arising from the reproductive
tract can have a selective action on the gonadotropic activity of the pituitary has, however, been demonstrated in the chicken. In this species the
placing of an irritant in the magnum part of the oviduct will selectively
depress LH release, FSH release being unaffected (151).

The suckling stimulus may also have an effect on the gonadotropic
function of the anterior pituitary. Desclin (62) has observed that in
spayed post-partum rats, whose main galactophores have been cut, the
suckling stimulus prevents the release of gonadotropin from the anterior
pituitary. Cytological studies of the pituitaries of these animals showed
that the basophils did not increase either in size or in number as they
regularly do in the nonsuckled animal after ovariectomy.

That the gonads, through the action of their hormones, can affect the
activity of the pituitary has been well established, and experiments dealing
with this problem were reviewed in 1950 in Volume II of *The Hormones* by
Evans and Simpson (see also Greep and Jones, 120, 121). Recently, more
light has been thrown on the interaction between hormones and the neurogenic mechanisms controlling the pituitary.

It has been shown that in the rat[11] a specific neurogenic stimulus is essential for the discharge of the ovulating hormone and that this stimulus passes to the pituitary within restricted but predictable time limits (82–84). Blocking agents (Dibenamine or atropine) given before 2 P.M. on the day of pro-estrus in 4-day–cycle rats prevented ovulation on the following day, whereas if given after 4 P.M. they were ineffective. Moreover, if the rats were anesthetized with pentobarbital during the critical period (2 P.M. to 4 P.M.) on the day of pro-estrus their ovulation was delayed by 24 hours. Anesthesia repeated daily between 2 P.M. and 4 P.M. postponed ovulation for several days. It was found that the minimal duration of the stimulus necessary for complete ovulation in the rat was between 20 and 35 minutes, although evidence was obtained that normally the duration of stimulus was longer than the minimal, so ensuring an excess of the ovulating hormone. If progesterone was given on the first day of diestrus, then the cycle (in 4-day–cycle rats) was extended by 1 day, thus becoming a 5-day cycle. Continued daily injections of progesterone retarded ovulation for as many days as the injections were given. If a second dose of progesterone was given on the third day of diestrus in a rat with such an artificial 5-day cycle, then ovulation was accelerated by 1 day, the cycle becoming a 4-day cycle again. In rats which normally showed a 5-day cycle, injection of progesterone on the third day caused ovulation on the fourth day. Injection of estrogen into rats with normal and artificial 5-day cycles on the second day of diestrus resulted in ovulation on the fourth day (80). Everett (80) has discussed these findings in relation to the normal control of the estrus cycle in the rat. He considers that when estrogen levels are elevated progesterone facilitates ovulation, whereas, if estrogen levels are low, ovulation is postponed by progesterone administration. These effects may ensue either from a modification of the threshold of LH release mechanism to estrogen or by alterations in estrogen metabolism. Since the induction of premature ovulation in 5-day–cyclic rats by progesterone can be blocked by Dibenamine or atropine, it would appear that at least some of the effects of progesterone are mediated through the central nervous system. The effect of progesterone in restoring estrous cycles in rats showing persistent estrus after hypothalamic lesions has already been noted (122).

This ovulation-stimulating effect of progesterone in the presence of suitable quantities of estrogen has been observed in other species. Es-

[11] In the fowl, recent experiments with adrenergic blocking agents have shown that the neurogenic stimulus for the release of the ovulation-inducing hormone passes to the pituitary some 14 hours prior to follicle rupture (van Tienhoven et al., 249c). If the blocking agents are administered some 38 hours prior to expected ovulation, ovulation will again be suppressed presumably through the inhibition of release of the hormone necessary for maturation of the follicle (Fraps and Conner, 105a).

trogen and progesterone together will induce ovulation in the rabbit, although neither are effective if given alone (233).   Progesterone given at the beginning of estrus, that is, when circulating estrogen is probably at a high titer, hastens ovulation in heifers (129) and in sheep (Simpson, quoted by Dutt, 76).   When administered before follicular growth has set in, progesterone can inhibit or delay ovulation in the heifer, sheep, and pig (see review by Dutt, 76).

The effect of progesterone and estrogen in combination on the gonadotropic potency of the pituitary in the monkey (*Macaca mulatta*) has been studied by Salhanick, Hisaw, and Zarrow (232).   In the ovariectomized monkey progesterone alone in either moderate or large doses had no effect on the content of gonadotropin in the pituitary.   Treatment, however, with moderate doses of estradiol (10 μg.) and progesterone (2 to 20 mg.), neither of which was effective when given alone, could produce within 20 days a complete depletion of gonadotropic activity from the pituitary when they were given together.

The ovarian hormones undoubtedly have important roles in regulating the gonadotropic activity of the anterior pituitary, and their effects are mediated at least in part through the central nervous system; the possibility of direct action on the adenohypophysis has not, however, been ruled out.

7. *Gonadotropic Potency of the Anterior Pituitary during the Estrous Cycle and Pregnancy*

Although it is well established that the gonadotropic content of the pituitary varies during the estrous cycle (see review by Burrows, 38), there has been considerable discussion as to the interpretation of these variations. It is assumed by some that the amount of hormone in the gland as determined on assay is closely correlated with the rate of secretion of the hormone into the blood stream.   Others hold that the assay value indicates the quantity of hormone being stored up in the gland or the amount remaining after liberation of the hormone into the blood.   If this is so, then the assay result is of no value in assessing the activity of the gland or of the blood levels of the hormone.

These problems have recently been discussed by Nalbandov (202), who considers that of the several ways in which the pituitary may function the following are the two most worthy of serious consideration.   First, the gland may be producing and storing hormone regardless of the needs of the target tissues, such hormone being released as necessary in response to stimuli; secondly, the rate of hormone formation and liberation may be regulated strictly by the needs of the target tissues.   Some recent experiments on this question are of interest.   Robinson and Nalbandov (223) assayed individual pituitaries from 33 sows killed throughout the estrous cycle (21 days) and found that the gonadotropic content was lowest during the 2 days of estrus.   It remained low after ovulation until the 8th day, when it increased suddenly, remaining high until the 20th day.   A very close correlation was found between the gonadotropic potency of the pituitary and the number and size of the follicles in the ovary.   Subsequent studies in sheep by Kammlade *et al.* (156) showed that there was a close correlation between the follicle size (but not follicle number) and gonadotropic potency of the pituitary throughout the cycle.   The potency increased from estrus to the 16th or 17th day, when the activity reached a maximum.   During the anestrous season, the gonadotropic content of the pituitary was found to be higher than during the breeding season.   This high potency was reflected in the ovaries, where the average diameter of the follicles was similar to that found in the breeding season; the total number of follicles was, however, somewhat reduced.   The authors postulate that anestrus in the sheep is due to an imbalance in the production of FSH and LH and not to a deficiency in the gonadotropic hormone complex. Evidence in accord with this view has been obtained by Dutt (76) and Robinson (226), who have shown that progesterone administered to the anestrous ewe will result in ovulation with estrus.   This observation is explicable on the basis that progesterone plays a role in the release of LH (129), thus altering the balance in favor of LH.

Reports on the gonadotropic activity of the pituitary during pregnancy are rather inconsistent; increases, decreases, and cyclic changes in potency having been described.   Some but not all of the discrepancies may be attributable to species differences and may depend on the extent to which gonadotropic function is assumed by the placenta (see Ladman and Runner, 162, for references).   Ladman and Runner (162) assayed pituitaries from pregnant mice and reported that the gonadotropic content was maximal at $12\frac{1}{2}$ to $15\frac{1}{2}$ days and minimal at $9\frac{1}{2}$ days and at $18\frac{1}{2}$ days; intermediate values were obtained at $6\frac{1}{2}$ days.   These assays were based on the ability of the pituitaries to induce ovulation in recipient pregnant mice at four stages of pregnancy, and it was thus possible to analyze the responsiveness of the assay animals during these stages.   If it be assumed that FSH is secreted at a relatively constant rate during pregnancy, then changes in the responsiveness of the ovaries of the assay animals are in all probability correlated with the quantity of endogenous LH in the circulation.   On this basis it was deduced that gonadotropin was released at an increasing rate as gestation proceeded and that between $8\frac{1}{2}$ and $11\frac{1}{2}$ days the gonadotropin release from the pituitary exceeded gonadotropin synthesis. This was followed by a phase when synthesis exceeded liberation. Finally, between 14½ and 17½ days, synthesis appeared to come to a standstill, whereas the release of gonadotropin was very rapid (see Fig. 5).

Nalbandov (202), on the basis of his studies on the sheep and sow, referred to above, considered that assays of pituitary gonadotropic potency did indeed measure the rate at which the gonadotropic complex was being produced and released into the blood stream at the time of autopsy. In support of this contention may be quoted the findings of Byrnes and Meyer (39) on the effect of physiological doses of estrogen on the rat pituitary, when the level of gonadotropin in the pituitary rose and fell as the secretory rate increased or decreased. On the other hand, the conclusions of Ladman and Runner (162) on the potency of the mouse pituitary and the rate of release of gonadotropin are not in accord with such a view, that is, if we are prepared to assume that FSH is secreted at a steady rate. This assumption, however, may not be justified. Further, if in the mouse the placenta were to produce significant quantities of LH, then this too would invalidate Ladman and Runner's conclusions. It is therefore clear that these experiments on the pregnant mouse do not necessarily contradict Nalbandov's views. Other experiments, however, on the gonadotropic potency of the pituitary during inanition are also not in line with such views; these experiments are discussed in the following section.

At present the concept that the gonadotropic potency of the pituitary reflects the rate of liberation into the blood stream of the hormones must be regarded with some reserve. It may do so only under certain conditions, and experiments on blood levels of gonadotropins are necessary to answer this question.

Gonadotropic Content of Human Pituitary. Bahn and his colleagues have shown that if it be assumed that the adult pituitary contains equal activities, by definition, of FSH and LH (1 "unit" of each per 3 mg. wet

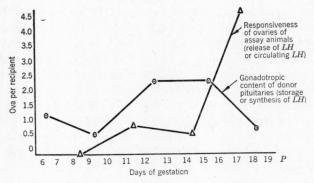

FIG. 5. Differentiation between storage and release of pituitary gonadotropin during gestation in the mouse. (From Ladman and Runner, 162.)

TABLE IV

USE OF PMS GONADOTROPIN FOR BREEDING GOATS IN THE ANESTROUS
SEASON

(Adapted from Folley, Greenbaum, and Roy, 98)

| Year | No. of goats injected | No. in estrus (*i.e.*, mated) | Goats kidding | |
			Number	Per cent of number injected
1945	14	8	1	7
1946	11	11	4	36
1947	19	16	5	26
Total	44	35	10	23

shedding of two to nine ova. Subsequent embryonic mortality reduces the litter size to just above normal. The use of PMS gonadotropin to increase the lamb crop in sheep is considered to be an economic proposition.[13]

Attempts to obtain twin calves from beef-type cows by the use of gonadotropins have not given encouraging results (126).

Superovulation. Considerable work has been carried out on the use of gonadotropins for producing superovulation in cows (see the excellent review by Willett, 256). Various gonadotropins and combinations of gonadotropins have been used with moderate success. FSH is usually injected subcutaneously, LH being provided exogenously by intravenous injection or endogenously by timing the injection of FSH so that follicular development corresponds with normal estrus; the necessary LH is then provided by the animal's own pituitary. The following procedures have given the most reliable results.

a. The injection of PMS gonadotropin during the follicular phase of the cycle (75, 99, 127). Injection during the luteal phase results in the development of cystic follicles.

b. The injection of PMS gonadotropin during mid-cycle accompanied with the expression of the corpus luteum by rectal manipulation (31, 75, 127).

c. The injection of horse pituitary gonadotropin at any stage of the cycle (99) or more particularly during the follicular phase (75).

[13] Wallace (254a) has studied the influence of dose levels, nutritive status of the animals, and stage of estrous cycle on the action of a single injection of PMS in the Romney ewe. He recommends the use of a single injection of 650–1,000 I.U. PMS given on the 12th, 13th, 14th, or 15th day of the cycle for increasing the lamb crop.

d. The injection of sheep pituitary FSH for several days before estrus followed by the intravenous injection of unfractionated sheep gonadotropin or human chorionic gonadotropin on the last day (43, 257).

e. The injection of a single dose of PMS gonadotropin 5 days before estrus with an intravenous injection of human chorionic gonadotropin on the 6th day (31, 163, 257).

Since the ovary of the calf is responsive to gonadotropic stimulation (43), an attempt has been made (171) to superovulate calves in the hope of obtaining ova for transfer experiments. Both ovulation and fertilization were obtained in the calf before the end of the first month of postnatal life, but the number of ova and the percentage fertilized were very low. Further research is required before the calf can be considered a suitable source of ova for transfer experiments.

D. CHORIONIC GONADOTROPIN

The physiology of human chorionic gonadotropin (HCG) has been considered in detail in Volume II of *The Hormones*, and mention will be made here only of some recent investigations.

The time of first appearance of HCG in the blood and urine has now been established with some certainty. In most cases HCG is present in the blood and urine 5 days prior to the expected start of menstruation. Serial assays have shown that the activity in the blood and urine levels off between day 24 and day 40 after the last normal menstrual period. After day 40 there is a rapid rise in activity which reaches a maximum about day 70. There is then a rapid fall in activity to day 90, after which the potency remains steady (243) (Figs. 7 and 8). Very similar results were obtained by Lyon, Simpson, and Evans (164), who, moreover, by the injection of detoxicated urine concentrates into hypophysectomized immature rats, demonstrated that after day 33 the gonadotropin has some follicle-stimulating activity in addition to the well-established luteinizing properties.

The observation of Brown and Bradbury (34) that HCG has a luteotropic effect in man has been confirmed by Segaloff, Sternberg, and Gaskill (236). As it was shown that the urinary prolactin was increased during the period of HCG administration, it was surmised that the luteotropic effects of HCG might be associated with the release of prolactin. Studies by Fried and Rakoff (107) are in agreement with this view (see also p. 371).

Important observations have recently been made by Diczfalusy and Loraine (72a) on sources of error in bioassays of serum human chorionic gonadotropin. These workers have shown that whereas the effect of HCG on the weight of the accessory reproductive organs of immature male rats is not influenced appreciably when the hormone is dissolved in human serum or plasma instead of saline, the effect on uterine weight was increased

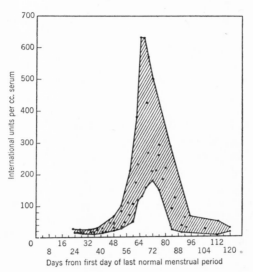

FIG. 7.   Range of the concentration of chorionic gonadotropin in the serum of women during early pregnancy.   (From Smith, Albert, and Randall, 243.)

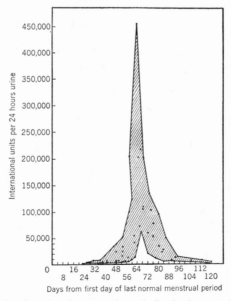

FIG. 8.   Range of values for the excretion of chorionic gonadotropin in the urine during early pregnancy.   (From Smith, Albert, and Randall, 243.)

two-fold when the hormone was dissolved in serum or plasma. Assays based on uterine weight are therefore considered to be unsuitable for the estimate of HCG in untreated serum or plasma. Assays based on ovarian weights were found to be both inaccurate and insensitive for the quantitative determination of HCG in body fluids.

E. PREGNANT MARE'S SERUM GONADOTROPIN

Recent research has confirmed the belief of Cole and Goss, and of Rowlands (see Volume II of *The Hormones*), that the endometrial cups are the site of formation of the gonadotropin found in the blood of the pregnant mare. The gonadotropic potency of the blood of mares carrying twin foals, and therefore having two sets of endometrial cups, is much greater than the potency of the blood in mares with one foal (231). Further studies have been made by Clegg, Boda, and Cole (48) on the relationship between the development of the cups and the initial appearance of the gonadotropin in the blood (Table V). Both appear about the same time (when the fetus has a crown-rump length of 2.0 cm.). Desquamation of the cups begins at a fetal crown-rump length of 10 to 20 cm. and is complete at 30 cm. The disappearance of gonadotropin from the blood corresponds with the completion of desquamation of the cups. Cytochemical studies with the McManus periodic acid method gave evidence favoring the belief that the gonadotropin was produced by the epithelial cells of the endometrial cups rather than from the decidual-like stromal cells. The interesting suggestion is made that in the early stages of development the cups are acting as endocrine glands, *i.e.*, are passing their secretion directly in the blood stream; in the later stages an exocrine function is also assumed, when large quantities of the hormone are passed with other secreted ma-

TABLE V

AVERAGE AMOUNT OF GONADOTROPIN PER MARE IN ENDOMETRIAL CUPS PLUS CUP SECRETION AT VARYING STAGES OF PREGNANCY (RESULTS OBTAINED IN 1950)
(Adapted from Clegg, Boda, and Cole, 48)

Crown-rump length of fetus (cm.)	No. of cases	Average weight of cups plus secretion (g.)	Gonadotropin, I.U.
2.0–4.9	12	3.5	21,000
5.0–9.9	14	8.0	56,000
10.0–14.9	11	5.5	73,000
15.0–19.9	4	10.5	150,000
20.0–24.9	9	8.6	133,000
25.0–29.9	10	5.2	42,000
30.0–34.9	3	2.9	14,000

terial into the lumen of the glands.   From there the secretion passes into
the space between the chorion and endometrium, where it forms and col-
lects in saclike structures in the allantochorion—the allantochorionic
pouches.   The gonadotropin in this secreted material is gradually absorbed into the fetal circulation.

F. Menopause Urinary Gonadotropin

In Volume II of, *The Hormones* it was concluded that the gonadotropin
derived from the urine of women in the menopause was mainly follicle-
stimulating in effect.   This view, however, has recently been contested by
Borth *et al.* (28b) who claim that such gonadotropin possess marked ICSH
activity as well as stimulating follicular growth.   Loraine and Brown
(163b) have confirmed this observation in the course of a study of assay
methods for human menopausal gonadotropin.

III. The Anterior-Pituitary Lactogenic Hormone (Prolactin)

A. Cellular Origin of Prolactin

The problem of elucidating the type of anterior-pituitary cell which
secretes lactogenic hormone has been attacked by cytological methods in
conjuction with physiological observations.   Histochemical methods for
the detection of prolactin, like those used for the pituitary gonadotropins,
hardly exist as yet.   Ladman and Barnett (161) have applied a reaction
for sulfhydryl and disulfide groups to the anterior pituitary of the rat.
Positive reactions were obtained in cells which the authors believe, though
without much conviction, might be classified as acidophils.   However,
since other anterior-lobe hormones contain these groups, these observations
throw little light on the origin of prolactin.   The cellular origin of prolactin
was hardly dealt with in Volume I of this treatise but soon after its publication the subject was discussed at some length by White (255).

In the pituitary of the ox, acidophils and basophils are not distributed
evenly, the cortical zone being predominantly acidophilic and the medullary zone mainly basophilic.   Ox pituitaries have been suitably dissected
so that extracts of "acidophilic" and "basophilic" zones could be assayed
for prolactin activity by accepted methods.   Like Azimov and Altman
(8) before them, Friedman and Hall (111) found more prolactin activity in
the cortical than in the medullary zone, suggesting that prolactin is secreted by the acidophils.   Since the latter workers found that the "basophilic" zone exhibited more gonadotropic activity than the "acidophilic"
zone, it can be concluded that prolactin and FSH are secreted by different
types of cell.   More recently this conclusion has found support in the work
of Herlant (141), referred to on p. 316, who by differential centrifugation
of pituitary homogenates obtained granules which were believed to orig-

inate in the acidophils and which exhibited pigeon crop-stimulating activity but no gonadotropic properties.

Schooley and Riddle (234) reported an increase in the number of acidophils in the pituitary of the pigeon at the beginning of the incubation period, when endogenous prolactin is stimulating the crop glands. The inception of incubation was accompanied by intense degranulation of the acidophil cells. Differential cell counts on the rat pituitary by Everett and Baker (85) showed that parturition was followed by a 100 % increase in the proportion of acidophils, and these cells showed an accumulation of secretory granules, corresponding, they believed, to the increased pituitary prolactin content reported some years ago by Turner and his colleagues (see Meites and Turner, 199).

More recently, Dawson (58) has claimed that a particular type of acidophil, the carminophil cell already referred to in section II.A., is the cell which secretes prolactin. The carminophils, which were first described by Friedgood and Dawson (108) and which form a small proportion of the acidophils, were so-called because they retain the dye, azocarmine, much more tenaciously than the ordinary acidophils or alpha cells under the conditions of differentiation used by Dawson, retaining a full red color while the alpha cells are colored faint pink. In a study of the hypophysis of the cat, Dawson (58) observed that the proportion of carminophils underwent a marked increase just before parturition and that secretory activity as indicated by degranulation was correlated with the beginning of lactation. Lacour (160) also doubts that the ordinary acidophil cell is the source of prolactin. She observed mammary secretion in a certain proportion of rats, both male and female, bearing estrogen-induced pituitary adenomata and was struck by the fact that in those animals which showed evidence of mammary secretion the adenomata contained the orangeophil epsilon cells of Romeis. Further study showed that these cells increased in number towards the end of pregnancy and were in evidence in the pituitaries of rats killed during lactation. Her observations could be interpreted as evidence that prolactin is secreted by the orangeophils of Romeis.

The apparently conflicting observations of Dawson (58) and Lacour (160) could be reconciled if it could be shown that the carminophils of Dawson are identical with Romeis' orangeophil cells. Some histologists assume they are the same, but as yet there is no general agreement on this point. The staining procedures involved are so complicated that it is difficult to feel certain about comparisons of results obtained by the two methods. Moreover it must be remembered that azocarmine is not always a well-defined compound with a constant composition irrespective of its source, and also that some variation in the response of pituitary cells to azocarmine may occur in relation to different methods of fixation. Since

the identification of the carminophil cell as the source of prolactin depends
on a rather subtle differentiation for which there is no clear-cut end point
and involving the use of a dye of far from standard composition, it seems
safer to reserve judgment for the present as to whether prolactin originates
in the alpha cell or from some special type of acidophil such as the carminophil or orangeophil cell.[14]

B. Role of Prolactin in Mammary Development

The discovery by Stricker and Grueter (246) of the presence of a lactogenic hormone in anterior-pituitary extracts was followed by claims that
anterior-pituitary extracts contain a factor which will evoke growth of the
mammary duct and lobule-alveolar systems.   Some of the earlier workers
denied that anterior-pituitary extracts promote mammary growth, but
today the evidence is virtually overwhelming, as we shall see, that at least
one anterior-pituitary hormone, prolactin, is concerned in the development
of the mammary gland.   As an example of the more recent work along
these lines, we ourselves have found (54) that unfractionated ox anterior-
pituitary extracts will evoke mammary alveolar growth in the immature
gonadectomized-adrenalectomized rat, which presumably has no source of
steroid hormones (steroprived rat).   There has been much controversy as
to whether the anterior-pituitary hormones which promote or help to promote mammary growth are specific mammogenic hormones or whether the
hypophyseal contribution can be wholly ascribed to the action of one or
more of the six generally accepted and well-characterized anterior-pituitary
hormones.   The history of the pituitary "mammogen" theory will not be
considered in detail here, since this controversial question was treated at
some length in Volume I of *"The Hormones"* (101) and later by Mayer and
Klein (183) and Folley (91).   It should, however, be pointed out that
Trentin and Turner (250) now believe that growth of the mammary duct
and alveolar systems can be called forth by one and the same pituitary
factor and not by different ones as once believed, this factor being protein in
nature rather than lipoid-soluble as formerly postulated.   Turner (251) has
tabulated the results of the assay of a number of anterior-pituitary preparations for prolactin and mammogen activities, respectively.   The former
was assayed by its effect on the pigeon crop-glands and the latter by a
method depending upon the production of minimal alveolar growth in the
mammae of spayed virgin mice receiving estrone.   Since the ratio of pro-

[14] Payne (206b) has described the appearance in the pituitaries of broody fowls of
a special type of acidophil which he calls the "broody cell."   In view of the fact that
prolactin injections can, in favorable circumstances, cause broodiness in fowls of the
correct genotype it seems possible that the "broody cells" may be the source of
prolactin.

lactin to mammogenic activities varied from 2.1 to 352.0, Turner concluded that prolactin and pituitary mammogen are not identical substances.

Meanwhile, whatever the ultimate fate of the pituitary "mammogen" hypothesis of Turner may be, evidence that prolactin possesses the ability to promote mammary alveolar growth continues to accumulate. Of the earlier work, the most convincing and impressive was that of Lyons (165), who injected small amounts of purified prolactin into certain galactophores of the mammae of rabbits (spayed females) possessing the necessary mammary development and obtained not only clear-cut lactational responses but also histological evidence of cellular hyperplasia of the alveolar tissue. This "lactational" growth of Lyons was characterized by the presence of numerous mitoses in the alveoli and also by the fact that the number of cells per alveolus was on the average greater in the prolactin-injected sectors than in control sectors of the same gland. The doses used were small enough for the responses to be localized to sectors communicating with the injected ducts, thus providing evidence that the action of the injected hormone upon the alveolar epithelium was a direct one. However, the experimental animals possessed intact pituitaries, with the result that the role of other anterior-pituitary hormones, endogenously produced, which might act on the mammary epithelium in concert with prolactin, either directly or via target gland such as the thyroid or adrenal cortices, was unknown. In the present state of knowledge the only other pituitary hormone which appears likely to be involved in a direct action on the mammary epithelium is somatotropin. The same considerations apply also to the experiments of Desclin (60, 61), who found that prolactin (admittedly not pure but stated to be very little contaminated with FSH, LH, thyroid-stimulating hormone (TSH), and adrenocorticotropic hormone (ACTH) activities) caused acinar growth in spayed female rats, and to those of Williams (259), who reported that injections of prolactin into lactating female mice from which the young had been removed retarded involution of the mammary lobule-alveolar system.

Lyons (167) has recently followed up his earlier work (166), which had the object of elucidating the hormonal factors necessary experimentally to evoke growth of the mammary lobule-alveolar system in the hypophysectomized rat to a degree equal to that attained by the end of pregnancy. His results implicate prolactin, to a high degree of probability, as one (probably not the only one), if the anterior-pituitary factors which are necessary in addition to the gonadal steroids. In the course of this work it was found that considerable, though not complete, growth of the mammary lobule-alveolar system in hypophysectomized-ovariectomized rats could be evoked by suitable treatment with estrone, progesterone, and ʻᶜᵉd prolactin, the steroids themselves being ineffective in the absence of prolactin. The mammary lobule-alveolar growth evoked by this triad of hormones, however, was not as extensive as could be obtained by substituting for the purified prolactin a cruder preparation known to contain ACTH and somatotropin. Later, Lyons, Li, and Johnson (168) reported that the mammary lobule-alveolar growth-promoting action of the hormone triad, estrone + progesterone + purified prolactin, in hypophysectomized-spayed rats was enhanced by addition of purified somatotropin (Fig. 9). Omission of prolactin from this hormonal tetrad resulted in loss of mammary alveolar growth-promoting activity, though duct growth, as evidenced by the presence of club-shaped end buds, continued (Lyons, private communication). Essentially similar results, unpublished at the time of writing, have since been obtained by Lyons and his colleagues in the immature male rat, hypophysectomized and orchidectomized (Lyons, Li, Cole, and Johnson, private communication[15]). Lyons and colleagues (private communication) have also shown that an extract of 12-day rat placentas acts in the gonadectomized-hypophysectomized rat like a combination of prolactin and somatotropin so far as mammary growth is concerned. This latter finding harmonizes with many other results suggesting that the placenta secretes prolactin (section III.E) and is in accord with the fact, observed many years ago (see Folley, 91, for review), that mammary growth continues to completion in mice hypophysectomized during pregnancy, provided the placentas are retained.

Besides confirming many of the above-mentioned observations of Lyons, Nelson (205, 206) has reported experiments on the hormonal factors necessary to maintain pseudopregnancy in hypophysectomized rats which carry important and obvious implications about the role of the pituitary in mammary growth. These ingenious experiments show that pseudopregnancy with its characteristic mammary lobule-alveolar development can be maintained in the absence of the hypophysis by treatment with estrogen + prolactin or by PMS + HCG + prolactin. The design of these experiments was of necessity such that they cannot tell us whether, in respect to its effect on mammary growth, the prolactin was acting solely in its capacity as a luteotropic principle maintaining the secretion of progesterone by the corpora lutea or whether, in addition, it exerted a direct growth-promoting action on the alveolar epithelium. The important point is that the results clearly show that unless one makes the rather unlikely assumption that the prolactin preparation used was contaminated with the specific mammogenic factors postulated by Turner and his school,

---

[15] See Lyons et al. (167a). It may be noted that Daane and Lyons (57a) have reported a synergistic action of prolactin with oestrogen and progesterone in promoting mammary lobule-alveolar growth in castrated male mice equal to that of the mid-pregnant female.

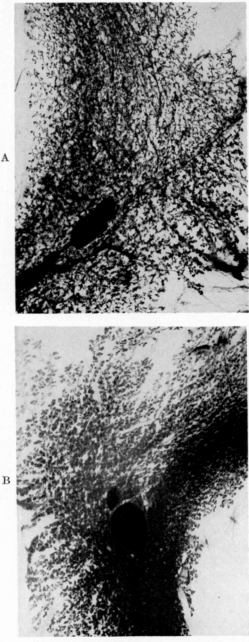

Fig. 9.   *A*. Whole mount of mammary gland of hypophysectomized-ovariectomized adult female rat injected daily for 14 days post-operatively with estrone (1 μg.), progesterone (4 mg.), and prolactin (2 mg.).

B. Whole mount of mammary gland of hypophysectomized-ovariectomized adult female rat treated post-operatively as above but receiving in addition growth hormone (40 μg./day).

Magnification was 2.8.   (By courtesy of Dr. W. R. Lyons.)

the mammary lobule-alveolar growth characteristic of pseudopregnancy requires only the intervention of known pituitary factors.

In view of these recent experiments on the hypophysectomized rat it seems clear that complete growth of the mammary alveolar system can be evoked by well-characterized anterior-pituitary hormones, prolactin and probably somatotropin, acting in concert with the ovarian steroids, estrogen and progesterone, there being no need to postulate the intervention of specific pituitary mammogenic hormones. On present evidence then, we may conclude that these comprise the hormonal influences which bring about mammary development in normal animals during pregnancy. As far as the rat is concerned it is probable that, as emphasized, for instance, by Desclin (69), prolactin plays a dual role, having, on the one hand, a direct mammogenic effect, and on the other, an indirect effect by virtue of its luteotropic action (section III.E) in maintaining the secretion of progesterone by the corpus luteum; it seems likely that prolactin, in fact, acted both as a mammogen and as a luteotropin in the hypophysectomized pseudopregnant rats of Nelson (205, 206). Such a dual role for prolactin in pregnancy will apply only to species in which the hormone exhibits a luteotropic action; as will be made clear in a later section, the luteotropic action of prolactin has so far been demonstrated unequivocally only in the rat.

C. PROLACTIN AND LACTOGENESIS

The power to initiate lactation in morphologically complete and functionally competent mammary tissue, *under suitable circumstances,* is perhaps the best known and most characteristic biological property of prolactin. The qualification must be made because purified prolactin is ineffective in the absence of the hypophysis unless adrenal glucocorticoids (or ACTH) are also administered. The relevant experimental findings and how they gave birth to the idea of a pituitary lactogenic complex have been discussed in recent reviews (91, 102, 184). On the other hand, those for whom the concept has any philosophic validity would, perhaps, rather discuss these results in terms of the "permissive" action of corticoids as postulated by Ingle (151b). The historic experiments of Stricker and Grueter (246), which in the perspective of today must be regarded as constituting the discovery of prolactin (an historically interesting first-hand account of which has recently been given by Stricker, 245), and numerous subsequent studies carried out since show, however, that prolactin is the limiting factor in most experimental situations involving the initiation of lactation in intact animals. Experimental lactogenesis in the pseudopregnant rat (221) is an exception, however, for here we have a case in which the role of the pituitary-adrenal axis, emphasized in a discussion of the status of prolactin as a lactogenic hormone by Folley and Young (104), stands out clearly, Reece having shown that far better lactational responses were obtained by administration of adrenal cortical extract together with prolactin than by administration of prolactin alone.

The elegant intra-mammary-duct injection experiments of Lyons (165), which were mentioned in the preceding section and which have been confirmed by Meites and Turner (197) and more recently by T. R. Bradley in unpublished work in our laboratory, although they do not prove that prolactin is the sole anterior-pituitary hormone concerned in lactogenesis, leave little room for doubt that its action in this respect on the mammary epithelium is a direct one. That being so it is at first sight a little surprising that Sonenberg et al. (244), who administered prolactin labeled with I^{131} to female rats, found no significant localization of radioactivity in the mammary tissue, though in one animal autoradiography showed a heavy concentration of radioactivity in the corpora lutea, now believed to be a target tissue for prolactin. Cox (57), on the other hand, detected considerable radioactivity in the mammary tissue and milk of mice a few hours after the injection of prolactin-I^{131}. However, the objections to the labeling of protein hormones by iodination of their aromatic groups with radioactive iodine are so obvious as to need no mention here;[16] perhaps the results of Sonenberg and associates should not, therefore, be regarded as conclusive evidence against accumulation of injected prolactin in its principal target organ, the mammary alveoli. More recently, Williams and Turner (258) have used prolactin labeled with I^{131} in an attempt to find out which component of the mammary gland cell has a particular affinity for the hormone. They injected the labeled hormone direct into the mammary ducts of rabbits and some hours later removed the treated mammae, homogenized the tissue, and submitted the homogenate to fractional centrifugation. Most of the radioactivity was associated with the mitochondrial fraction and almost as much with the microsomes. It is difficult to know what conclusions to draw from these results, since one cannot be sure that the I^{131} remained attached to the hormone protein after its absorption by the cell.

Further insight into the intimate mechanism of the lactogenic action of prolactin can come only from biochemical investigations, and it may be instructive at this point to summarize the progress already made in this direction. Let us first consider briefly the biochemical phenomena, ob-

[16] Prolactin labeled with S^{35} in the methionine residues has been prepared by Kraintz and Talmage (158a) by the incubation of ox-pituitary slices with methionine-S^{35} followed by the extraction of the hormone from the slices. This appears to be a development of the work of Melchior and Halikis (199a) who showed that methionine-S^{35} was actively incorporated into the proteins of the male rat pituitary in vitro.

TABLE VI

Respiratory Metabolism of Slices of Rat Mammary Gland during Pregnancy,
Lactation, and Involution

(Folley and French, 96)

Stage	Days	$-Q_{O_2}$		R.Q.	
		Glucose (0.3%)		Glucose (0.3%)	
		+	−	+	−
Pregnancy	20	1.3 ± 0.1	1.5 ± 0.05	0.83 ± 0.01	0.62 ± 0.03
Lactation	1	4.4 ± 0.3	4.0 ± 0.3	1.00 ± 0.05	0.73 ± 0.01
	8	7.1 ± 0.6	4.5 ± 0.5	1.62 ± 0.03	0.76 ± 0.01
	15	10.3 ± 0.4	5.2 ± 0.4	1.60 ± 0.06	0.78 ± 0.02
	22	9.6 ± 0.3	6.3 ± 0.2	1.53 ± 0.03	0.74 ± 0.02
Weaning	2	5.5 ± 0.9	5.0	0.76 ± 0.03	0.64

served in mammary tissue *in vitro*, which accompany lactogenesis and in
which, therefore, prolactin (perhaps along with other members of the
pituitary lactogenic compex acting directly or via their target glands) is
almost certainly involved.   Table VI, which is constructed from the results
of Folley and French (96), shows that the endogenous respiration of mammary tissue taken from rats at the end of pregnancy is low ($-Q_{O_2} = 1.5$)
and is not increased by addition of glucose to the medium.   At this stage,
the R.Q. of the tissue, even in the presence of glucose, is well below unity.
On the first day of lactation the endogenous $-Q_{O_2}$ has risen to a value of 4.0
and the R.Q. (in glucose) is now unity, while by the 8th day *post partum*
the tissue is responsive to glucose, in the presence of which $-Q_{O_2}$ is now
7.1 and the R.Q. has a value of 1.62.   Clearly, lactogenesis involves the
acquisition by the tissue of the power to utilize glucose with R.Q. > 1.
Further, Folley and French (97) have shown that although lactating rat
mammary tissue, unlike the udder tissue of ruminants, does not utilize
acetate when present as sole substrate, it utilizes it in the presence of
glucose with R.Q. > 1.   These results were interpreted as evidence that
lactating mammary tissue can synthesize fat from small molecules (acetate,
glucose)—a theory which was later substantiated by experiments with
labeled substrates (15, 17).   There is evidence that lipogenesis from small
molecules can proceed slowly in the mammary gland during late pregnancy
(16, 218); thus the lactogenic complex, when unopposed, seems to confer
upon mammary tissue the power rapidly to effect a process (lipogenesis)
which proceeds only slowly in its absence or when it is countered by inhib-

TABLE VII

EFFECT OF INSULIN, ADDED *in vitro*, ON LIPOGENESIS IN MAMMARY GLAND SLICES
FROM A LACTATING RAT

(From Balmain, Folley, and Glascock, 17)

The substrates were 1-C^{13}-2-tritio-acetate + C^{14}-glucose.

	Isotope content of Ca salts of mixed fatty acids after 3 hours		
	C^{14} c.p.m./mg. C	T c.p.m./mg. combustion H_2O	C^{13} atom % excess
Control	381	95	0.054
Insulin (1 I.U./ml.)	805	202	0.14

itory influences. It has also been shown (Table VII) that lipogenesis from glucose by slices of mammary gland from lactating rats is markedly potentiated by the addition of insulin to the medium (13, 15–18). Since this effect of insulin can be demonstrated only with lactating tissue and not with tissue taken from rats killed at the 20th day of pregnancy or after weaning (13), it would appear that acquisition of sensitivity to this interesting action of insulin is a property which is bound up with lactogenesis (Fig. 10). In other words, this particular response to insulin is evinced only in tissue which is under the influence of pituitary lactogenic hormones.

Studies on the enzyme systems of mammary tissue at various stages of the lactation cycle are also beginning to add to our knowledge of the biochemical events associated with lactogenesis. Greenbaum and Greenwood (118) have shown that the activities of glutamic dehydrogenase and glutamic-aspartic transaminase in rat mammary tissue rise sharply after parturition. These enzymes are probably concerned in the provision of amino acid precursors for the synthesis of milk protein. Similarly, Glock and McLean (112) have shown that the levels of activity of glucose-6-phosphate dehydrogenase and 6-phosphogluconate dehydrogenase in rat mammary tissue undergo a marked increase shortly after parturition. These are enzymes of the direct oxidative pathway of carbohydrate metabolism discussed by Dickens (72), and their presence in lactating mammary tissue in high concentration would seem to confirm the suggestion (17, 94) that the "Dickens cycle" may be an important element in the oxidative metabolism of the mammary gland.

It might be expected from the intra-mammary-duct injection responses that it would be possible to demonstrate a lactogenic effect of prolactin on

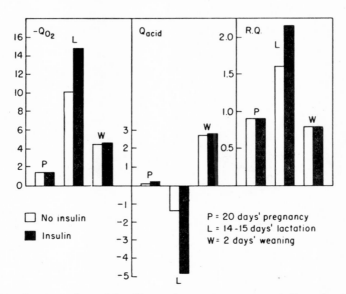

FIG. 10. *In vitro* effect of insulin on the respiratory metabolism (in glucose + acetate) and acetate utilization of rat mammary gland tissue during pregnancy, lactation, and involution. The results are taken from Balmain and Folley (13).

slices of mammary tissue *in vitro*. Following from the work on the respiration of mammary tissue described above, Balmain and Folley (14) showed that if one incubates mammary gland slices from lactating rats in Warburg microrespirometers containing Krebs' bicarbonate-saline in equilibrium with oxygen-carbon dioxide gas mixture and containing acetate + glucose as substrates, the total gas pressure progressively rises because the R.Q. of the tissue is greater than unity. The curve of net pressure change with time, the *composite respiration curve* as it is called, thus has a positive slope. The metabolism of tissue taken from rats at the end of pregnancy, on the other hand, is such that the over-all pressure, as measured under those conditions, slowly falls, the R.Q. at this stage being less than unity (Fig. 11). Lactogensis thus involves a marked change in the over-all pattern of the gas exchange of mammary tissue which can easily be detected by standard manometric methods.

The above-mentioned simple manometric indication of lactogenic effects must be used with due regard to the fact that a change in the slope of the composite respiration curve from negative to positive, or an increase in a slope of small positive value, may result from causes other than an increase in R.Q. For example, an increase in the production of lactic acid (glycolysis) or other acids, which would displace carbon dioxide from the buffer, would increase the slope of the composite respiration curve.

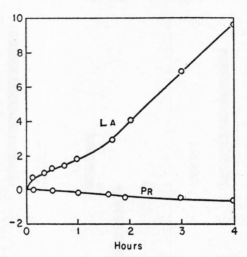

FIG. 11. Total gas exchange of mammary gland slices from rats killed on the 14th day of lactation (La) and 20th day of pregnancy (Pr), respectively. The ordinate shows net gas evolution as μl. gas/mg. final dry weight, uptake being calculated as O_2 and output as CO_2. (From Balmain and Folley, 14.)

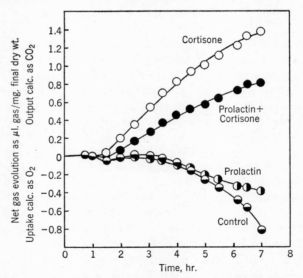

FIG. 12. *In vitro* effect of cortisone on the respiration of mammary gland slices (approximately 200 mg. wet weight) from a rat killed on the 20th day of pregnancy. The slices were incubated at 37°C. in 3 ml. Krebs' bicarbonate-saline (pH 7.4) containing 0.02 M sodium acetate + 0.3% glucose. The gas phase was 95% O_2 and 5% CO_2. Purified prolactin (22 I.U./mg.) and cortisone (free alcohol) were each added to a final concentration of 0.5 mg./ml. (From results of Balmain and Folley, 14.)

Balmain and Folley (14) found that prolactin added to the medium had no effect on the composite respiration curve of mammary gland slices from rats killed at the 20th day of pregnancy.   Addition of cortisone, on the other hand, did increase the slope of the curve, usually changing it from negative to positive (Fig. 12).   It seems unlikely, however, that this action of cortisone had any relation to lipogenesis, since in other experiments it was subsequently shown that cortisone decreased rather than increased the incorporation of acetate carbon into the fatty acids of mammary slices from rats killed just before or just after parturition (16).   There was no evidence of a synergistic effect of prolactin and cortisone when present together such as one might expect from the afore-mentioned studies on lactogenesis *in vivo*.   By contrast with these disappointing negative results with tissue taken at the end of pregnancy, tissue taken from rats during the first few days of lactation was responsive to the addition of prolactin to the medium, the hormone causing an increase in the slope of the composite respiration curve, which at this stage usually has a small positive slope (Fig. 13).   However, quite apart from the fact that it is uncertain whether responses of this nature observed in mammary tissue from rats already

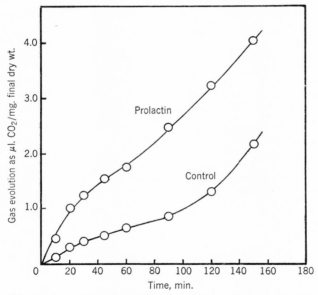

Fig. 13.   The *in vitro* effect of purified prolactin on the respiration of mammary gland slices (approximately 200 mg. wet weight) from a rat killed on the 4th day of lactation.   The slices were incubated at 37°C. in 3 ml. Krebs' bicarbonate-saline (pH 7.4) containing 0.02 M sodium acetate + 0.3% glucose.   The gas phase was 95% O_2 , 5% CO_2 .   Purified prolactin (22 I.U./mg.) was added to a final concentration of 0.5 mg./ml.   (Results from Balmain and Folley, 14.)

lactating should be considered as in essence lactogenic or galactopoietic (see below), more recent studies (30) indicate that this effect may be due not to prolactin itself but rather to another factor of pituitary origin present as a contaminant. Thus the amounts of all the prolactin preparations studied which were necessary to evoke the response were rather large and bore little obvious relation to their prolactin activities as measured by the pigeon crop test. Moreover, similar effects were evoked by some but not all of a number of preparations of somatotropin tried, by other anterior-lobe hormones, and by some posterior-lobe preparations. The preparations which evoked the response in the smallest concentrations were preparations of intermedin ("B") which were active in concentrations down to 2.5 μl. per milliliter, and so it seems likely that the effects obtained with prolactin and other anterior-pituitary preparations were due to contamination with small quantities of "B". It may thus be concluded that so far it has not been possible to demonstrate *in vitro* any effects of prolactin on the metabolism of mammary gland tissue which could be considered as essentially lactogenic (or galactopoietic) effects.[17]

Sgouris and Meites (238) investigated the inactivation of prolactin *in vitro* by a number of tissues and reported that of the tissues studied, the most active in this respect were the mammary gland and ovary of the rat and the crop gland of the pigeon, all of which are prolactin target tissues. Later, Sgouris and Meites (239) reported that while mammary gland slices from lactating rats will rapidly inactivate prolactin added to the medium, slices taken from rats at the end of pregnancy are without effect. If, as Sgouris and Meites (239) appear tacitly to believe, the interaction between a pituitary protein hormone and its target organ involves the destruction or inactivation of the former,[18] it could be argued that these results suggest that mammary tissue at the end of pregnancy is unresponsive to prolactin but becomes responsive at or soon after parturition.

[17] A recent more comprehensive study in this laboratory (Bradley, unpublished) has shown that prolactin (E. R. Squibb & Sons No. 71713, 22.4 I.U./mg.) at a concentration of 500 μg./ml. medium gives a statistically significant effect on the slope of the composite respiration curve of mammary slices from rats at days 17–20 of pregnancy as well as on lactating mammary slices. By contrast, intermedin (650 I.U./mg.) at a dose level of 15 μg./ml. is completely inactive on pregnant rat mammary tissue but, like prolactin, is significantly active on lactating rat mammary tissue. It may therefore be that the effect observed with prolactin is an intrinsic property of the hormone after all.

[18] The question of hormone consumption by a target organ has recently been considered at some length by Wijnans (255a) with particular reference to the irreversible removal of gonadotropin from the blood by the gonads. Wijnans concludes that the experimental results on the whole support the view that the gonads inactivate gonadotropin, and that this process is one of the factors maintaining the equilibrium between pituitary and gonads.

Any treatment of the role of prolactin in lactogenesis must include some consideration of current views on the mechanism of the initiation of copious milk secretion at parturition.   The most recent detailed reviews of this subject are those by Folley and Malpress (102) in Volume I of *The Hormones* and by Mayer and Klein (184) and Folley (91).   The theory which has occupied most attention during the last few years was that put forward by Meites and Turner (196) on the basis of extensive studies of the prolactin content of the pituitary in laboratory animals in different reproductive phases or after various experimental procedures.   According to this theory, the factor determining the onset of lactation at parturition is an increase in the rate of secretion of prolactin by the anterior pituitary, manifested by an increased prolactin content of the gland removed at autopsy, which is evoked by the action of estrogen circulating in the body fluids.   The indirect "lactogenic" effect of estrogen is believed to be held in abeyance during pregnancy by the action of progesterone, the level of which is supposed to fall at parturition in relation to that of estrogen, leaving the field clear for the latter to call forth the secretion of prolactin by the anterior lobe, thus initiating lactation.   This ingenious theory has been discussed fully and critically in the reviews just cited, and in those by Folley and Malpress (102) and Folley (91) the validity of some of the key evidence put forward in its favor was called into question.   Since these reviews were written, Meites and Turner (197) have reported additional experiments intended to meet some of the criticisms to which their theory has been subjected.   It may be noted that they seem to have overlooked an interesting paper by Atkinson and Leathem (6) which provides evidence, hitherto lacking, in favor of one of the steps of their argument, namely, the fall in progesterone relative to estrogen supposed to occur at parturition. In histological studies on mice killed at parturition, Atkinson and Leathem found evidence of biological effects of estrogen but not of progesterone. Nevertheless, in our view none of this more recent evidence provides any cogent reason for the alteration of the opinion previously expressed by one of us (91, 102) that though the Turner-Meites theory is both ingenious and attractive, the evidence in its favor is not sufficiently unequivocal to allow of its unqualified acceptance as a general theory applicable in broad outline to all species of mammal.   Indeed, it may be noted that one of its originators has recently reported results (193) which are difficult to reconcile with the Turner-Meites theory.   Mammary growth was evoked in gonadectomized rabbits by treatment with estrogen and progesterone; lactation duly resulted when either of the steroids was withdrawn and prolactin given, but not if the administration of *both* estrogen and progesterone was continued together with prolactin.   The Turner-Meites theory does not provide for the inhibition of the lactogenic action of exogenous prolactin by a combination of estrogen and progesterone. In a continuation of this work, Meites and Sgouris (194) have since reported experiments which show that whether or not administration of prolactin causes lactogenesis under these circumstances depends upon the relative dosage levels of prolactin, on the one hand, and the estrogen-progesterone combination, on the other. These results, as do somewhat similar ones in the rat reported by Klein and Mayer (157) and Desclin (69), strongly suggest that a peripheral antagonism between ovarian hormones and prolactin must play a part in experimental lactogenesis which is at least as important as the influence of these hormones on the secretion of prolactin by the anterior pituitary.

In a later section, evidence which is impressive as regards the rat at least, will be presented in favor of the concept that prolactin is a luteotropic hormone, or in other words, that prolactin is the hormone which provides the stimulus for continued corpus luteum function. During pregnancy, as we shall see, the luteotropic stimulus may come from the placenta as well as, or instead of, from the pituitary. If this is so, it is difficult to see how any theory of lactation initiation, such as the Turner-Meites theory, which postulates a low level of prolactin secretion during pregnancy relative to that obtaining during lactation, can hold the field—at least with respect to species in which prolactin is the luteotropic hormone and in which the corpus luteum remains functional during the whole of pregnancy. In species in which the luteotropic mechanism demands that prolactin be secreted in significant amounts during pregnancy, what possible mechanisms of lactogenesis at parturition can be suggested? First, it may be that the luteotropic effect of prolactin is evinced at lower concentrations in the body fluids than is its lactogenic action, so that the initiation of lactation requires a stepping-up at parturition of the rate of pituitary prolactin secretion which could perhaps be brought about by some such mechanism as postulated by the Turner-Meites theory. A second possibility, one which obviates the need for postulating a change in the rate of secretion of prolactin at parturition, was discussed by Mayer and Klein (184). This once more predicates the notion that the stimulation of a target organ by a tropic hormone involves the destruction of the latter, with the corollary that there would be competition between different target organs for available supplies of the tropic hormone. On this view, it seems possible that the demands of the corpus luteum of pregnancy on the available prolactin might leave insufficient hormone for the initiation of secretory changes in the mammary gland. Only when the corpus luteum of pregnancy regresses at parturition would there be sufficient prolactin available to initiate lactation. The corpus luteum of lactation in such forms as the rat presents a difficulty here, and it would be necessary to assume either that it needs less prolactin for its maintenance than the

corpus luteum of pregnancy or that the mammary gland, once it is functioning, takes priority.   A third possibility, again postulating a constant
rate of prolactin secretion, is that the production of other members of the
lactogenic hormone complex during pregnancy is too low to permit of the
initiation of lactation irrespective of how much prolactin is secreted and
that parturition involves a sudden increase in the rate of secretion of these
other members of the lactogenic complex.

The last possibility to be considered now, and perhaps the most attractive since it is more general in its applicability to various species, is based on
the old idea that lactation is held in check during pregnancy by a hormonal
inhibitor which nullifies the lactogenic action of prolactin and other anterior-pituitary lactogenic hormones.   Nelson (204) long ago put forward a
theory of this type for the guinea pig, in which he postulated an inhibitory
role for estrogen during pregnancy.   Later Folley and Malpress (100, 102)
proposed a "double threshold" theory which postulated two thresholds for
opposite actions of estrogen upon lactation, a lower one for stimulation and
a higher one for inhibition.   This theory really stemmed from the well-
known "lactogenic" effects of estrogens manifested, often spectacularly, in
farm animals (see review by Malpress, 170).   It was considered that at
parturition the level of estrogen in the body would fall, bringing it into
the "lactogenic zone" between the two thresholds, thus at one stroke
removing an inhibition possibly operating on the mammary gland itself, *i.e.*,
peripherally, and replacing it by a positive and unopposed stimulus causing
the anterior pituitary to secrete prolactin and other lactogenic hormones at
a maximum rate.   However, it has recently become clear that the combination of estrogen and progesterone is a much more potent inhibitor of
lactation than estrogen alone (see Fauvet, 87; Barsantini, Masson and
Selye, 21; Masson, 177; Walker and Matthews, 254, for the rat; Meites
and Sgouris (193) for the rabbit; Cowie *et al.* (56) for the goat; and Romani
and Recht (227) for man), which lends support to the concept, for which
Fauvet has been a vigorous protagonist for many years, that estrogen is
not an inhibitor of lactation under physiological conditions.   If lactation
is in fact held in check during the later stages of pregnancy by a hormonal
inhibitor, then we must conclude that the inhibitor is estrogen and progesterone acting synergistically; it cannot be progesterone by itself because
long ago it was shown that as much as 15 mg. progesterone daily had no
deleterious effect on established lactation in the rat (89).   Even more pertinent is the recent demonstration by Desclin (69) that 10 mg. progesterone
daily does not prevent the inception of secretory phenomena in the mammae of spayed rats which otherwise regularly follows the daily injection
of 30 I.U. prolactin.   On the other hand, a combination of 10 mg. progesterone and 0.1 mg. estradiol benzoate daily completely nullified the

lactogenic action of the prolactin. Similarly, Canivenc and Mayer (41) found that while 2.5 mg. progesterone daily did not prevent the secretory distension of the mammary alveoli in the rat which follows ovariectomy on the 12th day of pregnancy, 2.5 mg. progesterone together with 10 I.U. estradiol did inhibit the secretory changes. However, the results of these workers are puzzling in one respect: they state that 5.0 mg. progesterone daily by itself inhibited the appearance of secretion in the mammae. Perhaps sufficient estrogen was secreted by the placentas to form an inhibitory combination with 5.0 mg. progesterone daily but not with half this dose.

Recent work focusses attention upon the ovary as the source of a hormonal inhibitor which prevents lactation during pregnancy. Desclin (69) has shown that if cyclic rats are given daily injections of prolactin (30 I.U.), the cycles are interrupted (luteotropic effect) and mammary lobule-alveolar growth occurs, but the alveoli are devoid of secretion. In spayed rats, however, some mammary alveolar growth still occurs (mammogenic effect), but at autopsy the alveoli are distended with secretion. The inhibitor of secretion operating in the intact rat, which must presumably be a combination of estrogen and progesterone, could, however, be overcome if the prolactin dose was made large enough (200 I.U. daily), in which case secretory changes occurred in the mammae. These results are in harmony with those of Meites and Sgouris (193) in the rabbit cited earlier. The observations of Canivenc and Mayer (41) (see also Mayer and Canivenc, 181, and Canivenc, 40), who showed that secretory changes in the mammae of the pregnant rat quickly follow ovariectomy at the 12th day, also point to the same conclusion.

The problem of the initiation of copious milk secretion at parturition remains a baffling and complex enigma for which it is still difficult to put forward a theory capable of explaining all the observations, often on the surface conflicting, which have been made on various species. In an endeavor to contribute to the unification of concepts in this field one of the present authors (93, 94) has advanced a modified version of the "double threshold" theory which takes account of the potent inhibitory action of estrogen and progesterone in combination. The theory may be summarized as follows: (1) Deductions based on determinations of the prolactin content of the hypophysis are unsafe, since there is no evidence that changes in the pituitary prolactin content reflect alterations in the rate of secretion of the hormone (see Folley and Malpress, 102 and Folley, 91, for discussion). The development of reliable methods for the assay of blood levels of prolactin would be helpful in this respect. (2) Low levels of estrogen in the body fluids are indirectly "lactogenic" because they stimulate the secretion of prolactin and perhaps other anterior-pituitary hormones concerned in lactogenesis; higher levels tend to prevent lactogenesis perhaps by virtue of a direct action on the mammary gland.   *(3)* Low doses of estrogen may be deprived of their "lactogenic" activity by the simultaneous administration of progesterone, the hormonal combination then acting synergistically as an inhibitor.   This is the factor which holds lactation in check during pregnancy.   *(4)* The progesterone level decreases at parturition relative to that of estrogen, thus removing the inhibition and allowing lactogenesis to occur.

D. Role of Prolactin in the Maintenance of Lactation— Galactopoiesis

It has long been known that the integrity of the anterior pituitary is essential for the maintenance of lactation.   For references to experiments on hypophysectomy and attempted replacement therapy in lactating animals which prove this the reader should refer to Volume I of *The Hormones* (102) and to later reviews by Mayer and Klein (184) and Folley (91).   An interesting question, and one so difficult that so far it has not been definitely answered, is this: how far is the failure of lactation after hypophysectomy due to loss of prolactin and how far to the loss of other anterior-pituitary hormones which might also be concerned, directly or indirectly, in the maintenance of lactation?   Posed in a different way the question becomes: what part do the various anterior-pituitary hormones play in the maintenance of lactation?

This problem could be solved only by an experimental attack involving the withdrawal of one anterior-lobe hormone at a time by use of specific antihormone preparations, or more feasibly, by replacement experiments with various combinations of purified anterior-lobe hormones in animals hypophysectomized during lactation.   The first method has hardly yet been applied to this problem, the only paper on the subject of which we are aware being an early one of Young (264), who reported that injection of an antiserum raised to an admittedly impure prolactin preparation slightly decreased lactation in mice as judged by the growth rate of their sucklings. The possibilities for application of the second method of attack not only to laboratory rodents but also to larger animals such as goats are daily becoming more real with the advent of highly purified preparations of anterior-pituitary hormones.   In our laboratory, Cowie is carrying out replacement studies with purified anterior-lobe hormone preparations on rats hypophysectomized on the fourth day of lactation.   In connection with such studies it is necessary to remember that the milk-ejection reflex (see Cowie *et al.*, 55, for definition and terminology) is destroyed by the removal of the posterior lobe, which means that the experimental subjects must be given oxytocin twice or thrice a day so that if milk is secreted, the sucklings whose growth rate provides the only available measure of lacta-

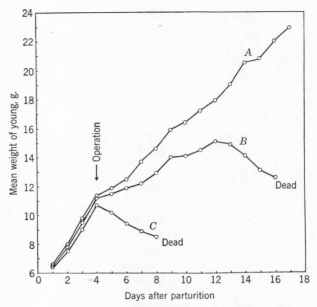

Fig. 14. Replacement therapy in hypophysectomized lactating rats.

A. Growth curve of young of three rats neurohypophysectomized on day 4 of lactation. The rats were injected three times daily after operation with oxytocin to allow
young to obtain milk.

B. Growth curve of young of two rats hypophysectomized on day 4 of lactation and
thereafter injected daily with prolactin (50 I.U.) and ACTH (4 I.U.) from day 4 to
day 11. Oxytocin injections continued until all the young had died.

C. Growth curve of young of five rats hypophysectomized on day 4 of lactation and
thereafter given oxytocin three times daily.

tional performance, can withdraw it from the mammae. Cowie has found
that prolactin alone (25 I.U. twice daily) had virtually no lactation-maintain-
ing effect in rats hypophysectomized on the fourth day of lactation; neither
had purified somatotropin (2 mg. twice daily). Prolactin and somatotropin together had a slight replacement effect but the combination prolactin + ACTH was better, though lactation maintenance was still not
complete (Fig. 14). The hormonal triad, prolactin + STH + ACTH, has
so far proved no better than prolactin + ACTH. These preliminary
results of Cowie, as far as they go, seem to harmonize with the suggestion
of Folley and Young (104) that prolactin and ACTH are components of
an anterior-pituitary galactopoietic complex. Work is proceeding in our
laboratory on a technique for hypophysectomy in the goat (Cowie, unpublished), and as soon as this difficult operation has been perfected, it is
intended to extend these studies to the larger animal, which yields suffi-

cient milk to enable its composition to be studied, so that the replacement effect of purified anterior-lobe hormones on the secretion of the various milk constituents, as well as on the gross milk yield, can be investigated.

Hitherto, most information about the hormonal mechanisms governing the maintenance of lactation has been given by studies of galactopoiesis. It may be pertinent at this point to recall that the word *galactopoiesis* has come into use as a result of independent suggestions by Folley and Young (103) and Bergman and Turner (24) to denote the process of experimentally evoking an increase in milk yield in an animal already lactating. It seems likely that the hormonal mechanisms involved in galactopoietic phenomena are similar to, if not identical with, those concerned in the maintenance of normal lactation. The tacit assumption here is that pituitary hormones which exhibit galactopoietic activity are likely to be intimately concerned in the maintenance of lactation, but, of course, the converse is not necessarily true. Thus treatment with ACTH actually decreases temporarily the milk yield of cows in declining lactation (51, 88, 240); yet there is abundant evidence that the integrity of the pituitary-adrenal mechanism is essential for the maintenance of lactation (see reviews by Mayer and Klein, 184; Folley, 92). The earlier experiments of Folley and Young, reviewed by Young (265) and Folley and Young (105), indicated that the relationship between galactopoietic potency and prolactin activity within a series of ox anterior-lobe extracts was not very close. Other biological properties of these extracts, connected in particular with their power to influence carbohydrate metabolism (diabetogenic activity), were shown to be more intimately related to galactopoietic power, and Folley and Young were led to adopt the concept of a pituitary galactopoietic hormone complex in which other pituitary hormones as well as prolactin were believed to be involved. Investigations by these authors and their collaborators were continued with the object of identifying other components of this hormone complex, and later studies (51) have confirmed earlier indications that the galactopoietic activity of prolactin in the cow in declining lactation is relatively low. Thus single injections of *ca.* 1000 I.U. purified prolactin had no significant effects on the milk yield of groups of cows in declining lactation. These animals could not be considered as inherently refractory to galactopoietic hormones since others chosen at random from the same herds, and tested in the same series of experiments, responded satisfactorily to single injections of other galactopoietic preparations (see below). It might be objected that the dose of prolactin given per kilogram was not impressively large; on the other hand, other groups of cows in the same experiment responded to single injections of amounts of unfractionated ox anterior-lobe extract containing much less prolactin as assayed by the pigeon crop response. Somewhat similar results have been reported by other workers. Biavati and Fiori (25) found that injections of 2000 to 4000 I.U. prolactin every third day had no significant effect on the milk yield of cows in middle and late lactation, though the treatment did appear to decrease the rate of decline in milk yield in the earlier stages. Donker and Petersen (74), on the other hand, reported that injections of 50 mg. prolactin daily actually *decreased* the milk yield of their cows. More recently, in our laboratory Dr. D.S. Flux (unpublished) has failed to obtain significant galactopoietic responses to single injections of *ca.* 1000 I.U. purified prolactin in nulliparous, spayed goats in which lactation had been induced by treatment with estrogen and progesterone. It is only fair to say, however, that these same animals, which at the time of treatment had been lactating for about a year and were giving remarkably constant daily milk yields, failed also to respond to injections of somatotropin as well as of thyroxine, the latter a well-known galactopoietic agent in the cow.

If we conclude, as we surely must, that there is little evidence that prolactin possesses any appreciable galactopoietic activity, at least in farm animals, it of course does not necessarily follow that continued secretion of prolactin is not essential for the maintenance of lactation in the cow and goat or for that matter any other species; it may merely be that prolactin is not a limiting factor in the declining phase of lactation in the cow and goat.

It may be asked at this point what is responsible for the galactopoietic activity of unfractionated anterior-pituitary extracts if not prolactin. The correlation between diabetogenic activity and galactopoietic power, noted by Folley and Young, suggested an answer as soon as it was shown by Cotes, Reid, and Young (52) that purified somatotropin is diabetogenic. Purified somatotropin was accordingly tested for galactopoietic activity in lactating cows by Cotes *et al.* (51) in the series of experiments mentioned above and shown to be strongly active, sufficiently so to account for practically all of the galactopoietic activity of unfractionated ox anterior-pituitary extracts, at least as displayed in single-injection tests. In tests involving repeated injections over considerable periods, thyrotropin may contribute to the galactopoietic effect of the extracts, since thyroxine is a potent galactopoietic agent. The discovery of the galactopoietic activity of somatotropin has since received ample confirmation (73, 74, 137).[19]

The question whether the continued secretion of prolactin is essential for the maintenance of lactation is bound up to some extent with another intriguing problem, namely, whether the respective constellations of anterior-pituitary hormones which have been postulated with some reason as

---

[19] The galactopoietic activity of somatotropin has also been confirmed in cows by Chung *et al.* (45a), Wrenn and Sykes (262a), Brumby and Hancock (35a), and Shaw *et al.* (239a), and in sheep by Jordan and Shaffhausen (155a). The subject has been recently reviewed and discussed by Folley (94a).

governing lactogenesis and lactation maintenance, respectively, are identical or not.   If they are identical, then milk secretion may be regarded as a process which occurs in functionally competent mammary tissue whenever the necessary constellation of anterior-lobe hormones is secreted in the correct proportions and is unopposed by inhibitory influences acting peripherally.   On this view the continued secretion of prolactin would be essential for the continuance of lactation.   If the two hormone constellations are not identical, then the role of prolactin in lactation might be confined to a "trigger-like" action responsible for its initiation.   The first idea seems to be the more likely if for no other reason than that it harmonizes with the theory put forward by Selye (237) according to which prolactin is secreted reflexly by the anterior-pituitary in response to the suckling stimulus.   The considerable amount of the earlier evidence which has been adduced in support of this theory will not be recapitulated here, even in summary; readers will find it discussed in reviews by Folley (90, 91) and Mayer and Klein (184).   It may, however, be relevant to mention experiments on the transection of the pituitary stalk in pregnant and lactating rabbits which have led Jacobsohn (152) to question the general validity of Selye's theory of the neural control of prolactin secretion.   In continuation of earlier experiments on rats (154), Jacobsohn found that mammary involution following stalk section was slower than that resulting from hypophysectomy or from removal of the young.   Since the operation obliterated all neural paths between the brain and pituitary and an attempt was made to prevent regeneration of the pituitary portal vessels by interposing a barrier of "white paraffin," Jacobsohn was inclined to interpret these and her earlier results as evidence that factors other than neural ones must, or at least can, elicit the secretion of anterior-pituitary hormones concerned in lactation.   It may be questioned, however, whether the measures taken to prevent re-establishment of the pituitary portal circulation were sufficiently rigorous to enable one to regard these findings as conclusive.   Moreover, since, as Jacobsohn was fully aware, the operation also interrupted the milk-ejection reflex mechanism, the engorgement of the glands with secretion, because of the inability of the sucklings to remove it, must have been partly responsible for the observed involutionary changes in the mammae.   Experiments by Meites and Turner (198), in continuation of their earlier work, suggest a relationship between suckling and pituitary prolactin secretion, that is, if the pituitary prolactin content is any guide to the latter, for the pituitaries of suckled rabbits always contained more prolactin than those of nonsuckled ones.

However, if we accept Selye's theory, a difficulty arises here in respect of species in which prolactin is the luteotropic hormone.   Prolactin in its role of luteotropin must be secreted at times, such as during the estrous or menstrual cycle or in pregnancy, when the suckling stimulus does not operate; hence there must be some stimulus other than the suckling reflex capable of evoking the secretion of prolactin. This alternative stimulus might well come from changes in the relative levels of estrogen and/or progesterone in the blood, as suggested by Turner and his school on the somewhat debatable basis of their studies of the prolactin potency of the anterior pituitary referred to earlier in this chapter. There is certainly no lack of evidence of the "lactogenic" action of estrogen, particularly in farm animals; this can be explained only on the assumption that estrogen can evoke the secretion of anterior-pituitary hormones including prolactin. The question arises, does estrogen attack the pituitary directly or through the mediation of a center in the hypothalamus? Evidence that estrogen may evoke secretion of anterior-pituitary hormones, including prolactin, by direct action on the anterior lobe has been provided by Jacobsohn (153), who showed that estrogen will bring about secretory changes in the mammae of stalk-sectioned rabbits and rats in which precautions as afore-mentioned were taken to prevent the regeneration of the portal vessels. The significance of these results is, of course, bound up with the efficacy of these precautionary measures. In so far as these results indicate that the secretion of prolactin can be triggered by a mechanism which does not involve the hypothalamus, they are supported by recent results of Everett (81), who obtained evidence in rats of luteotropic effects emanating from pituitaries autotransplanted under the kidney capsule and thus free from hypothalamic control.[20] It is, of course, possible that the anterior pituitary can function away from the control of the hypothalamus and that the role of the latter is merely to "modulate" pituitary activity in conformity with the needs of the body. It should be noted that Everett's results differ from those of Desclin (67), who also obtained luteotropic responses in rats with transplanted pituitaries, in that no estrogen treatment was necessary to activate the autografted glands. Moreover, Desclin (63) believes that cytological changes in the anterior pituitary of the rat of the type seen during pregnancy, which must be related to the secretion of a luteotropic hormone (presumably prolactin), can be experimentally evoked in two ways—by a neurogenic mechanism (suckling, sterile coitus, cervical stimulation) and also by estrogen acting directly. It is evident that further work on the mechanism of control of hypophyseal prolactin secretion, concerned both with the afferent pathways of the suckling reflex and the effect of sex hormones on prolactin release, is urgently required.

[20] In a definitive paper describing these experiments (81a) Everett considers that removal of the pituitary gland from its normal relationship with the hypothalamus not only *permits* continued luteotropic activity, but actually *favors* it.

E. Luteotropic Action of Prolactin

The idea that a third gonadotropin,[21] in addition to FSH and LH, is concerned in the regulation of ovarian function arose nearly a decade and a half ago. Astwood and Fevold (4) were among the first to put forward this idea in definitive form when they suggested that the function of the corpus luteum, as distinct from its formation, was under the control of a pituitary luteotropic hormone different from LH. The subsequent identification of luteotropin with the lactogenic hormone, prolactin, by Evans, Simpson, and Lyons (78), who concluded that prolactin was the only purified hypophyseal hormone capable of maintaining luteal function in hypophysectomized rats, seemed to go some way towards explaining many of the observations made during the thirties, notably by Riddle and his school, on the "anti-gonad" action of prolactin. Evidence for the anti-gonad and more particularly the luteotropic actions of prolactin obtained prior to 1947–1948 will not be recapitulated here for it has been considered in Volume I of this book (102) and in reviews by White (255), Mayer (178), Folley (91), and Voss (253a).

More recent work has added to the evidence for the luteotropic action of prolactin in the rat. Desclin (60, 65) observed luteotropic effects of prolactin in intact virgin female rats as shown by interruption of the estrous cycles and by the occurrence of uterine deciduoma reactions in response to trauma, by mammary acinar development, and by vaginal mucification. The mammary growth was probably a result of the dual action of prolactin, as a direct mammogen and as a luteotropic hormone evoking the secretion of progesterone. Prolongation of corpus luteum function in cyclic rats by prolactin administration beginning at the end of estrus has also been observed by Mayer (178) and Mayer and Canivenc (181). Nine days after the first injection the corpora lutea were voluminous, the vaginal epithelium mucified, and the mammae well developed. Prolactin, however, proved incapable of prolonging the function of the corpus luteum of pregnancy beyond normal term and of preventing its involution following removal of the gravid uterus (178, 185, 186). Mayer and Canivenc (182), however, have summarized indirect evidence that prolactin, probably of placental origin, exerts a luteotropic effect during normal pregnancy in the rat. They report that ovariectomy at the 12th day of pregnancy is followed by secretory changes in the mammae. The inhibitory effect of the ovary on lactogenesis can be mimicked by the administration of estradiol +

---

[21] The existence of yet another gonadotropin has been postulated; experiments on male White Leghorn chickens by Nalbandov et al. (202c) have led these workers to believe that androgen secretion in the chicken is controlled not only by LH but also by a gonadotropin which has properties distinct from those of mammalian LH.

progesterone or progesterone alone if enough be given (see also Canivenc and Mayer, 41; Mayer and Canivenc, 181; Canivenc, 40). Thus the absence of lactation during pregnancy must depend on the operation of a luteotropic influence. Evidence that this influence is probably prolactin emanating from the placenta is cited on page 372. In rats deprived of their young at birth, prolactin has been shown to prolong the life of the corpus luteum formed following the post-partum ovulation (*i.e.*, the corpus luteum of lactation) (178). The French workers (157, 178) emphasize the differences between the various types of corpus luteum (cyclic, progestational, gestational, lactational) in the rat with respect to their functional responses to exogenous prolactin in appropriate experimental situations.

Desclin (64, 65) has confirmed the earlier observations of Evans and his colleagues on the luteotropic action of prolactin in the hypophysectomized rat as shown by the occurrence of the deciduoma reaction, the histology of the corpus luteum, and the mucification of the vagina. He has further reported (66) that the luteotropic effect of prolactin is enhanced by concurrent estrogen administration. Thus there is now little room for doubt that prolactin is a luteotropic hormone, perhaps the sole luteotropic hormone, in the rat, though it is not certain that it is wholly responsible for the lactation anestrus characteristic of this form. Desclin (62) found that the appearance of castration cells in the pituitaries of rats spayed at parturition, the main milk ducts being sectioned to prevent the withdrawal of milk, was inhibited by application of the suckling stimulus. Since the appearance of castration cells in the hypophysis of rats spayed at parturition from which the young were removed could not be prevented by administration of prolactin, he concluded that a direct effect of the suckling stimulus on the gonadotropic function of the pituitary is a factor in the induction of the lactation anestrus.

So far there is no unequivocal evidence that prolactin is capable of exerting a luteotropic function in species other than the rat; even yet it may be premature to conclude that prolactin is the specific luteotropic hormone. Thus in the rabbit, Mayer (178) and Klein and Mayer (157) found that prolactin would not prolong the function of the corpus luteum of pseudopregnancy. The factors concerned in the maintenance of corpus luteum function in the rabbit as well as the rat have been discussed in reviews by Klein and Mayer (157) and Mayer (179).

The evidence for a luteotropic action of prolactin in primates is not at all conclusive. In the monkey, Bryans (36) has confirmed earlier observations of Hisaw (144) that the luteal phase of the menstrual cycle cannot be prolonged by injections of prolactin, though Bryans like Hisaw was able to prolong the cycle by injection of human chorionic gonadotropin and could demonstrate that the corpus luteum was functional during the prolonged luteal phase.

The position regarding women is of course of particular interest in view of the possibility of clinical use of prolactin in the capacity of a luteotropic hormone for treating menorrhagia and threatened abortion (see Kupperman, Fried, and Hair, 159). In women, various workers have reported that prolactin administration during the luteal phase will not increase the length of the menstrual cycle (29, 146, 159), though according to Holmstrom and Jones (146) the regression of the corpus luteum is nevertheless somewhat delayed. Fried and Rakoff (107) were able significantly to prolong the luteal phase of the cycle by combined treatment with prolactin and HCG, either hormone alone at the same respective dosage level having no effect. They therefore suggest that prolactin and HCG synergistically exert a luteotropic effect in women. Despite the fact that other investigators (e.g., Bradbury et al., 29; Segaloff, Sternberg, and Gaskill, 236) have shown that HCG if given in high enough doses is able by itself to prolong the luteal phase of the menstrual cycle, it seems possible that endogenous prolactin may be concerned in some way in the luteotropic effect of HCG, for Segaloff and co-workers observed an enhanced urinary output of prolactin during the period of HCG administration. The concept that prolactin and HCG may together be concerned in corpus luteum maintenance in the normal woman should be considered along with the findings of Everett (79) on the control of progesterone metabolism in the corpus luteum of the rat. Everett's observations, though perhaps not conclusive, suggested that HCG was involved in the formation or, at any rate, in the accumulation of cholesterol in the rat corpus luteum and prolactin in the transformation of cholesterol into progesterone. Miller and Everett (200) later reported that the accumulation of cholesterol in the rat corpus luteum following LH administration was accompanied by an increase in the ascorbic acid content. Following the administration of high doses of prolactin there was an indication that the ascorbic acid was decreased. The available evidence is therefore not unanimously against a luteotropic function of prolactin in man, and the evidence on the positive side is reinforced by the studies of Coppedge and Segaloff (50) on the urinary excretion of prolactin in women during the menstrual cycle, in which peak values were observed during that period of the luteal phase when luteal function is believed to be at its height. For references to earlier studies on prolactin excretion in the urine the reader is referred to reviews by Meites and Turner (195) and Voss (253).

Before concluding this section it is necessary to give some consideration to the luteotropic function of the placenta. It has been known for many years that in certain species the placenta can exert a luteotropic effect and in some cases is able to substitute for the pituitary in maintaining pregnancy and mammary lobule-alveolar growth in its absence. Astwood and Greep (5) prepared from rat placenta a luteotropin, which they called

cyonin, believed to be different from the known hypophyseal hormones
and also from human and equine cyonins. More recently, Averill, Ray,
and Lyons (7) have shown that pregnancy can be maintained in hypophysectomized rats by daily implantations of 12-day rat placentas. Since
the treatment was ineffective in the absence of the ovaries a luteotropic
effect was almost certainly involved. Histological evidence (hypertrophied luteal cells, vaginal mucification, mammary acinar growth) of luteotropic effects of placental grafts has been reported by Mayer and Canivenc
(180) and Canivenc (40). The nature and identity of the placental luteo-
tropins in various species is of considerable interest. In view of the evidence for the luteotropic action of HCG considered above, there would
seem to be little mystery surrounding the identity of the placental luteotropin in man. In the rat, on the other hand, there are indications that
the placental luteotropin may be prolactin itself, or at least a substance
with similar biological properties. Thus, Averill *et al.* (7) were able to
elicit local pigeon crop-gland responses to intradermal injections of acid-
acetone extracts of 12-day rat placentas, and Canivenc (40) obtained similar
responses to the implantation over the pigeon crop of portions of placental
grafts from rats. Canivenc and Mayer (42), by use of the local crop test
detected a prolactin-like substance in the placenta of the rat from the 10th
day onwards. Despite uncertainties attending the specificity of local
crop responses to implantation of whole tissue or tissue extracts one is
tempted, in view of the considerable evidence for the luteotropic action of
prolactin in the rat, to conclude that the luteotropic substance of the rat
placenta is prolactin itself. Circumstantial evidence that the placenta of
the rat secretes prolactin has been provided by Mayer and Canivenc (182).
As stated earlier, these workers have shown that ovariectomy on the 12th
day of pregnancy results in secretory changes in the mammae; if, however,
hysterectomy is performed as well, the mammae remain devoid of secretion, showing that the secretory stimulus comes from the placenta, possible
effects of the fetus and of uterine distension having been discounted in
other experiments. The lactogenic effect of the missing placentas could
be replaced by 200 I.U. prolactin daily, when the secretory changes in the
mammae were once more seen. References to earlier reports of the occurrence of prolactin, or at least crop-stimulating substances, in placental
tissue of various species will be found in reviews by Voss (253) and Folley
(91). If the placental luteotropin is prolactin, there still remains the
problem whether the placenta is able to elaborate prolactin or whether it
acts as a storehouse for hypophyseal prolactin which it abstracts from the
blood. Since the rat is able to dispense with the hypophysis after mid-
pregnancy provided the placentas survive, it seems doubtful whether these
latter can store enough prolactin to last for 10 days. The present indica-

tions are that the placenta of certain species can elaborate a hormone with biological properties similar to those of hypophyseal prolactin.

F. Prolactin and the Mammalian Male Reproductive System

Prolactin occurs in the male pituitary, hence its role in the male has been a subject of speculation. If metabolic effects such as those mentioned in the next section should be shown unequivocally to be a property of prolactin itself, they would, of course, in the main, apply equally to males and females. But, in addition, specific effects of prolactin on the male reproductive system in mammals are being currently studied. Anti-gonad actions of prolactin in male birds were reviewed by Riddle and Bates (221b).

Fiori and his colleagues (28a, 87a, b) have reported that relatively low doses of prolactin stimulate the testicular interstitial tissue of the male rat causing it to produce testosterone which in turn stimulates the male accessories. The possibility that prolactin exerts some effect directly on the male accessory organs themselves is suggested by recent results of Pasqualini (206a) who reported that administration of prolactin together with testosterone increased the secretion of the seminal vessicles of male rats to a degree above that shown by controls receiving testosterone alone. Dr. M. Sonenberg (private communication) has found that Zn^{65} is concentrated in the ventral prostate of the rat under the influence of prolactin and testosterone, either hormone alone being ineffective.

G. Metabolic Actions of Prolactin in Mammals

Earlier work, mostly by Riddle and his collaborators, on metabolic effects of prolactin in birds, *i.e.*, calorigenic effects, the production of splanchnomegaly, and effects on carbohydrate metabolism were reviewed by Riddle and Bates (221b). It is only more recently that metabolic effects of the hormone have been reported in mammals, although actions of this nature are to be expected in view of the lactogenic action of prolactin which involves profound alterations in protein, fat, and carbohydrate metabolism as well as considerable fluid and electrolyte shifts. The possibility that some of the actions ascribed to prolactin by the pioneer workers may have been due to the presence of small amounts of other anterior-pituitary hormones in the preparations used cannot be overlooked; nor is it certain that such considerations may not be applicable to some of the more recently discovered responses described below.

Various metabolic effects reminiscent of some of those ascribed at one time or another to somatotropin have been reported for purified preparations of prolactin. Sinkoff and Bodo (241a) report that prolactin diminishes the insulin hypersensitivity of hypophysectomized or adrenalectomized-hypophysectomized dogs. Since the somatotropin content of their prolactin was small, these authors believe that if this anti-insulin action is not inherent in prolactin itself then it must be a property of a separate anti-insulin or diabetogenic hormone other than somatotropin or ACTH. A diabetogenic response to injections of purified prolactin, in the sense of a transient hyperglycaemia, has been reported in mammals and amphibia with surgically reduced pancreatic tissue (Houssay and Anderson, 147b, c; Houssay et al., 148a). Geschwind and Li (111a) have reported that pro-lactin preparations increase the width of the epiphyseal plate of the tibia of the hypophysectomized male rat. The response differs in certain re-spects from that due to purified somatotropin, particularly in being more pronounced in males than females, but it is not yet certain whether or not it is an inherent property of the prolactin molecule. Reiss (221a) found that prolactin decreased the fatty acid content of the skin and carcass of the rat, but Li et al. (163a) failed to confirm this. The ubiquity of pro-lactin with respect to responses concerned with the care and nutrition of the embryo or the young is emphasized by Houssay's (147a) finding that the hormone causes the production of a jellylike mucous secretion by the oviduct of the toad. Obvious examples in birds and mammals have been described elsewhere in this chapter.

H. Effects of Prolactin in Birds

Bailey (12b) has reported an interesting physiological as well as morpho-logical study of the "brood spots" or "incubation patches" of passerine birds, which adds to the steadily lengthening list of responses involving prolactin which may be classified as concerned with care of the young. Com-plete incubation patches could be produced in nonbreeding birds by treat-ment with estrogen, but this, however, was ineffective in the absence of the hypophysis. In hypophysectomized birds estrogen by itself produced hyperaemia in the patch area, prolactin being required as well for the complete response; evidently the estrogen treatment had evoked prolactin secretion in the subjects with intact pituitaries. The case for the implica-tion of prolactin was further strengthened by the finding that the pituitaries of gulls exhibiting incubation patches contained more prolactin than those without patches. These findings appear to harmonize with those of Riddle et al. (222a) and Nalbandov and Card (202a) on the induction with pro-lactin of broodiness in female poultry possessing the genes for broodiness. On the other hand, Nalbandov et al. (202b) believe that broodiness induced by injections of prolactin in cocks is not a primary response to prolactin but is due primarily to lowered production of testosterone which springs from the "anti-gonad" action of prolactin (see Riddle and Bates, 221b) in inhibiting the secretion of FSH by the anterior lobe. Bailey (12a) has shown that prolactin exerts an "anti-gonad" action in the male sparrow even in the presence of a strong stimulus to pituitary function, for it prevented the increase in testis size due to intense illumination.

I. Assay of Prolactin

There have been no striking improvements in methods of assay of prolactin since this subject was reviewed by White (225), Meites and Turner (199), and Voss (253a). In our view the most accurate method available is still the pigeon crop-weight method (involving systemic injection of the hormone), the 20-year-old prototype of which was described by Riddle, Bates, and Dykshorn (222). The drawbacks of this method are, first, that in order to achieve satisfactory precision one must go to considerable expense both in pigeons and hormone and, secondly, the more general one that on theoretical grounds an avian bioassay cannot be the most satisfactory way of assaying a hormone the most interest and momentous functions of which are displayed in mammals. The results of some 10 years' experience in our laboratory with a variant of the systemic crop-weight assay have recently been statistically analyzed by Clarke and Folley (47). Surprisingly, it turned out that the number of birds needed to attain given fiducial limits of error when inbred White Carneau or Silver King pigeons were used, was no less than in previous work (95) with "ragamuffin" pigeons of mixed breeds and unknown ages. For a "4-point" assay it was estimated that 10 "pure-bred" birds per treatment would give 5 % fiducial limits of 76 % to 131 %, 15 birds per treatment would give limits of 88 % to 122 %, and 20 birds limits of 85 % to 118 %. The analysis showed that the precision of the assay was greatest for young pigeons not more than 3 months old (Fig. 15). Coppedge and Segaloff (50) and Segaloff (235) have used a modified version of the systemic crop-weight method for determining prolactin, or at least crop-stimulating activity, in human urine. The relatively small amount of activity in the urine necessitates the preparation of a concentrated extract, and all the pigeons are given a "booster" dose of hypophyseal prolactin to bring the response into the most sensitive portion of the dose-response curve. This would appear to entail the disadvantage that the urinary activity is determined as the difference between two relatively large quantities.

In the quest for a method more sensitive yet free from the various objections, e.g., that of nonspecificity, which may be made against the ingenious local (intradermal) crop test of Lyons and Page (169), Brown, Woodbury, and Sayers (32) have studied the effect of prolactin on the uptake of P^{32} by the pigeon crop-gland in vivo. Injection of prolactin increased the uptake of P^{32} by the crop glands and also their total P content. Both responses were regarded as potentially useful for assay purposes and indeed the same authors were able later to use the P^{32} uptake to show that

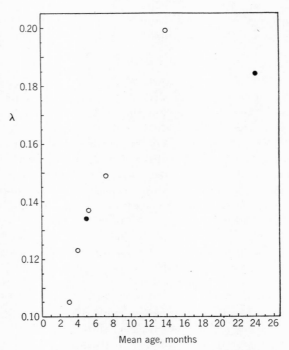

FIG. 15.   Prolactin assay by pigeon crop-weight method.   Relation between mean age of birds and index of precision (λ).   The solid dots represent groups whose ages were not known but were estimated from degree of gonad development.   (Constructed from results of Clarke and Folley, 47.)

simultaneous administration of ACTH decreases the crop response to prolactin (33).   Brown *et al.* (32) interpreted some of their findings as indicating that prolactin stimulation increases the rate of nucleic acid synthesis in the crop glands—a result in agreement with the previous findings of McShan *et al.* (189), who showed that the crop-gland response to prolactin was accompanied by a marked increase in the tissue pentose nucleic acid, deoxypentose nucleic acid increasing to a notably smaller extent.   Recent work in our laboratory (241) also suggests a relationship between nucleic acid metabolism and the growth response of the pigeon crop-glands to prolactin.   Dr. Marian Silver showed that administration to pigeons of high doses of the folic acid antagonist, aminopterin, greatly diminished the response of the crop glands to prolactin.   Despite the surprising fact that, even though the effect of the aminopterin was reinforced by maintaining the birds throughout the experimental period on a diet deficient in folic acid, no overt symptoms of folic acid deficiency developed, it seems safe to conclude that the reduction in the response was

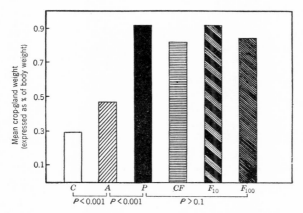

FIG. 16. The effect of aminopterin on the response of the pigeon crop-gland to prolactin.

C   = non-injected controls (8 birds).

A   = aminopterin + prolactin (10 birds).
      (10 mg./day aminopterin for 10 days beginning 6 days before the first injection of prolactin; 4 mg./day prolactin for 4 days.)

P   = prolactin alone (8 birds).

CF = citrovorum factor (3 mg./day) + aminopterin + prolactin (4 birds).

F_{10} = folic acid (10 mg./day) + aminopterin + prolactin (4 birds).

F_{100} = folic acid (100 mg./day) + aminopterin + prolactin (8 birds).
      (Injections of CF or F were begun 24 hours before the aminopterin treatment.)

(Results from Silver, 241.)

due to folic acid deprivation, since the inhibition could be largely abolished by simultaneous administration of folic acid or citrovorum factor (Fig. 16). Many of the results obtained in this study, which concerned not only the crop-gland response to prolactin but also the growth responses of the mammary gland and uterus of the rat to estrogen, indicate that whatever the stimulus, folic acid is necessary for the growth of these tissues instead of being specifically involved in the mechanism of hormonal action on the tissues. Much recent work on folic acid metabolism suggests that the vitamin is in some way related to the synthesis of nucleic acids; the results of Silver (241) on the crop response are thus in general harmony in this respect with those of McShan *et al.* (189). Incidentally, McShan and associates also showed that the growth of the pigeon crop glands in response to prolactin is accompanied by an increase in the succinic dehydrogenase activity of the tissue. Other enzyme studies on the hormonally stimulated crop glands were reported by Kocsis and Abood (158), who found that prolactin stimulation increases the acid phosphatase content.

No really satisfactory mammalian method of assay of prolactin has yet been devised, though this must continue to be a goal for future effort. Astwood (3) has discussed various responses in the rat, dependent upon maintenance of luteal function, *i.e.*, luteotropic responses, some of which could possibly be developed into quantitative assay methods, though so far they have been used only as qualitative, or at best semiquantitative, indicators.[22]   Use of such responses for the assay of prolactin preparations would of course involve the assumption that prolactin is the specific and sole luteotropic hormone, at least for the rat—an assumption which though not unreasonable in the light of current knowledge is perhaps not yet entirely without hazard.

The most attractive possibility for a mammalian assay method for prolactin would appear to be offered by the elegant and dramatic lactogenic responses to prolactin injected directly into the mammary duct system in the rabbit described first by Lyons (165) and discussed in sections III.B and III.C.   In our laboratory, Mr. T. R. Bradley, at the time of writing, is investigating the possibility of developing this response into a quantitative assay method.   The possibility of doing so was foreshadowed by the results given in Lyons' original publication and also by implication in the review of Meites and Turner (199).   Our experience indicates that the chief difficulty to overcome arises from the differences in responsiveness between various glands in the same rabbit or even between different "sectors" (or lobes?) in a given gland.   Bradley's results (unpublished) appear to indicate that the minimum volume of solution necessary to secure penetration of the hormone into the remotest ramifications of the whole system of alveolar lumina may be a significant factor here.   As emphasized earlier, strictly localized responses obtained by the Lyons technique point to a direct action of the hormone on the mammary epithelium, which ought to have its counterpart with surviving tissue *in vitro* if the necessary environmental conditions to simulate those obtaining *in vivo* can be hit upon.   Bradley has therefore also studied the possibility of utilizing for quantitative assay the effects of prolactin *in vitro* on the gas exchange of mammary slices taken from rats killed in early lactation as revealed by the technique used first by Balmain and Folley (14).   However, as stated in section III.C of this chapter it has been found that these effects were possibly due not to prolactin itself but to a contaminant of the preparation, perhaps intermedin.   This disappointment should not, however, discourage further search for an *in vitro* prolactin assay technique, which would be so useful from many points of view.

[22] Van der Kuy *et al.* (159a) have recently described a method for the rough standardization of prolactin based on the luteopropic effect in the rat.   Hypophysectomized rats are brought into estrus with gonadotropins and the dose of prolactin necessary to abolish estrus determined.

REFERENCES

1. Abrams, M. E., Marshall, W. A., and Thomson, A. P. D. *Nature* **174**, 311 (1954).
1a. Andrews, F. N. *Iowa State Coll. J. Sci.* **28**, 9 (1953).
2. Asdell, S. A. Patterns of Mammalian Reproduction. Comstock, Ithaca, 1946.
3. Astwood, E. B. *Ciba Colloq. Endocrinol.* **5**, 74 (1953).
4. Astwood, E. B., and Fevold, H. L. *Am. J. Physiol.* **127**, 192 (1939).
5. Astwood, E. B., and Greep, R. O. *Proc. Soc. Exptl. Biol. Med.* **38**, 713 (1938).
6. Atkinson, W. B., and Leathem, J. H. *Anat. Record* **95**, 147 (1946).
7. Averill, S. C., Ray, E. W., and Lyons, W. R. *Proc. Soc. Exptl. Biol. Med.* **75**, 3 (1950).
8. Azimov, G. I., and Altman, A. D. *Compt. rend. acad. sci. U.R.S.S.* **20**, 621 (1938).
9. Bahn, R. C., Lorenz, N., Bennett, W. A., and Albert, A. *Proc. Soc. Exptl. Biol. Med.* **82**, 777 (1953).
10. Bahn, R. C., Lorenz, N., Bennett, W. A., and Albert, A. *Endocrinology* **52**, 135 (1953).
11. Bahn, R. C., Lorenz, N., Bennett, W. A., and Albert, A. *Endocrinology* **52**, 605 (1953).
12. Bahn, R. C., Lorenz, N., Bennett, W. A., and Albert, A. *Endocrinology* **53**, 455 (1953).
12a. Bailey, R. E. *Condor* **52**, 247 (1950).
12b. Bailey, R. E. *Condor* **54**, 121 (1952).
13. Balmain, J. H., and Folley, S. J. *Biochem. J.* **49**, 663 (1951).
14. Balmain, J. H., and Folley, S. J. *Arch. Biochem. and Biophys.* **39**, 188 (1952).
15. Balmain, J. H., Folley, S. J., and Glascock, R. F. *Biochem. J.* **52**, 301 (1952).
16. Balmain, J. H., Folley, S. J., and Glascock, R. F. *Nature* **169**, 447 (1952).
17. Balmain, J. H., Folley, S. J., and Glascock, R. F. *Biochem. J.* **56**, 234 (1954).
18. Balmain, J. H., French, T. H., and Folley, S. J. *Nature* **165**, 807 (1950).
18a. Barrnett, R. J. *Endocrinology* **55**, 484 (1954).
19. Barrnett, R. J., and Greep, R. O. *Science* **113**, 185 (1951).
20. Barrnett, R. J., and Greep, R. O. *Endocrinology* **49**, 337 (1951).
21. Barsantini, J. C., Masson, G., and Selye, H. *Rev. can. biol.* **5**, 407 (1946).
22. Benoit, J., and Assenmacher, I. *Compt. rend. soc. biol.* **145**, 1112 (1951).
23. Benoit, J., and Assenmacher, I. 2e Réunion des Endocrinologistes de la langue française, p. 33 (1953).
23a. Benoit, J., and Assenmacher, I. *Arch. anat. microscop. morphol. exptl.* **42**, 334 (1953).
24. Bergman, A. J., and Turner, C. W. *J. Dairy Sci.* **23**, 1229 (1940).
25. Biavati, F., and Fiori, C. *Nuova vet.* **26**, 363 (1950).
26. Bissonnette, T. H. *Proc. Roy. Soc. (London)* **B110**, 322 (1932).
27. Bissonnette, T. H. *J. Comp. Psychol.* **22**, 93 (1936).
28. Bissonnette, T. H. *Physiol. Zoöl.* **14**, 379 (1941).
28a. Borgatti, G., and Fiori, W. *Riv. biol. (Perugia)* **43**, 199 (1951).
28b. Borth, R., Lunenfeld, B., and de Watteville, H. *Experientia* **10**, 266 (1954).
29. Bradbury, J. T., Brown, W. E., and Gray, L. A. *Recent Progr. Hormone Research* **5**, 151 (1950).
30. Bradley, T. R., Folley, S. J., Landgrebe, F. W., and Mitchell, G. M. *Biochem. et Biophys. Acta* **13**, 449 (1954).
31. Brock, H., and Rowson, L. E. *J. Agr. Sci.* **42**, 479 (1952).

32. Brown, R. W., Woodbury, D. M., and Sayers, G. *Proc. Soc. Exptl. Med.* **76,** 639 (1951).
33. Brown, R. W., Woodbury, D. M., and Sayers, G. *J. Clin. Endocrinol. and Metabolism* **12,** 939 (1952).
34. Brown, W. E., and Bradbury, J. T. *Am. J. Obstet. Gynecol.* **53,** 749 (1947).
35. Bruner, J. A. *J. Clin. Endocrinol.* **11,** 360 (1951).
35a. Brumby, P. J., and Hancock, J. *New Zealand J. Sci. Technol.* A, **36,** 417 (1955).
36. Bryans, F. E. *Endocrinology* **48,** 733 (1951).
37. Burkhardt, J. *J. Agr. Sci.* **37,** 64 (1947).
38. Burrows, H. Biological Actions of Sex Hormones, 2nd ed. University Press, Cambridge, 1949.
38a. Burt, A. S., and Velardo, J. T. *J. Clin. Endocrinol. and Metabolism* **14,** 979 (1954).
39. Byrnes, W. W., and Meyer, R. K. *Endocrinology* **49,** 449 (1951).
40. Canivenc, R. *Arch. Anat., Strasbourg* **34,** 105 (1952).
41. Canivenc, R., and Mayer, G. *Compt. rend. soc. biol.* **145,** 1692 (1951).
42. Canivenc, R., and Mayer, G. *Compt. rend. soc. biol.* **147** 1067 (1953).
43. Casida, L. E., Meyer, R. K., McShan, W. H., and Wisnicky, W. *Am. J. Vet. Research* **4,** 76 (1943).
44. Catchpole, H. R. *Federation Proc.* **6,** 88 (1947).
45. Catchpole, H. R. *J. Endocrinol.* **6,** 218 (1949).
45a. Chung, A. C., Shaw, J. C., and Gill, W. M. *J. Dairy Sci.* **36,** 589 (1953).
46. Clark, W. E. le Gros, McKeown, T., and Zuckerman, S. *Proc. Roy. Soc. (London)* **B126,** 449 (1939).
47. Clarke, P. M., and Folley, S. J. *Ciba Colloq. Endocrinol.* **5,** 90 (1953).
48. Clegg, M. T., Boda, J. M., and Cole, H. H. *Endocrinology* **54,** 448 (1954).
49. Cole, H. H. *Iowa State Coll. J. Sci.* **28,** 133 (1953).
50. Coppedge, R. L., and Segaloff, A. *J. Clin. Endocrinol.* **11,** 465 (1951).
51. Cotes, P. M., Crichton, J. A., Folley, S. J., and Young, F. G. *Nature* **164,** 992 (1949).
52. Cotes, P. M., Reid, E., and Young, F. G. *Nature* **164,** 209 (1949).
53. Cowie, A. T. Pregnancy diagnosis tests. Commonwealth Agricultural Bureaux. Joint Publ. 13 (1948).
54. Cowie, A. T., and Folley, S. J. *Endocrinology* **40,** 274 (1947).
55. Cowie, A. T., Folley, S. J., Cross, B. A., Harris, G. W., Jacobsohn, D., and Richardson, K. C. *Nature* **168,** 421 (1951).
56. Cowie, A. T., Folley, S. J., Malpress, F. H., and Richardson, K. C. *J. Endocrinol.* **8,** 64 (1952).
57. Cox, P. L. *Anat. Record* **109,** 285 (1951).
57a. Daane, T. A., and Lyons, W. R. *Endocrinology* **55,** 191 (1954).
57b. Dauzier, L., Ortavant, R., Thibault, C., and Wintenberger, S. *Ann. endocrinol. (Paris)* **14,** 553 (1953).
58. Dawson, A. B. *Am. J. Anat.* **78,** 347 (1946).
59. DeGroot, J. The significance of the hypophysial portal system. Doctorate thesis, University of Amsterdam, (1952).
60. Desclin, L. *Compt. rend. soc. biol.* **140,** 1182 (1946).
61. Desclin, L. *Compt. rend. soc. biol.* **140,** 1184 (1946).
62. Desclin, L. *Endocrinology* **40,** 14 (1947).
63. Desclin, L. *Bruxelles-Méd.* **22,** 30 May (1948).
64. Desclin, L. *Compt. rend. soc. biol.* **142,** 1436 (1948).

65. Desclin, L.   *Ann. endocrinol. (Paris)* **10**, 1 (1949).
66. Desclin, L.   *Compt. rend. soc. biol.* **143**, 1154 (1949).
67. Desclin, L.   *Colloq. intern. centre natl. recherche sci. (Paris)* **32, 1950,** 69 (1951).
68. Desclin, L.   *Ciba Colloq. Endocrinol.* **4**, 21 (1952).
69. Desclin, L.   *Ann. endocrinol. (Paris)* **13**, 120 (1952).
70. Dey, F. L.   *Endocrinology* **33**, 75 (1943).
71. Dey, F. L., Fisher, C., Berry, C. M., and Ranson, S. W.   *Am. J. Physiol.* **129**, 39 (1940).
72. Dickens, F.   *Ciba Colloq. Endocrinol.* **6**, 1 (1953).
72a. Diczfalusy, E., and Loraine, J. A.   *J. Clin. Endocrinol. and Metabolism* in press (1955).
73. Donker, J. D., and Petersen, W. E.   *J. Animal Sci.* **10**, 1074 (1951).
74. Donker, J. D., and Petersen, W. E.   *J. Dairy Sci.* **35**, 503 (1952).
74a. Donovan, B. T., and Harris, G. W.   *Nature* **175**, 74 (1955).
75. Dowling, D. F.   *J. Agr. Sci.* **39**, 374 (1949).
76. Dutt, R. H.   *Iowa State Coll. J. Sci.* **28**, 55 (1953).
77. Ershoff, B. H.   *Vitamins and Hormones* **10**, 79 (1952).
78. Evans, H. M., Simpson, M. E., and Lyons, W. R.   *Proc. Soc. Exptl. Biol. Med.* **46**, 586 (1941).
79. Everett, J. W.   *Endocrinology* **41**, 364 (1947).
80. Everett, J. W.   *Endocrinology* **43**, 389 (1948).
81. Everett, J. W.   *Anat. Record* **118**, 297 (1954).
81a. Everett, J. W.   *Endocrinology* **54**, 685 (1954).
82. Everett, J. W., and Sawyer, C. H.   *Endocrinology* **47**, 198 (1950).
83. Everett, J. W., and Sawyer, C. H.   *Endocrinology* **52**, 83 (1953).
84. Everett, J. W., Sawyer, C. H., and Markee, J. E.   *Endocrinology* **44**, 234 (1949).
85. Everett, N. B., and Baker, B. L.   *Endocrinology* **37**, 83 (1945).
86. Farquhar, M. G., and Rinehart, J. F.   *Endocrinology* **54**, 516 (1954).
86a. Farquhar, M. G., and Rinehart, J. F.   *Endocrinology* **55**, 857 (1954).
87. Fauvet, E.   *Arch Gynäkol.* **171**, 342 (1941).
87a. Fiori, W.   *Riv. Biol. (Perugia)* **44**, 137 (1952).
87b. Fiori, W., and Lasagna, G.   *Boll. soc. ital. biol. sper.* **27**, 561 (1951).
88. Flux, D. S., Folley, S. J., and Rowland, S. J.   *J. Endocrinol.* **10**, 333 (1954).
89. Folley, S. J.   *Nature* **150**, 266 (1942).
90. Folley, S. J.   *Brit. Med. Bull.* **5**, 142 (1947).
91. Folley, S. J.   *In* A. S. Parkes, Marshall's Physiology of Reproduction, 3rd ed. Longmans, Green & Co., London, 1952, Chapter 20.
92. Folley, S. J.   *In* J. M. Yoffey, The Suprarenal Cortex.   Butterworth, London, 1953, p. 85.
93. Folley, S. J.   *In* E. W. Dempsey, Sex and Internal Secretions, 3rd ed.   Williams & Wilkins, Baltimore, in press, 1955.
94. Folley, S. J.   Recherches récentes sur la physiologie et la biochimie de la sécrétion lactée.   Masson et Cie, Paris. and Desoer, Liège. (1954).
94a. Folley, S. J.   *In* R. W. Smith, O. H. Gaebler, and C. N. H. Long, The Hypophyseal Growth Hormone, Nature and Actions.   Blakiston, Philadelphia, 1955, Chapter 27.
95. Folley, S. J., Dyer, F. J., and Coward, K. H.   *J. Endocrinol.* **2**, 179 (1940).
96. Folley, S. J., and French, T. H.   *Biochem. J.* **45**, 270 (1949).
97. Folley, S. J., and French, T. H.   *Biochem. J.* **46**, 465 (1950).
98. Folley, S. J., Greenbaum, A. L., and Roy, A.   *J. Endocrinol.* **6**, 121 (1949).

99. Folley, S. J., and Malpress, F. H. *Proc. Roy. Soc. (London)* **B132,** 164 (1944).
100. Folley, S. J., and Malpress, F. H. *Abstr. 17th Intern. Physiol. Congr.,* p. 340 (1947).
101. Folley, S. J., and Malpress, F. H. *In* G. Pincus and K. V. Thimann, The Hormones. Academic Press, New York, 1948, Vol. 1, Chapter 15.
102. Folley, S. J., and Malpress, F. H. *In* G. Pincus and K. V. Thimann, The Hormones. Academic Press, New York, 1948, Vol. 1, Chapter 16.
103. Folley, S. J., and Young, F. G. *J. Endocrinol.* **2,** 226 (1940).
104. Folley, S. J., and Young, F. G. *Lancet* **240,** 380 (1941).
105. Folley, S. J., and Young, F. G. *11th Intern. Congr. Chem. 1947* **4,** 77 (1952).
105a. Fraps, R. M., and Conner, M. H. *Nature* **174,** 1148 (1954).
106. Frey, E. *Acta Anat.* **4,** 123 (1947).
107. Fried, P. H., and Rakoff, A. E. *J. Clin. Endocrinol. and Metabolism* **12,** 321 (1952).
108. Friedgood, H. B., and Dawson, A. B. *Endocrinology* **22,** 674 (1938).
109. Friedgood, H. B., and Dawson, A. B. *Endocrinology* **26,** 1022 (1940).
110. Friedgood, H. B., and Dawson, A. B. *Endocrinology* **30,** 252 (1942).
111. Friedman, M. H., and Hall, S. R. *Endocrinology* **29,** 179 (1941).
111a. Geschwind, I. I., and Li, C. H. *In* R. W. Smith, O. H. Gaebler, and C. N. H. Long, The Hypophyseal Growth Hormone, Nature and Actions. Blakiston, Philadelphia, 1955, Chapter 3.
112. Glock, G. E., and McLean, P. *Biochem. J.* **56,** 171 (1954).
113. Goldberg, R. C., and Chaikoff, I. L. *Anat. Record.* **112,** 265 (1952).
114. Green, J. D. *Am. J. Anat.* **88,** 225 (1951).
115. Green, J. D. *Ciba Colloq. Endocrinol.* **4,** 72 (1952).
116. Green, J. D., and Harris, G. W. *J. Endocrinol.* **5,** 136 (1947).
117. Green, J. D., and Harris, G. W. *J. Physiol.* **108,** 359 (1949).
118. Greenbaum, A. L., and Greenwood, F. C. *Biochem. J.* **56,** 625 (1954).
119. Greep, R. O., and Barrnett, R. J. *Endocrinology* **49,** 172 (1951).
120. Greep, R. O., and Jones, I. C. *In* E. S. Gordon, Symposium on Steroid Hormones. Univ. of Wisconsin Press, Madison, 1950, p. 330.
121. Greep, R. O., and Jones, I. C. *Recent Progr. Hormone Research* **5,** 197 (1950).
122. Greer, M. A. *Endocrinology* **53,** 380 (1953).
123. Hafez, E. S. E. *J. Agr. Sci.* **42,** 189 (1952).
124. Halmi, N. S. *Endocrinology* **47,** 289 (1950).
125. Halmi, N. S. *Endocrinology* **50,** 140 (1952).
126. Hammond, J., Jr. *J. Agr. Sci.* **39,** 222 (1949).
126a. Hammond, J., Jr. *Vitamins and Hormones* **12,** 157 (1954).
127. Hammond, J., Jr., and Bhattacharya, P. *J. Agr. Sci.* **34,** 1 (1944).
128. Hansel, W., and Trimberger, G. W. *J. Animal Sci.* **10,** 719 (1951).
129. Hansel, W., and Trimberger, G. W. *J. Dairy Sci.* **35,** 65 (1952).
130. Harris, G. W. *Physiol. Revs.* **28,** 139 (1948).
131. Harris, G. W. *J. Physiol.* **107,** 418 (1948).
132. Harris, G. W. *Proc. Roy. Soc. Med.* **41,** 661 (1948).
133. Harris, G. W. *J. Physiol.* **111,** 347 (1950).
134. Harris, G. W., and Jacobsohn, D. *Proc. Roy. Soc. (London)* **B139,** 263 (1952).
135. Hart, D. S. *J. Agr. Sci.* **40,** 143 (1950).
136. Hart, D. S. *J. Exptl. Biol.* **28,** 1 (1951).
137. Hays, E. *Recent Progr. Hormone Research* **8,** 503 (1953).
138. Herlant, M. *Bull. Acad. Belg. Cl. Sci.* [5] **28,** 588 (1942).

139. Herlant, M. *Arch. biol. (Liége)* **54**, 225 (1943).

140. Herlant, M. *Nature* **164**, 703 (1949).

141. Herlant, M. *Ann. endocrinol. (Paris)* **13**, 611 (1952).

142. Hill, M., and Parkes, A. S. *Proc. Roy. Soc. (London)* **B115**, 14 (1934).

143. Hillarp, N-Å. *Acta Endocrinol.* **2**, 11 (1949).

144. Hisaw, F. L. *Yale. J. Biol. and Med.* **17**, 119 (1944).

145. Hisaw, F. L. *Physiol. Revs.* **27**, 95 (1947).

146. Holmstrom, E. G., and Jones, W. J. *Am. J. Obstet. Gynecol.* **58**, 308 (1949).

147. Hotchkiss, R. D. *Arch. Biochem.* **16**, 131 (1948).

147a. Houssay, B. A. *Rev. soc. argentina biol.* **23**, 275 (1947).

147b. Houssay, B. A., and Anderson, E. *Rev. soc. argentina biol.* **25**, 91 (1949).

147c. Houssay, B. A., and Anderson, E. *Endocrinology* **45**, 627 (1949).

148. Houssay, B. A., Biasotti, A., and Sammartino, R. *Compt. rend. soc. biol.* **120**, 725 (1935).

148a. Houssay, B. A., Rodriguez, R. R., and Cardeza, A. F. *Rev. soc. argentina biol.* **24**, 33 (1953).

149. Hume, D. M. *Ciba Colloq. Endocrinol.* **4**, 87 (1952).

150. Hume, D. M. *Ann. Surg.* **138**, 548 (1953).

151. Huston, T. M., and Nalbandov, A. V. *Endocrinology* **52**, 149 (1953).

151a. Ifft, J. D. *Anat. Record* **117**, 395 (1953).

151b. Ingle, D. J. *J. Clin. Endocrinol. and Metabolism* **14**, 1272 (1954).

152. Jacobsohn, D. *Acta Physiol. Scand.* **19**, 10 (1949).

153. Jacobsohn, D. *Acta Physiol. Scand.* **19**, 19 (1949).

154. Jacobsohn, D., and Westman, A. *Acta Physiol. Scand.* **9**, 284 (1945).

155. Jefferson, J. M. *J. Anat.* **75**, 106 (1940).

155a. Jordan, R. M., and Shaffhausen, D. D. *J. Animal Sci.* **13**, 706 (1954).

156. Kammlade, W. G., Jr., Welch, J. A., Nalbandov, A. V., and Norton, H. W. *J. Animal Sci.* **11**, 646 (1952).

157. Klein, M., and Mayer, G. *Colloq. intern. centre natl. recherche sci. (Paris)* **32**, 1950, 73 (1951).

158. Kocsis, J. J., and Abood, L. G. *Endocrinology* **54**, 108 (1954).

158a. Kraintz, L., and Talmage, R. V. *Anat. Record* **117**, 537 (1953).

159. Kupperman, H. S., Fried, P., and Hair, L. Q. *Am. J. Obstet. Gynecol.* **48**, 228 (1944).

159a. van der Kuy, A., van Soest, E. M., and van Rooye-Belle, A. G. C. *Koninkl. Ned. Akad. Wetenschap. Proc.* **56**, 62 (1953).

160. Lacour, F. *Compt. rend. soc. biol.* **144**, 248 (1950).

161. Ladman, A. J., and Barrnett, R. J. *Endocrinology* **54**, 355 (1954).

162. Ladman, A. J., and Runner, M. N. *Endocrinology* **53**, 367 (1953).

163. Laing, J. A. *J. Agr. Sci.* **35**, 72 (1945).

163a. Li, C. H., Ingle, D. J., Prestrud, M. C., and Nezamis, J. E. *Endocrinology* **44**, 454 (1949).

163b. Loraine, J. A., and Brown, J. B. *Acta Endocrinol.* **17**, 250 (1954).

164. Lyon, R. A., Simpson, M. E., and Evans, H. M. *Endocrinology* **53**, 674 (1953).

165. Lyons, W. R. *Proc. Soc. Exptl. Biol. Med.* **51**, 308 (1942).

166. Lyons, W. R. *In* Essays in Biology in Honor of Herbert M. Evans. Univ. of California Press, Berkeley and Los Angeles, 1943, p. 315.

167. Lyons, W. R. *Colloq. intern. centre natl. recherche sci. (Paris)* **32**, 1950, 29 (1951).

167a. Lyons, W. R., Li, C. H., Cole, R. D., and Johnson, R. E. *J. Clin. Endocrinol. and Metabolism* **13**, 836 (1953).

168. Lyons, W. R., Li, C. H., and Johnson, R. E. *J. Clin. Endocrinol. and Metabolism* **12**, 937 (1952).
169. Lyons, W. R., and Page, E. *Proc. Soc. Exptl. Biol. Med.* **32**, 1049 (1935).
170. Malpress, F. H. *Brit. Med. Bull.* **5**, 161 (1947).
171. Marden, W. G. R. *J. Agr. Sci.* **43**, 381 (1953).
172. Marion, G. B., Smith, V. R., Wiley, T. E., and Barrett, G. R. *J. Dairy Sci.* **33**, 885 (1950).
173. Markee, J. E., Everett, J. W., and Sawyer, C. H. *Recent Progr. Hormone Research* **7**, 139 (1952).
174. Markee, J. E., Sawyer, C. H., and Hollinshead, W. H. *Endocrinology* **38**, 345 (1946).
175. Markee, J. E., Sawyer, C. H., and Hollinshead, W. H. *Recent Progr. Hormone Research* **2**, 117 (1948).
176. Marshall, F. H. A. *Biol. Revs.* **17**, 68 (1942).
177. Masson, G. M. C. *Anat. Record* **102**, 513 (1948).
178. Mayer, G. *Arch. sci. physiol.* **5**, 247 (1951).
179. Mayer, G. *Arch. Anat., Strasbourg* **34**, 305 (1952).
180. Mayer, G., and Canivenc, R. *Compt. rend. soc. biol* **144**, 410 (1950).
181. Mayer, G., and Canivenc, R. *Compt. rend. soc. biol.* **145**, 100 (1951).
182. Mayer, G., and Canivenc, R. *Compt. rend. assoc. anat., 39ᵉ réunion* 9 pp. (1952).
183. Mayer, G., and Klein, M. *Ann. nutrition et aliment.* **2**, 113 (1948).
184. Mayer, G., and Klein, M. *Ann. nutrition et aliment.* **3**, 667 (1949).
185. Mayer, G., and Klein, M. *Compt. rend. assoc. anat., 36ᵉ réunion* p. 478 (1949).
186. Mayer, G., and Klein, M. *Compt rend. soc. biol.* **143**, 1195 (1949).
187. McCann, S. M. *Am. J. Physiol.* **175**, 13 (1953).
188. McManus, J. F. A. *Nature* **158**, 202 (1946).
189. McShan, W. H., Davis, J. S., Soukop, S. W., and Meyer, R. K. *Endocrinology* **47**, 274 (1950).
190. McShan, W. H., and Meyer, R. K. *Endocrinology* **50**, 294 (1952).
191. McShan, W. H., Rozich, R., and Meyer, R. K. *Endocrinology* **52**, 215 (1953).
192. Meites, J. *Iowa State College J. Sci.* **28**, 19 (1953).
193. Meites, J., and Sgouris, J. T. *Endocrinology* **53**, 17 (1953).
194. Meites, J., and Sgouris, J. T. *Endocrinology*, **55**, 530 (1954).
195. Meites, J., and Turner, C. W. *J. Clin. Endocrinol.* **1**, 918 (1941).
196. Meites, J., and Turner, C. W. *Endocrinology* **30**, 711, 719, 726; *ibid.* **31**, 340 (1942).
197. Meites, J., and Turner, C. W. *Research Bull. Missouri Agr. Expt. Sta.* No. **415**, (1948).
198. Meites, J., and Turner, C. W. *Research Bull. Missouri Agr. Expt. Sta.* No. **416**, (1948).
199. Meites, J., and Turner, C. W. *In* C. W. Emmens, Hormone Assay. Academic Press, New York, 1950, Chapter 10.
199a. Melchior, J. B., and Halikis, M. N. *J. Biol. Chem.* **199**, 773 (1952).
199b. Metuzáls, J. *Acta Anat.* **20**, 258 (1954).
200. Miller, D. C., and Everett, J. W. *Endocrinology* **42**, 421 (1948).
200a. Mirsky, A. I., Stein, M., and Paulish, G. *Endocrinology* **55**, 28 (1954).
201. Moore, W. W., and Nalbandov, A. V. *Endocrinology* **53**, 1 (1953).
202. Nalbandov, A. V. *Iowa State College J. Sci.* **28**, 45 (1953).
202a. Nalbandov, A. V., and Card, L. E. *J. Heredity* **36**, 35 (1945).
202b. Nalbandov, A. V., Hochhauser, M., and Dugas, M. *Endocrinology* **36**, 251 (1945).

202c. Nalbandov, A. V., Meyer, R. K., and McShan, W. H. *Anat. Record* **110,** 475 (1951).
203. Nelson, M. M., Lyons, W. R., and Evans, H. M. *Endocrinology* **52,** 585 (1953).
204. Nelson, W. O. *Physiol. Revs.* **16,** 488 (1936).
205. Nelson, W. O. *Colloq. intern. centr. natl. recherche sci.* **32, 1950,** 19. (1951).
206. Nelson, W. O. *Ciba Colloq. Endocrinol.* **4,** 402 (1952).
206a. Pasqualini, R. Q. *Prensa méd. Argentina* **40,** 2658 (1953).
206b. Payne, F. *Anat. Record* **86,** 1 (1943).
207. Pearse, A. G. E. *J. Pathol. Bacteriol.* **61,** 195 (1949).
208. Pearse, A. G. E. *Stain Technol.* **25,** 95 (1950).
209. Pearse, A. G. E. *J. Endocrinol.* **7,** 48P (1951).
210. Pearse, A. G. E. *J. Pathol. Bacteriol.* **64,** 791 (1952).
211. Pearse, A. G. E. *J. Pathol. Bacteriol.* **64,** 811 (1952).
212. Pearse, A. G. E. *Ciba Colloq. Endocrinol.* **4,** 1 (1952).
213. Pearse, A. G. E. Histochemistry, Theoretical and Applied. Churchill, London, 1953.
214. Pearse, A. G. E. *J. Pathol. Bacteriol.* **65,** 355 (1953).
215. Phillips, R. W., Fraps, R. M., and Frank, A. H. *Am. J. Vet. Research* **6,** 165 (1945).
216. Popa, G. T., and Fielding, U. *J. Anat.* **65,** 88 (1930).
217. Popa, G. T., and Fielding, U. *J. Anat.* **67,** 227 (1933).
218. Popják, G., Folley, S. J., and French, T. H. *Arch. Biochem.* **23,** 509 (1949).
219. Purves, H. D., and Griesbach, W. E. *Endocrinology* **49,** 244 (1951).
220. Purves, H. D., and Griesbach, W. E. *Endocrinology* **49,** 427 (1951).
220a. Purves, H. D., and Griesbach, W. E. *Endocrinology* **55,** 785 (1954).
221. Reece, R. P. *Proc. Soc. Exptl. Biol. Med.* **40,** 25 (1939).
221a. Reiss, M. *Endocrinology* **40,** 294 (1947).
221b. Riddle, O., and Bates, R. W. *In* E. Allen, Sex and Internal Secretions, 2nd ed., Williams & Wilkins, Baltimore, 1939, chapter 20.
222. Riddle, O., Bates, R. W., and Dykshorn, S. W. *Am. J. Physiol.* **105,** 191 (1933).
222a. Riddle, O., Bates, R. W., and Lahr, E. L. *Am. J. Physiol.* **111,** 352 (1935).
223. Robinson, G. E., Jr., and Nalbandov, A. V. *J. Animal Sci.* **10,** 469 (1951).
224. Robinson, T. J. *J. Agr. Sci.* **40,** 275 (1950).
225. Robinson, T. J. *J. Agr. Sci.* **41,** 6 (1951).
226. Robinson, T. J. *J. Endocrinol.* **10,** 117 (1954).
227. Romani, J., and Recht, P. *Ann. endocrinol. (Paris)* **9,** 247 (1948).
228. Romeis, B. *In* W. von Möllendorff and W. Bargmann, Handbuch der Mikroskopischen Anatomie des Menschen. Springer, Berlin, 1940, Vol. 6, Part 3.
229. Rowan, W. *Nature* **115,** 494 (1925).
230. Rowan, W. *Proc. Boston Soc. Nat. History* **39,** 151 (1929).
231. Rowlands, I. W. *J. Endocrinol* **6,** 184 (1949).
232. Salhanick, H. A., Hisaw, F. L., and Zarrow, M. X. *J. Clin. Endocrinol. and Metabolism* **12,** 310 (1952).
233. Sawyer, C. H., Everett, J. W., and Markee, J. E. *Proc. Soc. Exptl. Biol. Med.* **74,** 185 (1950).
233a. Scharrer, E. *Experientia* **10,** 264 (1954).
233b. Scharrer, E., and Scharrer, B. *Recent Progr. Hormone Research* **10,** 183 (1954).
234. Schooley, J. P., and Riddle, O. *Am. J. Anat.* **62,** 313 (1938).
235. Segaloff, A. *Ciba Colloq. Endocrinol.* **5,** 106 (1953).
236. Segaloff, A., Sternberg, W. H., and Gaskill, C. J. *J. Clin. Endocrinol.* **11,** 936 (1951).

237. Selye, H.   *Am. J. Physiol.* **107,** 535 (1934).
237a. Severinghaus, A. E.   *Physiol. Revs.* **17,** 556 (1937).
238. Sgouris, J. T., and Meites, J.   *Am. J. Physiol.* **169,** 301 (1952).
239. Sgouris, J. T., and Meites, J.   *Am. J. Physiol.* **175,** 319 (1953).
239a. Shaw, J. C., Chung, A. C., and Bunding, I.   *Endocrinology,* **56,** 327 (1955).
240. Shaw, J. C., Hatziolos, B. C., Leffel, E. C., Chung, A. C., Gill, W. M., and Gilbert, J.   *Univ. Maryland Agr. Expt. Sta. Misc. Publ.* No. **139,** (1952).
241. Silver, M.   *J. Endocrinol.* **10,** 95 (1954).
241a. Sinkoff, M. W., and De Bodo, R. C.   *Arch. exptl. Pathol. Pharmakol.* **219,** 100 (1953).
242. Siperstein, E., Nichols, C. W., Jr., Griesbach, W. E., and Chaikoff, I. L.   *Anat. Record* **118,** 593 (1954).
243. Smith, R. A., Albert, A., and Randall, L. M.   *Am. J. Obstet. Gynecol.* **61,** 514 (1951).
244. Sonenberg, M., Money, W. L., Keston, A. S., Fitzgerald, P. J., and Godwin, J. T.   *Endocrinology* **49,** 709 (1951).
245. Stricker, P.   *Colloq. intern. natl. recherche sci.* **32, 1950,** 15 (1951).
246. Stricker, P., and Grueter, F.   *Compt. rend. soc. biol.* **99,** 1978 (1928).
247. Thomson, A. P. D.   *J. Physiol.* **113,** 425 (1951).
248. Thomson, A. P. D.   *Proc. Roy. Soc. (London)* **B142,** 126 (1954).
249. Thomson, A. P. D., and Zuckerman, S.   *Nature* **171,** 970 (1953).
249a. Thomson, A. P. D., and Zuckerman, S.   *Nature* **175,** 74 (1955).
249b. Thomson, A. P. D., and Zuckerman, S.   *Proc. Roy. Soc. (London)* **B142,** 437 (1954).
249c. van Tienhoven, A., Nalbandov, A. V., and Norton, H. W.   *Endocrinology* **54,** 605 (1954).
250. Trentin, J. J., and Turner, C. W.   *Research Bull. Missouri Agr. Expt. Sta.* No. **418,** (1948).
251. Turner, C. W.   *In* C. W. Emmens, Hormone Assay.   Academic Press, New York, 1950, Chapter 11.
252. Vazquez-Lopez, E.   *J. Endocrinol.* **6,** 158 (1949).
253. Voss, H. E.   *Ergeb. Physiol.* **44,** 96 (1941).
253a. Voss, H. E.   *Arzneimittel-Forsch.* **4,** 467 (1954).
254. Walker, S. M., and Matthews, J. I.   *Endocrinology* **44,** 8 (1949).
254a. Wallace, L. R.   *J. Agr. Sci.* **45,** 60 (1954).
255. White, A.   *Vitamins and Hormones* **7,** 253 (1949).
255a. Wijnans, M.   *Acta Physiol. et Pharmacol. Neerl.* **3,** 199, 214 (1954).
256. Willett, E. L.   *Iowa State College J. Sci.* **28,** 83 (1953).
257. Willett, E. L., McShan, W. H., and Meyer, R. K.   *Proc. Soc. Exptl. Biol. Med.* **79,** 396 (1952).
258. Williams, W. F., and Turner, C. W.   *Proc. Soc. Exptl. Biol. Med.* **85,** 524 (1954).
259. Williams, W. L.   *Anat. Record* **93,** 171 (1945).
260. Wislocki, G. B.   *Anat. Record* **69,** 361 (1937).
261. Wislocki, G. B.   *Research Publ. Assoc. Research Nervous Mental Disease* **17,** 48 (1938).
262. Wislocki, G. B., and King, L. S.   *Am. J. Anat.* **58,** 421 (1936).
262a. Wrenn, T. R., and Sykes, J. F.   *J. Dairy Sci.* **36,** 1313 (1953).
262b. Xuereb, G. P., Prichard, M. M. L., and Daniel, P. M.   *Quart. J. Exptl. Physiol.* **39,** 199, 219 (1954).
263. Yeates, N. T. M.   *J. Agr. Sci.* **39,** 1 (1949).

263a. Yeates, N. T. M.   *In* J. Hammond, Progress in the Physiology of Farm Animals, Butterworth, London, 1954, Vol. 1, Chapter 8.
264. Young, F. G.   *Biochem. J.* **32,** 656 (1938).
265. Young, F. G.   *Brit. Med. Bull.* **5,** 155 (1947).
266. Zarrow, M. X., and Bastian, J. W.   *Proc. Soc. Exptl. Biol. Med.* **84,** 457 (1953).
267. Zavadovskiĭ, M. M.   Hormonal Stimulation of Multifoetation in Sheep.   Moscow [see *Animal Breed. Abstr.* **13,** 179 (1945)].
268. Zubirán, S., and Gómez-Mont, F.   *Vitamins and Hormones* **11,** 97 (1953).
269. Zuckerman, S.   *J. Endocrinol.* **5,** 15P (1947).
270. Zuckerman, S.   *Ciba Colloq. Endocrinol.* **4,** 213 (1952).
271. Zuckerman, S.   *Lancet* **266,** 739, 789 (1954).

CHAPTER IX

Hormones of the Posterior Pituitary

By F. W. LANDGREBE, B. KETTERER, and H. WARING

CONTENTS

I. Introduction

The pituitary gland has a double embryonic origin: an epithelial up-growth (hypophysis) from the stomodeal region unites with a downgrowth from the third ventricle of the brain (infundibulum). The adult derivatives from these two rudiments are shown in the following table.

Embryonic	Adult	
Hypophysis (epithelial)	pars tuberalis pars glandularis pars intermedia	} anterior lobe. } posterior lobe.
Infundibulum (nervous)	pars nervosa	

Fresh or acetone-dried pituitary glands of domestic animals such as ox, pig, sheep, which are the main sources of pituitary material for the manufacture of extracts, are readily divided at the hypophyseal cleft into anterior and posterior lobes, as indicated by the above scheme. Since most of our information results from a study of the pharmacology of such extracts, this scheme has been retained in spite of Zuckerman's (225) physiologically more appropriate definition of the posterior and anterior lobes. The posterior lobe is of both epithelial and neural origin and can be desig-

389

nated a neurointermediate lobe. However, there are exceptions, *e.g.*, in the human pituitary the pars intermedia tissue is found in the anterior lobe and the posterior lobe is purely neural; in the whale, the pars nervosa is clearly separated by a fibrous capsule (76).

Appraisal of the endocrine status of any tissue requires, *inter alia*, information regarding dysfunction evoked by its removal as well as information on the effect of injecting extracts of such a tissue. The surgical removal of the posterior lobe without damage to the anterior lobe is a difficult operation; also, doubt still exists regarding the exact limitation of endocrine function between the posterior lobe and its associated hypothalamic elements. So it is not surprising that we have more unequivocal information about the effect of injections than of extirpations. The injection of unfractionated posterior-lobe extracts from an animal such as the ox shows that the following seven effects are evoked by posterior-lobe excitants: (*1*) Increase in blood pressure after intravenous injection into anesthetized or spinal animals; (*2*) contraction of the mammalian uterus; (*3*) diuresis in mammals; (*4*) antidiuresis in mammals; (*5*) potentiation of water passage in through skin of anura; (*6*) milk let down in mammals; and (*7*) melanophore expansion in lower vertebrates. Many other results of the injection of extracts have been observed, including other effects on the circulation, on smooth muscle, and on carbohydrate, water, and salt metabolism. Those which are well substantiated are set out in Table I of our previous review (218).

Of the seven effects of posterior-lobe extracts mentioned above, the first six are attributed to neural-lobe tissue and the last one to intermediate-lobe tissue. In the present article we shall consider the pars nervosa and the pars intermedia separately, and have confined ourselves to an attempt to bring the material of our previous review up to date.

II. Neural Lobe

A. Seat of Origin of Posterior-Lobe Properties

There is little doubt that the melanophore-expanding ("B") hormone is produced by the intermediate lobe, and it has been generally accepted, though with little evidence, that "B" is released from the intermediate lobe direct into the circulation.

The relationship between the pressor, antidiuretic, and oxytocic properties and the pars nervosa is, however, difficult to establish. There is evidence that all three properties arise from the pars nervosa.

The discovery of gland cells (pituicytes) among the fibers of the pars nervosa has led to work which indicates that these gland cells are the source of activity (216). Similar gland cells have been found in the hypothalamus

(77).   Although the evidence for the pituicyte theory is inconclusive, it is suggestive, *viz.:*

1. The pituicytes are atrophied after nerve section, which results in loss of activity.

2. Gersh (77) described osmophile granules present or absent in pituicytes according to the activity of the tissue.   This was not confirmed by others (101).

3. Wang (215) described granules in the pituicytes the presence of which was also correlated with the presence of activity.

Leveque and Scharrer (138), however, have stated categorically that the Hortega method used by Wang is unsuitable for the study of the cytology of secretion.

More recently, various workers have used chrome-alum hemotoxylin which according to Bargmann (13a) and Leveque and Scharrer (138), selectively stains material invariably associated with vasopressor, antidiuretic, and oxytocic hormones.   In the absence of activities, the gland does not stain; in their presence it stains deeply, but the stainable material is found in the perivascular spaces and not in the pituicytes.   Scharrer concludes that the pituicytes are not the secretory elements but that nerve cells in the hypothalamus produce the material which flows down the nerve tracts and is stored in the pars nervosa.   Additional evidence (14) for this view is that stainable material accumulates where interruptions to the nerve tract are made, and that physiological conditions, such as dehydration, which produce an increased secretion of antidiuretic hormone (ADH) result in a diminution of stainable material within the gland and in the tract. This hypothesis seems to accord well with the facts, but the staining method may not be specific to the activities themselves.   It also stains, for example, the anterior pituitary cells said to be responsible for the secretion of thyrotropic hormone (169).   The Gomori-stainable material can be extracted with an ethyl-alcohol–chloroform mixture, the "hormones" remaining behind (101a).

B. BIOLOGICAL ASSAY

Three responses are in current use for the assay of neural-lobe activities (30).   The first is the rise of blood pressure produced by an extract after *intravenous* injection into a fully anesthetized or spinal animal.   This property of the extract is called its pressor effect.   The second response is the contraction of the isolated uterus of a guinea pig or rat *in vitro*.   This is called the oxytocic action of the extract.   The third is the antidiuretic action of the extract in intact unanesthetized animals.

The accuracy in routine assays is usually about 20 % and this meets the requirements of the British and United States pharmacopoeias. Greater accuracy for research purposes can be obtained by repetitive assays.

1. Assay of Pressor Activity

Several methods have been described for the assay of pressor activity, of which we may note three:

1. Injection of extracts into anesthetized dogs (86, 175).

2. Injection of extracts into spinal cats (105).

3. Injection of extracts into anesthetized rats (130).

2. Assay of Oxytocic Activity

Three methods are in current use for the assay of this activity:

1. Isolated guinea pig uterus (30).

2. Rat uterus. The use of this tissue was first suggested by Holton (107). We have further investigated and improved the details of technique and find it an accurate and reliable method for assay of both whole and fractionated extracts. The method is similar to (*1*), except that the temperature at which the experiment is conducted is preferably 30°C., and the saline used contains less calcium. Careful selection of animals

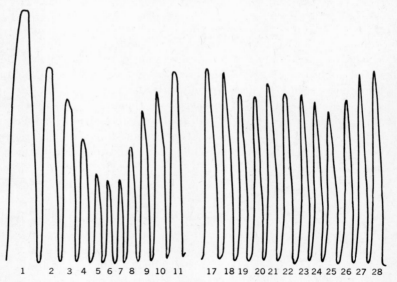

Fig. 1. Assay of oxytocic activity in rat uterus. (*a*) 1—0.1; 2—0.02; 3—0.016; 4—0.012; 5—0.009; 6—0.006; 7—0.006; 8—0.009; 9—0.012; 10—0.016; 11—0.02; (all responses are in I.U.s); (*b*) shows the consistency of responses to a series of equal doses. Responses 19 to 26 inclusive are to the injection of 0.016 I.U., and responses 17, 18, 27, and 28 are to 0.02 I.U. (50 ml. bath).

and the recording of vaginal smears daily prior to the test ensures that the animal is in diestrus when the uterus is excised. This preparation is more accurate and reliable than the guinea pig uterus (Fig. 1). When the fractionated extracts "Pitressin" and "Pitocin" (Parke, Davis) are measured using this and the rat blood pressure method, they are found to contain 4 % of oxytocic and pressor activity, respectively (128), *i.e.*, the results are similar to those obtained with the cat and guinea pig uterus.

3. Avian depressor. This method, developed by Coon (38), depends on the fact that oxytocic activity causes a purely depressor response in .he blood pressure of an anesthetized bird.

3. *Assay of Antidiuretic Activity*

The method first generally used for assay of antidiuretic activity is that of Burn (30). Unanesthetized rats are hydrated by means of a stomach tube, and doses of extract are injected subcutaneously. The delay in diuresis caused by various doses of known and unknown is used as a criterion of potency. Discrimination between doses differing by 20 % can be obtained only with difficulty, and the preparation is not very sensitive. A further criticism of methods using subcutaneous injection is that if the injected extract contains considerable inert material, this might delay absorption of the activity and so give erroneous results. Similar methods have been suggested using hydrated rats (79, 95), dogs (66), or mice (81), but methods based on intravenous injection are advisable. Such methods have recently been suggested by Ginsburg and Heller (80, 99). They assay the antidiuretic activity by intravenous injection of the extract into unanesthetized rats or mice which have previously received two doses of water by stomach tube. Heller (98), using mice, has developed a rapid and very sensitive technique which will detect doses as low as 10 microunits per 10 g. body weight (Fig. 2). Dicker (54) has recently published an even more refined and sensitive technique using the rat under ethanol anesthesia, in which the water load is maintained constant throughout the experiment.

C. Physiology and Pharmacology

When our last review (217) was written, extracts of the posterior pituitary were known to possess a number of different pharmacological properties of which only the antidiuretic activity had been shown with certainty to have physiological significance. Since then our knowledge of the function of the *mammalian* neurohypophysis has been extended to include the control of milk ejection. With other vertebrate classes our knowledge is still at the pharmacological level.

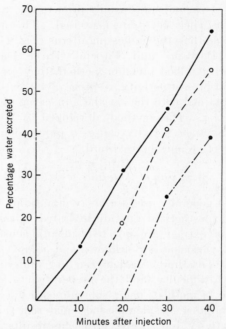

FIG. 2.   Effect of intravenous injections of *vasopressin* on water diuresis of mice. O———O = 12.5 µU. *vasopressin*/10 g. body weight (mean of 12 animals). ●–·–· ● = 25 µU./10 g. (10 animals). ●———● = controls injected with 0.9% NaCl solution (17 animals). Injections given at zero time, immediately after third water load.

1. *Water and Salt Economy*

a. Mammals. The neurohypophysis plays an important part in the maintenance of mammalian water and salt balance. The disease diabetes insipidus, characterized by polyuria and polydipsia, is due to dysfunction of the neurohypophysis and can be corrected by injections of posterior pituitary extracts. Extracts administered in physiological doses to normal animals secreting a moderate volume of urine produce an antidiuresis. This can be obtained with negligible effect on the glomerular filtration rate, showing that the extract acts on the renal tubules (21). Microdissection and microchemical studies indicate that the antidiuretic hormone acts on Henle's loop (222).

Water and salt metabolism appear to be under the influence of at least three endocrine tissues: the anterior pituitary (220, 221), the adrenal cortex (74, 152, 180), and the neurohypophysis.

The anterior lobe is concerned, apart from its adrenocorticotropic activity, since in hypophysectomized animals it is difficult to restore the ability to excrete a normal water load by administering adrenocortical extracts. Boss, Osborn, and Renzi (22a) showed that this was due to a lower glomerular filtration rate after hypophysectomy. Some experiments indicate that this in turn may be due to a lack of "growth hormone," since extracts of the latter restore a normal glomerular filtration rate in hypophysectomized dogs (22, 222) and also cause sodium and potassium retention in hypophysectomized rats (223).

The part played by the adrenal cortex and the neurohypophysis is well illustrated by some recent experiments of Chester Jones (114) on water and salt excretion in adrenalectomized rats with and without diabetes insipidus. Rats with diabetes insipidus had the same food intake as controls and excreted the same total amount of sodium. Adrenalectomized rats could not excrete a water load, lost sodium, and accumulated potassium. When, however, rats with diabetes insipidus were adrenalectomized, the total amount of water consumed dropped to about half its previous level, and the sodium and potassium excretion moved to levels not very different from those of controls. These animals could not deal with a heavy water load. A functional neurohypophysis without adrenal cortices disturbed sodium balance more than the presence of functional adrenal cortices without a neurohypophysis and more than the absence of both. This might mean that the neurohypophysis causes excretion of sodium, but, on the other hand, in rats with diabetes insipidus the sodium balance seems normal.

Evidence that injections of posterior pituitary extracts cause salt uresis is equivocal. Physiological doses of "Pitressin" have no consistent effect on salt uresis in man (34, 149, 150). An increased salt excretion was rarely recorded. Very much larger doses, however, of 3 to 10 I.U. did cause a salt uresis (142, 184). Weston et al. (219) related the onset of salt uresis after continued dosage with large quantities of "Pitressin" to the much expanded extracellular fluid volume resulting from the water retention. Data from other species are also conflicting (179, 183, 192, 219) but suggest that different states of hydration are responsible for the different responses. Thus Anslow et al. (11) found that a chloride uresis and a sodium uresis in dogs occurred in response to injections of pituitary extracts only when they were under water load. Kerpel-Fronius and Vönöczky (118) obtained similar results in the rabbit.

It has been postulated that secretion of the antidiuretic hormone is regulated by osmoreceptors situated somewhere in the carotid vascular bed (207). These receptors respond to supranormal blood concentrations of sodium chloride. Recently, by means of intradural ligation of the carotid network, Verney has located the osmoreceptors in the proencephalon (111a). The connection between the osmoreceptors and the neurohypophysis is

presumably nervous, and it is possible to influence the secretion of the antidiuretic hormone by purely nervous means.   Thus an antidiuresis can be
brought about by (1) strong emotion (207), (2) direct electrical stimulus of
the neurohypophysis (91), and (3) the use of the drugs acetyl choline and
nicotine (29, 214).   Conversely alcohol can cause a diuresis by completely
depressing the secretion of the antidiuretic hormone (203).

Assay methods for antidiuretic activity are now sufficiently sensitive to
measure it in serum and urine.   The concentration in jugular-vein blood
and in the urine following administration of hypertonic saline has been investigated.   About 10 % of the antidiuretic activity of an infused extract
is excreted (7).   The urinary antidiuretic substance is of high molecular
weight, although active substances of small molecular weight can be produced by heat treatment and pressure dialysis (7).   Its activity is destroyed by treatment with thioglycolate.   Because of these properties it
has been compared with the Van Dyke protein and with the active substance of high molecular weight found in certain posterior-lobe extracts.

Although there seems to be considerable evidence that the antidiuretic
activity found in urine and blood samples is of pituitary origin, the presence of antidiuretic activity has been correlated with bacterial contamination.   Krieger, Butler, and Kilvington (124) found that certain strains of
B. coli, found in the urinary tract, thrive in the urine samples and elaborate
antidiuretic substances.   When bacteriostatic conditions were maintained
in the sample, no antidiuretic activity appeared in the urine of dehydrated
rats (123).

b. Other Vertebrates.   Information relating to fish, reptiles, and birds is
scanty.   Fish have not been shown to exhibit an antidiuresis in response
to injections of mammalian pituitary extracts (217).   The fowl responds
with an antidiuresis due to a combination of tubular reabsorption and reduced glomerular flow (217).   The response produced in the crocodile by
these extracts is due solely to reduced glomerular filtration (217).

The function of the neurohypophysis in the water economy of amphibia
has, on the other hand, been quite extensively investigated in recent years.
Amphibia are of particular interest because of the special problems created
by a skin permeable to water.

In 1921 Brunn (27) showed that frogs in contact with water, when injected with posterior lobe pituitary (PLP), increased their water content.
Since frogs do not drink, since submerged frogs do not lose water through
their skin, and since frog kidneys can excrete urine several times faster than
water can be taken up by the skin, we can say that the Brunn effect may
be caused by an increased water intake through the skin and/or a reduced
elimination through the kidneys.   Experiments with ligated kidney ducts

leave no doubt that water can be taken in through the skin (see Barker-Jorgensen (15) for review).

With regard to the effect of pituitary extract on the kidney, a combination of direct observation, injection into the renal portal vein so that the tubes but not the glomeruli are subjected to PLP, and inulin clearance experiments, show that *both* potential sites, *i.e.*, tubes and glomeruli, are affected (15, 178). And in different *Anura* one or other may be differentially affected, *e.g.*, in *Bufo* the tubes are more sensitive than the glomerulus and in *Rana* the reverse is true (15). Although of no physiological significance, we may note in passing that no pituitary diuretic effect has been described in amphibia comparable to that common in anesthetized mammals. On the other hand, unanesthetized artificially water-loaded amphibia exhibit, as do mammals, an antidiuretic response to PLP (124b).

Work and discussion has ranged round the Brunn effect on three counts: (1) Permeability of the skin and locus of the retained fluid, (2) the precise nature of the PLP fraction responsible, and (3) its ecological significance.

(1) *Permeability of the skin and locus of retained fluid.* Stewart (194a) placed frogs in hypotonic and hypertonic sucrose solutions so that the same osmotic gradient resulted—with the gradient leading to water entering the body in the former, and in the reverse sense in the latter. Since in comparable experiments the outflow was four to five times greater than the inflow, it is concluded that the skin shows greater resistance to inflow. Addition of PLP reduced this resistance.

Capraro and Tiengo (33a), using isolated *Rana* skin, showed that PLP increases water passage through skin proportionately more when there is isotonic solution on each side than when the external medium is hypotonic. This suggests that PLP is effective chiefly on active transport of water, and the same conclusion follows from the work of Capraro and Bernini (33) using heavy water. Sawyer (178) has shown that frogs ceased to imbibe water in response to pituitrin from solutions more concentrated than their tissue fluids. It follows that under the influence of pituitary, water cannot be transferred against an osmotic gradient. The action involved is therefore different from the ADH effect on kidney tubules.

Using radio tracer techniques Ussing (201a) has shown that water uptake is correlated with an increased potential difference across the skin and with the intake of sodium ions. Fuhrman and Ussing (72a) showed that PLP increases the electric potential across isolated skin, and using radioactive sodium, showed that after the addition of hormones more work has to be done to transport Na against the electrical force. Using simultaneous measurement of electric potential across the skin and influx and outflux of chloride and sodium ions, Barker-Jorgensen *et al.* (15b) showed with *Bufo* and *Rana* that chloride and sodium can be *actively* taken up and that it is possible to stimulate separately the mechanisms for uptake of sodium and chloride. However, the pituitary role was not studied.

Ewer (64) using *Bufo* showed that there is a significant increase in fluid held in the lymph spaces after injection of PLP. She also showed that fluid can be resorbed from the bladder.

(2) *Precise pituitary excitant responsible.* There is no experimental evidence to show the existence of different excitants acting on the kidneys and skin; the cutaneous effect always follows and overlaps the total kidney effect. Work with a variety of extracts indicates that we are merely dealing with threshold phenomena, the kidney being either more or less sensitive according to the animal and extract used (15, 178).

Up to 1945, work was chiefly done on *Rana temporaria* (Europe) and *Rana pipiens* (America). The chief points emerging from this work were that in terms of the total Brunn effect:

a. "Pitocin" is roughly twice as potent as "Pitressin," but both have a potent effect.

b. Survey of a wide variety of pituitary materials from different species (65a, 96a, 137a) shows quite clearly that the water balance titer does not parallel either the "Pitressin" or "Pitocin" results. Furthermore, those animals which, owing to their environment, might be expected to need "water balance" activity have large amounts of this activity in their pituitaries.

These two kinds of data led Heller (96a) to suggest as one possibility that besides manufacturing pressor and oxytocic substances, the PLP produces a separate "water balance principle" (W.B.P.). No claim has been made to have separated this putative principle from the other two well-established excitants, but in this connection it is interesting to note that crustacean eye-stalk (99a) extract has W.B. effects in amphibia but no antidiuretic effect in mammals.

The alternative to postulating a separate W.B.P. has been put forward by Heller (96) and Barker-Jorgensen (15). In essence their view is that W.B.P. is the phylogenetic precursor of A.D.H. We can elaborate this proposition in this way. Suppose that the posterior lobe produces two chemically similar excitants ("Pitressin" and "Pitocin") which, respectively, have not quite identical configuration in all vertebrate pituitaries. Some plausibility is attributed to this proposition by the demonstration that "Pitressin" from sheep and that from pig have different amino acid contents; the latter has lysine instead of arginine—see Section II, below D. If this general proposition were true and if, in the evolution of function, the physiological *raison d'être* of pituitary was control of water exchange through frog skin, to be replaced later by effect on mammalian Henle's loop (*i.e.*, true antidiuretic effect), then extracts from mammalian pituitary might well contain pituitary excitants which were not a good fit on the amphibian receptors. So in dealing with "near fits," it would not be surprising to find that of the two fractions from the *mammalian* pituitary, in some amphibia one excitant would make a near fit and in other amphibia the other would. In fact, whereas mammalian "Pitocin" is twice as potent as "Pitressin" on *Rana*, the reverse is true for *Bufo* (15, 62a, 63).

The precise role of anterior lobe pituitary (ALP) in antidiuresis is not clear (as with the antidiuretic picture with mammals), but its significance appears to lie in its general metabolic role. Thus Levinsky (138a) showed that ALP reduces water intake to "Pitocin," and Levinsky and Sawyer (138b), besides confirming this, showed that the absence of the ALP was compensated for in some respects by injection of thyroxine.

(*3*) *Ecological significance of Brunn or water balance effect.* The Brunn effect offers obvious potential advantages to an animal living an amphibious existence. Some birds and mammals have adapted to aridity by means of a more impervious skin and a hypertonic urine. Although no amphibian has been described as secreting hypertonic urine, from the point of view of water conservation alone they do even better and exhibit anuria presumably owing to cessation of glomerular filtration (15); this would presumably rapidly have deleterious side effects. But the limiting factor in amphibia is the uncontrolled water loss from the skin in dry situations. Relevant to this, Levinsky and Sawyer (138b) have shown that removal of the pituitary does not affect the rate of dehydration but impedes the rate at which a dehydrated frog regains water; and furthermore the PLP of dehydrated frogs contains less excitant, indicating that the excitant is being used more under conditions of dehydration. With this in mind, and with the observation that some amphibia are clearly more independent of water than others, the significant questions for appraisal of ecological relations are the following: Does permeability of skin vary between species inhabiting dry and wet niches? Is there a difference in general tissue tolerance to desiccation? Do arid species exhibit greater speed of water uptake when presented with water? Unfortunately, too few species have been investigated, but the little information we have is consistent with the view that all amphibia lose water through their skin in dry surroundings at the same rate, but that dry-living forms are able to withstand greater degrees of desiccation and can, when they make contact with water, replace their losses more rapidly (see, for example, ref. 15).

2. *Milk Ejection*

It has long been known that injection of extracts of the posterior pituitary produces a flow of milk from cannulated teats of lactating animals (73, 155).

In the discharge of milk from the mammary glands during suckling the process of "let down" seems to be of major importance and is necessary for the recovery of the full yield of milk (65). This process involves an active reflex response on the part of the mother (39). The view that this maternal reflex process of milk ejection involves the posterior pituitary (61) has recently gained strong experimental support. Electrical stimulation of the infundibular stem in anesthetized lactating rabbits produced ejection of milk from cannulated teats (43), and Andersson (8) obtained milk ejection in unanesthetized sheep and goats in response to stimuli in the vicinity of the supraoptic nucleus. Cross and Harris (44) found in rabbits that stimulation was ineffective after lesions had been made in the anterior median eminence. Such lesions abolished the milk-ejection reflex unless replacement therapy was given in the form of 50/200 milliunits (mU) of posterior pituitary extract. Similarly, removal of the posterior lobe in lactating rats resulted in the litters obtaining little or no milk unless posterior pituitary extract was given to the mother (92). These results seem to establish the physiological role of the neurohypophysis in milk ejection.

There is evidence to suggest that the oxytocic principle is the physiological milk-ejection hormone, though various workers have found that extracts fractionated for their vasopressor activity have more effect than can be accounted for by their contamination with oxytocic activity (160, 200). This pointed to the possibility that the effect was due to a separate principle present in neural-lobe extracts. The recent preparation of the two fractions, *oxytocin* and *vasopressin*, in a state of probable purity has permitted further investigation of this question. Whittlestone (224) found in the lactating sow that 100 I.U. of *vasopressin* had an activity represented by about 20 I.U. *oxytocin*. Cross and Van Dyke (45) showed that the method using the lactating-rabbit mammary gland is more sensitive (3/20 mU) to *oxytocin* than the lactating sow method and consider it to be the best available method for assessing milk-ejection activity. They found that 100 I.U. of *vasopressin* had a milk-ejection activity represented by 17 I.U. *oxytocin*. Cross (42) concludes that the mammary test is not specific for *oxytocin* and favors the view that oxytocic activity is due to the physiological milk-ejection hormone.

D. PURIFICATION AND CHEMISTRY

Two polypeptides have recently been isolated from posterior-lobe material which account for the main pharmacological activities associated with neural-lobe extracts. This does not necessarily mean that under physiological conditions neural-lobe activities exist in this form, and many arguments can be put forward for the concept of a unitary neural-lobe hormone. The present section will be devoted to the isolation and characterization of the fractionated activities; a discussion of the unitary hormone concept will be deferred to a separate section.

1. *Purification*

As early as 1919 Dudley (59) showed that oxytocic activity was more readily extracted by butanol than was pressor activity. The fact that oxytocic activity is in general more soluble in organic solvents than pressor activity was made the basis of a number of the earlier techniques for the fractionation of these activities. In 1928, Kamm and his collaborators (116) devised a separation depending on the solubility of oxytocic activity in a mixture of glacial acetic acid and ether. Stehle and Fraser (193) later developed a method depending on precipitation from methyl alcohol or ethyl alcohol with ethyl acetate. In 1941, Irving, Dyer, and du Vigneaud further purified Kamm's pressor fraction by utilizing the fact that in electrophoresis pressor activity moves towards the cathode six times as fast as oxytocic activity (109). A comparison of the total recovery and the fractionations achieved by these three methods is shown in Table I (summarized from Irving and du Vigneaud (110)).

Potts and Gallagher (168) fractionated pressor and oxytocic activities according to their affinity for a cation-exchange material. Pressor activity was adsorbed in preference to oxytocic activity.

The isolation of the fractionated activities as pure substances was achieved in du Vigneaud's laboratories by the use of a countercurrent distribution machine of the type developed by Craig (40). In 1949 Liver-

TABLE I

YIELDS OF OXYTOCIC AND PRESSOR ACTIVITY OBTAINED FROM EARLY FRACTIONATION
PROCEDURES

Preparation	Potency (International unit/mg.).		Recovery of activity (%).	
	Pressor activity	Oxytocic activity	Pressor activity	Oxytocic activity
Kamm *et al.* (1928)				
Pressor fraction	80	15	16	3
Oxytocic fraction	160	6	1.5	38
Stehle and Fraser (1935)				
Pressor fraction	200	10	40	2
Oxytocic fraction	4	250	0.2	14
Irving *et al.* (1941)				
Pressor fraction	200	26	4	0.5
Oxytocic fraction	22	146	5	34

more and du Vigneaud (140), using this technique, prepared an oxytocic fraction which gave the distribution curve of a pure substance in the solvent system in which it was isolated. Its probable purity was supported by an amino acid analysis (162, 163) in which eight amino acids occurred in approximately equimolecular proportions. Livermore and du Vigneaud used Parke-Davis' "Pitocin" as starting material, but in later work (163) beef posterior lobes were used as a source. The crude extract was treated according to a modified Kamm procedure in order to obtain the partial purification necessary for countercurrent distribution. Both the solvent systems 2-butanol:0.05 % acetic acid (partition coefficient of oxytocic activity 0.4) and 2-butanol:0.01M ammonium hydroxide (partition coefficient 1.8) were used successfully, but the former was preferred. It is curious that the first pure preparations were estimated to contain over 800 units per milligram, whereas subsequent preparations contained only 500 units per milligram, even in one case after a 1000-transfer distribution was performed (161). The discrepancy is probably due to errors in assay technique.

This highly purified material had milk-ejecting activity equivalent to its oxytocic activity (45, 224). Less than 0.5 I.U. per milligram of antidiuretic activity was found and no pressor activity could be detected by the cat blood pressure method.

Oxytocic activity purified in this way is called *oxytocin* and has been characterized as a crystalline flavianate. Doubly refractile needles with a melting point 190° to 200°C. and containing 29.5 % to 31.7 % flavianate were obtained. The potency of the *oxytocin* flavianate corresponded to its *oxytocin* content (161).

In the case of pressor activity the solvent system n-butanol:0.1 M p-toluenesulfonic acid was suitable for countercurrent distribution after preliminary fractionation of beef posterior-lobe extracts. An apparently pure substance with a pressor potency of 400 to 500 I.U. per milligram was obtained on countercurrent distribution (201). The pure substance is called *vasopressin*. Though identical *oxytocin* was prepared from beef and hog pituitaries, beef *vasopressin* and hog *vasopressin* were not identical. The partition coefficient of hog material in the solvent system n-butanol:0.09 M p-toluene-sulfonic acid was 0.66, whereas that from ox material was 1.25. This was later shown to be due to a different amino acid composition. The most potent hog vasopressin obtained had a potency of only 175 I.U. per milligram, but the authors suggest that a certain amount of inactivation took place (164).

Vasopressin was similarly potent in I.U. per milligram whether assayed for antidiuretic or for pressor activity. This indicates that these activities are due to the same chemical substance. However, *vasopressin* does exhibit a low degree of oxytocic activity when tested by the accepted methods of assay. This oxytocic activity seems to be intrinsic in *vasopressin*. For each 100 units of pressor-antidiuretic activity, *vasopressin* possessed oxytocic activity represented by approximately 5 I.U. when estimated by the isolated rat uterus method or by 13 to 15 I.U. when determined by the chicken blood-pressure method (165). Whittlestone also found that *vasopressin* contained milk-ejecting activity equivalent to about 8 I.U. of oxytocin (224).

In 1953 Maier-Hüser *et al.* (141) described a new method for partially purifying oxytocic activity preliminary to countercurrent distribution. An innovation in this method was the use of a silica adsorbent. Both pressor and oxytocic activities were adsorbed to silica from a dilute acetic acid (0.3 %) extract in the cold, but oxytocic activity was selectively eluted by hot dilute acetic acid (0.5 %). Both the adsorption and the elution were performed in the one day. This oxytocic fraction was further purified by extraction from aqueous solution with *n*-butanol and then further extracted from butanol-octanol solution with 0.1 % acetic acid. The potency, degree of fractionation, and yield attained by this method were comparable with those achieved by the procedure of Kamm *et al.* (116)

Fromageot *et al.* (72) recently published a procedure for recovering the pressor activity remaining on the silica adsorbent and purifying it by a new method to 450 to 500 I.U. per milligram. The silica was packed into a column and washed with an eluent containing 25 g. of anhydrous sodium sulfate, 0.02 g. of trimethylcetylammonium bromide, and 1 ml. of glacial acetic acid per liter. Pressor activity was removed from this eluate by adsorption on to salicylic acid. The salicylic acid was dissolved in ether and the mixture extracted with distilled water. This active aqueous solution was then freeze-dried and subjected to a 24-transfer countercurrent distribution between water and *n*-butanol containing 10 mg. of salicylic acid per milliliter. A qualitative amino acid analysis indicated that this procedure produced a substance identical with the *vasopressin*.

2. Chemical Analysis

When du Vigneaud and his collaborators isolated *oxytocin* and *vasopressin* as pure substances a complete analysis was possible. Pierce and du Vigneaud (162) examined a hydrolyzate of *oxytocin* for amino acids. The eight amino acids: leucine, isoleucine, tyrosine, proline, glutamic acid, aspartic acid, glycine, and cystine and also ammonia were detected. With the exception of tyrosine and cystine, which gave low values, the amino acids occurred in equimolecular proportions. The molar ratio of ammonia to the amino acids was 3.46. In a subsequent study (163) the precaution was taken of hydrolyzing (with 6 N HCl at 132°C. for 16 hours) under an atmosphere of nitrogen. Under these conditions the molar ratios of cystine and tyrosine to the other amino acids was nearer 1 and the molar ratio of ammonia to any amino acid was a closer approximation to 3. The earlier anomalies were apparently artifacts of hydrolysis.

An elementary analysis was also performed. Correcting for moisture content (9.65 %) the following figures were obtained: C 50.12 %, H 6.84 %, N 16.12 %, S 6.15 %, and ash 0.11 %. These figures are very close to what would be obtained with a hypothetical molecule composed of 1 mole each of the above amino acids together with 3 moles of ammonia, i.e., C 50.4 %, H 6.68 %, N 16.4 %, and S 6.2 %.

In a similar fashion Turner et al. (201) analyzed vasopressin (prepared from beef posterior lobes) for amino acids and ammonia. In this case the eight amino acids phenylalanine, tyrosine, proline, glutamic acid, aspartic acid, glycine, arginine, and cystine were found to occur in equimolecular proportions. Ammonia was present in a molar ratio of 3:1 to any one amino acid. Thus six of the amino acids which occur in oxytocin also occur in vasopressin. However, whereas oxytocin contains leucine and isoleucine, vasopressin contains phenylalanine and arginine. The examination of chromatograms of hydrolyzates of pressor material for a peak in the isoleucine-leucine position should be a fairly sensitive chemical method for detecting contamination with oxytocin. It should be possible to detect 0.7 % contamination by this method (this represents about 3.5 I.U. per milligram oxytocic activity).

The amino acid spectrum of hog vasopressin differed from that of beef vasopressin in that arginine was replaced by lysine (164). Oxytocin of bovine and porcine origin was, however, identical in composition, in potency, and in the melting point of the flavianate (161).

These figures for amino acid analysis have been confirmed by Acher and Chauvet (3) and by Tuppy (199).

3. Physicochemical Data

a. Molecular Weights. The preparation of pure oxytocin and vasopressin, the determination of the structures of these substances by degradation studies, and finally the proof of these structures by synthesis (209, 211) has permitted the exact determination of minimum molecular weights. Thus the values for oxytocin, beef vasopressin, and hog vasopressin are 1007, 1084, and 1056, respectively. Pierce and du Vigneaud (163) had previously published preliminary determinations of the molecular weight of oxytocin by a thermoelectric osmometer method. Values of 928 and 802 were obtained, indicating that oxytocin occurs as an octapeptide monomer.

b. Electrophoretic Properties. Mobility studies were performed on oxytocin over a wide pH range by Kunkel et al. (126). The filter paper electrophoresis method of Kunkel and Tiselius (127) was used. From these results *oxytocin* was shown to have an isoelectric point of pH 7.7.   For this determination, monovalent buffers were used.   In polyvalent buffers, however, it was indicated that the isoelectric point would be higher and the value of pH 8.5 suggested by the preliminary work of Cohn *et al.* (36) was arrived at from mobility determinations carried out in polyvalent buffers.   Taylor *et al.* (196) used similar methods to determine the iso-electric point of *vasopressin* and obtained a value of pH 10.9.

By using starch and glass bead supporting media (125) sufficient material could be handled for the examination of the migration of biological activity (126, 196).   When *vasopressin* (completely free of the substance *oxytocin*) was examined in this way, the pressor peak exhibited some oxyto-cic activity.   When equal quantities of *oxytocin* and *vasopressin* were mixed and subjected to electrophoresis, a single peak of pressor activity was found, but there were two peaks of oxytocic activity: a large one corresponding to *oxytocin* and a small one corresponding to *vasopressin*.   This is addi-tional evidence that *vasopressin* has intrinsic oxytocic activity, *i.e.*, the methods for assay of oxytocic activity are not specific for *oxytocin*.

4. *Structure and Synthesis of Oxytocin and Vasopressin*

Within four years of the isolation of *oxytocin* as a pure substance, the structures of the octapeptide amides *oxytocin* and *vasopressin* had been de-duced from degradative studies and proved by synthesis.   The chief credit for this great achievement is due to du Vigneaud and his collaborators. Fromageot's school in Paris and Tuppy in Vienna have independently ar-rived at the same structural formulas for *vasopressin* and *oxytocin*, respec-tively.

In polypeptides not containing cystine the amino acid residues may be arranged in either a simple unbranched chain or a simple ring structure. Cystine has two α-amino groups and so may form up to four peptide bonds instead of the usual one or two.   If more than one α-amino group is in-volved, the following polypeptide structural forms are also possible:

1. The cystine may be involved in a ring structure which may itself be either (*a*) at the end of a straight chain, bearing a free α-amino group or a free carboxyl group (or amide); (*b*) within a straight-chain structure, or (*c*) within a simple polypeptide ring.

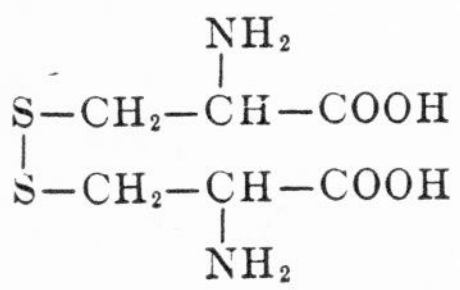

$$NH_2$$
$$|$$
$$S-CH_2-CH-COOH$$
$$|$$
$$S-CH_2-CH-COOH$$
$$|$$
$$NH_2$$

FIG. 3.   Cystine.

2. The cystine may be involved in a branched-chain structure, linking two chains together as in the case of insulin.

To determine the structure of a complex molecule, it is broken into smaller determinable components. Ideally, the experiments should be such that only one hypothetical structure will account for all the degradation products produced. Final proof of such a structure can be obtained only by synthesis.

As a first step Mueller *et al.* (147) studied the effect of breaking the cystine disulfide bond of *oxytocin* by oxidation with performic acid. This treatment is known to convert the amino acid residue of cystine to two cysteic acid residues. Neither free cysteic acid nor free cysteic acid amide could be detected after this treatment, indicating that both halves of the cystine residue are in a peptide chain. Countercurrent distribution and paper chromatography showed that *oxytocin* oxidized by performic acid contained only one significant component. This component had the same amino acid composition as *oxytocin* except that the cystine had disappeared and cysteic acid was now present in a molar ratio of 2. Thus no fragmentation of the polypeptide had occurred, indicating that cystine was not involved in a branched-chain structure but in a ring structure. Similarly, breakage of the cystine disulfide bond by desulfurization in the presence of a Raney nickel catalyst produced a substance which could not be fractionated (51). After desulfurization the cystine residue of *oxytocin* was replaced by two alanine residues, but otherwise the amino acid composition remained unchanged.

Oxytocin could be fragmented by the action of bromine, which reacts with oxytocin, before or after oxidation with performic acid, to give two readily separable components (149). One component proved to be a dipeptide composed of cysteic acid and 3,5-dibromotyrosine and the other a heptapeptide of composition (Asp, CySO₃H, Glu, Gly, Ileu, Leu, Pro)[1] (171).

Davoll *et al.* (51) tested for free amino groups in *oxytocin* and desulfurized *oxytocin* by Sanger's technique (176) whereby the action of dinitrofluorobenzene (DNFB) produces *N*-dinitrophenyl derivatives (N-DNP) of those residues which bear free amino groups. Levy's test (139), which converts amino acids with a free amino group to *N*-dithiocarboxy derivatives by the action of carbon disulfide, was also used on *oxytocin*. Both DNFB and carbon disulfide also react with the phenolic hydroxyl group of tyrosine. After DNFB treatment of *oxytocin* followed by hydrolysis, only *O*,*N*-*bis*-DNP tyrosine and *N*-DNP tyrosine could be recognized in the ethyl-

---

[1] This notation was devised by Brand and Edsall (26).

acetate–soluble fraction, although a third substance which was not identified was also present. O-DNP tyrosine but no free tyrosine was found in the water-soluble fraction, and the cystine content was low. Similarly after treating *oxytocin* with carbon disulfide followed by acidification to set free any substituted amino acid residues, the quantities of free tyrosine and cystine in the water-soluble fraction were much reduced. In the case of desulfurized *oxytocin*, DNFB treatment reduced the free tyrosine and free alanine content of hydrolyzates and produced N-DNP tyrosine, O-DNP tyrosine, O,N-*bis*-DNP tyrosine, and DNP alanine. The results of these experiments implied that both cystine and tyrosine might bear free α-amino groups. However, when Ressler, Trippett, and du Vigneaud (171) made DNP derivatives of *oxytocin* which had been oxidized by performic acid, DNP cysteic acid and only O-DNP tyrosine occurred in hydrolyzates DNP derivatives of the dipeptide and heptapeptide fragments resulting from the action of bromine on performic-acid–oxidized *oxytocin* were also produced. The DNP derivative of the dipeptide was composed of DNP cysteic acid and O-DNP 3,5-dibromo tyrosine. Thus there is no evidence from this later work that the tyrosine has a free amino group. N- or O,N-*bis*-DNP tyrosine were never detected. It was found that if the hydrolyzate of DNP *oxytocin* was analyzed without being extracted with ethyl acetate, O-DNP tyrosine could be recovered in molar ratios as high as 0.71. So the tyrosine residue in *oxytocin* probably does not possess a free amino group. The presence of N-DNP derivatives of tyrosine would be accounted for by fragmentations and side reactions during DNFB treatment. Thus it was concluded that the dipeptide fragment was $CySO_3H$ .Tyr. Synthetic $CySO_3H$.Tyr and its isomer Tyr.$CySO_3H$ gave the expected DNP derivatives, indicating that inversions do not occur during DNFB treatment, and the properties of $CySO_3H$.Tyr. and the dipeptide fragment were parallel. Consequently, unless rearrangements occur during performic acid treatment, *oxytocin* has the sequence cystinyl-tyrosine, and the cystine residue has a free amino group, α to its peptide bond with tyrosine. DNP isoleucine was recovered from hydrolyzates of the DNFB-treated heptapeptide fragment, indicating that bromine splits a tyrosyl isoleucine link in *oxytocin*.

Finally, by studying peptides in partial hydrolyzates of *oxytocin*, desulfurized *oxytocin*, and the DNP derivative of the heptapeptide fragment, du Vigneaud, Ressler, and Trippett (210) were able to propose a structure for *oxytocin*.

The heptapeptide fragment was useful for the following reasons: (*1*) It contained only one cysteic acid residue, and this was not the residue the linkages of which have been accounted for by Ressler *et al.* (171); (*2*)

TABLE II

PEPTIDES FROM A PARTIAL HYDROLYSATE OF OXYTOCIN (210)

	Peptide	Origin of peptide
1	Asp.CySO₃H	DNP heptapeptide
2	(Asp, Ala)	Desulfurized oxytocin
3	CySO₃H.Pro	DNP heptapeptide
4	(CySO₃H,Pro,Leu)	DNP heptapeptide
5	(CySO₃H,Pro,Leu,Gly)	DNP heptapeptide
6	(CySO₃H,Asp,Glu)	Oxytocin, partial hydrolyzate subsequently treated with bromine
7	(Tyr,CyS-SCy,Asp,Glu)	Oxytocin
8	(Ala,Asp,Glu,Leu or Ileu)	Desulfurized oxytocin
9	(Tyr,CyS-SCy,Asp,Glu,Leu or Ileu)	Oxytocin

In this table where the sequence is known, the amino acids are separated by periods, and where unknown, by commas.

DNP-isoleucine and a number of DNP-isoleucyl-peptides could be removed by extraction with ethyl acetate, leaving in the aqueous phase peptides farther from the isoleucine end of the heptapeptide; (3) a special solvent system to distinguish between leucine and isoleucine was not required, since the latter occurred as the DNP-derivative. Table II shows the significant peptides found in these hydrolyzates.

The sequences in peptides 1 and 3 were determined by making DNP derivatives. On the assumption that no rearrangement took place during oxidation or desulfurization, the peptides show that *oxytocin* has the sequence:

$$\text{Ileu.Glu.Asp.Cys.Pro.Leu.Gly.}$$
$$|$$
$$\text{(Cys.Tyr.)}$$

Ressler *et al.* (171) have shown that the dipeptide fragment has the sequence CySO₃H.Tyr, and that when this is split off, the remaining heptapeptide fragment has a free amino group on the isoleucine residue. This suggests a link between tyrosine and isoleucine, but a peptide containing isoleucine and tyrosine was never recovered from partial hydrolyzates. That such a link does occur, however, was demonstrated when performic-acid–oxidized *oxytocin* was subjected to an Edman degradation (60), when cysteic acid, tyrosine, and isoleucine were removed in sequence. Thus the amino acid structure of *oxytocin* is:

$$\text{CyS.Tyr.Ileu.Glu.Asp.CyS.Pro.Leu.Gly.}$$

It is assumed that the amino acids have the L-configuration.

This formula does not account for the 3 moles of ammonia per mole of *oxytocin* which are liberated on hydrolysis. It was assumed that aspartic and glutamic acids occurred as the amides asparagine and glutamine, respectively. That glycine occurs as glycinamide was deduced from the following evidence: (*1*) *Oxytocin* is not attacked by carboxypeptidase; (*2*) the thiohydantoin method for carboxyl end group determination does not affect *oxytocin*; (*3*) if *oxytocin* is heated between 90° and 100°C. for 1 hour, 1 mole of ammonia is released; if then the thiohydantoin method is applied, glycine is released; (*4*) *oxytocin* has an isoelectric point of pH 7.7, which is consistent with the ionization of the amino group and the tyrosine-phenolic group, but which would not be expected if a carboxyl group were also capable of ionization.

Du Vigneaud *et al.* (211, 211a) synthesized an octapeptide of this proposed structure and found it was active in the chicken blood pressure and rat uterus tests and that it was also active in causing milk ejection and bringing about labor in the human female. The product was purified by counter-current distribution and the activity was found to be concentrated in a single peak. Material from the peak tube was indistinguishable in biological potency with the best preparations of natural *oxytocin*. They were also identical in specific rotation, melting point, and crystalline form of the active flavianate, in partition coefficients in 2-butanol/acetic acid and 2-butanol/ammonia, and in electrophoretic mobilities at pH 4.6 and pH 10.7.

The procedure of the synthesis (see Fig. 4) was governed by the lability of the cystine disulfide bond and the relative instability of the peptide bond between tyrosine and isoleucine. Thus *oxytocin* was finally produced from the protected, benzyl nonapeptide amide *N*-carbobenzoxy-*S*-benzyl-cysteinyl-isoleucyl glutaminyl-asparagyl-*S*-benzyl-cysteinyl-prolyl-leucyl-glycinamide by debenzylation and aeration. The benzylation freed the amino group and the two thiol groups, and the aeration oxidized the two thiol groups to form a disulfide bond, and hence the pentapeptide ring of *oxytocin*.

The tosyl tripeptide amide (I) was synthesized by a novel method. Tosyl-glutamic acid was treated with phosphorus pentachloride to give 1-tosylpyrrolid-5-one-2-carboxyl chloride. This was coupled with asparagine and the reslting *N*-(1'-tosylpyrrolid-5'-one-2'-carbonyl)-asparagine was treated with aqueous ammonia, yielding tosyl-glutaminyl-asparagine. The tosyl group was removed and the dipeptide amide coupled with tosyl-isoleucyl chloride, thus giving the tripeptide amide (I). The preparation of the tetrapeptide amide (II) is as follows. Ethylleucylglycinate was condensed with carbobenzoxyproline by the isovaleryl mixed anhydride procedure of Vaughan and Osato (206). The product was reduced

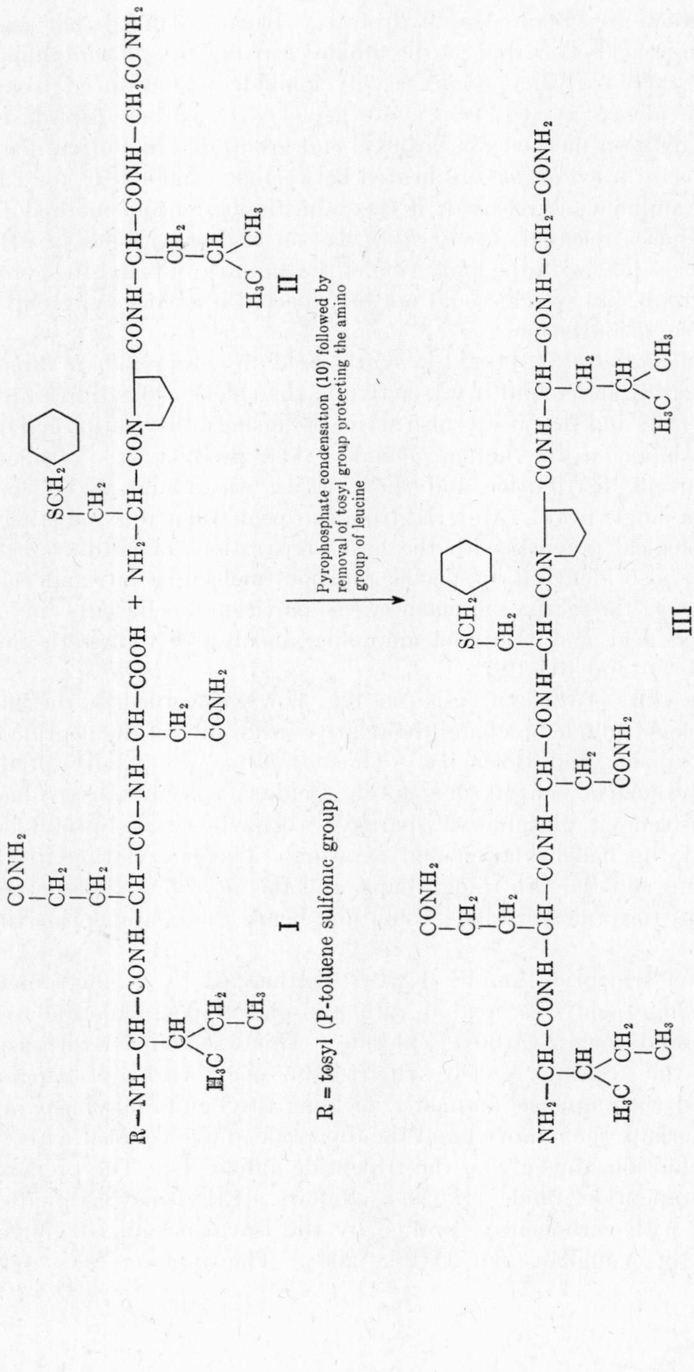

FIG. 4. Synthesis of *oxytocin*.

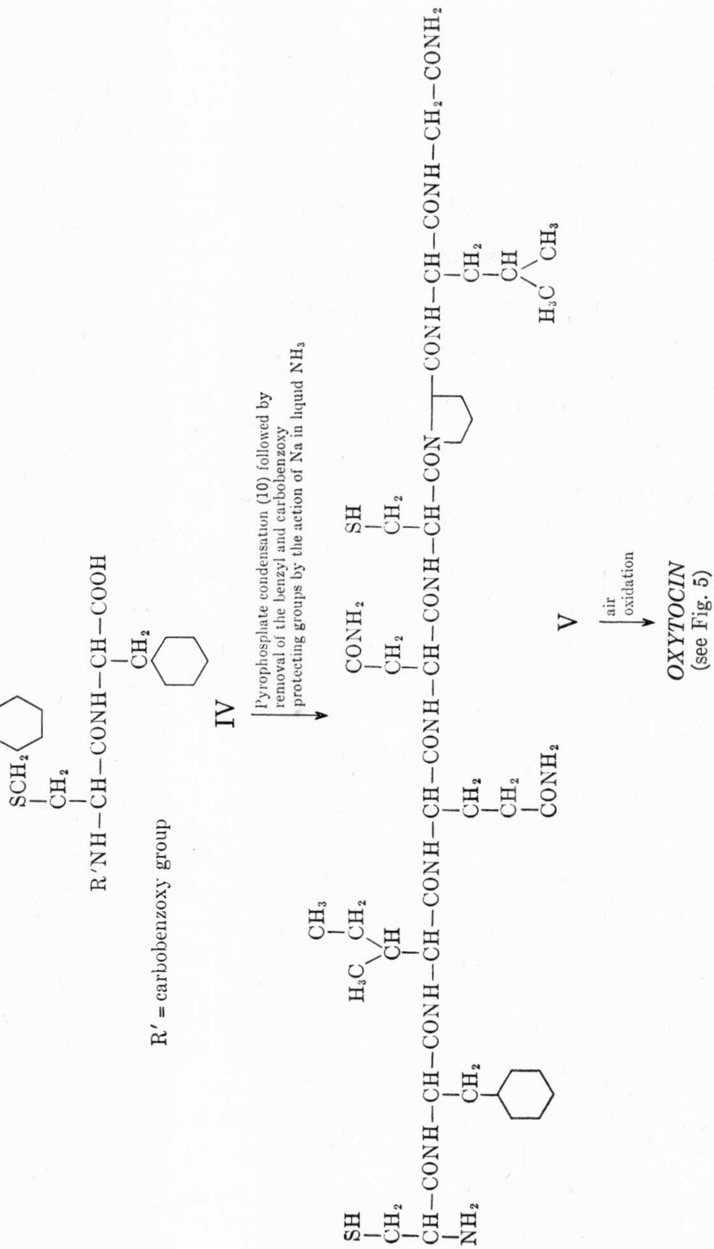

Fig. 4. Synthesis of *oxytocin*.

catalytically and then coupled with *bis*-di-carbobenzoxycystinyl *bis*-dichloride. The saponified product was reduced and benzylated in liquid ammonia to give *S*-benzyl cysteinyl-prolyl-leucyl-glycine. Esterification to the corresponding benzyl ester hydrochloride and then treatment with methanolic ammonia gave the tetrapeptide amide (II).

A structure for *oxytocin* was first proposed by Tuppy (199), forestalling by a month du Vigneaud and his colleagues, who did not publish the formula of *oxytocin* until it had been proved by synthesis. Tuppy's proposed structure was based on the following evidence. Performic-acid–oxidized *oxytocin* was partially hydrolyzed with acid and also digested with the proteolytic enzyme from *Bacillus subtilis*. The following peptides were discovered in the acid hydrolyzate $CySO_3H.Tyr$; $Ileu.Glu$; $Asp.CySO_3H$; $CySO_3H.(Pro, Leu)$, and $Leu.Gly$. The enzymic digest was fractionated in a four-compartment electrophoresis cell. The acidic fraction contained the two main peptides $CySO_3H.(Tyr, Ileu, Gly)$ and $Asp.(CySO_3H, Pro, Leu)$. The *N*-terminal residues in these derivatives were determined by making DNP-derivatives. The basic fraction from the enzymic digest contained material which reacted with ninhydrin to give a yellow color and yielded only glycine on hydrolysis. Its behavior on a chromatogram was indistinguishable from that of glycinamide. The peptides from the acidic hydrolyzate establish the sequences $CySO_3H.Tyr.Ileu.Glu.$ and $Asp.CySO_3H.Pro.Leu$ in the two tetrapeptides isolated from the enzymic digest. Tuppy put forward the following structure for performic-acid–oxidized *oxytocin*:

$$CySO_3H.Tyr.Ileu.Glu(NH_2).Asp(NH_2).CySO_3H.Pro.Leu.Gly(NH_2)$$

This necessitated the following assumptions: (*1*) that glutamic and aspartic acids occurred as the amides which, together with glycinamide, accounted for the 3 moles of ammonia which are released by the hydrolysis of 1 mole of *oxytocin*; (*2*) that $CySO_3H.Tyr.Ileu$ is an *N*-terminal sequence; this had already been demonstrated by Mueller *et al.* (148); (*3*) that a glutamyl-aspartyl linkage occurs even though peptides containing both glutamic and aspartic acid were never isolated.

Assuming that the two cysteic residues of performic-acid–oxidized *oxytocin* arise from the oxidative breaking of a single cystine residue, *oxytocin* then has the structure:

$$CyS.Tyr.Ileu.Glu(NH_2)Asp(NH_2)CyS.Pro.Leu.Gly(NH_2)$$

The results of this elegant study are in complete accordance with the findings of du Vigneaud's school.

   b. Vasopressin. Degradative studies of beef *vasopressin* were conducted on lines similar to those for *oxytocin*. Thus Popenoe and du Vigneaud (166) found that performic-acid treatment broke the cystine disulfide bond of *vasopressin*, producing two cysteic acid residues, without causing a fragmentation. From DNP derivatives it was found that *vasopressin* and performic-acid–oxidized *vasopressin* had a free amino group on the cystine residue and a free amino group on a cysteic acid residue, respectively, while in both substances the tyrosine-phenolic group was free to act with DNFB. Like *oxytocin*, *vasopressin* and performic-acid–oxidized *vasopressin* were fragmented by the action of bromine. However, only one product, having the composition Phe.(Glu,Asp,CySO$_3$H,Pro,Arg,Gly), could be isolated. This corresponds to the heptapeptide fragment Ileu.(Glu,Asp,CySO$_3$H, Pro,Leu,Gly) from similar treatment of *oxytocin*. However, the complementary fragment CySO$_3$H.Tyr could not be recovered from bromine-treated *vasopressin*. That CySO$_3$H.Tyr is the *N*-terminal sequence in performic-acid–oxidized *vasopressin* was clearly shown by an Edman degradation. The phenylalanine residue of the heptapeptide has a free amino group, indicating that bromine breaks a tyrosyl-phenylalanine linkage. Popenoe and du Vigneaud (167) subjected performic-acid–oxidized *vasopressin* to partial hydrolysis, and the significant peptides obtained are shown in Table III. Peptide 1 confirms the sequence CySO$_3$H.Tyr.Phe which is suggested by the above work. The amino and the carboxylic acid groups of one of the cysteic acid residues of performic-acid–oxidized *vasopressin* are now accounted for. Peptide 2 shows that the carboxyl end of the other cysteic acid residue is linked to the peptide (Pro,Arg,Gly), and consequently according to peptide 3 its amino end must be linked to aspartic. Peptides 4, 5, and 6 then show that performic-acid–oxidized *vasopressin* must have the sequence:

CySO$_3$H.Tyr.Phe.Glu.Asp.CySO$_3$H.(Pro,Arg,Gly)

No peptides were found in these acid hydrolyzates which threw light on the (Pro,Arg,Gly) grouping. The *C*-terminal sequence was clarified by

TABLE III

PEPTIDES FROM A PARTIAL HYDROLYSATE OF VASOPRESSIN (167)

Peptide
1   (CySO$_3$H,Tyr,Phe)
2   CySO$_3$H.(Pro,Arg,Gly)
3   (Asp,CySO$_3$H)
4   (Glu,Asp,CySO$_3$H)
5   (Phe,Glu,Asp)
6   (Glu,Asp,CySO$_3$H,Pro,Arg,Gly)

du Vigneaud, Lawler, and Popenoe (210) who found that the action of trypsin on *vasopressin* produced two fractions separable by paper chromatography. One of these fractions behaved as glycinamide and gave glycine on hydrolysis. The other fraction contained the other seven amino acids. Since Neurath and Schwert (151) have shown that only those bonds involving the carboxyl group of arginine and lysine are affected by trypsin, the liberation of glycinamide from *vasopressin* indicates the *C*-terminal sequence arginylglycinamide. In support of this, when glycinamide is split off from *vasopressin* and incubated with arginase, some urea is produced, whereas arginase has no effect on the intact hormone. Thus du Vigneaud *et al.* were able to propose the following structure for *vasopressin*:

$$\text{CyS.Tyr.Phe.Glu(NH}_2\text{).Asp(NH}_2\text{).CyS.Pro.Arg.Gly(NH}_2\text{)}$$

Du Vigneaud *et al.* (209) suggested that hog *vasopressin* has the same structure as beef *vasopressin* except that lysine replaces arginine. This was proved when a substance of the formula proposed for hog *vasopressin* was synthesized and shown to be active in the pressor-antidiuretic assay. The procedure of the synthesis was identical with that for *oxytocin* except that ε-tosyl-lysine replaced leucine and phenylalanine replaced isoleucine. Subsequently a synthetic bovine *vasopressin* with the expected biological properties was prepared (208). In this synthesis, however, some of the intermediates were prepared by new methods.

The formula for beef *vasopressin* was confirmed by Acher and Chauvet (3) from independent degradative studies. *Vasopressin* prepared by the method of Fromageot *et al.* (72) was the starting point. Performic acid oxidation did not fragment *vasopressin* but converted the cystine residue to two cysteic acid residues, one of which was *N*-terminal. Tryptic digestion of performic-acid–oxidized *vasopressin* liberated glycinamide which, occurring as the amide, consequently occupied the *C*-terminal position. In a partial acid hydrolyzate of performic-acid–oxidized *vasopressin* the following peptides were identified: $\text{CySO}_3\text{H.Tyr}$; Phe.Glu; Glu, Asp; $\text{Asp.CySO}_3\text{H}$; CySO_3H.(Pro, Arg); Pro.Arg. and Pro.Arg.Gly. These indicate the sequences: $\text{CySO}_3\text{H.Tyr}$; $\text{Phe.Glu.Asp.CySO}_3\text{H}$, and $\text{CySO}_3\text{H.Pro.Arg.Gly}$. Since it has been shown that glycine is *C*-terminal, the $\text{CySO}_3\text{H.Tyr}$. must be *N*-terminal. Thus, assuming that glutamic acid and aspartic acid occur as the amides, this evidence permitted the proposal of the following structure for beef *vasopressin*:

$$\text{CyS.Tyr.Phe.Glu(NH}_2\text{)Asp(NH}_2\text{).CyS.Pro.Arg.Gly(NH}_2\text{)}.$$

This is in full agreement with the findings of du Vigneaud and associates.

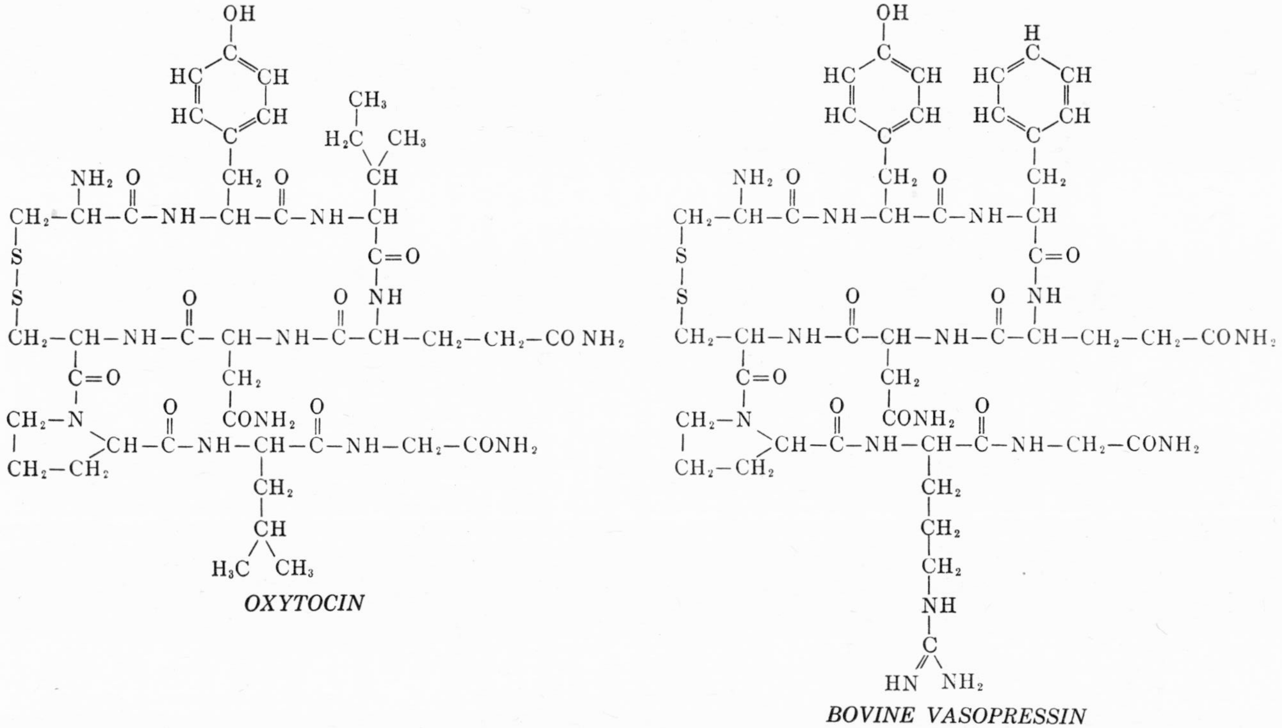

FIG. 5.   *Oxytocin and bovine vasopressin.*

E. ONE- AND MULTI-HORMONE HYPOTHESES

Although the octapeptides *oxytocin* and *vasopressin* account for the main pharmacological actions of neural lobe extracts, there is a certain amount of evidence that the neural-lobe activities are not elaborated and secreted in the form of these polypeptides.

Biological activity in press juice from fresh pituitaries is associated with material which sediments rapidly in the ultracentrifuge (85, 174) and which does not dialyze, but these properties are not shown in extracts made in the usual way by boiling in dilute acetic acid.

These phenomena may simply be due to chance adsorption, of no physiological significance, of the small molecular *oxytocin* and *vasopressin* to inert substances. However, the concept of a large labile molecule with all neural-lobe activities has been current since it was first proposed by Abel in 1920 and could explain these phenomena.

In 1942, by using mild conditions, van Dyke *et al.* (204) isolated a purified protein from beef posterior lobes which he suggested might be the unitary hormone. It possessed oxytocic, pressor, and antidiuretic activities in the same proportions in which they occur in the gland and its potency was 17 I.U. per milligram. Its molecular weight was about 30,000, and its isoelectric point was at pH 4.8. An elementary analysis was performed, and in 1950 van Dyke and Block (205) published a complete amino acid analysis. A hypothetical molecule of molecular weight 30,000 and containing one molecule each of *oxytocin* and of *vasopressin* would have a similar biological potency. If the activities are, in fact, present in the gland in this form, it would account for about 12 % of the dry weight of the gland. This is hardly likely if the pituicyte theory is correct, but is feasible if the Scharrer hypothesis is true (see p. 391). Unfortunately, tests for purity were not exhaustive, and there was evidence of electrophoretic inhomogeneity. The stability of the biological activity of the protein differed strikingly from that of the fractionated activities by being inactivated by cysteine.

The biological evidence which bears on this problem must be interpreted with caution. Dicker and Tyler (57) showed that the ratio of pressor to oxytocic activity might be as high as 44 to 1 in pituitaries of fetuses and young animals and that this ratio increased with age. They also showed that the oxytocic content of the pituitary was reduced independently of the pressor activity during parturition and lactation, particularly during lactation.

Thus on the basis of these findings, if a protein such as that of van Dyke *et al.* (204) is elaborated by the pituitary, the different activities can be secreted separately.

If a unitary hormone were secreted into the blood stream, one stimulus might bring about all responses. Peeters *et al.* (159) found that the stimulus of milking provoked an antidiuresis in lactating cows, and Cross (41) found an antidiuresis when hydrated rabbits suckle their young. The intracarotid injection of hypertonic saline caused milk ejection in the goat (9) and increased uterine motility in the dog. Coitus resulted in milk ejection in human beings (93) and antidiuresis in the human being and rat (62). However, Cross found that whereas the milk-ejecting response in rabbits could be mimicked by 50 to 200 mU of "Pitocin," the antidiuresis was mimicked by only 0.5 to 1.0 mU of "Pitressin." The simplest interpretation of this is that a unitary hormone containing equal amounts of pressor and oxytocic activities does not circulate. However, one needs to be particularly cautious in a case like this where the action of the hormone at two different target organs is compared with that of pharmacological extracts. It is possible that a target organ might deal with the hormone and with the corresponding activity in a pharmacological extract quite differently.

Thus no definite conclusions can yet be drawn as to whether or not oxytocic–milk-ejecting and pressor-antidiuretic activities occur in the one molecule in physiological conditions. It is possible that a single substance is elaborated but that separate activities are released.

III. Intermediate Lobe

A. Seat of Origin of Melanophore-Expanding Hormone

Of the various excitants previously mentioned as present in whole extracts of ox or pig posterior lobes, we have yet to discuss melanophore-expanding activity ("B"). With the pituitaries of domestic animals, the intermediate lobe cannot be dissected free from the other lobes for the routine manufacture of extracts. This lobe is associated with the posterior lobe on dissection of the whole gland, and there is enough evidence to leave no doubt that "B" is produced by the intermediate lobe. This is summarized in our previous review (217), and new evidence has been obtained to further substantiate this view (144). In animals such as the human, however, where the intermediate-lobe cells have migrated into the anterior lobe, "B", as would be expected, is associated with anterior-lobe extracts. The presence of large amounts of the activity in certain other anterior-lobe extracts can be explained by careless dissection, contamination, or diffusion of activity between death and dissection (186). Only a trace of "B" is found in ox anterior lobes carefully dissected within a few minutes of death of the donor (128).

Since all the methods used to assay "intermediate-lobe extracts" use this property of melanophore expansion in amphibia or fish, the latter response has for most become a definition of intermediate-lobe *hormone*. It is possible (217) that the intermediate lobe secretes more than one activity, since a number of properties have been ascribed to extracts rich in melanophore-expanding activity. Nevertheless, for the present, we too have used melanophore-expanding activity to designate intermediate-lobe extracts.

B. BIOLOGICAL ASSAY

In our last review (217) we recommended the use of *Xenopus laevis* for the assay of this activity. The melanophore-expanding activity is measured by microscopic determination of melanophore expansion, using five arbitrary stages denoted numerically 1 to 5 (104) for recording purposes. This method has been described in detail, together with a criticism of other methods, by Landgrebe and Waring (137).

Since then, other methods have been devised. One of the main criticisms of the method of Landgrebe and Waring is the subjective nature of the reading of the melanophore index. In 1952 Thing (197), however, confirmed the reliability of this subjective assessment by comparing the results with those obtained simultaneously on the same animals by an objective photoelectric method. He measured changes in reflectance from a defined portion of the skin brought about by melanophore expansion. Thing found that this photoelectric method was no more reliable or precise than the use of the melanophore index of Hogben and Gordon (104) but was technically more difficult.

Ketterer and Remilton (120) applied standard statistical methods to this method of assay and found that in spite of the arbitrary melanophore index, the regression of response on logarithm of the dose is approximately linear. In a typical crossover assay using groups of six animals, 95% fiducial limits of prediction potency were calculated by Irwin's method (111). With responses expanding the melanophores to an approximate mean position between contraction and expansion (m.i. = 3), which is the response aimed at for accurate assay, it was calculated that the true potency might be expected to lie between 0.92 P and 1.09 P, where P is the calculated dose in micrograms corresponding to a fixed response.

Whereas Landgrebe and Waring found that test animals used only occasionally, but meanwhile kept on an illuminated white background, gradually increased in sensitivity over a period of six months, Ketterer and Remilton found that if the test animals were in daily use for periods up to four months, consistent responses were obtained to the same dose. However, after a long period this advantage is offset by increasing variance obtained in the response, and it is suggested that the animals be rested with

feeding, on a black background, every two or three months if they are in
continuous use.

Of the other methods recently suggested for the assay of this activity,
most have used photoelectric methods of recording *in vitro* preparations.
Rigler and Holzbauer's (173) *in vitro* method is very sensitive; however,
the criticisms we have previously made of such methods are still valid, and
the suggested subjective method still remains the most satisfactory.

C. Physiology and Pharmacology

Only the melanophore-excitant activity of intermediate-lobe extracts has
so far been shown to have a physiological role in the intact animal (106,
157, 216).   The role of "B" in chromatic physiology has been extensively
investigated, and a brief discussion of the work is included in our previous
review (217).   There are two main difficulties in assessing the physiological
significance of the intermediate lobe.   One is that the pars intermedia alone
cannot be removed surgically from experimental animals; thus any dysfunction which might be evoked by its removal cannot be studied.   The
other difficulty is that no reliable assay method has yet been devised which
is sensitive enough to measure the melanophore-dispersing activity present
in mammalian blood and urine.

Many workers (52, 145) have used the melanophore expansion obtained
in amphibia after the injection of urine, first suggested by Konsuloff (122),
as a test for pregnancy.   Our own work, however, suggests that the slight
(Melanophore Index—less than 3) melanophore expansion obtained with
some urines is not due to "B," and Hobson (103) (Table IV) has found
no correlation between results obtained with the Hogben (129) and the
Konsuloff pregnancy tests providing that none of the latter tests was considered positive unless the urine raised the melanophore index of *Xenopus*
from 1 to 3 or more.

In view of the difficulty of measuring the activity in blood and tissue

TABLE IV

PARALLEL PREGNANCY TESTS USING HOGBEN AND KONSULOFF METHODS

Urine samples.	Hogben		Konsuloff	
	−ve	+ve	−ve	+ve
Nonpregnant	53	0	49	4
Pregnant	0	51	51	0
Total	53	51	100	4

fluids, almost all our information is derived from the results of injection of extracts. Of the pharmacological activities of these extracts, other than melanophore-expanding activities, those concerned with dark adaptation, carbohydrate metabolism, and melanin synthesis are under investigation in many laboratories.

Jores (115) believed that "B" played some part in night vision and claimed that nocturnal animals have more "B" in their pituitary than diurnal ones and that the amount increased on dark adaptation. In view of the close association of melanophore-expanding activity and the eye in lower animals, this is a very interesting concept. Jores assumed that the function of the hormone was to act as a catalyst for the regeneration of visual purple, and he claimed that local application of the hormone to the human eye reduced the time of dark adaptation from about 50 to about 11 minutes. This was, however, re-examined by Buschke (31), who obtained entirely negative results. It was only recently that further systematic investigations were carried out on this problem.

Hanaoka found that extracts of "B" accelerated the *in vivo* (87) and *in vitro* (88) regeneration of visual purple in the Japanese toad. He also claimed that injection of a purified extract of melanophore-expanding activity subcutaneously in man shortens the time of dark adaptation and also considerably increases sensitivity.

Figure 6 (89) shows Hanaoka's results on the effect of "B" on dark adap-

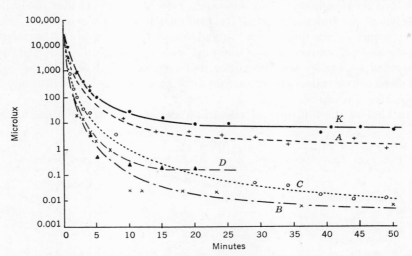

FIG. 6. The effect of subcutaneous injection of 200 I.U. of melanophore expanding activity on dark adaptation and light sensitivity in man (89). Curve *A*: 35 sec. after injection. Curve *B*: 2 min. 0.7 sec. after injection. Curve *C*: 5 min. 55 sec. after injection. Curve *D*: 8 min. 10 sec. after injection. Curve *K*: control, before injection.

tation and light sensitivity in man at various intervals of time after the subcutaneous injection of 200 I.U.   This work can easily be criticized but deserves repetition.

Of the various effects on carbohydrate metabolism attributed to "B"-containing extracts, it would appear that "B" itself is not responsible for any direct effect on blood sugar or for an antagonistic effect to injected insulin.   It is still doubtful whether "B" is responsible for Collip's (37, 53) specific metabolic effect.   Though our earlier extracts were capable of antagonizing the hyperglycemic action of adrenaline, this property seems somewhat doubtful in the more recently purified extracts (p. 422) obtained from pig material (131).   Recent *in vitro* work, though, does lend some credence to the view that "B" may play some part in carbohydrate metabolism.   Bradley *et al.* (25) found that a highly purified extract of "B" from pig material (p. 422) was the most active (1.25 μg. per milliliter) extract tested in increasing the respiratory exchange of mammary tissue *in vitro*. This effect might be due to an increased respiratory quotient resulting from accelerated lipogenesis or to an increase in the rate of glycolysis.

Bullough (28) has investigated the effects of "B"-containing extracts on the epidermal mitotic rate *in vitro* and has evidence that these extracts stimulate mitosis by facilitation of the glucokinase reaction.   It would seem that the extracts do not stimulate any other step in the course of energy production from glucose in these experiments.

There is strong evidence for the participation of "B" in melanin synthesis in the skin of amphibia, but this role of the activity in mammals is not so certain (217).

The correlation between pituitary-adrenal-cortex function and skin pigmentation is not clear, but the increase in melanin sometimes found after ACTH therapy (84) may be partly or wholly due to the "B" content of most of the commercially available ACTH extracts (see p. 425).

D.   PURIFICATION AND CHEMISTRY

Stehle (187) in 1936, and later, Landgrebe *et al.* (135) suggested methods to prepare potent extracts of this activity.   More recently, Landgrebe and Mitchell (131) have described a method yielding a much more potent extract than before.   Since pig glands have been shown to be five times as potent as ox glands in "B" (136), dried pig posterior-lobe powder was used as starting material.   Some workers have deliberately destroyed pressor and oxytocic contamination by alkaline treatment, but since this treatment changes the character of the "B" (134), it was avoided.   The method allows recovery of pressor and oxytocic activity.   A high yield of "B" is obtained in a final product many times more potent than any previously described and virtually free of oxytocic and pressor activities.

In view of the close chemical similarity of "ACTH" and "B" (see p. 424), we purified the latter using modifications of techniques already suggested for ACTH (12).

Dried pig posterior-lobe powder is extracted with glacial acetic acid at 50°C. for 5 minutes. After centrifuging, the active principle is precipitated with ether and the precipitate dried and dissolved in dilute acetic acid. The activity is then adsorbed on powdered oxycellulose and eluted with dilute hydrochloric acid. This is then adjusted to pH 6.5 with ammonium hydroxide and centrifuged and 5 volumes of acetone are added to the supernatant. The resulting precipitate is dried, and contains about 25% of the original activity. This final product is 500 times as potent as the International Standard ox posterior-lobe powder, if good original material is used. The final potency depends upon that of the original material, which itself can vary from 3 to 10 I.U. per milligram. If good ox material assaying nearly 2 I.U. per milligram is used as initial material, this same method will produce an extract containing about 200 I.U. per milligram. Hence either the product obtained by this method from pig material is more highly purified or the "polypeptide" obtainable from pig glands is different from that from ox pituitaries and is 5 times as potent. If this is true, the fact that Stehle has prepared an extract from ox material containing 300 I.U. per milligram (191) would indicate that our final preparation from pig material is by no means pure. Further evidence for the possible difference between the ox and the pig "polypeptides" is obtained from the results of caustic soda treatment (131). This results in 80% destruction of the activity, whereas with ox material the potency is doubled. It may be that in all extracts "B" itself is destroyed by such treatment and that a hypothetical substance "B.1" (134), which shares with "B" the ability to expand the melanophores of test animals, is produced from a precursor by such treatment. Further evidence to support this possibility has been obtained by Ketterer and Remilton (120) who found that simple precipitation of a crude ox extract with acetone produced material which was not potentiated by alkali from an extract that originally was capable of potentiation. This might be explained if the precursor of "B.1" is not precipitated with acetone under these conditions. If, however, this concept is accepted, the results of caustic soda treatment of our highly purified pig material produce no evidence for the nonidentity of pig and ox melanophore-expanding polypeptides. The results could be explained by the loss of the "B.1" precursor in the more highly purified pig extracts. The increased potency of some "B"-containing extracts after alkali treatment has been investigated by a number of other workers (e.g., 35, 189), and is interesting from another point of view (see p. 424).

Investigations are proceeding on the chemistry of this purified extract from pig posterior lobes. Little is yet known other than that a preparation containing 500 I.U. per milligram contains the following amino acids: alanine, aspartic, glycine, glutamic, leucine, lysine, proline, tryptophan, tyrosine, and valine (132). These include all the amino acids found in any quantity by Benfey (17) in Stehle's highly purified material made from ox glands; thus as yet no evidence is provided for the possible difference between the two polypeptides.

Stehle (190) suggested that purified extracts of this type can be assayed by their tryptophan content (since this amino acid is not present in the other hormones of the posterior lobe). Our own extracts were therefore measured by Stehle's modification (190) of the method of May and Rose (143), and we used tryptophan itself as a standard. Comparison of the tryptophan content of an extract assaying 500 I.U. per milligram and one assaying 950 I.U. per milligram shows about 10 % and about 15 % tryptophan, respectively, but we have insufficient confidence in the method to draw definite conclusions regarding the validity of Stehle's stuggestion.

We previously found the "B" activity in a simple ox posterior-lobe extract had an isoelectric point in the region of pH 4.1 (217). Ketterer and Kirk (119), using filter paper electrophoresis technique, found the isoelectric point of the bulk of the "B" activity in a number of different preparations to be in the neighborhood of pH 4.8. Rigler and Holzbauer (173), on the other hand, produced evidence suggesting that "B" activity has a basic isoelectric point. Ketterer and Kirk's electrophoretic patterns indicated a diversity of "B" active substances with different mobilities, none of which, however, moved towards the cathode at pH 7.2. A similar diversity of "B" active substances on electrophoresis was also observed by Thing (198). Chromatographic experiments on our purified extract from pig material, however, yield no evidence that more than one substance is involved (132).

E. SEPARATE IDENTITY OF "B" AND ACTH

When the source of origin of "B" and the adrenal ascorbic-acid–depleting (AAD) property of "ACTH" extracts is considered, it is surprising that the separate identity of the two activities was ever in question. Nevertheless, many workers have suggested that these two activities are due to one and the same substance (112, 195). These claims were largely initiated by the fact that most commercial extracts of "ACTH" contain large amounts of "B," owing to the fact that these extracts are made from whole pituitary glands or from badly dissected glands or, less likely, from pig anterior lobes into which pars intermedia cells have migrated. Recent work indicates this possibility in some varieties of pig as in the human being (128).

It is clear, though, that in the preparation of extracts, "B" activity behaves chemically very much like AAD activity. Morris (146), however, and Reinhardt *et al.* (170) have produced evidence that these two activities can reside in different molecular entities. The latter workers found that the AAD activity in one of their preparations was destroyed by heating in alkali, whereas its "B" activity was increased. Care must be taken in drawing conclusions from this type of work, since some "B" preparations, *e.g.*, those from pig and certain ox extracts (131, 135), are in fact destroyed by the usual treatment with alkali.

Landgrebe and Morris (133) used the method of purification suggested for "B" on carefully dissected and collected posterior lobes and also on the corresponding anterior lobes, and assayed the final products for both melanophore expanding activity and for AAD activity. The extract from the posterior lobe was found to contain 950 I.U. per milligram of "B" and 3 I.U. per milligram of AAD, while that from the anterior lobe was found to contain 6 I.U. per milligram of AAD and 100 I.U. per milligram of "B". The amount of "B" found in these anterior lobe extracts is small when the potency of the posterior lobe extract is considered. The amount of AAD in the posterior lobe extract, however, might indicate that a certain amount of AAD activity is intrinsic in the "B" polypeptide or that some AAD activity is elaborated in the posterior lobe. This is being further investigated, and to date, a single observation indicates that it is unlikely: these extracts have been purified by electrophoresis and a product obtained which seems to be homogeneous in the ultracentrifuge (134A) and which contains about 1500 I.U. "B" per milligram and less than 0.2 I.U. AAD per milligram (133).

The effect of the usual caustic soda treatment on these purified preparations from both anterior and posterior lobes of the pig pituitary is also interesting. The melanophore expanding activity of material obtained from the posterior lobe is destroyed (131), whereas the purified anterior lobe extract is of similar potency after treatment and shows the usual prolonged response (132). It may be, therefore, that while the hypothetical substance "B.1" may be present in the *posterior* lobe of the ox, it is not present in the posterior lobe of the pig but may be present in the anterior lobe of the pig pituitary.

Mialhe-Voloss (144), with crude extracts of ox anterior and posterior lobes found, using the Pincus maintenance test for the measurement of corticotropic activity, that both posterior and anterior lobes were similarly potent and that melanophore-expanding activity was much higher in the posterior-lobe extracts. Other workers, *e.g.*, Reinhardt *et al.* (170), have been able partially to fractionate AAD and "B" from extracts containing both activities, so that it would appear that AAD and "B" are not identical but that the polypeptide responsible for "B" activity may have intrinsic AAD activity.

TABLE V

ASSAYS OF "B" AND AAD WITH COMMERCIAL "ACTH" EXTRACTS

"ACTH" extract	"B" I.U./mg.	Potentiation	F.I.	B.1 = nt I.U./mg.	AAD I.U./mg.
$8/9$	2.6	×3	0.8	7.8	2.5
$11/12$	2.1	×0.25	2.0	0.5	0.3
$18/19$	2.0	×2.5	0.8	5.0	1.0
$26/29$	4.3	×2		8.6	1.29
Int. Std.	0.35	×4	3.7	1.4	1.0

Assays of "B" and AAD with a number of commercial[2] ACTH extracts (128) do not show parallelism. Results of a few such assays are shown in Table V.

It is interesting to speculate on the hypothesis that there is a precursor in pituitary extracts which, on caustic soda treatment, is converted into B.1 (see p.   ). It might be that this precursor is part or the whole of the molecule of ACTH (218). If this is so, alkaline treatment of our ACTH extracts and subsequent assay for "B" and AAD might show better parallelism. This is in fact so, but the results are not sufficiently parallel to substantiate the hypothesis (see Table V). It is rather interesting, however (since all the extracts recorded are made from whole pig pituitaries), that, except in one case, No. 11/12, where the AAD potency was very low, the extracts all show potentiation after treatment. This we have found not to occur with either crude or purified pig posterior-lobe extracts; thus it does seem possible that this potentiation is a property of the anterior-lobe material and that B.1, if it exists, emanates from the anterior lobe in the pig.

REFERENCES

1. Abel, J. J., and Nagayama, T. *J. Pharmacol.* **15**, 347 (1920).
2. Abrahams, V. C., and Pickford, M. *J. Physiol.* **122**, 56P (1953).
3. Acher, R., and Chauvet, J. *Biochim. et Biophys. Acta.* **12**, 487 (1953).
4. Adolph, E. F. *Am. J. Physiol.* **117**, 366 (1936).
5. Ames, R. G., and Van Dyke, H. B. *Proc. Soc. Exptl. Biol. Med.* **75**, 417 (1950).
6. Ames, R. G., and Van Dyke, H. B. *Endocrinology* **50**, 350 (1952).
7. Ames, R. G., Moore, D. H., and Van Dyke, H. B. *Endocrinology* **46**, 215 (1950).
8. Andersson, B. *Acta Physiol. Scand.* **23**, 1 (1951).
9. Andersson, B. *Acta Physiol. Scand.* **23**, 8 (1951).
10. Anderson, G. W., Blodinger, J., and Welcher, A. D. *J. Am. Chem. Soc.* **74**, 5309 (1952).
11. Anslow, W. P., Jr., Wesson, L. G., Jr., Balomey, A. A., and Taylor, J. G. *Federation Proc.* **7**, 3 (1948).

---

[2] Our best thanks are due to Dr. Tindall of Organon Limited for supplying these various extracts.

12. Astwood, E. B., Raben, M. S., Payne, R. W., and Grady, A. B. *J. Am. Chem. Soc.* **73,** 2969 (1951).

13. Astwood, E. B., Raben, M. S., and Payne, R. W. *Recent Progr. Hormone Research* **7,** 1 (1952).

13a. Bargmann, W. *Z. Zellforsch.* **34,** 610 (1949).

14. Bargmann, W., and Scharrer, E. *Am. Scientist* **39,** 255 (1951).

15. Barker-Jorgensen, C. *Acta Physiol. Scand.* **22,** Suppl., 78 (1950).

15a. Barker-Jorgensen, C. *Acta Physiol. Scand.* **30,** 171-177 Fasc. 2–3 (1954).

15b. Barker-Jorgensen, C., Levi, H., and Zerahn, K. *Acta Physiol. Scand.* **30,** 178-190 Fasc. 2–3 (1954).

16. Belehradek, J., and Huxley, J. S. *Brit. J. Exptl. Biol.* **5,** 89 (1927).

17. Benfey, B. G. *Brit. J. Pharmacol.* **8,** 435 (1953).

18. Biassotti, A. *Compt. rend. soc. biol.* **86,** 361 (1923).

19. Birnie, J. H., Eversole, W. J., Boss, W. R., Osborn, C. M., and Gaunt, R. *Endocrinology* **47,** 1 (1950).

20. Birnie, J. H., Jenkins, R., Eversole, W. J., and Gaunt, R. *Proc. Soc. Exptl. Biol. Med.* **20,** 83 (1949).

21. Bjering, T. *Arch. exptl. Pathol. Pharmakol.* **176,** 255 (1934).

22. De Bodo, R. C., Schwarz, I. L., Greenberg, J., Hurtz, N., Earle, D. P., Jr., and Farber, S. J. *Proc. Soc. Exptl. Biol. Med.* **76,** 612 (1951).

22a. Boss, W. R., Osborn, C. M., Renzi, A. A. *Endocrinology* **50,** 66 (1952).

23. Boylston, G. A., and Ivy, A. C. *Proc. Soc. Exptl. Biol. Med.* **38,** 644 (1938).

24. Boyd, E. M., and Brown, M. *Am. J. Physiol.* **122,** 191 (1938).

25. Bradley, T. R., Folley, S. J., Landgrebe, F. W., and Mitchell, G. M. *Biochim. et Biophys. Acta* **13,** 449 (1954).

26. Brand, E., and Edsall, J. T. *Ann. Rev. Biochem.* **16,** 224 (1947).

27. Brunn, F. *Z. ges. exptl. Med.* **25,** 170 (1921).

28. Bullough, W. S. Personal communication.

29. Burn, G. P., and Singh, G. R. *Brit. J. Pharmacol.* **6,** 471 (1951).

30. Burn, J. H., Finney, D. J., and Goodwin, L. G. Biological Standardisation. Oxford Univ. Press, London, 1950.

31. Buschke, W. *Klin. Wochschr.* **13,** 1785 (1934).

32. Buxton, P. A. Animal Life in Deserts. Longmans, London, 1923.

33. Capraro, V., and Bernini, G. *Nature* **169,** 454 (1952).

33a. Capraro, V., and Tiengo, M. *Arch. sci. biol.* (*Bologna*) **36,** 308 (1952).

34. Chalmers, T. M., Lewis, A. A. G., and Pawan, G. L. S. *J. Physiol.* **112,** 238 (1951).

35. Chen, G., and Geiling, E. M. K. *J. Pharmacol.* **78,** 222 (1943).

36. Cohn, M., Irving, G. W., Jr., and du Vigneaud, V. *J. Biol. Chem.* **137,** 635 (1941).

37. Collip, J. B. *Am. J. Physiol.* **119,** 381 (1937).

38. Coon, J. M. *Arch. intern. pharmacodynamie* **62,** 79 (1939).

39. Cowie, A. T., Folley, S. J., Cross, B. A., Harris, G. W., Jacobsohn, D., and Richardson, K. C. *Nature* **168,** 421 (1951).

40. Craig, L. C. *J. Biol. Chem.* **155,** 519 (1944).

41. Cross, B. A. *Nature* **166,** 612 (1950).

42. Cross, B. A. *J. Endocrinol.* **9,** ix (1953).

43. Cross, B. A., and Harris, G. W. *Nature* **166,** 994 (1950).

44. Cross, B. A., and Harris, G. W. *J. Endocrinol.* **8,** 148 (1952).

45. Cross, B. A., and van Dyke, H. B. *J. Endocrinol.* **9,** 232 (1953).

46. Croxatto, H., Barnafi, L., Rojas, G., Reyes, A., and Infanti, A. *Nature* **171,** 82 (1953).

47. Croxatto, H., Rojas, G., and Barnafi, L. *Science* **113**, 494 (1951).
48. Dale, H. H. *Biochem. J.* **4**, 427 (1909).
49. Dale, H. H., and Dudley, H. W. *J. Pharmacol.* **18**, 27 (1921).
50. Das, N., Chash, B. W., and Guha, B. C. *J. Pharmacol.* **18**, 27 (1921).
51. Davoll, H., Turner, R. A., Pierce, J. G., and du Vigneaud, V. *J. Biol. Chem.* **193**, 363 (1951).
52. De Bourgraaf, J. F., and Dingemanse, E. *Ned. Tijdschr. Geneesk.* **90** (No. 42) (1946).
53. Derrick, J. B., and Collip, J. B. *Can. J. Research* **E31** (No. 2) 117, 125 (1953).
54. Dicker, S. E. *J. Physiol.* **122**, 149 (1953).
55. Dicker, S. E., and Ginsburg, M. *Brit. J. Pharmacol. Chem. Therap.* **5**, 497 (1950).
56. Dicker, S. E., and Tyler, C. *J. Physiol.* **120**, 141 (1953).
57. Dicker, S. E., and Tyler, C. *J. Physiol.* **121**, 206 (1953).
58. Dow, C., and Zuckerman, S. *J. Endocrinol.* **1**, 387 (1939).
59. Dudley, H. W. *J. Pharmacol.* **14**, 295 (1919).
60. Edman, P. *Acta Chem. Scand.* **4**, 283.
61. Ely, F., and Petersen, W. E. *J. Dairy Sci.* **24**, 211 (1941)
62. Eranko, O., Friberg, O., Karvonnen, M. J. *Acta Endocrinol.* **12**, 197 (1953).
62a. Ewer, R. F. *J. Exptl. Biol.* **27**, 40 (1950).
63. Ewer, R. F. *J. Exptl. Biol.* **28**, 374 (1951).
64. Ewer, R. F. *J. Exptl. Biol.* **29**, 429 (1952).
65. Folley, S. J. *Brit. Med. Bull.* **5**, 142 (1947).
65a. Fontaine, M., and Raffy, A. *Compt. rend. soc. biol.* **114** (1-2) 6 (1950).
66. Fraser, A. M. *J. Physiol.* **100**, 233 (1941).
67. Fraser, A. M. *Rev. can. biol.* **9**, 54 (1950).
68. Freeman, M., Gulland, F. N., and Randall, S. S. *Biochem. J.* **29**, 2208 (1935).
69. Freudenberg, K., and Biller, H. *Naturwissenschaften* **24**, 523 (1936).
70. Freudenberg, K., Weiss, E., and Biller, H. *Z. physiol. Chem.* **233**, 172 (1935).
71. Friberg, O. *Acta Endocrinol.* **12**, 193 (1953).
72. Fromageot, P., Acher, R., Clauser, H., and Maier-Hüser, H. *Biochim. et Biophys. Acta* **12**, 424 (1953).
72a. Fuhrman, F. A., and Ussing, H. H. *J. Cellular Comp. Physiol.* **38** (No. 1) 109 (1951).
73. Gaines, W. L. *Am. J. Physiol.* **38**, 285 (1915).
74. Gaunt, R., Birnie, J. H., and Eversole, W. J. *Physiol. Revs.* **29**, 281 (1949).
75. Geiling, E. M. K. *Bull. Johns Hopkins Hosp.* **57**, 123 (1935).
76. Geiling, E. M. K., and Oldham, F. K. *J. Am. Med. Assoc.* **116**, 302 (1941).
77. Gersh, I. *Am. J. Anat.* **64**, 407 (1939).
78. Gilman, A., and Goodman, L. *J. Physiol.* **90**, 113 (1937).
79. Ginsburg, M. *J. Pharmacol.* **6**, 411, (1951).
80. Ginsburg, M., and Heller, H. *J. Endocrinol.* **9**, 267 (1953).
81. Glaubach, S., and Molitor, H. *Arch. exptl. Pathol. u. Pharmakol.* **166**, 243 (1932).
82. Gulland, F. N., and Randall, S. S. *Biochem. J.* **29**, 378 (1935).
83. Gulland, F. N., and Randall, S. S. *Chemistry & Industry*, p. 422 (1936).
84. Hall, T. C., McCracken, B. H., and Thom, G. W. *J. Clin. Endocrinol.* **13** (No. 3) 243 (1953).
85. Ham, G. C., and Rosenfeld, M. *Bull. Johns Hopkins Hosp.* **71**, 18 (1942).
86. Hamilton, H. C., and Rowe, L. W. *J. Lab. Clin. Med.* **2**, 120 (1916).
87. Hanaoka, T. *Ann. zool. japon.* **24**, 137 (1951).

88. Hanaoka, T. *Nature* **172**, 866 (1953).
89. Hanaoka, T. *Japan. J. Physiol.* **2**, 9 (1951).
90. Hare, K., Hickey, R. C., and Hare, R. S. *Am. J. Physiol.* **134**, 240 (1941).
91. Harris, G. W. *J. Physiol.* **107**, 430 (1948).
92. Harris, G. W., and Jacobsohn, D. *Proc. Roy. Soc. (London)* **B139**, 265 (1952).
93. Harris, G. W., and Pickles, V. R. *Nature* **172**, 1049 (1953).
94. Heller, H. *Arch. Exptl. Pathol. Pharmacol.* **157**, 298 (1930).
95. Heller, H. *J. Physiol.* **99**, 246 (1941).
96. Heller, H. *J. Physiol.* **100**, 125 (1941).
96a. Heller, H. *Biol. Revs.* **20**, 147 (1945).
97. Heller, H. *Experientia* **6**, 368 (1950).
98. Heller, H. *J. Endocrinol.* **8**, 227 (1952).
99. Heller, H., and Blackmore, K. E. *J. Endocrinol.* **8**, 224 (1952).
99a. Heller, H., and Smith, B. *J. Exptl. Biol.* **25**, 388 (1948).
100. Heller, H., and Urban, F. F. *J. Physiol.* **85**, 502 (1935).
101. Hickey, R. C., Hare, K., and Hare, R. S. *Anat. Record* **81**, 319 (1941).
101a. Hild, W., and Zetler, G. *Z. ges. exptl. Med.* **120**, 236 (1953).
102. Hill, A. V., Parkinson, J. L., and Solandt, D. Y. *J. Exptl. Biol.* **12**, 397 (1935).
103. Hobson, B. M. Unpublished.
103a. Hogben, L. Comparative Physiology of Internal Secretions. Macmillan, New York, 1927.
104. Hogben, L., and Gordon, C. *J. Exptl. Biol.* **7**, 286 (1930).
105. Hogben, L., Schlapp, W., and MacDonald, A. D. *Quart. J. Exptl. Physiol.* **14**, 301 (1924).
106. Hogben, L. *Proc. Roy. Soc. (London)* **B131**, 111 (1942).
107. Holton, P. *Brit. J. Pharmacol.* **3**, 328 (1948).
108. Ingram, W. R., Ladd, L., and Benbow, J. T. *Am. J. Physiol.* **127**, 544 (1939).
109. Irving, G. W., Jr., Dyer, H. M., and du Vigneaud, V. *J. Am. Chem. Soc.* **63**, 503 (1941).
110. Irving, G. W., Jr., and du Vigneaud, V. *Ann. N. Y. Acad. Sci.* **43**, 273 (1943).
111. Irwin, J. O. *J. Hyg.* **43**, 121 (1943).
111a. Jewell, P. A., and Verney, E. B. *J. Endocrinol.* **9**, Proc., ii (1953).
112. Johnson, S., and Hogberg, B. *Nature* **169**, 286 (1952).
113. Jones, A. M., and Schlapp, W. *J. Physiol.* **87**, 144 (1936).
114. Jones, I. C. *J. Endocrinol.* **9**, Proc. xxxviii (1953).
115. Jores, A., and Hotop, H. *Z. vergl. Physiol.* **20**, 699 (1934).
116. Kamm, O., Aldrich, T. B., Grote, I. W., Rowe, L. W., and Bugbee, E. P. *J. Am. Chem. Soc.* **50**, 573 (1928).
117. Kamm, O., Grote, I. W., and Rowe, L. W. *J. Biol. Chem.* **92**, Proc. lxix (1931).
118. Kerpel-Fronius, E., and Vönöczky, J. *Z. Vitamin-, Hormon- u. Fermentforsch.* **4**, 149, (1951).
119. Ketterer, B., and Kirk, R. L. *J. Endocrinol.* **11**, 19 (1954).
120. Ketterer, B., and Remilton, E. *J. Endocrinol.* **11**, 7 (1954).
121. Ketterer, B., and Remilton, E. *J. Endocrinol.* **11**, 14 (1954).
122. Konsuloff, S. *Klin. Wochschr.* **13**, 776 (1934).
123. Krieger, V. I., and Kilvington, T. B. *Australian J. Exptl. Biol. Med. Sci.* **29**, 77 (1951).
124. Krieger, V. I., Butler, H. M., and Kilvington, T. B. *J. Obstet. Gynaecol. Brit. Empire* **58**, 5 (1951).
124a. Krough, A. The Anatomy and Physiology of Capillaries. Yale Univ. Press, New Haven, 1929.

124b. Kuang, M. H. *Federation Proc.* **9,** 63 (1950).
125. Kunkel, H. G., and Slater, R. J. *Proc. Soc. Exptl. Biol. Med.* **80,** 42 (1952).
126. Kunkel, H. G., Taylor, S. P., Jr., and du Vigneaud, V. *J. Biol. Chem.* **200,** 559 (1953).
127. Kunkel, H. G., and Tiselius, A. *J. Gen. Physiol.* **35,** 89 (1951).
128. Landgrebe, F. W. Unpublished.
129. Landgrebe, F. W., and Hobson, B. M. *Brit. Med. J.* **ii,** 17 (1949).
130. Landgrebe, F. W., Macaulay, M. H. I., and Waring, H. *Proc. Roy. Soc. Edinburgh* **B62,** 202 (1946).
131. Landgrebe, F. W., and Mitchell, G. M. *Quart. J. Exptl. Physiol.* **39,** 11 (1954).
132. Landgrebe, F. W., and Mitchell, G. M. Unpublished.
133. Landgrebe, F. W., and Morris, C. J. O. R. Unpublished.
134. Landgrebe, F. W., Munday, K., and Waring, H. *Australian J. Exptl. Biol. Med. Sci.* **28,** 619 (1950).
134a. Landgrebe, F. W., Mitchell, G. M., Porath, J., and Roos, A. Unpublished.
135. Landgrebe, F. W., Reid, E., and Waring, H. *Quart. J. Exptl. Physiol.* **32,** 121 (1943).
136. Landgrebe, F. W., and Waring, H. *Australian J. Exptl. Biol. Med. Sci.* **27,** 331 (1949).
137. Landgrebe, F. W., and Waring, H. *In* C. W. Emmens, Hormone Assay. Academic Press, New York, 1950.
137a. Lazo-Wasem, E. A., and Weisel, G. F. *Biol. Bull.* **102** (Pt. 1), 25 (1952).
138. Leveque, T. F., and Scharrer, E. *Endocrinology* **52,** 436 (1953).
138a. Levinsky, N. G. *Endocrinology* **51** (No. 2) 110 (1952).
138b. Levinsky, N. G., and Sawyer, W. H. *Endocrinology* **51,** 110 (1952).
139. Levy, A. L. *J. Chem. Soc.,* p. 404 (1950).
140. Livermore, A. H., and du Vigneaud, V. *J. Biol. Chem.* **180,** 365 (1949).
141. Maier-Hüser, H., Clauser, H., Fromageot, P., and Plongeron, R. *Biochim. et Biophys. Acta* **11,** 252 (1953).
142. Manchester, R. C. *Proc. Soc. Exptl. Biol. Med.* **29,** 717 (1932).
143. May, C. E., and Rose, E. R. *J. Biol. Chem.* **54,** 213 (1922).
144. Mialhe-Voloss, C. *Compt. rend.* **45** (No. 1) 189 (1953).
145. Moretti, G. F., and Rives, M. *Gynecol et Obstet.* **48** (No. 1) 79 (1949).
146. Morris, C. J. O. R. *Lancet* **i,** 1210 (1952).
147. Mueller, J. M., Pierce, J. G., Davoll, H., and du Vigneaud, V. *J. Biol. Chem.* **191,** 309 (1951).
148. Mueller, J. M., Pierce, J. G., and du Vigneaud, V. *J. Biol. Chem.* **204,** 861 (1953).
149. Murphy, R. F. J., and Stead, E. A., Jr. *J. Clin. Invest.* **30,** 1055 (1951).
150. Nelson, W. P., and Welt, L. G. *J. Clin. Invest.* **31,** 392 (1952).
151. Neurath, H., and Schwert, G. W. *Chem. Revs.* **46,** 69 (1950).
152. Oberman, R. R. *Physiol. Revs.* **31,** 285 (1951).
153. O'Connor, W. J. *Quart. J. Exptl. Physiol.* **36,** 21 (1951).
154. Oldham, F. K. *Anat. Record.* **72,** 265 (1938).
155. Ott, I., and Scott, J. C. *Proc. Soc. Exptl. Biol. Med.* **8,** 48 (1910).
156. Overton, E. *Verhandl. phys. med. Ges. Wurzburg* **36,** 22 (1904).
157. Parker, G. H. Colour Change of Animals in Relation to Nervous Activity. Univ. Pennsylvania Press, Philadelphia, 1936.
158. Pasqualini, R. Q. Papel de la hipofis en la regulación de la diuresis: Dissertation, Buenos Aires 1935.

159. Peeters, G., Coussens, R., Bouckaert, J. P.., and Oyaert, W. *Arch. intern. Pharmacodynamie* **80**, 355 (1949).
160. Petersen, W. E. *Proc. Soc. Exptl. Biol. Med.* **50**, 298 (1942).
161. Pierce, J. G., Gordon, S., and du Vigneaud, V. *J. Biol. Chem.* **194**, 929 (1952).
162. Pierce, J. G., and du Vigneaud, V. *J. Biol. Chem.* **182**, 359 (1950).
163. Pierce, J. G., and du Vigneaud, V. *J. Biol. Chem.* **186**, 77 (1950).
164. Popenoe, E. A., Lawler, H. C., and du Vigneaud, V. *J. Am. Chem. Soc.* **74**, 3713 (1952).
165. Popenoe, E. A., Pierce, J. G., du Vigneaud, V., and van Dyke, H. B. *Proc. Soc. Exptl. Biol. Med.* **81**, 506 (1952).
166. Popenoe, E. A., and du Vigneaud, V. *J. Biol. Chem.* **205**, 133 (1953).
167. Popenoe, E. A., and du Vigneaud, V. *J. Biol. Chem.* **206**, 353 (1954).
168. Potts, A. M., and Gallagher, T. F. *J. Biol. Chem.* **140**, Proc., 103 (1941).
169. Purves, H. D., and Greisbach, W. E. *Endocrinology* **49**, 427 (1951).
170. Reinhardt, W. O., Geschwind, I. I., Porath, J. O., and Li, C. H. *Proc. Soc. Exptl. Biol. Med.* **80**, 439 (1952).
171. Ressler, C., Trippett, S., and du Vigneaud, V. *J. Biol. Chem.* **204**, 861 (1953).
172. Rey, R. Recherches experimentales sur l'économie de l'eau chez Batraciens: Dissertation, Paris, 1937.
173. Rigler, R., and Holzbauer, M. *Arch. exptl. Pathol. u. Pharmakol.* **219**, S456–S465 (1953).
174. Rosenfeld, M. *Bull. Johns Hopkins Hosp.* **66**, 398 (1940).
175. Rowe, L. W. *Endocrinology* **13**, 205 (1929).
176. Sanger, F. *Biochem. J.* **39**, 507 (1945).
177. Sawyer, W. H. *Am. J. Physiol.* **164**, 44 (1951).
178. Sawyer, W. H. *Am. J. Physiol.* **164**, 457 (1951).
178a. Sawyer, W. H., and Sawyer, M. K. *Physiol. Zool.* **25**, 84 (1952).
179. Sartorius, O. W., and Roberts, K. *Endocrinology* **45**, 273 (1949).
180. Sayers, G. *Physiol. Revs.* **30**, 241 (1950).
181. Scala, F. *Arch. zool. ital.* **23**, 283 (1936).
182. Sealock, R. R., and du Vigneaud, V. *J. Pharmacol.* **54**, 433 (1935).
183. Shannon, J. A. *J. Exptl. Med.* **76**, 387 (1942).
184. Smith, F., and Mackay, E. M. *Proc. Soc. Exptl. Biol. Med.* **34**, 116 (1936).
185. Smith, M. I., and McClosky, W. T. *J. Pharmacol.* **24**, 371 (1925).
186. Spaul, E. A. *J. Exptl. Biol.* **5**, 166 (1927).
187. Stehle, R. L. *J. Pharmacol.* **57**, 1 (1936).
188. Stehle, R. L. *J. Biol. Chem.* **102**, 573 (1953).
189. Stehle, R. L. *Rev. can. biol.* **3**, 48 (1944).
190. Stehle, R. L. *Rev. can. biol.* **4**, 37 (1945).
191. Stehle, R. L. *Brit. J. Pharmacol.* **8**, 435 (1953).
192. Stehle, R. L., and Bourne, W. *J. Physiol.* **60**, 229 (1925).
193. Stehle, R. L., and Fraser, A. M. *J. Pharmacol.* **55**, 136 (1935).
194. Stewart, W. C. *Am. J. Physiol.* **151**, 412 (1949).
194a. Stewart, W. C. *Am. J. Phys.* **157**, 412 (1949).
195. Sulman, F. G. *Nature* **169**, 588 (1952).
196. Taylor, S. P., Jr., du Vigneaud, V., Kunkel, H. G. *Federation Proc.* **12** (1953).
197. Thing, E. *Acta Endocrinol.* **10**, 295 (1952).
198. Thing, E. *Acta Endocrinol.* **14**, 113 (1953).
199. Tuppy, H. *Biochim. et Biophys. Acta* **11**, 449 (1953).
200. Turner, C. W., and Cooper, W. D. *Endocrinology* **29**, 320 (1941).

201. Turner, R. A., Pierce, J. G., and du Vigneaud, V.   *J. Biol. Chem.* **191,** 21 (1951).
201a. Ussing, H. H.   *Acta Physiol. Scand.* **28,** fas. 1 (1953).
202. Vandemark, N. L., and Hays, R. L.   *Am. J. Physiol.* **170,** 518 (1952).
203. van Dyke, H. B., and Ames, R. G.   *Acta Endocrinol.* **7,** 110 (1951).
204. van Dyke, H. B., Chow, B. F., Greep, R. O., and Rothen, V.   *J. Pharmacol. Exptl. Therap.* **74,** 190 (1942).
205. van Dyke, H. B., and Block, R. J.   *Nature* **165,** 975 (1950).
206. Vaughan, J. R., Jr., and Osato, R. L.   *J. Am. Chem. Soc.* **73,** 5553 (1951).
207. Verney, E. B.   *Proc. Roy. Soc. (London)* **B135,** 25 (1947).
208. du Vigneaud, V., Gish, D. T., and Katsoyannis, P. G.   *J. Am. Chem. Soc.* **76,** 4752 (1954).
209. du Vigneaud, V., Lawler, H. C., and Popenoe, E. A.   *J. Am. Chem. Soc.* **75,** 4880 (1953).
210. du Vigneaud, V., Ressler, C., and Trippett, S.   *J. Biol. Chem.* **205,** 949 (1953).
211. du Vigneaud, V., Ressler, C., Swan, J. M., Roberts, C. W., Katsoyannis, P. G., and Gordon, S.   *J. Am. Chem. Soc.* **75,** 4879 (1953).
211a. du Vigneaud, V., Ressler, C., Swan, J. M., Roberts, C. W., and Katsoyannis, P. G.   *J. Am. Chem. Soc.* **76,** 3115 (1954).
212. du Vigneaud, V., Sealock, R. R., Sifford, R. H., Kamm, O., and Grote, I. W.   *J. Biol. Chem.* **100,** xciv (1953).
213. Walker, A. M.   *Am. J. Physiol.* **127,** 519 (1939).
214. Walker, J. M.   *Quart. J. Med.* **18,** 51 (1949).
215. Wang, K. J.   *Chinese J. Physiol.* **13,** 405 (1938).
216. Waring, H.   *Biol. Revs.* **17,** 120 (1942).
217. Waring, H., and Landgrebe, F. W.   *In* Pincus and Thimann, The Hormones, Vol. 2, p. 427.   Academic Press, New York, 1950.
218. Waring, H., and Ketterer, B.   *Nature* **171,** 862 (1953).
219. Weston, R. E., Hanenson, I. B., Crossman, J., Berdasco, G., and Wolfman, M.   *J. Clin. Invest.* **32,** 611 (1953).
220. White, H. L., Heinbecker, P., and Rolf, D.   *Am. J. Physiol.* **149,** 404 (1947).
221. White, H. L., Heinbecker, P., and Rolf, D.   *Am. J. Physiol.* **156,** 67 (1949).
222. White, H. L., Heinbecker, P., and Rolf, D.   *Am. J. Physiol.* **157,** 47 (1949).
223. Whitney, J. E., Bennett, L. L., and Li, C. H.   *Proc. Soc. Exptl. Biol. Med.* **79,** 584 (1952).
224. Whittlestone, W. G.   *J. Endocrinol.* **8,** 89 (1952).
225. Zuckerman, S.   *Lancet* **266,** 789 (1954).

CHAPTER X

The Chemistry and Physiology of the Thyroid

BY RULON W. RAWSON, JOSEPH E. RALL, AND
MARTIN SONENBERG

CONTENTS

During the past decade research in the field of thyroid physiology has been more intense than ever before. This research, which has been carried on by physiologists, biochemists, biophysicists, and clinical investigators, has been most rewarding. The recent acceleration in thyroid research can probably be attributed to the fact that our modern tools of study have permitted an approach to some of the previously unanswerable problems with workable methods. The availability of radioactive isotopes of iodine and other elements has made it possible to investigate dynamically various functions of the thyroid in physiologic equilibrium. The various methods of chromatography have made it possible to separate the various amino acids of the thyroid and to identify the circulating thyroid hormones, and the discovery of various goitrogenic inhibitors of the thyroid has made it possible to separate some major steps in the synthesis of thyroid hormone.

In Volume II of *The Hormones* the late Dr. William T. Salter presented a complete and admirable review of literature on the biochemistry and physiology of the thyroid up to 1949. In this volume, the authors have concentrated their discussions on studies reported since 1949. The older literature has been referred to, however, when such reports provided information needed to clarify certain facets in the discussion.

I. Morphology of the Thyroid

A. ANATOMY AND COMPARATIVE ANATOMY OF THE THYROID

1. *Gross Anatomy of the Thyroid*

The thyroid is present in all vertebrates and some chordates. Perhaps the most primitive forms to concentrate iodine (and this is presumed to represent thyroid function) are amphioxus and the ascidions, *Perophora annecteus*, *Styela montereyensis*, and *Cima intestinalis*. The iodine is collected in the stolonic septum in relatively high concentration (242). The form of iodine in these structures is not known.

The thyroid is variously located in the general region of the neck and thorax, its precise location varying with the species. In elasmobranchs it is a loose unpaired aggregate of follicles. In teleosts it is distributed in paired fashion along the ventral aorta. In reptiles only a single lobe is present, lying over the pericardium. In most mammals, including man, two lobes are present, more or less adherent to the trachea below the level of the larynx. The average weight of the thyroid in adult man is between 15 and 25 g., although in one goitrous area it was found to be 30 g. (568). Presumably the weight is inversely correlated with the amount of iodine in the diet (470, 566).

A great deal has been done on the role of the thyroid in the economy of lower animals. The cold-blooded species are of particular interest. Several recent reviews describe some of the available data (197, 415). In general, it appears that O_2 consumption of fish and amphibia is not affected by thyroid hormone. It is reported that thyroid increases oxygen consumption of salamanders and thyroidectomy decreases O_2 consumption (715). General body activity was reported to be increased by thyroxine (205, 305). In certain selachians antithyroid drugs had no effect, whereas in teleosts the same compounds (thiourea) caused a fall in blood iodine and exophthalmos (395, 500). It has been suggested that there is a difference between mammalian and piscine thyroid gland extract (666). Extracts of parrot fish thyroids were said to stimulate O_2 consumption of *Bathystoma*, whereas extracts of mammalian thyroid tissue were ineffective, even though the two extracts had similar actions in rats (668). However, Berg and Gorbman have shown that at least in the platyfish, the iodinated compounds in the thyroid are identical with those in mammalian thyroids (62).

The thyroid in man derives its blood supply from two superior thyroidal arteries arising from the external carotids and two inferior thyroidal arteries arising from the subclavian or the thyrocervical trunk. The blood flow per gram of thyroid tissue is very abundant and probably exceeded only by that of the adrenal. A recent review summarizes in detail the anatomy and function of the thyroid in cold-blooded vertebrates (415).

The innervation of the thyroid appears to concern only the blood vessels (494). It has been reported that in the dog continuous stimulation of the cervical sympathetics by previous anastomosis to the phrenic nerve, produced exophthalmos and signs of hyperthyroidism (214). This may be due to indirect effect upon hypophyseal secretion of thyrotropic hormone.

2. *Microscopic Anatomy of the Thyroid*

The thyroid is composed of small spheroidal structures lined with a single layer of cells and filled with a homogeneous refractile material known as colloid which is a protein, thyroglobulin. The spheroidal structures are variously known as acini, follicles, and alveoli, and in man average 300 μ in diameter (787). Under physiological conditions the activity of the thyroid is positively correlated with the height of the thyroid cells (558). Under great stimulation there is infolding and the development of papilliferous growths in the acini. The resting or atrophic thyroid shows low cells lining very large acini which are distended with colloid.

More recently, the finer details of the cytology of the thyroid have been investigated with the electron microscope (89, 472). These studies show a brush border and cilia on the acinar end of the thyroid cells. These cilia are about 0.2 to 0.4 μ in length. A brush border similar to this is usually found (small intestine, proximal convoluted tubule) in cells engaged in absorptive activity or (parietal cells of stomach, ependymal cells of choroid plexus) in secretion. In the thyroid cells, a network which appears canalicular in nature can be seen. These structures are about 0.08 μ wide and may be 1 μ long.

The physiological activity of the thyroid appears to be correlated with the size and extent of these structures. TSH or thiouracil produces an increase in size and ramifications of the canalicular structures, and either hypophysectomy or administration of thyroxine produces atrophy of the structures. There appears to be no evidence for reversal of polarity of secretion of the cell (89, 387), and the colloid droplets may be seen leaving the cell and entering the colloid. The very close apposition of the capillaries to the thyroid cell seen in electron micrographs suggests that secretion of hormone is affected by resorption of colloid by the cell and release into the capillary.

Nuclei, nucleoli, mitochondria, and terminal bars are present in the cell, but the Golgi apparatus of older cytologists is not seen with electron microscopy (89). X-ray and ultraviolet absorption by the thyroid has been studied (183, 228, 737) and may be a means of determining iodine content.

3. Chemical Anatomy of the Thyroid

A bewildering array of elements and organic compounds have been described as in the thyroid or as possessing an especial predilection for the thyroid. The distribution of iodine in the thyroid will be discussed below.

In general, elements of the VIIth periodic group are concentrated in varying degrees in the thyroid. Except for iodine, it appears that the vertebrates do not synthesize organic compounds from these elements, and, therefore, their concentration in the thyroid represents an equilibrium with their concentration in blood. Bromine, technetium, rhenium, astatine, chlorine, and manganese are elements that fall in the VIIth periodic group, and all have been shown to be concentrated, at least temporarily, in the thyroid (54, 55, 56, 273, 274, 275, 327, 511, 803). Rhenium (as $H Re O_4$) labeled with radioactive rhenium is concentrated in the thyroid to an extent of 25 to 100 times its concentration in blood. Rapid urinary excretion, however, causes a rapid fall in blood and thyroidal rhenium, with the result that in two days essentially all the rhenium has been excreted (56). Manganese follows essentially the same pattern of uptake and loss (161). All of these compounds wash iodine out of the thyroid, and all in large enough dosage cause goiter (54). Furthermore, bromine and chlorine and fluorine have been reported to increase the goitrogenic action of thiouracil (783). In rats made hyperthyroid with thyroxine, the uptake of radioactive bromine by the thyroid was depressed (9). A considerable amount of work has been done on astatine (eka-iodine or element 85), all the isotopes of which are radioactive. Its concentration in guinea pig, rat, monkey, and human thyroid appears to be $\frac{1}{10}$ to $\frac{1}{4}$ that of iodine. No real information is, however, available about organic compounds of astatine (129, 273, 274, 275, 327, 650). This element is of possible therapeutic interest because it emits alpha particles.

Antimony appears to be concentrated in the thyroid to a greater extent than in any other tissue of the body (87, 135, 363, 431, 674).   There is some dispute as to the effect of antimony administration on the thyroid gland and animal organism.   Kramer reports no effect of antimony on the histology of the thyroid or status of the animal (363).   Westrick reports that antimony intensifies the effect of thyroxine (on loss of body weight and increase in O_2 consumption), and furthermore antimony alone causes thyroidal hyperplasia (772).   Sulfur as sulfate labeled with S^{35} appears in the colloid 48 hours after administration in quantities sufficient for autoradiographs (496).   Sulfur as CNS— probably does not selectively concentrate in the thyroid when labeled with S^{35} (798), although some data based on chemical techniques suggest substantial thyroidal concentration (445).   Sulfur in thiourea appears to localize in the thyroid, where it is rapidly oxidized to sulfate by the thyroid (644).

The ribosenucleic acid and deoxyribosenucleic acid content of thyroid cytoplasm, nucleolus, and nucleus has been investigated in animals under treatment with thiouracil or thyroxine (143, 561).   In general, more ribosenucleic acid is found under conditions of cellular hypertrophy.

The thyroid has been found to have an unusually high content of hydrolyzable hexosamine (368).   The Vitamin C content of the thyroid has been determined and most of it found in mitochondria (758).

The thyroid gland has also been studied from a histochemical standpoint. A comprehensive survey of the literature to 1949 has been reported (146). Dempsey has reported the presence of peroxidase granules in thyroid cells (147).   Histochemical techniques have also suggested the presence of phosphatase, protease, and oxidase (147, 151, 152, 154, 155) in the thyroid. The abundance of these enzymes under different physiological states has been studied.   A mucolytic enzyme whose activity is increased by TSH has been described in the thyroid (399).

The thyroid gland and particularly the stromal network fluoresce: colloid shows a variable degree of natural fluorescence (147, 247, 248).

Glycogen has not been demonstrated in the thyroid (149).   It has also been suggested, on the basis of colloid basophilia, that colloid has a high content of ribonucleic acid (146).   This is further supported by the evidence that digestion of colloid with ribonuclease destroys its basophilic staining reaction and that the staining affinity of colloid at various pH's agrees with that known for ribosenucleic acid.   Gersh has suggested on a histochemical basis that polysaccharide, partly hyaluronic acid, is in the colloid as a glycoprotein (226, 227).

An extensive studying of the staining of thyroidal colloid with a variety of histochemical techniques reported recently, has shown that the basophilia of colloid is due to either COOH or OSO_3H groups and that probably there is little hyaluronic acid in colloid (195).

Autoradiography is another method of studying the thyroid—in particu-

lar the location and relative concentration of iodine in various conditions
(388).   Review of this rather large literature is impossible.

B. EMBRYOLOGY

The thyroid is derived from endoderm of the primitive pharynx and can
be first detected as an outpocketing in the region of the 1st and 2nd pharyngeal pouches in an embryo of five or six primitive segments.   This anlage
enlarges and grows caudally, leaving a thin duct attached to the pharynx.
In man, this duct and its pharyngeal attachment atrophies, except for a
very narrow strip of follicles extending upward a centimeter or two from
the isthmus of the thyroid.

Recently evidence has been presented suggesting that in the salmon the
thyroid is derived from mesoderm as a thickening of the pericardium (722).
If confirmed, this report suggests that a reinvestigation of the embryology
of the thyroid in other forms may be in order.

Histologically discrete cords of cells may be seen in a human embryo of
8 mm.   By about the 14th week of embryonic life the cells have become
organized into well-defined glandular structures.   Studies with radioiodine
show that at about this time the thyroid begins to concentrate appreciable
iodine and colloid appears (111).   Quantitative studies of iodine concentration by the fetal thyroid have been done in the cow.   The concentration
of I^{131} in the fetal thyroid was seven times more than that in the maternal
thyroid, although the fetal blood I^{131} was lower than the maternal blood
I^{131} (244).   The accumulation of iodine in the fetal bovine thyroid first
occurred at 60 days and was related to length and body weight (796).

I^{131} was observed to concentrate in the embryonic chick thyroid at 10
days (69, 735).   By the second half of incubation the chick thyroid could
synthesize thyroxine and diiodotyrosine (70).

The chronological sequence of the development of iodine accumulation
in the fetal rat has also been studied (243).

Two structures in the embryo, the ultimobranchial bodies and the
internal epithelial body, which are derived from the 4th pouch are supposed by some anatomists to contribute to the thyroid (495), and said by
others to disappear (348).   It appears that probably there is species variation in this respect, since the rat, for example, shows certain differences
in histology between central and peripheral follicles, suggesting a different
origin for these areas of the thyroid.   In man, there are occasional mis-
directions in the embryologic journey of the thyroid.   The lingual thyroid
located at the base of the tongue is presumed to represent a failure of migration, particularly since it is almost never associated with the presence
of any thyroid tissue in the normal location (539).   Thyroglossal duct
cysts represent failure or atrophy of this structure.   Very much more

rarely the thyroid may be found intralingually, sublingually, intratracheally, intraesophageally, or in the mediastinum.

II. Prethyroid Iodine Metabolism

Iodine is usually ingested by the animal organism as iodide and is absorbed from the gastrointestinal tract. There are many older experiments reported of "iodine balance" studies, but these are extremely difficult from an analytical viewpoint and may be subject to marked error. Elmer and Salter have written extensive reviews which cover these and many other aspects of iodine metabolism, and the reader is referred to these publications (181, 630). More recently, radioisotopes of iodine have made possible a much more precise accounting of iodine balance. In general, iodide is readily absorbed from the gastrointestinal tract. The volume of distribution of iodide in man approaches about 40 % of the body weight but requires at least 5 hours for equilibration (481). The kinetics of iodide metabolism have been discussed in great detail recently (575). More specifically, iodide is distributed between plasma and erythrocytes (human) approximately the same as chloride $(i.e., \frac{\text{cell } I^{131}}{\text{plasma } I^{131}} = 0.67)$, and on the basis of water content the cell concentration appears to equal the plasma concentration (73, 541, 761). Iodide is also absorbed from the skin, and it has been estimated that as much as 300 μg. of iodide may be absorbed from bathing in certain waters (163, 463). Iodide is concentrated by salivary glands, stomach, and mammary glands. These secretions have recently been studied very carefully in man with I^{131} and found to concentrate iodide in the following ratio:

$$\frac{\text{Saliva } I^-}{\text{Plasma } I^-} = 40$$

$$\frac{\text{Gastric Juice } I^-}{\text{Plasma } I^-} = 30$$

$$\frac{\text{Milk } I^-}{\text{Plasma } I^-} = 30$$

(315).
Recently an iodinated protein has been described in milk which is not thyroxine bound to a protein carrier (749). In mice, I^{131} is secreted by the mammary gland of the lactating female in such quantity that sterilization of the young occurred (623, 624). Normally these mechanisms do not account for significant loss of iodine from the body. Renal excretion of iodide, on the other hand, is substantial, amounting in man to approximately 30 ml. of plasma cleared per minute (339). Interestingly enough,

the renal excretion of iodide is independent of plasma concentration of iodide (115).   Chloride excretion, on the other hand, is dependent upon the concentration of chloride in plasma, urine flow, and acid-base balance but generally is slower than iodide excretion.   Urine flow seems to have no effect on iodide clearance (507).   Hypophysectomy definitely decreases (in rats) urinary clearance of iodide (14).   The effect of cortisone in iodide metabolism will be discussed below.   Myxedema and renal disease decrease the rate of excretion of iodide by the kidney (447).

Iodide is also excreted in the sweat and appears to be dependent on the amount of sweating, although no recent data are available.   The thyroid rapidly accumulates iodide and under normal circumstances retains it for a considerable period of time.   Many workers have described the kinetics of iodide distribution, renal excretion, and thyroidal uptake.   One may use any of several methods of describing the rates of transfer of iodide. Using the clearance concept, it appears that the normal human thyroid clears approximately 16 ml. of plasma of its iodide per minute (483). Roughly the same figure put another way is that the normal nonrenal loss of iodine from plasma (this is largely thyroidal uptake), occurs at a rate of 3.9 % per hour (339).   In general, if radioiodide is introduced into the blood stream, it diffuses into the extravascular iodide space and is accumulated by the thyroid and excreted by the kidney.   The rate of loss from plasma is approximated by a double exponential curve of the familiar form, $Q = Ae^{-\alpha_1 t} + Be^{-\alpha_2 t}$ (619).   Similar double exponential curves may be obtained over the thyroid and in the urine.   If the first 1 to 2 hours is not analyzed very carefully, all these decay rates approximate single exponential functions quite closely.   A study of simultaneously determined blood, urine, and thyroid measurements has been made and shows that these rates are approximately the same (339).   This means that after the iodide phase of loss from blood is completed and before substantial thyroidal loss of I^{131} has occurred, approximately 25 % of the dose will be in the thyroid and 60 % in the urine in man (37, 298, 299, 443, 533, 663, 769).   As one might expect, there is a good correlation between thyroidal uptake of iodine and thyroid hormone secretion.   Therefore, the use of I^{131} in one manner or another has become an extremely widely used test of thyroid function and is particularly adapted to the diagnosis of hyperthyroidism.   The various combinations and permutations possible in measuring the thyroid, the urine, or the blood for radioactivity at varying times after administration of I^{131} have been investigated *in extenso*.   In general, the effort has been to develop a simple procedure that differentiates normal patients from those with hyperthyroidism; a review of these tests is of more clinical than physiological importance.

Although distribution of iodide in body compartments and renal excretion of iodide are independent of concentration, the uptake of iodide by the thyroid is extremely sensitive to variations in iodide concentration. In patients with hyperthyroidism a tracer dose of I^{131} is handled essentially the same by the thyroid whether carrier-free or whether carrier NaI up to 100 μg. is added.   Carrier iodide of 1000 μg. causes substantial reduction in the rate of uptake, although the absolute iodide uptake may not be depressed (115, 662).   Stanley has suggested that in hyperthyroid patients the level of iodide in the blood necessary to inhibit biosynthesis of thyroid hormone is lower than in normal patients (685).   In rats a level of iodide in the serum of 35 μg. % or more inhibited biosynthesis, although it did not completely inhibit some temporary uptake of iodide (792, 795).   Interestingly enough, after about 2 days of exposure of rats to a level of iodide in the serum of 35 μg. % or more, the biosynthetic function returned (795). The uptake of iodine by the thyroid will be discussed from a biochemical standpoint below, but it is possible to separate two distinct phases in the entry of iodine into the thyroid.   The first mechanism of accumulation of iodide by the thyroid is by concentration of iodide as such.   This has been termed the "iodide trap."   In normal rats, this results in a concentration of iodide in thyroid of approximately 25 to 500 times that in blood (714, 747, 748).   One of the goitrogenic drugs such as thiouracil or relatively large "carriers" of sodium iodide by depressing or abolishing thyroid hormone synthesis reveals this trap and shows the concentration of iodide as such by the thyroid (450, 709, 714).   A mechanism for this trapping has been studied by Wyngaarden, who demonstrated fixation of iodide, as iodide, by homogenates of thyroid tissue (800).   Thiocyanate did not reverse the binding of iodide to thyroid gland homogenate, and propylthiouracil prevented the binding.   These are two slightly discordant notes. Whether the formation of a protein-anion complex occurred or whether actual oxidation of iodide and chemical union with some organic compound occurred is not certain.   The effect of a wide variety of agents on trapping of iodide by the thyroid and on biosynthesis of thyroid hormone will be discussed below.

III. Intrathyroidal Iodine Metabolism

The iodine precursor of the thyroid hormone is accumulated by the thyroid gland as inorganic iodide.   Its conversion into thyroxine involves a series of chemical reactions, many of which may well be enzymatic.

Presumably the first step in the conversion of accumulated inorganic iodide to organic iodine by the thyroid involves the oxidation of iodide to free iodine or hypoiodite (32, 709).   This is presumptive, inasmuch as free iodine has never been isolated from the thyroid gland, although suggestive evidence for its existence obtained by chromatography has recently been presented (190).   It would appear that this oxidation of iodine occurs very rapidly and that the oxidized form of iodine reacts immediately with proteins or amino acids to form organic iodine. This speculation is made on the basis of observations (33, 448, 450, 709, 746, 748) that treatment of animals with certain antithyroidal agents which prevent the formation of organic iodine, results in the accumulation of inorganic iodide. Chromatography of extracts of thyroids reveals the presence of inorganic iodide (164, 714) with a maximum accumulation in the thyroid 1 hour after injection. That the antithyroid agents act as reducing agents and thus prevent the oxidation of inorganic iodide is supported by the observation (644) that after the administration of thiourea and its localization in the thyroid, this substance is oxidized to inorganic sulfate. In addition, thiourea-like drugs may prevent the oxidation of iodide to the free halogen by inhibiting the appropriate enzyme involved in this oxidation (147). Cytochrome oxidase and peroxidase have been suggested as the enzymes which catalyze the conversion of iodide. Moreover, thiouracil is an inhibitor of peroxidase (147, 361, 613), an enzyme reported to be in thyroid tissue (751). Recently, however, it has been suggested (191) that the oxidation of iodide to iodine is nonenzymatic, with the oxidizing agent being the cupric ion.

Evidence for the enzymatic oxidation of inorganic iodide is meager. It is known that thyroid slices are capable of synthesizing labeled iodinated compounds from radioactive iodide (476). These organic precursors may originate in the thyroids of sheep, man, dog, or rat (595). Previously, the integrity of the cell was considered crucial, since thyroid homogenates were unable to produce iodinated organic compounds (638). Recently, however, not only homogenates (764) but cell-free preparations (191) of thyroid tissue have produced organically bound iodine. The addition of a cell-free preparation of thyroid tissue to iodide ion, cupric ion, and tyrosine resulted in the iodination of tyrosine (191, 764). Not only is the iodination of tyrosine in thyroid slices inhibited by the absence of oxygen but by the usual inhibitors of cytochrome oxidase, i.e., cyanide, azide, sulfide, and carbon monoxide (638). It has been suggested that other oxidizing enzymes are also in the thyroid (147, 154) and that they may be affected by some, but not all, of these enzyme inhibitors. Thiocyanates and thiourea are effective in preventing substitution processes in the thyroid (211, 710), the former by depressing the uptake of iodide and the latter by preventing the conversion of inorganic iodide to organic iodine derivatives.

Biological milieu other than thyroid tissue are capable of producing iodinated compounds with an iodide precursor, including slices of intestine (701) and unpasteurized milk (346). The addition of xanthine to the xanthine oxidase present in milk results in the liberation of hydrogen peroxide, which in the presence of peroxidase could oxidize iodide to iodine —a heuristic model indeed. The iodine would then be capable of reacting with tyrosine to give diiodotyrosine. It has been demonstrated (771) that horse-radish peroxidase will oxidize iodide and may promote the coupling of two diiodotyrosine molecules. After the injection of hens with radioactive iodine, radioiodinated organic compounds bound to proteins may be found in the yolks of eggs, one of which has been demonstrated as diiodotyrosine (599). Some of the lower forms, like the algae, *Laminaria flexicaulis*, may liberate iodine from iodide, possibly with cytochrome oxidase (608). Since there is inhibition by pyrophosphate and fluorides, other enzyme systems may participate as well.

Certainly, all *in vitro* reactions which result in the production of iodinated proteins require iodine in its oxidized form but not as iodide (563). Although the thyroid may be crucial for the oxidation of iodide to iodine, the administration of free iodine will result in iodinated proteins not present in the thyroid (174).

At present, several possibilities exist for the conversion of free iodine or hypoiodite to thyroxine. Iodine may react directly with tyrosine to form diiodotyrosine, two molecules of which couple to form thyroxine. Secondly, iodine may react with tyrosine to produce both monoiodotyrosine and diiodotyrosine to yield triiodothyronine, which in turn may be iodinated to form thyroxine. Thirdly, thyronine may be iodinated to yield the tetraiodothyronine, thyroxine, directly or consecutively from the mono-, di-, and tri-iodo derivatives of thyronine.

The first series of reactions has actually been demonstrated chemically (285, 754). Diiodotyrosine can be oxidized directly to thyroxine by hydrogen peroxide in alkaline solution (282). Diiodotyrosine has been found in thyroid gland hydrolyzates as well as in the extracts of nonhydrolyzed glands (258, 260, 611, 729, 732), and represents about 60 % of the total iodine of the thyroid (206, 287) subsequent to alkaline hydrolysis and 30 % after enzymatic hydrolysis (588). More recently, monoiodotyrosine has been found in direct extracts of thyroid tissue and thyroid hydrolyzates (194, 258, 260, 611, 711, 713, 729) and by specific activity measurements (711) would appear to be the precursor of diiodotyrosine. Excessive amounts of iodide will temporarily inhibit organic iodine synthesis in the rat (791, 792, 794, 795). The conversion of diiodotyrosine into thyroxine in alkaline solutions has been demonstrated (754). The presence of thyroxine in thyroid gland extracts and hydrolyzates (258, 260, 611, 732) has been well documented. With specific activity measurements evidence has been presented that diiodotyrosine is a precursor of thyroxine (107). However, since monoiodotyrosine was an unknown constituent of the thyroid at the time of these studies, it may well have contaminated the diiodotyrosine fraction. Specific activity studies with impure substances would have questionable validity.

A simple oxidative mechanism has been suggested (282, 331) for the conversion of diiodotyrosine to thyroxine.   The initial step in the proposed reaction would be the oxidation of the diiodophenolic ion by removing one electron from the oxygen atom with the production of a free radical (I).   Another diiodotyrosine molecule is oxidized by the loss of one electron in the *para* position to the diiodophenolic group with the production of a second free radical (II).   Both of these free radicals would be formed in the same biological system.   The addition of these two free radicals (I and II) would lead to an intermediate product phenoxydienone (III).

The free radical theory has not been the only suggestion to account for the formation of an ether.   One could also visualize (488) an oxidative mechanism which involved the loss of two electrons from one of the resonance forms of the diiodophenolic ion.   There would then be ready addition of the carbonium ion formed with a negatively charged group, the diiodophenolic ion.   The latter would have the strongest negative charge at a biological pH where the strongly acidic diiodophenolic group would be significantly ionized.

Thus the over-all reaction can be visualized as the condensation of two diiodotyrosine molecules to give thyroxine via I, II, and III above:

Although the mechanism of the union of two diiodotyrosine molecules to form a thyroxine molecule is not clearly defined, it is known that this condensation is enhanced by oxidative agents as well as by free iodine (286, 565). The condensation of two diiodotyrosine molecules would lead to an intermediary product whose decomposition would yield dehydroalanine, which in turn would be oxidized to pyruvic acid or hydrated to serine (281, 522). Although hypophysectomy reduces the formation of thyroxine from diiodotyrosine (107), it does not abolish the formation of thyroxine (18) but merely decreases the rate of conversion of diiodotyrosine.

Whether the triiodothyronine isolated from thyroid gland hydrolyzates (264, 589) represents the intermediate in the conversion of diiodotyrosine to thyroxine has not yet been fully resolved. *In vitro*, the iodination of 3,5-diiodothyronine gives both 3,5,3'-triiodothyronine (591, 593) as well as thyroxine (593). Triiodothyronine could also be formed by the condensation of a molecule of monoiodotyrosine with a molecule of diiodotyrosine. Triiodothyronine may well be a metabolite of thyroxine by deiodination notwithstanding the lack of action of deiodase on thyroxine. Triiodothyronine may be present in thyroid tissue unrelated (461) to thyroxine.

Many have found it difficult to accept the rearrangement of two molecules of diiodotyrosine to give a molecule of thyroxine, particularly if the tyrosine residues are already in peptide linkage. It has been suggested (633) that the thyroid gland elaborates an iodine-free thyroglobulin which may then be iodinated to a greater or lesser extent, depending upon the supply of iodine as well as upon other physiological conditions. Certainly, the iodine content of thyroglobulins may vary depending upon the state of thyroid function as well as other factors (462). The prevention of iodine incorporation into the colloidal material of thyroid follicles may be accomplished with various goitrogenic agents despite an increase in the colloid (35). This suggests a continuation of protein synthesis without iodination and the production of hormonally inactive material. Such schemes would assume the iodination of a preformed thyronine present in peptide linkage in the iodine-free globulin. The presence of thyronine in thyroglobulin has not yet been demonstrated.

Proteins of nonthyroidal origin have been iodinated by incubation in an alkaline medium and thyroxine recovered after hydrolysis (2, 71, 524, 563, 564). This does not mean, of course, that thyroxine may not have been formed by the union of two diiodotyrosine molecules. Until all the tyrosine in serum albumin is iodinated, no thyroidal activity is produced (480). Thereafter one atom equivalent of iodine suffices to give marked endocrine activity, suggesting that this latter iodine acts as an oxidizing agent. With proteins deficient in tyrosine, no thyroxine will be produced. When nonthyroidal animal proteins are iodinated *in vivo* by injecting solutions of free iodine, the hypothyroidism of athyreotics may be relieved (174).

It has been suggested (606) that monoiodotyrosine and diiodotyrosine may act as carriers of iodine, since they are easily deiodinated by a thyroid deiodase, an enzyme which has no effect on thyroxine, triiodothyronine, or diiodothyronine (598, 605). The activity of this deiodase is enhanced by the administration to the animal of thyroid-stimulating hormone (597). The liberated iodine is then utilized by the thyroid (602) in the iodination of thyronine.   Perhaps monoiodotyrosine and diiodotyrosine are precursors of thyroxine only insofar as their iodine content is concerned.   This would not be inconsistent with the data on specific activity determinations, if one assumes that the iodine liberated is not mixed with the iodide coming to the thyroid from the blood.   Further experiments with ring labeled tyrosine and iodinated tyrosine will be necessary before one can conclude that the phenyl ring of tyrosine is a precursor of the diphenyl ring of thyroxine.   Monoiodohistidine has also been isolated from enzymatically hydrolyzed thyroglobulin in accord with the occurrence of this substance as well as diiodohistidine from artificially iodinated globins (208, 590). The kinetics are such that much more monoiodotyrosine is produced than monoiodohistidine (713).   Only by iodination with small amounts of iodine are the monoiodinated amino acids obtained in large quantities.

Iodine may be incorporated directly into a preformed iodine-free protein or first united with amino acids which are in turn organized into the protein molecule.   Nevertheless, most agree that more than 95 % of the iodine ends up in a protein molecule, thyroglobulin.   Most of the iodine is stored in the colloid of the follicles after a brief sojourn in the follicular epithelium. Thyroid-stimulating hormone decreases the interval during which iodine remains in the epithelium (385).   The bulk of the iodine exists in combination with a protein which occurs in the follicle and may be extracted with isotonic saline.   This unique iodinated protein, thyroglobulin, has been prepared in essentially pure form (157, 158, 294), despite certain variations in composition which attend physiological and pathological changes (106). These variations are in terms of degree of iodination, even within the same species (158, 462), despite an essential constancy of the amino acid composition (461).   Radioactive thyroglobulin has been prepared by administering radioactive iodine to the organism (596, 590) or by incubating thyroid slices in a milieu containing radioactive iodine (637).   With the use of such preparations and salting-out techniques it can be shown that in a normal animal both the radioactivity and the total protein can be precipitated in a parallel fashion (603).   However, after stimulation with thyroid-stimulating hormone only the radioactivity precipitates in the range of normal thyroglobulin, whereas more than 60 % of the protein behaves unlike thyroglobulin.   The proteins obtained from the thyroids of patients with thyrotoxicosis, prepared for operation with iodine, appear similar to those found in normal patients, except for the absolute and relative concentrations of iodine (270, 461).

Because of the variation noted in the total extent of iodination, it has been suggested (629) that proteinogenesis precedes iodination.   The latter occurs when the tyrosine already exists in peptide linkage and not as free tyrosine.   Certainly, the formation of iodinated amino acids is as efficient or more efficient when the tyrosine is in peptide association with other molecules (522, 600).   Despite the variation in iodine content of thyroglobulin, which depends to a large extent on the level of blood iodine and the rate of thyroxine formation and release, the ratio of thyroxine iodine to total iodine is relatively constant at about 30 % (790).   It would appear that normal thyroglobulin and thyroglobulin from well-differentiated fetal thyroids as well as the protein obtained from animals treated with TSH, or from patients with hyperthyroidism, all have the same amino acid composition.

Although the thyroid hormone secreted by the thyroid is part of the thyroglobulin molecule, the latter per se does not circulate in blood.   It is presumed that the proteolytic enzyme found in thyroid tissue (151, 156, 178, 333) catalyzes the proteolysis of thyroglobulin with the liberation of thyroid hormone.   The proteolytic activity of the thyroid is increased by TSH (150, 178), decreased by iodides (153), and manifested by an increase in the number of colloid droplets in the follicle.   There is an increased proteolytic activity in severe toxic goiter (153).   Conversely, the proteolytic activity of the thyroid is diminished by hypophysectomy and in colloid goiter (152).   Presumably, fragments of lower molecular weight than thyroglobulin diffuse through the thyroid epithelium to circulate in blood. This enzyme has been separated from thyroglobulin (734) and is able to catalyze the fragmentation of thyroglobulin into peptides of thyroxine. This enzyme, in the presence of cysteine hydrochloride and thyroglobulin will have a pH maximum at 3.5 and will liberate monoiodotyrosine, diiodotyrosine, and thyroxine with very small amounts of iodide (586) and triiodothyronine (592).   The protease recovered from the thyroid is inhibited by fluoride, cyanide, and cupric ion (404).   These products are similar to those noted with tryptic hydrolysis of thyroglobulin (588), except that the latter yields no iodides.   Dipeptides and tripeptides have been hydrolyzed by peptidases present in aqueous extracts of beef thyroid tissue (765).   Preparations of cathepsin isolated from thyroid tissue also contain a nuclease which liberates soluble phosphate from ribosenucleic acid (405).

Although thyroxine is most often considered to be the thyroid hormone, natural thyroxine, which is levorotatory, exists in peptide linkage in the thyroid gland as an integral part of the protein thyroglobulin (289).   This protein was described many years ago (321, 504) and is the storage form of the thyroid hormone.   Thyroglobulin has a molecular weight of approximately 700,000 (294, 295, 296) and an isoelectric point of pH 5.   It has been observed (413) that thyroglobulin may dissociate reversibly with variations in concentration, ionic strength, hydrogen ion concentration, or dielectric constant.   Thus the protein of 700,000 molecular weight may represent a polymer of a smaller fragment, or the latter may be a true hydrolytic product of thyroglobulin.   It is heat-coagulable and is more soluble in salt solution than in water.   However, thyroglobulin may be precipitated from a solution which contains 42 % to 49 % by volume of 3.5 M phosphate solution (587)—a useful identifying criterion.   Although appearing homogeneous when subjected to ultracentrifugation and electrophoresis, thyroglobulin can be shown to contain three constituents (158) by solubility measurements in a solvent of high ionic strength.   Since this protein can be recovered directly from the thyroid follicle (150, 574), and not necessarily by extraction of thyroid tissue, amino acid analyses can be considered to reflect accurately the composition of this protein and not contaminating bound substances from the epithelium.   Although the total content of tyrosine and thyronine residues remains constant in thyroglobulin, the degree of iodination of these aromatic moieties may vary depending upon the thyroid gland from which the thyroglobulin originates (145).   The thyroglobulin iodine content of many species varies between 0.1 % and 0.8 % (158).   The total iodine content, for example, of dog thyroglobulin is 0.38 % (601).   The purity of thyroglobulin does not depend on its iodine content (584).   In glands from thiouracil-treated animals, which are poor in iodine, there is less diiodotyrosine and more tyrosine (145).   On the other hand, it has been reported that after treatment of animals with antithyroid drugs thyroglobulin had an electrophoretic mobility, solubility, and composition different from the thyroidal protein of normal animals (145, 604).   By salting-out techniques there is no difference in the thyroglobulin from normal and thyrotropin-treated animals (604).   Thyroxine and diiodotyrosine as well as tyrosine and tryptophane have been isolated in pure and levorotatory form from thyroglobulin (287, 288, 289) after enzymatic hydrolysis.   By histochemical techniques it would appear that thyroglobulin has carbohydrate reacting groups (227).

Thyroxine, obtained from mammalian thyroid tissue by drastic alkaline hydrolysis (343), has as its empiric formula $C_{15}H_{11}O_4NI_4$; 65.4 % of the weight of this molecule may be accounted for on the basis of its iodine content.   Both thyroxine and diiodotyrosine give reactions characteristic of phenol and tyrosine as well as amino acids in general, *i.e.*, ninhydrin reaction (88).   In addition, they give a characteristic color reaction with nitrous acid (344).   Although these iodinated amino acids are recovered as the levorotatory form from the enzymatic hydrolysis of thyroglobulin, alkaline

hydrolysis causes racemization with no resultant optical activity.   Sodium
dl-thyroxine crystallizes with five molecules of water and assumes the
triclinic form (326).

The rate of secretion of thyroid hormone from the thyroid has been determined in various species.   In general, it has been found that the rates of
iodine entry and hormonal iodine output are constant and equal to each
other (167), with no diurnal variation.   Thiouracil will increase, whereas
hypophysectomy and treatment with thyroxine will decrease, the rate of
release of radioactive iodine labeled substances from the thyroid (21, 544,
789).   One must recognize, however, that the apparent rate of loss of
radioiodine from the thyroid is a function of the absolute amount of thyroid
hormone secreted as well as of that fraction of iodine which when released
from the thyroid hormone is reutilized by the thyroid.   In normal human
thyroids, the biological half life of metabolic radioactive iodine is approximately 100 days (94).   With a variety of techniques (430, 453, 525, 575,
614, 634, 684, 685, 724, 736) the daily thyroid hormone turnover in man
has been estimated between 60 and 360 μg. of *dl*-thyroxine.   In the chick
it has been reported (497) that thyroid hormone is secreted at the daily
rate of 2.8 μg. per 100 g. of body weight, with more being liberated by fast-
feathering, than by slow-feathering, strains (79).   Using the classic method
of goiter inhibition, it has been found (65, 308) that the duck secretes 18
μg. of thyroxine per day by the first week of life.   One strain of rats maintained on an iodine-deficient diet has an uncorrected rate of secretion of
iodine-labeled substances of 10 % per day, which is equivalent to a discharge of about 2.5 μg. of *l*-thyroxine per day.

IV. Postthyroid Iodine Metabolism

A. Blood Iodine

It has been known for many years that much of the iodine in the blood
represents thyroid hormone, and there are myriad investigations which
show the relationship between blood iodine and the status of the thyroid.
The normal amount of iodine in the serum of man is between 4 and 8 μg.
per 100 ml.   The clinical material on this has been summarized recently
(545).

Thyroxine and triiodothyronine have now been conclusively identified
in the blood of rats and man (258–262, 372, 538, 612, 705, 707, 712).

The rat appears to have relatively a greater proportion of triiodothyronine than man, but in all cases thyroxine appears to account for 90 % to
95 % of the organic iodine in blood and triiodothyronine for a few per cent.
The most recent data obtained with labeled thyroxine demonstrated that
thyroxine entered red cells but that the red cell concentration was only 25 %
that of plasma (482).

When proteins of serum are precipitated, almost all the blood iodine and approximately 95 % of added thyroxine are precipitated (733). Furthermore, the iodine in blood and also added thyroxine cannot be dialyzed from blood (234). It has seemed, therefore, that the thyroid hormone is bound in some way to protein. Analysis of protein fractions for iodine has been done (632, 706), and, although most of the iodine was in albumin, the highest concentration was in α-globulins. More recently, Schmid (642) has found the highest iodine:protein ratio in fraction VI, which is a mixture of α-globulins. Classical, free electrophoretic analysis of serum from a patient given I^{131} revealed that the radioactivity was in several protein fractions (658). Electrophoresis on filter paper, however, permits ready sampling of different areas and actually separates protein components. It has been shown that in serum to which labeled thyroxine was added, or in serum from a patient previously given I^{131}, 75 % to 90 % of the radioactivity may be found in a rather discrete band just between α-1 and α-2 globulin (245, 318, 381, 440, 441, 578). Most of the remaining activity is found in albumin, which has been shown to be capable of binding thyroxine *in vitro* (394). More recently, the binding capacity of this specific protein (interalpha) has been investigated (144). Triiodothyronine is also bound in part to this interalpha protein (144). Of probably fortuitous occurrence is the fact that thyroglobulin has the same electrophoretic mobility at pH 8.6 as thyroxine in serum (578).

In patients with carcinoma of the thyroid and with no normal thyroid tissue remaining, an iodinated protein that migrates with albumin was found (318, 577). This liberated mainly monoiodotyrosine on hydrolysis and on sedimentation in the ultracentrifuge had a sedimentation constant of about 3.8 Svedbergs. The exact significance of this unusual iodinated material is not clear.

Electrophoresis at pH 4.5 of serum to which labeled thyroxine was added shows that thyroxine moves in the band of proteins known as M_2 (576). These proteins are acidic α-2 glycoproteins. The sedimentation constant of the thyroxine-binding protein has been determined in the ultracentrifuge and is approximately 3 S. (514).

B. THE METABOLISM OF THYROXINE

Since thyroxine accounts for most of the iodine in the blood, many investigations have been reported on its manner of breakdown and excretion. A recent review summarizes the important kinetic considerations involved in thyroxine iodine or thyroid hormone metabolism (575). Another comprehensive review summarizes the data up to 1949 (473). In the human being, thyroxine is well absorbed from the gastrointestinal tract (19) and quickly appears in the blood. Upon intravenous administration,

l-thyroxine[131] disappears from the blood at a double exponential rate, the final component having a half time of 3.8 days (17). The rate of disappearance of l-thyroxine from the blood appears to be slower (8- to 12-day half time), however, and if numerous early samples are taken, the curve of plasma radioactivity is well represented by the sum of four exponentials (542). The volume of distribution of the earliest phase upon extrapolation to time zero is approximately 4 % of the body weight, and the extrapolation of the slowest component to zero time gave about 20 % of the body weight. d-Thyroxine disappears from the blood at an even more rapid rate than l-thyroxine. Several authors have removed plasma from patients given I[131] and infused this labeled thyroid hormone into other patients. In general, it seems that the rate of loss of endogenously labeled thyroid hormone is more rapid than that of labeled thyroxine (277, 482, 736). In no instance, however, were samples taken for an adequate period of time, to be sure that the slower component of loss was measured. An unexplained phenomenon was the finding that when labeled hormone was transfused into thyrotoxic recipients, it was turned over more rapidly than in euthyroid recipients (277).

This difference between endogenously labeled hormone and labeled thyroxine was not observed in the rat by one group (257, 259).

In a series of investigations by Albert et al., however, a rather marked difference was found in the rat between the metabolism of exogenously labeled thyroxine and endogenously labeled thyroid hormone. In both instances liver, carcass, gastrointestinal tract, urine, feces, and thyroid were measured for 5 to 12 days (15, 16, 328). In the case of labeled thyroxine, the ratio of carcass to liver plus gastrointestinal radioactivity in 1 hour was about 1.3. It fell until at the end of 5 days it was about 0.4. In the case of endogenously labeled thyroid hormone, the ratio of carcass to liver plus gastrointestinal tract activity did not fall and was approximately 4 in 11 days. It is important to note that endogenously labeled thyroid hormone was formed by giving iodide[131], with the result that considerable time was required for secretion of labeled hormone. Furthermore, instead of "Flash" labeling, there was continuous labeling. These factors may account for the discrepancy. The secretion of triiodothyronine which is formed from I[131] by the rat may play a role in the case of the endogenously labeled hormone and not in the case of labeled thyroxine. In all events the liver played a major role in the excretion of the thyroxine containing some 50 % of the remaining radioactivity 16 days after its administration. The nature of the radioactivity found in the bile has been investigated, and a compound tentatively identified as a glucuronide of thyroxine has been isolated (91, 704, 705). This compound is hydrolyzed to thyroxine by β-glucuronidase and is hydrolyzed in the gastrointestinal tract.   It is produced by perfused livers and liver slices but not by liver homogenates or spleen slices (91).   The quantitative determination of the biliary secretion in man shows that in general about 10% of the radioactivity administered as I^{131}-labeled l-thyroxine appeared in the bile in 6 or 7 days (329).   Another report described biliary excretion of radioactivity after I^{131}-labeled thyroxine in normal rats, those treated with desiccated thyroid, and those treated with thiouracil (355).   The thyroidectomized and thiouracil-treated rats showed a diminished biliary excretion of radioactivity over a 6-hour period.   It appears as though there is a quantitative difference between rats and man in the catabolism of thyroxine.   In rats about two-thirds of the radioactivity is eventually excreted in the feces and one-third in the urine (16).   In man, approximately two to three times as much iodine from thyroxine is excreted in the urine as appears in the feces (17).   Another study using l-thyroxine labeled with I^{131} showed somewhat different results.   Over a 6-day period about twice as much radioactivity was found in the feces as in the urine (329).

The role of the liver in the metabolism of thyroxine has also been investigated by transplantation of the thyroid into the spleen so that all of the thyroid hormone is delivered directly to the liver.   In spite of this, the animals grew satisfactorily, the precipitable iodine in serum was normal, and there were no changes generally (78).   It has also been reported that the intrasplenic injection of thyroxine results in about the same metabolic effect as subcutaneous injection (473).   The distribution of labeled thyroxine in the nuclei, mitochondria, and supernatant fractions of liver cells has also been studied (402).   Somewhat over half the radioactivity was found in the supernatant fraction, about one-fourth in the mitochondria, and the rest in the nuclei.   Thyroxine metabolism has also been studied in the dog, rat, and mouse (118, 267, 708).

The thyroid has been examined by several workers after the administration of labeled thyroxine and appears not to concentrate thyroxine, since the ratio of thyroidal to urinary I^{131} is essentially the same after radiothyroxine or radioiodide (61, 482).   The thyroid thus accumulates the iodide released upon deiodination of thyroxine.

The pituitary concentration of thyroxine has been investigated, and it appears that in the rabbit there is definite localization of radiothyroxine in the posterior lobe and in the tuber cinereum (133, 290).   Even after rather large doses of thyroxine[131], this concentration in pituitary was noted in the rabbit (324).   The monkey also shows a concentration of thyroxine in the pituitary (132).   No significant concentration is found in the pituitary of the rat, cat, or guinea pig (132, 257, 328).   Thyroxine is also eliminated in the urine but in rather small quantity.   After a tracer dose of I^{131} when equilibrium has been more or less achieved, usually less than 5% of the urinary radioactivity is present as thyroxine (538).   There is a suggestion that other nonthyroxine, organic iodine compounds may appear in the urine.

A considerable number of investigations have been reported on the effect of various agents and procedures on the metabolism of thyroxine. The effect of hyperthyroidism has been studied in rats and in man (61, 355). In general, no marked difference is noted other than the difference in collection by the thyroid of the iodine derived from thyroxine. There are data to suggest increased utilization, in stress and as a result of epinephrine, of thyroid hormone in rats (84, 188). Recently in human beings fluctuations in the level of protein-bound serum iodine have been observed under situations of emotional tension (300). This may, of course, be due to any one of a large number of factors such as variations in release of thyroid hormone, in excretion, or in distribution of the hormone.

The effect of a thyroxine antagonist (the butyl ester of 3:5-diiodo-4-hydroxybenzoic acid) on the metabolism of thyroxine has been studied. In thyroidectomized rats, this compound increased the elimination of radioactivity if the thyroxine was labeled in the prime positions but had essentially no effect if the thyroxine was labeled in the 3:5 positions (585). Sodium iodide was without effect, and diiodotyrosine slightly increased the catabolism of thyroxine only when it was labeled with I^{131} in the prime positions. In all instances the urinary excretion of I^{131} was the only measure of thyroxine degradation utilized. Other workers using intact rats found that butyl 3:5-diiodo-4-hydroxybenzoic acid decreased the elimination of radioactivity after the administration of thyroxine or triiodothyronine labeled with I^{131} in the prime positions (775, 779). Labeled triiodothyronine was also excreted more slowly when the same ester was administered. In all the above reports, the I^{131} was attached to the prime positions. The explanation offered by the later group is that the butyl ester competes with thyroxine for the enzyme which deiodinates thyroxine and, therefore, being deiodinated more slowly, it is excreted more slowly. Support for this argument is the fact that this same ester is in rats a rather potent inhibitor of the effect of thyroxine on oxygen consumption, but actually enhances the increased oxygen consumption from triiodothyronine (419). It has also been reported that pantothenate hastened the disappearance of thyroxine (nonlabeled) and that either thiamine hydrochloride or niacin prolonged the duration of action of thyroxine (473).

There are many difficulties in comparing work from different investigators, since the size of the dose of thyroxine, the route of administration, and the position of the label (e.g., 3', 5', 3, or 5 position) play important roles (257, 585). In general, the more thyroxine administered, the more will be found in the stool. If the radioactive label is on the prime positions, it is somewhat more labile than if on the other ring (585).

The interesting observation that 2,4-dinitrophenol lowers the PBI of rats was reported recently (238). Very recently this has been investigated in greater detail, and it was shown that 2,4-dinitrophenol hastened the loss of labeled thyroxine from serum, decreased the rate of loss of labeled iodine from the thyroid, and depressed the protein-bound iodine of serum (237). Furthermore, in spite of a lower PBI there was no change in pituitary cytology.

A recent and rather extensive investigation of precipitable iodine in the tissues of normal dogs has been reported (102). The concentration of precipitable iodine in heart, lungs, spleen, small intestine, pancreas, and testis was about the same as that of serum. PBI in skeletal muscle was lower than PBI of serum, and PBI's of liver and kidney were greater than that of serum. Recently, it has been suggested on the basis of studies with I^{131} in rats that there may be a large pool of iodine in nonthyroid tissues which is not in equilibrium with exogenous I^{131} for periods of a week or more (15). A rough calculation of the data presented by Carr and Riggs, however, suggests that if the data on nonthyroidal iodine in the dog can be applied to man, this is probably not the case, because approximately two-thirds of the iodine can be then accounted for in the thyroid. Difficulty in iodine analysis and species difference certainly prevent a final opinion.

The metabolism of labeled triiodothyronine has been investigated. It appears, in man, to disappear from the circulation much more rapidly than thyroxine, the slowest rate of loss from blood having a half time of about 2 days (338, 542). The glucuronide of triiodothyronine has been identified in the bile (607). Precise and complete studies of its degradation are at the moment lacking, however. Triiodothyronine was originally described as an unknown compound which was found after the administration of labeled thyroxine (259). It has been suggested that triiodothyronine is derived extrathyroidally from the partial deiodination of thyroxine (265, 779). However, Roche, Lissitzky, and Michel (594) investigated nonthyroidal tissues for the presence of an enzyme capable of deiodinating thyroxine to triiodothyronine and could find none. They did describe a deiodase which deiodinated monoiodotyrosine and diiodotyrosine but which is ineffective with thyroxine and triiodothyronine. This deiodase was found in the thyroid gland. The fate of radioactive diiodotyrosine has been recently investigated in rats and man. It was rapidly deiodinated and rapidly excreted, and did not localize in the liver to any appreciable extent (328, 337). When the butyl ester of 3:5-diiodo-4-hydroxybenzoic acid was administered with diiodotyrosine, it markedly reduced the excretion of iodine in the urine (779).

A series of publications has presented data suggesting that thyroxamine may be the active thyroid hormone (370, 371, 717-720). Thyroxamine was not isolated from blood, but its action was similar to that of naturally occurring thyroid hormone.   An increase in the protein-bound iodine of serum occurring after the long-continued administration of sodium iodide has been described (138).   This material, which is an organic compound of iodine, is not thyroxine.   Its nature, function, and significance are unknown.

V. Agents Affecting Growth and Function of the Thyroid

It is well known that both the growth and function of the thyroid can be readily influenced by altering either the hormonal or nutritional environment of the organism.   Such methods of altering the gland's structure or function, although not always within the physiologic range, might justifiably be classified as physiologic stresses on the thyroid.   In recent years, there have been described many chemical agents which also alter the thyroid's function and growth.   Notwithstanding the fact that these agents usually exert their action by interfering with or augmenting certain physiologic functions of the thyroid, they are pharmacologic in action and will be discussed as such.

A. Hormonal Control of Thyroid Function

The most dramatic hormonally induced alterations in the thyroid result from removal of the pituitary or from the administration of pituitary extracts rich in thyrotropic hormone.   In recent years, several studies have been directed at determining the capacity of the thyroid to exert its normal functions in the absence of any stimulus from the pituitary.   It has been reported (747) that the iodide-trapping mechanism of the thyroid functions at about 10 % of its normal capacity after removal of the pituitary.   In this study, it was also observed that the thyroids of hypophysectomized animals failed to bind iodine to protein and that these functions of the thyroid were restored by administering thyrotropic hormone. In another study (477) it has been reported that the thyroids of hypophysectomized rats were capable of concentrating only a fraction of the I^{131} trapped by normal thyroid tissue and that within the 30 hours that these rats were followed, diiodotyrosine was synthesized, but not thyroxine. Studies done by another group (18, 543) on hypophysectomized rats revealed that such animals were capable of concentrating one-tenth the radioiodide collected by the thyroids of intact rats.   Furthermore, the rate of loss of labeled thyroid hormone from the thyroid fell to one-tenth of the normal rate within 5 days of removing the pituitary.   It has also been found that although the thyroids of hypophysectomized rats bind I^{131} to protein very slowly, eventually more than 90 % of the collected iodine is bound to protein.   Furthermore, in this study I^{131} was found in the thyroxine fraction in the thyroids of hypophysectomized rats, but the proportion of thyroxine to diiodotyrosine was less than in the thyroids of intact rats.

Recently it has been reported that isotopic labeling techniques can be applied in studying the targets of various preparations of pituitary hormones (679, 680). Pituitary extracts rich in thyrotropic and gonadotropic hormones have been labeled by coupling them with diazobenzene sulfonic acid into which S^{35} had been incorporated (681). When this preparation was administered to male chicks, the radioactivity was found to be concentrated in the thyroid, gonads, and liver. Esterification of similar pituitary preparations with S^{35} labeled sulfate resulted in a radioactive preparation which when injected into chicks or rats was found to be concentrated in the thyroid, testes, liver, and retro-orbital tissues (679, 680).

Another study (340) done in chicks revealed three effects of the thyroid-stimulating hormone which occurred in the following order: a loss of previously deposited radioactive iodine, growth of the thyroid as indicated by an increased cell height, and finally an increased avidity for radioactive iodine. In another study (548) the loss of total thyroid iodine and changes in the thyroid mean acinar cell height have been followed at varying intervals after administration by injection of one Junkmann-Schöller unit of TSH. A 20% loss of thyroid iodine was observed at the end of 6 hours and a maximum loss of 75% by the end of 24 hours. There was no increase in mean cell height of the thyroid until after 18 hours. This effect became maximum at the end of 30 hours.

In human beings, it has also been demonstrated that the earliest effect induced by the administration of TSH is a loss of thyroid hormone. It has been observed that the intramuscular administration of thyrotropic hormone to patients who had previously received large tracer doses of radioactive iodine is followed by a prompt release of protein-bound I^{131} into the circulation and a decrease in radioactivity in the thyroid (59).

It has been suggested that this purging effect of TSH occurs as the result of an activation of a proteolytic enzyme which hydrolyzes thyroglobulin and releases thyroxine into the circulation (152). A digestion of intrafollicular colloid and a transport across the cellular wall of the follicles of what is presumed to be the thyroid hormone have been demonstrated by histochemical techniques. A proteolytic enzyme which is capable of hydrolyzing hemoglobin and thyroglobulin has recently been isolated from the thyroid (451). It would appear from the above studies that the primary action of thyrotropic hormone is to release thyroxine from the intrafollicular thyroglobulin. This action possibly occurs in association with a proteolytic enzyme. Growth of thyroid tissue and the increased iodide-concentrating function of the thyroid appear to occur consequently to the release of hormone from the gland.

In another study, however, two of these functions of the pituitary have been separated (253). It has been found that if the pituitary is separated from the hypothalamus, growth of the thyroid fails, but the iodide-concentrating function of the thyroid is not altered. From these studies it has been suggested that the pituitary may secrete two thyroid-stimulating factors, one of which has a growth effect and the other a metabolic effect.

A recent investigation (165) has resulted in an apparent separation of two other effects which previously had been attributed to the thyrotropic hormone. It has been reported that the exophthalmos-producing factor of the pituitary can be separated by chemical fractionation from the thyroid-stimulating principle. If the observations of these two investigative groups are confirmed, further study may either identify the exophthalmos-producing factor with the above suggested growth-promoting factor or with the metabolic fraction of the thyrotropic hormone. On the other hand, such studies may make it even more complicated by presenting us with three different pituitary hormones which would be related to thyroid function.

The metabolism of thyrotropic hormone has been studied, and it appears that the thyroid gland itself may play a major role in this process. Studies (558) done on patients with untreated hyperthyroidism have revealed that they excrete no active thyrotropic hormone in the urine. Normal medical students excrete easily measurable amounts of this hormone but considerably less than that excreted by totally thyroidectomized patients.

Studies done on the serum of patients with various types of thyroid disease have revealed similar results. In one study, in which changes in the mean cell heights of guinea pig thyroids were used as the assay method, no thyrotropic activity was found in the sera of untreated thyrotoxic patients, a small amount in the sera of such patients under treatment with derivatives of thiourea, and great amounts in patients with untreated myxedema (532). In another study, the effects of sera from patients with various disorders of the thyroid were tested for their effect on metamorphosis and on the mean cell heights of tadpole thyroids. In about half of the hypothyroid patients studied, the sera were found to have increased amounts of thyrotropic activity. Three acromegalic patients were also found to have increased thyrotropic activity in the serum. Patients with hyperthyroidism were found to have thyrotropic activity about equal to that of normal human beings (137).

These observations have been explained by some on the basis of a theory that the pituitaries of thyrotoxic patients are suppressed by the increased circulating thyroid hormone of this malady. Furthermore, it is postulated that the pituitaries of totally thyroidectomized patients excrete a readily demonstrable thyroid-stimulating factor because of a compensatory increased activity of the anterior pituitary. On the other hand, it has been postulated that the normal thyroid alters the thyrotropic hormone and that the thyroid of Graves' disease inactivates even more of this pituitary hormone. To test this thesis a study (559) with tissue culture techniques was undertaken. Explants of rabbit thyroid tissue or of control tissues from the same animals were bathed in Tyrode's solution containing varying amounts of thyrotropic hormone for 1 to 3 days. The bathing media were removed and assayed by the cell height technique for thyroid-stimulating activity. It was observed that one rabbit thyroid was capable of inactivating as much as 12 units of thyrotropic hormone, and that explants of thymus or of lymph nodes, both of which tissues are enlarged in Graves' disease, were capable of inactivating as much as 6 units of TSH. None of the other control tissues inactivated any of the exposed TSH. Furthermore, explants of thyroid tissue did not alter the gonadotropic activity of the pituitary extracts used (548.) It was also found that explants of well-involuted thyroid tissue taken from patients with Graves' disease after preoperative treatment with iodides were capable of inactivating nearly twice the amount of TSH that was inactivated by normal thyroid tissue taken at operations for parathyroid adenomas. Explants of colloid goitrous tissue failed to inactivate any TSH (550). Subsequent studies have demonstarated that TSH inactivated by exposure to thyroid tissue can be reactivated by treatment with certain reducing agents such as thiouracil or 5-aminothiodiazole-2-thiol (552). Thus it is suggested that the thyrotropic hormone in exerting its action on the thyroid is inactivated through some oxidative enzyme system and possibly acts as a hydrogen donator to some unidentified enzyme system in the thyroid.

It has been reported that the administration of desiccated thyroid to patients with Graves' disease did not suppress the iodide-concentrating function of the thyroid (768). On the basis of these observations, it has been suggested that the pituitary is not involved in hyperthyroidism, since it is thought that the administration of thyroid should depress any hyper-functioning pituitary. On the other hand, it has also been reported that rats made goitrous by the administration of thiouracil when treated with thiouracil and dl-thyroxine in a dose of 50 µg. daily for 14 days manifest only a partial involution of their goitrous thyroids.

Studies reported by several investigators suggest that the products of both male and female gonads and of the adrenal may alter thyroid function. Twenty years ago (688) it was reported that the thyroids of mature guinea pigs responded to thyrotropic hormone with a greater degree of hyperplasia when the hormone was administered during the luteal phase of the ovary than they did during the follicular phase. In another study (468) in rats on a diet deficient in iodine it has been reported that estrone and diethylstilbesterol not only increased the involutional action of ad-

ministered iodides but also increased the storage of iodine by the thyroid.
It has also been reported (468) that rats on an iodine-deficient diet when
treated with testosterone, estrone, progesterone, or pregnenolone had a
greater avidity for radioiodine than did their controls.   In the same study,
it was also found that estradiol, estriol, and diethylstilbesterol inhibited
the uptake of radioiodine by the thyroids of rats on an iodine-deficient
diet.   In women (526) with normal menstrual cycles, the uptake of I^{131}
has been the same throughout the menstrual cycle.   However, there was a
decreased uptake of I^{131} in the post-partum period.   This phenomenon
may be related to the fact that normal pregnancy in human beings is associated with significant rises in the serum protein-bound iodine level.
The maximum rise is observed in the last trimester (426).

   There have been repeated reports from one laboratory that parahydroxy-
propriophenone, a very weak estrogen, inhibits the goitrogenic action of
propylthiouracil in the rat (108, 369).   Other investigators have failed to
confirm this observation (390, 469, 646).

   Two investigative groups (467, 677) have observed that whereas adrenalin when administered to rats produces a decreased uptake of I^{131} by
the thyroid, the same stimulus when administered to adrenalectomized
rats causes a marked increase in the collection of I^{131}.   These studies have
been pursued in rats on an iodine-deficient diet receiving ACTH or various
steroids of adrenal origin.   It has been observed that ACTH, cortisone,
Compound A, Compound L, and desoxycorticosterone if administered in
large enough doses cause a decreased uptake of I^{131} by the thyroid.   Remissions in patients with Graves' disease treated with ACTH have been reported (204).

   The effect of cortisone or of ACTH on the response of the hypophysectomized rat's thyroid to administered thyrotropic hormone has been studied.   It has been observed (549) that cortisone or ACTH inhibited the
uptake of I^{131} in response to treatment with TSH but did not prevent the
growth response.   It has likewise been observed (501, 502) that the administration of cortisone with TSH to hypophysectomized dogs did not
alter the effect of TSH on the thyroid's growth.   These apparent inhibitory
effects of cortisone as evidenced by a decreased trapping of I^{131} have been
explained on the basis of an increased renal clearance of the iodide (323).

B. The Effects of Environment on the Thyroid

   Several investigators (104, 689, 743) have reported that the exposure of
laboratory animals to cold results in a stimulus to the thyroid.   In two of
these studies the stimulus was quantitated by demonstrating an increased
mean cell height of the thyroid, and in another study an increased collection and turnover of radioactive iodine was observed.   It might be postu-

lated that this stimulus was excited by an effect of the cold on some temperature control center in the midbrain. Support for this thesis comes from the fact that stalk-sectioned animals do not demonstrate any change in the thyroid on exposure to the cold (744). Since it has been demonstrated that animals in the cold require more thyroxine to prevent the goitrogenic effect of thiouracil than do those exposed to warmer temperatures (148), the effects of cold might be explained on the basis of an increased need for thyroid hormone by the peripheral tissues, with the stimulus mediated via the midbrain and pituitary. This effect of cold on the thyroid has also been demonstrated in the thyroids of newly hatched chicks (309). When the eggs were incubated at temperatures of 96.8°F., the thyroids of the newly hatched chicks weighed 7.38 mg., whereas the thyroids of chicks hatched from eggs which had been incubated at 102.2°F. weighed 2.19 mg.

The effect of general body irradiation on the uptake of radioiodine by the thyroid has been recently investigated (85, 320, 465). With the smaller doses, 800 to 1000 r, there was observed at 2 hours an increased uptake of I^{131} which lasted for 1 day, following which there occurred a decreased uptake of I^{131}. Animals exposed to the larger doses of X-ray manifested increased uptakes of I^{131}. The decreased uptake of I^{131} observed initially might be attributed to an increased output of adrenal steroids. The increased uptake, on the other hand, might be attributed to starvation as the result of X-ray sickness. At any rate, it has been demonstrated that the thyroids of starved animals have an increased avidity for radioiodine (104).

It is of interest that the exposure of mice to darkness results in a stimulus to the thyroid, as evidenced by increases in the growth of the thyroid and in its avidity for I^{131} (531). On the other hand, continuous exposure to light results in a suppression of growth and function of the thyroid.

Stress such as that produced by the injection of formalin or by surgical trauma has been reported to depress the thyroid's avidity for I^{131}. Forced muscular exercise which resulted in less depression of the thyroid's avidity for radioiodine was, however, followed by an increased urinary excretion of iodide (74). These changes might be attributed to the effects of adrenal steroids on the body economy.

C. Nutritional Effects on the Thyroid

The well-known nutritional effects of an iodine deficiency on the thyroid have recently been reinvestigated (104). In this study, the effects of an iodine-deficient diet were observed on the following indices: the total and protein-bound iodine levels of the serum; total thyroid iodine; thyroid weight; and the avidity of the thyroid for I^{131}. The animals studied were sacrificed at intervals of 10, 20, 34, 106, and 237 days after instituting this dietary regime. It is of interest that an increased avidity for I^{131} developed within 10 days of beginning this diet, when the total thyroid iodine was 81 % of normal. Maximum avidity for I^{131} was observed at 20 days, when the total thyroid iodine was 61 % that of the control thyroids. There was no significant increase in thyroid weights, however, until after 106 days of this dietary regime, when the total thyroid iodine was less than 20 % that of the control thyroids and the serum total and protein-bound iodine levels were approximately half those of the control rats. Here again we have an apparent separation between the metabolic and growth changes in the thyroid which presumably were mediated via the pituitary. The metabolic changes occurred much before the increased growth in thyroid tissue was observed. Unfortunately, this cannot be stated unequivocally without observations at shorter invervals between the 34th and 106th days and without cell height measurements at all periods of observation.

Alterations in thyroid function have been produced also by administering in excess a variety of foods, i.e., cabbage (112), rape seed (345), and soybeans (653). A thorough study of foods which might alter thyroid function has been reported recently (31, 254). The effects of 61 different foods on the accumulation of I^{131} were studied in normal human thyroids. It was reported that several vegetables such as spinach, lettuce, cabbage, rutabaga, turnips, and strawberries caused a decrease in the accumulation of I^{131} when taken in great enough quantities. The most potent vegetable inhibitor of the thyroid was the rutabaga. The goitrogen from this vegetable has been isolated and identified as L-5-vinyl-2-thioöxazolidone (36). At present, it is impossible to tell whether or not these agents account for the development of some human goiters.

In a study on the effect of proteins and amino acids on the endocrine system, it has been found that rats on a diet deficient in phenylalanine had small thyroids (636). Assays of the pituitaries and sera of these rats for thyrotropic hormone might be helpful in clarifying the mechanism by which this phenomenon occurred.

D. PHARMACOLOGIC AGENTS AFFECTING THE THYROID

Chemical control of thyroid function has recently been realized not only in the laboratory but also in the clinic. Such chemical control of thyroid function was probably first observed by Austin Flint (199), who nearly a century ago wrote that he preferred treating thyrotoxic patients with hydrocyanic acid, since he had observed this agent to have a sedative effect in patients with this malady. The next demonstration of a chemical inhibitory effect on the thyroid came from the observation by Marine and associates (432) that methyl cyanide had a thyroid inhibitory effect in rabbits. Goiters, with low metabolic rates, were then reported in patients being treated for their hypertension with potassium thiocyanate (43). Then the observations by Mackenzie, Mackenzie, and McCollum (416, 417) that sulfaguanidine, and by Richter and Clisby (572) that thiocarbamide were goitrogenic in the rat excited intensive searches for effective chemical inhibitors to thyroid function. Several investigators (34, 38, 96, 449) undertook intensive searches for nontoxic chemical compounds which exerted inhibitory actions on the thyroid and which might be useful in controlling the overactive thyroids of thyrotoxic patients. By now a long list of agents with varying chemical structures have been found to exert some antithyroid activity (see Table I). Most of these thyroid inhibitors have been found to be goitrogenic to varying degrees. The thiocarbamides constitute the largest series of agents studied. A second group is made up of aniline derivatives and has been labeled by one group of investigators the aromatic thyroid inhibitors (190). A third group has been defined as "interfering ions" (801, 802). There are still other thyroid-inhibiting or goitrogenic compounds which do not fit into any of the above groups.

The thiocarbamides, *i.e.*, thiouracil, etc., have been demonstrated to interfere with thyroid function by preventing the oxidation of iodide and thus preventing the utilization of iodine in the synthesis of thyroid hormone (32). It has been suggested that these agents exert this effect by inhibiting an oxidative enzyme necessary for the oxidation of iodide (146, 151).

A theory with experimental support has been presented that the aromatics (sulfonamides, *para*-aminobenzoic acid, resorcinol, etc.) and possibly iodides in excess compete with tyrosine for the oxidized iodine in the thyroid gland (190). This interference with the iodination of tyrosine interferes with the synthesis of thyroid hormone and is followed by chemical hypothyroidism.

It has been demonstrated that thiocyanate interferes with the trapping of iodide by thyroid slices (211). It has also been demonstrated *in vivo* that thiocyanate discharges stored iodide from the thyroid under the control of thiouracil. Studies recently reported by one group (801, 802) have demonstrated that several monovalent anions, *i.e.*, perchlorate, chlorate, hypochlorite, periodate, iodate, biiodate, and nitrate share with thiocyanate the properties of blocking the iodide trap of the thyroid and of discharging iodide from the gland. These agents have also been found to have certain goitrogenic properties. Recently, it has been demonstrated that potassium perchlorate is an effective agent in controlling the overactive thyroid of Graves' disease (235).

Most of these agents have been found to possess goitrogenic properties which are generally attributed to a compensatory increased production of

TSH by the pituitary, secondary to a fall in circulating thyroid hormone. No doubt this explanation is at least in part true, as evidenced by the absence of demonstrable TSH in the pituitaries of animals made goitrous by the administration of thiouracil and by the fact that such goitrous responses to these thyroid inhibitors do not occur in hypophysectomized animals.   However, it has been demonstrated that a significant increase in the mean cell height occurs in thyroids taken from rats within 24 hours of starting treatment with thiouracil before the serum protein-bound iodine has fallen significantly (552).   Furthermore, two investigative groups (220, 221) have demonstrated that thiouracil and related compounds when administered with thyrotropic hormone augment the action of administered thyrotropic hormone.   This augmentation of TSH by these agents may account for the increase in size of goiters observed in some patients treated with some of these agents even before their metabolic rates have reached euthyroid levels.

From the practical point of view, many of these agents have been found to have unusual value in the treatment of hyperthyroidism.   Although prolonged treatment of Graves' disease with these agents is usually effective as long as the drugs are given, the per cent of lasting remissions after cessation of therapy has been disappointing.   Probably the greatest merit of these agents has been in the preparation of such patients for thyroidectomy. The major advantage of such a preparation for operation is that the patient can be brought to a euthyroid state and be treated as a patient with a non-toxic goiter.

Another well-known inhibitor to the thyroid is iodide.   This halogen is well known to the clinician as an effective inhibitor in controlling the hyperthyroidism of Graves' disease.   Its effects are quite different from those produced by thiouracil or other goitrogenic agents, since they result in an involution of the hyperplastic goiter of this malady and in a storage of thyroglobulin in the thyroid follicles.   By following the histologic changes in serial biopsies taken before any therapy and after control of the hyperthyroidism with thiouracil, and in the same thyroids which were removed after continued treatment with thiouracil and added iodides, it has been demonstrated that this involutional or therapeutic effect of iodide can be separated from the nutritive role of iodide.   In this study (553) the pretreatment biopsies showed the classic thyroid hyperplasia of Graves' disease, which was not decreased in the biopsies taken after treatment with thiouracil had restored the patients to euthyroidism.   However, the addition of iodides caused an involution of the thyroid (Fig. 1).   Since the thyroglobulin iodine values in the operatively removed thyroid were very low, *i.e.* 7.0 mg. per 100 g. of tissue, it can be said that the involutional effect of iodide occurred notwithstanding the fact that thiouracil was given in a

TABLE I
Agents Affecting Thyroid

Compound	Formula	Iodide accum. blocked	I^{131} uptake	Iodine conversion	Thyroid weight	Ref.
A. Inorganic Anions						
1. Iodide	I^-	x	↓		↓	32
2. Fluoride	F^-				→	498
3. Thiocyanate	CNS^-	x	↓		↓←	35, 42, 797
4. Nitrate	NO_3^-	x	↓			802
5. Chlorate	ClO_3^-	x	↓			802
6. Biiodate	$H(IO_3)_2^-$	x	↓			802
7. Hypochlorite	ClO^-	x	↓			802
8. Iodate	IO_3^-	x	↓			802
9. Periodate	IO_4^-	x	↓			802
10. Perchlorate	ClO_4^-	x	↓			802
B. Metals						
1. Antimony	Sb_2O_3		↓	↓	←	772
C. Thiocarbamide Derivatives						
1. Thiourea	$HS-C(=NH)-NH_2$				←	35, 416, 573, 637
2. Thiosemicarbazone	$R-C(H)=N\cdot N(H)-C(=S)-NH_2$				⇵?	35, 505

649, 686	←	→	→	
35, 113	←			
382, 687, 788	↑?			
35	←			

3. 2-Mercaptoimidazole

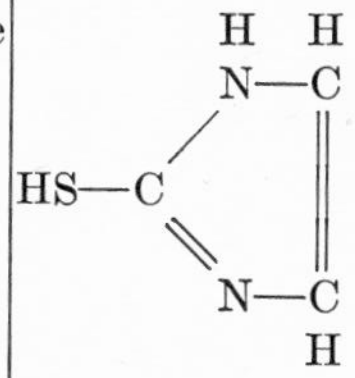

$$\begin{array}{ccc} H & H & \\ N-C & = & C \\ | & & \\ HS-C & & N-C-H \end{array}$$

4. 2-Thiohydantoin

$$\begin{array}{ccc} O = C & = & C \\ N & & \\ HS-C & & N-C-H_2 \end{array}$$

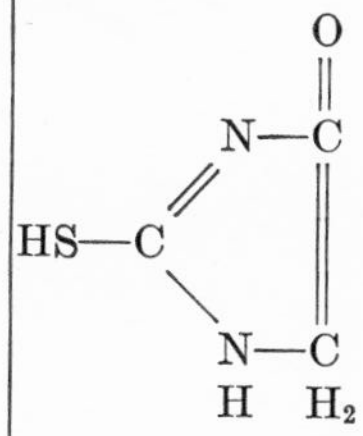

5. Ergothioneine

$$H - C - CH_2 - \overset{+}{C} - N(CH_3)_3$$
$$COO^-$$

$$\begin{array}{ccc} H & & \\ N-C & = & C \\ | & & \\ HS-C & & N-C-H \end{array}$$

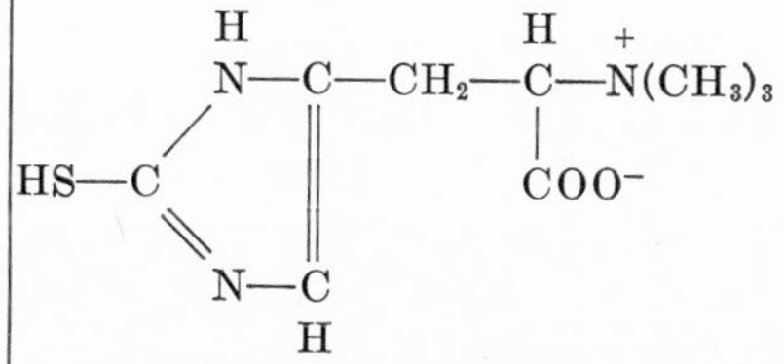

6. Aminothiazole

$$\begin{array}{ccc} NH_2 - C - N & & C = C \\ & S & H \quad H \end{array}$$

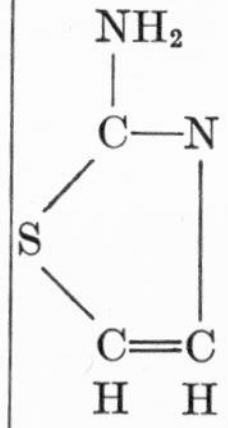

TABLE I (*Continued*)

Compound	Formula	Iodide accum. blocked	I131 uptake	Iodine conversion	Thyroid weight	Ref.
C. Thiocarbamide Derivatives						
7. L-5-Vinyl-2-thioöxazolidone			→	→	←	36
8. 2-Mercaptothiazole			→		←	649
9. 2-Thiouracil			→	→	←	35, 746

Compound	Structure				References
10. 5-Iodo-2-thiouracil	(structure)	→	→	←	52,105,784
11. Thiopyridone-2	(structure)			→	114
12. Thiopiperidone-2	(structure)			→	114
13. Promizole	(structure)			←	192, 487

TABLE I (Continued)

Compound	Formula	Iodide accum. blocked	I131 uptake	Iodine conversion	Thyroid weight	Ref.
D. Aniline Derivatives						
1. *p*-Aminobenzoic acid			→		↑	35
2. *p*-Amino salicylic acid					↑	117, 278, 350
3. Phenothiazine			→			702

4. Amphenone "B"		→	→	←	312
5. Sulfonamides			→	←	210, 416, 637
6. Antistine				→	225

TABLE I (Continued)

Compound	Formula	Iodide accum. blocked	I^{131} uptake	Iodine conversion	Thyroid weight	Ref.
D. Aniline Derivatives 7. Phenylbutazone			→			250
E. Aromatic Phenols 1. Resorcinol			→	→	↑	166

2. *p*-Hydroxypropio-phenone	↓?	469, 512
3. Hesperidine methylchalcone	←	562
F. Miscellaneous 1. Nitrogen mustard	→	664

TABLE 1 (Continued)

Compound	Formula	Iodide accum. blocked	I131 uptake	Iodine conversion	Thyroid weight	Ref.
F. Miscellaneous 2. 4-Methyl-6-hydroxy-pyrimidine-2-α-thioisobutyric acid	OH—C=N, CH, C=C, N=C—CH₃, H—C—H, H₃C—C—SH, COOH (pyrimidine ring structure)				→	474

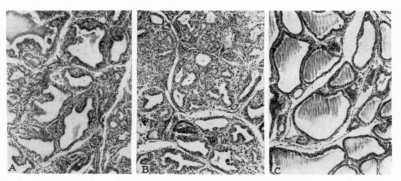

FIG. 1. Sections of biopsies and operatively removed thyroid from one patient in various phases of treatment.

A. Biopsy taken before beginning any treatment. The classic hyperplasia of Graves' disease is illustrated.

B. Biopsy taken after treatment with thiouracil had restored patient to euthyroid state. Compared to A, the hyperplasia is not decreased.

C. Section of thyroid taken from operatively removed thyroid after continued treatment with thiouracil and added sodium iodide. The involutional effect of iodide is demonstrated.

dose great enough to prevent the utilization of iodine in the synthesis of thyroid hormone.

It has been suggested (793) that iodides exert their therapeutic effects by preventing the trapping of iodide. Another group of investigators (190) have suggested that iodide works much like the aromatic goitrogens by competing with tyrosine for any oxidized iodine. Notwithstanding the experimental evidence presented by both of these groups, it must be pointed out that the hyperplastic thyroids of Graves' disease after successful treatment with iodide contain even greater than normal amounts of iodinated thyroglobulin (270).

It has also been suggested (548, 552) that this therapeutic effect of iodide in Graves' disease is due to an inhibitory action on the reaction that occurs between thyroid cell and thyrotropic hormone. Evidence for this thesis comes from the observations that: (1) iodide inhibits the action of TSH on the thyroid of hypophysectomized rats; (2) the *in vitro* inactivation of TSH by explants of thyroid tissue is inhibited by adding iodide to the medium; and (3) whereas the urine of untreated thyrotoxic patients contains no active thyrotropic hormone, a thyroid-stimulating factor is very readily demonstrated in the urine of a thyrotoxic patient shortly after instituting treatment with iodide.

This thesis may be further supported by the observation (679) that pituitary preparations rich in thyrotropic hormone labeled by esterification with S^{35} labeled sulfate are concentrated in the thyroids of rats to a significantly greater degree when the animals are receiving an iodine-deficient diet than when the animals are receiving adequate or excess amounts of iodides.

Of the other halogens, chloride and bromide are without inhibitory effect on the thyroid. There is some evidence, however, that fluoride (498) might exert some inhibitory effect on the thyroid.

VI. Actions of Thyroid Hormone

A. Relation to Structure

"Thyroid hormone" has been used as a generic term to indicate any substance that will relieve human myxedema when properly administered (631). As such, this definition would not require that this substance be thyroidal in origin or have a specific physical and chemical constitution. However, almost all contain iodine substituted in an inner aromatic ring of a chemical grouping named thyronine (279). Some bromine substituted thyronines have hormonal activity (396) as well as the diphenyl thioether analogue of thyroxine (397). At present, various forms of the thyroid hormone exist including thyroglobulin, various degradation products of thyroglobulin, thyroxine recovered from thyroglobulin (342) or synthesized chemically (283), other substituted thyronines (27), various crystalline products from the hydrolysis of iodinated proteins (635), and the circulating and active form of the thyroid hormone. One cannot justly claim that the substance with the greatest biological activity per mole is indeed the thyroid hormone. It has been reported (6) that thyroxine polypeptides obtained from tryptic digests of thyroglobulin have a greater biological effect than thyroxine.

With the study of the structural analogues of thyroxine, some insight has been gained as to what portions of the structure of thyroxine are necessary for its physiological action (212, 217, 490) and what substitutions make for the most effective antithyroxine agents.

For thyroxine activity the hydroxyl on the outer ring may be present in either the 2' or 4' (489) position, and the formation of a methyl ether at the hydroxyl group will decrease thyroxine activity (48). The two halogens at 3' and 5' appear necessary only for maximal activity, iodine being more effective than bromine or chlorine (1, 48, 386, 396, 569). The oxygen in the ether linkage between the two rings can be successfully replaced by a sulfur (280, 397), although the diphenyl ether configuration is crucial (86). The side chain (R) at position 1 of the inner ring must be a polar group such as $CHNH_2COOH$, NH_2, $-CH= CH COOH$, $-CH_2CH_2COOH$, and $-COOH$, although tetraiodothyroacetic acid and triiodothyroacetic acid have only a tenth of the activity of triiodothyronine in the prevention of goiter (523). Such a variety suggests that a simple compound itself may be active, because most of these compounds have only one reactive group. In general, the diiodothyronine framework provides the optimum starting point for maximal hormonal activity. In mammalian studies, thyroxine itself (where R is alanine, all four X's are I, and the hydroxyl is in the 4' position) has until now consistently proved the most active single compound. Triiodothyronine, which is similar to thyroxine except that there is an iodine atom absent at the 5' position, is more active than thyroxine in increasing oxygen consumption (263, 265). 4-(4'-Hydroxyphenoxy)-3,5-diiodophen-ylpropionic acid tested for tadpole metamorphosing effects (45) was 2.9 times as active as thyroxine under the conditions of testing. The high specificity of the thyroxine core for hormonally active material was demonstrated by the synthesis and testing of "isothyroxine," a compound with the same molecular weight and elemental analysis as thyroxine (284). "Isothyroxine" was hormonally inactive.

Several nitro ethers of N-acetyldiiodotyrosine not only showed antithyroxine activity, but in large doses had some weak thyroidal activity (799).

After an evaluation of the studies with iodinated phenoxyacetic acid it was apparent (356) that 2, 4, 6 positions were important for the distribution of the halogen. Most compounds which were active thyroxine antagonists (213, 418, 799) contained iodine in the 2 and 6 positions counting from the oxygen bridge. 2',6'-Diiodothyronine exhibited thyroxine inhibition as well (130). The alkyl esters of 3,5-diiodo-4-OH benzoic acid (776) as well as the monoiodo derivative (683) also formed a series of potent antithyroxine agents, with the butyl ester most effective (654). Hydroxylating the alkyl group increased the antithyroxine activity of the lower esters (780). The simplest substances tested having antithyroxine activity are those which contain predominantly the diiodophenoxy group (418, 777, 778). It is interesting that on the basis of studies with radioactive thyroxine and the butyl ester of 3,5-diiodo-4-OH benzoic acid, the site of action of this thyroxine analogue was considered to be in the blocking of the conversion of thyroxine to triiodothyronine (419, 774). It is of further interest that the physiologic effect of triiodothyronine was enhanced and its excretion diminished by this analogue (419). The block to thyroidal uptake of I^{131} by N-butyl 3,5-diiodo-4-hydroxybenzoate appeared to be by no other mechanism than the breakdown of this compound to iodide, which then exerted the same effect as inorganic iodide (90).

Thyronine (534) and a thyroxine-free peptone (4) have been reported effective against thyrotoxicosis and experimental hyperthyroidism. Dibromotyrosine and diiodotyrosine have also been claimed (7, 8, 620) to depress various aspects of thyroid function, but this has been questioned (47). 3-Fluorotyrosine (362, 403) and 3-fluoro-4-hydroxyphenylacetic acid (442) have also been studied. The latter may exert some noncompetitive effects (45). Although the metabolic response of rats to thyroxine or desiccated thyroid is lowered by methylthiouracil (3) and animals made hypothyroid by thiouracil are less responsive metabolically to thyroxine (49), one gains no insight into the structure of thyroid hormone structure from such studies. This may well represent a toxic effect of thiouracil derivatives rather than a peripheral antagonism to thyroxine (83).

Other agents appear to be antithyroxine agents, but they very likely do not exert their action as authentic thyroxine antagonists. The suggestion (103) that 1,7-dimethylxanthine was a peripheral antagonist of thyroxine has not been substantiated (44, 246, 782). The antithyroxine activity reported for cholesterol or carotene (46, 433, 437, 628, 659, 669) seems unrelated to structural analogues. Although vitamins may offset the toxic effects of thyroid administration, this protective action of the vitamins more likely reflects the overcoming of a relative vitamin deficiency rather than an antithyroxine action of the vitamin (170).

The principal generalization which can be made (45, 213) is that the configuration

has exhibited antithyroxine activity with a wide variety of different groups substituted on each end.

B. Fundamental Actions

The extreme variety of effects noted after the administration of thyroid hormone may well reflect a primary action of this hormonal substance a one biochemical site.   All the changes noted may then be the consequence of this fundamental action.   The ubiquitous nature of thyroid hormone effects may be appreciated from the number and types of enzymes affected (Table II).   Since diffuse changes are induced after concentrations of thyroxine in body fluids of 10^{-7} M, it has been tempting to consider this hormone as acting either as a catalyst on "the fundamental reaction" or in a more general fashion as a coenzyme for many reactions.   Of course, the concentration at any histological or biochemical site may well be many times in excess of this figure.   This "reaction" is as yet unidentified, although many suggestions have been offered.   Perhaps all oxygen consumption and indirectly the various metabolic processes are regulated by the effect of thyroxine on cytochrome c (168).   However, it is difficult to feel secure in the specificity of action of thyroxine on cytochrome c when adrenalectomy, like thyroidectomy, will produce a fall in total body cytochrome c (169).   Until the relationship of this iron-containing enzyme to the other enzymes is established, it is presumptuous to conclude that thyroxine affects certain enzymes like xanthine oxidase, cholinesterase, and lipase via its effect on cytochrome c.

More recently the hypothesis has been presented (375) that thyroxine may exert its metabolic effects by "uncoupling" a specific oxidative phosphorylation occurring at a rate-limiting step.   The decrease in metabolic efficiency which would accompany such a process might be more than offset by the enhanced rate of oxidation, which would yield, in a given period, more total utilizable energy.   Indeed, it has been found that thyroxine *in vitro* depresses the ratio of esterified, *i.e.*, high-energy, phosphorus to oxygen of tissue preparations (307, 376, 434, 435, 491).   Not only thyroxine but also what may be the active thyroid hormone, triiodothyronine, will dissociate phosphorylation from respiration and even depress the respiration absolutely (423).   Other substituted phenols will have a similar action (332).   Oxidative phosphorylation may indeed be the pivotal area for the action of thyroid hormone, for the association of the tricarboxylic acid cycle and cell respiration through phosphorylation is less tenuous (393).   The crucial role of enzymes in the effect of thyroxine on phosphorylation is given further support in the observed reduction by enzyme poisons of the elevated P^{32} turnover following treatment with thyroid hormone (240).   That the ubiquitous high-energy phosphorus compounds may control to some extent many phases of metabolism may be appreciated from the study (11) where decreased oxygen consumption because of swelling mitochondria was in turn attributed to a decrease in adenosine triphosphate which was present in the hyperthyroid state.

In general it may be stated that except for the afore-mentioned demonstration of an *in vitro* effect of thyroxine on oxidative phosphorylation, there has been no *in vitro* response to thyroxine or thyroglobulin which has been

TABLE II
THYROID EFFECTS ON ENZYMES

Enzyme	Source	Species	Concentration as affected by thyroidectomy or thiouracil			Concentration as affected by thyroid administration			Reference
			↑	0	↓	↑	0	↓	
I. *Oxidizing enzymes*									
A. Cytochrome	Heart, Kidney, Skeletal muscle, Liver	Lamb and Dog			X				177
	Liver	Rat				X			433
	Spleen						X		
	Brain						X		
	Liver	Rat				X	X		728
B. Cytochrome c	Muscle	Rat				X	X		730
	Liver, Kidney, Heart, Skeletal muscle	Rat				X	X		168
C. Succinoxidase	Skeletal muscle	Dog			X				175, 176
	Brain	Rat						X	618
	Liver	Rat				X	X		728
							X		452, 672, 673, 727, 785, 786
					X				401
D. Lactic acid dehydrogenase	Liver	Rat	TU X	TX X				X	750
E. Pyruvic acid oxidase	Brain	Rat					X		618

TABLE II (*Continued*)

Enzyme	Source	Species	Concentration as affected by thyroidectomy or thiouracil			Concentration as affected by thyroid administration			Reference
			↑	0	↓	↑	0	↓	
F. D-Amino acid oxidase	Liver Kidney	Rat				X			352, 353, 617
							X		
	Liver	Rat			X				97, 352
G. Xanthine oxidase	Liver	Rat					X		567
H. Choline oxidose	Liver	Rat					X		672, 673
II. *Esterases* A. Lipase	Serum	Rabbit						X	351
				X					760
B. Cholinesterase	Serum	Human			X	X			26, 233
C. Pseudocholinesterase	Plasma	Rat						X	292
			X					X	293
D. Alkaline phosphatase	Femur	Rat				X			781
	Serum	Human				X			58
	Serum	Rat	X		X				421
	Intestine	Rat			X	X			527
	tine					X			456
	Liver	Rat			X	X			456, 457
				X				X	357
				X				X	366
	Kidney	Rat			X		X		357
					X				366, 421
								X	438
					X	X			456, 457
	Thyroid	Mouse					X		268
	Kidney	Guinea pig			X				366
	Spleen	Rat	X						366
	Tibia	Rat					X		438
	Thyroid	Rat			X	X			691
	Milk	Cow	X					X	110

TABLE II (*Continued*)

Enzyme	Source	Species	Concentration as affected by thyroidectomy or thiouracil			Concentration as affected by thyroid administration			Reference
			↑	0	↓	↑	0	↓	
E. Acid phosphatase	Liver	Rat					X		457
					X		X		357
					X				366
					X	X			456
	Kidney	Rat					X		357
					X	X			456
							X		457
	Thyroid	Rat	X					X	691
	Intestine	Rat			X	X			456
				X			X		457
F. Adenosinetriphosphatase	Liver	Rat				X	X		491
							X		673
G. Creatinephosphokinase	Skeletal muscle	Rabbit						X	28
III. *Carbohydrases* Amylase	Liver	Rat				X			639
IV. *Proteolytic enzymes* Cathepsin	Liver	Rat				X			439
V. *Amidases* Arginase	Liver	Rat					X		400, 357
						X			140
VI. *Transferases* Hexokinase	Skeletal muscle	Rat				X			672, 673
	Brain	Rat					X		673

consistent and reproducible enough to isolate the site of action of thyroid hormone.

C. Nitrogen Metabolism

Many aspects of nitrogen metabolism are affected by the administration of thyroid hormone. Frequently, one may have to accept the over-all observation on the nitrogen balance without being able to evaluate the indirect contributions of altered metabolic rate, appetite, or absorption from gut. It would appear, for example, that the subnormal growth of cretins is related to some extent to the decreased food intake associated with the decreased metabolic rate.

Total nitrogen balance was studied (503) in normal patients treated with thyroid hormone, and it was found that the negative nitrogen balance could be accounted for on the basis of increased urea excretion. Among nitrogen products, thyroid hormone is considered (82) to act on "deposit" protein, the protein of extracellular fluid, which is in excess in myxedema. It has been reported that when myxedematous patients are treated with thyroid hormone, the increased nitrogen excretion is associated with a sodium diuresis, whereas normal subjects excrete an excess of potassium with their nitrogen diuresis (95). This lends support to the concept that the protein which is mobilized in myxedema is extracellular.

In experimental animals that have been thyroparathyroidectomized, there is a higher level of blood urea than in control rats (513) and an increased nitrogen excretion (306). The surgical procedure and reduced food intake put the animal into a negative nitrogen balance which becomes positive when the food intake assumes normal proportions (383). With paired feeding, normal and thyroidectomized rats have almost identical nitrogen balances (383). However, treatment with thiouracil will also induce negative nitrogen balance. In hyperthyroid rats there were increases in the urinary nitrogen, ammonia, uric acid, and creatinine (699). In hyperthyroid animals on a high carbohydrate diet and in thyroidectomized animals (625) on a constant diet, there was a greater excretion of nitrogen in urine than in control situations. The administration of thyroxine normalized the urinary nitrogen excretion. The increase in plasma amino acids which follows evisceration is decreased by thyroidectomy and increased by thyroxine (77). This emphasizes the catabolic role of thyroxine in nitrogen metabolism rather than its role in promoting deamination or urea synthesis. Whether the thyroid hormone is primarily anabolic or catabolic, may depend to a large extent on the dose at which it is administered as well as on the metabolic state of the organism at the time of administration of this hormone.

Thyroxine does not lead to a negative nitrogen balance in adrenalectomized rats (310, 510). In experimental burns, where there is a marked negative nitrogen balance, there is no reduction of the urinary nitrogen after thyroidectomy (651, 804). The adrenal rather than the thyroid appears to be the crucial gland in the negative nitrogen balance of burns (651, 804). Vitamin A did not modify the decreased nitrogen utilization noted with thyroid treatment of rats (93). In these hyperthyroid rats, there was no change in the ammonia or uric acid excretion, but there was a decreased urinary allantoin. Vitamin B_{12} did reduce the negative nitrogen balance of rats made hyperthyroid with thyroxine (626), suggesting that B_{12} spares proteins and that this vitamin may be involved even in the action of thyroid hormone.

It has been found that thyroid hormone will promote the utilization of proteins entering the organism, as measured by the ability to increase the liver nitrogen of previously starved rats (678). With the use of N^{15}-labeled glycine, it has been found (306) that the rate of protein catabolism is decreased in thyroidectomized rats, whereas the rate of amino acid catabolism in the same animals was increased to such an extent that a negative nitrogen balance ensued. The rate of synthesis of protein from amino acids in thyroidectomized and control animals was the same. In rats made hyperthyroid and given heavy water, there was a larger concentration of deuterium in the proteins of the liver than in control animals (335). Thyroxine inhibited glutamic acid oxidation by rat kidney cortex (193). Liver slices from thyroidectomized rats liberated less nitrogen and formed less amino nitrogen than those from normal rats (354). These net rates, of course, need not apply in human beings, but it is of interest that in human myxedema the blood globulin is increased and accordingly the total blood protein is moderately elevated (159, 752), while the administration of thyroxine decreases the plasma proteins at the expense of the globulins (752). In myxedema the spinal fluid protein is likewise higher than normal (725). This is similar to findings in rats made hypothyroid by thyroidectomy where there was an increase in the NPN of blood and plasma globulin, more specifically the α-globulin. The total plasma protein was increased while the plasma albumin was not significantly altered (384). This increase in plasma proteins could be reduced somewhat by a restriction of dietary intake. However, in the fowl, it has been noted (696) that the administration of thyroxine will decrease the plasma proteins at the expense of the albumins while the globulins remain normal. In rabbits, the administration of thyroid hormone increases the concentration of albumin and fibrinogen in plasma and bone marrow but causes a decrease in the globulin of these tissues (492). This was not confirmed in another study (12) where it was found that rabbits made hyperthyroid showed a constant decrease in total blood proteins with a decrease of albumins and an increase of globulins.

The protein nitrogen of the kidneys is increased in rats treated with thyroxine, although this nitrogenous product is increased with thiouracil treatment, as though this drug promoted protein synthesis or decreased protein catabolism. Thyroidectomy of rats at birth leads to a decrease in muscle mass as well as to a deficient amount of myosin (647). It has been shown (648) that thyroidectomized rats have a carcass containing less protein and more fat than control rats. The liver and kidney weights were reduced in such animals as well as the total and relative protein contents of both organs (383). However, in contradistinction to thyroidectomy, liver protein in thiouracil-treated rats is increased above that of ad libitum fed controls. Thyroxine, on the other hand, will increase both liver weight and liver protein (693).

The thyroid hormone is intimately involved in creatine and creatinine metabolism. It has been known (652) for some time that there is a creatinuria and associated decrease in creatinine excretion in Graves' disease. This metabolic defect is corrected when the Graves' disease is treated with iodide (508). Patients with hyperthyroidism show a decreased tolerance for creatine, insofar as such patients excrete more of an administered dose of creatine than do normal patients (515, 571, 726). In experimental animals, the relationship of the thyroid to creatine metabolism is similar to that noted in man. Experimental hyperthyroidism in rats results in a profound creatinuria (479). The creatine and phosphocreatine content of the muscles of the rabbit are increased after thyroidectomy and decreased after the administration of thyroid substance (755). It has been suggested (5) that this disorder in creatine metabolism may be nonspecific, inasmuch as insulin and adrenalin as well as thyroid hormone will cause a decrease in creatine content of heart and skeletal muscle. However, the creatinuria induced by adrenalin is not manifested in thyroidectomized animals (124). It has been found (773) that thyroxine or thyrotropic hormone, when administered to the intact animal, causes a loss of stored creatine with no increase in the rate of creatine synthesis. There is faulty conversion of creatine to creatinine in hyperthyroid patients, with an increased transformation of creatine to its anhydride in hypothyroid patients (773). In a series of investigations (123) on the creatinuria of guinea pigs it has been found that removal of the thyroid and thymus decreased urinary creatine, thymectomy and gonadectomy increased creatinuria, and removal of the thyroid, thymus, and gonads had no effect on creatine excretion. Castration after thyroidectomy will increase urinary creatine (125), while creatinuria can be induced by thyroxine in the absence of thyroid, thymus, or gonads (126).

The role of the thyroid in nucleic acid metabolism has only recently been investigated. Thyroxine increases both the pentosenucleic acid as well as the deoxypentosenucleic acid of rat kidney (427, 429), whereas thyroidectomy decreases these same purine and pyrimidine derivatives in kidney (428). Oddly enough, thiouracil has an effect similar to that of thyroxine (428), suggesting that this thiopyrimidine has an additional action beyond its ability to decrease the production of thyroid hormone. Human beings receiving thyroxine do not show any change in the level of their blood uric acid, although they may show a decrease in urinary uric acid (100). In another study, urinary uric acid was unchanged by the administration of thyroxine or triiodothyronine (555). In thyroidectomized human beings, there is no increased uric acid excretion (100).

The metabolism of other nitrogenous products seems to be related to the thyroid. In patients made hyperthyroid with thyroxine, there is a decrease in blood glutathione levels, whereas in hypothyroidism induced by methylthiouracil there is an increase in the level of this tripeptide (99). There is no correlation in patients between ergothionine levels in blood and thyroid activity (380). It appears that thyroidectomized animals synthesize less acetylcholine, whereas hyperthyroid animals produce more of this compound (120, 325). However, since the formation of acetylcholine from pyruvate and choline requires the presence of coenzyme A, it has also been suggested (120) that the decreased acetylcholine synthesis in thyroidectomized animals is only a reflection of decreased coenzyme A formation.

D. Thyroid and Carbohydrate Metabolism

The effect of the thyroid hormone on digestion and absorption of carbohydrate and on glucose degradation and utilization has been studied by few investigators. There are many clinical reports of hyperglycemia in hyperthyroid patients (230). Intravenous glucose appears to be metabolized normally in hyperthyroid man (411). Another study in normal and hyperthyroid subjects showed no difference in the absorption of galactose from the small bowel (478). A careful study in rats showed that desiccated thyroid produced an increased rate of absorption of glucose, xylose, and galactose from the gastrointestinal tract (25). There is some evidence that the thyroid increases the rate of utilization of glucose, for it has been found that the blood sugar of eviscerated hyperthyroid rats fell more rapidly than in control eviscerated rats (464). Furthermore, in rats fed glucose, experimental hyperthyroidism decreased the amount of glycogen formed in the liver (119). In hyperthyroid patients there is indirect evidence that liver glycogen content is normal (570). Net splanchnic glucose production has been reported to be essentially normal in hyperthyroid subjects (484). Houssay investigated carbohydrate metabolism in partially pancreatectomized dogs and found that the administration of thyroid converts these animals to a diabetic state (319). More recently, radioiodine thyroidectomy of diabetic dogs has been investigated, and the loss of thyroid did not appear to influence the diabetes (486).

Pentose excretion in the rat is increased with thyroid feeding and decreased after treatment with thiouracil (609). There is some evidence that the thyroid affects intermediary carbohydrate metabolism. For example, in experimental hyperthyroidism an elevation of the pyruvic acid in

blood was found (536). The blood lactic acid fell after thyroidectomy in
dogs, and the rise in blood lactate produced by adrenaline was less than
normal in thyroidectomized dogs (521). The thyroid also affects acetylation of p-aminobenzoic acid. In normal subjects given 500 mg. of p-aminobenzoic acid, approximately 88 % was acetylated. Liver disease and hypothyroidism did not affect this, but the fraction acetylated was below normal
in hyperthyroid subjects (229).

E. Thyroid and Fat Metabolism

It has been long known that in man hypothyroidism is quite regularly
accompanied by hypercholesterolemia. In addition the level of neutral
fat and phospholipid is elevated in hypothyroidism (201, 516, 517). Hyperthyroidism is irregularly accompanied by a fall in the level of these
fatty substances of blood. The level of fat in the diet plays a major role
in the development of hypercholesterolemia in the rat, for starvation or a
severely limited food intake can prevent hypercholesterolemia induced
by hypothyroidism (184). Contrariwise, a high-fat diet protects animals
against the lethal effect of large doses of thyroxine (251). Furthermore,
the administration of thyroid will lower the level of cholesterol in the serum
of rats fed a high-cholesterol and high-fat diet (767). Lipoproteins of S_f
10-20 size have been reported to be increased in amount in the serum of
hypothyroid subjects (236).

The partial understanding of the mechanisms whereby thyroxine controls fat metabolism has recently been achieved. The synthesis of phospholipids in the liver has been shown to be increased in rats treated with
thyroxine and decreased in rats given thiouracil (200). Phospholipid turnover in the thymus has been reported to be decreased by desiccated thyroid, although nucleic acid turnover was increased (209). The same
investigators also found that thyroid increased phospholipid and nucleic
acid turnover in liver. The excretion of cholesterol in the bile is controlled
in part by the thyroid and plays a role in regulation of the level of cholesterol in serum. The biliary excretion of cholesterol is regularly reduced in
hypothyroid rats and increased in hyperthyroid rats (616). Cholic acid
secretion in the bile is apparently lowered in both hypothyroid and hyperthyroid rats (723). In experiments with both deuterium and tritium labeling the synthesis of cholesterol was found to be increased in hyperthyroid
rats and decreased in hypothyroid rats (436, 615). The turnover time of
visceral cholesterol paralleled that of cholesterol synthesis. Exposure of
hypothyroid rats to a cold environment had no effect on the rate of cholesterol synthesis (436). In contrast to the effect of thyroid on nitrogen
metabolism, there appears to be a consistent gradation of effect of thyroid
on fat metabolism from hypothyroidism to euthyroidism to hyperthy-

roidism.   There are equivocal data on the level of cerebrosides in blood in hypo- and hyper-thyroidism (142).

In human myxedema the electrophoretic pattern of serum is essentially normal except for an elevation of the β-globulin (425).

The role of the thyroid in atherosclerosis has been extensively investigated in animals and man.   A recent study of eight patients who had been hyperthyroid on an average of seven years and who had elevated serum cholesterols, showed at autopsy an essentially "normal" amount of atherosclerosis (72).   In dogs, thiouracil feeding per se appears to have no effect on the development of atherosclerosis but does potentiate the atherosclerosis induced by the feeding of cholesterol (692).   Desiccated thyroid, on the other hand, protects against the development of atherosclerosis in the chicken subsequent to the feeding of cholesterol (139).   In rabbits after atherosclerosis had been induced by the feeding of cholesterol, a normal diet, 2,4-dinitrophenol, and thyroxine did not accelerate regression of these lesions (40).

F. Electrolyte and Water Metabolism

Thyroid hormone appears to be involved in the metabolism of a rather large number of mineral elements.

Studies of the effect of the thyroid on sodium and potassium are confined almost exclusively to man and are subject to some dispute (82).   Boothby and his associates found no consistent effect of intravenous thyroxine on either sodium or potassium.   Byrom (95), however, in a later study reported that in the hypothyroid or normal man, thyroxine (in a massive dose) caused a loss of both these elements.   In the hypothyroid subjects the loss of sodium was much greater than that of potassium, whereas in the normal subjects more potassium was lost.   He suggested that this meant that the fluid accumulated by the myxedematous patient was largely extracellular but that in the normal subject an intense thyroxine effect could cause loss of intracellular water and salts.   More recently, two studies have been reported with thyroxine and triiodothyronine, and both studies failed to reveal a consistent effect on the over-all balance of sodium or potassium (30, 555).

Thyroid hormone has a profound effect on water, however.   In myxedematous patients given thyroxine or triiodothyronine, there is a marked diuresis, and one report shows an increase in the level of sodium and chloride in serum, suggesting that enough water was excreted to cause a relative concentration of extracellular fluid (555).

The effect of thyroid hormone on calcium metabolism is not yet entirely clear.   This is hardly surprising, since calcium intake, renal function, vitamin D, nitrogen balance, activity, etc., exert such marked effects on calcium metabolism that smaller effects can easily be masked. It was first noted that in hyperthyroid patients an increase in urinary calcium could be detected (358). Later it was shown that in rabbits the administration of desiccated thyroid causes a loss of calcium (509). Several studies in man have shown that patients with hyperthyroidism, if kept on a rather low calcium intake, excreted more calcium than normal subjects (39, 579, 581). These same investigators showed that hypothyroid human subjects tended to excrete less calcium than did normal subjects (580). In patients with hyperthyroidism who showed hypercalcuria (four of six) treatment of the hyperthyroidism with thiouracil caused a fall in urinary calcium to normal values (249). However, in two more recent studies with both thyroxine and triiodothyronine no consistent effect was seen on calcium excretion or balance (30, 555). There was in no instance any change in the level of calcium in the blood as a result of change in thyroid activity.

A recent report of pathologic examination of vertebrae from patients with active hyperthyroidism showed excess destruction in all cases. The earlier clinical reports on the effects of hyperthyroidism on the skeleton are well reviewed in this article (202).

Phosphorus metabolism is markedly affected by the thyroid. Either thyroxine or triiodothyronine causes a loss of phosphorus in both urine and stool (30, 555, 579, 580, 581). If one attempts to account for the phosphorus loss on the basis of nitrogen loss (using the ratio of these two as found in normal muscle), there is a considerable excess in phosphorus excretion (555). The source of this phosphorus is not clear. Thyroid has no effect on the level of phosphorus in the blood, however. Thyroid hormone has also been reported to affect the phosphorus content of cow's milk (110).

No consistent effect of thyroxine or triiodothyronine on chloride excretion in urine or stool in man has been found (555). However, earlier investigators found that the feeding of desiccated thyroid to cats caused a decreased urinary excretion of chloride in spite of diuresis (537), according to one report; according to another report, thyroxine or desiccated thyroid caused an increase in urinary chloride (215). The adrenal may play a role in these responses, since Gaunt has found that in rats thyroxine increases the diuresis after a water load. Previous adrenalectomy abolished this effect of thyroid (221). A study of chloride excretion in the sweat of normal and hyperthyroid subjects may help in explaining these differences. It was found that the chloride content of sweat was decreased in hyperthyroid subjects; the more severe the hyperthyroidism, the less chloride was found in the sweat (360).

Iron metabolism appears to be affected by thyroid function. In rabbits thyroidectomy caused a rise of 15 % to 25 % in the serum iron and a slight fall in tissue iron. Thyroxine caused a reversion of these levels to normal

(528).   In man the serum iron has been reported by one group to be high in hyperthyroidism, and has been reported by another group to increase in patients with hyperthyroidism after treatment (203, 655).

Two groups of investigators have reported that the level of bound magnesium in the serum is elevated in hyperthyroidism and below normal in myxedema (162, 676).

A more recent report shows that nondiffusible magnesium of plasma is unchanged in patients with definite alterations in thyroid function (131).

G. Thyroid and Vitamin Metabolism

A vast literature on this subject was reviewed in 1943 (170); the reader is directed to this reference.

1. *Vitamin A*

The thyroid is necessary for the conversion of carotene to Vitamin A, and carotene does not prevent the development of signs of Vitamin A deficiency in hypothyroid animals (172, 330, 341, 762).   In myxedematous subjects treatment with desiccated thyroid was said to decrease blood carotene and increase blood Vitamin A (127).   In cows and goats, thyroxine appears to decrease the carotene content of stool, and thiouracil increases it (109).   Thyroid feeding may have improved absorption of carotene or increased its conversion to Vitamin A.

The effect of Vitamin A on the thyroid is less well understood.   It has been reported that Vitamin A deficiency does not affect iodine uptake by the thyroid but does diminish incorporation of iodine into thyroxine (762). On the other hand, a very extensive investigation showed that either Vitamin A lack or Vitamin A excess increased radioiodine uptake by the thyroid (466).

Vitamin A has also been reported to protect animals against the rise in O_2 consumption caused by desiccated thyroid (628).   Further studies showed that Vitamin A in large dosage decreased the TSH content of rat pituitary (627).

There is conflicting evidence on the relationship between Vitamin A and thyroxine with respect to amphibian metamorphosis, with some data suggesting an antagonism between the two substances (189, 198, 407, 770).

2. *Vitamin B*

Thiamine requirements appear to be increased in hyperthyroidism, and the urinary excretion of thiamine is increased in hyperthyroidism (134, 302, 643).   The paralysis in *Discoglossus pictus* induced by very large doses of thiamine hydrochloride is prevented by thyroxine (22).   Pigeons in whom a thiamine deficiency had been induced have been reported to show a reduc-

tion in the calorigenic effect of thyroxine (622).   Riboflavin deficiency has
been reported in hypothyroid rabbits and in myxedematous patients (252,
347).   A lack of riboflavin has been reported to alter the histologic picture
of the thyroid without altering its weight (76).   In hyperthyroid rats there
is an increased need for riboflavin (171).   Thyroidectomy or thiouracil
appeared to lower the N' methyl nicotinamide excretion, whereas this
defect is corrected by thyroxine (98).   It was suggested that thyroxine
might participate in the methylation of nicotinic acid.

Vitamin B_6 , in large dosage, has been reported to cause hypofunction of
the thyroid of rabbits (101).   Vitamin B_6-deficient rats have a lower oxygen
consumption than normally fed controls but the same oxygen consumption
as pair fed controls (57).   Signs of Vitamin B_6 deficiency were unaffected
by hypothyroidism.

The administration to rats of large amounts of iodocasein causes loss
of body weight and eventual death.   Vitamin B_{12} appears to partially
protect rats from these effects (75, 182, 698).   However, Vitamin B_{12}
does not inhibit the increase in O_2 consumption secondary to thyroprotein
feeding (460).   The diet is reported to affect the antagonism between B_{12}
and thyroxine, for it is observed in animals on a soy flour diet and not seen
with rats on a wheat flour diet (529).   Other reports indicate that B_{12}
does not protect against thyroxine administration but a fraction of liver
does (75, 185, 187).   Dried penicillin mycelia and aureomycin mash but
none of the B vitamins have been reported to antagonize the feeding of
desiccated thyroid (186).   Vitamin B_{12} itself apparently has no effect on
the thyroid as measured by radioiodine uptake (rats) (458, 759).   In mice
Vitamin B_{12} will increase the growth rate and iodinated casein abolishes
this effect (459).   Vitamin B_{12} will inhibit in rats the growth-depressing
effect of thiouracil, although it has no effect on the reduction in I^{131} thyroidal uptake caused by thiouracil (458).   Thyroidal hypertrophy of the
B_{12}-supplemented rats was less than in those given thiouracil alone (458).
Of some interest is the fact that dinitrophenol will cause a retardation
in body and testis weight, which is reversed by liver fractions (187).

Citrovorum factor is said to be excreted in excessive quantity in the
urine of hyperthyroid rats (173).   If the rats are also deficient in folic
acid, there is no change in excretion of citrovorum factor from the feeding of
thyroid.

3. Vitamin C

Considerable work has been reported on Vitamin C deficiency and the
thyroid, but in general it is contradictory or inconclusive.   Even the effect
of scurvy on the thyroid is not clear, for both marked changes and no
changes have been reported (10, 64, 291, 410, 444, 610, 645, 742, 763).

The effect of TSH on the normal and scorbutic guinea pig is also not clear and has been recently reviewed (763). Both thyroxine and triiodothyronine catalyze the cupric-ascorbic acid oxidation system and are roughly equally effective (224). The possibility of formation of free radicals was suggested (222, 223) as a mechanism for this action.

H. Effect of Thyroid on Oxygen Consumption

The remarkable effect of thyroid hormone on oxygen consumption was first demonstrated many years ago by Magnus Levy (420), and very well quantitated in normal and hyperthyroid human subjects (60, 81, 454). The decay curves of the effect of thyroxine in patients with myxedema have been carefully investigated (80). Relatively little work was done on this recently until triiodothyronine was identified in plasma, synthesized (261, 264, 592), and shown to have physiologic activity (265). Now, experiments in man and rats have shown that triiodothyronine is roughly three to four times as potent in elevating oxygen consumption as is thyroxine (30, 263, 266, 297, 446, 555, 731). There are marked differences between these two compounds, however, in onset of action and duration of action. A single dose of thyroxine, given intravenously, requires about 10 days before its peak effect on BMR is seen. After this the basal oxygen consumption falls off in exponential fashion, with a half time of about 15 days. Recently, it was noted that in guinea pigs a rise in oxygen consumption could be seen 4 hours after the administration of thyroxine (406). Triiodothyronine, administered in a single dose intravenously, has its peak effect in 24 to 36 hours and thereafter declines in exponential fashion, with a half time of about 8 days. A careful study of comparative effects of different amounts of these two agents disclosed that the ratio of total increase in oxygen consumption $\frac{T_3 \Delta O_2}{T_4 \Delta O_2}$ was 4 or 5 for low doses and actually less than 1 for high doses (446).

There is a recent report that in rats thyroxine caused less increase in O_2 consumption in females than in males. Castration increased the sensitivity of females to the calorigenic action of thyroxine (530).

One aspect of oxygen consumption has been used as a test for thyroid hormone. In this test survival time of animals, placed in a closed vessel, has been measured. Thyroxine or triiodothyronine caused a definite decrease in survival time (665, 731).

Much work has been done on the respiration of tissues from normal, thyroxine-treated, and thyroidectomized animals. The central nervous system (455), muscle, kidney and liver (92), and cardiac muscle (50, 51, 740) show an increased O_2 utilization after thyroxine treatment and decreased O_2 consumption after thyroidectomy.

There is some discrepancy in the results, but in general most tissues are affected with the exception of the brain, spleen, and gonads (51).

Catheterization technique has been employed to study in the intact human being oxygen consumption of brain and of viscera. Absence of the thyroid causes a marked decrease in cerebral oxygen consumption, although hyperthyroidism does not affect cerebral O_2 consumption (640, 641). Net splanchnic oxygen consumption in hyperthyroid patients was increased even more than basal oxygen consumption (485).

I. THYROID AND GROWTH AND METAMORPHOSIS

The most dramatic effect of thyroid hormone on growth—its control of metamorphosis in amphibia—was first noted by Gudernatsch in 1912, and it soon became apparent that the thyroid was necessary for metamorphosis in the tadpole and that feeding of thyroid hormone (269) could markedly accelerate metamorphosis. Actually, thyroid hormone in sufficient quantity will cause metamorphosis of the salamander, which ordinarily spends its entire life in the larval form (738). Furthermore, acceleration of tadpole metamorphosis is so sensitive an index of thyroid hormone that it has been extensively used as an assay procedure (141, 217). Thyroxine causes metamorphosis in very small doses. It is of interest that triiodothyronine is approximately three times as effective as thyroxine (621). Diiodothyronine and even diiodotyrosine are said to be effective in very large doses but the possibility of contamination with small amounts of thyroxine or triiodothyronine exists. The converse effect is also seen, since thyroidectomy or hypophysectomy prevent tadpole metamorphosis (24, 671).

There are some groups of urodeles which are permanently larval forms (Proteidae and Sirenidae). One species, *Typhlomolge*, is of considerable interest because some specimens have no demonstrable thyroid and the remaining specimens studied had rudimentary thyroids (739). The other species of permanently larval forms, however, have normal thyroids, and it appears that thyroxine or desiccated thyroid will not cause metamorphosis in these forms.

Recently it has been shown that an antihistaminic (the HCl salt of benzyhydryl,2-(1-piperidyl)-ethyl ether) inhibits the metamorphogenic effect of triiodothyronine and delays spontaneous metamorphosis (271). Interestingly enough, cortisone does not affect metamorphosis in tadpoles (367) and has no effect on the tadpole thyroid. Even in mundane nonmetamorphosing fauna, however, the thyroid has a profound effect on growth.

In fish, investigation of the effects of thyroidectomy and thyroid feeding is somewhat difficult. Growth of certain fish (hybrid strain of *Xiphophorus hellerii* and *Platypoeclus maculatus*) was retarded by thiourea (239), and hyperplasia of the thyroid was seen. This has also been noted in reticulatus and in guppies (304, 670). The effect of thyroid on growth of fish is less uniform, with some observers finding that thyroid powder accelerated growth and abolished the effect of thiourea, and others finding that thyroid had no effect on the inhibition of growth caused by thiourea (316, 667, 670). Also in some fish long-continued feeding of thyroid has been reported to cause growth of monsters (256, 364).

Maintenance of fish in complete darkness appears to stimulate thyroidal growth (547).

Changes in the epidermis and in the eyes and head can be observed in fish given thyroid (303, 374, 377, 378, 582).

Change in salinity has an effect on the thyroid of fresh water teleosts: an increase in salinity decreases thyroidal activity (499). Normal growth is impossible in the absence of the thyroid in man, rats, mice, monkeys, goats, sheep, and rabbits (276, 317, 661, 703). In adult monkeys it has been reported that thyroidectomy was without effect, but a recent and comprehensive survey showed that thyroidectomy with I^{131} in monkeys caused signs and symptoms of myxedema very similar to those found in man (197, 414, 518, 519, 520). Undoubtedly the effect of thyroid hormone on growth represents the sum of the effects of thyroid hormone on a very large number of biochemical processes whose acceleration is necessary for gross increase in animal size. Most of these will be discussed in other sections, but there are a few specific effects of thyroid hormone on growth or organs which might be mentioned here. Excessive doses of thyroxine will cause a marked loss of weight and eventual death of most animals. Certain vitamin and liver supplements will partially protect against this and are discussed earlier. A rather surprising report suggests that l-chloramphenicol protects against the lethal effect of large doses of thyroxine and partially protects against weight loss (232). d-Chloramphenicol, on the other hand, produces results similar to those produced by the administration of thyroxine.

Growth of cartilage as measured by incorporation of S^{35} is at least partially controlled by thyroid hormone being increased by thyroxine and decreased by thiouracil (179). Eruption of teeth is markedly accelerated by thyroxine (334). The thyroid hormone plays a role in molting in reptiles and in plumage in birds (493, 805). In hypophysectomized rats thyroxine markedly accelerates skeletal maturation (560). Epiphyseal closure in immature rats treated with thyroxine occurred early and before adult size was reached. In hypophysectomized rats both growth hormone and thyroxine were necessary for optimal skeletal growth (29, 660).

In tadpoles, thyroxine stimulates the ossification of long bones (207).

J. The Effects of Thyroid Hormone on Various Organ Systems

The clinical symptoms observed in patients with either hyperthyroidism or hypothyroidism suggest specific effects of the thyroid hormone on

several organ systems of the body.   Some of these organ effects have recently been more accurately defined by studies in patients in the hyperthyroid or hypothyroid state or by studies in laboratory animals.

1. *The Cardiovascular Renal System*

The cardiovascular changes in hyperthyroidism often-times produce the
patient's most bothersome symptoms and the greatest challenge to the
therapist.   Tachycardia and a wide pulse pressure are quite characteristic
of this malady.   In patients with severe or long-standing hyperthyroidism
the heart failure is often relatively insensitive to therapy with digitalis.
The cardiac output is increased in hyperthyroidism and is below normal in
the myxedematous patient (216, 485, 641).   In hyperthyroidism, there is
an increased mean and systolic pressure in the right ventricle without
change in the diastolic pressure.   Thus there exists a normal pulmonary
vascular resistance.   Whereas these effects have always been attributed to
the increased work demands imposed by the organism's increased rate of
metabolism, it has been suggested (546) that there is a specific cardiotoxic
effect of the thyroid hormone which is independent of its metabolic effects.
Another group of investigators have reported that the hearts of animals
of various species when made thyrotoxic are insensitive to vagal stimulation
(311).   It has also been reported that the hearts of rats made hypothyroid
by the administration of methylthiouracil are less likely to develop ventricu-
lar arrhythmias on the injection of calcium chloride than are the hearts of
euthyroid animals (424).

In myxedema, there is a decreased blood flow to the skin, whereas in hyperthyroidism the blood flow through the skin and musculature is increased
(180, 694, 695).   The cerebral blood flow is markedly decreased in myxedema.   This has been attributed to an increased cerebrovascular resistance
(640).   It has been reported that hyperthyroidism is not associated with
any change in renal blood flow (128).   On the other hand, the same investigators have reported that myxedema is associated with a reduction in
renal blood flow and decreased clearance of urea, rate of glomerular filtration, and tubular secretory capacity.   The administration of desiccated
thyroid increases the renal blood flow and the tubular excretory capacity.
It has also been reported that hyperthyroidism is not associated with any
change in hepatic blood flow (128).

2. *The Nervous System*

The nervousness in patients with hyperthyroidism has been recognized
as a prominent feature of the disease since the malady was first described.
Similarly the sluggishness and even apathy of hypothyroidism is recognized
as one of the prominent features of this syndrome.   In one study it has
been observed (641) that in myxedema there is not only a decreased rate of

cerebral blood flow but also a decreased rate of oxygen and of glucose consumption by the brain. It is of interest that these indices in hyperthyroidism were found to be within normal limits (640). Studies (121) on the oxygen consumption by brain slices of hyperthyroid rats have revealed an increased oxygen consumption for 2 hours only. Electroencephalographic studies done on athyreotic patients have typically revealed diminished voltage, absent α waves and slow frequency, with a reversion towards normal after treatment with desiccated thyroid (63).

One study indicates that there is no impaired conduction by peripheral nerves in myxedema. However, after a normal reflex contraction in response to the tapping of the Achilles tendon there is a marked delay in the time required for relaxation of the muscle (373). This phenomenon would indicate a defect in muscle function.

3. *The Gonads*

Characteristically, thyrotoxic women describe less profuse menses than they had prior to the onset of their disease. Rarely we are confronted by a patient with amenorrhea which is corrected after control of the hyperthyroidism. Severe hypothyroidism is usually associated with menorrhagia and metrorrhagia. Myxedema of a profound type and of long standing is often associated with amenorrhea. Studies have been reported on one myxedematous patient who had been amenorrheic for four years and who during her control period had no cornified cells in the vaginal smears. Nine days after administering 1 mg. of triiodothyronine this patient abruptly showed 60 % cornification in the vaginal smear. She then had an ovulatory menstrual period 30 days later. It has been reported that athyreotic rabbits and baboons are capable of developing ovarian follicles but not of ovulating (116, 231). Yet it has been reported that the administration of thyroxine does not alter the gonadotropic activity of rat pituitaries (219).

It has been reported (68) that hypothyroidism decreases the sensitivity of mice to estrone and that hyperthyroidism has a reverse effect. Changes in the thyroid status, however, did not alter the response to 3,17β-estradiol. In the male gonad there is no characteristic change produced by hyperthyroidism. It is of interest, however, that in a group of 83 young males with cryptorchidism 54 were said to have had congenital thyroid disease. In 5 cases with hypothyroidism descent of the testis was induced by the administration of thyroid hormone (389). In another study (700) done in bulls it was found that myxedema induced in young bulls by the administration of thiouracil did not affect the sperm. In the older bull, however, such a myxedematous state was associated with poorly mobile and abnormal sperm which returned to normal on correction of the myxedema by withdrawing the antithyroid agent. Gynecomastia is seen quite frequently in male patients with hyperthyroidism. The mechanisms of this phenomenon or the reports by some female patients with this malady that their breasts become larger with the onset of symptoms are far from being clarified. However, it should be pointed out that the administration of iodinated casein to cows may temporarily increase the production of milk (721, 745). Whether these effects on mammary tissue are due to a direct effect on the breast, to a general metabolic effect, or to a direct effect on the gonads has not been resolved.

4. *The Adrenals*

It has been reported that the adrenals of patients with Graves' disease are relatively insensitive to stimulation with adrenocorticotropic hormone (301, 690). On the other hand, adrenal hyperplasia has been produced in experimental animals following the administration of thyroid hormone (716). Furthermore, in another study it was observed that rats maintained over a long period of time on thiouracil had small adrenals and failed to survive exposure to the cold. Since the pituitaries of animals with altered states of thyroid function have been demonstrated to contain normal amounts of ACTH, these phenomena cannot be attributed to any change in the pituitary (272).

5. *The Gastrointestinal Tract*

Severely thyrotoxic patients may have diarrhea and myxedematous patients usually suffer with constipation. The constipation of athyreosis may be attributed to decreased peristalsis of the entire gastrointestinal tract, and the diarrhea of hyperthyroidism may be attributed to increased peristaltic activity. It is interesting, however, that in both myxedema and hyperthyroidism there is a significant incidence of achlorhydria. In myxedema, a 53% incidence of absolute achlorhydria has been reported (398). In Graves' disease, it has been found that 38% of a large group of cases had achlorhydria (398). This phenomenon is easily explained in myxedema as being secondary to the generally decreased body metabolism. It is less easily explained in hyperthyroidism unless there is an insensitivity of the stomach to vagal stimulation similar to the reported insensitivity of hearts to vagal stimulation in experimental hyperthyroidism. It has been demonstrated experimentally that thyroidectomy reduces the time required to produce a perforating peptic ulcer in guinea pigs treated with histamine (756). It has also been observed that whereas thyroxine does not protect against the development of fatal peptic ulceration, desiccated thyroid does (757).

Notwithstanding the fact that the liver of severely thyrotoxic patients has been reported to have certain impaired functions, there are no known specific effects of thyroxine on the liver except for a loss of glycogen observed in experimental hyperthyroidism.

It has been reported that thyroidectomy is followed by a fall in hemoglobin but that the administration of thyroxine causes only a slight increase in the hemoglobin level. The administration of thyroxine has been reported to cause a fall in lymphocytes (422). It has also been reported that the addition of thyroxine to a mixture of fibrinogen and thrombin delays coagulation. This effect is attributed to an inactivation of thrombin by thyroxine (23).

K. Drug Action and Bacteria

1. *Drugs*

The data on the effect of variations in thyroidal activity on the response to, and the metabolism of, assorted pharmacologically important drugs are meager. The older literature is completely contradictory as to whether thyroid feeding increases or decreases susceptibility to morphine poisoning. The relatively more recent data suggest that thyroidectomized rabbits and mice are more sensitive to morphine than normal controls (322, 412). This may be true, even though another investigation found that there was no difference in the narcotic effect of morphine between normal and thyroxine-treated mice (753). Work on man, relating thyroid and morphine, is fragmentary and uncontrolled. More recently the effect of alterations in thyroidal activity on the susceptibility to methadone has been extensively investigated (697). In general, either thiouracil or methimazole produced a definite reduction in susceptibility of rats to methadone, and thyroid increased the susceptibility as measured by per cent fatality for each dose. Thiouracil or thyroidectomy reduced the increase in pain threshold from methadone, although thyroid feeding did not affect it. The metabolism of methadone in liver slices in both thiouracil-treated and thyroidectomized rats was slower than normal. Thyroid feeding appears to increase resistance of rats to pentobarbital, whereas thyroidectomy diminishes it (583). The lowered resistance of the thyroidectomized rats corresponded to a slower detoxication of pentobarbital in the liver, but the increase in resistance of the thyroxine-treated animals was not accompanied by any change in detoxication. Thyroidectomy increased the recovery period and increased the acute fatality with thiopental and propallylanol, although thyroxine feeding did not alter either (313).

On the other hand, thyroxine appears to sensitize rabbits to the toxic effects (pulmonary edema) of large doses of phenobarbital (41). The effect of thyroxine on some carcinogens has been investigated, and it appears that thyroxine reduces the incidence of carcinogenesis after dibenzanthracene or methylcholanthrene, whereas thiouracil increases the incidence (53). This is presumably secondary to the effect of the thyroid on blood flow through the skin (see above). Somewhat unexpected was the finding that dibenzanthracene inhibited the toxic effects of thyroxine as measured by the anoxia survival time.

The increased sensitivity of hyperthyroid subjects to adrenaline has been known for some time. A recent article summarizes the evidence for the conclusion that hyperthyroidism causes an increased sensitivity to adrenaline and that thyroid deficiency causes tolerance to adrenaline (535). It also appears that the elevation in blood sugar (guinea pigs) after adrenaline is reduced by thyroidectomy (122). The toxicity of noradrenaline appears to be unaffected by thyroxine (365). Thyroxine also appears to enhance the effect of adrenaline on augmenting the effect of electrical stimulation of the phrenic nerve in a phrenic nerve-diaphragm preparation (160). Variable effects of myxedema in one dog on vascular reactivity to adrenaline, angiotonin, and tetraethylammonium chloride are reported (506). The mechanism of the action of thyroxine on adrenaline effect seems to be clarified by reports that there is an adrenaline-destroying enzyme in blood whose concentration is lowered by treatment with thyroxine and increased by thiouracil (336). Furthermore, thyroxine decreases the level of amine oxidase in the liver, which enzyme is known to play an important role in the destruction of adrenaline (682). Thyroxine is also reported to diminish the erythema subsequent to acetyl choline injection (359).

2. Bacterial Infection and Sensitivity

The thyroid appears to affect the development and course of some infectious diseases. Treatment with thiouracil of guinea pigs given tuberculosis seems to result in a shortening of survival time (218). On the other hand, thiouracil treatment of mice did not affect the development of infection after a standard dose of hymenolepis eggs (379). Treatment with large doses of thyroid markedly decreased resistance to such an infection. Thyroxine has been reported to synergize the curative effect of sulfanilamide on pneumococcal infection in mice (656, 657). Rats treated with iodoprotein were less severely parasitized from a standard dose of *Notoedres muris* than were normal rats, and thiouracil-treated rats were more severely parasitized (392). Thiouracil has been reported to increase the mortality of mice from poliomyelitis and thyroid to increase the incubation time (314). Thyroxine has been reported to have no effect on the susceptibility of mice to the MM virus (241).

The most recent study on the susceptibility of mice to the Lansing strain of poliomyelitis as affected by hypo- and hyper-thyroidism revealed no consistent change (675), although there were minor deviations in the course of the disease.

Large doses of thyroxine have been reported to lower the survival time of mice infected with murine pneumonitis and the destruction of the thyroid with radioiodine to increase the resistance of mice to this virus (766).

Thyroxine has been reported to cause a decreased mortality in rats from *Micrococcus pyogenes* (656, 657). The same report also found that thyroxine increased the antibody titer from typhoid. There are several studies of the effects of thyroxine and cortisone on the reactivity of sensitive guinea pigs to tuberculin. Cortisone treatment decreased the hypersensitivity and thyroxine increased the extent of the response (408). Later, it was shown that treatment of the guinea pigs with propylthiouracil did not affect the response of guinea pigs to BCG but abolished the desensitizing action of ACTH or cortisone (409). Thyroxine increases sensitivity to BCG, but this effect is reduced by cortisone. Other investigators have found that thyroxine decreases and thiouracil increases the response to PPD of guinea pigs sensitized with BCG. The reaction to old tuberculin, however, is not affected (391).

In rabbits the anaphylactic changes subsequent to the administration of horse serum are accelerated by thyroxine (349). There is a suggestion that cortisone antagonizes the effect of thyroxine.

Arthritis produced by the intra-articular injection of egg albumen in sensitized guinea pigs is increased by thyroxine or TSH (741). Cortisone decreases the inflammatory response.

VII. Physiologic Aspects of Thyroid Tumors

Studies done during the past decade indicate that both benign and cancerous tumors of the thyroid may result from prolonged and intense growth stimuli of a physiologic nature. Furthermore, recent studies have demonstrated that many cancers of the thyroid can be made to respond to the organism's need for thyroid hormone and to assume the functions of normal thyroid tissue.

It has been demonstrated by several investigators that prolonged treatment of rats or mice with thiouracil or related drugs results in the production of benign and malignant tumors of the thyroid. Rats treated with allyl thiourea and 2-acetylamino-fluorene have been observed to develop both benign and cancerous tumors of the thyroid (66, 67). In a study done on mice it has been reported that the administration of propylthiouracil to mice of a low-tumor strain resulted in the development of nonmetastasizing tumors which were not transplantable (136). Similar treatment of mice of a high-tumor strain resulted in the development of metastasizing transplantable cancers of the thyroid (475). In another study it has been reported (471, 554) that benign tumors develop in Sprague-Dawley rats which have been treated with thiouracil. In this same study transplantable tumors were produced only if the rats were receiving dibenzanthracene sub-cutaneously at the same time.   These observations would suggest that the prolonged and intensive stimulus to growth of the thyroid, presumably mediated by the pituitary, contributes to the development of tumors of the thyroid.   Whether or not these tumors are cancerous apparently depends on the genetic background or upon the exposure to a carcinogen.

Studies on the function of thyroid tumors have revealed that the capacity of benign tumors to trap radioactive iodine depends on the degree of histologic differentiation of the tumor.   The highly undifferentiated tumors are incapable of collecting or retaining iodide, whereas those tumors presenting immature but definite follicular structure are capable of retaining iodine but usually less than that trapped by normal thyroid tissues (551, 557).

In one extensive study (196) in which the autoradiographic technique was used to determine the capacity of 100 cancers of the thyroid to concentrate I^{131}, it was observed that 46 were capable of concentrating iodine. Although those tumors with some follicular structure were the tumors most likely to pick up I^{131}, there were some less differentiated tumors which did concentrate the isotope.   In no instance did a tumor concentrate more than a fraction of the iodine picked up by normal thyroid tissue.

By studying 57 patients with cancers of the thyroid which had metastasized to the skeleton or to the lungs, it has been demonstrated (556) that complete removal or destruction of the normal thyroid resulted in the metastases assuming the function of normal thyroid in 29 patients.   The evidence for function was based on the demonstration that one or more of the metastatic lesions in these 29 patients concentrated I^{131}.   Furthermore, in several of these patients it has been demonstrated that their tumors were capable of secreting thyroxine.   It has also been demonstrated in a small series of patients that some cancers of the thyroid are capable of responding to treatment with TSH, as evidenced by an induced or an increased capacity of the metastatic lesions to concentrate I^{131}.

The prolonged administration of thiouracil or of tapazole, both of which agents augment the action of administered TSH, to 49 patients who had been previously thyroidectomized has resulted in a markedly increased capacity of the tumors to concentrate radioiodine in 31 cases.

Thus it has been demonstrated that such tumors can be forced to assume the function of normal thyroid tissue.   From the practical point of view, such induced physiologic control of these cancers has permitted the administration of cancericidal doses of I^{131} (540).

REFERENCES

1. Abderhalden, E., and Wertheimer, E.   *Z. ges exptl. Med.* **63**, 557 (1928).
2. Abelin, I.   *Arch. exptl. Pathol. Pharmakol.* **181**, 250 (1936).

3. Abelin, I. *Arch. intern. pharmacodynamie* **75,** 187 (1947).
4. Abelin, I. *Biochem. Z.* **286,** 160 (1936).
5. Abelin, I. *Helv. Physiol. et Pharmacol. Acta* **9,** 74 (1951).
6. Abelin, I., and Huber, P. *Acta Endocrinol.* **6,** 1 (1951).
7. Abelin, I., and Kipfer, H. *Arch. intern. pharmacodynamie* **82,** 99 (1950).
8. Abelin, I., and Parhon, C. I., Jr. *Klin. Wochschr.* **12,** 1167 (1933).
9. Abelin, I., and Poretti, G. *Schweiz. med. Wochschr.* **82,** 1186 (1952).
10. Abercrombie, W. F. *Am. J. Pathol.* **11,** 469 (1935).
11. Aebi, H. *Helv. Physiol. et Pharmacol. Acta* **10,** C43 (1952).
12. Agnoletto, A., and Agnoletto, C. *Folia Endocrinol. (Pisa)* **3,** 159 (1950).
13. Albert, A. *Endocrinology* **48,** 334 (1951).
14. Albert, A. *J. Clin. Endocrinol.* **11,** 762 (1951).
15. Albert, A., Ford, E., and Lorenz, N. *Endocrinology* **53,** 50, 1953.
16. Albert, A., and Keating, F. R., Jr. *Endocrinology* **51,** 427 (1952).
17. Albert, A., and Keating, F. R., Jr. *J. Clin. Endocrinol.* **9,** 1406 (1949).
18. Albert, A., and Lorenz, N. *Proc. Soc. Exptl. Biol. Med.* **77,** 204 (1951).
19. Albert, A., Rall, J. E., Keating, F. R., Power, M. H., and Williams, M. *J. Clin. Endocrinol.* **9,** 1392 (1949).
20. Albert, A., Rawson, R. W., Riddell, C. B., Merrill, P., and Lennon, B. E. *Endocrinology* **40,** 361 (1947).
21. Albert, A., and Tenney, A. *Proc. Soc. Exptl. Biol. Med.* **77,** 202 (1951).
22. Alibrandi, A. *Ricerca sci.* **19,** 1179 (1949).
23. Allegretti, N., Buta, S., and Milkovic, S. *Arkiv. Kemi* **22,** 207 (1950).
24. Allen, B. M. *Quart. Rev. Biol.* **4,** 325 (1929).
25. Althausen, T. L. *J. Am. Med. Assoc.* **115,** 101 (1940).
26. Ambrus, C., and Ambrus, J. *Z. Vitamin-, Hormon- u. Fermentforsch.* **2,** 464 (1948–1949).
27. Anderson, A. B., Harington, C. R., and Lyon, D. M. *Lancet* **224,** 1081 (1933).
28. Askonas, B. A. *Nature* **167,** 933 (1951).
29. Asling, C. W., Becks, H., Simpson, M. E., and Evans, H. M. *Anat. Record* **104,** 225 (1949).
30. Asper, S. P., Jr., Selenkow, H. A., and Plamondon, C. A. *Bull. Johns Hopkins Hosp.* **93,** 164 (1953).
31. Astwood, E. B. *Ann. Internal Med.* **30,** 1087 (1949).
32. Astwood, E. B. *Ann. N. Y. Acad. Sci.* **50,** 419 (1949).
33. Astwood, E. B. *Harvey Lectures* **40,** 195 (1944–1945).
34. Astwood, E. B. *J. Pharmacol. Exptl. Therap.* **78,** 79 (1943).
35. Astwood, E. B., and Bissell, A. *Endocrinology* **34,** 282 (1944).
36. Astwood, E. B., Greer, M. A., and Ettlinger, M. G. *Science* **109,** 631 (1949).
37. Astwood, E. B., and Stanley, M. M. *Western J. Surg. Obstet. Gynecol.* **55,** 625 (1947).
38. Astwood, E. B., Sullivan, J. Bissell, A., and Tyslowitz, R. *Endocrinology* **32,** 210 (1943).
39. Aub, J. C., Bauer, W., Heath, C., and Ropes, M. *J. Clin. Invest.* **7,** 97 (1929).
40. Bainborough, A. R., and McMillan, G. C. *Arch. Pathol.* **54,** 204 (1952).
41. Bariety, M., and Kohler, D. *Compt. rend. soc. biol.* **145,** 184 (1951).
42. Barker, M. H. *J. Am. Med. Assoc.* **106,** 762 (1936).
43. Barker, M. H., Lindberg, H. A., and Wald, M. H. *J. Am. Med. Assoc.* **117,** 1591 (1941).
44. Barker, S. B. *Endocrinology* **37,** 484 (1945).

45. Barker, S. B.   *Physiol. Revs.* **31,** 205 (1951).
46. Barker, S. B., Dirks, H. B., Jr., Garlick, W. R., and Klitgaard, H. M.   *Proc. Soc. Exptl. Biol. Med.* **78,** 840 (1951).
47. Barker, S. B., Kiely, C. E., Jr., Dirks, H. B., Jr., Klitgaard, H. M., Wang, S. C., and Wawzonek, S.   *J. Pharmacol. Exptl. Therap.* **99,** 202, (1950).
48. Barker, S. B., Kiely, C. E., Jr., Klitgaard, H. M., Dirks, H. B., Jr., Wang, S. C., and Wawzonek, S.   *Endocrinology* **48,** 70 (1951).
49. Barker, S. B., Kiely, C. E., Jr., and Lipner, H. J.   *Endocrinology* **45,** 624 (1949).
50. Barker, S. B., and Klitgaard, H. M.   *Am. J. Physiol.* **170,** 81 (1952).
51. Barker, S. B., and Schwartz, H. S.   *Proc. Soc. Exptl. Biol. Med.* **83,** 500 (1953).
52. Barrett, H. W., Gassner, F. X., and Dittmer, K.   *Endocrinology* **48,** 189 (1951).
53. Bather, R., and Franks, W. R.   *Rev. can. biol.* **11,** 51 (1952).
54. Baumann, E. J., and Metzger, N.   *Proc. Soc. Exptl. Biol. Med.* **70,** 536 (1949).
55. Baumann, E. J., Searle, N. Z., Yalow, A. A., Siegel, E., and Seidlin, S. M.   *Federation Proc.* **11,** 184 (1952).
56. Baumann, E. J., Zizmer, N., Oshry, E., and Seidlin, S. M.   *Proc. Soc. Exptl. Biol. Med.* **72,** 502 (1949).
57. Beaton, J. R., Beare, J. L., Beaton, G. H., White, J. M., and McHenry, E. W.   *J. Nutrition* **51,** 599 (1953).
58. Bechgaard, P.   *Acta Med. Scand.* **114,** 293 (1943).
59. Becker, D. V., Rall, J. E., Peacock, W. C., and Rawson, R. W.   *J. Clin. Invest.* **32,** 149 (1953).
60. Benedict, F. G., Emmes, L. E., Roth, P., and Smith, H. M.   *J. Biol. Chem.* **18,** 139 (1914).
61. Benua, R. S., Albert, A., and Keating, F. R., Jr.   *Trans. Am. Goiter Assoc.,* p. 218 (1952).
62. Berg, O., and Gorbman, A.   *Proc. Soc. Exptl. Biol. Med.* **83,** 751 (1953).
63. Bertrand, I., Delay, J., and Guillain, J.   *Compt. rend. soc. biol.* **129,** 395 (1938).
64. Bessesen, D. H.   *Am. J. Physiol.* **63,** 245 (1923).
65. Biellier, H. V., and Turner, C. W.   *Poultry Sci.* **29,** 248 (1950).
66. Bielschowsky, F.   *Brit. J. Exptl. Pathol.* **25,** 90 (1944).
67. Bielschowsky, F.   *Brit. J. Exptl. Pathol.* **26,** 270 (1945).
68. Biggers, J. D., and Claringbold, P. J.   *Australian J. Biol. Sci.* **6,** 305 (1953).
69. Blanquet, P., Stoll, R., and Capot, L.   *Compt. rend. soc. biol.* **146,** 1103 (1952).
70. Blanquet, P., Stoll, R., Maraud, R., and Capot, L.   *J. méd. Bordeaux et Sud-Ouest* **130,** 605 (1953).
71. Blum, F., and Strauss, E.   *Z. physiol. Chem.* **127,** 199 (1923).
72. Blumgart, H. L., Freedberg, A. S., and Kurland, G. S.   *Am. J. Med.* **14,** 665 (1953).
73. Boatman, J. B., and Moses, C.   *Am. J. Physiol.* **164,** 783 (1951).
74. Bogoroch, R., and Timiras, P.   *Endocrinology* **49,** 548 (1951).
75. Bolene, C., Ross, O. B., and MacVicar, R.   *Proc. Soc. Exptl. Biol. Med.* **75,** 610 (1950).
76. Bologna, U., and Piccioni, V.   *Ricerca sci.* **21,** 1820 (1950).
77. Bondy, P. K.   *Endocrinology* **45,** 605 (1949).
78. Bondy, P. K.   *Proc. Soc. Exptl. Biol. Med.* **77,** 638 (1951).
79. Boone, M. A., Davidson, J. A., and Reineke, E. P.   *Poultry Sci.* **29,** 195 (1950).
80. Boothby, W. M., and Beldes, E. J.   *Proc. Staff Meetings Mayo Clinic* **1,** 166 (1926).
81. Boothby, W. M., Berkson, J., and Plummer, W. A.   *Ann. Internal Med.* **11,** 1014 (1937).

82. Boothby, W. M., Sandiford, I., Sandiford, K., and Slosse, J. *Trans. Assoc. Am. Physicians* **40**, 195 (1925).
83. Borell, U., and Holmgren, H. *Endocrinology* **42**, 427 (1948).
84. Botkin, A. L., and Jensen, H. *Endocrinology* **50**, 68 (1952).
85. Botkin, A. L., Praytor, E. H., Austing, M. E., and Jensen, H. *Endocrinology* **50**, 550 (1952).
86. Bovarnick, M., Bloch, K., and Foster, G. L. *J. Am. Chem. Soc.* **61**, 2472 (1939).
87. Brady, F. J., Lawton, A. H., Cowie, D. B., Andrews, H. L., Ness, A. T., and Ogden, G. E. *Am. J. Trop. Med.* **25**, 103 (1945).
88. Brand, E. B., and Kassell, B. *J. Biol. Chem.* **131**, 489 (1939).
89. Braunsteiner, H., Fellinger, K., and Pakesch, F. *Endocrinology* **53**, 123 (1953).
90. Brayne, M. K., and Maclagan, N. F. *J. Endocrinol.* **9**, 90 (1953).
91. Briggs, F. N., Braver, R. W., Taurog, A., and Chaikoff, I. L. *Am. J. Physiol.* **172**, 561 (1953).
92. Brophy, D., and McEachern, D. *Proc. Soc. Exptl. Biol. Med.* **70**, 120 (1949).
93. Brown, E. F., and Morgan, A. F. *J. Nutrition* **35**, 439 (1948).
94. Burns, F. J., Fish, W. A., Hackett, J. W., and Hickey, F. C. *J. Appl. Physiol.* **4**, 15 (1951).
95. Byrom, F. B. *Clin. Sci.* **1**, 273 (1933–1934).
96. Bywater, W. G., McGinty, D. A., and Jenesel, N. D. *J. Pharmacol. Exptl. Therap.* **85**, 14 (1945).
97. Cagan, R. N., Gray, J. L., and Jensen, H. *J. Biol. Chem.* **183**, 11 (1950).
98. Calvo, J. M., Boehme, C. C., and Goemine, J. *Bol. soc. biol. Santiago Chile* **6**, 88 (1949).
99. Capra, P. *Arch. sci. med.* **88**, 536 (1946).
100. Capra, P. *Arch. sci. med.* **93**, 353 (1952).
101. Capretti, G., and Magnani, B. *Giorn, clin. med.* (*Parma*) **32**, 417 (1951).
102. Carr, E. A., Jr., and Riggs, D. S. *Biochem. J.* **54**, 217 (1953).
103. Carter, G. S., and Jenkins, G. N. *Nature* **154**, 639 (1944).
104. Catz, B., El-Rawi, I., and Geiger, E. *Am. J. Physiol.* **172**, 291 (1953).
105. Catz, B., Petit, D. W., and Starr, P. *J. Clin. Endocrinol.* **11**, 978 (1951).
106. Cavett, J. W., Rice, C. O., and McClendon, J. F. *J. Biol. Chem.* **110**, 673 (1935).
107. Chaikoff, I. L., and Taurog, A. *Ann. N. Y. Acad. Sci.* **50**, 377 (1949).
108. Chamorro, A. *Compt. rend. soc. biol.* **143**, 1540 (1949).
109. Chanda, R., Clapham, H. M., McNaught, M. L., and Owen, E. C. *Biochem. J.* **50**, 95 (1951).
110. Chanda, R., and Owen, E. C. *Biochem. J.* **50**, 100 (1951).
111. Chapman, E. M., Corner, G. W., Jr., Robinson, D., and Evans, R. D. *J. Clin. Endocrinol.* **8**, 717 (1948).
112. Chesney, A. M., Clawson, T. A., and Webster, B. *Bull. Johns Hopkins Hosp.* **43**, 261 (1928).
113. Cheymol, J., Chabrier, P., and Gay, Y. *Arch. intern. pharmacodynamie* **87**, 321 (1951).
114. Cheymol, J., Renault, J., and Pazin, M. *Arch. intern. pharmacodynamie* **93**, 143 (1953).
115. Childs, D. S., Keating, F. R., Jr., Rall, J. E., Williams, M., and Power, M. H. *J. Clin. Invest.* **29**, 726 (1950).
116. Chu, J. P. *Endocrinology* **34**, 90 (1944).
117. Clausen, K. H., and Kjerulf-Jensen, K. *Nord. Med.* **45**, 475 (1951).
118. Clayton, J. C., Free, A. A., Page, J. E., Somers, G. F., and Woollett, E. A. *Biochem. J.* **46**, 598 (1950).

119. Coggeshall, H. C., and Greene, J. A. *Am. J. Physiol.* **105,** 103 (1933).
120. Cohen, A. G. N., and Minz, B. *Arch. sci. physiol.* **4,** 145 (1950).
121. Cohen, R. A. *Proc. Soc. Exptl. Biol. Med.* **32,** 1446 (1935).
122. Comsa, J. *Am. J. Physiol.* **161,** 550 (1950).
123. Comsa, J. *Compt. rend. soc. biol.* **140,** 299 (1946).
124. Comsa, J. *Compt. rend. soc. biol.* **140,** 613 (1946).
125. Comsa, J. *Compt. rend. soc. biol.* **141,** 511 (1947).
126. Comsa, J. *Compt. rend. soc. biol.* **141,** 513 (1947).
127. Concha, E., Atria, A., and Sabah, D. *Rev. med. Chile* **78,** 791 (1950).
128. Corcoran, A. C., and Page, I. H. *J. Clin. Endocrinol.* **7,** 801 (1948).
129. Corson, D. R., Mackenzie, K. R., and Segrè, E. *Physiol. Revs.* **58,** 672 (1940).
130. Cortell, R. E. *J. Clin. Endocrinol.* **9,** 955 (1949).
131. Cosgrove, J. B. R., and Perry, W. F. *Can. J. Research* **E27,** 10 (1949).
132. Courrier, R., Horeau, A., Marois, M., and Morel, F. *Compt. rend.* **232,** 776 (1951).
133. Courrier, R., Horeau, A., Marois, M., and Morel, F. *Compt. rend. soc. biol.* **143,** 935 (1949).
134. Cowgill, G. R., and Palmieri, M. L. *Am. J. Physiol.* **105,** 146 (1933).
135. Cowie, D. B., Lawton, A. H., Ness, A. T., Brady, F. J., and Ogden, G. E. *J. Wash. Acad. Sci.* **35,** 192 (1945).
136. Dalton, A. J., Morris, H. P., and Dubnik, C. S. *Federation Proc.* **5,** 219 (1946).
137. D'Angelo, S. A., Paschkis, K. E., Gordon, A. S., and Cantarow, A. *J. Clin. Endocrinol.* **11,** 1237 (1951).
138. Danowski, T. S., Huff, S. J., Wirth, P. M., Hill, G. C., Green, M. H., and Fettermann, G. H. *J. Clin. Endocrinol.* **11,** 1254 (1951).
139. Dauber, D., Horlick, L., and Katz, L. N. *Am. Heart J.* **38,** 25 (1949).
140. de Angelis, W., Fignolo, W., Holm, N., and Barsantini, J. C. *Arch. soc. biol. Montevideo* **19,** 27 (1952).
141. Deanesly, R., and Parkes, A. S. *J. Endocrinol.* **4,** 324 (1945).
142. De Candia, S., and Nava, G. *Folia Endocrinol. (Pisa)* **3,** 817 (1950).
143. DeGasperis, A. *Biol. Latina* **4,** 155 (1951).
144. Deiss, W. P., Albright, E. C., and Larson, F. C. *Proc. Soc. Exptl. Biol. Med.* **84,** 513 (1953).
145. Deltour, G. H., and Bekaert, J. *Compt. rend. soc. biol.* **147,** 388 (1953).
146. Dempsey, E. W. *Ann. N. Y. Acad. Sci.* **50,** 336 (1949).
147. Dempsey, E. W. *Endocrinology* **34,** 27 (1944).
148. Dempsey, E. W., and Astwood, E. B. *Endocrinology* **32,** 509 (1943).
149. Dempsey, E. W., and Singer, M. *Endocrinology* **38,** 270 (1946).
150. de Robertis, E. *Am. J. Anat.* **68,** 317 (1941).
151. de Robertis, E. *Anat. Record* **80,** 219 (1941).
152. de Robertis, E. *Ann. N. Y. Acad. Sci.* **50,** 317 (1949).
153. de Robertis, E. *Western J. Surg. Obstet. Gynecol.* **56,** 253 (1948).
154. de Robertis, E., and Grasso, R. *Endocrinology* **38,** 137 (1946).
155. de Robertis, E., and Nowinski, W. W. *J. Clin. Endocrinol.* **6,** 235 (1946).
156. de Robertis, E., and Nowinski, W. W. *Science* **103,** 421 (1946).
157. Derrien, Y., Michel, R., Pedersen, K. O., and Roche, J. *Biochim. et Biophys. Acta* **3,** 436 (1949).
158. Derrien, Y., Michel, R., and Roche, J. *Biochim. et Biophys. Acta* **2,** 454 (1948).
159. Deusch, G. *Deut. Arch. klin. Med.* **134,** 342 (1920).
160. deVisscher, M., and Dijkmans, J. *Arch. intern. physiol.* **57,** 440 (1950).
161. Deysach, L. J., and Ray, T. W. *Proc. Soc. Exptl. Biol. Med.* **71,** 188 (1949).

162. Dine, R. F., and Lavietes, P. H. *J. Clin. Invest.* **21**, 781 (1942).
163. Dirnagl, K., and Presch, H. R. *Klin. Wochschr.* **31**, 525 (1953).
164. Dobyns, B. M., and Barry, S. R. *J. Biol. Chem.* **204**, 517 (1953).
165. Dobyns, B. M., and Steelman. S. L. *Endocrinology* **52**, 705 (1953).
166. Doniach, I., and Fraser, R. *Lancet* **i**, 855 (1950).
167. Dougherty, J., Gross, J., and Leblond, C. P. *Endocrinology* **48**, 700 (1951).
168. Drabkin, D. L. *J. Biol. Chem.* **182**, 335 (1950).
169. Drabkin, D. L. *J. Biol. Chem.* **182**, 351 (1950).
170. Drill, V. A. *Physiol. Revs.* **23**, 355 (1943).
171. Drill, V. A., and Overman, R. R. *Am. J. Physiol.* **135**, 474 (1942).
172. Drill, V. A., and Truat, A. P. *Endocrinology* **40**, 259 (1947).
173. Drysdale, G. R., Betheil, J. J., Lardy, H. A., and Baumann, C. A. *Arch. Biochem. and Biophys.* **33**, 1 (1951).
174. Dvoskin, S. *Endocrinology* **40**, 334 (1947).
175. Dye, J. A., and Maughan, G. H. *Proc. Soc. Exptl. Biol. Med.* **26**, 439 (1929).
176. Dye, J. A., and Maughan, G. H. *Proc. Soc. Exptl. Biol. Med.* **26**, 441 (1929).
177. Dye, J. A., and Waggener, R. A. *Am. J. Physiol.* **85**, 1 (1928).
178. Dziemian, A. J. *J. Cellular Comp. Physiol.* **21**, 339 (1943).
179. Dziewiatkowski, D. *J. Biol. Chem.* **189**, 717 (1951).
180. Eichna, L. W., and Wilkins, R. W. *Bull. Johns Hopkins Hosp.* **68**, 512 (1941).
181. Elmer, A. W. Iodine Metabolism and Thyroid Function. Oxford University Press, London, 1938.
182. Emerson, G. A. *Proc. Soc. Exptl. Biol. Med.* **70**, 392 (1949).
183. Engström, A. *Discussions Faraday Soc.* **9**, 427 (1950).
184. Entenman, C., Chaikoff, I. L., and Reichert, F. L. *Endocrinology* **30**, 794 (1942).
185. Ershoff, B. H. *Proc. Soc. Exptl. Biol. Med.* **71**, 209 (1949).
186. Ershoff, B. H. *Arch. Biochem.* **28**, 359 (1950).
187. Ershoff, B. H. *Metabolism, Clin. and Exptl.* **2**, 175 (1953).
188. Ershoff, B. H., and Golub, O. J. *Arch. Biochem.* **30**, 202 (1951).
189. Eufinger, H., and Gottlieb, J. *Klin. Wochschr.* **12**, 1397 (1933).
190. Fawcett, D. M., and Kirkwood, S. *J. Biol. Chem.* **204**, 787 (1953).
191. Fawcett, D. M., and Kirkwood, S. *J. Biol. Chem.* **205**, 795 (1953).
192. Feldman, W. H., Hinshaw, H. C., and Mann, F. C. *Proc. Staff Meetings Mayo Clinic* **19**, 25 (1944).
193. Feldott, G., and Lardy, H. A. *Federation Proc.* **10**, 182 (1951).
194. Fink, K., and Fink, R. M. *Science* **108**, 358 (1948).
195. Fisher, E. R. *Arch. Pathol.* **56**, 275 (1953).
196. Fitzgerald, P., and Foote, F. W. *J. Clin. Endocrinol.* **9**, 1153 (1949).
197. Fleischman, W. Comparative Physiology of the Thyroid and Parathyroid Glands. Charles C Thomas, Springfield, Ill., 1951.
198. Fleischman, W., and Kann, S. *Wien. klin. Wochschr.* **47**, 1488 (1936).
199. Flint, A. H. A Treatise on the Principles and Practice of Medicine. H. C. Lea, Philadelphia, 1866, p. 301.
200. Flock, E. V., Bollman, J. L., and Berkson, J. *Am. J. Physiol.* **155**, 402 (1948).
201. Foldes, F. F., and Murphy, A. J. *Proc. Soc. Exptl. Biol. Med.* **62**, 218 (1946).
202. Follis, R. H., Jr. *Bull. Johns Hopkins Hosp.* **92**, 405 (1953).
203. Forattini, C., and Selmi, W. *Folia Endocrinol.* (*Pisa*) **3**, 869 (1950).
204. Forsham, P. H., Thorn, G. W., Prunty, F. T. G., and Hills, A. G. *J. Clin. Endocrinol* **8**, 15 (1948).
205. Fortune, P. Y. *Nature* **171**, 483 (1953).
206. Foster, G. L. *J. Biol. Chem.* **83**, 345 (1929).

207. Fox, E., and Irving, J. T.   *S. African J. Med. Sci.* **15,** 11 (1950).
208. Fraenkel-Conrat, H.   *Arch. Biochem.* **27,** 109 (1950).
209. Fraenkel-Conrat, J., and Li, C. H.   *Endocrinology* **44,** 487 (1949).
210. Franklin, A. L., and Chaikoff, I. L.   *J. Biol. Chem.* **148,** 719 (1943).
211. Franklin, A. L., Chaikoff, I. L., and Lerner, S. R.   *J. Biol. Chem.* **153,** 151 (1944).
212. Frieden, E., and Winzler, R. J.   *J. Biol. Chem.* **176,** 155 (1948).
213. Frieden, E., and Winzler, R. J.   *J. Biol. Chem.* **179,** 423 (1949).
214. Friedgood, H. B., and Cannon, W. B.   *Endocrinology* **26,** 142 (1940).
215. Fujimaki, Y., and Hildebrandt, F.   *Arch. exptl. Pathol. Pharmakol.* **102,** 226 (1924).
216. Fullerton, C. W., and Harrop, G. A.   *Bull. Johns Hopkins Hosp.* **46,** 203 (1930).
217. Gaddum, J. H.   *J. Physiol. (London)* **64,** 246 (1927).
218. Gadeke, R., and Jacob, W.   *Klin. Wochschr.* **29,** 229 (1951).
219. Gallone, L., and Gelluzzi, W.   *Arch. fisiol.* **51,** 12 (1951).
220. Gassner, F. X., Hopwood, M. L., Herrold, E. A., and Plummer, A. J.   *Trans. Am. Goiter Assoc.,* p. 403 (1950).
221. Gaunt, R., Corsden, M., and Liling, M.   *Endocrinology* **35,** 105 (1944).
222. Gemmill, C. L.   *Am. J. Physiol.* **167,** 349 (1951).
223. Gemmill, C. L.   *J. Biol. Chem.* **192,** 749 (1951).
224. Gemmill, C. L.   *Am. J. Physiol.* **172,** 286 (1953).
225. Gerlach, U., and Blaich, W.   *Ärztl. Wochschr.* **8,** 461 (1953).
226. Gersh, I.   *Federation Proc.* **6,** 392 (1947).
227. Gersh, I.   *J. Endocrinol.* **6,** 282 (1950).
228. Gersh, I., and Caspersson, T.   *Anat. Record* **78,** 303 (1940).
229. Gershberg, H., and Kuhl, W. J., Jr.   *J. Clin. Invest.* **29,** 1625 (1950).
230. Geyelin, H. R.   *Arch. Internal Med.* **16,** 975 (1915).
231. Gillman, J., and Gilbert, C.   *J. Obstet. Gynaecol. Brit. Empire* **60,** 445 (1953).
232. Ginoulhiac, E.   *Boll. soc. ital, biol. sper.* **27,** 1738 (1951).
233. Gitman, L., Greenblatt, I. J., and Mitchell, N.   *Proc. Soc. Exptl. Biol. Med.* **71,** 179 (1949).
234. Gley, E., and Bourcet, P.   *Compt. rend.* **130,** 1721 (1900).
235. Godley, A. F., and Stanbury, J. B.   *J. Clin. Endocrinol.* **14,** 70 (1954).
236. Gofman, J. W., Jones, H. B., Lindgren, F. T., Lyon, T. P., Elliott, H. A., and Strisower, B.   *Circulation* **2,** 161 (1950).
237. Goldberg, R. C.   *Federation Proc.* **13,** 56 (1954).
238. Goldberg, R. C., and Chaikoff, I. L.   *Endocrinology* **49,** 613 (1951).
239. Goldsmith, E. D., Nigrelli, R. F., Gordon, A. S., Charipper, H. A., and Gordon, M.   *Endocrinology* **35,** 132 (1944).
240. Goldstein, M. S.   *J. Biol. Chem.* **199,** 923 (1952).
241. Gollan, F.   *Proc. Soc. Exptl. Biol. Med.* **67,** 362 (1948).
242. Gorbman, A., and Creaser, C. W.   *J. Exptl. Zool.* **89,** 391 (1942).
243. Gorbman, A., and Evans, H. M.   *Endocrinology* **32,** 113 (1943).
244. Gorbman, A., Lissitzky, S., Michel, O., Michel, R., and Roche, J.   *Compt. rend. soc. biol.* **145,** 1642 (1951).
245. Gordon, A. H., Gross, J., O'Connor, D., and Pitt-Rivers, R.   *Nature* **169,** 19 (1952).
246. Gordon, A. S., Charipper, H. A., and Goldsmith, E. D.   *Anat. Record* **89,** 566 (1944).
247. Grafflin, A. L.   *J. Morphol.* **65,** 297 (1939).
248. Grafflin, A. L.   *J. Morphol.* **70,** 535 (1942).
249. Green, J., and Lyall, A.   *Lancet* **260,** 828 (1951).

250. Green, T. W., White, W. E., Engelman, E. P., and Krupp, M. A. *Proc. Soc. Exptl. Biol. Med.* **82**, 155 (1953).
251. Greenberg, S. M., and Deuel, H. J., Jr. *J. Nutrition* **42**, 279 (1950).
252. Greene, J. A. *Am. J. Med. Sci.* **195**, 618 (1938).
253. Greer, M. A. *Trans. Am. Goiter Assoc.* p. 207 (1952).
254. Greer, M. A., and Astwood, E. B. *Endocrinology* **43**, 105 (1948).
255. Griesbach, W. E., and Purves, H. D. *Brit. J. Exptl. Pathol.* **24**, 185 (1943).
256. Grobstein, C., and Bellamy, A. W. *Proc. Soc. Exptl. Biol. Med.* **41**, 363 (1939).
257. Gross, J., and Leblond, C. P. *J. Biol. Chem.* **184**, 489 (1950).
258. Gross, J., and Leblond, C. P. *Endocrinology* **48**, 714 (1951).
259. Gross, J., and Leblond, C. P. *Proc. Soc. Exptl. Biol. Med.* **76**, 686 (1951).
260. Gross, J., Leblond, C. P., Franklin, A. E., and Quastel, J. H. *Science* **111**, 605 (1950).
261. Gross, J., and Pitt-Rivers, R. *Lancet* **ii**, 766 (1951).
262. Gross, J., and Pitt-Rivers, R. *Lancet* **i**, 439 (1952).
263. Gross, J., and Pitt-Rivers, R. *Lancet* **i**, 593 (1952).
264. Gross, J., and Pitt-Rivers, R. *Biochem. J.* **53**, 645 (1953).
265. Gross, J., and Pitt-Rivers, R. *Biochem J.* **53**, 652 (1953).
266. Gross, J., Pitt-Rivers, R., and Trotter, W. R. *Lancet* **i**, 1044 (1952).
267. Gross, J., and Schwartz, S. *Cancer Research* **11**, 614 (1951).
268. Grunt, J. A., and Leathem, J. H. *Proc. Soc. Exptl. Biol. Med.* **72**, 218 (1949).
269. Gudernatsch, J. F. *Wilhelm Roux' Arch. Entwicklungmech. Organ.* **35**, 457 (1912).
270. Gutman, A. B., Benedict, E. M., Baxter, B., and Palmer, W. W. *J. Biol. Chem.* **97**, 303 (1932).
271. Hahn, P., and Poupa, O. *Nature* **167**, 84 (1951).
272. Halmi, N. S., and Bogdanove, E. M. *Proc. Soc. Exptl. Biol. Med.* **77**, 518 (1951).
273. Hamilton, J. G. *Radiology* **39**, 541 (1942).
274. Hamilton, J. G., Asling, C. W., Garrison, W. M., Scott, K. G., and Axelrod-Heller, D. *Proc. Soc. Exptl. Biol. Med.* **73**, 51 (1950).
275. Hamilton, J. G., and Soley, M. H. *Proc. Natl. Acad. Sci. U. S.* **26**, 483 (1940).
276. Hammett, F. S. *Am. J. Physiol.* **68**, 1 (1924).
277. Hamolsky, M. W., Freedberg, A. S., Kurland, G. S., and Wolsky, L. *J. Clin. Invest.* **32**, 453 (1953).
278. Hanngren, A. *Lancet* **ii**, 117 (1952).
279. Harington, C. R. *Biochem. J.* **20**, 300 (1926).
280. Harington, C. R. *Biochem. J.* **43**, 434 (1948).
281. Harington, C. R. *J. Chem. Soc.* p. 193 (1944).
282. Harington, C. R. *Proc. Roy. Soc. (London)* **B132**, 223 (1944).
283. Harington, C. R., and Barger, G. *Biochem. J.* **21**, 169 (1927).
284. Harington, C. R., and McCartney, W. *J. Chem. Soc.*, p. 892 (1929).
285. Harington, C. R., and Pitt-Rivers, R. *Nature* **144**, 205 (1939).
286. Harington, C. R., and Pitt-Rivers, R. *Biochem. J.* **39**, 157 (1945).
287. Harington, C. R., and Randall, S. S. *Biochem. J.* **23**, 373 (1929).
288. Harington, C. R., and Randall, S. S. *Biochem. J.* **25**, 1032 (1931).
289. Harington, C. R., and Salter, W. T. *Biochem. J.* **24**, 456 (1930).
290. Harper, E. O., and Mattis, P. A. *Federation Proc.* **10**, 306 (1951).
291. Harris, K. D., and Smith, E. A. *Am. J. Physiol.* **84**, 599 (1928).
292. Hawkins, R. D., and Nishikawara, M. *Endocrinology* **45**, 108 (1949).
293. Hawkins, R. D., Nishikawara, M., and Mendel, B. *Endocrinology* **43**, 167 (1948).
294. Heidelberger, M., and Palmer, W. W. *J. Biol. Chem.* **101**, 433 (1933).

295. Heidelberger, M., and Pedersen, K. O. *J. Gen. Physiol.* **19**, 95 (1935).
296. Heidelberger, M., and Svedberg, T. *Science* **80**, 414 (1934).
297. Heming, A. E., and Holtkamp, D. E. *J. Clin. Endocrinol. and Metabolism* **13**, 880 (1953).
298. Hertz, S., and Roberts, A. *J. Clin. Invest.* **21**, 31 (1942).
299. Hertz, S., Roberts, A., and Salter, W. T. *J. Clin. Invest.* **21**, 25 (1942).
300. Hetzel, B. S., and Hine, D. C. *J. Clin. Endocrinol. and Metabolism* **12**, 296 (1952).
301. Hill, S. R., Jr., Reiss, R. S., Forsham, P. H., and Thorn, G. W. *Trans. Am. Goiter Assoc.*, p. 243 (1950).
302. Himwich, H. E., Goldfarb, W., and Cowgill, G. R. *Am. J. Physiol.* **99**, 689 (1932).
303. Hoar, W. S. *Publ. Ontario Fish. Research Lab.* **No. LXXI**, 1 (1951).
304. Hoar, W. S., and Bell G. M. *Can. J. Research* **D28**, 126 (1950).
305. Hoar, W. S., MacKinnon, D., and Redlich, A. *Can. J. Zool.* **30**, 273 (1952).
306. Hoberman, H. D., and Graff, J. *Yale J. Biol. and Med.* **23**, 195 (1950).
307. Hoch, F. L., and Lipmann, F. *Federation Proc.* **12**, 218 (1953).
308. Hoffmann, E. *Poultry Sci.* **29**, 109 (1950).
309. Hoffman, E., and Shaffner, C. S. *Poultry Sci.* **29**, 365 (1950).
310. Hoffmann, F., Cori, O., and Cori, A. T. *Acta Physiol. Latinoamer.* **1**, 84 (1951).
311. Hoffmann, F., and Hoffmann, E. J. Prensas de la Universidad de Chile, 1944.
312. Hogness, J. R., Lee, N. D., and Williams, R. H. *Endocrinology* **52**, 378 (1953).
313. Holck, H. G. O., and Hillyard, I. W. *J. Pharmacol. Exptl. Therap.* **103**, 347 (1951).
314. Holtman, D. F. *Science* **103**, 137 (1946).
315. Honour, A. J., Myant, N. B., and Rowlands, E. N. *Clin. Sci.* **11**, 449 (1952).
316. Hopper, A. F. *Anat. Record* **108**, 554 (1950).
317. Horsley, V. A. *Proc. Roy. Soc. (London)* **B38**, 5 (1884).
318. Horst, W., and Rösler, H. *Klin. Wochschr.* **31**, 13 (1953).
319. Houssay, B. A. *Endocrinology* **35**, 158 (1944).
320. Hursh, J. B., Van Valkenburg, P. A., and Mohney, J. B. *Radiology* **57**, 411 (1951).
321. Hutchison, R. *J. Physiol.* **23**, 178 (1898–1899).
322. Ikonen, M. V., Konyuchenko, T. U., and Kuznetzova, S. M. *Zhur. Eksp. Biol. i Med.* **13**, 86 (1929); cf. *C. A.* **24**, 5380 (1930).
323. Ingbar, S. H. *Endocrinology* **53**, 171 (1953).
324. Jensen, J. M., and Clark, D. E. *J. Lab. Clin. Med.* **38**, 663 (1951).
325. Jimenez, F. V. *Tesis quim. Univ. Chile* **2**, 1 (1950).
326. Joel, N., and Canepa, F. G. *Acta Cryst.* **4**, 283 (1951).
327. Johnson, G. L., Leininger, R. F., and Segrè, E. *J. Chem. Phys.* **17**, 1 (1949).
328. Johnson, H. W., and Albert, A. *Endocrinology* **48**, 669 (1951).
329. Johnson, P. C., and Beierwaltes, W. H. *J. Lab. Clin. Med.* **41**, 676 (1953).
330. Johnson, R. M., and Baumann, C. A. *J. Biol. Chem.* **171**, 513 (1947).
331. Johnson, T. B., and Tewkesbury, L. B. *Proc. Natl. Acad. Sci. U. S.* **28**, 73 (1942).
332. Judah, J. D. *Biochem. J.* **49**, 271 (1951).
333. Kamner, M. E., Peranio, A., and Bruger, M. *Endocrinology* **46**, 353 (1950).
334. Karnofsky, D., and Cronkite, E. P. *Proc. Soc. Exptl. Biol. Med.* **40**, 568 (1939).
335. Karp, A., and Stetten, DeW. Jr. *J. Biol. Chem.* **179**, 819 (1949).
336. Kawamoto, K., Yoshida, H., and Sato, H. *Symposia on Enzyme Chem. (Japan)* **7**, 92 (1952).

337. Keating, F. R.   J. Clin. Endocrinol. **11**, 758 (1951).
338. Keating, F. R., and Albert, A.   J. Clin. Invest. **32**, 580 (1953).
339. Keating, F. R., Power, M. H., Berkson, J., and Haines, S. F.   J. Clin. Invest. **26**, 1138 (1947).
340. Keating, F. R., Rawson, R. W., Peacock, W. C., and Evans, R. D.   Endocrinology **36**, 137 (1945).
341. Kelley, B., and Day, H. G.   J. Biol. Chem. **175**, 863 (1948).
342. Kendall, E. C.   J. Am. Med. Assoc. **64**, 2042 (1915).
343. Kendall, E. C.   J. Biol. Chem. **39**, 125 (1919).
344. Kendall, E. C., and Osterberger, A. E.   J. Biol. Chem. **40**, 265 (1919).
345. Kennedy, T. H., and Purves, H. D.   Brit. J. Exptl. Pathol. **22**, 241 (1941).
346. Keston, A. S.   J. Biol. Chem. **153**, 335 (1944).
347. Kinde, N. N.   Proc. Soc. Exptl. Biol. Med. **23**, 812 (1926).
348. Kingsbury, B. F.   Am. J. Anat. **18**, 329 (1915).
349. Kjems, E.   Acta Pathol. Microbiol. Scand. **31**, 18 (1952).
350. Kjerulf-Jensen, K., and Wolffbrandt, G.   Acta Pharmacol. Toxicol. **7**, 376 (1951).
351. Klein, G.   Acta Endocrinol. **1**, 248 (1948).
352. Klein, J. R.   J. Biol. Chem. **128**, 659 (1939).
353. Klein, J. R.   J. Biol. Chem. **131**, 139 (1939).
354. Kline, D. L.   Endocrinology **45**, 596 (1949).
355. Klitgaard, H. M.   Proc. Soc. Exptl. Biol. Med. **82**, 578 (1953).
356. Klitgaard, H. M., Dirks, H. B., Jr., Barker, S. B., Wang, S. C., and Wawzonek, S.   Endocrinology **48**, 525 (1951).
357. Kochakian, C. D., and Bartlett, M. N.   J. Biol. Chem. **176**, 243 (1948).
358. Koeppen, H.   Neurol. Centr. **11**, 219 (1892).
359. Köhler, V., Penew, L., and Barthel, M.   Klin. Wochschr. **27**, 591 (1949).
360. Koivusalo, M., and Pekkarinen, A.   Acta Endocrinol. **13**, 138 (1953).
361. Kracht, J., and Kracht, U.   Arch. exptl. Pathol. **213**, 429 (1951).
362. Kraft, K.   Z. physiol. Chem. **245**, 58 (1936).
363. Kramer, L. B.   Bull. Johns Hopkins Hosp. **86**, 179 (1950).
364. Krochert, G.   Z. exptl. Pathol. Therap. **98**, 214 (1936).
365. Kroneberg, G., and Hüter, F.   Klin. Wochschr. **29**, 649 (1951).
366. Kroon, D. B.   Acta Endocrinol. **2**, 227 (1949).
367. Kuusisto, A. N., and Telkkä, A.   Acta Endocrinol. **13**, 61 (1953).
368. Kuzin, A. M., and Gladyshev, B. N.   Biokhimiya **15**, 316 (1950).
369. Lacassagne, A.   Ciba Colloquia Endocrinol. **4**, 245 (1952).
370. Lachaze, A., and Thibault, O.   Bull. soc. chim. biol. **33**, 1456 (1951).
371. Lachaze, A., and Thibault, O.   Bull. soc. chim. biol. **33**, 1458 (1951).
372. Laidlaw, J. C.   Nature **164**, 927 (1949).
373. Lambert, E. H., Underdahl, L. O., Beckett, S., and Mederos, L. O.   Trans. Am. Goiter Assoc., p. 43 (1951).
374. Landgrebe, F. W.   J. Exptl. Biol. **18**, 162 (1941).
375. Lardy, H. A.   In L. F. Wolterink, The Biology of Phosphorus.   Michigan State College Press, East Lansing, Mich., 1951.
376. Lardy, H. A., and Feldott, G.   Ann. N. Y. Acad. Sci. **54**, 636 (1951).
377. LaRoche, G.   Rev. can. biol. **11**, 431 (1953).
378. LaRoche, G.   Rev. can. biol. **11**, 439 (1953).
379. Larsh, J. E., Jr.   J. Parasitol. **36**, 473 (1950).
380. Larson, F. C., and Albright, E. C.   Am. J. Med. Sci. **222**, 26 (1951).
381. Larson, F. C., Deiss, W. P., and Albright, E. C.   Science **115**, 626 (1952).
382. Lawson, A., and Rimington, C.   Lancet i, 586 (1947).

383. Leathem, J. H.   Symposium on Protein Metabolism, Hormones and Growth, p. 17, Rutgers University Press, New Brunswick, 1952.
384. Leathem, J. H., and Seeley, R. D.   *Endocrinology* **42,** 150 (1948).
385. Leblond, C. P.   *J. Am. Pharm. Assoc. Sci. Ed.* **40,** 595 (1951).
386. Leblond, C. P., and Grad, B.   *J. Pharmacol. Exptl. Therap.* **94,** 125 (1948).
387. Leblond, C. P., and Gross, J.   *Endocrinology* **43,** 306 (1948).
388. Leblond, C. P., and Sue, P.   *Compt. rend. soc. biol.* **133,** 543 (1940).
389. Lederer, J.   *Ann. endocrinol. Paris* **12,** 621 (1951).
390. Lederer, J.   *Arch. intern. pharmacodynamie* **93,** 128 (1953).
391. Leech, F. B., and Paterson, A. B.   *J. Endocrinol.* **8,** 96 (1952).
392. Leech, F. B., and Spence, T.   *Parasitology* **41,** 224 (1951).
393. Lehninger, A. L.   *Harvey Lectures*, Ser. **49,** 176 (1953–1954).
394. Lein, A.   *Federation Proc.* **11,** 91 (1952).
395. Leloup, J., and Olivereau, M.   *Compt. rend. soc. biol.* **144,** 772 (1950).
396. Lerman, J., and Harington, C. R.   *J. Clin. Endocrinol.* **9,** 1099 (1949).
397. Lerman, J., Harington, C. R., and Means, J. H.   *J. Clin. Endocrinol. and Metabolism* **12,** 1306 (1952).
398. Lerman, J., and Means, J. H.   *J. Clin. Invest.* **11,** 167 (1932).
399. Levine, M. D.   *J. Endocrinol.* **6,** 288 (1950).
400. Lightbody, H. D., Witt, E., and Kleinman, A.   *Proc. Soc. Exptl. Biol. Med.* **46,** 472 (1941).
401. Lipner, H. J., and Barker, S. B.   *Endocrinology* **52,** 367 (1953).
402. Lipner, H. J., Barker, S. B., and Winnick, T.   *Endocrinology* **51,** 406 (1952).
403. Litzka, G.   *Arch. exptl. Pathol. Pharmakol.* **183,** 436 (1936).
404. Llamas, R.   *Anales inst. biol. Univ. nacl. Mex.* **18,** 15 (1947).
405. Llamas, R., Roca, J., and Ondarza, R.   *Anales inst. biol. Univ. nacl. Mex.* **21,** 269 (1950).
406. Logan, R. E., and Lein, A.   *Federation Proc.* **10,** 85 (1951).
407. Logaras, G., and Drummond, J. C.   *Biochem. J.* **32,** 964 (1938).
408. Long, D. A., and Miles, A. A.   *Lancet* **258,** 492 (1950).
409. Long, D. A., Miles, A. A., and Perry, W. L. M.   *Lancet* **260,** 1392 (1951).
410. Löwy, E.   *Z. ges. exptl. Med.* **38,** 407 (1923); quoted from Drill, V. A.   *Physiol. Revs.* **23,** 355 (1943).
411. Lozner, E. L., Winkler, A. W., Taylor, F. H., and Peters, J. P.   *J. Clin. Invest.* **20,** 507 (1941).
412. Lund, C. C., and Benedict, E. B.   *New Engl. J. Med.* **201,** 345 (1929).
413. Lundgren, H. P.   *J. Phys. Chem.* **42,** 177 (1938).
414. Lusted, L., Pickering, D. E., Fisher, D. A., and Smyth, F. S.   *Am. J. Diseases Children* **86,** 426 (1953).
415. Lynn, W. G., and Wachowski, H. E.   *Quart. Rev. Biol.* **26,** 123 (1951).
416. Mackenzie, C. G., and Mackenzie, J. B.   *Endocrinology* **32,** 185 (1943).
417. Mackenzie, J. B., Mackenzie, C. G., and McCollum, E. V.   *Science* **94,** 518 (1941).
418. Maclagan, N. F., Sheahan, M. M., and Wilkinson, J. H.   *Nature* **164,** 699 (1949).
419. Maclagan, N. F., Sprott, W. E., and Wilkinson, J. H.   *Lancet* **263,** 915 (1952).
420. Magnus-Levy, A.   *Berlin klin. Wochschr.* **32,** 650 (1895).
421. Magrassi, B.   *Arch. sci. med.* **95,** 65 (1933).
422. Majumdar, A. C.   *Indian J. Physiol. and Allied Sci.* **4,** 50 (1950).
423. Maley, G. F., and Lardy, H. A.   *J. Biol. Chem.* **204,** 435 (1953).
424. Malinow, M. R., Batlle, F. F., and Malamud, B.   *Am. J. Physiol.* **172,** 743 (1953).
425. Malmros, H., and Swahn, B.   *Acta Med. Scand.* **145,** 361 (1953).

510 RULON W. RAWSON, JOSEPH E. RALL, AND MARTIN SONENBERG

426. Man, E. B., Heinemann, M., Johnson, C. E., Leary, D. C., and Peters, J. P. *J. Clin. Invest.* **30**, 137 (1951).
427. Mandel, L., Jacob, M., and Mandel, P. *Compt. rend. soc. biol.* **145**, 1231 (1951).
428. Mandel, L., Jacob, M., and Mandel, P. *Experientia* **8**, 426 (1952).
429. Mandel, P., Mandel, L., and Jacob, M. *Compt. rend.* **232**, 1513 (1951).
430. Maqsood, M. *Nature* **166**, 735 (1950).
431. Maren, T. H., and Otto, G. F. *Federation Proc.* **7**, 243 (1948).
432. Marine, D., Baumann, E. J., Spence, A. W., and Cipra, A. *Proc. Soc. Exptl. Biol. Med.* **29**, 772 (1932).
433. Markoff, G. N. *Beitr. pathol. Anat. u. allgem. Pathol.* **94**, 377 (1935).
434. Martius, C., and Hess, B. *Arch. Biochem. and Biophys.* **33**, 486 (1951).
435. Martius, C., and Hess, B. *Arch. exptl. Pathol. Pharmakol.* **216**, 45 (1952).
436. Marx, W., Gustin, S. T., and Levi, C. *Proc. Soc. Exptl. Biol. Med.* **83**, 143 (1953).
437. Marx, W., Meserve, E. R., and Deuel, H. J., Jr. *Proc. Soc. Exptl. Biol. Med.* **67**, 385 (1948).
438. Mathies, J. C., Goodman, E. D., and Palm, L. *Am. J. Physiol.* **168**, 352 (1952).
439. Mathies, J. C., Palm, L., and Gaebler, O. H. *Endocrinology* **49**, 571 (1951).
440. Maurer, W., and Reichenbach, L. *Naturwissenschaften* **39**, 261 (1952).
441. Maurer, W., and Schild, K. T. *Klin. Wochschr.* **29**, 514 (1951).
442. May, R. *Deut. med. Wochschr.* **74**, 374 (1949).
443. McArthur, J. W., Rawson, R. W., Fluharty, R. G., and Means, J. H. *Ann. Internal Med.* **29**, 229 (1948).
444. McCarrison, R. *Indian J. Med. Research* **7**, 633 (1920).
445. McClendon, J. F., Foster, W. C., and Reed, E. *Biochem. J.* **47**, 53 (1950).
446. McConahey, W. M., Blackburn, C. M., Keating, F. R., and Albert, A. *Trans. Am. Goiter Assoc.* p. 3 (1953).
447. McConahey, W. M., Keating, F. R., Jr., and Power, M. H. *J. Clin. Invest.* **30**, 778 (1951).
448. McGinty, D. A. *Ann. N. Y. Acad. Sci.* **50**, 403 (1949).
449. McGinty, D. A., and Bywater, W. G. *J. Pharmacol. Exptl. Therap.* **85**, 129 (1945).
450. McGinty, D. A., and Sharp, E. A. *J. Clin. Endocrinol.* **6**, 473 (1946).
451. McQuillan, M. T. Biochemical Studies on the Thyroid Gland. Ph.D. Thesis, University of Melbourne, Australia, 1952.
452. McShan, W. H., Meyer, R. K., and Erway, W. F. *Arch. Biochem.* **15**, 99 (1947).
453. Means, J. H. The Thyroid and Its Diseases, 2nd ed. Lippincott, Philadelphia, 1948.
454. Means, J. H. *J. Biol. Chem.* **21**, 263 (1915).
455. Méhes, G., and Pintér, I. *Acta Phys. Acad. Sci. Hung.* **2**, 207 (1951).
456. Meier, A. L. *Acta Anat.* **16**, 97 (1952).
457. Meier-Burkhardt, R. E. *Acta Anat.* **16**, 298 (1952).
458. Meites, J. *Proc. Soc. Exptl. Biol. Med.* **75**, 193 (1950).
459. Meites, J. *Proc. Soc. Exptl. Biol. Med.* **82**, 626 (1953).
460. Meites, J., and Shay, J. C. *Proc. Soc. Exptl. Biol. Med.* **76**, 196 (1951).
461. Michel, R. *2nd Intern. Congr. Biochem., Paris,* p. 75, (1952).
462. Michel, R., and Lafon, M. *Compt. rend. soc. biol.* **140**, 634 (1946).
463. Miller, O. B., and Selle, W. A. *J. Invest. Dermatol.* **12**, 19 (1949).
464. Mirsky, I. A., and Broh-Kahn, R. H. *Am. J. Physiol.* **117**, 6 (1936).
465. Mole, R. H., and Blatt, O. *Proc. Roy. Soc. Med.* **46**, 250 (1953).
466. Money, W. L., Fager, J., Lucas, V., and Rawson, R. W. *J. Clin. Endocrinol.* **11**, 747 (1951).

467. Money, W. L., Kirschner, L., Kraintz, L., Merrill, P., and Rawson, R. W. *Trans. Am. Goiter Assoc.* p. 213 (1950).
468. Money, W. L., Kraintz, L., Fager, J., Kirschner, L., and Rawson, R. W. *Endocrinology* **48**, 682 (1951).
469. Money, W. L., Lucas, V., Fager, J., and Rawson, R. W. *J. Clin. Endocrinol.* **11**, 973 (1951).
470. Money, W. L., Rall, J. E., and Rawson, R. W. *J. Clin. Endocrinol. and Metabolism* **12**, 1495 (1952).
471. Money, W. L., and Rawson, R. W. *Cancer* **3**, 321 (1950).
472. Monroe, B. G. *Anat. Record* **116**, 345 (1953).
473. Monroe, R. A., and Turner, C. W. *Univ. Missouri Coll. Agr. Research Bull.* **446**, (August 1949).
474. Morelli, A., and Genazzini, E. *Clin. terap.* **4**, 351 (1953).
475. Morris, H. P., Dalton, A. J., and Green, C. D. *J. Clin. Endocrinol.* **11**, 1281 (1951).
476. Morton, M. E., and Chaikoff, I. L. *J. Biol. Chem.* **147**, 1 (1943).
477. Morton, M. E., Perlman, I., Anderson, E., and Chaikoff, I. L. *Endocrinology* **30**, 495 (1942).
478. Moseley, V., and Chornack, F. W. *J. Clin. Invest.* **26**, 11 (1947).
479. Mukherjee, R., and Mitchell, H. H. *J. Nutrition* **37**, 303 (1949).
480. Muus, J., Coons, A. H., and Salter, W. T. *J. Biol. Chem.* **139**, 135 (1941).
481. Myant, N. B., Corbett, B. D., Honour, A. J., and Pochin, E. E. *Clin. Sci.* **9**, 405 (1950).
482. Myant, N. B., and Pochin, E. E. *Clin. Sci.* **9**, 421 (1950).
483. Myant, N. B., Pochin, E. E., and Goldie, E. A. G. *Clin. Sci.* **8**, 109 (1949).
484. Myers, J. D. *J. Clin. Invest.* **29**, 1421 (1950).
485. Myers, J. D., Brannon, E. S., and Holland, B. C. *J. Clin. Invest.* **29**, 1069 (1950).
486. Neal, W. B., Jr., Dragstedt, L. R., Rogers, G. R., and McKeague, G. *Am. J. Physiol.* **168**, 29 (1952).
487. Nemir, R. L., Schulman, I., and Clemons, H. *Am. Rev. Tuberc.* **62**, 618 (1950).
488. Neuberger, A. *Ann. Rev. Biochem.* **18**, 243 (1949).
489. Niemann, C., and Mead, J. F. *J. Am. Chem. Soc.* **63**, 2685 (1941).
490. Niemann, C., and Redemann, C. E. *J. Am. Chem. Soc.* **63**, 1549 (1941).
491. Niemeyer, H., Crane, R. K., Kennedy, E. P., and Lipmann, F. *Federation Proc.* **10**, 229 (1951).
492. Nihei, Y. *Tohoku J. Exptl. Med.* **49**, 39 (1947).
493. Nobel, G. K., and Bradley, H. T. *Biol. Bull.* **64**, 284 (1933).
494. Nonidez, J. F. *Am. J. Anat.* **57**, 135 (1935).
495. Norris, E. H. *Am. J. Anat.* **20**, 411 (1916).
496. Odeblad, E. *Nord. Med.* **48**, 1585 (1952).
497. Odell, T. T., Jr. *Endocrinology* **51**, 265 (1952).
498. Ogilvie, A. L. *J. Dental Research* **32**, 386 (1953).
499. Olivereau, M. *Compt. rend. soc. biol.* **144**, 775 (1950).
500. Olivereau, M. *Compt. rend. soc. biol.* **144**, 832 (1950).
501. O'Neal, L. W., and Heinbecker, P. *Endocrinology* **53**, 60 (1953).
502. O'Neal, L. W., and Heinbecker, P. *Endocrinology* **53**, 239 (1953).
503. Ord, W. M., and White, E. *Brit. Med. J.* **ii**, 217 (1893).
504. Oswald, A. *Z. physiol. Chem.* **32**, 121 (1901).
505. Otto, H. *Z. Ärztl. Fortbild.* **47**, 118 (1953).
506. Page, I. H., and McCubbin, J. W. *Circulation* **5**, 390 (1952).
507. Pahaut, J., Govaerts, J., and Bonhomme, P. *Nature* **172**, 545 (1953).

508. Palmer, W. W., Carson, D. A., and Sloan, L. W. *J. Clin. Invest.* **6,** 597 (1929).
509. Parhon, M. *Mém. soc. biol.* **72,** 620 (1912).
510. Pasqualetti, A. T. *Farm. Chilena* **24,** 450 (1950).
511. Perlman, I., Morton, M. E., and Chaikoff, I. L. *Am. J. Physiol.* **134,** 107 (1941).
512. Perrault, M. *Presse méd.* **58,** 1010 (1950).
513. Persike, E. C. *Endocrinology* **42,** 356 (1948).
514. Petermann, M., Robbins, J.,and Hamilton, M. B. *J. Biol. Chem.,* **208,** 369 (1954).
515. Peters, J. H., Schwartz, R., Mermelstein, H., Nefores, M. N., and Mansuy, M. M. *J. Clin. Invest.* **30,** 799 (1951).
516. Peters, J. P., and Man, E. B. *J. Clin. Invest.* **22,** 715 (1943).
517. Peters, J. P., and Man, E. B. *J. Clin. Invest.* **29,** 1 (1950).
518. Pickering, D. E., and Fisher, D. A. *Am. J. Diseases Children* **86,** 11 (1953).
519. Pickering, D. E., and Fisher, D. A. *Am J. Diseases Children* **86,** 147 (1953).
520. Pickering, D. E., Fisher, D. A., Scott, K. G., van Wagenen, G., and Smyth, F. S. *Am. J. Diseases Children* **86,** 574 (1953).
521. Pittoni, A., and Barbieri, E. *Boll. soc. ital. biol. sper.* **28,** 1745 (1952).
522. Pitt-Rivers, R. *Biochem. J.* **43,** 223 (1948).
523. Pitt-Rivers, R. *Lancet* **265,** 234 (1953).
524. Pitt-Rivers, R., and Randall, S. S. *J. Endocrinol.* **4,** 221 (1945).
525. Plummer, H. S., and Boothby, W. M. *Am. J. Physiol.* **55,** 295 (1921).
526. Pochin, E. E. *Clin. Sci.* **11,** 441 (1952).
527. Ponz, F. *Rev. español. fisiol.* **1,** 173 (1945).
528. Prina, C. *Arch. sci. med.* **91,** 478 (1951).
529. Prinzie, A. *Ann. endocrinol. (Paris)* **12,** 250 (1951).
530. Prueter, R. D., Warson, M. D., and Ferguson, J. K. W. *Can. J. Med. Sci.* **31,** 99 (1953).
531. Puntriano, G., and Meites, J. *Endocrinology* **48,** 217 (1951).
532. Purves, H. D., and Griesbach, W. E. *Brit. J. Exptl. Pathol.* **30,** 23 (1949).
533. Quimby, E. H., and McCune, D. J. *Radiology* **49,** 201 (1947).
534. Raab, W. *Wien, Arch. inn. Med.* **23,** 321 (1932).
535. Raab, W. *J. Am. Med. Assoc.* **128,** 249 (1945).
536. Rabbi, A., and Rossi, C. A. *Boll. soc, ital. biol. sper.* **26,** 1114 (1950).
537. Radcliffe, C. E. *Endocrinology* **32,** 415 (1943).
538. Rall, J. E. *J. Clin. Endocrinol.* **10,** 996 (1950).
539. Rall, J. E. Unpublished observations.
540. Rall, J. E., Foster, C. G., and Peacock, W. C. *J. Clin. Invest.* **31,** 149 (1953).
541. Rall, J. E., Power, M. H., and Albert, A. *Proc. Soc. Exptl. Biol. Med.* **74,** 460 (1950).
542. Rall, J. E., Robbins, J., Becker, D., and Rawson, R. W. *J. Clin. Invest.* **32,** 596 (1953).
543. Randall, R. V., and Albert, A. *Endocrinology* **48,** 327 (1951).
544. Randall, R. V., Lorenz, N., and Albert, A. *Endocrinology* **48,** 339 (1951).
545. Rapport, R. L., and Curtis, G. M. *J. Clin. Endocrinol.* **10,** 735 (1950).
546. Rasmussen, H. *Acta Med. Scand. Suppl.* **115** (1941).
547. Rasquin, P. *Bull. Am. Museum. Natl. Hist.* **93,** 501 (1949).
548. Rawson, R. W. *Ann. N. Y. Acad. Sci.* **50,** 491 (1949).
549. Rawson, R. W. *Ciba Colloq. Endocrinol.* **4,** 294 (1952).
550. Rawson, R. W., Graham, R. M., and Riddell, C. B. *Ann. Internal Med.* **19,** 405 (1943).
551. Rawson, R. W., McArthur, J. W., Dobyns, B. M., Fluharty, R. G., and Cope, O. *Trans. Am. Goiter Assoc.,* p. 187 (1947).

552. Rawson, R. W., and Money, W. L. *Recent Progr. Hormone Research* **4,** 397 (1949).
553. Rawson, R. W., Moore, F. D., Peacock, W. C., Means, J. H., Cope, O., and Riddell, C. B. *J. Clin. Invest.* **24,** 869 (1945).
554. Rawson, R. W., and Rall, J. E. *Med. Clin. N. Amer.* **36,** 639 (1952).
555. Rawson, R. W., Rall, J. E., Pearson, O. H., Robbins, J., Poppell, H. F., and West, C. D. *Am. J. Med. Sci.* **226,** 405 (1953).
556. Rawson, R. W., Rall, J. E., and Robbins, J. *Arch. Internal Med.* **92,** 299 (1953).
557. Rawson, R. W., Skanse, B., Marinelli, L. D., and Fluharty, R. G. *Cancer* **2,** 279 (1949).
558. Rawson, R. W., and Starr, P. *Arch. Internal Med.* **61,** 726 (1938).
559. Rawson, R. W., Sterne, G. D., and Aub, J. C. *Endocrinology* **30,** 240 (1942).
560. Ray, R. D., Asling, C. W., Simpson, M. E., and Evans, H. M. *Anat. Record* **107,** 253 (1950).
561. Reich, M. *Boll. soc. ital. biol. sper.* **25,** 1063 (1949).
562. Reilly, W. A., Scott, K. G., and White, W. E. *Proc. Soc. Exptl. Biol. Med.* **81,** 682 (1952).
563. Reineke, E. P. *Ann. N. Y. Acad. Sci.* **50,** 450 (1949).
564. Reineke, E. P., and Turner, C. W. *J. Biol. Chem.* **149,** 555 (1943).
565. Reineke, E. P., and Turner, C. W. *J. Biol. Chem.* **162,** 369 (1946).
566. Remington, R. E., and Remington, J. W. *J. Nutrition* **15,** 539 (1938).
567. Remy, C., Richert, D. A., Westerfeld, W. W., and Tepperman, J. *Proc. Soc. Exptl. Biol. Med.* **73,** 573 (1950).
568. Rice, C. O. *Arch. Surg.* **36,** 96 (1938).
569. Richards, C. E., Brady, R. O., and Riggs, D. S. *J. Clin. Endocrinol.* **9,** 1107 (1949).
570. Richardson, H. B., Levine, S. Z., and Dubois, E. F. *J. Biol. Chem.* **67,** 737 (1926).
571. Richardson, H. B., and Shorr, E. *Trans. Assoc. Am. Physicians* **50,** 156 (1935).
572. Richter, C. P., and Clisby, K. H. *Arch. Pathol.* **33,** 46 (1942).
573. Richter, C. P., and Clisby, K. H. *Proc. Soc. Exptl. Biol. Med.* **48,** 684 (1941).
574. Rienhoff, W. F. *Arch. Surg.* **19,** 986 (1929).
575. Riggs, D. S. *Pharmacol. Revs.* **4,** 284 (1952).
576. Robbins, J., Petermann, M., and Rall, J. E. *J. Biol. Chem.* **212,** 403 (1955).
577. Robbins, J., and Rall, J. E. *J. Clin. Endocrinol. and Metabolism* **13,** 852 (1953).
578. Robbins, J., and Rall, J. E. *Proc. Soc. Exptl. Biol. Med.* **81,** 530 (1952).
579. Robertson, J. D. *Lancet* **241,** 129 (1941).
580. Robertson, J. D. *Lancet* **241,** 216 (1941).
581. Robertson, J. D. *Lancet* **242,** 672 (1942).
582. Robertson, O. H. *J. Exptl. Zool.* **94,** 229 (1949).
583. Robillard, E., Guénel, J., Pellerin, J., D'Iorio, A., and Crevier, M. *Rev. can. biol.* **10,** 472 (1951).
584. Roche, J. *Rend. ist. super. sanità* **13,** 938 (1950).
585. Roche, J., Deltour, G. H., and Michel, R. *Compt. rend. soc. biol.* **147,** 385 (1953).
586. Roche, J., Deltour, G. H., Michel, R., and Lissitzky, S. *Compt. rend. soc. biol.* **144,** 1647 (1950).
587. Roche, J., Derrien, Y., and Michel, R. *Compt. rend. soc. biol.* **141,** 299 (1947).
588. Roche, J., Jutisz, M., Lissitzky, S., and Michel, R. *Biochim. et Biophys. Acta* **7,** 257 (1951).
589. Roche, J., Lissitzky, S., and Michel, R. *Ann. pharm. franç.* **10,** 166 (1952).
590. Roche, J., Lissitzky, S., and Michel, R. *Biochim. et Biophys. Acta* **8,** 339 (1932).

591. Roche, J., Lissitzky, S., and Michel, R. *Biochim. et Biophys. Acta* **11**, 215 (1953).
592. Roche, J., Lissitzky, S., and Michel, R. *Biochim. et Biophys. Acta* **11**, 220 (1953).
593. Roche, J., Lissitzky, S., and Michel, R. *Compt. rend.* **234**, 997 (1952).
594. Roche, J., Lissitzky, S., and Michel, R. *Compt. rend.* **234**, 1228 (1952).
595. Roche, J., Michel, O., Deltour, G. H., and Michel, R. *Ann. endocrinol. (Paris)* **13**, 1 (1952).
596. Roche, J., Michel, O., and Michel, R. *Compt. rend. soc. biol.* **144**, 506 (1950).
597. Roche, J., Michel, O., Michel, R., and Gorbman, A. *Compt. rend. soc. biol.* **147**, 234 (1953).
598. Roche, J., Michel, O., Michel, R., and Lissitzky, S. *Compt. rend. soc. biol.* **147**, 232 (1953).
599. Roche, J., Michel, O., Michel, R., and Marois, M. *Compt. rend. soc. biol.* **145**, 1833 (1951).
600. Roche, J., and Michel, R. *Bull. soc. chim. biol.* **31**, 144 (1949).
601. Roche, J., Michel, R., and Lafon, M. *Compt. rend. soc. biol.* **141**, 301 (1947).
602. Roche, J., Michel, R., Lissitzky, S., and Michel, O. *Compt. rend.* **232**, 2148 (1951).
603. Roche, J., Michel, R., Michel, O., Deltour, G. H., and Lissitzky, S. *Biochim. et Biophys. Acta* **6**, 572 (1951).
604. Roche, J., Michel, R., Michel, O., Deltour, G. H., and Lissitzky. S. *Compt. rend. soc. biol.* **144**, 917 (1950).
605. Roche, J., Michel, R., Michel, O., and Lissitzky, S. *Biochim. et Biophys. Acta* **9**, 161 (1952).
606. Roche, J., Michel, R., Michel, O., and Lissitzky, S. *Compt. rend. soc. biol.* **145**, 288 (1951).
607. Roche, J., Michel, R., and Tata, J. *Biochim. et Biophys. Acta* **11**, 543 (1953).
608. Roche, J., Nguyen van Thoai, and Lafon, M. *Compt. rend. soc. biol.* **143**, 1327 (1949).
609. Roe, J. H., and Coover, M. O. *Proc. Soc. Exptl. Biol. Med.* **75**, 818 (1950).
610. Rondoni, P., and Montagnani, M. *Sperimentale* **69**, 659 (1915).
611. Rosenberg, I. N. *J. Clin. Endocrinol.* **11**, 1063 (1951).
612. Rosenberg, I. N. *J. Clin. Invest.* **30**, 1 (1951).
613. Rosenberg, I. N. *Science* **116**, 503 (1952).
614. Rosenblum, I. *Federation Proc.* **10**, 111 (1951).
615. Rosenman, R. H., Friedman, M., and Byers, S. O. *Circulation* **5**, 589 (1952).
616. Rosenman, R. H., Friedman, M., and Byers, S. O. *Science* **114**, 210 (1951).
617. Rossiter, R. J. *J. Biol. Chem.* **135**, 431 (1940).
618. Rossiter, R. J. *J. Endocrinol.* **2**, 165 (1940).
619. Rotblat, J., and Marcus, R. Proc. Isotopes Techniques Conf., Oxford, July 1951.
620. Roth, P. *Bull. musée natl. hist. nat. Paris* **13**, 611 (1941).
621. Roth, P. *Ann. endocrinol. (Paris)* **14**, 857 (1953).
622. Rubino, F. *Boll. soc. ital. biol. sper.* **26**, 1018 (1950).
623. Rugh, R. *J. Morphol.* **89**, 323 (1951).
624. Rugh, R. *Proc. Soc. Exptl. Biol. Med.* **83**, 762 (1953).
625. Rupp, J., Paschkis, K. E., and Cantarow, A. *Endocrinology* **44**, 449 (1949).
626. Rupp, J., Paschkis, K. E., and Cantarow, A. *Proc. Soc. Exptl. Biol. Med.* **76**, 432 (1951).
627. Sadhu, D. P. *Am. J. Physiol.* **152**, 263 (1948).
628. Sadhu, D. P., and Brody, S. *Am. J. Physiol.* **149**, 400 (1947).

629. Salter, W. T.   The Chemistry and Physiology of Hormones.   Am. Assoc. Advancement Sci., Washington, D. C., 1944, p. 104.
630. Salter, W. T.   The Endocrine Function of Iodine.   Harvard University Press, Cambridge, Mass., 1940.
631. Salter, W. T.   The Hormones, Vol. II.   Academic Press, New York, 1950, p. 190.
632. Salter, W. T.   *Ann. N. Y. Acad. Sci.* **50,** 358 (1949).
633. Salter, W. T., Cortell, R. E., and McKay, E. A.   *J. Pharmacol. Exptl. Therap.* **85,** 310 (1945).
634. Salter, W. T., deVisscher, M., McAdams, G. B., and Rosenblum, I.   *J. Clin. Endocrinol.* **11,** 1512 (1951).
635. Salter, W. T., and Lerman, J.   *Trans. Assoc. Am. Physicians* **53,** 202 (1938).
636. Samuels, L. T.   Personal communication.
637. Schachner, H., Franklin, A. L., and Chaikoff, I. L.   *Endocrinology* **34,** 159 (1944).
638. Schachner, H., Franklin, A. L., and Chaikoff, I. L.   *J. Biol. Chem.* **151,** 191 (1943).
639. Scharles, F. H., Robb, P. D., and Salter, W. T.   *Am. J. Physiol.* **111,** 130 (1935).
640. Scheinberg, P.   *J. Clin. Invest.* **29,** 1010 (1950).
641. Scheinberg, P., Stead, E. A., Jr., Brannon, E. S., and Warren, J. V.   *J. Clin. Invest.* **29,** 1139 (1950).
642. Schmid, K.   *J. Am. Chem. Soc.* **75,** 60 (1953).
643. Schneider, E., and Bruger, A.   *Klin. Wochschr.* **17,** 905 (1938).
644. Schulman, J., Jr.   *J. Biol. Chem.* **186,** 717 (1950).
645. Schulze, E., and Linnemann, H.   *Arch. exptl. Pathol. Pharmakol.* **189,** 448 (1938).
646. Scott, C. C., Kroc, R. L., and Stasilli, N. R.   *Endocrinology* **50,** 607 (1952).
647. Scow, R. O.   *Am. J. Physiol.* **173,** 199 (1953).
648. Scow, R. O.   *Endocrinology* **49,** 522 (1951).
649. Searle, C. E., Lawson, A., and Morley, H. U.   *Biochem. J.* **49,** 125 (1951).
650. Segrè, E., Mackenzie, K. R., and Corson, D. R.   *Phys. Rev.* **57,** 1087 (1940).
651. Sellers, E. A., You, S. S., and You, R. W.   *Endocrinology* **47,** 148 (1950).
652. Shaffer, P. A.   *Am. J. Physiol.* **23,** 1 (1908–1909).
653. Sharpless, G. R., Pearsons, J., and Prato, G. S.   *J. Nutrition* **17,** 545 (1939).
654. Sheahan, M. M., Wilkinson, J. H., and Maclagan, N. F.   *Biochem. J.* **48,** 188 (1951).
655. Sicuteri, F., and Minnini, G.   *Arch. studio fisiopatol. e. clin. ricambio* **14,** 35 (1950).
656. Sidorkina, M. Ya.   *Doklady Akad. Nauk S. S. S. R.* **73,** 1287 (1950) [*C. A.* **45,** 762 (1951)].
657. Sidorkina, M. Ya.   *Doklady Akad. Nauk S. S. S. R.* **77,** 357 (1951) [*C. A.* **45,** 7227 (1951)].
658. Silver, S., and Reiner, M.   *Bull. N. Y. Acad. Med.* **26,** 277 (1950).
659. Simkins, S.   *J. Clin. Endocrinol.* **7,** 574 (1947).
660. Simpson, M. E., Asling, C. W., and Evans, H. M.   *Yale J. Biol. and Med.* **23,** 1 (1950).
661. Simpson, S.   *Quart. J. Exptl. Physiol.* **6,** 119 (1913).
662. Skanse, B.   *Acta Med. Scand.* **131,** 251 (1948).
663. Skanse, B.   *Acta Med. Scand. Suppl.* 235 (1949).
664. Skowran, S., and Jordan, M.   *Bull. intern. acad. polon. sci. Classe méd.,* p. 111 (1949).
665. Smith, A. U., Emmens, C. W., and Parkes, A. S.   *J. Endocrinol.* **5,** 186 (1946–1948).
666. Smith, D. C., and Brown, F. C.   *Biol. Bull.* **102,** 278 (1952).

667. Smith, D. C., and Everett, G. M.   *J. Exptl. Zool.* **94,** 229 (1943).
668. Smith, D. C., and Matthews, S. A.   *Am. J. Physiol.* **153,** 215 (1948).
669. Smith, D. C., and Perman, J. M.   *Endocrinology* **27,** 110 (1940).
670. Smith, D. C., Sladek, S. A., and Kellner, A. W.   *Physiol. Zool.* **26,** 117 (1953).
671. Smith, P. E.   *Anat. Record* **11,** 57 (1916).
672. Smith, R. H., and Williams-Ashman, H. G.   *Nature* **164,** 457 (1949).
673. Smith, R. H., and Williams-Ashman, H. G.   *Biochim. et Biophys. Acta* **7,** 295 (1951).
674. Smith, R. L.   *Federation Proc.* **6,** 205 (1947).
675. Smith, S. C., Rasmussen, A. F., Jr., Elvehjem, C. A., and Clark, R. F.   *Proc. Soc. Exptl. Biol. Med.* **82,** 269 (1953).
676. Soffer, L. J., Cohn, C., Grossman, E. B., Jacobs, M., and Sobotka, H.   *J. Clin. Invest.* **20,** 429 (1941).
677. Soffer, L. J., Gabrilove, J. L., and Dorrance, W. R.   *Proc. Soc. Exptl. Biol. Med.* **76,** 763 (1951).
678. Solganils, R. I.   *Biokhimiya* **17,** 649 (1952).
679. Sonenberg, M.   Personal communication.
680. Sonenberg, M.   *Ciba Colloq. Endocrinol.* **4,** 229 (1952).
681. Sonenberg, M., Keston, A. S., Money, W. L., and Rawson, R. W.   *J. Clin. Endocrinol.* **10,** 1269 (1952).
682. Spinks, A., and Burn, J. H.   *Brit. J. Pharmacol.* **7,** 93 (1952).
683. Sprott, W. E., Wilkinson, J. H., and Maclagan, N. F.   *J. Endocrinol.* **9,** xxxii (1953).
684. Stanbury, J. B., Brownell, G. L., Riggs, D. S., Perinetti, H., del Castillo, E., and Itoiz, J.   *J. Clin. Endocrinol.* **12,** 191 (1952).
685. Stanley, M. M.   *J. Clin. Endocrinol.* **9,** 941 (1949).
686. Stanley, M. M., and Astwood, E. B.   *Endocrinology* **44,** 588 (1949).
687. Stanley, M. M., and Astwood, E. B.   *Lancet* **ii,** 905 (1947).
688. Starr, P., and Patton, H.   *Endocrinology* **18,** 113 (1934).
689. Starr, P., and Roskelley, R.   *Am. J. Physiol.* **130,** 549 (1940).
690. Statland, H., and Lerman, J.   *Trans. Am. Goiter Assoc.,* p. 227 (1950).
691. Steger, K.   *Acta Anat.* **11,** 246 (1951).
692. Steiner, A., Kendall, F. E., and Bevans, M.   *Am. Heart J.* **38,** 34 (1949).
693. Sternheimer, R.   *Endocrinology* **25,** 899 (1939).
694. Stewart, H. J., and Evans, W. F.   *Am. Heart J.* **20,** 715 (1940).
695. Stewart, H. J., and Evans, W. F.   *Arch. Internal Med.* **69,** 808 (1942).
696. Sturkie, P. D.   *Endocrinology* **49,** 565 (1951).
697. Sung, C., and Way, E. L.   *J. Pharmacol. Exptl. Therap.* **108,** 1 (1953).
698. Sure, B., and Easterling, L.   *J. Nutrition* **42,** 221 (1950).
699. Sure, B., Ford, Z. W., Jr., Theis, R. M., and Goldfischer, M.   *Endocrinology* **28,** 806 (1941).
700. Swanson, E. W., and Bootman, J. P.   *J. Dairy Sci.* **36,** 246 (1953).
701. Swenson, R. E., and Curtis, G. M.   *J. Clin. Endocrinol.* **8,** 934 (1948).
702. Talmage, R. U., Nachimson, H., Kraintz, L., and Green, J. A.   *Science* **118,** 191 (1953).
703. Tatum, A. L.   *J. Exptl. Med.* **17,** 634 (1913).
704. Taurog, A., Briggs, F. N., and Chaikoff, I. L.   *J. Biol. Chem.* **191,** 29 (1951).
705. Taurog, A., Briggs, F. N., and Chaikoff, I. L.   *J. Biol. Chem.* **194,** 655 (1952).
706. Taurog, A., and Chaikoff, I. L.   *J. Biol. Chem.* **176,** 639 (1948).
707. Taurog, A., and Chaikoff, I. L.   *J. Biol. Chem.* **176,** 699 (1948).
708. Taurog, A., Chaikoff, I. L., and Entenman, C.   *Endocrinology* **40,** 86 (1947).

709. Taurog, A., Chaikoff, I. L., and Feller, D. D. *J. Biol. Chem.* **171,** 189 (1947).
710. Taurog, A., Chaikoff, I. L., and Franklin, A. L. *J. Biol. Chem.* **161,** 537 (1945).
711. Taurog, A., Chaikoff, I. L., and Tong, W. *J. Biol. Chem.* **178,** 997 (1949).
712. Taurog, A., Chaikoff, I. L., and Tong, W. *J. Biol. Chem.* **184,** 99 (1950).
713. Taurog, A., Tong, W., and Chaikoff, I. L. *J. Biol. Chem.* **184,** 83 (1950).
714. Taurog, A., Tong, W., and Chaikoff, I. L. *J. Biol. Chem.* **191,** 677 (1951).
715. Taylor, A. *J. Exptl. Zool.* **81,** 135 (1939).
716. Tepperman, J., Engel, F. L., and Long, C. N. H. *Endocrinology* **32,** 373 (1943).
717. Thibault, O. *Ann. endocrinol. (Paris)* **12,** 674 (1951).
718. Thibault, O. *J. Physiol.* **45,** 233 (1953).
719. Thibault, O., and Lachaze, A. *Compt. rend.* **232,** 1318 (1951).
720. Thibault, O., and Lachaze, A. *Compt. rend. soc. biol.* **145,** 797 (1951).
721. Thomas, J. W., and Moore, L. A. *J. Dairy Sci.* **36,** 657 (1953).
722. Thomopoulos, T. *Compt. rend.* **227,** 1262 (1948).
723. Thompson, J. C., and Vars, H. M. *Proc. Soc. Exptl. Biol. Med.* **83,** 246 (1953).
724. Thompson, W. O., McLellan, L. L., Thompson, P. K., and Dickie, L. F. N. *J. Clin. Invest.* **12,** 235 (1933).
725. Thompson, W. O., Thompson, P. K., Silveus, E., and Dailey, M. E. *Arch. Internal Med.* **44,** 368 (1929).
726. Tierney, N. A., and Peters, J. P. *J. Clin. Invest.* **22,** 595 (1943).
727. Tipton, S. R. *Am. J. Physiol.* **161,** 29 (1950).
728. Tipton, S. R., Leath, M. J., Tipton, I. H., and Nixon, W. L. *Am. J. Physiol.* **145,** 693 (1946).
729. Tishkoff, G. H., Bennett, R., Bennett, V., and Miller, L. L. *Science* **110,** 452 (1949).
730. Tissières, A. *Arch. intern. physiol.* **54,** 305 (1946).
731. Tomich, E. G., and Woollett, E. A. *Lancet* i, 726 (1953).
732. Tong, W., Taurog, A., and Chaikoff, I. L. *J. Biol. Chem.* **191,** 665 (1951).
733. Treverrow, V. *J. Biol. Chem.* **127,** 737 (1939).
734. Trikojus, V. M. Proc. Isotope Techniques Conf., Oxford, July 1951.
735. Trunnell, J. B., and Brayer, F. T. *J. Clin. Endocrinol. and Metabolism* **13,** 88 (1953).
736. Tubianan, M. *Compt. rend. soc. biol.* **145,** 1011 (1951).
737. Turchini, J. *Bull. histol. appl. physiol. et pathol. et tech. microscop.* **14,** 17 (1937).
738. Uhlenhuth, E. *Biol. Bull.* **42,** 143 (1922).
739. Uhlenhuth, E. *Biol. Bull.* **45,** 303 (1923).
740. Ullrick, W. C., and Whitehorn, W. V. *Am. J. Physiol.* **171,** 407 (1952).
741. Ungar, G., Damgaard, E., and Weinstein, H. G. *Am. J. Physiol.* **166,** 340 (1951).
742. Uotila, U. *Virchow's Arch. pathol. Anat. u. Physiol.* **301,** 535 (1938).
743. Uotila, U. *Endocrinology* **25,** 605 (1939).
744. Uotila, U. *Endocrinology* **26,** 129 (1940).
745. Usuelli, F., and Piana, A. *Boll. soc. ital. biol. sper.* **26,** 1439 (1950).
746. Vanderlaan, W. P., and Bissell, A. *Endocrinology* **39,** 157 (1946).
747. Vanderlaan, W. P., and Greer, M. A. *Endocrinology* **47,** 36 (1950).
748. Vanderlaan, J. E., and Vanderlaan, W. P. *Endocrinology* **40,** 403 (1947).
749. van Middlesworth, L., Tuttle, A. H., and Threlkeld, A. *Science* **118,** 749 (1953).
750. Vestling, C. S., and Knoepfelmacher, A. A. *J. Biol. Chem.* **183,** 63 (1950).
751. Villamil, M. F., and Mancini, R. E. *Rev. soc. argentina biol.* **23,** 219 (1947).
752. Villar Caso, J., Zofmann, A. E., and Rivero Fontan, J. L. *Rev. españ. enfermedad. aparato digest. y nutrición* **10,** 446 (1951).
753. Vollmer, H., and Buchholz, C. *Arch. exptl. Pathol. Pharmakol.* **155,** 185 (1930).

518   RULON W. RAWSON, JOSEPH E. RALL, AND MARTIN SONENBERG

754. von Mutzenbecher, P. *Z. physiol. Chem.* **261**, 253 (1939).
755. Wang, E. *Acta Med. Scand.* **105**, 1 (1939).
756. Watman, R. N., and Nasset, E. S. *Am. J. Physiol.* **157**, 216 (1949).
757. Watman, R. N., and Nasset, E. S. *Am. J. Physiol.* **166**, 131 (1951).
758. Wawrzyniak, M. *Ann. Univ. Mariae Curie-Sklodoruska, Lublin, Poland,* **DD6,** 417 (1951).
759. Wayne, E. J., MacGregor, A. G., and Miller, H. *Lancet* **258**, 327 (1950).
760. Weber, G., and Drechsler, K. *Am. J. Physiol.* **162**, 289 (1950).
761. Weir, E. G., and Hastings, A. B. *J. Biol. Chem.* **129**, 547 (1939).
762. Weise, C. E., Mehl, J. W., and Deuel, H. J., Jr. *J. Biol. Chem.* **175**, 21 (1948).
763. Weisenfeld, S., and Rawson, R. W. *Trans. Am. Goiter Assoc.*, p. 259 (1952).
764. Weiss, B. *J. Biol. Chem.* **201**, 31 (1953).
765. Weiss, B. *J. Biol. Chem.* **205**, 193 (1953).
766. Weiss, E., Moulder, J. W., and Itatoni, M. K. *J. Infectious Diseases* **90**, 21 (1952).
767. Weiss, S. B., Marx, L., and Marx, W. *Endocrinology* **50**, 192 (1952).
768. Werner, S. C. *Bull. N. Y. Acad. Med.* **29**, 523 (1953).
769. Werner, S. C., Quimby, E. H., and Schmidt, C. *J. Clin. Endocrinol.* **9**, 342 (1949).
770. Weslaw, W., and Wrobleski, B. *Z. ges. exptl. Med.* **105**, 497 (1939).
771. Westerfeld, W. W., and Lowe, C. *J. Biol. Chem.* **145**, 463 (1942).
772. Westrick, M. L. *Proc. Soc. Exptl. Biol. Med.* **82**, 56 (1953).
773. Wilkins, L., and Fleischmann, W. *J. Clin. Invest.* **25**, 360 (1946).
774. Wilkinson, J. H., and Maclagan, N. F. *J. Endocrinol.* **9**, xliv (1953).
775. Wilkinson, J. H., and Maclagan, N. F. *Lancet* **ii**, 1024 (1953).
776. Wilkinson, J. H., Sheahan, M. M., and Maclagan, N. F. *Biochem. J.* **49**, 710 (1951).
777. Wilkinson, J. H., Sheahan, M. M., and Maclagan, N. F. *Biochem. J.* **49**, 714 (1951).
778. Wilkinson, J. H., Sheahan, M. M., and Maclagan, N. F. *Biochem. J.* **54**, 491 (1953).
779. Wilkinson, J. H., Sprott, W. E., Bowden, C. H., and Maclagan, N. F. *Biochem. J.* **56**, 215 (1954).
780. Wilkinson, J. H., Sprott, W. E., and Maclagan, N. F. *Biochem. J.* **54**, 16 (1953).
781. Williams, H. L., and Watson, E. M. *Endocrinology* **29**, 258 (1941).
782. Williams, R. H. *J. Clin. Endocrinol.* **5**, 217 (1945).
783. Williams, R. H., Jaffe, H., and Soloman, B. *Am. J. Med. Sci.* **219**, 1 (1950).
784. Williams, R. H., Tagnon, R. F., Jaffe, H., Towery, T. R., and Rogers, W. F., Jr. *J. Clin. Endocrinol.* **8**, 597 (1948).
785. Williams-Ashman, H. G. *Biochem. J.* **42**, li (1948).
786. Williams-Ashman, H. G. *J. Endocrinol.* **5**, xc (1948).
787. Wilson, G. E. *Anat. Record* **42**, 243 (1929).
788. Wilson, M., and McGinty, D. A. *Am. J. Physiol.* **156**, 377 (1949).
789. Wolff, J. *Endocrinology* **48**, 284 (1951).
790. Wolff, J., and Chaikoff, I. L. *Endocrinology* **41**, 295 (1947).
791. Wolff, J., and Chaikoff, I. L. *Endocrinology* **42**, 468 (1948).
792. Wolff, J., and Chaikoff, I. L. *Endocrinology* **43**, 174 (1948).
793. Wolff, J., and Chaikoff, I. L. *J. Biol. Chem.* **172**, 855 (1948).
794. Wolff, J., and Chaikoff, I. L. *J. Biol. Chem.* **174**, 555 (1948).
795. Wolff, J., Chaikoff, I. L., Goldberg, R. C., and Meier, J. R. *Endocrinology* **45**, 504 (1949).

796. Wolff, J., Chaikoff, I. L., and Nichols, C. W., Jr.   *Endocrinology* **44,** 510 (1949).
797. Wolff, J., Chaikoff, I. L., Taurog, A., and Rubin, L.   *Endocrinology* **39,** 140 (1946).
798. Wood, J. L., and Kingsland, N.   *J. Biol. Chem.* **185,** 833 (1950).
799. Woolley, D. W.   *J. Biol. Chem.* **164,** 11 (1946).
800. Wyngaarden, J. B., Stanbury, J. B., and Du Toit, C. H.   *J. Clin. Endocrinol.* **11,** 1259 (1951).
801. Wyngaarden, J. B., Stanbury, J. B., and Rapp, B.   *Endocrinology* **52,** 568 (1953).
802. Wyngaarden, J. B., Wright, B. M., and Ways, P.   *Endocrinology* **50,** 537 (1952).
803. Yagi, Y., Michel, R., and Roche, J.   *Bull. soc. chim. biol.* **35,** 289 (1953).
804. You, S. S., You, R. W., and Sellers, E. A.   *Endocrinology* **47,** 156 (1950).
805. Zawadowsky, B.   *Endokrinologie* **10,** 23 (1932).

CHAPTER XI

Chemistry of Steroid Hormones

BY H. HIRSCHMANN

CONTENTS

The discovery of the remarkable therapeutic effects of cortisone has stimulated chemical research on steroid hormones to such an extent that a full presentation within the confines of this chapter is not possible. Many of the methods discovered in recent years can be and often were put to a great variety of uses. To present this wealth of material as succinctly as possible, an attempt has been made to survey procedures rather than to describe the syntheses of individual compounds. This seemed the more justified as there are now three excellent recent reviews dealing with the preparation of cortisone and cortisol (68, 272, 301). In presenting proofs of structure or of configuration greater conciseness is often possible by selecting the facts which seem to establish most clearly a given point rather than by following the historical development. Having chosen this course the author must offer his apologies to those investigators whose pioneering efforts do not receive their due credit. The literature was sur-

521

veyed as far as possible up to the end of 1953, but a few more recent publications could still be included. Material already discussed in Volume I has not been reviewed again unless subsequent developments necessitated the revision of earlier conclusions. The vast subject of total synthesis could be dealt with only very briefly. Steroid spectroscopy, although a most important tool both in synthesis and analysis, could not be included. However, a very thorough survey of ultraviolet spectra has recently been made by L. Dorfman (80). Dobriner *et al.* (79) have made available their large collection of infrared spectra, and Bernstein and Lenhard (23) have dealt extensively with the absorption characteristics of steroids in concentrated sulfuric acid. Finally, reference should be made to the classical treatise on steroid chemistry by Fieser and Fieser (93), which gives an authoritative account of the field up to November 1948.

I. Nomenclature—Abbreviations

Some basic principles of steroid nomenclature, the significance of the terms α and β, etc., have been set forth in Volume I of *The Hormones* (p. 561). The customary numbering system is again reproduced in Chart 1.

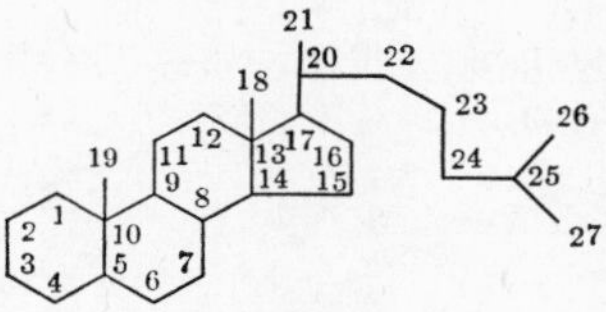

CHART 1.

The National Research Council Subcommittee on Steroid Nomenclature has proposed a number of changes[1] similar to but not identical with those adopted at a Ciba Foundation Conference. The major revisions which will be followed in this chapter are: Position and configuration indices (the latter without parentheses) will always precede the functional group to which they refer. Inversion of configuration at a ring junction will be indicated by a prefix stating the position and configuration of the hydrogen (or functional group) at this ring juncture. At C-17, however, the stated configuration will be that of the side chain, which need be specified only if it is the unnatural (α) configuration. Unknown configurations will be indicated by ξ. Etianic and alloetianic acid will be used instead of etiocholanic and etioallocholanic acid.

As the systematic names of polyfunctional steroids are often cumbersome, liberal use of trivial names will be made. Those not yet used in Volume I include: 17β-estradiol (previously known as α-estradiol) for the

[1] This report is available from the office of Chemical Abstracts, Columbus, Ohio.

more potent isomer of $\Delta^{1,3,5(10)}$-estratriene-3,17-diol; epitestosterone for 17α-hydroxy-Δ^4-androsten-3-one; epiandrosterone for 3β-hydroxyandrostan-17-one; dehydroepiandrosterone for 3β-hydroxy-Δ^5-androsten-17-one (this term should not be confused with the obsolete "epi-Dehydroandrosteron" which had been employed to designate the 3-epimer (277)); cortisol for 11β,17,21-trihydroxy-Δ^4-pregnene-3,20-dione (Kendall's Compound F) (this term was suggested by Shoppee (301) in preference to hydrocortisone, which is longer and could be confused with dihydrocortisone, which has been used by some for the 4,5-reduction product); epicortisol for 11α,17,21-trihydroxy-Δ^4-pregnene-3,20-dione; cortisone for 17,21-dihydroxy-Δ^4-pregnene-3,11,20-trione (Kendall's Compound E), 11-deoxycortisol for 17,21-dihydroxy-Δ^4-pregnene-3,20-dione (Reichstein's Compound S). The important urinary excretion products 3α,11β,17,21-tetrahydroxypregnan-20-one and 3α,17,21-trihydroxypregnane-11,20-dione will be named urocortisol and urocortisone, respectively, rather than designated by the somewhat loose terms "tetrahydro-F" and "tetrahydro-E."

In the charts and formulas the following abbreviations will be employed: Me for CH_3 ; Et for C_2H_5 ; Bu for $\overset{\backprime}{C}_4H_9$; φ (phenyl) for C_6H_5 ; Ar for an aromatic radical; Ac (acetyl) for CH_3CO; Ts (tosyl = p-toluenesulfonyl) for $CH_3 \cdot C_6H_4 \cdot SO_2$; Ms (mesyl = methanesulfonyl) for CH_3SO_2 ; NBS for N-bromosuccinimide; NIS for N-iodosuccinimide; NBA for N-bromoacetamide; pyr. for pyridine; col. for collidine; W-K for Wolff-Kishner reduction; Opp. for Oppenauer oxidation. A wavy line in the formulas indicates that the configuration is either unknown or irrelevant. In aliphatic structures, bonds indicated by solid triangles (as in Chart 7) are pointing forward (towards the observer), and those by broken lines are directed to the rear. If not marked in this manner, the configuration of aliphatic compounds and of C-20 in the steroids is indicated by a projection into a plane. This projection is obtained by arranging the molecule so that the bonds which lead from the asymmetric center to the atoms written above and below it point away from the observer. (For examples see Charts 7 and 10.)

II. Stereochemistry

A. GENERAL CONSIDERATIONS

Probably no concept has contributed more to the understanding of the chemical behavior of the steroids as it is affected by the geometry of the molecule than Barton's (18) developments of the modern stereochemistry of cyclohexane (123). Since the carbon skeleton of this compound can be arranged in two distinct strain-free forms which have become known as boat and as chair, it was thought for a long time that the molecule could assume either shape with *equal* facility. Inspection of molecular models

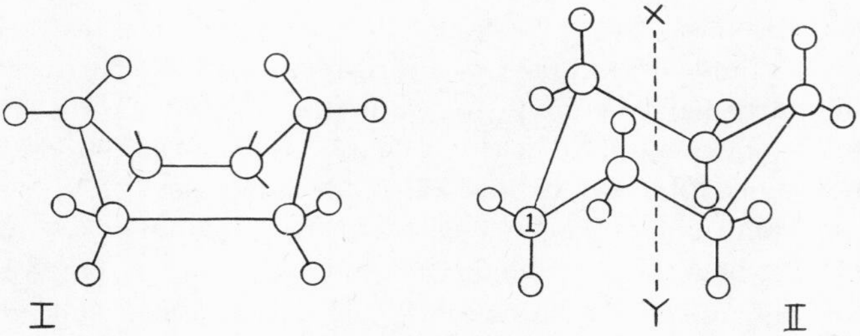

Fig. 1. Cyclohexane; I boat, II chair.

(Fig. 1) shows that the hydrogen atoms attached to adjacent carbon atoms at the bottom of the boat (I) are at the shortest possible distance from each other and that the separation of two hydrogens located at stern and bow is even less.   In the chair form (II), on the other hand, all hydrogens are at the maximal distance from those at adjacent carbon atoms.   The greater stability of this arrangement has been demonstrated by Hassel (123) and others by a great variety of experimental techniques.   In the chair form all 6 carbon atoms are equivalent.   This can readily be seen by rotating the model around the axis X-Y.   Rotation through 60° yields the mirror image, rotation through 120°, a structure indistinguishable from the original.   The hydrogen atoms attached to each carbon atom are not equivalent geometrically.   At each carbon, one carbon hydrogen bond is parallel to the symmetry axis (X-Y) and is termed axial,[2] while the other, which radiates outward, is termed equatorial.   The distance of two substituents at adjacent carbon atoms that are *trans* to each other will be quite different if the two groups are axial or equatorial.   Equatorial substituents of cyclohexane are close only to substituents at adjacent carbon atoms, whereas axial substituents in addition encroach upon axial groups in *meta*[3] positions   On the basis of this geometric differentiation a number of rules have been set forth (18) which describe the stereochemical behavior of steroids and of related structures with greater reliability than earlier attempts at generalization, such as the rules of Skita and of Vavon (117, 240, 306).

1. At a given asymmetric center substituents are generally more stable in the equatorial than in the axial position.   (This is illustrated by reactions which permit the equilibration of epimers and by the reduction of ketones with sodium and alcohol, which yields predominantly the equatorial hydroxyl.)   (See ref. 54 for exception.)

2. At a given carbon atom substituents are more sterically hindered if axial than if equatorial.   (Examples: Equatorial hydroxyl groups esterify

[2] This term replaces (19) "polar" which was used previously.

[3] The terms *"ortho,"* *"meta,"* and *"para"* will be used in the same sense as in aromatic chemistry.

faster; equatorial esters hydrolyze faster; axial hydroxyl groups are more rapidly converted to the ketone with chromic acid, which, in the rate-determining step, is believed to attack the carbon-bound hydrogen; in phase partition, compounds with an equatorial hydroxyl are relatively more soluble in polar solvents than their epimers (291).)

3. The catalytic hydrogenation of ketones in acidic media gives predominantly axial hydroxyl groups. (This implies an attachment of the catalyst to the side from which the *ortho-meta* carbon bonds recede (306), *i.e.*, a carbonyl at C-1 would be reduced from above (Fig. 1, II).)

4. 1,2-Elimination reactions which operate by an ionic mechanism or 1,2-rearrangements proceed most readily if the bonds broken lie in one plane and face opposite directions. In the case of the elimination reactions the condition is satisfied if the substituents eliminated are both axial.

5. Similarly in the opening of 1,2-epoxides, the reagent attacks preferentially that carbon atom at which the newly formed bond can be axial, thus retaining the axial hydroxyl group at the other.

Obviously the utility of these rules and of others formulated by Barton depends on the certainty with which the α and β substituents at the various asymmetric carbon atoms of the steroid nucleus can be classified as axial or equatorial. Such a correlation can be made for most steroids without ambiguity if it can be assumed that the ring system possesses minimal angular strain and that those rings which can assume various shapes under this condition are predominantly in the chair form just as they are in cyclohexane. (In the all *trans*-linked steroids ordinarily only ring A has such flexibility.) The predominance of the all chair form for typical steroids (without ring bridges or other unusual steric features) is supported by dipole measurements (239) on 3,17-diketones with either *cis* or *trans* fusion of rings A and B. On the basis of this chair model the substituents of rings A, B, and C can be classified as set forth in Table I. Only in so far as the orientations of the substituents at C-17 and C-15 approximate those which would obtain if ring D were six-membered, can they be considered as axial or equatorial and then only with respect to ring C. Mechanical models indicate that the α and β bonds at C-17 are turned somewhat upward from such positions. This results in a closer approach of the β substituent to the methyl group (C-18) and a greater separation of the α substituent from the α-hydrogen at C-14. It might therefore be anticipated that the β-position at C-17 is more hindered than the α. As will be shown, this is not the case, and C-17 conforms to rules 1 and 2 but not to 3. The β-position at C-17 therefore can be considered as quasi-equatorial, the α as quasi-axial. A possible explanation for this behavior has been suggested by von Euw and Reichstein (328). The terms axial and equatorial cannot be applied in any way to C-16.

TABLE I

GEOMETRY OF RING SUBSTITUENTS

Position	Config. at C-5				Position	Config. at C-5			
	α		β			α		β	
	Config.		Config.			Config.		Config.	
	α	β	α	β		α	β	α	β
1	a	e	e	a	8	—	a	—	a
2	e	a	a	e	9	a	—	a	—
3	a	e	e	a	10	—	a	—	†
4	e	a	a	e	11	e	a	e	a
5	a	—	—	*	12	a	e	a	e
6	e	a	e	a	13	—	a	—	a
7	a	e	a	e	14	a	—	a	—

* Axial with respect to Ring A and equatorial to B.
† Axial with respect to Ring B and equatorial to A.
a = axial; e = equatorial.

B. REVISION AT C-17

Until 1947 no stereochemical correlation of 17-alkyl steroids containing a 17-hydroxy group had been made with those not so oxygenated. However, since the inversion at C-17 abolishes the corticoid activity of potent adrenal steroids, it seemed plausible that the active compounds possessed the same orientation of the side chain regardless of the presence or absence of a hydroxyl group at C-17. In 1946, Sorkin and Reichstein (315) provided convincing evidence that the side chains of the sterols, of the bile acids, and of the 17-deoxy steroids of the adrenal are β-oriented (Vol. I, p. 574), thus reversing a previous tentative assignment. Whereas this change was incorporated in the presentations of Volume I, the evidence necessitating the corresponding reversals of the assignments at C-17 in 17-hydroxysteroids appeared too late to be included. As will be seen this revision affects the stereonomenclature of the 17-hydroxysteroids with and without a side chain at C-17. With few exceptions therefore, compounds designated in Volume I as 17(α) or 17(β) (or 17"α" or 17"β", Vol. I, p. 567)) actually have the reverse configuration and henceforth will be named according to the configurations now established.

The chemical reactivity of 17-hydroxysteroids depends quite markedly on their configuration. Esters of testosterone hydrolyze at a faster rate than those of epitestosterone (276). In contrast to their epimers (303)

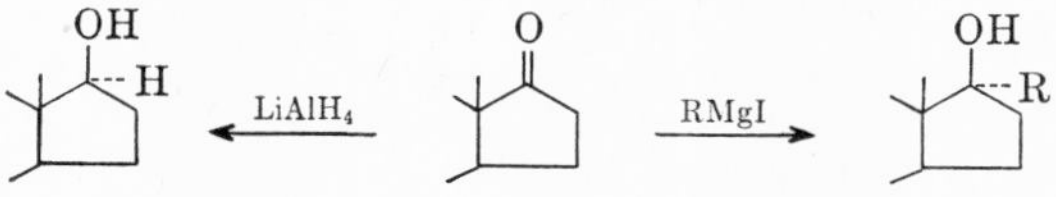

CHART 2. Addition reactions of 17-ketones.

17-hydroxy-20-ketosteroids with the natural configuration cannot be acetylated at C-17 with pyridine and acetic anhydride. Conversely the reactivity of the 20-carbonyl group is greater in the natural than in the synthetic
series (328). As stated in the preceding section inspection of molecular
models does not permit an unequivocal selection of the more hindered
configuration. When the hydrolysis rates of both 17-epimers of methyl
3β-hydroxyalloetianate were compared, the isomer related to the bile
acids (which therefore possesses the 17β configuration) reacted at a faster
rate (328). By analogy then, testosterone and the compounds which have
been linked with it sterically like the more potent estradiol (Vol. I, pp. 361,
373) are 17β-hydroxysteroids (118), whereas cortisol and its 17-hydroxy-
lated companions from the adrenal cortex are 17α-hydroxy compounds.
This dissimilarity in the orientation of the hydroxyl groups is supported
also by addition reactions of 17-ketosteroids (II). Lithium aluminum
hydride furnishes predominantly compounds with the configuration of
testosterone (I) or the more potent estradiol (245). The closely related
Grignard reagents, which would be expected to add to the double bond from
the same direction, yield predominantly 17-hydroxy-17-alkyl compounds
(III), which are epimeric at C-17 to the natural corticoids.

A direct correlation of pregnane derivatives with hydroxyl and with
hydrogen at C-17 can be made through the Serini reaction, which converts
20-acetates of 17,20-glycols into 20-ketones by treatment with zinc. The
process is stereospecific, since a given glycol will yield only a single 20-
ketone. Its configuration is dependent on the configuration of the starting
compound at C-17 but not at C-20. The reaction has been interpreted as
a pinacolic shift and as such would be expected to proceed with inversion
at C-17 (299) (Chart 3). The results[4] (92, 96, 299, and earlier studies
cited in these references) are in accord with this formulation only if the
configurations of the starting glycols at C-17 are assigned as deduced from
the studies of reactivity described above.

20-Ketopregnanes can be converted to the acetates of 17-hydroxysteroids
by the action of peroxy acids. The reaction is again stereospecific, yielding
a single isomer (V, VII) which depends in its configuration on that of the

---

[4] The reaction of the $17\beta,20\beta$-glycol (96) seems to require reinvestigation, since
the experiments of Salamon (283) cast real doubts on the identity of the starting material used (158).

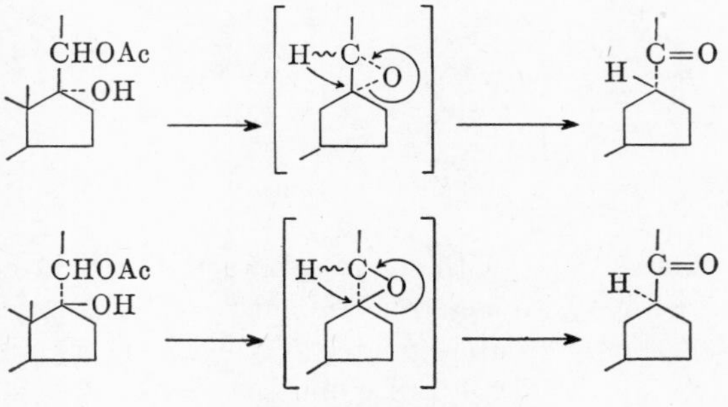

CHART 3. Serini reaction.

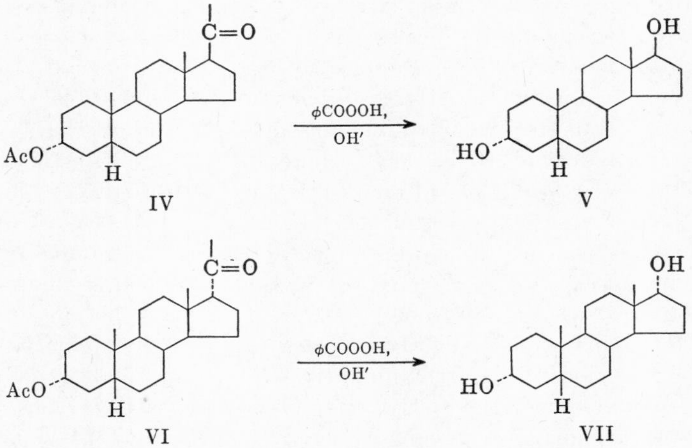

CHART 4. Peroxy acid degradation of 20-ketones.

starting compound (IV, VI) at C-17 (116). Studies on sterically known systems have shown that this reaction proceeds with retention of configuration (320, 235). Hence, substance V, which is derived from 3α-acetoxy-pregnan-20-one (IV), must be etiocholane-3α,17β-diol. Since V has also been prepared from Δ⁵-androstene-3β,17β-diol (278), which in turn has been converted to testosterone by reactions not affecting C-17, the 17β configuration of testosterone and of the numerous substances which have been related to it has been demonstrated in a most convincing manner.

C. Configuration of C-20

The naturally occurring 20-hydroxysteroids fall into four structural types (I–IV), depending on the number and location of the hydroxyl groups attached to adjacent carbon atoms. Obviously the asymmetry of C-20 admits the possibility of finding two epimeric forms for each of these types. The contention of Marker et al. that the naturally occurring compounds

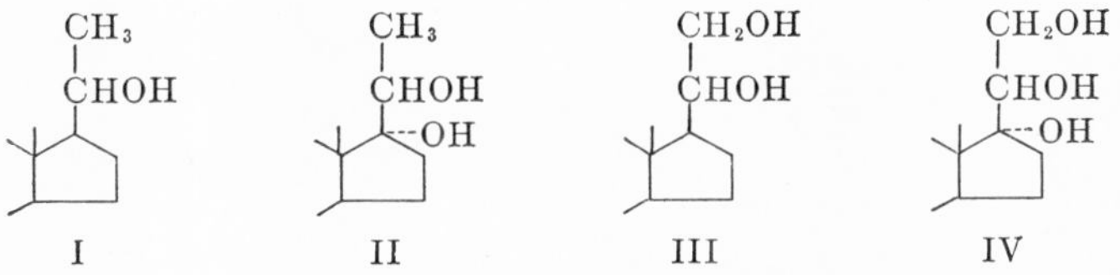

CH$_3$ CH$_3$ CH$_2$OH   CH$_2$OH
CHOH   CHOH   CHOH   CHOH
       --OH   --OH

I   II   III   IV

CHART 5. Types of 20-hydroxysteroids.

belong to a single steric series (215), which was termed 20α, differing from the products (20β) that result from the catalytic reduction of 20-ketones, has not stood the test of time. Even among the simplest compounds (type I) species differences exist. The pregnanediols, etc., which have been isolated from human urine thus far have all proved to be 20α compounds, whereas the predominant isomers in the urine of pregnant mares are 20β (36, 161, Vol. I, p. 620). The reduction of 20-ketones in the laboratory does not take a uniform course either. Although catalytic reduction with platinum apparently has given 20β compounds as the chief product in every instance, this is not always true if nickel is used (157). Lithium aluminum hydride also gave usually but not invariably (156, 158, 188, 322) 20β-hydroxysteroids as the main products. Sodium borohydride, which permits more selective reduction (rates: C-3 > C-20 > C-11 (212, 243, 309)), and aluminum isopropoxide (219) have been studied less extensively. They appear to give chiefly 20β-hydroxy compounds. Reduction with sodium and alcohol has been used as a synthetic route to 20α-hydroxy steroids (Vol. I, p. 428), but again the proportion of isomers has been variable. It is clear that the correlation of configuration at C-20 requires more reliable tools than the mode of formation from the ketone, be it biological or chemical.

A solution of the problem is largely due to Sarett (287), who related the four structural types (I to IV) derived from 3α-hydroxy-11-ketopregnane and from 3,11-diketopregnane by the sequence of reactions A to C. In series A and B the only reactions which rupture a linkage at C-20 are the formation of the epoxides (VII, XI) from the tosylates. This process is known to occur with inversion at the tosylated carbon atom. In sequence C the linkage between C-20 and its oxygen remains intact even if the conversion of the 21-tosylate (XV) into a 21-thioether (XVI) proceeds again via an epoxide.[5] Therefore, if the product of sequence A (IX) is 20α, the starting compound was 20β. The starting compound of B (X) is 20α, since its product (XII) is the epimer of the one obtained in A (IX). The 17,20-glycol obtained in C (XVII) is the 20-epimer of that used for B.

[5] In a related system studied by Lardon and Reichstein (197) a neighboring hydroxyl group participated in the opening of the epoxide ring. Such a complication can be excluded here, since both the substituted and the entering group are located at C-21.

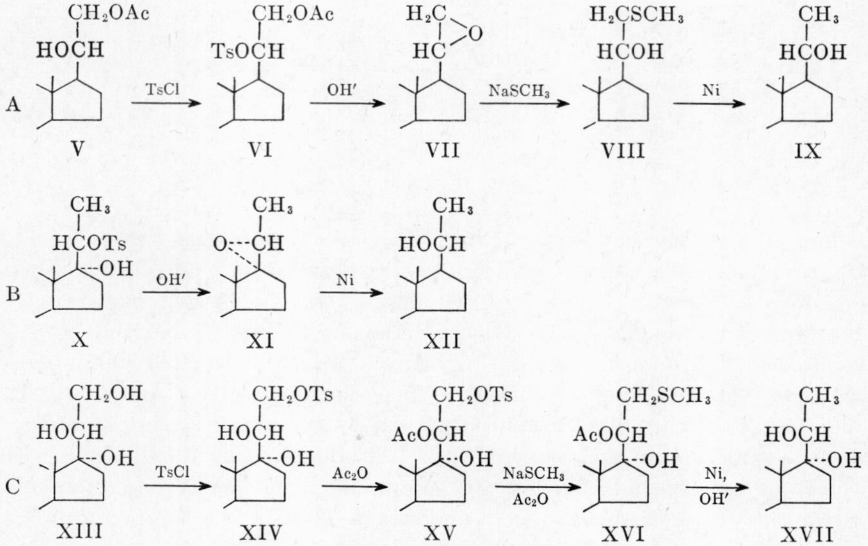

A CH_2OAc / HOCH (V) — TsCl → CH_2OAc / TsOCH (VI) — OH′ → $H_2C{>}O$ / HC (VII) — $NaSCH_3$ → H_2CSCH_3 / HCOH (VIII) — Ni → CH_3 / HCOH (IX)

B CH_3 / HCOTs ‥OH (X) — OH′ → CH_3 / O:‥CH (XI) — Ni → CH_3 / HOCH (XII)

C CH_2OH / HOCH ‥OH (XIII) — TsCl → CH_2OTs / HOCH ‥OH (XIV) — Ac_2O → CH_2OTs / AcOCH ‥OH (XV) — $NaSCH_3$, Ac_2O → CH_2SCH_3 / AcOCH ‥OH (XVI) — Ni, OH′ → CH_3 / HOCH ‥OH (XVII)

CHART 6. Correlation of 20-hydroxysteroids.

Hence, the starting compound of C was 20β. The 20-hydroxysteroids of types I to IV correlated in this manner conformed to two generalizations: (1) in one steric series (20β) the acetates were always more dextrorotatory than their epimers, and (2) acetylation of a 20α-hydroxy group decreased, that of a 20β-hydroxy increased, the molecular rotation. Since changes of structure relatively distant from the asymmetric center at C-20 are not expected to affect the sign of these rotational differences, a correlation of all 20-hydroxysteroids with the normal β configuration of the side chain became possible. It showed that the terms α and β which had independently (Vol. I, pp. 429, 567) and arbitrarily been assigned to 20-hydroxysteroids of different types all signified the same configuration. Furthermore with the exception of Reichstein's Compound O, all 20-hydroxysteroids thus far isolated from cattle adrenals have the 20β configuration.

The steric significance of this convention of designating the 20-stereo-isomers was first investigated by Fieser and Fieser (92), who analyzed the results obtained in the *cis* hydroxylation of $\Delta^{17,20}$-ethylenes with osmium tetroxide. Such olefins can exist in two isomeric forms, of which the *trans* (XIX) places the hydrogen and the *cis* (XVIII) the methyl group at C-20 into the proximity of ring C. The latter arrangement could be expected to lead to steric repulsion and hence to lesser stability. The configuration of the resulting glycol at C-20, of course, will depend on the direction of the attack by osmium tetroxide, but this can be diagnosed by the configuration of the glycol at C-17. With one exception (286, *vide*

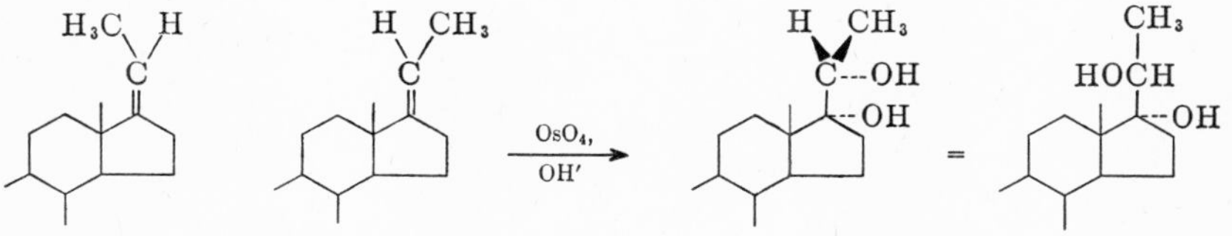

XVIII XIX XX

CHART 7. *Cis*-hydroxylation of 17(20)-ethylenes.

D 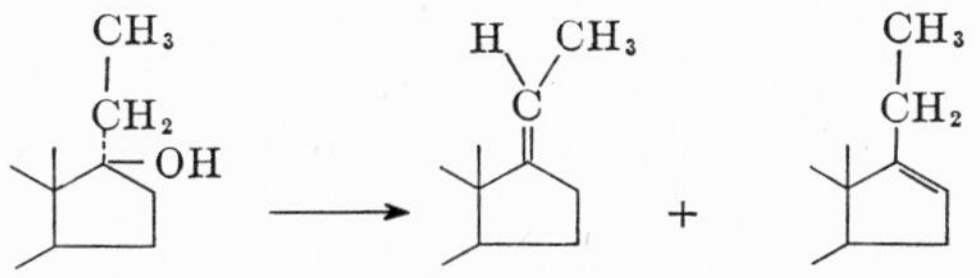

XXI XIX XXII

E 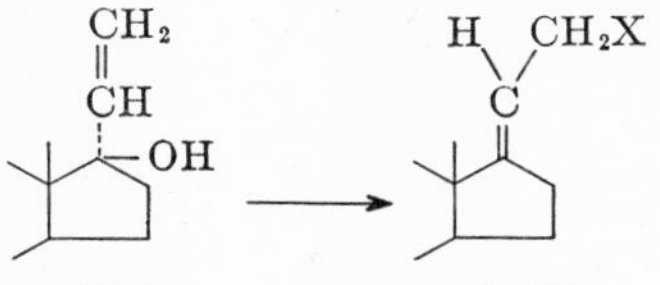

XXIII XXIV

F 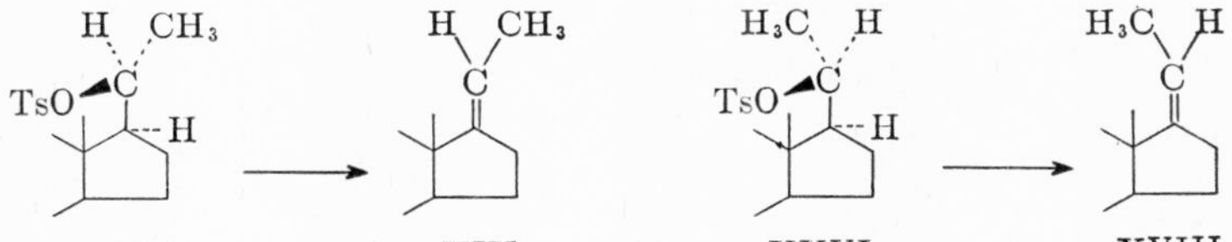

XXV XIX XXVI XVIII

CHART 8. Formation of 17(20)-ethylenes.

infra) the main products isolated from these reactions were 17α, 20β-dihydroxy compounds. This signifies hydroxylation from the rear, and if the starting compound can be assumed to be the more stable *trans* olefin, the configuration of the product at C-20 (relative to the remainder of the molecule) is fully determined.

The olefins which were used in these hydroxylation reactions were obtained mainly[6] by three types of procedures, *viz.*, (*D*) dehydration of 17β-hydroxysteroids, (*E*) allylic shift of a 17β-hydroxy-Δ^{20}-olefin, and (*F*)

[6] Other procedures are: The Wolff-Kishner reduction of 3β-acetoxy-$\Delta^{5,16}$-pregnadien-20-one (102), which gave the same $\Delta^{5,17}$-pregnadien-3β-ol as was obtained by treating 17-ethinyl-Δ^{5}-androstene-3β,17β-diol with sodium and alcohol (279) (the latter reaction evidently is a variation of process E.); the rearrangement of 17,21-dibromo-20-ketones to a *trans*-Δ^{17}-ethylene (330, Section IV, G); treatment of 20-aminopregnanes with nitrous acid which yields besides 20-alcohols, Δ^{20} and *trans*-Δ^{17}-ethylenes (287).

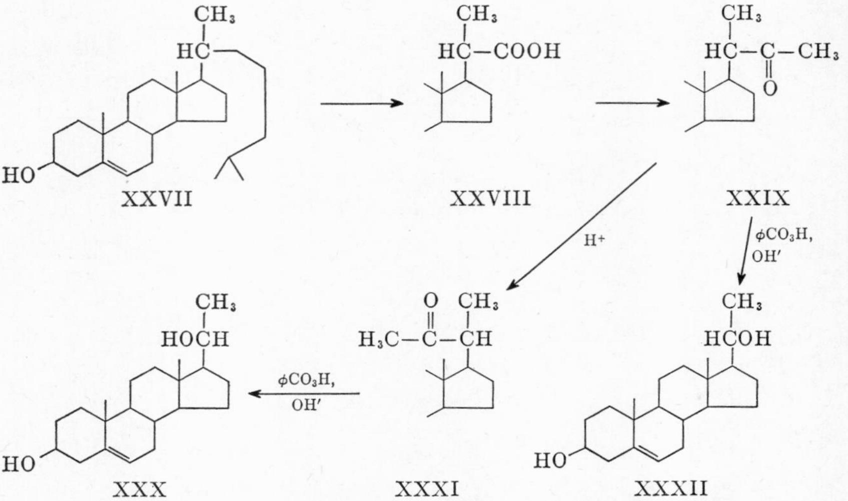

CH₃
HC—
HO
XXVII

CH₃
HC—COOH
XXVIII

CH₃
HC—C—CH₃
O
XXIX

H⁺

ϕCO₃H, OH'

CH₃
HOCH
HO
XXX

O CH₃
‖ |
H₃C—C—CH
XXXI

CH₃
HCOH
HO
XXXII

ϕCO₃H, OH'

CHART 9. Correlation of 20-hydroxysteroids with cholesterol.

dehydration of a 20α or β hydroxy compound by treating its tosylate with a nitrogenous base. As Klyne (187) has pointed out, the geometry of the products obtained in reaction F should depend on the configuration of the starting compound. The arrangement most favorable for elimination (C-17 → H and C-20 → tosyloxy bonds antiparallel) would yield different olefins from 20α and 20β compounds. Experiments with simple[7] tosylates (155, 286, 287) support this contention and provide a correlation of 20-hydroxy compounds and 17,20-glycols consistent with that derived by sequence B. No comparable restrictions exist for the steric course of reactions D and E, and the preferential formation of the trans-Δ¹⁷⁽²⁰⁾-olefin appears to be quite plausible. Hydroxylation of the Δ¹⁷⁽²⁰⁾-ethylenes from D gave predominantly, and of those from E gave exclusively, 17α,20β-glycols. Since this consistency supports the thesis of the Fiesers, these ethylenes are formulated as trans. Evidence derived from X-ray data which also favors this structure has been reported by Shoppee (302).

The very detailed X-ray analyses (59) of cholesteryl iodide have also been adduced (159, 187) for the study of this problem. According to these data the configuration of cholesterol at C-20 is as indicated in XXVII. (In obtaining this projection the methyl at C-20 is again assumed to be turned to the rear.) Cholesterol has been oxidized to the bisnor acid (XXVIII) (337), which as the acid chloride was treated with dimethyl cadmium to

---

[7] The results obtained with 20-tosylates containing an acetoxy group at C-21 do not conform to this pattern. The α-isomer failed to yield an olefin, and the β gave in low yield the trans rather than the cis-Δ¹⁷-ethylene (286).

yield the ketone XXIX. The latter on peroxy acid oxidation (with temporary protection of the double bond) and hydrolysis gave Δ^5-pregnene-$3\beta,20\alpha$-diol (XXXII) (338). If the ketone was first isomerized with acid, the same treatment yielded Δ^5-pregnene-$3\beta,20\beta$-diol (XXX). Since such peroxy acid degradations proceed without inversion (Section II, B) the configurations of the 20-hydroxysteroids as determined by degradation from cholesterol are in accord with those derived from the hydroxylation of 17(20)-ethylenes. Additional support for these assignments from the work of Prelog and co-workers will be presented in the next section. An opposing view is held by Ryer and Gebert (281), who considered certain lactones too hindered to be readily formed. These interpretations of molecular models, however, do not appear to be justified to this reviewer.

D. Absolute Configuration

The spatial relationships that exist between the various asymmetric centers of the steroid nucleus were determined relative to one center of asymmetry. The customary point of reference is carbon atom 10 in its usual configuration, *i.e.*, that found in cholesterol and practically every naturally occurring steroid. For the sake of pictorial representation it was arbitrarily assumed that the angular methyl group at C-10 faces the observer if the molecule appears in the usual way (with ring A in the lower left corner). It was not known, however, whether this assumption was consistent with one made by Emil Fischer (101) about sugars when by defining (+)-saccharic acid he assigned the structure given in Chart 10 to dextrorotatory D-glyceraldehyde. A correlation of these two arbitrary conventions will be of real concern to the biochemist if he wishes to compare for instance the stereospecificity of dehydrogenases acting on steroidal and aliphatic alcohols. A correlation would in addition establish the actual configuration of the steroids, since recent work (27, 195, 343) has shown that the Fischer convention of representing aliphatic molecules depicts in all probability the true spatial distribution of bonds around the asymmetric center.

A solution of this problem should be at hand if the configuration of one asymmetric center of the steroid nucleus can be compared with that of an aliphatic compound sterically related to glyceraldehyde. Unfortunately the results of such studies have not been consistent with each other. In principle, at least, the most reliable approach is chemical degradation,

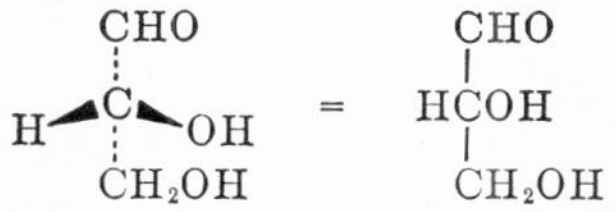

$$\begin{array}{cc} \text{CHO} & \text{CHO} \\ | & | \\ \text{H}{-}\text{C}{-}\text{OH} & = \quad \text{HCOH} \\ | & | \\ \text{CH}_2\text{OH} & \text{CH}_2\text{OH} \end{array}$$

Chart 10. Model and projection of D-glyceraldehyde.

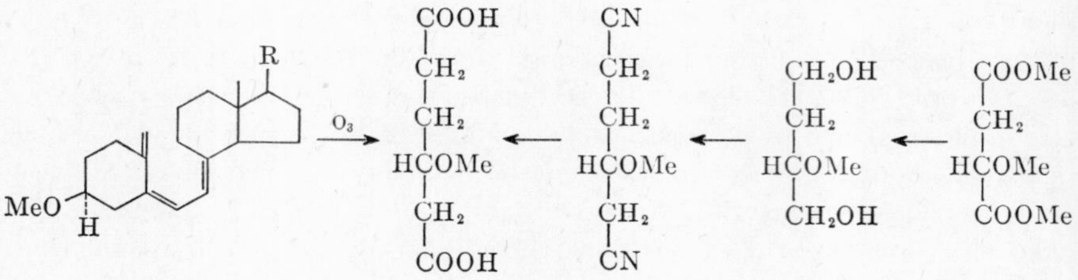

$$
\begin{array}{ccccc}
 & \text{COOH} & \text{CN} & & \\
 & | & | & & \\
 & \text{CH}_2 & \text{CH}_2 & \text{CH}_2\text{OH} & \text{COOMe} \\
 & | & | & | & | \\
\xrightarrow{\ O_3\ } & \text{CH}_2 & \text{CH}_2 & \text{CH}_2 & \text{CH}_2 \\
 & | & | & | & | \\
 & \text{HCOMe} & \text{HCOMe} & \text{HCOMe} & \text{HCOMe} \\
 & | & | & | & | \\
 & \text{CH}_2 & \text{CH}_2 & \text{CH}_2\text{OH} & \text{COOMe} \\
 & | & | & & \\
 & \text{COOH} & \text{CN} & & \\
\text{I} & \text{II} & \text{III} & \text{IV} & \text{V}
\end{array}
$$

CHART 11. Correlation of calciferol with glyceraldehyde.

provided the reactions cannot possibly invert the asymmetric center investigated. This mode of attack was used in Reichstein's laboratory (22, 196) on carbon atom 3 of calciferol which is derived by photolysis from ergosterol. According to X-ray evidence, the light reaction has not altered the configuration at C-3, which is therefore β. Ozonization of the methyl ether (I) furnished chemically and optically pure $(-)$-methoxy-adipic acid (II), characterized further as the dianilide. The reference sample was obtained from the dimethyl ester (V) of L-methoxysuccinic acid by reducing the ester groups to alcohols. These were successively replaced by tosyloxy, iodo, and cyano groups. The dicyano compound (III) was hydrolyzed with alkali in dilute methanol to yield β-methoxy-adipic acid contaminated with large amounts of various hexenedioic acids formed by elimination of methanol largely, it seems, at the cyano stage. As it is not unlikely that an α-β unsaturated nitril would undergo a Michael addition with methoxide, this step could have resulted in racemization but obviously not in inversion. The β-methoxyadipic acid was isolated only as the dianilide, which appeared to be chemically and optically pure. Unfortunately, however, the rotation of the pure dianilide is very low and hence does not furnish a sensitive index of optical purity. Lardon and Reichstein therefore considered their results only as preliminary. The sign of rotation of the dianilide would indicate that the acids from calciferol and from L-malic acid are not identical but optical antipods and therefore that the steroid convention is the reverse of the Fischer convention.

Studies using indirect methods of comparison, however, have led to the opposite conclusion. Prelog and his collaborators (62, 255, 256, 258) have developed an elegant procedure which is based on studies of asymmetric synthesis by McKenzie and others. The asymmetric center to be investigated is that of a secondary alcohol R_1R_2CHOH which is esterified with phenylglyoxylic acid. The resulting ester (VII) is treated with methyl magnesium iodide and hydrolyzed. If the groups R_1 and R_2 differ sufficiently in bulk, the resulting phenyllactic acid (atrolactic acid) (IX) is

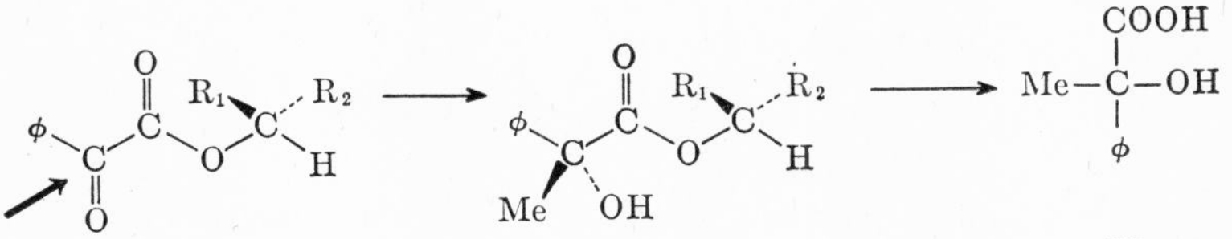

CHART 12. Configuration by asymmetric synthesis.

optically active. The phenyl, ketone, and ester group of VII can be expected to lie in one plane. If the hydrogen lies in the same plane[8] and if the alkyl group R_1 is smaller than R_2, the Grignard reagent ought to attack preferentially from the less hindered frontal side (arrow) and give on hydrolysis a mixture of atrolactic acids in which the D($-$)-isomer (IX) predominates. If the positions of R_1 and R_2 are reversed as in the epimeric alcohol, the resulting acid will be dextrorotatory. The predominant configuration of the acid therefore is linked in a predictable manner with that of the original alcohol. When the method was tested on aliphatic or cyclic alcohols of known configuration, the results agreed in every case with expectation. The steroids investigated (androstan-17β-ol, cholestan-7α-ol, cholestan-7β-ol, and allopregnan-20β-ol) contained a secondary alcohol group flanked on the one side by the relatively small methylene or methyl group and on the other by the bulkier tri- or tetra-alkylmethane. The results were consistent with each other and indicated that the steroid and Fischer conventions agree.

The molecular rotation of a steroid has often been looked upon as the sum of contributions of the various asymmetric centers. The difference, e.g., of the molecular rotations of a pair of epimeric alcohols is qualitatively and quantitatively independent of changes in configuration or structure that are made at a distant part of the molecule. With decreasing distance of asymmetric centers changes at one will generally also affect the other, demonstrating that the concept of a fixed contribution of a given asymmetric center is at best an approximation. Nevertheless the sign of the difference of a pair of epimeric alcohols often does not change even if structural or configurational changes occur in close vicinity of the asymmetric center. Stokes and Bergmann (317) were able to relate the sign of this difference in saturated steroids to the degree of alkylation at adjacent carbon atoms. If one of these is a methylene group and the other a tri- or tetra-alkylated methane, the alcohol represented by partial structure A

[8] Rotation around the C—O bond of the alcohol will alter the position of R_1 and R_2 relative to this plane. However, Prelog has shown that the effect of these other conformations on the steric result should largely cancel out. See also Cram and Elhafez (58) for a somewhat different derivation of the same final result in related cases.

CHART 13. Alcohols with dextrorotatory contribution.

is usually[9] more dextrorotatory than its epimer. The same observation (234) has been made with some monocyclic terpenes[10] which have been related to glyceraldehyde (104, 106). Furthermore, similar studies (233) have been reported for allylic alcohols derived from steroids and from terpenes of known configuration. In this case the structural feature which chiefly determines the contribution of the alcohol group appears to be its spatial relationship to the double bond. The contribution was found to be strongly positive for cyclohexenols of type B and negative for epimeric structures. The consistency of these data is quite striking and unless the structural features responsible for the regularities were misinterpreted, the observations demonstrate that the steroid and Fischer conventions agree. This would indicate that the customary representation of the steroid molecule with the angular methyl groups towards the observer pictures the actual molecule and not its mirror image.[10a]

III. Total Syntheses

The difficulties which beset the total synthesis of a nonaromatic steroid hormone are well brought out if one considers the numerous possibilities for stereoisomerism. Since cortisone (I), for example, has six asymmetric centers, 64 stereoisomers or 32 racemic pairs are possible. The partly aromatic steroids, which have fewer asymmetric centers, offered an easier

[9] An exception are the 6-hydroxysteroids with the normal (β) configuration at C-5 (317).

[10] The reverse correlation between structure and the sign of rotation had been reported by Stokes and Bergmann for aliphatic alcohols and had led them to suggest that the Fischer and the steroid conventions do not agree. It seems somewhat dubious, however, whether the extent of alkylation of the α carbon atoms is really *the* determining factor in the rotation of aliphatic secondary alcohols. For instance, the molecular rotations given by Freudenberg (105) for the series HCOH with Et above and R below are: $\mathrm{R} =$ methyl ($-10.3°$), ethyl ($0°$), propyl ($+5°$), isopropyl ($-15.4°$). See also Klyne and Stokes (190).

[10a] This view has received strong support from very recent degradations (57a, 264a) of cholesterol. These permitted the direct comparison of fragments which contained C-20 as the sole asymmetric center, with aliphatic reference substances that were linked to glyceraldehyde. In view of this important advance, it is of particular interest that the configuration of C-20 relative to the steroid nucleus as set forth in Section II,C, has been confirmed by a new approach (6a).

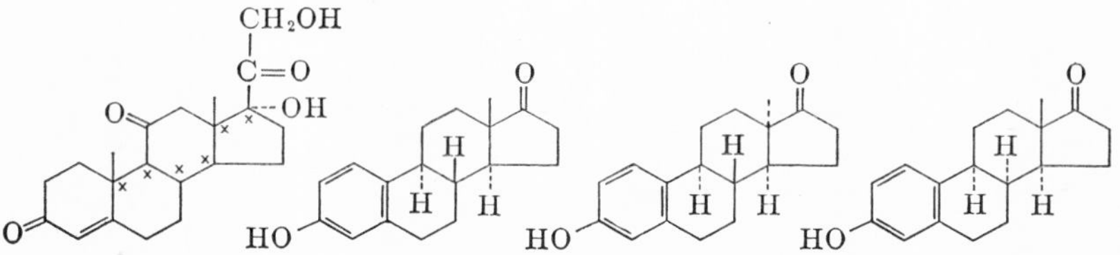

CHART 14.

target and were attacked first.   The total synthesis of equilenin (Vol. I, p. 352) with two asymmetric centers was followed by that of estrone (II), which has four (8 racemic pairs).

The first total synthesis of a racemic stereoisomer of estrone by Bachmann and associates has already been described (Vol. I, p. 356).   By the use of very similar procedures, Anner and Miescher (4) succeeded in preparing the same (±)-isomer and four more racemic pairs.   These included (±)-estrone, which was resolved to yield the natural hormone.   Johnson *et al.* (172) devised a new synthetic procedure, which again yielded estrone and three additional racemic pairs.   One of these, identified as (±)-lumiestrone (III), was obtained along with (±)-estrone from a common precursor by reactions which should lead to isomers differing only in the configuration at C-13.   This synthesis, therefore, fully confirmed Butenandt's views about the nature of the light reaction which converts estrone to lumiestrone (Vol. I, p. 379).   The steric relationships between the other synthetic isomers are not clear.[11]   Of the four obtained by the Swiss workers only one ((±)-estrone-e) possessed estrogenic potency comparable to that of natural estrone.   Estrone-e has tentatively (29) been assigned structure IV.   A simpler synthesis of estrone in which no other isomers were encountered has since been described by Johnson and Christiansen (174).

The great goal of total synthesis of nonaromatic steroids was first reached in 1951 almost simultaneously by two groups of investigators, one headed by Sir Robert Robinson (44) of Oxford and the other by R. B. Woodward (346) of Harvard University.   In the synthesis of epiandrosterone (VIII) by the British workers, contact was made with a product of natural origin already at the tricyclic stage.   This diketone (VI), which had been totally synthesized in 1947 (57) and identified with a degradation product of the sterols and of the bile acids (260), was converted to VII and identified with material from the oxidation of cholesterol (193).   As the natural product

[11] Birch (29) has presented a very plausible scheme of correlation based on the assumption that all intermediates, prior to introducing asymmetry at C-14 in the Anner-Miescher and at C-13 in the Johnson synthesis, as well as the final products, were homogeneous.   If Birch's argument is applied to the findings as now revised (172) conflicting assignments result.

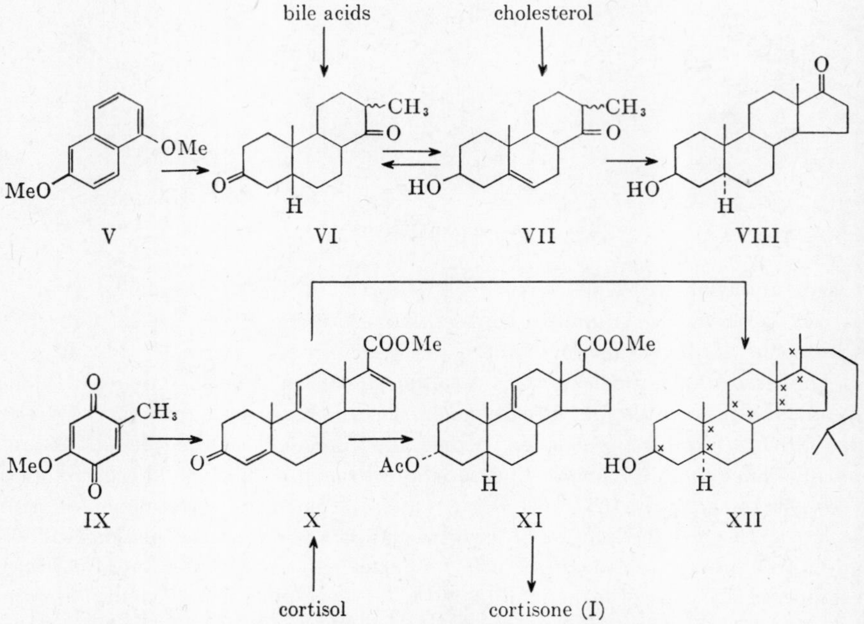

CHART 15. Some products of Robinson and Woodward syntheses.

(VII) was more readily available by far, it was used as a relay to continue the synthesis of epiandrosterone. Woodward and collaborators accomplished the synthesis of a nonaromatic steroid (X) without such aid. Their success was due in large measure to the stereospecificity of the reactions chosen to introduce the asymmetric centers. At most steps and particularly at all the early ones, their procedures could be expected to yield the desired isomer as the main product. This approach to total synthesis not only benefits the yields but avoids the necessity of carrying numerous stereoisomers of unknown configurations through the various steps in parallel reactions until at the end the desired isomer can be selected by its identity with natural material. The product (X) of the Woodward synthesis proved to be identical with a degradation product of cortisol, and this natural material apparently was used to continue the synthesis of cholestan-3β-ol (XII) and of methyl 3α-acetoxy-$\Delta^{9(11)}$-etianate (XI), which in turn had been converted (152) to an intermediate used in a partial synthesis of cortisone. The methods of partial synthesis have also established many other links between products of the Woodward or Robinson syntheses and important naturally occurring steroids. In this formal sense it may be said that their total syntheses have also been accomplished. However, the first *de facto* total synthesis of an adrenal steroid is due to

Sarett and his collaborators (288, 290), who prepared cortisone in a highly stereospecific manner.   Another synthesis of (±)-cortisone acetate starting from a tricyclic intermediate of Woodward's has since been reported by Barkley *et al.* (16).   A remarkably simple total synthesis of (±)-epiandrosterone and of its 13-epimer, (±)-lumiepiandrosterone, has been accomplished by Johnson *et al.* (173).   Although no less than six asymmetric centers were established in two successive reductions, the desired isomer was obtained as the chief product.   Other splendid achievements in this field were the total synthesis of methyl (±)-3-ketoetianate by Wilds *et al.* (342) and of (±)-5α and β-D-homoandrostane-3,17-a-dione by Wieland *et al.* (339).

IV. Partial Syntheses, Structures, and Chemical Properties

A. Phenolic and Other 19-Norsteroids

The main route from readily accessible steroids to estrogens has been the high-temperature aromatization of $\Delta^{1,4}$-3-ketones (VI → I), according to Inhoffen (Vol. I, p. 361).   The reaction conditions have been further improved by Hershberg *et al.* (134), who exposed the dienone VI in mineral oil briefly to the rather heroic temperature of 530°C.   If the aromatization is carried out by means of acid in an anhydrous medium, a rearrangement occurs leading to an inactive compound originally formulated as VII (Vol. I, p. 361) in analogy to the behavior of a naturally occurring dienone, santonin.   However, Woodward and Singh (345) while studying a more closely related model (differing from the steroids only in the absence of

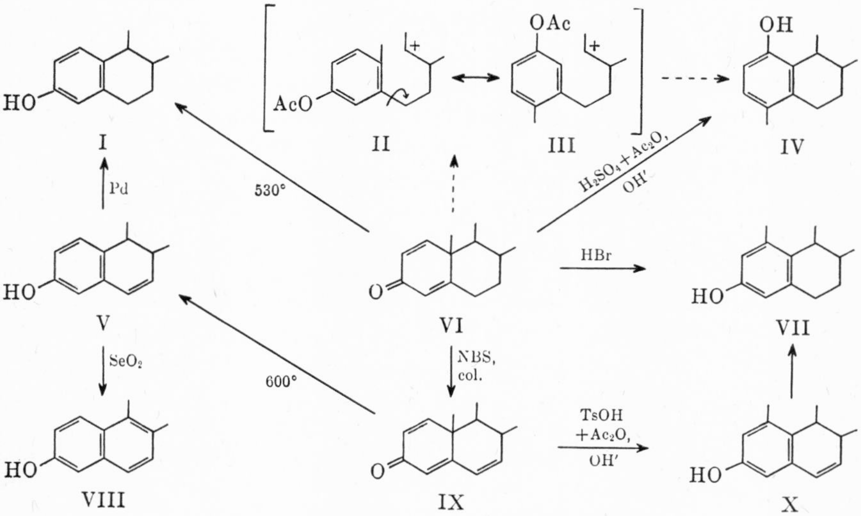

CHART 16. Aromatization of ring A.

rings C and D) observed that in this case the methyl retained its *para* relationship to the C—O bond and proposed structure IV for the steroid. This structure has been verified by further aromatization and comparison with synthetic compounds (83, 84, 344). (The reaction *may* involve rupture of the 9-10 linkage (II) followed by rotation around the 5-6 bond (III) and re-establishment of ring B.) Two methods have been found to avoid this type of rearrangement. If the starting compound contains an additional double bond in the 6-7 position (IX) as in $\Delta^{1,4,6}$-androstatriene-3,17-dione, the rearrangement product (X) can be reduced to a different methylestrone (VII) which is estrogenic (the potency in rats is about one half that of estrone) (77). This compound is the main rearrangement product of the dienone VI if the reaction is conducted in an aqueous medium (concentrated hydrochloric or hydrobromic acids) (82). The structure of the 1-methylestrone so obtained was again proved by further aromatization (81). If the $\Delta^{1,4,6}$-trien-3-one (IX) derived from testosterone acetate is subjected to pyrolysis, the 17-acetate of 17β-Δ^6-dehydroestradiol (V) results, which can be reduced to that of 17β-estradiol (I) or (as the diacetate) be oxidized with selenium dioxide to 17β-dihydroequilenin (VIII) diacetate (76). The reactions proceed in good yield and therefore afford a more convincing correlation of configuration at C-17 than that previously given by Marker (213). The dihydroequilenin isolated from the urine of pregnant mares (164) therefore has the 17α configuration (see also 300).

These reactions and the analogous conversions of Δ^6-dehydroestrone to estrone and equilenin (184) provide additional evidence (Vol. I, p. 370) that these two estrogens possess identical configurations at the juncture of rings C and D. This problem (185) and the related question of the nature of this juncture have received a great deal of attention as a result of the observations on the estrogenic activities of the doisynolic acids (Vol. I, p. 363). Stereospecific syntheses (8) and other studies (10, 12) have reaffirmed that rings C and D of all natural estrogens are *trans* linked with each other just as they are in the nonaromatic steroids from which they can be prepared by high-temperature reactions.[12] This arrangement is less stable[13]

[12] There was less reason to suspect that this process would alter the configuration of either C-8 or C-9, since the *trans* fusion of rings B and C represents a stable arrangement. This is confirmed by the stability of 7-ketoestrone and its derivatives to conditions which would permit isomerization at C-8 (247). Accordingly estrone is formulated as $8\beta,9\alpha$.

[13] An exception to this rule has recently been reported for certain 15-ketosteroids (17). One factor contributing to this reversal of stability is probably the presence of a side chain at the β side of C-17. 14β-Compounds are more stable if a side chain at C-17 has the α rather than the β configuration, whereas the reverse has been found for 14α-steroids (195a). Very recently Dreiding (80a) has proposed an interesting alternative explanation which ascribes the decisive difference between these 15-ketos-

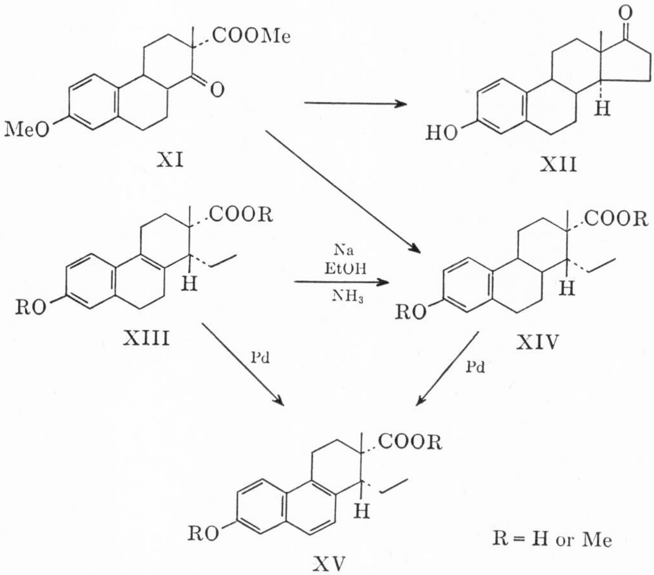

CHART 17. Configuration of doisynolic acid.

than *cis* fusion of the two rings, and inversions at C-14 are observed when the *trans* compounds are exposed to palladium catalysts at high temperatures (250°C.) (9). This reaction does not depend on the presence of aromatic rings. It is not observed at 80°C. even on prolonged exposure. If ring D is opened as in the doisynolic acids, no inversion occurs on treatment with palladium at 250°C.

The C-D-*cis* compounds which result from the epimerization of the natural estrogens at C-14 have very little estrogenic activity. The reverse has been observed in the doisynolic acid series (XIV). *Cis*-bisdehydrodoisynolic acid (XV, R = H) (methyl at C-13 *cis* to H at C-14) is a potent estrogen, but the *trans* acid is not (128). Among the known doisynolic acids, again the most potent isomer (XIV) belongs to the *cis* series, as it can be formed (3) from the dimethyl derivative of *cis*-Δ⁸-dehydrodoisynolic acid (XIII) (2, 127) and be dehydrogenated (3) to *cis*-bisdehydrodoisynolic acid (XV). This doisynolic acid (XIV) probably agrees with estrone in the configurations at C-8 and C-9, since both compounds have been prepared from the same isomer of the keto ester (XI) (3, 4). The methyl

---

teroids and the partly aromatic steroids to the absence of a double bond between C-8 and C-9. This is believed to prevent the epimerization of the *trans* C-D system *at C-14* since the product would not be able to assume a favorable conformation with only one of the three alkyl substituents of ring C at C-13 and C-14 in an axial position.

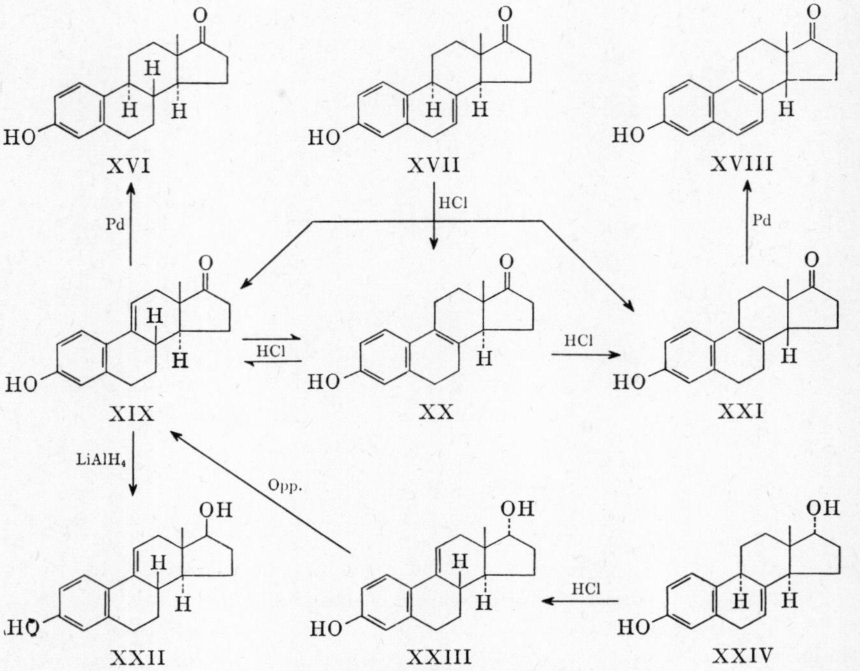

CHART 18. Isomerization of equilin.

ether of the (±)-acid produced estrus in the ovariectomized rat at an oral dose of 0.05 μg.

Banes *et al.* (14, 15, 140) have disentangled the complex mixture which results when equilin (XVII) is treated with hydrochloric and acetic acids (Vol. I, p. 376). The three main products (XIX, XX, XXI) show by their intense absorption in the ultraviolet that the 4th double bond is in conjugation with the aromatic ring. Their spectra are clearly different from that of Δ⁶-dehydroestrone (248). Compound XIX showed an absorption peak at 263.5 mμ, the two others, near 275 mμ. By comparison with the spectra of related structures with known positions of the double bond (126), compound XIX is considered to have 9(11), the others, 8(9) unsaturation. The configuration of compound XIX at the various asymmetric centers is established by its reduction to estrone (XVI), that of XXI by its low-temperature dehydrogenation to 14β-equilenin (d-isoequilenin) (XVIII) and by a comparison of the infrared spectrum of the acetate with that of the *cis*-racemate, which was synthesized by Heer and Miescher (129). The structure of XX as Δ⁸-dehydroestrone is less certain since it could not be dehydrogenated to equilenin. The chemical and physical properties of 14β-Δ⁸-dehydroestrone (XXI) agree quite closely with those of "isoequilin

A," the product originally isolated from this reaction mixture (165). The structure assigned to this slightly impure older preparation therefore appears to be correct. $\Delta^{9(11)}$-Dehydroestrone (XIX) was obtained also by Oppenauer oxidation from an unidentified diol (Compound 3) isolated from the urine of pregnant mares (164). Its structure as 17α-$\Delta^{9(11)}$-dehydro-estradiol (XXIII) follows from this observation, from its nonidentity with the epimer XXII prepared from the ketone XIX with lithium aluminum hydride, and from its preparation from 17α-dihydroequilin (XXIV) (15). The diol can be isolated from mares' urine only if the conjugated estrogens are cleaved with acid but not if they are split with dioxane (120). It, therefore, appears to be an artifact which could arise from a 17α-estradiol hydroxylated in the 11 position or from 17α-dihydroequilin. The latter possibility appears to be more probable, since there is evidence for the presence of the precursor (15). $\Delta^{9(11)}$-Dehydroestrone (XIX) has been isolated from the ketonic fraction of such urines. It is probably again an artifact derived from equilin (XVII).

Interest in Δ^4-3-ketosteroids that lack the angular methyl group between rings A and B was aroused by the high progestational activity of a 19-nor-progesterone which had been prepared from strophanthidin by Ehrenstein (Vol. I, p. 446). The product (originally designated as 10-norprogesterone) has proved to be a mixture of stereoisomers from which 19-nor-10ξ,14β,17α-progesterone has been isolated (85). A procedure far simpler than this very arduous route from strophanthidin has been devised by Birch (28). The method has been greatly improved by Wilds and Nelson (341), who prepared 19-nortesterone from estrone in yields of over 70 %. The reduction of the phenolic methyl ether (XXV) is carried out in liquid ammonia and ether with lithium and alcohol. This yields an enolic ether (XXVI) which can be cleaved with mineral acid to the α-β unsaturated ketone (XXVIII). The position of the double bond between C-4 and C-5 can be deduced from the location of the absorption maximum (240 mμ). The only asymmetric center affected by these reactions is C-10. It is probable but not yet certain that the hydrogen at this site is β-oriented. As ring A aromatic compounds of various types are readily obtained (*vide supra*), the procedure has afforded easy access to 19-nor-Δ^4-3-ketosteroids with the same configurations at the other asymmetric centers as their normal homologues with the 19-methyl group. The resulting 19-norprogesterone is four to

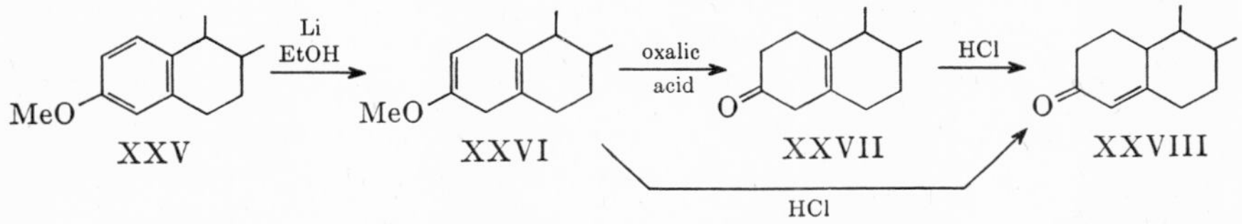

CHART 19. Synthesis of 19-nor-Δ^4-3-ketosteroids.

eight times as potent as progesterone (74); 19-nordeoxycorticosterone (284) is about twice as effective as deoxycorticosterone in regulating the sodium potassium ratio; 19-nortestosterone on the other hand, is inferior to testosterone as an androgen but equal to it in its myotrophic (protein-anabolic) effect (136).

B. 6-Hydroxylated Compounds

1. *6β-Hydroxy-3,5-cycloandrostan-17-one. Hydrolysis of Sulfates*

The bulk of the steroids excreted in the urine of man is in the form of water-soluble derivatives comprising both glucuronidates and sulfates. As far as is known the hydrolytic cleavage of a glucosidic linkage does not affect the bond between the oxygen and carbon of the alkyl moiety and therefore does not alter the configuration of the alcohol. The situation with sulfates is more complex. Burwell (40) examined the hydrolysis of (+)-sodium *s*-butyl sulfate (I) at about 100°C. and observed inversion of configuration upon alkaline hydrolysis. Acid hydrolysis proceeded very much faster and led to an alcohol with retained configuration accompanied by the racemate. The extent of racemization varied considerably with experimental conditions and was strongly influenced by the acid used. It can be concluded that acid hydrolysis can proceed by two different mechanisms attacking either the C—O or the S—O bond of the ester grouping. If acid hydrolysis of steroid sulfates takes a similar course, the configuration of the excreted ester can not be deduced reliably from that of the alcohol isolated after hydrolysis. Lieberman *et al.* (207) in a careful study of the hydrolysis of representative 3α and 3β sterol sulfates of the types thus far encountered naturally (5-*allo* and Δ⁵) observed *complete* retention of configuration upon treatment with hydrochloric acid at room temperature. It is not clear to what extent the differences in the structure of the substrates or in the reaction conditions are responsible for the different results with steroidal and alkyl sulfates.

The C—O bond of steroidal sulfates is not always retained in hydrolytic reactions. This has been demonstrated in studies of the origin of a new urinary steroid isolated by Dingemanse and Huis in't Veld (66). The compound was liberated from a conjugated precursor by a process of simultaneous heating and extraction of the unacidified urine. It proved identical with a substance obtained by treating the tosylate of dehydroepiandrosterone with aqueous acetone in the presence of potassium acetate (20, 42). This reaction proceeds by rearrangement, as has been shown by extensive studies in the cholesterol series. The 3,5-cyclo-6-hydroxy structure (III) first proposed for such products (formerly known as *i*-steroids) by Wallis *et al.* (332) has been verified in numerous investigations. These include a direct demonstration of the bond between C-3 and C-5 by conversion to a A-norsteroid (IV) (292, 304) and a reduction to cholestan-6β-ol (VII) (305).

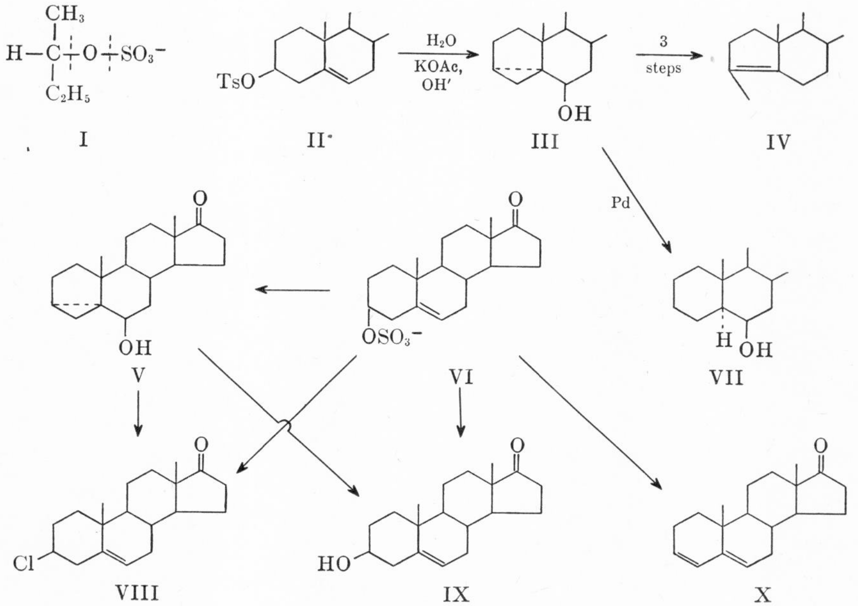

CHART 20.

The *i*-cholesterol therefore is 3,5-cyclocholestan-6β-ol and the urinary product 6β-hydroxy-3,5-cycloandrostan-17-one (V). The rearrangement products are very sensitive to acid. The urinary compound on treatment with hydrochloric acid gave, depending on the temperature, either 3β-chloro-Δ^5-androsten-17-one (VIII) or dehydroepiandrosterone (IX) as the main product. These observations prompted the Dutch workers to propose that dehydroepiandrosterone is an artifact formed from the *i*-steroid by the customary use of hydrochloric acid. This suggestion was received with skepticism by many investigators, and there is indeed no need to make such an assumption. Synthetic dehydroepiandrosterone sulfate (VI) duplicates in every way the behavior of the urinary excretion product (318). It furnishes dehydroepiandrosterone (IX), the chloro compound (VIII), and the $\Delta^{3,5}$-diene (X) on acid hydrolysis. In neutral solution under the conditions[14] of Dingemanse and Huis in't Veld, the 3,5-cyclo compound (V) is obtained in high yield. Although this reaction offers a very plausible and adequate explanation of the findings of the Dutch workers, a definite disposition of the controversy still seems to require the unequivocal[15] identification of the conjugated excretion product.

[14] Solvolysis in dioxane gave a 17-ketosteroid precipitable with digitonin which presumably was dehydroepiandrosterone (48).

[15] The product isolated by Munson *et al.* (Vol. I, p. 485) was characterized as a sulfate

2. 6-Hydroxysteroids

6-Hydroxy compounds with the normal steroid skeleton have aroused renewed interest with the demonstration that Δ^4-3-ketones can be 6β-hydroxylated by adrenal tissue and by certain microorganisms (see Chapter XII, "Steroid Hormone Metabolism"). Furthermore, 6α-hydroxy compounds with 5α and β hydrogen have been isolated from human urine (206). A firm basis for assignments of configuration at C-6 was laid in the cholesterol series. Cholesterol acetate (I) on treatment with peroxy acid furnishes both 5,6-epoxides (II, VI) (254). One of these (VI) on treatment with lithium aluminum hydride could be cleaved to yield two diols (251). The one with the tertiary hydroxyl group (V) (which could also be obtained from a 4,5-epoxide) formed a cyclic carbonate (IX) (252). This is possible only if the hydroxyl at C-5 has the same orientation as the 3β-hydroxyl group. This proves the β configuration also for the epoxide VI and for the 6-hydroxy group in its main reduction product (X) (cholestane-$3\beta,6\beta$-diol). Hydrolytic cleavage of either epoxide forms the same triol 3-monoacetate (III) (253). It is the $5\alpha,6\beta$ compound expected according to rule 5 (Section II, A) since the 6-mesylate (IV) can be converted to the α-epoxide (II, R = H) (108). (The formation of epoxides proceeds by inversion of the mesylated carbon atom.) The diacetate (VII) of the triol, therefore, possesses an equatorial acetate at C-3 and an axial one at C-6. This situation permits partial saponification to yield the 6-monoacetate (VIII), which was oxidized at C-3 (XII) and then dehydrated with thionyl chloride and pyridine to yield the 6β-acetoxy-Δ^4-3-ketone (XV) (87). The course of this reaction depends on the dehydrating agent used. Hydrogen chloride leads to a different 6-acetoxy-Δ^4-3-ketone unless the reaction is carried out at a very low temperature in a solvent completely freed of alcohol (137). The product obtained under these precautions is unstable, as it will isomerize to the epimer if exposed to hydrogen chloride in chloroform containing some alcohol (89, 137). The unstable isomer therefore has the original 6β configuration, and the reaction represents the conversion of an axial to an equatorial substituent. The 6β acetate can be solvolyzed to the parent compound with alcoholic alkali without incurring inversion or other changes (Vol. I, p. 440). The same product was obtained when the 5-hydroxy diacetate was dehydrated with thionyl chloride, solvolyzed to the Δ^4-$3\beta,6\beta$-diol (XI) (250), and then oxidized with manganese dioxide (314) or sodium dichromate (89). The unsaturated diol (XI) therefore has retained its 6β configuration and the coprostane-$3\beta,6$-diol (XIII) derived from it by reduction (257) can be expected to be likewise the 6β-isomer. These assignments of configurations at C-6 for 5-normal, 5-*allo*, and Δ^4-

---

that yielded dehydroepiandrosterone on acid hydrolysis. This does not preclude the possibility that it might have been the sulfate of the 3,5-cyclocompound.

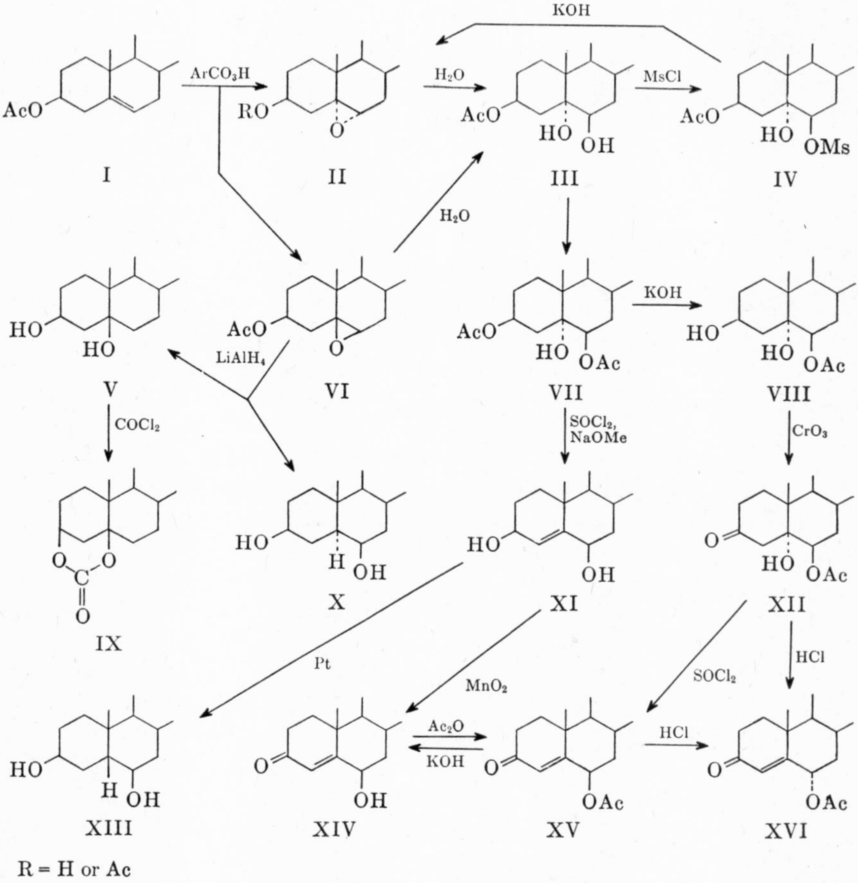

CHART 21. Configuration of 6-hydroxysteroids.

compounds are confirmed particularly for 5-*allo* compounds by many additional observations. In general 6-epimers differ sufficiently in their mode of synthesis, in their reactions, and in their molecular rotations to permit a diagnosis of configurations[16] without the necessity of direct comparison with a compound with rigorously proved orientation at C-6.

C. Δ^4-3-KETONES

As the presence of a Δ^4-3-ketone is a common characteristic of the androgenic, progestational, and cortical hormones, methods for the preparation

[16] The 6-acetoxyprogesterone described earlier (Vol. I, p. 440) on reinvestigation was shown to be the 6β-isomer (13). Its high progestational activity could not be confirmed.

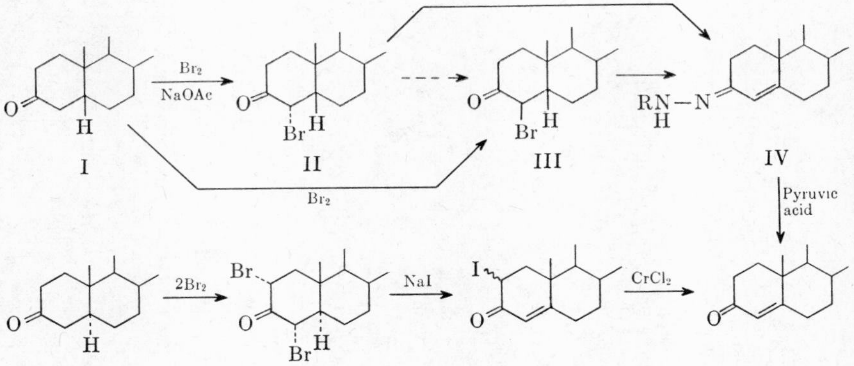

CHART 22. Δ^4-3-Ketones from 3-ketosteroids.

of this grouping command widespread interest. They vary according to the manner in which rings A and B are joined at C-5. Until recently the preparation of Δ^4-3-ketones (VIII) from 3-keto-5β-steroids (I) via the 4-bromide (III) (Vol. I, p. 418) has been an unsatisfactory procedure. The low yields have been ascribed repeatedly to the configuration of the bromine, which is β or equatorial (91, 99) and hence unfavorably disposed towards elimination with pyridine (rule 4, Section II, A). As was first shown by Mattox and Kendall (223), this difficulty can be circumvented by the formation of a hydrazone which loses hydrogen bromide spontaneously at room temperature to form the α-β unsaturated hydrazone (IV). The most suitable derivative appears to be the semicarbazone, which can be split quantitatively under mild conditions in the presence of a hydrazine acceptor such as pyruvic acid (133, 191, 227). More detailed studies of the bromination of 3-ketones of the 5-normal series have revealed the complexity of the reaction (171, 191, 222). Although the 4-bromide is the main product, it is not stable in the presence of hydrogen bromide and produces mixtures containing 2-bromo, 2,4-dibromo, as well as unbrominated, ketone. To reduce the presence of 2-brominated products, Mattox and Kendall (222) brominated in the presence of only a small amount of hydrogen bromide and neutralized the acid formed in the reaction by the addition of sodium acetate. The bromide isolated under such conditions appears to be the 4α-isomer[17] (II) (167). It also dehydrobrominated very readily as the hydrazone. Brominations in dimethylformamide containing toluenesulfonic acid have furnished the β isomer in good yield (167).

[17] Spectrographic evidence for this configuration has been obtained thus far in only one case where the yields were rather low. It is probable that the 4α-bromide is the primary product, which normally is not isolated as it epimerizes to the more stable β-isomer in the presence of hydrogen bromide (53, 54).

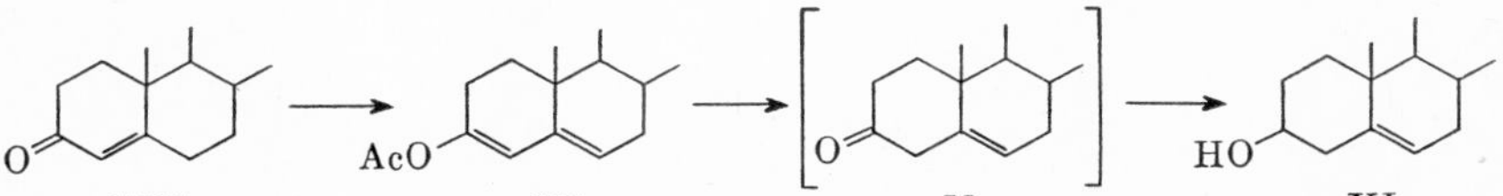

CHART 23. Δ^5-Sten-3β-ols from Δ^4-3-ketones.

The product isolated in the monobromination of 3-keto-5-*allo*-steroids is the 2α-bromide (55, 99), which can be converted to Δ^4-3-ketones albeit in poor yield (Vol. I, p. 417).   The second bromine also enters at C-2, but the product rearranges in the presence of hydrogen bromide (78) to the 2α,4α-dibromide (VI).[18] Treatment with sodium iodide substitutes the bromine at C-2 and eliminates the one at C-4 (VII).   The reductive removal of the iodine can be accomplished with chromous chloride, zinc, or even collidine (268).

The third major route to α-β unsaturated ketones, that from 5-6 unsaturated steroids via the dibromide (Vol. I, p. 572), has also been improved by better methods of bromination and debromination (90, 177). The reverse reaction is of interest particularly in the preparation of tagged Δ^5-unsaturated steroids, since a widely used procedure for the introduction of isotopic carbon into the steroid nucleus furnishes Δ^4-3-ketones (Section V, A).   The double bond is shifted into the 5-6 position by preparation of the enol acetate (IX).   Treatment with sodium borohydride in (dilute) alcohol gives mainly Δ^5-3-hydroxysteroids with the β configuration at C-3 (21, 64, 295).   The reaction probably involves solvolysis by the alkaline medium to the Δ^5-3-ketone (X), which is reduced faster to the alcohol (XI) than it rearranges to the Δ^4-3-ketone (VIII).   The reaction with lithium aluminum hydride proceeds by a different mechanism and furnishes the Δ^5-3β-hydroxysteroids in inferior yields (63).

The usual practice in hormone synthesis has been to prepare the α-β unsaturated ketone as one of the last steps.   If this is not done, blocking agents are often needed to protect this rather reactive group against changes which are to modify the remainder of the molecule.   Such protective agents are particularly useful if they are selective and mask only some of the carbonyl groups present, permitting others to react.   Enol ethers (XII) (179, 296), thioenol ethers (XIII) (266), pyrrolidyl derivatives (XIV) (132, 151), and ketals (XV) (5, 51) have all been used successfully for this purpose.   They are formed and cleaved under conditions of acid catalysis[19]

[18] Configurations assigned on the basis of spectrographic evidence (175).   The ease of dehydrobromination has suggested the axial (β) arrangement at C-4 (67).

[19] The reaction with pyrrolidine often proceeds without acid by azeotropic distillation of the water formed in the reaction.   The conditions of hydrolysis are satisfied also by very low acidity.   The positions of the double bonds in the pyrollidyl compounds at C-3 and C-5 rather than at C-2 and C-4 are not certain but are sug-

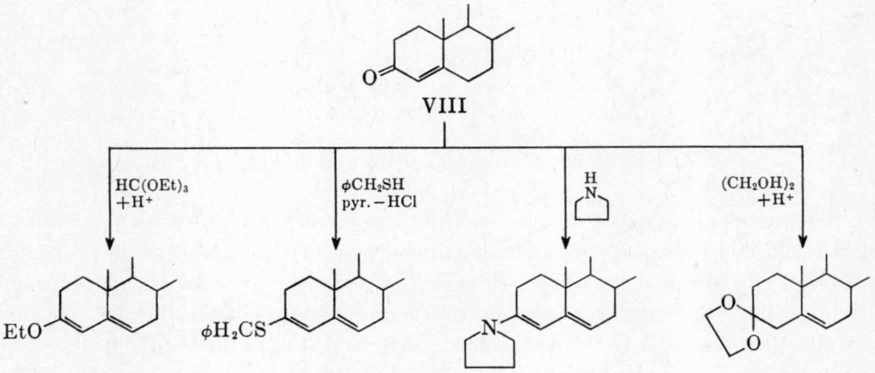

CHART 24. Protection of Δ^4-3-ketones.

which can be sufficiently mild so as to preserve acid-sensitive groupings such as an 11β-hydroxy group. The first three modes of protection can be applied without blocking additional saturated carbonyl groups that may be present at C-11, C-17, or C-20. Ethylene glycol if used in excess in the presence of toluenesulfonic acid forms ketals not only with Δ^4-3-ketones but also with saturated carbonyl groups at C-17 or C-20 but not at C-11 (5, 139). This reaction therefore provides important intermediates for the synthesis of 11-hydroxysteroids as, *e.g.*, in the preparation of cortisol from cortisone (5) or of 11β-hydroxyprogesterone from 11-ketoprogesterone (210). Acetylation of a hydroxy group at C-21 will block ketal formation at C-20 both in reaction with the glycol (5) or in exchange with the ketal of mesityl oxide (51). If the amount of ethylene glycol is limited to 1 mole, the course of the reaction depends on the concentration of the catalyst (139). Δ^4-Androstene-3,17-dione reacted preferentially at C-3 with lower, and at C-17 with higher, concentrations of toluenesulfonic acid. If the ketal is prepared by exchange with that of butanone, the reaction proceeds with ketones at C-3 and C-20 but not at C-17 (60). Δ^4-3-Ketones can be regenerated from their ketals under milder conditions of hydrolysis than are required for the liberation of 20-ketones (313). The blocking agents, therefore, possess sufficient versatility to serve a great variety of synthetic purposes. An interesting alternative to the protection of Δ^4-3-ketones in reactions with metal hydrides has been proposed by Sondheimer *et al.* (311), who found that the Δ^4-3-hydroxysteroids which result from this treatment can be selectively reoxidized to the ketone with manganese dioxide. Al-

---

gested by the rotations. Evidence for the shift of the double bond in the case of the ketals was provided by Fernholz and Stavely but neglected until recalled by Antonucci *et al.* (6). This shift of double bond to the β-γ position has been observed also with ketals of aliphatic α-β unsaturated ketones like mesityl oxide (51).

cohol groups which are not adjacent to double bonds are not affected by this oxidant at room temperature under normal conditions.

D. INTRODUCTION OF OXYGEN AT C-11

As the presence of an oxygen atom at C-11 appears to be essential for the anti-inflammatory effect of the corticoids, an unprecedented effort has been made in the last few years to find new routes to the synthesis of 11-oxygenated steroids. There are only a few naturally occurring compounds besides the adrenal hormones which are known to contain oxygen in this position. They are found among the heart poisons obtained from the skin of the Japanese toad (228) and from certain plants of the species *Strophantus sarmentosus*. After a long search, the variety of *S. sarmentosus* which yields the 11-oxygenated (183) aglycone, sarmentogenin (II), was identified (43, 199, 326); the conversion of the substance into cortisone has been accomplished (198), but at the moment, at least, the starting material is not available in quantity. The simplest point of departure for *introducing* oxygen at C-11 by chemical means are steroids which are oxygenated in the adjacent 12-position. Several procedures which utilize the 12-hydroxybile acid, deoxycholic acid, have been described (Vol. I, p. 578), and a few additional ones will be reported below. The bile acids served well for the commercial synthesis of cortisone for several years, but their supply is limited and more abundant starting compounds were needed. Some of these like hecogenin (III) also contain oxygen at C-12 (331), but the prob-

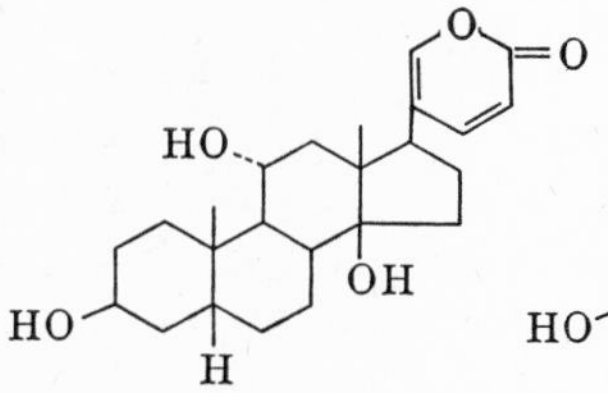

I
Gamabufogenin
from Japanese toad

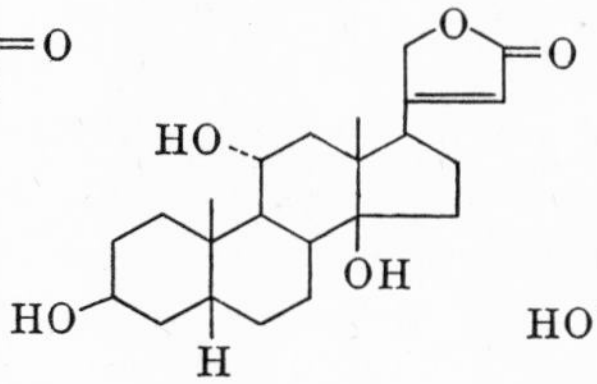

II
Sarmentogenin

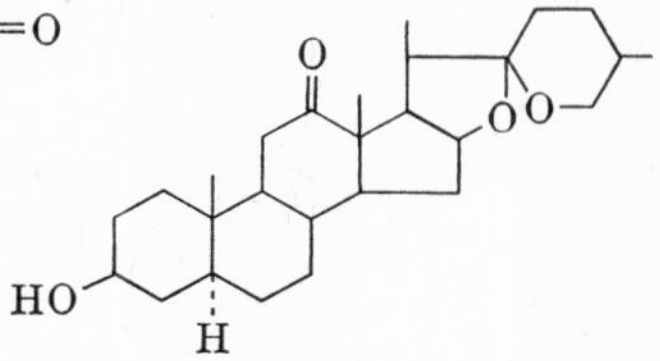

III
Hecogenin

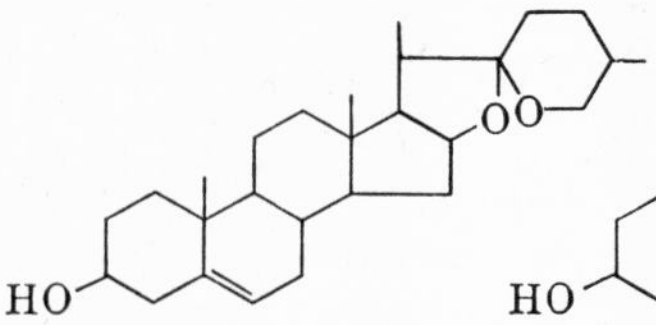

IV
Diosgenin

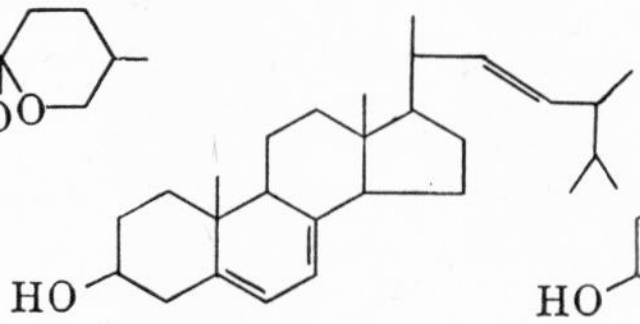

V
Ergosterol

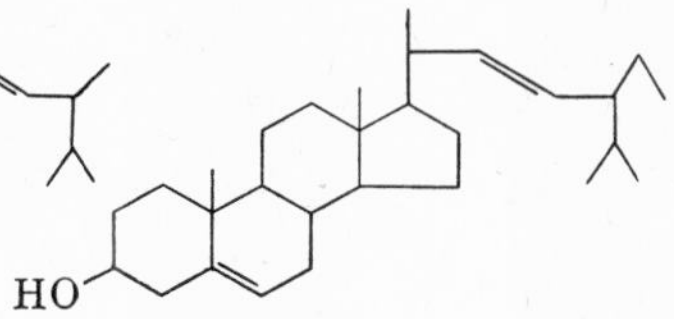

VI
Stigmasterol

CHART 25.

lem of transposing this function to C-11 had to be met by different methods
(56, 75, 166, 293).   An altogether new approach was made when steroids
containing functional groups in ring B rather than C (diosgenin (IV),
ergosterol (V), stigmasterol (VI), and other Δ^5-unsaturated compounds)
were used for the synthesis of 11-ketones.   As already stated, methods for
the total synthesis of 11-ketosteroids have also been devised.   But in spite
of these many great advances, the technique which at the moment, at least,
appears to be of the greatest practical value for oxygenation at C-11 is not
one of organic chemistry.   The spectacular success in finding microorganisms which introduce 11α and even 11β hydroxyl groups into various
steroids is being reported in the chapter on steroid metabolism.

1. Syntheses from $\Delta^{7,9(11)}$-Dienes

The preparation of the starting materials, the $\Delta^{7,9(11)}$-dienes, from
abundant natural products like diosgenin or ergosterol largely followed the
paths laid out by Windaus and his collaborators in their classical studies of
the provitamins D.   Oxidation of a Δ^5-3β-acetoxysteroid (I) with chromic
acid or better with t-butyl chromate (142, 244) introduces a keto group at
C-7 (III) which on reduction with lithium aluminum hydride furnishes
predominantly the 7β-hydroxy compound[20] (94).   The 7(8) double bond
can be established by heating of the benzoate to yield VII (263).   A somewhat similar and more widely used procedure involves reaction with N-bro-
mosuccinimide to yield the 7α-bromide (II) (25), which can be dehydrobrominated with tertiary amines to the same diene (25, 271).   Unfortunately II, being an allylic bromide, also gives large amounts of the isomeric
$\Delta^{4,6}$-diene.   This complication is avoided if the Δ^5-stenol is oxidized to the
$\Delta^{4,6}$-dienone V.   This conversion can be accomplished by oxidation with
manganese dioxide at elevated temperature (312), by oxidation with benzo-
quinone in the presence of aluminum t-butoxide (335), or by other procedures (265).   Reduction of the enol acetate (VI) with sodium borohydride
furnishes again the 5,7-diene (VII) (65, 264).   The selective hydrogenation
of its 5(6) double bond is best accomplished by nickel catalysis (146, 200,
275).   The Δ^7-steroid (VIII) can also be obtained in good yield from the
Δ^5-7-ketone (III) by step-wise catalytic reductions to the 7α-hydroxy-5-
allosteroid (IV) and esterification with, and then elimination of, methane-
sulfonic acid (142).   Oxidation with mercuric acetate completes the synthesis of the required $\Delta^{7,9(11)}$-diene (XII) (270).

The product obtained by these procedures has the 5α configuration,
necessitating a rather circuitous route for the subsequent introduction of

[20] The configurations of 7-hydroxysteroids with a 5–6 double bond or 5α-hydrogen
were determined by Heymann and Fieser (153).   The 7-halides are formulated on the
basis of these results and of a comparison of their molecular rotations (26).

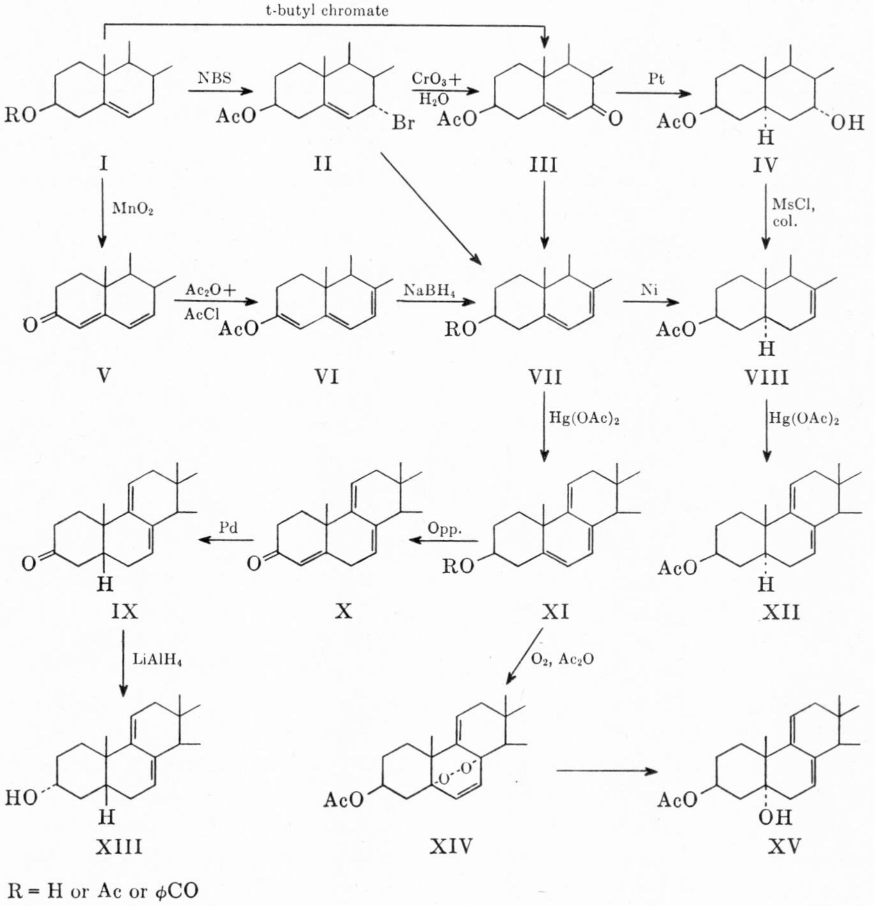

CHART 26. Preparation of $\Delta^{7,9(11)}$-dienes.

R = H or Ac or ϕCO

the Δ^4-3-ketone (see Section IV, C).   To obtain more favorable conditions for this step, two alternatives have been proposed.   Oxidation of the $\Delta^{5,7,9(11)}$-trienol (XI) according to Oppenauer's method shifts the 5(6) double bond to the 4(5) position (X), which in some compounds (Vol. I, p. 424) permits reduction predominantly to the 5β-isomer, particularly if the hydrogenation is carried out in an alkaline medium (176, 333, 340). The molecular environment is favorable enough in the sapogenin series to permit the conversion of XI to XIII, a $\Delta^{7,9(11)}$-diene with β configuration at C-5 (347).   The $\Delta^{5,7,9(11)}$-triene (XI) can be converted by the action of oxygen and light to the 5α,8α-peroxide (XIV), which can be reduced to the 5α-hydroxy $\Delta^{7,9(11)}$-diene (XV) (30, 202).   The presence of a hydroxy group at C-5 allows the facile establishment of the 4(5) double bond as soon as the alcohol function at C-3 is oxidized to a carbonyl group (32).

The conversion of $\Delta^{7,9(11)}$-dienes with the *allo* configuration at C-5 to 11-ketones has been accomplished in many laboratories. The main results are summarized in Chart 27. Oxidation with 1 mole of an aromatic peroxy acid (peroxybenzoic (47) or monoperoxyphthalic acid (146)) furnished an unsaturated epoxide which could be expected to be either a $\Delta^{9(11)}$-7,8-epoxide or a Δ^{7}-9,11-epoxide (XVI). The decision between these two structures was complicated by the fact that the reaction product yielded under different conditions two different α-β unsaturated ketones (146). Treatment with boron trifluoride in benzene furnished the Δ^{8}-11-ketone (XXV), acid hydrolysis, the Δ^{8}-7-ketone (XXII). The isolation of probable intermediates in these rearrangements and consideration of reaction mechanisms, however, made it quite clear that the epoxide must have the 9,11-oxido structure (XVI). If it is treated with boron trifluoride in benzene (31) for a very brief time or with boron trifluoride in ether (31, 143), or with magnesium bromide (11), an unsaturated 11-ketone (XX) results which still has the double bond in the 7(8) position (143). Its configuration at C-9 is abnormal (β), since reduction of the ethylenic bond furnishes a stereoisomer (XXVI) of the natural ($8\beta,9\alpha$) 11-ketone (XXXI) to which it isomerizes on treatment with alkali (31). The epimerization of the unsaturated ketone proceeds much more readily. It occurs (XIX) upon cautious treatment with alumina, whereas prolonged exposure or treatment with boron trifluoride in benzene yields the Δ^{8}-11-ketone (XXV). Whereas catalytic reduction of this compound furnished still another stereoisomer (probably $8\alpha,9\alpha$) (XXXII) (70), lithium in liquid ammonia gave the natural 11-ketone (XXXI) in good yields (294, 313). This sequence, epoxidation, (step-wise) isomerization, and reduction to XXX or XXXI, appears to be the best route from the diene to 11-oxygenated steroids (141).

In contrast to this straightforward rearrangement of the epoxide with boron trifluoride, the reaction in aqueous acid seems to proceed by allylic shift. Very brief exposure (146) or adsorption on acid-washed alumina (47) yielded a Δ^{8}-7,11-diol (XVII).[21] This can be oxidized to the unsaturated diketone (XVIII) and reduced with zinc and acid to the saturated diketone (XXIV) with the natural configuration at C-8 and C-9. This steric result is due to the greater stability of this arrangement, since reduction with zinc in ether-methanol furnishes an isomer (believed to be $8\alpha,9\alpha$) which readily

---

[21] The symmetrical structure of this compound leaves little doubt that the reactions in aqueous acid cannot be used for determining the structure of the original epoxide (XVI). The Δ^{8}-7,11-diol may well be an intermediate in the formation of the Δ^{8}-7-ketone (XXII) to which it has been converted under conditions similar to but not identical with those prevailing in the acid hydrolysis (144).

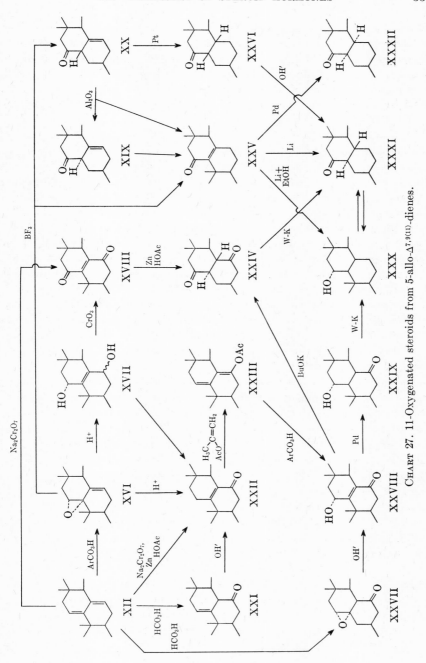

CHART 27. 11-Oxygenated steroids from 5-allo-$\Delta^{7,9(11)}$-dienes.

isomerizes with acetic acid to the natural 8β,9α configuration (38).   The
selective removal of the 7-ketone group is achieved by Wolff-Kishner[22]
reduction or better by formation of the 7-dithioketal and its desulfurization
by nickel.   The unsaturated diketone can also be prepared directly with
sodium dichromate though in lower yield (95) or by a sequence employing
N-bromosuccinimide in acidified t-butanol-water, silver nitrate, and chromic acid (98).

If the original 7,9(11)-diene is oxidized with an aliphatic peroxy acid
like peroxyformic, the 7(8) double bond is attacked first (37).   The products appear to be $\Delta^{9(11)}$-unsaturated 7-ketones (XXI) or 7,8-epoxides (72),
compounds which readily isomerize with mild alkali to the conjugated
Δ^8-7-ketone (XXII).   This can be utilized by another peroxidation of its
enol acetate (XXIII) to yield the 11α-hydroxy-Δ^8-7-ketone (XXVIII) (73).
This compound is also available by oxidation of the original 7,9(11)-diene
with 2 moles of peroxyformic acid (37, 72) and alkaline hydrolysis of the
resulting 9,11-epoxy-7-ketone (XXVII).   More vigorous alkaline hydrolysis (37) or better, treatment with potassium t-butoxide (267) furnishes
the saturated diketone (XXIV).   Alternatively, the 11α-hydroxy-Δ^8-7-
ketone can be converted to the saturated 11α-hydroxy compound (XXX)
by reduction of the ethylenic double bond and reductive removal of the
keto group by the methods already described (69, 72).   Additional procedures have been reported by Heusser et al. (144, 150) and Laubach et al.
(201).

The presence of a 5α-hydroxy group does not interfere with the conversion of the 7,9(11)-diene to the 11-ketone via the 9,11-epoxide (31, 32, 39),
but inversion to the normal series (5β hydrogen) alters the course of oxidation with aromatic peroxy acids (100, 144, 146).   The initial attack is at
the 7(8) double bond, yielding both a $\Delta^{9(11)}$-unsaturated 7,8-epoxide and
7-ketone (XXI).   The epoxide isomerizes with boron trifluoride to the
Δ^8-7-ketone (XXII) (144) or yields on brief acid hydrolysis a Δ^8-7,11-diol
(XVII) (146).   All these products can be converted to 11-ketones by
processes analogous to those described in the 5-allo-series (73, 100, 146).
The results with other oxidants are likewise similar to those observed
with 5α-compounds and provide additional routes to the saturated 11-
ketone (98, 100).

2. Syntheses from 12-Ketones

Several new routes have been developed for transforming 12- into 11-
ketosteroids.   One of the older ones (Vol. I, p. 585) was based on bromination of the 12-ketone followed by gentle hydrolysis to the 11-hydroxy-12-

---

[22] Contrary to older beliefs 11-keto groups can also be removed by this technique
(236).   If this is desired higher temperatures and longer reaction times are employed.

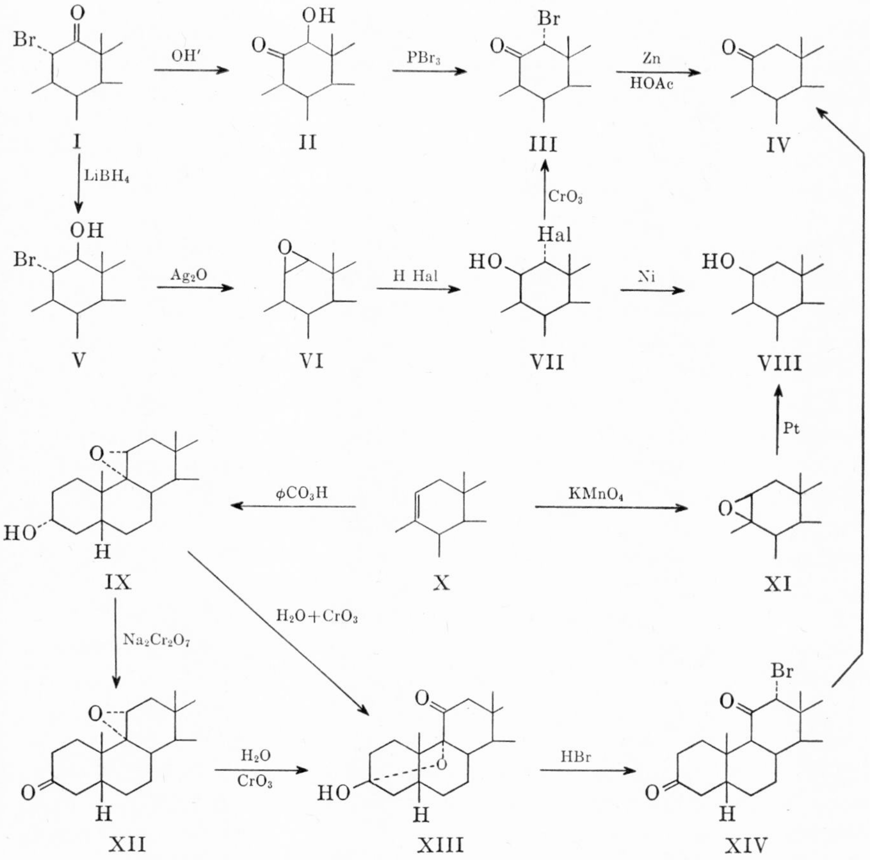

CHART. 28. 11-Oxygenated steroids from 12-ketones.

ketone. If the hydrolysis of the bromoketone (I) is carried out at elevated temperature, equilibration of the ketols occurs, yielding predominantly an 11-ketone with an equatorial hydroxyl (β) at C-12 (II). This can be brominated with phosphorus tribromide and reduced to yield the 11-ketone (IV) (35). This scheme is useful with bile acids, but the terminal bromination step has made it inapplicable to sapogenins (75). This limitation does not apply to a new procedure, which effects the conversion in very satisfactory yields (56, 293). Reduction of the bromoketone (I) with lithium borohydride gave a 12β-hydroxy derivative (V) which readily dehydrobrominates to form the 11,12-β-epoxide (VI). This is reopened with hydrogen halide to give the expected (rule 5) di-axial 11β-hydroxy-12α-halogen derivative (VII). The iodide or bromide could be reduced with nickel to the 11β-hydroxysteroid (VIII), and the bromide gave the bromo ketone (III) on oxidation and the 11-ketone on subsequent reduction. A very similar sequence of reactions starting from the less readily accessible 11,12-ethylene has been developed by Fuerst and Scotoni.(109).

12-Ketones can be converted to the 9(11)-ethylene (X) (Vol. I, p. 580) and thence by two new procedures to the 11-oxygenated products. The reactions are applicable only to compounds with normal (β) configuration at C-5. In this case oxidation with permanganate gave the 9,11-β-epoxide (XI) in fair yield (52). This could be reduced to the 11β-hydroxy compound (VIII) (rule 5). Oxidation of the ethylene with peroxy acids furnished the 9,11-α-epoxide (IX). This structure has proved to be very inert (97) unless activated by some vicinal group. (Several examples of this were given in the preceding section.) In the Heymann-Fieser procedure (152) activation is provided by a keto group at C-3 which can form a hemiketal with a 9α-hydroxy group (XIII). Several methods were developed for its utilization. The one illustrated here, reaction with hydrogen bromide, is analogous to the opening of the Kendall 3α,9α-epoxide (Vol. I, p. 584). Treatment of the resulting 12-bromoketone (XIV) with zinc and acid completes the synthesis of the 11-ketone (IV).

3. Other Reactions in Ring C

The steric course of reductions of 11-ketones has become well defined. Reduction with sodium (138, 145) or lithium (313) and an alcohol either at its boiling point or in liquid ammonia yields the 11α isomer in accordance with rule 1. All other effective procedures, hydrogenation with platinum (328), lithium aluminum hydride (289), lithium borohydride (334), or sodium borohydride (152, 241), gave the 11β-hydroxy compounds almost (5) exclusively. The β-hydroxy group is axial and in *meta* position to both angular methyl groups which likewise have β and axial orientations. Reactions of the hydroxy group, therefore, meet great steric hindrance from these bulky substituents, and acetylations with pyridine and acetic anhydride have not proved feasible. 11β-Hydroxysteroids, however, acetylate readily with acetic anhydride or isopropenyl acetate in the presence of toluenesulfonic or perchloric acids (242). The nature of the acid seems to play a critical part in the success of the operation (119), for whereas 11β-hydroxysteroids are relatively stable to toluenesulfonic acid, they dehydrate readily with hydrogen halides. As the bond linking this hydroxyl group is antiparallel to one connecting a hydrogen with an adjacent tertiary carbon atom (C-9), dehydration should proceed more readily in this direction than towards C-12. $\Delta^{9(11)}$-Desaturation occurs if 11β-hydroxysteroids are treated with hydrogen halides (45, 273), boron trifluoride (152), or phosphorus oxychloride and pyridine (119). It also accompanies the liberation of 11β-hydroxysteroids from their conjugates when urine is heated with acid

(298). Exposure to higher acid concentrations than are needed for dehydration can lead to a shift of the double bond possibly to the 8(9) (ref. 45) or 8(14) (ref. 211) position. Contrary to older beliefs (Vol. I, pp. 488, 570, 600) 11(12)-unsaturated compounds do not form under these conditions. They result from 12α-tosylates by elimination and possess in some cases high biological activity. Introduction of the 11(12) double bond into progesterone (229) triples its progestational activity but reduces (231) that of ethynyltestosterone (Vol. I, p. 446). 11-Desaturation sustains or moderately reduces the androgenic potency of testosterone (231) and the ability of deoxycorticosterone acetate to maintain the life of adrenalectomized dogs and rats (45, 329, 336).

The 11α-hydroxysteroids have become of interest chiefly because they are formed in excellent yields by microbiological oxidations. The equatorial 11α-hydroxyl group has about normal reactivity in acetylation reactions and is not particularly susceptible to dehydrations (Vol. I, p. 570). The reaction, however, proceeds with phosphorus oxychloride and pyridine (24) or by ionization of the tosylate (II) (24, 107) to form 9(11)-ethylenes (III). The latter process is the basis of a conversion of the 21-acetate (I) of epicortisol to that of cortisol (VII) (107). Addition of hypobromous acid to the double bond by an improved technique furnished the bromohydrin (IV), which could be reduced with zinc and alcohol to cortisol acetate. The halohydrins are remarkably effective in depositing glycogen in the

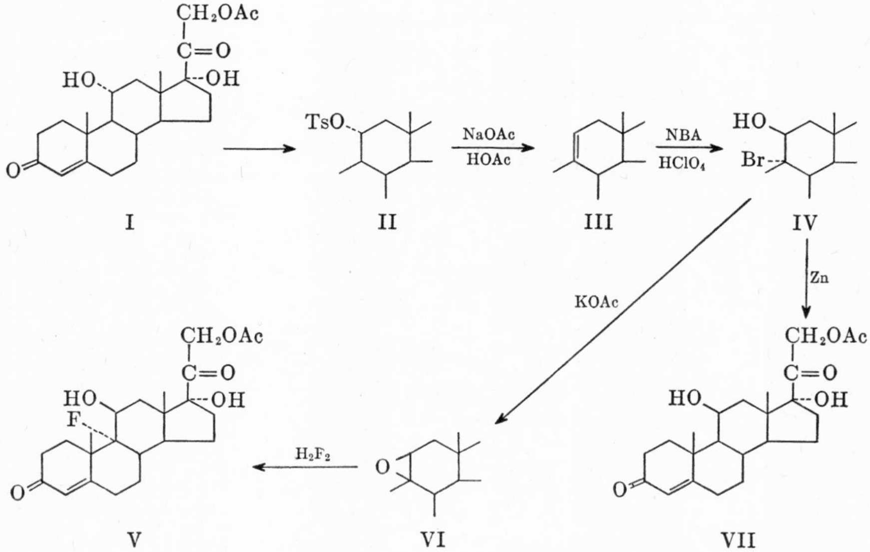

CHART 29. Cortisol from epicortisol.

rat liver.   In particular the fluorohydrin, 9α-fluorocortisol acetate (V), is
about 11 times, its oxidation product, 9α-fluorocortisone acetate, 9 times, as
potent as cortisone acetate in this test.   Another route to cortisol from
11α-hydroxysteroids via the 11-ketone has been described recently by Levin
et al. (203).

E. 16-OXYGENATED STEROIDS

The seven 16-hydroxylated steroids that have been identified as urinary
constituents belong to two structural types, viz., 16,17-glycols with 18 or
19 carbon atoms, and derivatives of 16-hydroxypregnane.   The stereochemistry of the 16,17-glycols has been elucidated by Huffman and Lott
(169) by their synthesis of urinary Δ^5-androstene-3β,16,17-triol (Vol. I,
p. 479).   The first steps, the conversion of the 17-ketone (V) to the ketol II,
have already been described (Vol. I, p. 377).   The structure of the ketol
acetate III as a 17β-acetoxy-16-ketone follows from its conversion to a
known 17β-acetoxyderivative IV by nickel desulfurization of the thioketal.
On catalytic reduction (316), the ketol acetate gave a glycol acetate VIII
with *cis* orientation of its hydroxyl groups, as deduced from their ability
to form a cyclic ketal with acetone (41).   Compound VIII, therefore, has
the 16β,17β configuration.   Although ketol II and its acetyl derivative III
are mutually interconvertible, the possibility of isomerization during these
reactions was considered.   It was virtually ruled out when the location
of the keto group at C-16 was corroborated for the ketol by independent
evidence and the configuration of its hydroxyl group confirmed by reduction to the 16β,17β-glycol VIII with sodium amalgam in an acid medium
(169).   The second glycol obtained in this reaction (VII) therefore should
be the 16-epimer, Δ^5-androstene-3β,16α,17β-triol.   It was identical with
the isolated compound.   Its 16,17-*trans* configuration is confirmed by reduction of the 5(6) double bond, which gave a product different from the

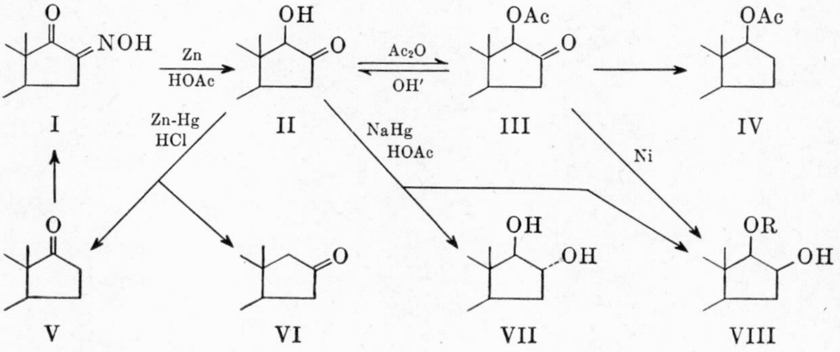

CHART 30. Configuration of 16,17-glycols.

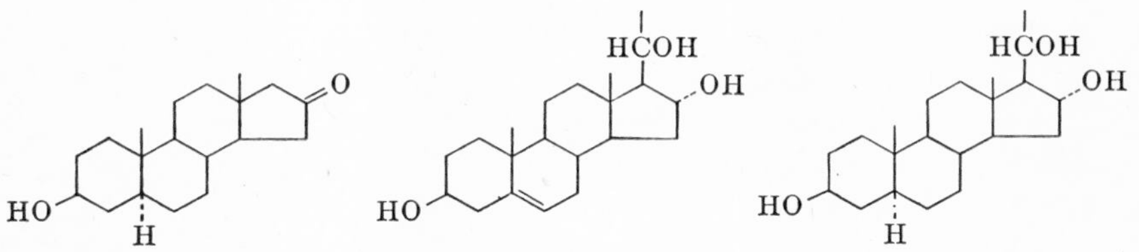

CHART 31.

other *cis* glycol (16α,17α) (Vol. I, p. 378).   Analogous syntheses have produced natural estriol (169), androstane-3α,16,17-triol (208), and etiocholane-3α,16,17-triol (208) along with their stereoisomers.   Insofar as *trans* orientation of the hydroxyl groups has been established,[23] the natural products should, therefore, likewise be 16α,17β-compounds.   Isomerization seems to take place if ketol II is subjected to a Clemmensen reduction, since both 16- and 17-ketones (VI and V) were obtained (170).   The 3β-hydroxyandrostan-16-one (IX) prepared in this manner proved to be identical with a compound isolated by Heard and McKay from the urine of pregnant mares (Vol. I, p. 481).

Three 16-hydroxysteroids with 21 carbon atoms have been found among urinary excretion products.   Δ⁵-Pregnene-3β,16α,20α-triol (X) was obtained from an adrenal tumor case (159), its reduction product allopregnane-3β,16α,20α-triol (XI) from human pregnancy urine (208), and allopregnane-3β,16α,20β-triol (XXI) from the urine of pregnant mares (Vol. I, p. 450).[24]   The basis of the stereochemical assignments at C-16 in this series of natural products are the reactions of the sapogenins (*e.g.*, XII), which demonstrate that the 5-membered ring attached to ring D must be free of strain, as it is if the substituents at C-16 and C-17 are *cis* to each other (161).   Since the conversion of diosgenin to cholesterol (217) established the β configuration of the carbon-carbon bond at C-17, the same assignment could be made for the carbon-oxygen bond at C-16 (161). The steric link to the pregnane compounds is provided by Marker's acetolysis reaction (Vol. I, p. 410), which has become one of the main avenues in the synthesis of the steroid hormones.   The reaction product (XIII) (218), the acetate of the pseudosapogenin,[24] can be oxidized to a keto ester (XIV) which shows considerable lability to acid or alkali (219).   Under these conditions a Δ¹⁶-20-ketone (XVI) is formed which can be utilized for

---

[23] This is conclusively proved for estriol but rests in the case of the other two triols mainly on a precariously small difference of optical rotations between the 16-epimers. Nevertheless it is probable that these assignments are also correct.   For additional support of the estriol configuration see Sheehan *et al.* (297).

[24] The structure previously reported for this compound (Vol. I) has been shown to be in error.

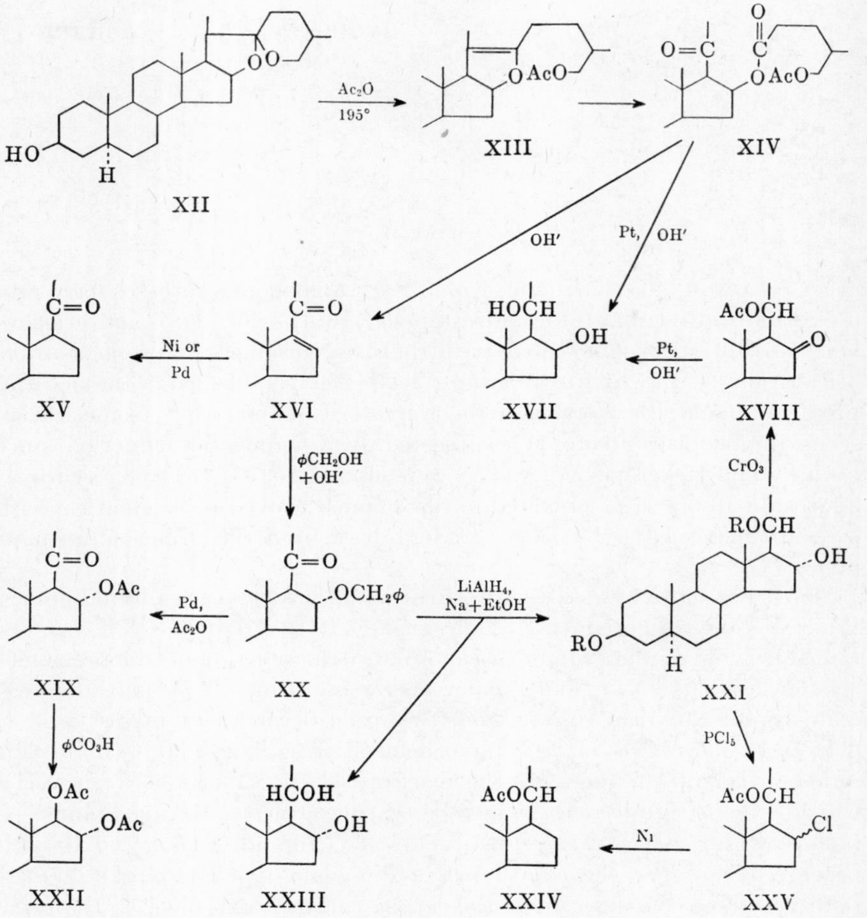

R = H or Ac

Some of the reactions were carried out with Δ⁵- compounds

CHART 32. Configuration of 16-hydroxylated allopregnanes.

hormone synthesis either directly (Section IV, G, 1) or after reduction of the 16(17) double bond (XV) (Vol. I, p. 423). Catalytic hydrogenation of XIV produced a 20-hydroxy derivative which has no tendency to eliminate the ester grouping and can be hydrolyzed to yield XVII. Since this series of reactions which converts tigogenin XII to allopregnane-3β,16,20-triol (XVII) does not affect C-16, the final product still has the 16β configuration (161). The opposite assignment (16α) must be made for the mares' triol (XXI, R = H), which (as the 3,20-diacetate (XXI, R = Ac)) can be converted to XVII by a sequence of reactions comprising oxidation of the free hydroxyl group to the 16-ketone (XVIII), reduction of this keto group, and hydrolysis of the acetates (161).

Δ^{16}-20-Ketones in the presence of alkali or acid react reversibly with alcohols to form 16-alkoxy derivatives[25] (112).   For preparatory purposes the use of benzyl alcohol is particularly attractive, since the resulting benzyl ethers (XX) can be cleaved by hydrogenolysis without the possibility of an inversion at C-16 (162).   If the 20-keto group in XX is reduced with lithium aluminum hydride, both 20-epimers are obtained.   The predominant epimer could be reduced to the mares' triol (XXI), thus demonstrating the 16α configuration for the benzyl ethers and their reaction products.   These include the triols X and XI which are derived from the less abundant 20-epimer (XXIII).   The configurations at C-20 in these products could be assigned when the 20-monoacetate of the mares' triol (XXI) was converted to the known 20β-acetoxyallopregnane (XXIV) by removal of the free hydroxyl groups (161).   If the hydrogenolysis of the benzyl ethers is done catalytically with palladium rather than with sodium and alcohol, the prior reduction of the 20-keto group is not necessary (160, 163).   Peroxybenzoic acid oxidation of the 16α-acetoxy-20-ketone (XIX) so obtained provided a link with a 16,17-acetoxy derivative (XXII) of androstane; this has fully confirmed the stereochemical assignments at C-16 and C-17 which were made independently for the C_{19} and C_{21} series. 16-Hydroxysteroids with the same configuration as these urinary excretion products have been obtained also by microbiological hydroxylations (249, 325).

F.   D-HOMOSTEROIDS

Compounds differing from normal steroids in having ring D six- rather than five-membered have become of considerable biochemical interest with Klyne's (186) startling demonstration that certain D-homosteroids are genuine constituents of urine.   The strain inherent in the *trans* fusion of rings C and D renders appropriately substituted steroids quite susceptible to enlargement of ring D.   17-Hydroxy-20-ketones would undergo such a change if either C-16 or C-13 severed its bond with C-17 and became attached to C-20.   A D-homosteroid with a methyl group at C-17 (IV) would result in the first case, at C-17a in the second (V or VI).   Thus far only the latter type of rearrangement of 17-hydroxy-20-ketones has been observed.[26] The reaction creates a new asymmetric center at C-17a, which permits the

---

[25] If this is to be avoided as in the conversion of XIV to XVI it is advantageous either to work with a sterically hindered solvent like *t*-butanol (238) or a nonalcoholic one like tetrahydrofuran (47).

[26] Von Euw and Reichstein (327) have described an isomerization product of I which is different from V and VI.   It has not been identified but may possess structure IV.

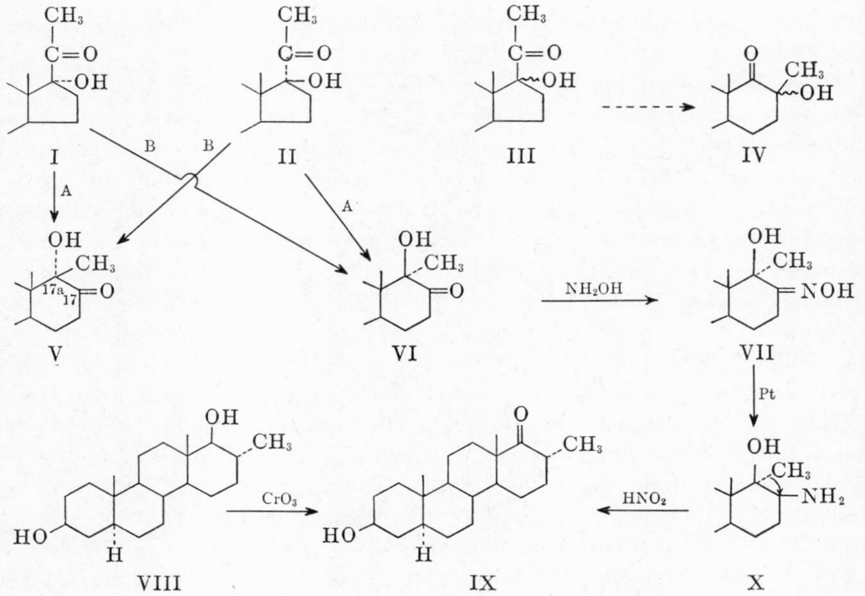

CH₃ structures across top labeled I, II, III, IV

I, II, III, IV; arrows A, B; V, VI, VII, VIII, IX, X

CH_3

I   II   III   IV

V   VI   NH₂OH   VII

Pt

OH / CH₃ / V

VI = O   NH₂OH →   VII =NOH

VIII   CrO₃   IX   HNO₂   X

CHART 33. Structure of uranediol.

existence of two isomers (V and VI). Both of these have been obtained in a rather stereospecific manner, with the result depending both on the configuration of the starting compound at C-17 and on the catalytic agent used to cause the rearrangement. Observations made in several laboratories have been interpreted by Turner (321), who related the steric result[27] of the rearrangement to the orientation of the carbonyl group in the starting compound. If it is directed towards the observer when the new bond is formed at C-20, the hydroxyl group will be established with β orientation, whereas a rearward direction of the keto group will lead to an α hydroxyl. If the rearrangement is brought about by alkali, the alcohol groups in I and II are partly present as the negatively charged alkoxide $(-O^-)$. As the charge should cause the carbonyl group to face in the opposite direction, the rearrangement can be expected to proceed mainly according to B. On the other hand, in the presence of complexing agents like boron trifluoride or alumina which have been postulated to form cyclic intermediates with the carbonyl and hydroxy group, the ketone would

[27] The configurations of these D-homosteroids were assigned originally on the basis of hydrolysis rates of the acetyl derivatives (303). If it is assumed that the equatorial acetate is more reactive, configurations are deduced which explain neither the formation nor the reactions of these compounds. These measurements are therefore being disregarded in this discussion.

CHART 34. 17a-Keto-D-homosteroids.

orient itself to the same side as the hydroxyl and the rearrangement would proceed according to A.   The recorded data (with the exception of the acid-catalyzed rearrangement of 17α-hydroxy-20-ketones (327)) are accounted for by these generalizations, and the configurations assigned to V and VI on this basis appear to be justified.   The oxime (VII) derived from VI was reduced catalytically in the presence of acetic acid.   The resulting amine, which can be expected to be axial (17β) (cf. rule 3) (189), rearranged to a ketone (IX) on treatment with nitrous acid (186, 259).   Since the carbon methyl bond at C-17a and the carbon nitrogen bond at C-17 lie in one plane, the migration of the methyl group from C-17a to the α side of C-17 is the expected course for this reaction (rule 4) (189).   The structure assigned to IX accounts for the inertness of the carbonyl group, which was at first mistaken for an epoxide.   The properties of the 17α-methyl-D-homoandrostan-3β-ol-17a-one so prepared agreed closely with the partial oxidation product (216) of Marker's uranediol (Vol. I, p. 447).   Identity was confirmed by direct comparison of the diketones (186, 189).   The diketone is stable to acid, again indicating the equatorial (17α) configuration of the methyl group.   The configuration of the hydroxyl group at 17a is not known from chemical evidence but has been suggested to be β on the basis of rotation measurements (36).   The structure of the uranediol makes it clear that it could not have formed from a normal steroid in the course of its isolation.[28]

If uranediol arises in the course of metabolism from an allopregnane derivative, its structure suggests bond migration involving the 16-17 linkage. Although this has not been observed in the rearrangements of 17-hydroxy-20-ketones, such a reaction occurs in the synthesis of 17a-keto-D-homosteroids (XIV) from the 17β-hydroxy-20-amine XIII with nitrous acid (149). This route has given easy access to androgens with a six-membered ring D. They are generally more potent than their lower homologues with the usual steroid structure (280).

[28] This appears not to be true for the urinary D-homosteroid of type V (Vol. I, p. 602), which in all probability was formed from the corresponding 17α-hydroxy-20-ketone (I) during chromatography on alumina.   Turner's categorical statement (321) that such compounds do not rearrange in contact with this adsorbent was not found to hold for prolonged exposure to alkaline alumina.   When magnesium silicate (205) was used in its stead the D-homocompound was no longer isolated from the urinary extract (154).

G. REACTIONS OF THE SIDE CHAIN

1. *Introduction of Oxygen at C-17 and C-21*

The degradations of the sapogenins, bile acids, and the abundant sterols with a double bond in the side chain afford ready access to 20-ketosteroids (I). It is natural therefore that most of the newer procedures of elaborating the side chain of the adrenal steroids are based on such a precursor. The bromination of 20-ketones was extensively studied by Marker and his collaborators. With minor exceptions, their findings have been confirmed and brought to fruition by subsequent developments. If 1 mole of bromine is used, bromination occurs primarily at C-17 (Vol. I, p. 436). But as the product is often not easily purified, it has been recommended (178) that the 17,21-dibromide (V) be prepared and treated with sodium iodide to obtain the very reactive 21-iodide (VI), which can be reduced selectively to the 17-monobromide (II) with sodium bisulfite (see, however, also (147)). Alternatively, a pure product is easily obtained by bromination of the enol acetate (XIII) (96). Treatment with a nitrogenous base like pyridine or collidine (178) converts the monobromide to the Δ^{16}-20-ketone (III), which represents a useful intermediate for the synthesis of 17α-hydroxysteroids

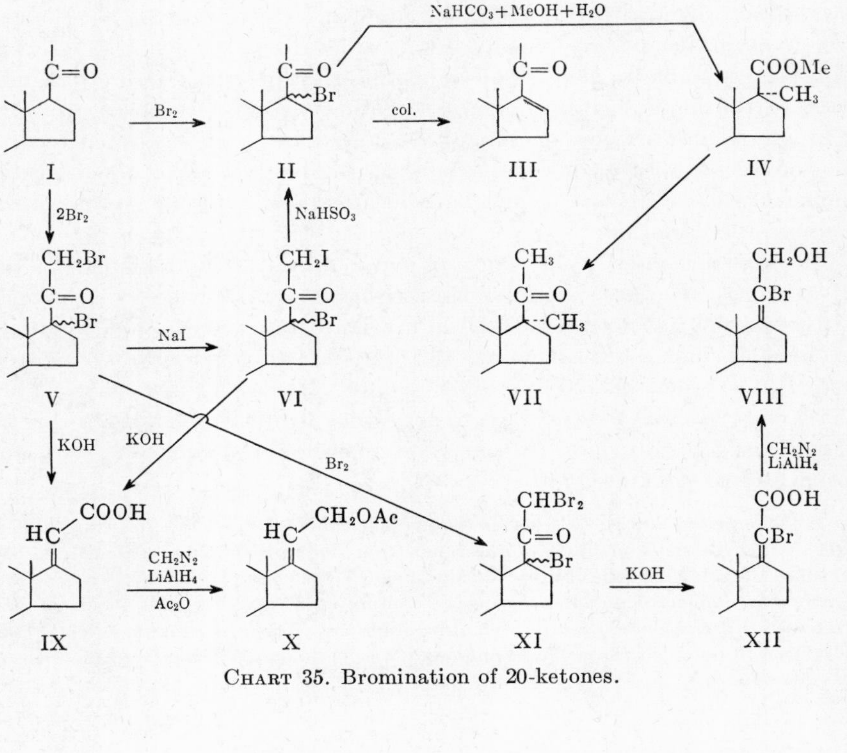

CHART 35. Bromination of 20-ketones.

(*vide infra*).   If the keto halides are treated with alcoholic alkali, rearrangements occur.   In the case of the monobromide the methyl ester of a 17-
methyletianic acid results (Vol. I, p. 438), which probably represents the
17α-methyl isomer (IV) (148).[29]   Such a product was converted through the
acid chloride to 17-methylprogesterone (VII), which proved to be at least
twice as potent as progesterone in the Corner-Allen test (147).   The rearrangement product of the 17,21-dihalides (V and VI) is an unsaturated acid
(IX) (178, 214) which upon methylation, reduction with lithium aluminum
hydride, and acetylation gave the *trans*-Δ^{17}-unsaturated 21-acetoxy derivative (X) (330).   This can be hydroxylated with osmium tetroxide to the
17α,20β,21-triol.   Although the preferential oxidation of the 21-mono-
acetate to 17α-hydroxy-21-acetoxy-20-ketones (XXII) is possible (Vol.
I, p. 592), the yields were quite unsatisfactory.   However, if the ethylene
(X) is treated with hydrogen peroxide and only a catalytic amount of
osmium tetroxide, compound XXII is obtained directly in good yields
(232).   The precise nature of the process was not established, but it was
shown that the 17,20,21-triol monoacetate was not an intermediate.   The
process may therefore be basically similar to three others which involve
hydroxylation of the 17(20) double bond in substrates containing a negative
substituent at C-20.   This substituent may be an acetoxy group (194), a
cyanide (285), or a bromide (330).   The required 20-bromide VIII is obtained by the rearrangement of the 17,21,21-tribromo-20-ketone (XI)
(330) and esterification and reduction of the resulting unsaturated bromo
acid (XII) to the unsaturated bromo alcohol (VIII).   Its acetate (XXVI)
is converted to the desired 17α-hydroxy-21-acetoxy-20-ketone (XXII)
with osmium tetroxide.   The process does not require the usual hydrolysis
of the osmate, which evidently is too unstable to be isolated.

    The 20-ketone (I) combines with hydrogen cyanide to form the cyano-
hydrin (XVI), which can be dehydrated with phosphorus oxychloride and
pyridine to yield the unsaturated cyanide XVII (285).   Treatment with
osmium tetroxide and hydrolysis of the osmate XVIII with sodium sulfite
furnished the 17α-hydroxy-20-ketone (XV).   This 17-hydroxylation procedure is equally applicable to 20-ketones containing a 21-acetoxy group
(XXIX).   The use of the costly osmium tetroxide is not essential, as
permanganate likewise converts the intermediate XXX to the 17α-hydroxy-
21-acetoxy-20-ketone (XXII) (130).   The yields of the bromo and of the
cyano procedure can be very satisfactory but vary quite markedly with
structural changes in distant parts of the molecule.

    [29] Configurations based on rotation data and biological activities.   Since this re-
arrangement probably proceeds by inversion at C-17, the starting compound would
then be expected to have a 17β bromine; this, however, is contrary to the view that
C-17 is brominated most readily from the rear (116).

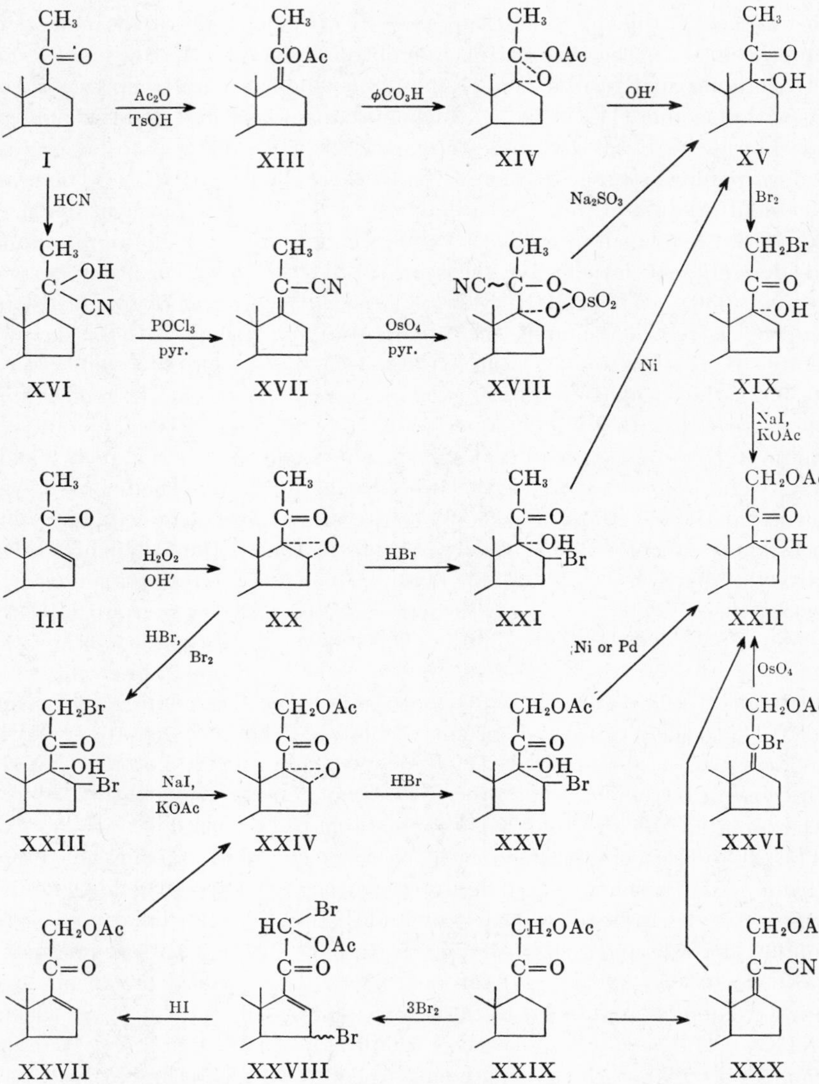

CHART 36. Introduction of hydroxyls at C-17 and C-21.

The 20-ketone (I) can form two types of enol acetates. Treatment with acetic anhydride and toluenesulfonic acid yields the Δ^{17} (XIII) (220), with isopropenyl acetate and toluenesulfonic acid chiefly the Δ^{20}-acetate (XXXIV) (237, 323). The former product, which is often obtained as a mixture of *cis* and *trans* isomers, is oxidized with peroxybenzoic (194) or monoperoxyphthalic acid (269). Cleavage of the resulting epoxide with alkali yields the desired 17α-hydroxy-20-ketone (XV).   With the 17-position blocked, bromination yields the 21-monobromide (XIX), which can be hydrolyzed to the 21-alcohol without undergoing rearrangement (194). Usually, however, the bromine is replaced by the acetoxy group by successive treatments with sodium iodide and potassium acetate (269).

Two other procedures (50, 181) introduce the 17α hydroxyl group by oxidation of the 16(17) double bond.   The Δ¹⁶-20-ketone (III) is available directly by degradation of the sapogenins (see Section IV, E) or from the saturated 20-ketones (I) by the processes already described.   The 16,17-epoxide (XX) is formed in high yield with alkaline hydrogen peroxide (181).   If it is to be converted to the 17α-hydroxy-20-ketone (XV), the ring is opened with hydrogen bromide and the bromohydrin (XXI) reduced with nickel (180), or alternatively the ring is opened with lithium aluminum hydride while the keto group is protected by formation of a ketal (182).   If the synthetic objective is the 17,21-dihydroxy-20-ketone, the ring opening with hydrogen bromide is followed by bromination at C-21 (XXIII) and successive substitution by iodide and acetate (181). As this reaction re-establishes the epoxide ring, it is again cleaved with hydrogen bromide.   Reduction completes the synthesis of the 17α-hydroxy-21-acetoxy-20-ketone (XXII).   The results obtained in the bromination of 21-acetoxy-20-ketones (XXIX) may not be typical, since the compound studied was also substituted at C-12.   This substitution has been shown to direct in ketones of type I the first bromine to C-21 rather than to C-17 (176).   This also occurred when there was an acetoxy group at C-21 (103).   In order to obtain the desired Δ¹⁶-20-ketone (XXVII) 3 moles of bromine were used in the presence of acetyl bromide (50).   The product was identified (49) as the unsaturated 15,21-dibromide XXVIII, which was reduced with hydrogen iodide.   The remaining steps to the 17α-hydroxy-21-acetoxy-20-ketone (XXII) via the epoxide XXIV were very similar to those already described.

Several of the syntheses mentioned utilized a 21-acetoxy-20-ketone as starting material.   Since this partial structure occurs also in deoxycorticosterone acetate, there was an obvious need for synthetic procedures which would furnish such ketol acetates from 20-ketones or other equally accessible sources.   The most direct way of introducing an acetoxy group at C-21, the reaction with lead tetraacetate (Vol. I, p. 587), often gives only fair yields.   In a manufacturing process developed in Germany (274) the 20-ketone is condensed with diethyl oxalate.   The resulting ester (XXXI) is hydrolyzed, the enolate XXXII treated with iodine, and finally the iodinated β-diketone (XXXIII) cleaved to yield the 21-iodo-20-ketone (XXXV).   This can also be prepared from the Δ²⁰-enol acetate (XXXIV) either by bromination and substitution with sodium iodide (237) or di-

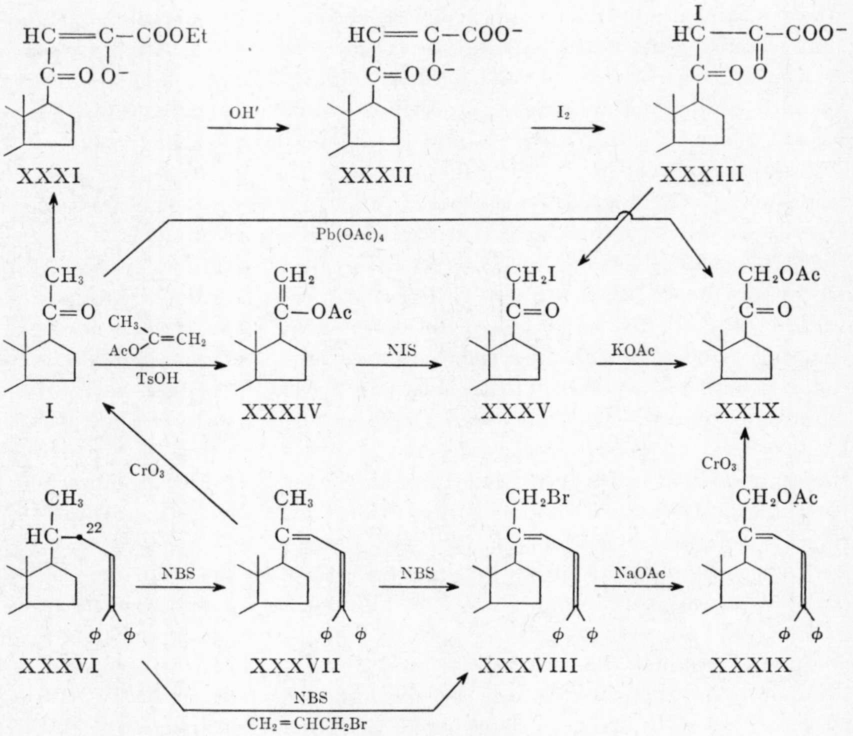

CHART 37. Hydroxylation at C-21.

rectly with N-iodosuccinimide (71). Substitution of the iodide by acetate completes the synthesis.

A very simple procedure applicable to bile acids has been developed in the Ciba laboratories. It is based on their splendid method for the degradation of the side chain (Vol. I, p. 415) which involved bromination of the intermediate XXXVI at C-22 with N-bromosuccinimide and dehydrobromination with heat or base to yield the diene XXXVII, which can be oxidized to the 20-ketone (I). If the diene is let to react again with N-bromosuccinimide, the bromine enters at C-21 (230). These three steps (XXXVI to XXXVIII) can be carried out in a single operation if N-bromosuccinimide is applied in allyl bromide (131) rather than in the customary carbon tetrachloride. The unsaturated solvent acts as an acceptor for the hydrogen bromide eliminated and is converted chiefly to a dibromopropane. The yields of XXXVIII are excellent, and since the product as an allylic bromide is easily substituted at C-21, the desired 21-acetoxy-20-ketone is readily secured by oxidation with chromic acid.

2. *Esters at C-17 and C-21*

The 21-acetates which result from many of these syntheses can be used as such for most biological and medical purposes. However, at times the hydrolysis to the free compounds is indicated—a process which can be attended by considerable loss. Some of this could be traced to air oxidation. If a 21-acetoxy-20-ketone (I) like deoxycorticosterone acetate is exposed to ethanolic potassium hydroxide under nitrogen, the free steroid is formed, but in the presence of oxygen large amounts are cleaved to the corresponding etianic acid (II) (137, 324). Reichstein and von Euw (261) have recommended hydrolysis with bicarbonate in aqueous methanol for ketol 21-acetates without (I) and with (III) a hydroxyl group at C-17; Mattox and Kendall (224) prefer the use of hydrochloric acid in dilute methanol for this purpose. The acid-catalyzed reaction converts a small amount of the 17α-hydroxy-21-acetoxy-20-ketone (III) to the 21,21-dimethoxyketone (IV) (221). This reaction becomes the main process in the absence of water and proceeds also from 16α-hydroxylated (VII) (325) and Δ¹⁶-unsaturated (VIII) (221) ketols under similar conditions.

The tertiary 17α-hydroxy group adjacent to a 20-ketone is inert to acetic anhydride and pyridine but will acetylate slowly with acetic anhydride in the absence of pyridine and much more rapidly in the presence of toluenesulfonic (168) or other acids (321, 322). Sodium acetate likewise catalyzes the reaction (310). Unlike the 11β-acetates, which can also be obtained under similar conditions of acid catalysis, 17α-acetoxy-20-ketones (V, VI) hydrolyze with alkali with surprising ease. The rate of reaction has been reported to equal (168), or even to exceed (310), that obtained with the very reactive 21-acetoxy group. In view of the ease of reversal, acetylation at C-17 can be used for the protection of this hydroxyl group.

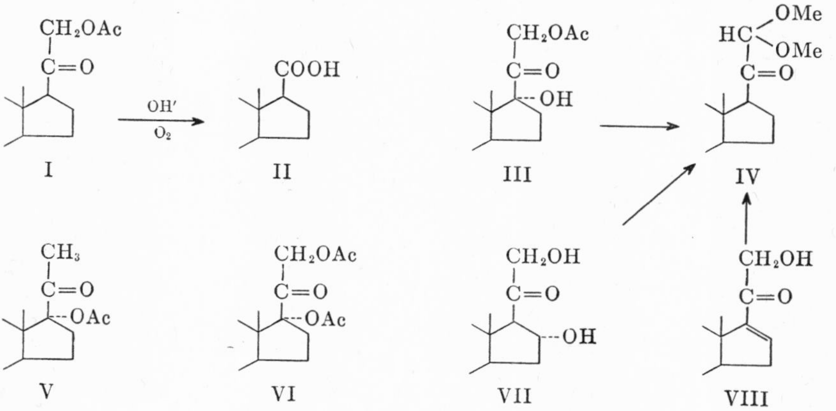

CHART 38.

H. ALDOSTERONE

Older studies particularly from the laboratories of Wintersteiner and of Kendall had shown that the mother liquors obtained in the crystallization of the more water-soluble adrenal steroids were remarkably effective in maintaining the life of adrenalectomized animals (Vol. I, p. 592). The potency of this crude material surpassed that of any of the known adrenal hormones that might be present. These observations suggested to some the existence of a hormone of unknown structure, to others a synergistic effect of known substances. Although this postulated synergism could not be duplicated with synthetic mixtures, the problem remained dormant for many years. In 1952 Grundy *et al.* (121) reported on the fractionation of adrenal extracts by paper chromatography and presented evidence for a potent mineral factor different from the known hormones. The isolation of the active principle in crystalline form was reported from London and Basel (308) and very shortly thereafter also from the Mayo Clinic (225, 226). A brilliant analysis by the same team of Swiss and British investigators (308a) has elucidated the structure which shows that the factor differs from corticosterone in having an aldehyde group at C-18 (Ia).[30] Accordingly it has been named aldosterone. This structure is tautomeric with the hemiacetal Ib, which admits the possibility of having two stereoisomers epimeric at C-18. Only one of these can form a lactone as in III. It is not known at the moment which of these tautomers represents the crystalline product. In solution at least the hemiacetal form appears to predominate. Aldosterone surpassed deoxycorticosterone in its effect on mineral metabolism by a factor of 50 to 100, depending on test conditions, and was at least 30 times as potent as deoxycorticosterone acetate when judged by its ability to maintain the life of adrenalectomized dogs (308).

The evidence supporting the structure of aldosterone has just been communicated (308a), and as yet rather few experimental details have been published. The analysis indicated the composition $C_{21}H_{30}O_5 \pm H_2$. The spectrographic properties of aldosterone and of its derivatives both in the ultraviolet and in the infrared as well as the soda fluorescence test indicated a Δ^4-3-ketone group (226, 307, 308). On treatment with excess of acetic anhydride in pyridine, aldosterone formed a diacetate (II) which contained no free hydroxyl group. This product had relatively little biological activity but could be reconverted to the parent compound by enzymatic hydrolysis. Reducing tests, infrared data, and the liberation

---

[30] The summary given here is based on the preliminary communications in *Experientia*. While this Chapter was in press the complete reports appeared in *Helvetica Chimica Acta* which disclosed many important additional observations such as the high potency of aldosterone in the glycogen deposition test (⅓ the activity of cortisone).

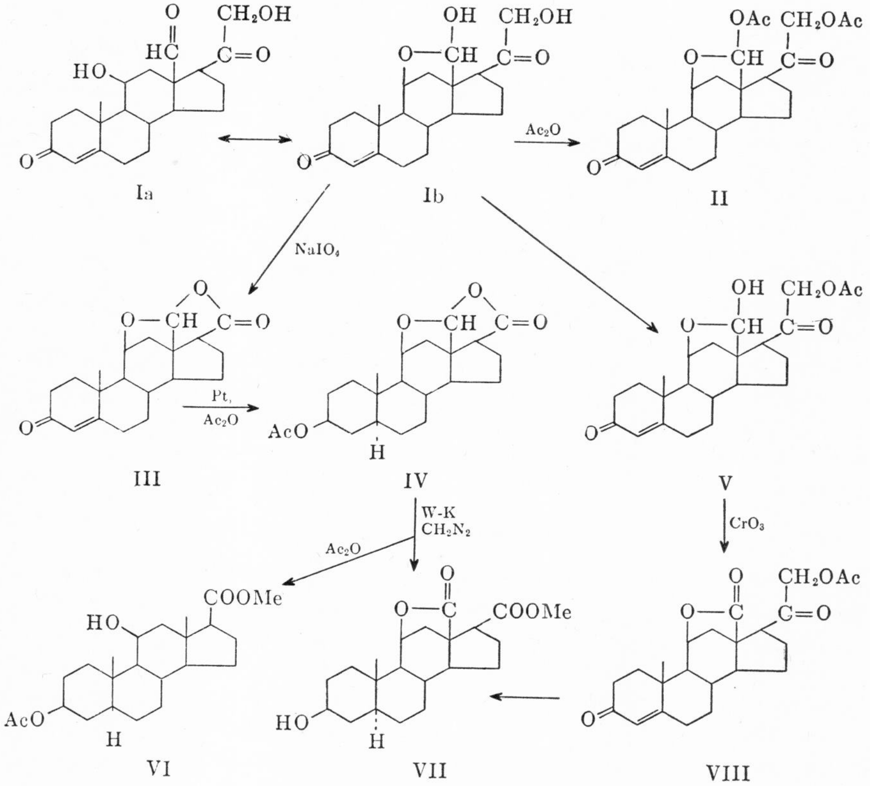

CHART 39. Aldosterone.

of formaldehyde with periodate or bismuthate suggested the presence of the usual ketol side chain. The steroid (III) formed in this cleavage, however, was not an acid but judging from its infrared spectrum a γ-lactone (308a). After reduction of the α-β unsaturated ketone grouping and acetylation, the resulting lactone (IV) was subjected to a Wolff-Kishner reduction which gave a neutral and an acidic fraction. The latter after methylation gave two products. One of these was acetylated and identified as methyl 3β-acetoxy-11β-hydroxyalloetianate (VI). This established the nature of the carbon skeleton and the presence of oxygen atoms at C-3, C-11, C-20, and C-21. If the side chain of aldosterone has the same 17β configuration as that of the etianate, the 5th oxygen should be at C-18 to permit the facile formation of the γ-lactone. When the 21-monoacetate (V) (inert to bismuthate) was oxidized with chromic acid, a different γ-lactone (VIII) formed. As the ketol acetate side chain was shown to be intact, this lactone should involve the oxygen at C-11, which therefore was present as a (free or derivatized) hydroxyl group even before hydrogenation (III → IV). In accordance with this conclusion, the spectrum of the diacetate (II) gave no evidence for an 11-ketone (226, 307). To account then for the formation of two five-membered lactones, one involving C–20 and the other C–11, the fifth oxygen had to be placed at C-18 (308a). The absence of a primary hydroxyl group in this position can be inferred from the spectrum of the diacetate (II), which showed no free hydroxyl group. The recorded data, therefore, are well accounted for if aldosterone is formulated as the hemiacetal of 11β,21-dihydroxy-3,20-diketo-Δ^4-pregnen-18-al. This structure is supported by additional observations, including a correlation of lactone VIII with the second carboxylate VII, which was obtained under the conditions of the Wolff-Kishner reaction evidently owing to a Cannizaro dismutation of the aldehyde. The only other steroid known to be oxygenated in position 18 (333a) is isorubijervine, a steroidal alkaloid which has been isolated from *Veratrum viride*.

V. Introduction of Isotopic Labels by Chemical Means

Aside from the occasional use of hetero atoms the elements employed for the labeling of sterols and steroid hormones have been the isotopes of carbon and of hydrogen. Isotopic carbon if inserted into the ring system provides a label of maximum permanence which seems ideal for many investigations. However, even a label which will be lost in certain reactions has its own distinct merits, as it may provide information about metabolic pathways difficult to secure by other means.

A. ISOTOPIC CARBON

Methods have been developed for the insertion of isotopic carbon into rings A or D. Procedures designed for the labeling of ring A have employed the Δ^4-3-ketone (I) both as starting compound and as final product. Treatment with ozone followed by other oxidants (hydrogen peroxide and periodic acid) (319) opens ring A with the loss of one carbon atom (C-4). The resulting keto acid (II) forms an enol lactone (III) which has been subjected to condensation reactions. Methyl magnesium iodide adds to the carbonyl group to form a hemiketal (IV) (110, 125) which cyclizes and dehydrates to the α-β unsaturated ketone (VIII) under the influence of acid, alkali, or piperidine. A likely intermediate is the diketone VII, which can be obtained by heating the hemiketal to 180°C. This Grignard reaction has given the highest yields of VIII whether based on the steroid or on the isotopic precursor. The procedure has been employed in the preparation of C-4 labeled cholestenone (110, 125), testosterone (110), and progesterone (111). In the last case the carbonyl group at C-20 had to be protected by the formation of an enol acetate.

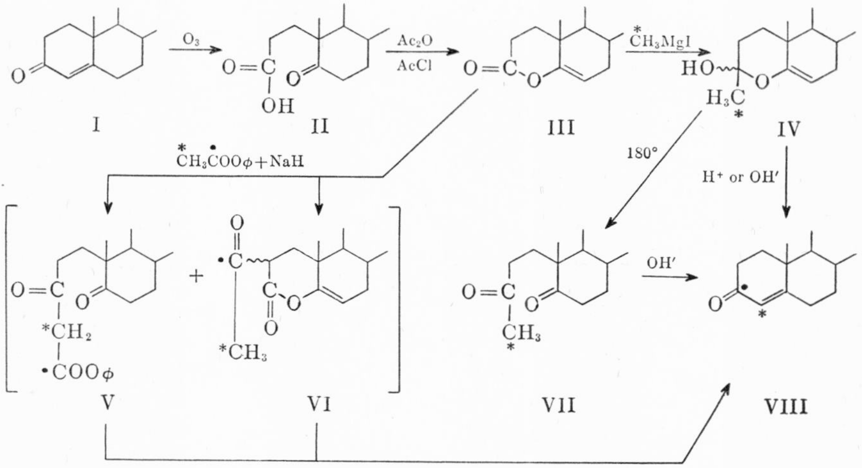

* Carbon derived from labeled methyl
• Carbon derived from labeled carboxyl

CHART 40. Labeling of ring A.

If the enol lactone III is condensed with phenyl acetate (319), the reaction can be expected to proceed either at the activated hydrogens of the
acetate or at those at C-2, producing intermediate V or VI, respectively.
When the reaction mixture was subjected to acid or alkali, the Δ^4-3-ketone
formed by hydrolysis, decarboxylation, and cyclization. Both compounds
V and VI if derived from methyl labeled acetate can be expected to yield
C-4 labeled Δ^4-3-ketones by this process. In the first case the carboxyl
group derived from acetic acid; in the second that of the lactone is lost by
decarboxylation. Repetition of the experiment with carboxyl labeled
acetate furnished the Δ^4-3-ketone in only slightly diminished isotopic yield.
The condensation therefore proceeds mainly via the intermediate VI and
is suitable also for the preparation of steroids labeled at C-3. The method
has been applied to the preparation of tagged cholestenone (319), testosterone (7, 319), and progesterone (122).

A third but evidently inferior method utilizes the Reformatsky condensation of the methyl ester of II with isotopic methyl bromoacetate. The
reaction has been studied with cholestenone (319) and methyl Δ^4-3-keto-
etianate (124), which in turn has been converted to progesterone and
deoxycorticosterone acetate. Depending on the labeling of the acetate in
either the methyl or carboxyl group, the isotope will again appear in the
4- or 3-position of the steroid.

The insertion of isotopic carbon into ring D is more laborious. It has
been carried out both with C_{19} (135) and C_{18} compounds (204) but seems
now of interest chiefly for the synthesis of estrogens. Ring D of the 17-

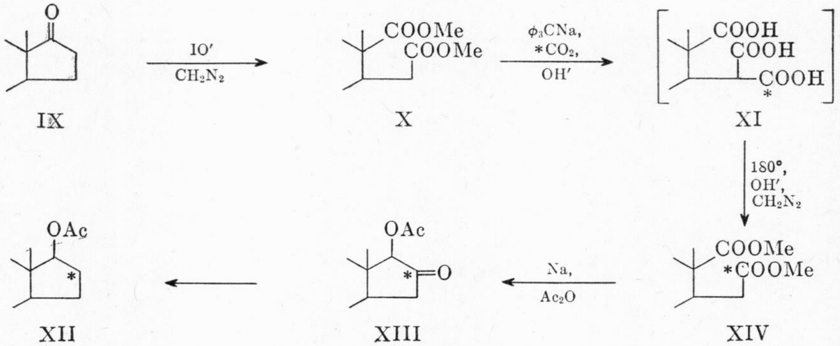

* Carbon derived from isotopic CO_2

CHART 41. Labeling of ring D.

ketosteroid (IX) is opened with hypoiodite (Vol. I, p. 364).   Methylation
of the reaction product furnished the dimethyl ester X which can be car-
boxylated with isotopic carbon dioxide in position 15 via the sodio derivative (204).   Decarboxylation after hydrolysis eliminates again a carboxyl
group containing about half of the isotope.   The concentration of isotope
per mole of steroid is therefore about half that of the original carbon dioxide.   The isotopic methyl ester (XIV) was cyclized with sodium in
liquid ammonia-ether according to the elegant procedure of Sheehan et al.
(297) and converted to the 17β-acetoxy compound (XII) by the method
of Huffman and Lott (Section IV, E).   This sequence of reactions has been
used in the synthesis of 17β-estradiol labeled in position 16.   The preparation of dehydroepiandrosterone also labeled at C-16 (135) followed
essentially a route of reconstituting ring D that has already been described
(Vol. I, p. 354).

The introduction of isotopic carbon into the side chain has also been
carried out with several steroids (progesterone tagged at C-21 (209, 262),
17-methyltestosterone (209), 17α-methylestradiol (34), and cholesterol
labeled at C-26(46, 61, 282)).

B. Isotopic Hydrogen

The three principal methods of introducing the isotopes of hydrogen
into steroids have been hydrogenation of double bonds, hydrogenolysis of
unwanted substituents, and catalytic exchange reactions.   Catalytic
hydrogenation of double bonds presents no special problem if the reaction
can be carried out in a nonhydroxylic solvent.   Ionizable hydrogen atoms
from acids, water, alcohols, etc., rapidly equilibrate with the hydrogen
molecules of the gas phase in the presence of the catalyst.   The equilibria
between deuterium and ordinary acetic acid are greatly in favor of intro-

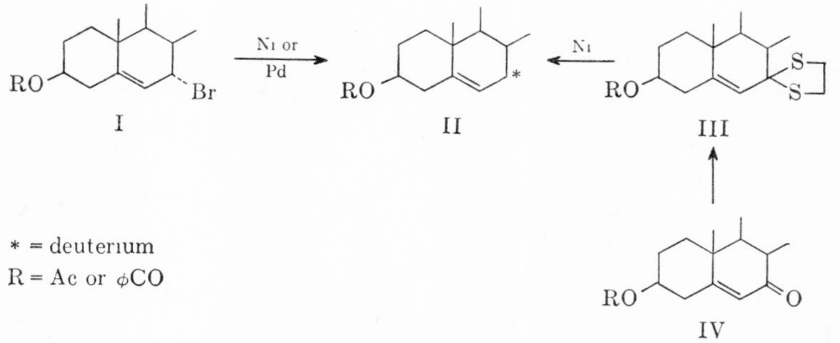

* = deuterium
R = Ac or ϕCO

CHART 42. Labeling by hydrogenolysis.

ducing the lighter isotope into the steroid (86).   Therefore, if hydroxylic solvents cannot be avoided, they should also be enriched in their ionizable hydrogens with the isotope to be incorporated.   Hydrogenation of double bonds has been employed to label estrone acetate in the 6,7-positions (246), 3β-acetoxyallopregnan-20-one in the 5,6-positions (194), and the acetate of methyl lithocholate in the 11,12-positions (86).   The bile acid has been degraded (Section IV, G) to 3α-hydroxypregnan-20-one, testosterone, progesterone (191), 17-hydroxyprogesterone (194), 11-deoxycortisol (192), and related substances.

The labeling of cholesterol and Δ^5-androstene-3β,17β-diol in position 7 provides examples of deuteration by hydrogenolysis (115).   The starting compounds were either the 7α-bromide (I) or the 7-ketone (IV), which are readily available from their 5(6)-unsaturated precursors (Section IV, D, 1).   Treatment of the bromide (I) or of the thioketal (III) of ketone IV with deuterized nickel gave the Δ^5-compounds labeled at C-7.

In stating the location of the isotope in these preparations it was tacitly assumed that catalytic hydrogenation or hydrogenolysis are not accompanied by exchange reactions between the isotopic hydrogen on the catalyst surface and the ordinary hydrogen atoms attached to the steroid.   This, however, cannot be taken for granted, since the hydrogen atoms of deuterium and ordinary cyclohexane equilibrate quite rapidly on a platinum surface (88).   Critical data on steroids are scarce and do not warrant as yet extended generalizations.   No significant exchange seemed to accompany the deuteration of methyl 3α-acetoxy-Δ^{11}-cholenate in acetic acid (DOAc) at room temperature with platinum (86), but deuterized cholesterol on reduction with tank hydrogen lost deuterium, probably from the 6-position (113).[31]   Conditions are more favorable for such exchange

---

[31] One would expect, therefore, that the catalytic deuteration of 3β-acetoxy-Δ^5-pregnen-20-one (194) introduced more than two atoms of deuterium.   According to a personal communication from Dr. T. F. Gallagher this was the case.

reactions if steroids in acetic acid are heated with heavy water and platinum (33). The isotopic hydrogen so incorporated is not uniformly distributed throughout the molecule (113); in fact the amount and location of isotope introduced by this method and retained on treatment with alkali is so dependent on the complete structure of the steroid that no generalizations appear to be possible at this time (1, 113, 114). Information on isotope distribution, however, is often essential for a quantitative and at times even for a qualitative interpretation of biological studies. The principal tool in locating deuterium or tritium has been the loss of label by degradation, substitution, oxidation of alcohols, and treatment of ketones with alkali. The last process, which exchanges isotope at carbon atoms adjacent to the carbonyl group, can be surprisingly slow. Complete removal of isotope from such positions, therefore, seems to be assured only if the treatment is continued to constant isotope content. Quite a few steroids have been prepared by this exchange reaction, and several were subjected to such an isotope analysis. Of particular interest is the distribution in cholesterol, since such preparations have been used in metabolic studies of fundamental importance. Deuterium was found chiefly at C-6 and in the terminus of the side chain (C-24 to C-27) (113). The exchange reaction has also been used for the incorporation of tritium into 3α-acetoxypregnane-11,20-dione, which in turn has been converted to radioactive cortisone (114).

REFERENCES

1. Anker, H. S., and Bloch, K.   *J. Am. Chem. Soc.* **66,** 1752 (1944).
2. Anner, G., and Miescher, K.   *Helv. Chim. Acta* **29,** 1889 (1946).
3. Anner, G., and Miescher, K.   *Helv. Chim. Acta* **30,** 1422 (1947).
4. Anner, G., and Miescher, K.   *Helv. Chim. Acta* **31,** 2173 (1948); *ibid.* **32,** 1957 (1949); *ibid.* **33,** 1379 (1950).
5. Antonucci, R., Bernstein, S., Heller, M., Lenhard, R., Littell, R., and Williams, J. H.   *J. Org. Chem.* **18,** 70 (1953).
6. Antonucci, R., Bernstein, S., Littell, R., Sax, K. J., and Williams, J. H.   *J. Org. Chem.* **17,** 1341 (1952).
6a. Arigoni, D., Riniker, B., and Jeger, O.   *Helv. Chim. Acta* **37,** 878 (1954).
7. Ashmore, J., Elliott, W. H., Doisy, E. A., Jr., and Doisy, E. A.   *J. Biol. Chem.* **200,** 661 (1953).
8. Bachmann, W. E., and Controulis, J.   *J. Am. Chem. Soc.* **73,** 2636 (1951).
9. Bachmann, W. E., and Dreiding, A. S.   *J. Am. Chem. Soc.* **72,** 1323 (1950).
10. Bachmann, W. E., Dreiding, A. S., and Stephenson, E. F. M.   *J. Am. Chem. Soc.* **73,** 2765 (1951).
11. Bachmann, W. E., Horwitz, J. P., and Warzynski, R. J.   *J. Am. Chem. Soc.* **75,** 3268 (1953).
12. Bachmann, W. E., and Ramirez, F.   *J. Am. Chem. Soc.* **72,** 2527 (1950).
13. Balant, C. P., and Ehrenstein, M.   *J. Org. Chem.* **17,** 1587 (1952).
14. Banes, D., and Carol, J.   *J. Biol. Chem.* **204,** 509 (1953).
15. Banes, D., Carol, J., and Haenni, E. O.   *J. Biol. Chem.* **187,** 557 (1950).

16. Barkley, L. B., Farrar, M. W., Knowles, W. S., and Raffelson, H.   *J. Am. Chem. Soc.* **75**, 4110 (1953).
17. Barnes, C. S., Barton, D. H. R., and Laws, G. F.   *Chemistry & Industry*, p. 616 (1953).
18. Barton, D. H. R.   *J. Chem. Soc.*, p. 1027 (1953).
19. Barton, D. H. R., Hassel, O., Pitzer, K. S., and Prelog, V.   *Science* **119**, 49 (1954).
20. Barton, D. H. R., and Klyne, W.   *Nature* **162**, 493 (1948).
21. Belleau, B., and Gallagher, T. F.   *J. Am. Chem. Soc.* **73**, 4458 (1951).
22. Bergstroem, S., Lardon, A., and Reichstein, T.   *Helv. Chim. Acta* **32**, 1617 (1949).
23. Bernstein, S., and Lenhard, R. H.   *J. Org. Chem.* **18**, 1146 (1953).
24. Bernstein, S., Lenhard, R., and Williams, J. H.   *J. Org. Chem.* **19**, 41 (1954).
25. Bide, A. E., Henbest, H. B., Jones, E. R. H., Peevers, R. W., and Wilkinson, P. A.   *J. Chem. Soc.*, p. 1783 (1948).
26. Bide, A. E., Henbest, H. B., Jones, E. R. H., and Wilkinson, P. A.   *J. Chem. Soc.*, p. 1788 (1948).
27. Bijvoet, J. M., Peerdeman, A. F., and van Bommel, A. J.   *Nature* **168**, 271 (1951).
28. Birch, A. J.   *J. Chem. Soc.*, p. 367 (1950).
29. Birch, A. J.   *Ann. Rept. Progr. Chem.*, p. 205 (1951).
30. Bladon, P., Clayton, R. B., Greenhalgh, C. W., Henbest, H. B., Jones, E. R. H., Lovell, B. J., Silverstone, G., Wood, G. W., and Woods, G. F.   *J. Chem. Soc.*, p. 4883 (1952).
31. Bladon, P., Henbest, H. B., Jones, E. R. H., Lovell, B. J., Wood, G. W., Woods, G. F., Elks, J., Evans, R. M., Hathway, D. E., Oughton, J. F., and Thomas, G. H.   *J. Chem. Soc.*, p. 2921 (1953).
32. Bladon, P., Henbest, H. B., Jones, E. R. H., Lovell, B. J., and Woods, G. F.   *J. Chem. Soc.*, p. 125 (1954).
33. Bloch, K., and Rittenberg, D.   *J. Biol. Chem.* **149**, 505 (1943).
34. Bocklage, B. C., Nicholas, H. J., Doisy, E. A., Jr., Elliott, W. H., Thayer, S. A., and Doisy, E. A.   *J. Biol. Chem.* **202**, 27 (1953).
35. Borgstrom, E., and Gallagher, T. F.   *J. Biol. Chem.* **177**, 951 (1949).
36. Brooks, R. V., Klyne, W., Miller, E., and Paterson, J. Y. F.   *Biochem. J.* **51**, 694 (1952).
37. Budziarek, R., Newbold, G. T., Stevenson, R., and Spring, F. S.   *J. Chem. Soc.*, p. 2892 (1952).
38. Budziarek, R., and Spring, F. S.   *J. Chem. Soc.*, p. 956 (1953).
39. Burke, D. C., Turnbull, J. H., and Wilson, W.   *J. Chem. Soc.*, p. 3237 (1953).
40. Burwell, R. L., Jr.   *J. Am. Chem. Soc.* **74**, 1462 (1952).
41. Butenandt, A., Schmidt-Thomé, J., and Weiss, T.   *Ber.* **72**, 417 (1939).
42. Butenandt, A., and Surányi, L. A.   *Ber.* **75**, 591 (1942).
43. Callow, R. K., and Taylor, D. A. H.   *J. Chem. Soc.*, p. 2299 (1952).
44. Cardwell, H. M. E., Cornforth, J. W., Duff, S. R., Holtermann, H., and Robinson, R.   *Chemistry & Industry*, p. 389 (1951); *J. Chem. Soc.*, p. 361 (1953).
45. Casanova, R., Shoppee, C. W., and Summers, G. H. R.   *J. Chem. Soc.*, p. 2983 (1953).
46. Chaikoff, I. L., Siperstein, M. D., Dauben, W. G., Bradlow, H. L., Eastham, J. F., Tomkins, G. M., Meier, J. R., Chen, R. W., Hotta, S., and Srere, P. A.   *J. Biol. Chem.* **194**, 413 (1952).
47. Chamberlin, E. M., Ruyle, W. V., Erickson, A. E., Chemerda, J. M., Aliminosa, L. M., Erickson, R. L., Sita, G. E., and Tishler, M.   *J. Am. Chem. Soc.* **75**, 3477 (1953).

48. Cohen, S. L., and Oneson, I. B. *J. Biol. Chem.* **204,** 245 (1953).
49. Colton, F. B., and Kendall, E. C. *J. Biol. Chem.* **194,** 247 (1952).
50. Colton, F. B., Nes, W. R., van Dorp, D. A., Mason, H. L., and Kendall, E. C. *J. Biol. Chem.* **194,** 235 (1952).
51. Constantin, J. M., Haven, A. C., Jr., and Sarett, L. H. *J. Am. Chem. Soc.* **75,** 1716 (1953).
52. Constantin, J. M., and Sarett, L. H. *J. Am. Chem. Soc.* **74,** 3908 (1952).
53. Corey, E. J. *J. Am. Chem. Soc.* **76,** 175 (1954).
54. Corey, E. J. *J. Am. Chem. Soc.* **75,** 2301 (1953).
55. Corey, E. J. *J. Am. Chem. Soc.* **75,** 4832 (1953).
56. Cornforth, J. W., and Osbond, J. M. *Chemistry & Industry,* p. 919 (1953).
57. Cornforth, J. W., and Robinson, R. *Nature* **160,** 737 (1947); *J. Chem. Soc.,* p. 1855 (1949).
57a. Cornforth, J. W., Youhotsky, I., and Popják, G. *Nature* **173,** 536 (1954).
58. Cram, D. J., and Elhafez, F. A. A. *J. Am. Chem. Soc.* **74,** 5828 (1952).
59. Crowfoot, D. *Vitamins and Hormones* **2,** 409 (1944).
60. Dauben, H. J., Jr., Loeken, B., and Ringold, H. J. *J. Am. Chem. Soc.* **76,** 1359 (1954).
61. Dauben, W. G., and Bradlow, H. L. *J. Am. Chem. Soc.* **72,** 4248 (1950).
62. Dauben, W. G., Dickel, D. F., Jeger, O., and Prelog, V. *Helv. Chim. Acta* **36,** 325 (1953).
63. Dauben, W. G., and Eastham, J. F. *J. Am. Chem. Soc.* **73,** 3260 (1951); *ibid.* **75,** 1718 (1953).
64. Dauben, W. G., and Eastham, J. F. *J. Am. Chem. Soc.* **73,** 4463 (1951).
65. Dauben, W. G., Eastham, J. F., Micheli, R. A., Takemura, K. H., Mandell, L., and Chemerda, J. M. *J. Am. Chem. Soc.* **75,** 3255 (1953).
66. Dingemanse, E., and Huis in't Veld, L. G. *J. Biol. Chem.* **195,** 827 (1952); *Acta Physiol. et Pharmacol. Neerl.* **2,** 229 (1951–1952).
67. Djerassi, C. *J. Am. Chem. Soc.* **71,** 1003 (1949).
68. Djerassi, C. *Vitamins and Hormones* **11,** 205 (1953).
69. Djerassi, C., Batres, E., Velasco, M., and Rosenkranz, G. *J. Am. Chem. Soc.* **74,** 1712 (1952).
70. Djerassi, C., Frick, W., Rosenkranz, G., and Sondheimer, F. *J. Am. Chem. Soc.* **75,** 3496 (1953).
71. Djerassi, C., and Lenk, C. T. *J. Am. Chem. Soc.* **75,** 3493 (1953).
72. Djerassi, C., Mancera, O., Romo, J., and Rosenkranz, G. *J. Am. Chem. Soc.* **75,** 3505 (1953).
73. Djerassi, C., Mancera, O., Velasco, M., Stork, G., and Rosenkranz, G. *J. Am. Chem. Soc.* **74,** 3321 (1952).
74. Djerassi, C., Miramontes, L., and Rosenkranz, G. *J. Am. Chem. Soc.* **75,** 4440 (1953).
75. Djerassi, C., Ringold, H. J., and Rosenkranz, G. *J. Am. Chem. Soc.* **73,** 5513 (1951).
76. Djerassi, C., Rosenkranz, G., Romo, J., Kaufmann, S., and Pataki, J. *J. Am. Chem. Soc.* **72,** 4534 (1950).
77. Djerassi, C., Rosenkranz, G., Romo, J., Pataki, J., and Kaufmann, S. *J. Am. Chem. Soc.* **72,** 4540 (1950).
78. Djerassi, C., and Scholz, C. R. *J. Am. Chem. Soc.* **69,** 2404 (1947).
79. Dobriner, K., Katzenellenbogen, E. R., and Jones, R. N. Infrared Absorption Spectra of Steroids. Interscience, New York, 1953.
80. Dorfman, L. *Chem. Revs.* **53,** 47 (1953).

80a. Dreiding, A. S. *Chemistry & Industry* p. 992 (1954).
81. Dreiding, A. S., and Pummer, W. J. *J. Am. Chem. Soc.* **75**, 3162 (1953).
82. Dreiding, A. S., Pummer, W. J., and Tomasewski, A. J. *J. Am. Chem. Soc.* **75**, 3159 (1953).
83. Dreiding, A. S., and Tomasewski, A. J. *J. Am. Chem. Soc.* **76**, 540 (1954).
84. Dreiding, A. S., and Voltman, A. *J. Am. Chem. Soc.* **76**, 537 (1954).
85. Ehrenstein, M. *Chimia (Switz.)* **6**, 287 (1952).
86. Eidinoff, M. L., Knoll, J. E., Fukushima, D. K., and Gallagher, T. F. *J. Am. Chem. Soc.* **74**, 5280 (1952).
87. Ellis, B., and Petrow, V. A. *J. Chem. Soc.*, p. 1078 (1939).
88. Farkas, A., and Farkas, L. *Trans. Faraday Soc.* **35**, 917 (1939).
89. Fieser, L. F. *J. Am. Chem. Soc.* **75**, 4377 (1953).
90. Fieser, L. F. *J. Am. Chem. Soc.* **75**, 5421 (1953).
91. Fieser, L. F., and Ettorre, R. *J. Am. Chem. Soc.* **75**, 1700 (1953).
92. Fieser, L. F., and Fieser, M. *Experientia* **4**, 285 (1948).
93. Fieser, L. F., and Fieser, M. Natural Products Related to Phenanthrene. Rheinhold, New York, 1949.
94. Fieser, L. F., Fieser, M., and Chakravarti, R. N. *J. Am. Chem. Soc.* **71**, 2226 (1949).
95. Fieser, L. F., and Herz, J. E. *J. Am. Chem. Soc.* **75**, 121 (1953).
96. Fieser, L. F., and Huang-Minlon. *J. Am. Chem. Soc.* **71**, 1840 (1949).
97. Fieser, L. F., and Rajagopalan, S. *J. Am. Chem. Soc.* **73**, 118 (1951).
98. Fieser, L. F., Schneider, W. P., and Wei-Yuan Huang. *J. Am. Chem. Soc.* **75**, 124 (1953).
99. Fieser, L. F., and Wei-Yuan Huang. *J. Am. Chem. Soc.* **75**, 4837 (1953).
100. Fieser, L. F., Wei-Yuan Huang, and Babcock, J. C. *J. Am. Chem. Soc.* **75**, 116 (1953).
101. Fischer, E. *Ber.* **24**, 2683 (1891).
102. Fischer, R., Lardelli, G., and Jeger, O. *Helv. Chim. Acta* **33**, 1335 (1950).
103. Fleisher, G. A., and Kendall, E. C. *J. Org. Chem.* **16**, 573 (1951).
104. Fredga, A., and Miettinen, J. K. *Acta Chem. Scand.* **1**, 371 (1947).
105. Freudenberg, K. Stereochemie. (See Table opposite p. 696.) Franz Deuticke, Leipzig and Wien, 1933.
106. Freudenberg, K., and Hohmann, W. *Ann.* **584**, 54 (1953).
107. Fried, J., and Sabo, E. F. *J. Am. Chem. Soc.* **75**, 2273 (1953); *ibid.* **76**, 1455 (1954).
108. Fuerst, A., and Koller, F. *Helv. Chim. Acta* **30**, 1454 (1947).
109. Fuerst, A., and Scotoni, R., Jr. *Helv. Chim. Acta* **36**, 1410 (1953).
110. Fujimoto, G. I. *J. Am. Chem. Soc.* **73**, 1856 (1951).
111. Fujimoto, G. I., and Prager, J. *J. Am. Chem. Soc.* **75**, 3259 (1953).
112. Fukushima, D. K., and Gallagher, T. F. *J. Am. Chem. Soc.* **73**, 196 (1951).
113. Fukushima, D. K., and Gallagher, T. F. *J. Biol. Chem.* **198**, 861, 871 (1952).
114. Fukushima, D. K., Kritchevsky, T. H., Eidinoff, M. L., and Gallagher, T. F. *J. Am. Chem. Soc.* **74**, 487 (1952).
115. Fukushima, D. K., Lieberman, S., and Praetz, B. *J. Am. Chem. Soc.* **72**, 5205 (1950).
116. Gallagher, T. F., and Kritchevsky, T. H. *J. Am. Chem. Soc.* **72**, 882 (1950).
117. Goering, H. L., and Serres, C., Jr. *J. Am. Chem. Soc.* **74**, 5908 (1952).
118. Goldberg, M. W., Sicé, J., Robert, H., and Plattner, P. A. *Helv. Chim. Acta* **30**, 1441 (1947).
119. Graber, R. P., Haven, A. C., Jr., and Wendler, N. L. *J. Am. Chem. Soc.* **75**, 4722 (1953).

120. Grant, G. A., and Beall, D. *Recent Progr. Hormone Research* **5**, 307 (1950).
121. Grundy, H. M., Simpson, S. A., and Tait, J. F. *Nature* **169**, 795 (1952).
122. Gut, M. *Helv. Chim. Acta* **36**, 906 (1953).
123. Hassel, O. *Quart. Revs. (London)* **7**, 221 (1953).
124. Heard, R. D. H., and Ziegler, P. *J. Am. Chem. Soc.* **72**, 4328 (1950).
125. Heard, R. D. H., and Ziegler, P. *J. Am. Chem. Soc.* **73**, 4036 (1951).
126. Heer, J., and Miescher, K. *Helv. Chim. Acta* **31**, 219 (1948).
127. Heer, J., and Miescher, K. *Helv. Chim. Acta* **31**, 229 (1948).
128. Heer, J., and Miescher, K. *Helv. Chim. Acta* **31**, 405 (1948).
129. Heer, J., and Miescher, K. *Helv. Chim. Acta* **31**, 1289 (1948).
130. Heer, J., and Miescher, K. *Helv. Chim. Acta* **34**, 359 (1951).
131. Heer, J., and Wettstein, A. *Helv. Chim. Acta* **36**, 891 (1953).
132. Herr, M. E., and Heyl, F. W. *J. Am. Chem. Soc.* **75**, 5927 (1953).
133. Hershberg, E. B. *J. Org. Chem.* **13**, 542 (1948).
134. Hershberg, E. B., Rubin, M., and Schwenk, E. *J. Org. Chem.* **15**, 292 (1950).
135. Hershberg, E. B., Schwenk, E., and Stahl, E. *Arch. Biochem.* **19**, 300 (1948).
136. Hershberger, L. G., Shipley, E. G., and Meyer, R. K. *Proc. Soc. Exptl. Biol. Med.* **83**, 175 (1953).
137. Herzig, P. T., and Ehrenstein, M. *J. Org. Chem.* **16**, 1050 (1951).
138. Herzog, H. L., Jevnik, M. A., and Hershberg, E. B. *J. Am. Chem. Soc.* **75**, 269 (1953).
139. Herzog, H. L., Jevnik, M. A., Tully, M. E., and Hershberg, E. B. *J. Am. Chem. Soc.* **75**, 4425 (1953).
140. Hess, S. M., and Banes, D. *J. Biol. Chem.* **200**, 629 (1953).
141. Heusler, K., Heusser, H., and Anliker, R. *Helv. Chim. Acta* **36**, 652 (1953).
142. Heusler, K., and Wettstein, A. *Helv. Chim. Acta* **35**, 284 (1952).
143. Heusler, K., and Wettstein, A. *Helv. Chim. Acta* **36**, 398 (1953).
144. Heusser, H., Anliker, R., Eichenberger, K., and Jeger, O. *Helv. Chim. Acta* **35**, 936 (1952).
145. Heusser, H., Anliker, R., and Jeger, O. *Helv. Chim. Acta* **35**, 1537 (1952).
146. Heusser, H., Eichenberger, K., Kurath, P., Daellenbach, H. R., and Jeger, O. *Helv. Chim. Acta* **34**, 2106 (1951).
147. Heusser, H., Engel, C. R., Herzig, P. T., and Plattner, P. A. *Helv. Chim. Acta* **33**, 2229 (1950).
148. Heusser, H., Engel, C. R., and Plattner, P. A. *Helv. Chim. Acta* **33**, 2237 (1950).
149. Heusser, H., Herzig, P. T., Fuerst, A., and Plattner, P. A. *Helv. Chim. Acta* **33**, 1093 (1950).
150. Heusser, H., Saucy, G., Anliker, R., and Jeger, O. *Helv. Chim. Acta* **35**, 2090 (1952).
151. Heyl, F. W., and Herr, M. E. *J. Am. Chem. Soc.* **75**, 1918 (1953).
152. Heymann, H., and Fieser, L. F. *J. Am. Chem. Soc.* **73**, 4054, 5252 (1951); *ibid.* **74**, 5938 (1952).
153. Heymann, H., and Fieser, L. F. *Helv. Chim. Acta* **35**, 631 (1952).
154. Hirschmann, F. B. Unpublished experiments.
155. Hirschmann, H. *J. Biol. Chem.* **140**, 797 (1941).
156. Hirschmann, H. *Ciba Colloquia Endocrinol.* **7**, 140 (1953).
157. Hirschmann, H., Daus, M. A., and Hirschmann, F. B. *J. Biol. Chem.* **192**, 115 (1951).
158. Hirschmann, H., and Hirschmann, F. B. *J. Biol. Chem.* **187**, 137 (1950).
159. Hirschmann, H., and Hirschmann, F. B. *J. Biol. Chem.* **184**, 259 (1950).

160. Hirschmann, H., Hirschmann, F. B., and Corcoran, J. W. *Federation Proc.* **12,** 218 (1953).
161. Hirschmann, H., Hirschmann, F. B., and Daus, M. A. *J. Biol. Chem.* **178,** 751 (1949).
162. Hirschmann, H., Hirschmann, F. B., and Daus, M. A. *J. Am. Chem. Soc.* **74,** 539 (1952).
163. Hirschmann, H., Hirschmann, F. B., and Farrell, G. L. *J. Am. Chem. Soc.* **75,** 4862, 6363 (1953).
164. Hirschmann, H., and Wintersteiner, O. *J. Biol. Chem.* **122,** 303 (1938).
165. Hirschmann, H., and Wintersteiner, O. *J. Biol. Chem.* **126,** 737 (1938).
166. Hirschmann, R., Snoddy, C. S., Jr., and Wendler, N. L. *J. Am. Chem. Soc.* **75,** 3252 (1953).
167. Holysz, R. P. *J. Am. Chem. Soc.* **75,** 4432 (1953).
168. Huang-Minlon, Wilson, E., Wendler, N. L., and Tishler, M. *J. Am. Chem. Soc.* **74,** 5394 (1952).
169. Huffman, M. N., and Lott, M. H. *J. Am. Chem. Soc.* **71,** 719 (1949); *J. Biol. Chem.* **172,** 789 (1948).
170. Huffman, M. N., and Lott, M. H. *J. Am. Chem. Soc.* **73,** 878 (1951); *ibid.* **75,** 4327 (1953).
171. Inhoffen, H. H., Koelling, G., Koch, G., and Nebel, I. *Chem. Ber.* **84,** 361 (1951).
172. Johnson, W. S., Banerjee, D. K., Schneider, W. P., Gutsche, C. D., Shelberg, W. E., and Chinn, L. J. *J. Am. Chem. Soc.* **74,** 2832 (1952).
173. Johnson, W. S., Bannister, B., Bloom, B. M., Kemp, A. D., Pappo, R., Rogier, E. R., and Szmuszkovicz, J. *J. Am. Chem. Soc.* **75,** 2275 (1953).
174. Johnson, W. S., and Christiansen, R. G. *J. Am. Chem. Soc.* **73,** 5511 (1951).
175. Jones, R. N., Ramsay, D. A., Herling, F., and Dobriner, K. *J. Am. Chem. Soc.* **74,** 2828 (1952).
176. Julian, P. L. *Recent Progr. Hormone Research* **6,** 195, 212 (1951).
177. Julian, P. L., Cole, W., Magnani, A., and Meyer, E. W. *J. Am. Chem. Soc.* **67,** 1728 (1945).
178. Julian, P. L., and Karpel, W. J. *J. Am. Chem. Soc.* **72,** 362 (1950).
179. Julian, P. L., Meyer, E. W., Karpel, W. J., and Cole, W. *J. Am. Chem. Soc.* **73,** 1982 (1951).
180. Julian, P. L., Meyer, E. W., Karpel, W. J., and Ryden, I. *J. Am. Chem. Soc.* **71,** 3574 (1949).
181. Julian, P. L., Meyer, E. W., Karpel, W. J., and Waller, I. R. *J. Am. Chem. Soc.* **72,** 5145 (1950).
182. Julian, P. L., Meyer, E. W., and Ryden, I. *J. Am. Chem. Soc.* **72,** 367 (1950).
183. Katz, A. *Helv. Chim. Acta* **31,** 993 (1948).
184. Kaufmann, S., Pataki, J., Rosenkranz, G., Romo, J., and Djerassi, C. *J. Am. Chem. Soc.* **72,** 4531 (1950).
185. Klyne, W. *Nature* **161,** 434 (1948).
186. Klyne, W. *Nature* **166,** 559 (1950).
187. Klyne, W. *Chemistry & Industry*, p. 426 (1951).
188. Klyne, W. *Ciba Colloquia Endocrinol.* **7,** 127 (1953).
189. Klyne, W., and Shoppee, C. W. *Chemistry & Industry*, p. 470 (1952).
190. Klyne, W., and Stokes, W. M. *Biochem. J.* **55,** xxviii (1953).
191. Koechlin, B. A., Kritchevsky, T. H., and Gallagher, T. F. *J. Biol. Chem.* **184,** 393 (1950).
192. Koechlin, B. A., Kritchevsky, T. H., and Gallagher, T. F. *J. Am. Chem. Soc.* **73,** 189 (1951).

193. Koester, H., and Logemann, W. *Ber.* **73,** 298 (1940).
194. Kritchevsky, T. H., and Gallagher, T. F. *J. Am. Chem. Soc.* **73,** 184 (1951).
195. Kuhn, W. *Z. Elektrochem.* **56,** 506 (1952).
195a. Lardon, A. *Helv. Chim. Acta* **32,** 1517 (1949).
196. Lardon, A., and Reichstein, T. *Helv. Chim. Acta* **32,** 1613, 2003 (1949).
197. Lardon, A., and Reichstein, T. *Helv. Chim. Acta* **34,** 756 (1951).
198. Lardon, A., and Reichstein, T. *Pharm. Acta Helv.* **27,** 287 (1952).
199. Lardon, A., and Reichstein, T. *Ciba Colloquia Endocrinol.* **7,** 65 (1953).
200. Laubach, G. D., and Brunings, K. J. *J. Am. Chem. Soc.* **74,** 705 (1952).
201. Laubach, G. D., Schreiber, E. C., Agnello, E. J., Lightfoot, E. N., and Brunings, K. J. *J. Am. Chem. Soc.* **75,** 1514 (1953).
202. Laws, G. F. *J. Chem. Soc.,* p. 4185 (1953).
203. Levin, R. H., Magerlein, B. J., McIntosh, A. V., Jr., Hanze, A. R., Fonken, G. S., Thompson, J. L., Searcy, A. M., Scheri, M. A., and Gutsell, E. S. *J. Am. Chem. Soc.* **76,** 546 (1954).
204. Levitz, M. *J. Am. Chem. Soc.* **75,** 5352 (1953).
205. Lieberman, S., and Dobriner, K. *J. Biol. Chem.* **161,** 269 (1945).
206. Lieberman, S., Fukushima, D. K., and Dobriner, K. *J. Biol. Chem.* **182,** 299 (1950).
207. Lieberman, S., Hariton, L. B., and Fukushima, D. K. *J. Am. Chem. Soc.* **70,** 1427 (1948).
208. Lieberman, S., Praetz, B., Humphries, P., and Dobriner, K. *J. Biol. Chem.* **204,** 491 (1953).
209. MacPhillamy, H. B., and Scholz, C. R. *J. Biol. Chem.* **178,** 37 (1949).
210. Magerlein, B. J., and Levin, R. H. *J. Am. Chem. Soc.* **75,** 3654 (1953).
211. Mancera, O., Barton, D. H. R., Rosenkranz, G., and Djerassi, C. *J. Chem. Soc.,* p. 1021 (1952).
212. Mancera, O., Zaffaroni, A., Rubin, B. A., Sondheimer, F., Rosenkranz, G., and Djerassi, C. *J. Am. Chem. Soc.* **74,** 3711 (1952).
213. Marker, R. E. *J. Am. Chem. Soc.* **60,** 1897 (1938).
214. Marker, R. E., Crooks, H. M., Jr., and Wagner, R. B. *J. Am. Chem. Soc.* **64,** 817 (1942).
215. Marker, R. E., Kamm, O., Wittle, E. L., Oakwood, T. S., and Lawson, E. J. *J. Am. Chem. Soc.* **60,** 1067 (1938).
216. Marker, R. E., and Rohrmann, E. *J. Am. Chem. Soc.* **61,** 2719 (1939).
217. Marker, R. E., and Turner, D. L. *J. Am. Chem. Soc.* **63,** 767 (1941).
218. Marker, R. E., Turner, D. L., and Ulshafer, P. R. *J. Am. Chem. Soc.* **64,** 1655 (1942).
219. Marker, R. E., Turner, D. L., Wagner, R. B., Ulshafer, P. R., Crooks, H. M., Jr., and Wittle, E. L. *J. Am. Chem. Soc.* **63,** 774, 779 (1941).
220. Marshall, C. W., Kritchevsky, T. H., Lieberman, S., and Gallagher, T. F. *J. Am. Chem. Soc.* **70,** 1837 (1948).
221. Mattox, V. R. *J. Am. Chem. Soc.* **74,** 4340 (1952).
222. Mattox, V. R., and Kendall, E. C. *J. Biol. Chem.* **185,** 593 (1950).
223. Mattox, V. R., and Kendall, E. C. *J. Biol. Chem.* **185,** 601 (1950).
224. Mattox, V. R., and Kendall, E. C. *J. Biol. Chem.* **188,** 287 (1951).
225. Mattox, V. R., Mason, H. L., and Albert, A. *Proc. Staff Meetings Mayo Clinic* **28,** 569 (1953).
226. Mattox, V. R., Mason, H. L., Albert, A., and Code, C. F. *J. Am. Chem. Soc.* **75,** 4869 (1953).

227. McGuckin, W. F., and Kendall, E. C. *J. Am. Chem. Soc.* **74**, 5811 (1952).
228. Meyer, K. *Helv. Chim. Acta* **32**, 1599 (1949).
229. Meystre, C., Tschopp, E., and Wettstein, A. *Helv. Chim. Acta* **31**, 1463 (1948).
230. Meystre, C., and Wettstein, A. *Helv. Chim. Acta* **30**, 1037 (1947).
231. Meystre, C., and Wettstein, A. *Helv. Chim. Acta* **32**, 1978 (1949).
232. Miescher, K., and Schmidlin, J. *Helv. Chim. Acta* **33**, 1840 (1950).
233. Mills, J. A. *J. Chem. Soc.*, p. 4976 (1952).
234. Mills, J. A. *Chemistry & Industry*, p. 218 (1953).
235. Mislow, K., and Brenner, J. *J. Am. Chem. Soc.* **75**, 2318 (1953).
236. Moffett, R. B., and Hunter, J. H. *J. Am. Chem. Soc.* **73**, 1973 (1951).
237. Moffett, R. B., and Weisblat, D. I. *J. Am. Chem. Soc.* **74**, 2183 (1952).
238. Mueller, G. P., Stobaugh, R. E., and Winniford, R. S. *J. Am. Chem. Soc.* **75**, 4888 (1953).
239. Nace, H. R., and Turner, R. B. *J. Am. Chem. Soc.* **75**, 4063 (1953).
240. Noyce, D. S., and Denney, D. B. *J. Am. Chem. Soc.* **74**, 5912 (1952).
241. Oliveto, E. P., Clayton, T., and Hershberg, E. B. *J. Am. Chem. Soc.* **75**, 486 (1953).
242. Oliveto, E. P., Gerold, C., Weber, L., Jorgensen, H. E., Rausser, R., and Hershberg, E. B. *J. Am. Chem. Soc.* **75**, 5486 (1953).
243. Oliveto, E. P., and Hershberg, E. B. *J. Am. Chem. Soc.* **75**, 488 (1953).
244. Oppenauer, R. V., and Oberrauch, H. *Anales asoc. quím. argentina* **37**, 246 (1949) [*C. A.* **44**, 3871 (1950)].
245. Papineau-Couture, G., Richardson, E. M., and Grant, G. A. *Can. J. Research* **27B**, 902 (1949).
246. Pearlman, W. H., and Pearlman, M. R. J. *J. Am. Chem. Soc.* **72**, 5781 (1950).
247. Pearlman, W. H., and Wintersteiner, O. *J. Biol. Chem.* **130**, 35 (1939).
248. Pearlman, W. H., and Wintersteiner, O. *J. Biol. Chem.* **132**, 605 (1940).
249. Perlman, D., Titus, E., and Fried, J. *J. Am. Chem. Soc.* **74**, 2126 (1952).
250. Petrow, V. A., Rosenheim, O., and Starling, W. W. *J. Chem. Soc.*, p. 677 (1938).
251. Plattner, P. A., Heusser, H., and Feurer, M. *Helv. Chim. Acta* **32**, 587 (1949).
252. Plattner, P. A., Heusser, H., and Kulkarni, A. B. *Helv. Chim. Acta* **31**, 1885 (1948).
253. Plattner, P. A., and Lang, W. *Helv. Chim. Acta* **27**, 1872 (1944).
254. Plattner, P. A., Petrzilka, T., and Lang, W. *Helv. Chim. Acta* **27**, 513 (1944).
255. Prelog, V. *Helv. Chim. Acta* **36**, 308 (1953).
256. Prelog, V., and Meier, H. L. *Helv. Chim. Acta* **36**, 320 (1953).
257. Prelog, V., and Tagmann, E. *Helv. Chim. Acta* **27**, 1880 (1944).
258. Prelog, V., and Tsatsas, G. *Helv. Chim. Acta* **36**, 1178 (1953).
259. Prins, D. A., and Shoppee, C. W. *J. Chem. Soc.*, p. 494 (1946).
260. Reich, H. *Helv. Chim. Acta* **28**, 892 (1945).
261. Reichstein, T., and von Euw, J. *Helv. Chim. Acta* **21**, 1181 (1938).
262. Riegel, B., and Prout, F. S. *J. Org. Chem.* **13**, 933 (1948).
263. Ringold, H. J., Rosenkranz, G., and Djerassi, C. *J. Am. Chem. Soc.* **74**, 3318 (1952).
264. Ringold, H. J., Rosenkranz, G., and Djerassi, C. *J. Am. Chem. Soc.* **74**, 3441 (1952).
264a. Riniker, B., Arigoni, D., and Jeger, O. *Helv. Chim. Acta* **37**, 546 (1954).
265. Romo, J., Ringold, H. J., Rosenkranz, G., and Djerassi, C. *J. Org. Chem.* **16**, 1873 (1951).
266. Romo, J., Romero, M., Djerassi, C., and Rosenkranz, G. *J. Am. Chem. Soc.* **73**, 1528 (1951).

267. Romo, J., Stork, G., Rosenkranz, G., and Djerassi, C. *J. Am. Chem. Soc.* **74**, 2918 (1952).
268. Rosenkranz, G., Mancera, O., Gatica, J., and Djerassi, C. *J. Am. Chem. Soc.* **72**, 4077 (1950).
269. Rosenkranz, G., Pataki, J., Kaufmann, S., Berlin, J., and Djerassi, C. *J. Am. Chem. Soc.* **72**, 4081 (1950).
270. Rosenkranz, G., Romo, J., Batres, E., and Djerassi, C. *J. Org. Chem.* **16**, 298 (1951).
271. Rosenkranz, G., Romo, J., and Berlin, J. *J. Org. Chem.* **16**, 290 (1951).
272. Rosenkranz, G., and Sondheimer, F. *Progr. Chem. Org. Nat. Products* **10**, 274 (1953).
273. Ruff, A., Shoppee, C. W., and Summers, G. H. R. *J. Chem. Soc.*, p. 3683 (1953).
274. Ruschig, H. *Angew. Chem.* **60**, 247 (1948).
275. Ruyle, W. V., Chamberlin, E. M., Chemerda, J. M., Sita, G. E., Aliminosa, L. M., and Erickson, R. L. *J. Am. Chem. Soc.* **74**, 5929 (1952).
276. Ruzicka, L., Furter, M., and Goldberg, M. W. *Helv. Chim. Acta* **21**, 498 (1938).
277. Ruzicka, L., and Goldberg, M. W. *Helv. Chim. Acta* **19**, 1407 (1936).
278. Ruzicka, L., Goldberg, M. W., and Bosshard, W. *Helv. Chim. Acta* **20**, 541 (1937).
279. Ruzicka, L., Goldberg, M. W., and Hardegger, E. *Helv. Chim. Acta* **22**, 1294 (1939); *ibid.* **25**, 1297 (1942).
280. Ruzicka, L., Wahba, N., Herzig, P. T., and Heusser, H. *Chem. Ber.* **85**, 491 (1952).
281. Ryer, A. I., and Gebert, W. H. *J. Am. Chem. Soc.* **74**, 41, 4336 (1952).
282. Ryer, A. I., Gebert, W. H., and Murrill, N. M. *J. Am. Chem. Soc.* **72**, 4247 (1950).
283. Salamon, I. *Helv. Chim. Acta* **32**, 1306 (1949).
284. Sandoval, A., Miramontes, L., Rosenkranz, G., Djerassi, C., and Sondheimer, F. *J. Am. Chem. Soc.* **75**, 4117 (1953).
285. Sarett, L. H. *J. Am. Chem. Soc.* **70**, 1454 (1948); *ibid.* **71**, 2443 (1949).
286. Sarett, L. H. *J. Am. Chem. Soc.* **70**, 1690 (1948).
287. Sarett, L. H. *J. Am. Chem. Soc.* **71**, 1165, 1169, 1175 (1949).
288. Sarett, L. H., Arth, G. E., Lukes, R. M., Beyler, R. E., Poos, G. I., Johns, W. F., and Constantin, J. M. *J. Am. Chem. Soc.* **74**, 4974 (1952).
289. Sarett, L. H., Feurer, M., and Folkers, K. *J. Am. Chem. Soc.* **73**, 1777 (1951).
290. Sarett, L. H., Johns, W. F., Beyler, R. E., Lukes, R. M., Poos, G. I., and Arth, G. E. *J. Am. Chem. Soc.* **75**, 2112 (1953).
291. Savard, K. *J. Biol. Chem.* **202**, 457 (1953).
292. Schmid, H., and Kaegi, K. *Helv. Chim. Acta* **33**, 1582 (1950).
293. Schmidlin, J., and Wettstein, A. *Helv. Chim. Acta* **36**, 1241 (1953).
294. Schoenewaldt, E. F., Turnbull, L., Chamberlin, E. M., Reinhold, D., Erickson, A. E., Ruyle, W. V., Chemerda, J. M., and Tishler, M. *J. Am. Chem. Soc.* **74**, 2696 (1952).
295. Schwenk, E., Gut, M., and Belisle, J. *Arch. Biochem. and Biophys.* **31**, 456 (1951).
296. Serini, A., and Koester, H. *Ber.* **71**, 1766 (1938).
297. Sheehan, J. C., Coderre, R. A., and Cruickshank, P. A. *J. Am. Chem. Soc.* **75**, 6231 (1953).
298. Shoppee, C. W. *Helv. Chim. Acta* **30**, 766 (1947).
299. Shoppee, C. W. *J. Chem. Soc.*, p. 1671 (1949).

300. Shoppee, C. W. *Chemistry & Industry*, p. 810 (1950).
301. Shoppee, C. W. *Ann. Rev. Biochem.* **22,** 261 (1953).
302. Shoppee, C. W. *Ciba Colloquia Endocrinol.* **7,** 140 (1953).
303. Shoppee, C. W., and Prins, D. A. *Helv. Chim. Acta* **26,** 185, 201 (1943).
304. Shoppee, C. W., and Summers, G. H. R. *J. Chem. Soc.*, p. 2528 (1952).
305. Shoppee, C. W., and Summers, G. H. R. *J. Chem. Soc.*, p. 3361 (1952).
306. Siegel, S. *J. Am. Chem. Soc.* **75,** 1317 (1953).
307. Simpson, S. A., and Tait, J. F. *Mem. soc. endocrinol.* **2,** 9 (1953).
308. Simpson, S. A., Tait, J. F., Wettstein, A., Neher, R., von Euw, J., and Reichstein, T. *Experientia* **9,** 333 (1953).
308a. Simpson, S. A., Tait, J. F., Wettstein, A., Neher, R., von Euw, J., Schindler, O., and Reichstein, T. *Experientia* **10,** 132 (1954); *Helv. Chim. Acta* **37,** 1163, 1200 (1954).
309. Soloway, A. H., Deutsch, A. S., and Gallagher, T. F. *J. Am. Chem. Soc.* **75,** 2356 (1953).
310. Soloway, A. H., and Fukushima, D. K. *J. Am. Chem. Soc.* **75,** 5442 (1953).
311. Sondheimer, F., Amendolla, C., and Rosenkranz, G. *J. Am. Chem. Soc.* **75,** 5930 (1953).
312. Sondheimer, F., Amendolla, C., and Rosenkranz, G. *J. Am. Chem. Soc.* **75,** 5932 (1953).
313. Sondheimer, F., Mancera, O., Rosenkranz, G., and Djerassi, C. *J. Am. Chem. Soc.* **75,** 1282 (1953).
314. Sondheimer, F., and Rosenkranz, G. *Experientia* **9,** 62 (1953).
315. Sorkin, M., and Reichstein, T. *Helv. Chim. Acta* **29,** 1218 (1946).
316. Stodola, F. H., Kendall, E. C., and McKenzie, B. F. *J. Org. Chem.* **6,** 841 (1941).
317. Stokes, W. M., and Bergmann, W. *J. Org. Chem.* **17,** 1194 (1952).
318. Teich, S., Rogers, J., Lieberman, S., Engel, L. L., and Davis, J. W. *J. Am. Chem. Soc.* **75,** 2523 (1953).
319. Turner, R. B. *J. Am. Chem. Soc.* **72,** 579 (1950).
320. Turner, R. B. *J. Am. Chem. Soc.* **72,** 878 (1950).
321. Turner, R. B. *J. Am. Chem. Soc.* **75,** 3484 (1953).
322. Turner, R. B. *J. Am. Chem. Soc.* **75,** 3489 (1953).
323. Vanderhaeghe, H., Katzenellenbogen, E. R., Dobriner, K., and Gallagher, T. F. *J. Am. Chem. Soc.* **74,** 2810 (1952).
324. Velluz, L., Petit, A., Pesez, M., and Berret, R. *Bull. soc. chim. France*, p. 123 (1947).
325. Vischer, E., Schmidlin, J., and Wettstein, A. *Helv. Chim. Acta* **37,** 321 (1954).
326. von Euw, J., Reber, F., and Reichstein, T. *Helv. Chim. Acta* **34,** 413 (1951).
327. von Euw, J., and Reichstein, T. *Helv. Chim. Acta* **24,** 879 (1941).
328. von Euw, J., and Reichstein, T. *Helv. Chim. Acta* **30,** 205 (1947).
329. von Euw, J., and Reichstein, T. *Helv. Chim. Acta* **31,** 2076 (1948).
330. Wagner, R. B., and Moore, J. A. *J. Am. Chem. Soc.* **72,** 3655, 5301 (1950).
331. Wagner, R. B., Moore, J. A., and Forker, R. F. *J. Am. Chem. Soc.* **72,** 1856 (1950).
332. Wallis, E. S., Fernholz, E., and Gephart, F. T. *J. Am. Chem. Soc.* **59,** 137 (1937).
333. Weidlich, H. A. *Die Chemie* **58,** 30 (1945).
333a. Weisenborn, F. L., and Burn, D. *J. Am. Chem. Soc.* **75,** 259 (1953).
334. Wendler, N. L., Huang-Minlon, and Tishler, M. *J. Am. Chem. Soc.* **73,** 3818 (1951).
335. Wettstein, A. *Helv. Chim. Acta* **23,** 388 (1940).

336. Wettstein, A., and Meystre, C.   *Helv. Chim. Acta* **32,** 880 (1949).
337. Wieland, P., and Miescher, K.   *Helv. Chim. Acta* **31,** 211 (1948).
338. Wieland, P., and Miescher, K.   *Helv. Chim. Acta* **32,** 1922 (1949).
339. Wieland, P., Ueberwasser, H., Anner, G., and Miescher, K.   *Helv. Chim. Acta* **36,** 1231 (1953).
340. Wilds, A. L., Johnson, J. A., Jr., and Sutton, R. E.   *J. Am. Chem. Soc.* **72,** 5524 (1950).
341. Wilds, A. L., and Nelson, N. A.   *J. Am. Chem. Soc.* **75,** 5366 (1953).
342. Wilds, A. L., Ralls, J. W., Tyner, D. A., Daniels, R., Kraychy, S., and Harnik, M.   *J. Am. Chem. Soc.* **75,** 4878 (1953).
343. Wood, W. W., Fickett, W., and Kirkwood, J. G.   *J. Chem. Phys.* **20,** 561 (1952).
344. Woodward, R. B., Inhoffen, H. H., Larson, H. O., and Menzel, K. H.   *Chem. Ber.* **86,** 594 (1953).
345. Woodward, R. B., and Singh, T.   *J. Am. Chem. Soc.* **72,** 494 (1950).
346. Woodward, R. B., Sondheimer, F., Taub, D., Heusler, K., and McLamore, W. M.   *J. Am. Chem. Soc.* **73,** 2403 (1951); *ibid.* **74,** 4223 (1952).
347. Yashin, R., Rosenkranz, G., and Djerassi, C.   *J. Am. Chem. Soc.* **73,** 4654 (1951).

CHAPTER XII

Steroid Hormone Metabolism

BY RALPH I. DORFMAN

CONTENTS

I. Introduction

This section is concerned with the metabolism of estrogens, progesterone, androgens, and the adrenocortical hormones. Those reactions which produce biologically active steroids (biosynthesis) and those reactions which tend to modify the steroid hormones will be considered. Classically, these phrases have referred to both the anabolic and catabolic aspects of metabolism, respectively. The term anabolic will be used to indicate those metabolic steps which transform simple or complex substances into steroid hormones, and our aims will be set to describe those anabolic or biosynthetic pathways which lead to steroids showing the maximum biological activity within any particular class of active substances. Once these steroid hormones are formed, they are subjected to a second series of reactions which, in general, lead to decreased or total loss of activity. The reactions in this category will be considered to be catabolic in nature. These catabolic changes may involve nuclear disruptions, or they may merely indicate oxidative or reductive changes of functional groups, the steroid nucleus remaining intact. Conjugation of the steroid hormones or their metabolites with sulfuric and glucuronic acid may also occur. This phase of steroid metabolism will not be discussed in this chapter but has been reviewed (80, 84, 172, 173, 195). Catabolic changes involving ring rupture have as yet not been studied in detail, although the weight of evidence points to a significant disruption of the steroid nucleus in the whole animal. Such changes will be discussed in the separate sections.

In some instances, metabolic transformations change the biological activity of steroids from one biological class to another, such as the conversion of the adrenocortical hormone, cortisol, to the androgens, 11β-hydroxy-androsterone and 11-ketoandrosterone. However, when the original type of activity has been modified, although a new type of activity arises, this change may be considered to be catabolic in nature.

The biogenesis of the steroid hormones is limited to specific glands and does not appear to be a general property of many cells in the mammalian organism. Four tissues of the body, namely, the testes, ovaries, adrenal, and placenta of pregnancy are capable of producing steroid hormones. Steroid catabolic reactions are not limited to specific tissues; rather they can be carried out by a variety of tissues, such as liver, kidney, spleen, and prostate.

Steroid reactions, anabolic and catabolic, are under control of specific enzyme systems. Many biosynthetic enzyme systems are located in specific tissues, whereas those concerned with catabolic changes are widely distributed in mammalian tissues. Enzymes exhibiting metabolic influences on steroids are not limited to mammalian tissue. Microorganisms, such as yeasts, molds, fungi, and bacteria possess enzyme systems capable of catalyzing metabolic transformations in both the phenolic and neutral steroids. The microbiological reactions, although capable of producing reactions associated with biogenesis, seem oriented more toward the destruction of the steroid hormones. The method of attack appears to be the introduction of hydroxyl groups in various positions of the steroid nucleus, thus producing rupture points for the ultimate destruction of the nucleus. These microbiological reactions are presented under the headings of the various types of steroid hormones elsewhere in this chapter.

Nomenclature is discussed elsewhere in this volume (Chapter XI), and the suggestions contained therein will be used here.

II. The Biosynthesis of the Steroid Nucleus

Cholesterol is a precursor of neutral steroid hormones but not of the phenolic steroids, estrogens. Labeled cholesterol is converted to pregnane-$3\alpha,20\alpha$-diol by the pregnant woman (16), to cortisol and corticosterone by perfusion through the cow adrenal (331), and to androsterone and 3α-hydroxyetiocholan-17-one (etiocholanolone) by patients bearing masculinizing malignant adrenal tumors (305). It is therefore necessary to consider, in some detail, the biosynthesis of cholesterol as a model for the formation of the steroid nucleus in the organism. It seems likely, but it is still not proved, that the nucleus of the steroid hormones is built up from a substance such as acetate in a manner similar to that found for cholesterol. To establish this point with certainty it will be necessary to degrade steroid hormones formed from labeled acetate, as has already been done for cholesterol.

Cholesterol is known to be synthesized by many animal cells including liver, kidney, lung, adrenal, skin, and intestine. The nervous system of the young, growing animal, before the nerves have become myelinated, synthesizes cholesterol, but once the nerve tissue has become myelinated, as is true in the adult animal, cholesterol synthesis by this tissue is of an extremely low order. Cholesterol synthesis is, in part, controlled by the concentrations of this substance in the organism. Thus, animals on low-cholesterol diets synthesize relatively large amounts of this compound, whereas an animal fed a diet containing high concentrations of this steroid produces minimal quantities.

The biogenesis of cholesterol is a complicated story which has been studied for many years, but it was not until isotopic methods were employed that real progress was made. Two important observations which stimulated studies on the biosynthesis of cholesterol consisted in the demonstration that deuterated cholesterol arises in rodents fed deuterium oxide (251), and, secondly, that labeled cholesterol arises from labeled acetate (18, 174). Bloch and his co-workers have continued these studies using both C^{13} and C^{14} singly and doubly labeled acetic acid.

Synthesis of cholesterol has been demonstrated by perfusion of various whole isolated organs (283), by tissue slices (18), by homogenates of fetal liver (245), and by water-soluble enzyme preparations. Bucher (26) and Bucher *et al.* (27) showed that C^{14}-labeled acetate may be incorporated into cholesterol when the substrate is incubated with a homogenate of liver containing phosphate buffer, nicotinamide, magnesium, adenosine-triphosphate (ATP), and diphosphonucleotide (DPN). Quantitatively, the incorporation of acetate into cholesterol was as efficient with the use of homogenates as previously found for slice preparations. Rabinowitz and Gurin (246) have prepared a particle-free, water-soluble enzyme preparation from rat liver homogenates which incorporates acetate carbon into cholesterol.

The original suggestions of Channon (49) and Robinson (252) that squalene may in fact be a precursor of cholesterol could not be efficiently tested until radioactive squalene was made available. This was done by the administration of squalene, obtained from sharks, to rats, together with C^{14}-labeled acetate. Under these conditions, enough C^{14}-labeled squalene accumulated in the livers of the treated animals so that this tagged compound could be isolated and identified (160, 161). The C^{14}-labeled squalene so obtained was fed, in turn, to mice, and C^{14}-labeled cholesterol was isolated from the livers. Squalene-C^{14} was a more efficient precursor of cholesterol than acetate, and the fatty acids which were isolated from the livers of the same animals had a specific activity so low that it was unlikely that squalene-C^{14} was first broken down to small particles such as acetate which then were converted to cholesterol (17). Similar results have been reported by Eidinoff *et al.* (83). To the experiments of Bloch, however, must be added the experiences of Popjak (242), who studied the biosynthesis of squalene and cholesterol from acetate-1-C^{14} by rat liver slices and by ovarian tissues of the laying hen. This investigator suggests, on the basis of relative specific activities of endogenous squalene and cholesterol, that "squalene as such is not an intermediate (or the immediate precursor) in the biosynthesis of cholesterol, although it may provide through some other intermediate isoprenoid units for sterol formation." The following scheme is suggested:

$$\text{Acetate} \rightarrow \text{isoprenoid unit} \rightarrow \text{X} \rightarrow \text{cholesterol}$$
$$\uparrow\downarrow$$
$$\text{Squalene}$$

A likely mechanism for the biosynthesis of cholesterol involves the intermediate isoprene which could arise from the following series of reactions (20, 173, 326).

$$2CH_3COOH \rightarrow CH_3COCH_2COOH \tag{1}$$

$$CH_3COCH_2COOH \rightarrow CH_3COCH_3 \tag{2}$$

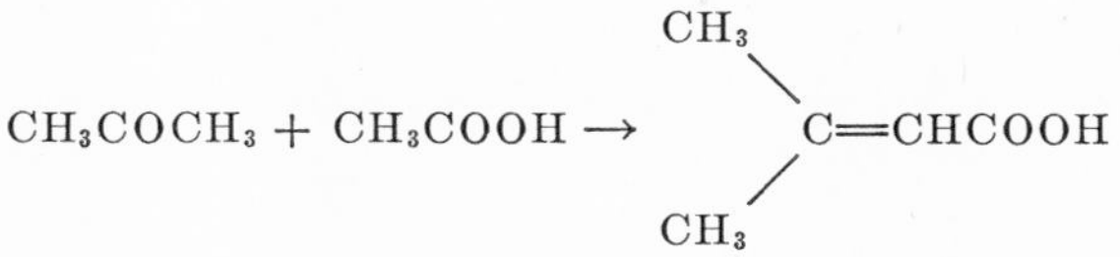

$$CH_3COCH_3 + CH_3COOH \rightarrow \quad \begin{array}{c} CH_3 \\ \diagdown \\ C\!\!=\!\!CHCOOH \\ \diagup \\ CH_3 \end{array} \qquad (3)$$

$$\begin{array}{c} CH_3 \\ \diagdown \\ C\!\!=\!\!CHCOOH \\ \diagup \\ CH_3 \end{array} \rightarrow \quad \begin{array}{c} CH_3 \\ \diagdown \\ C\!\!-\!\!CH\!\!=\!\!CH_2 \\ \diagup\!\!\diagup \\ CH_2 \end{array} \qquad (4)$$

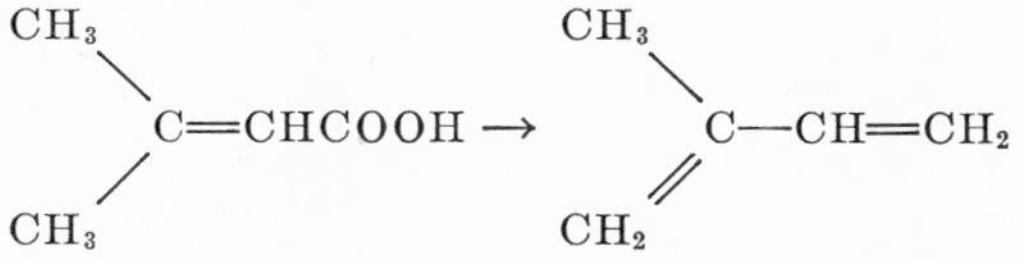

Isoprene would be converted to squalene and squalene to cholesterol. Figure 1 indicates the most likely distribution of acetate molecules in the cholesterol molecule (326).

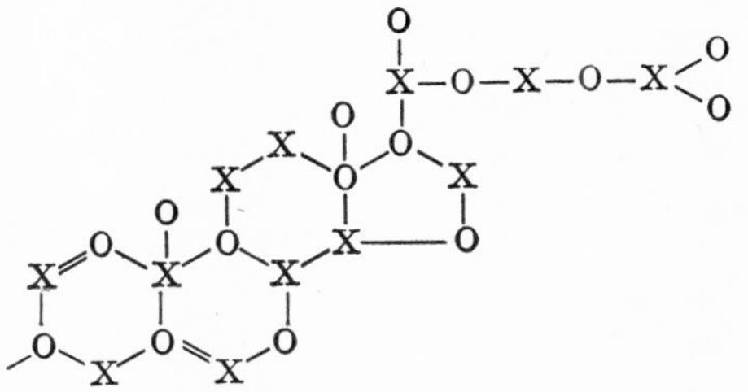

FIG. 1.   Origin of carbon atoms in cholesterol when biosynthesized from acetate. X = acetate carboxyl; O = acetate methyl.

III. Estrogens

A group of hormonally active steroids, estrogens, are characterized by a phenolic group in ring A and by their effectiveness in maintaining the female secondary sex characters such as the mammary glands, the uterus, and vagina (Chapter XIII).   The estrogens have been isolated from various endocrine tissues including the ovary, the testes, the adrenals, and the placenta of pregnancy.   The urine of most animals contain lesser or greater amounts of estrogenic substances, depending upon the species, the sex, and the age, and high concentrations in the urine as well as blood are associated particularly with pregnancy.   The naturally occurring estrogens are listed in Table I.   The ovary is the principal site of estrogen production in the nonpregnant female.   The cyclic nature of estrogen production is in part dependent upon the ovarian response to the piutitary gonadotropins follicle-stimulating hormone (FSH) and luteinizing hormone (LH) (Chapter XIII).   A small but regular amount of estrogens appear to be produced by the adrenal cortex in the female as well as the male, and the testis is unquestionably a source of estrogens in the male.   Actually, the

TABLE I
Naturally Occurring Estrogens

Estrogen	Source	Reference
17β-Estradiol	Placenta—human	Huffman *et al.* (148)
	Ovary—sow	MacCorquodale *et al.* (176)
	Testis—stallion	Beall (9)
	Testis—human	Goldzieher and Roberts (103)
	Urine—human	Smith *et al.* (290)
	Urine—normal female	Engel *et al.* (87)
	Urine—stallion	Levin (164)
	Urine—pregnant mare	Wintersteiner *et al.* (324)
Estrone	Ovary—sow	Westerfeld *et al.* (318)
	Testis—stallion	Beall (9)
	Adrenal—bovine	Beall (8)
	Urine—pregnant cow	Pearlman *et al.* (230)
	Urine—human male	Dingemanse *et al.* (63)
	Urine—human female	Engel *et al.* (87)
	Urine—pregnant mare	DeJongh *et al.* (60)
	Urine—stallion	Deulofeu and Ferrari (61) Haussler (111)
	Urine—bull	Marker (182)
	Urine—steer	Marker (183)
	Bile—pregnant cow	Pearlman *et al.* (230)
17α-Estradiol	Urine—pregnant mare	Hirschmann and Wintersteiner (142)
Estriol	Urine—pregnant human	Marrian (192); Doisy *et al.* (68)
	Urine—normal female	Engel *et al.* (87)
16-Ketoestrone	Urine—normal female	Serchi (284)
Equilen	Urine—pregnant mare	Girard *et al.* (102)
Hippulin	Urine—pregnant mare	Girard *et al.* (102)
Equilenin	Urine—pregnant mare	Girard *et al.* (102)
17β-Dihydro-equilenin	Urine—pregnant mare	Wintersteiner *et al.* (324)

stallion testis contains a uniquely high content of estrogens, being the richest tissue source of the hormone.

In the pregnant animal, estrogens are contributed by three different glands, of which one, the placenta, is the principal source; two other sources, ovary and adrenal, are of minor importance. The placenta of pregnancy

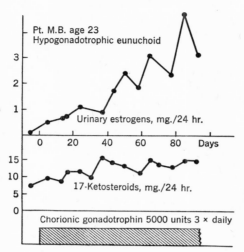

F IG. 2.   Excretion of urinary estrogens and 17-ketosteroids after treatment with chorionic gonadotropin.   From Maddock *et al.* (177).

produces relatively large amounts of estrogenic substances and shows an increased production of these hormones as gestation progresses.   Just before parturition, the total placental estrogen production may be as much as 100 times greater than that found at conception, and expulsion of the placenta causes a prompt return to the prepregnancy level.

The stimulus for estrogen production in the male is in part conditioned by the action of the luteinizing hormone of the anterior pituitary on the testis.   Administration, for example, of chorionic gonadotropin (prepared from human pregnancy urine) in doses of 500 international units three times weekly to a patient with hypogonadotropic eunuchoidism increases the estrogenic output of the testis more than 30-fold (Fig. 2).   The adrenocorticotropic hormone (ACTH) has the ability to stimulate the adrenals of either males or females to produce estrogens, but the relative production by this means is small as compared to the contributions made by the gonads.

Studies on human semen are consistent with the idea that the testis produces estrogenic steroids.   Extracts have been prepared which are capable of producing estrogenic responses in spayed rodents (105, 199, 250).   Diczfalusy (62) employed solvent partition and countercurrent distribution as well as fluorimetric analysis of extracts of human semen and demonstrated the presence of estrone, 17β-estradiol, and estriol.

A. Biosynthesis of Estrogens

The studies of Heard and co-workers (127, 128) on the biogenesis of estrogens have been particularly enlightening.   These studies consisted in the administration of C^{14}-labeled acetate and cholesterol to the pregnant mare followed by the isolation of estrone, equilin, and equilenin from the urine. Of particular interest is the difference in the radioactive carbon content of isolated estrone when cholesterol-4-C^{14} and acetate-1-C^{14} are administered. After administration of acetate-1-C^{14} definitive evidence for the incorporation of C^{14} into the estrone molecule was found, whereas the administration of cholesterol-4-C^{14} resulted in no C^{14} labeling of the estrone that was synthesized during the experiment. A second point of interest is the difference in specific activity between estrone, on the one hand, and the more highly unsaturated estrogens, on the other. For example, whereas estrone having a count of 641 was isolated from the urine after the administration of carboxyl-labeled acetate, the specific activity of equilin produced simultaneously was 304 and that of equilenin was 328. This suggests that the phenolic ring A of the highly unsaturated estrogens is not synthesized from acetate but rather that the aromatic portion of the nucleus originates from some other source in the body.

A considerable amount of speculation concerning the interrelationship between estrone and the unsaturated estrogens found in pregnant mare urine has been published, but no definitive experiments were done to establish precise interrelationships until C^{14}-labeled estrone became available. When estrone-16-C^{14} was administered intrajugularly to a pregnant mare in the 9th month of gestation, the urinary equilin and equilenin contained no significant radioactivity. In other words, equilin and equilenin are not metabolic products of estrone but must arise from an independent biosynthetic mechanism. It is possible, however, that these highly unsaturated compounds may be converted to estrone and in effect may be metabolic intermediates in the formation of the more highly active estrogens, estrone and 17β-estradiol. This possibility too appears to be unlikely, since if this were the case it would be expected that the specific activities of these compounds would be essentially the same when produced from acetate. This is not the case.

In summary, it may be said that the estrogens do not arise from cholesterol as much but may be built up from smaller particles such as acetate, and that there exist two independent routes of synthesis for estrogens, one for estrone and still another for the estrogens equilen and equilenin.

B. LOCALIZATION OF ESTROGENS

Albert and co-workers (1) prepared radioactive iodo-17β-estradiol which was not estrogenic at 1000 times the dose of 17β-estradiol. The iodinated steroid was administered subcutaneously to female mice, and 10 to 12 hours later the animals were sacrificed and individual tissues examined for radioactivity. The gastrointestinal tract contained 40 % of the total

I^{131}, with by far the greatest amount being contained in the contents rather than the walls. The authors reported that the radioactivity increased progressively down the gastrointestinal tract, as indicated by the fact that the duodenum, jejunum, and colon-cecum contained, respectively, 0.5 %, 3 %, and 4 % of the administered I^{131}. The feces contained about 35 % of the radioactive material. With respect to tissue concentrations the thyroid contained the highest amount of radioactivity per milligram, more than 100 times that for the whole body. Other tissues concentrating the radioiodine included the mammary gland, the skin, and the submaxillary glands.

Twombly et al. (301) studied the metabolism of radioactive dibromoestrone by administering the steroid intravenously to rabbits, a monkey, and dogs. The same steroid was administered intravenously also to three patients. No significant concentration of the steroid could be detected in tissues in either the animals or the patients.

In a series of papers, Daudel and Berger (11, 57, 58) reported the preparation of the radioactive synthetic estrogen, triphenylbromoethylene, and administration of the material to mice. After intraperitoneal administration the ovaries contained twice the radioactivity found in the blood at 12 hours but less than that in the blood at 31 hours. Twombly (300) indicated that direct contamination may have been the source of these results, since Patterson et al. (217) were unable to confirm these results when the compound was administered either intravenously or subcutaneously.

Triphenylbromoethylene had also been subcutaneously administered in the lumbar region to female rats (57). Radioactive bromine was reported to be concentrated in the pituitary (121 times), the adrenal (48 times), and thyroid and ovary (7 to 8 times) as compared with the concentration in blood. Twombly (300) was unable to confirm the concentration of radioisotope in the pituitary gland.

Diethylstilbestrol-C^{14} (or C^{14}-containing metabolites) was not found to be significantly concentrated after 10 and 21 hours in the mammary gland, mammary cancer, the uterus, adrenals, or pituitary of mice, a dog, and a rabbit. The livers contained 1 % to 5 % of the radioactivity, and the rabbit kidney contained 1.7 % of the administered radioisotope (300).

Radioactive dibromoestrone when injected into rabbits resulted in 25 % of the radioactivity being excreted in the feces and 16 % in the urine. Seventy per cent of the steroid appeared in the bile of a bile-fistula dog within 5 hours of administration, as compared with 4 % excreted in the urine. Studies on the excretion of radioactive dibromoestrone in patients with biliary fistulas have been reported. The steroid was administered intravenously and the steroid and its radiobromo metabolic products determined in various body fluids. Within 24 hours, 39 % of the radioactivity was found in the bile and 18 % in the urine (301, 302).

After 17α-methyl-C^{14}-estradiol was injected into normal adult male rats the C^{14} metabolites were found primarily in the feces, with a small amount appearing in the urine and no $C^{14}O_2$ appearing in the respiratory air. In rats bearing bile fistulas, the bile contained the major portion of radioactivity (19, 215). Estrone-16-C^{14} administered to rats resulted in the bulk of the C^{14} being excreted in the feces.

C. Catabolism of Estrogens

Knowledge of estrogen catabolism has been derived from experiments involving both *in vitro* and *in vivo* studies. Although early reports indicated that the relative concentrations of the three estrogens, estrone, 17β-estradiol, and estriol were dependent upon the presence or absence of certain endocrine tissues, this idea has not survived experimental trial. It appears more likely that the conversion of estrone to 17β-estradiol and the reverse reaction is dependent upon one or two enzyme systems which appear to be present in most tissues. The significant difference amongst tissues is quantitative rather than qualitative. In other words, a tissue such as the liver perhaps accomplishes these transformations to the greatest extent owing to the fact that this tissue contains the highest enzyme concentrations, as well as to the fact that liver tissue is relatively abundant in the organism.

The metabolic reactions of the estrogenic substances are summarized in Table II for *in vivo* studies and in Table III for *in vitro* studies.

Our over-all knowledge of estrogen metabolism in the human being is represented in Figure 3. Of the six steroids listed, four, including 17β-estradiol, estrone, estriol, and 16-ketoestrone, have been isolated from tissues and/or urine. The remaining two estrogens listed in the figure, enclosed in brackets, have not been isolated from either human tissue or urine. They are included in the scheme of metabolism on the basis that both steroids are possible theoretical intermediates and since one steroid, 16-keto-17β-estradiol, has been shown to be convertible to estriol. Some reactions are listed in Fig. 3 with question marks, since evidence for these conversions is lacking. Thus, the direct 16α-hydroxylation of either the 17β-hydroxy or 17-ketone is not known; rather the 16α-hydroxylation and reduction of the 17-ketone is known. The reduction of the 16-ketone to the 16α-hydroxyl group is known, but the oxidation of the 16α-hydroxyl group to the 16-ketone is not certain.

Zondek (332) as early as 1934 demonstrated that estrogens can be modified by liver tissue and that this change is due to enzymatic reactions. Cell-free preparations of liver were made and the name estrinase was sug-

TABLE II

REACTIONS INVOLVING PHENOLIC STEROID HORMONES AND RELATED SUBSTANCES UNDER *In Vivo* CONDITIONS

Reaction	Species	Substance administered	Products isolated from urine	References
17β-OH → 17-C=O	Rabbit ovari-ectomized-hysterecto-mized	17β-Estradiol	Estrone	Fish and Dorf-man (93)
	Guinea pigs males and females ovariecto-mized	17β-Estradiol	Estrone	Fish and Dorf-man (90–92)
	Rabbit fe-male	17β-Estradiol	Estrone	Heard *et al.* (124)
	Human male	17β-Estradiol	Estrone	Heard and Hoff-man (126)
	Pregnant monkey	17β-Estradiol	Estrone	Dorfman *et al.* (82)
17-C=O → 17α-OH	Rabbit ovari-ectomized-hysterecto-mized	17β-Estradiol	17α-Estradiol	Fish and Dorf-man (93)
	Rabbits fe-males	17β-Estradiol	17α-Estradiol	Heard *et al.* (124)
	Rabbits	Estrone	17α-Estradiol	Stroud (294)
	Dog	Estrone	17α-Estradiol (bile)	Pearlman *et al.* (231)
17-C=O → {17β-OH 16α-OH	Human male Human male Pregnant women	Estrone Estrone	Estriol Estriol	Pearlman and Pincus (228) Pearlman *et al.* (226)
16-C=O → 16α-OH	Human male	16-Ketoestrone 16-Keto-17β-estradiol	Estriol (colori-metric evi-dence)	Stimmel *et al.* (293)
17-C=O → 17β-OH	Human male Pregnant women	Estrone	17β-Estradiol	Pearlman *et al.* (226)

gested. Detailed discussions of liver inactivation are included in Volume I, page 389. The *in vitro* conversion of 17β-estradiol to estrone by acetone powders of beef liver was demonstrated by the isolation and identification of the product (162). Whether this enzyme is identical to that described by Sweat *et al.* (296) (see p. 648), which is active in the androgen series, is not known but not unlikely. The reverse reaction, conversion of estrone to 17β-estradiol, has also been demonstrated, including the isolation of the product (223).

Reactions with microorganisms, especially yeast, have been described in the estrogen series. These consist of oxidation of the 17β-hydroxyl group to the 17-ketone group and the reverse reaction (318a).

The term estronase has been employed by Bischoff and co-workers (13) to designate an enzyme system which can convert estrone to a more active

TABLE III

REACTIONS INVOLVING PHENOLIC STEROID HORMONES UNDER *In Vitro* CONDITIONS

Reaction	Source of enzyme	Substrate	Product	References
17β-OH → 17-C=O	Beef liver acetone powder	17β-Estradiol	Estrone	Ledogar and Jones (162)
	Liver (rat)	17β-Estradiol	Estrone	Pearlman and DeMeio (223) Ryan and Engel (257)
	Human tissues: placenta liver, etc.	17β-Estradiol	Estrone	Ryan and Engel (258)
17-C=O → 17β-OH	Various human tissues	Estrone	17β-Estradiol	Ryan and Engel (258)
	Liver (rat) perfusion	Estrone	17β-Estradiol	Levy and Fish (165)
17-C=O → 17α-OH	Liver (rat) perfusion	Estrone	17α-Estradiol	Levy and Fish (165)
17-C=O → {16α-OH 17β-OH	Liver (rat) homogenate	Estrone	Estriol	Levy and Fish (165)

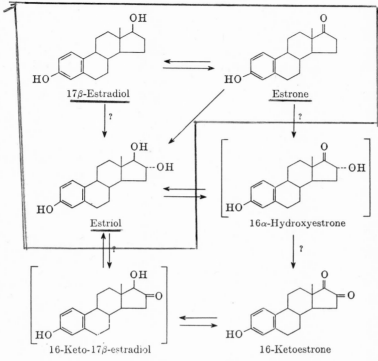

OH

O

HO

17β-Estradiol

HO

Estrone

?

OH

--OH

HO

Estriol

O

--OH

HO

16α-Hydroxyestrone

?

?

OH

=O

HO

16-Keto-17β-estradiol

O

=O

HO

16-Ketoestrone

FIG. 3. Metabolism of estrogens in man.

estrogen, most likely 17β-estradiol. This enzyme has been detected in a variety of tissues and seems not unlike the enzyme system discussed by Ryan and Engel (257, 258). Bischoff's studies indicated the following characteristics of this system: (1) in the uterus, added glucose was not required and NaF had no inhibitory effect; (2) rodent lung tissue did not require added glucose but NaF caused a marked inhibition, and methylene blue had an inhibitory effect on both testis tissue and red blood cells.

IV. Progesterone

Progesterone, which is the only reasonably active progestational substance in the body, is known to be produced by the corpus luteum, the placenta, and the adrenal cortex. The presence of this substance in the testis is strongly indicated by the finding that 3β-hydroxy-Δ^5-pregnen-20-one can be isolated from this gland, and, second, that this gland contains an enzyme system which is capable of converting the Δ^5-3β-hydroxy group to the Δ^4-3-ketone. Progesterone appears to have a number of important roles in endocrine physiology. Its activity as a progestational substance, a substance which has specific effects on the uterine and vaginal mucosa in addition to its important role in the maintenance of pregnancy, is matched by its importance as an intermediate in corticoid biosynthesis. Such important steroids as cortisol, corticosterone, and deoxycorticosterone are derived by biosynthetic hydroxylating reactions from progesterone and are discussed in the section dealing with the metabolism of the adreno-cortical hormones (p. 623).

A. Biosynthesis of Progesterone

The formation of the corpus luteum with its subsequent ability to produce progesterone is brought about by the combined action of anterior pituitary gonadotropic hormones (FSH and LH). It is quite likely that the correctly timed action of these two anterior pituitary hormones is essential for the biogenesis of progesterone in the corpus luteum. At just what stage in the biosynthesis these hormones exert their action is not known.

The placenta undoubtedly can produce progesterone from cholesterol. This has been demonstrated by the administration of deuterated cholesterol to a pregnant woman, resulting in the excretion of deuterated pregnanediol (16). It is quite likely, therefore, that cholesterol was converted to progesterone, which, in turn, was metabolized to the reduced diol.

The factors influencing the biogenesis of progesterone of the adrenal appear to be related to the presence of adrenocorticotropic hormone. Thus, in the adrenogenital syndrome, a condition which is characterized by high ACTH concentrations in the blood, there is a high production of pregnane-$3\alpha,20\alpha$-diol demonstrable by urinary analysis.

That 3β-hydroxy-Δ^5-pregnen-20-one is an intermediate in the biosynthesis of progesterone from cholesterol is indicated from the studies of Solomon *et al.* (291). These workers have demonstrated the conversion of cholesterol-C^{14} to radioactive 3β-hydroxy-Δ^5-pregnen-20-one and progesterone by perfusion experiments employing the human placenta.

B. Catabolism of Progesterone

Progesterone may be reduced as is illustrated in Fig. 4; references are contained in Table IV. These reactions are reductive in nature except for the oxidation in ring A of pregnenolone to progesterone. Reduction reaction may occur at the 3- and 20-ketone groups as well as at the unsaturated group between carbons 4 and 5, giving rise to a variety of reduced constituents which are known primarily from related urinary products and from a more limited number of *in vitro* experiments. 3β-Hydroxy-Δ^5-pregnen-20-one is probably the immediate precursor of progesterone and may be produced from cholesterol and/or acetate in four steroid-producing tissues including the corpus luteum, testis, adrenal, and the placenta.

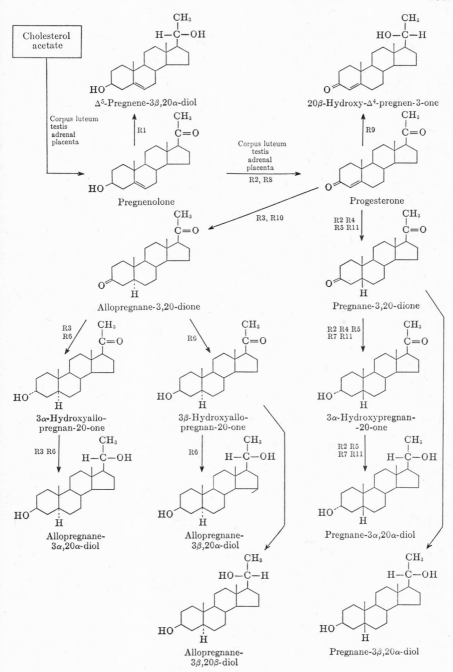

FIG. 4. Metabolism of progesterone and related steroids.

TABLE IV
REFERENCES FOR FIGURE 4.

Isolations

Progesterone	Sow ovary	Butenandt (38)
		Wintersteiner and Allen (322)
		Slotta et al. (289)
		Hartmann and Wettstein (110)
	Whale ovary	Prelog and Meister (243)
	Beef adrenal	Beall and Reichstein (10)
		Beall (7)
	Human placenta	Salhanick et al. (261)
		Pearlman and Cerceo (222)
Pregnenolone	Swine testis	Ruzicka and Prelog (256)
		Haines et al. (107)
Δ^5-Pregnene-3β,20α-diol	Mare urine, pregnancy	Marker and Rohrmann (188)
	Human urine, adrenal hyperactivity	Hirschmann and Hirschmann (139)
		Schiller et al. (275)
		Mason and Kepler (197)
Allopregnane-3,20-dione	Mare urine, pregnancy	Marker et al. (187)
	Human urine	Lieberman et al. (170)
		Dobriner et al. (67)
Pregnane-3,20-dione	Mare urine, pregnancy	Marker et al. (187)
	Human urine	Lieberman et al. (170)
3α-Hydroxyallopregnan-20-one	Human urine, pregnancy	Marker et al. (186)
	Human urine, cancer	Dobriner et al. (67)
	Human urine, normal	Lieberman et al. (170)
	Swine testis	Prelog et al. (244)
3β-Hydroxyallopregnan-20-one	Sow ovary	Slotta et al. (289)
		Wintersteiner and Allen (322)
		Hartmann and Wettstein (110)
		Butenandt and Westphal (40)
	Whale ovary	Prelog and Meister (243)
	Mare urine, pregnancy	Marker et al. (187)
	Sow urine, pregnancy	Marker and Rohrmann (191)
	Human urine, pregnancy	Pearlman et al. (229)
	Beef adrenal	Beall and Reichstein (10)
	Swine testis	Ruzicka and Prelog (256)
	Human placenta	Pearlman and Cerceo (222)
3α-Hydroxypregnan-20-one	Human urine, pregnancy	Marker and Kamm (184)
	Sow urine, pregnancy	Marker and Rohrmann (191)
	Human urine, cancer and normal	Dobriner et al. (67)
		Dobriner (64)
	Cow bile, pregnancy	Pearlman and Cerceo (221)

TABLE IV—(*Continued*)

Isolations

Allopregnane-3α,20α-diol	Bull urine	Marker (181)
	Human urine, pregnancy	Hartmann and Locher (109)
	Mare urine, pregnancy	Marker and Rohrmann (189)
	Cow urine, pregnancy	Marker (180)
	Human urine, female adrenal hyperplasia	Miller and Dorfman (210)
Allopregnane-3β,20α-diol	Human urine, pregnancy	Marker and Rohrmann (189)
	Mare urine, pregnancy	Marker and Rohrmann (188)
	Cow urine pregnancy	Marker (180)
	Bull urine	Marker (181)
Allopregnane-3β,20β-diol	Ox bile	Pearlman (219)
Pregnane-3α,20α-diol	Mare urine, pregnancy	Brooks *et al.* (23)
	Human urine, male	Engel *et al.* (86)
	Human urine, female	Venning and Browne (312)
	Human urine, castrate	Hirschmann (137)
	Human urine, adrenal cancer and virilism	Butler and Marrian (41)
		Mason and Kepler (197)
		Salmon *et al.* (262)
	Cow urine, pregnancy	Marker (180)
	Mare urine, pregnancy	Marker *et al.* (185)
	Bull urine	Marker (181)
	Chimpanzee urine	Fish *et al.* (95)
	Cow bile, pregnancy	Pearlman and Cerceo (221)
	Human placenta	Pearlman and Cerceo (222)
Pregnane-3β,20α-diol	Human urine, adrenal hyperplasia	Mason and Kepler (197)

Reactions

R1	Human	(*In vivo*)	Pregnenolone $\rightarrow$ Δ^5-Pregnene-3β,20α-diol	Ungar *et al.* (310)
R2	Human	(*In vivo*)	Pregnenolone $\rightarrow$ Pregnane-3α,20α-diol	Pearlman and Pincus (228)
				Ungar *et al.* (310)
	Rabbit	(*In vivo*)	Pregnenolone $\rightarrow$ Pregnane 3α,20α-diol	Pearlman and Pincus (228)
R3	Human	(*In vivo*)	Progesterone $\rightarrow$ Allopregnan-3α,20α-diol	Ungar *et al.* (310)
				Kyle and Marrian (159)
R4	Human	(*In vivo*)	Progesterone $\rightarrow$ 3α-Hydroxy-pregnan-20-one	Dorfman *et al.* (79)
				Venning and Ripstein (313)

TABLE IV—(*Continued*)

			Reactions	
R5	Rabbit	(*In vivo*)	Progesterone → Pregnane-3α, 20α-diol	Heard *et al.* (124)
	Human	(*In vivo*)	Progesterone → Pregnane-3α, 20α-diol	Venning and Browne (312) Buxton and Westphal (42) Dorfman *et al.* (79)
R6	Human	(*In vivo*)	Allopregnane- → Allopregnane- 3,20-dione 3α,20α-diol + Allopregnane- 3β,20α-diol	Ungar *et al.* (310)
R7	Human	(*In vivo*)	Pregnane-3, → Pregnane-3α, 20-dione 20α-diol	Ungar *et al.* (310)
R8	Adrenal perfusion		Pregnenolone → Progesterone	Hechter *et al.* (133)
	Testis, Adrenal, Ovary, Placenta, Corpus luteum,	(*In vitro*)	Pregnenolone → Progesterone	Samuels *et al.* (265)
	Rat testis	(*In vitro*)		Helmreich *et al.* (135)
R9	Bovine corpus luteum	(*In vitro*)	Progesterone → 20β-Hydroxy-Δ⁴-pregnen-3-one	Hayano *et al.* (119)
R10	Bovine adrenal	(*In vitro*)	Progesterone → Allopregnane-3,20-dione	Levy *et al.* (166)
R11	Rabbit liver	(*In vitro*)	Progesterone → Pregnane-3α, 20α-diol	Horwitt and Segaloff (146)

3β-Hydroxy-Δ^5-pregnen-20-one, once formed, may be reduced at carbon 20 to form the diol, Δ^5-pregnene-3β,20α-diol, or may undergo oxidation in ring A to form progesterone. The transformation from 3β-hydroxy-Δ^5-pregnen-20-one to the corresponding diol appears to be reversible, whereas the oxidation to progesterone is not. The reduction of the Δ^4-group to the pregnane and allopregnane forms is also indicative of one-way reactions. Further reductions lead to diketones, hydroxyketones, and dihydroxy pregnane and allopregnane derivatives.

A second type of metabolic change which can occur on the progesterone molecule is hydroxylation. Five hydroxylating systems which can either singly or in combination modify the nucleus, causing, in many instances, qualitative changes in biological activity, are known and are discussed in detail in the adrenocorticoid section (p. 629).

C. MICROBIOLOGICAL REACTIONS OF PROGESTERONE

Important advances have been made in the microbiological modifications of the progesterone molecule. These reactions include 6β-hydroxylation, 11α-hydroxylation, 16α-hydroxylation, 17α-hydroxylation, the formation of 17-ketosteroids, dehydrogenation at C-1 in ring A and the formation of the ring D lactone. These reactions, which are illustrated in Fig. 5 and Table

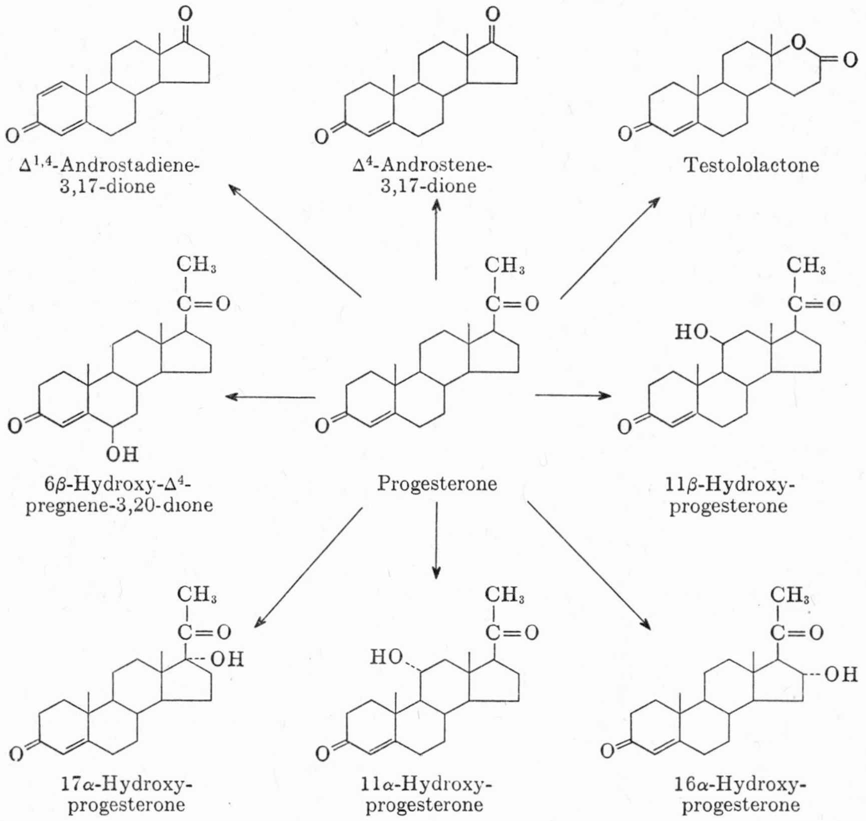

FIG. 5. Microbiological reactions of progesterone.

TABLE V
Microbiological Reactions of Progesterone

Reaction	Organism	Product	Reference
6β-Hydroxylation	*Gliocladium catenulatum*	6β-Hydroxy-Δ⁴-androstene-3,17-dione	Peterson *et al.* (235)
11α-Hydroxylation	*Rhizopus arrhizus*	11α-Hydroxyprogesterone	Murray and Peterson (214) Peterson *et al.* (236) Mansera *et al.* (179)
	Aspergillus niger	11α-Hydroxyprogesterone	Fried *et al.* (98)
16α-Hydroxylation	*Actinomycetes*	16α-Hydroxyprogesterone	Perlman *et al.* (232)
17α-Hydroxylation	*Cephalothecium roseum*	11α,17α-Dihydroxyprogesterone	Meister *et al.* (201a)
Δ⁴-Group → saturated group (5α)	*Rhizopus nigricans*	11α-Hydroxyallopregnane-3,20-dione	Peterson *et al.* (236)
	Penicillium chrysogenum	5α-Dihydrotestololactone	Fried *et al.* (97, 97a)
Δ⁴-Group → saturated group (5β)	*Actinomycetes*	16α-Hydroxypregnane-3,20-dione	Perlman *et al.* (232)
Formation of Δ¹-group	*Streptomyces lavendulae*	Δ¹,⁴-Androstadiene-3,17-dione 17β-Hydroxy-Δ¹,⁴-androstadien-3-one	Fried *et al.* (97, 97a)
	Fusarium solani	Δ¹,⁴-Androstadiene-3,17-dione	Vischer and Wettstein (314)
Oxidation of side chain and 17-C=O formation	*Fusarium solani*	Δ¹,⁴-Androstadiene-3,17-dione	Vischer and Wettstein (314)
	Gliocladium catenulatum *Penicillium lilacinum* Thom *Aspergillus flavus*	Δ⁴-Androstene-3,17-dione	Peterson *et al.* (235)

TABLE V—*(Continued)*

Reaction	Organism	Product	Reference
Oxidation of side chain and 17-C=O formation (*con't.*)	*Streptomyces lavendulae*	$\Delta^{1,4}$-Androstadiene-3,17-dione 17β-Hydroxy-$\Delta^{1,4}$-androstadien-3-one	Fried *et al.* (97, 97a)
Oxidation of side chain and ring D lactone formation	*Aspergillus flavus* *Penicillium adametzi*	Testololactone	Peterson *et al.* (235)
	Penicillium chrysogenum	Testololactone	Fried *et al.* (97, 97a)
	Cylindrocarpon radicola	Δ^1-Dehydrotestololactone	

V, are of particular value for the commercial production of cortisone, cortisol, and estrogens.

D. Localization of Progesterone

The fate of progesterone-21-C^{14} has been studied in the rat and in the mouse (249, 6). A portion (approximately 10%) of the C^{14} was recovered in the expired CO_2. Fecal (major) and urinary (minor) excretion of the isotope accounted for by far the bulk (about 80%) of the administered dose. The bulk of the fecal radioactivity was present in the neutral nonsaponifiable fraction (249). The pituitaries and adrenals of mice contained significant concentrations of C^{14}, whereas in the rat the pituitary concentration was high and no significant quantities of radiocarbon could be detected in the adrenal.

Heard *et al.* (127) also studied the administration of progesterone-21-C^{14} to mice with results in essential agreement to those reported by Riegel *et al.* (249) and Barry *et al.* (6). Within 100 hours after a single subcutaneous injection, 2.39% was found in the expired air as $C^{14}O_2$. By far the major portion of the $C^{14}O_2$ was excreted in the first 13 hours (2.14%). The urine contained 22% of the C^{14} within the 5-day period and the feces approximately the same amount, 20.55%. When progesterone-21-C^{14} was administered to a male rat and the excreta collected for 6 days, 11.8% appeared in the urine and 31.3% in the feces.

Gallagher and co-workers (99) administered progesterone-4-C^{14}, both intravenously and intramuscularly, to women. In both instances approximately one-third of the labeled carbon was recovered in the urine, with slightly more radioactivity being detected after intravenous administration. Most of the urinary substances were neutral ether-soluble compounds which were liberated from their complex by either acid or enzymatic hydrolysis. Only small amounts of activity were found in the combined acidic and phenolic fractions, and Gallagher *et al.* (99) have indicated the possibility that even this small radioactivity may be due to unhydrolyzed glucuronides which can be extracted by ether in a continuous extractor.

V. Androgens

Androgens are the products of the testis, ovary, adrenal cortex, and perhaps the placenta. The individual compounds are listed in Table VI.

TABLE VI
ANDROGENS OF TISSUES

Tissue	Steroid	Species	References
Testis	Testosterone	Bull Stallion Man Rabbit Hog	David *et al.* (59) Tagmann *et al.* (297) Savard *et al.* (269) Brady (21)
	Δ^4-Androstene-3,17-dione	Man	Savard *et al.* (269)
Adrenal cortex	Δ^4-Androstene-3,17-dione	Bovine Human (fetus)	Reichstein and Shoppee (247) Bloch *et al.* (15) Bloch *et al.* (14)
	Adrenosterone	Bovine	Reichstein and Shoppee (247) Bloch *et al.* (15)
	11β-Hydroxy-Δ^4-androstene-3,17-dione	Bovine	Bloch *et al.* (15)
	Androstane-3β,11β-diol-17-one	Bovine	Reichstein and Shoppee (247)
Blood	11β-Hydroxy-Δ^4-androstene-3,17-dione	Human adrenal venous (after ACTH)	Pincus and Romanoff (239)
	Testosterone	Dog—spermatic vein	West *et al.* (316)
	Δ^4-Androstene-3,17-dione		

The most active androgen, testosterone, is produced by the testis, perhaps by the ovary, and probably not by the adrenal.   The biosynthesis of testosterone is known to be conditioned or in part controlled by gonadotropic hormones (LH and FSH). Analysis of dog spermatic vein blood has yielded both testosterone and Δ^4-androstene-3,17-dione.

Four adrenal steroids may be designated as proandrogens, since these substances, as such, do not possess androgenic activity but during metabolism are converted in part to androgenic steroids.   Cortisone and cortisol may be converted in part to androgenic substances 11-ketoandrosterone, 11β-hydroxyandrosterone, 11β-hydroxy-Δ^4-androstene-3,17-dione, and adrenosterone.   Two pathways to the ring A saturated 17-ketosteroids

TABLE VII

PROANDROGENS OF TISSUES

Proandrogens	Source	Androgens formed	References
Cortisone Cortisol	Adrenal cortex	11-Hydroxyandros- terone 11-Ketoandrosterone Adrenosterone 11β-Hydroxy-Δ^4-an- drostene-3,17-dione	Burstein et al. (31–33) Dorfman et al. (74) Birke and Plantin (12a)
17-Hydroxyprogester- one 11-Deoxycortisol	Adrenal cortex	Androsterone Δ^4-Androstene-3,17- dione	Gallagher et al. (99) Dorfman et al. (74) Birke (12b)

have been indicated.   The Δ^4-3-ketosteroids of the C_{21} series may be converted to C_{19} steroids either before or after reduction of the Δ^4-double bond. The removal of the sidechain before reduction of the double bond results in the formation of 11β-hydroxy-Δ^4-androstene-3,17-dione and adrenosterone and the subsequent formation of the androgens, 11β-hydroxyandrosterone and 11-ketoandrosterone. The latter two steroids may also arise from side chain removal subsequent to ring A reduction (72).   A similar situation exists with respect to the formation of androgens from 17-hydroxyprogesterone and 11-deoxycortisol. These steroids can yield the androgens Δ^4-androstene-3,17-dione and androsterone (Table VII).

A. BIOSYNTHESIS OF ANDROGENS

Specific steroid-producing tissues appear to supply to the blood and tissues five principal androgens which include dehydroepiandrosterone,

Δ^4-androstene-3,17-dione, testosterone, 11β-hydroxy-Δ^4-androstene-3,17-dione, and adrenosterone. Testosterone may be a specific product of the testes, or actually this androgen may be synthesized in both the ovaries and testes. Δ^4-Androstene-3,17-dione is produced by the testes and probably by the ovaries as well. Evidence exists for the biosynthesis of five androgens by adrenal tissues. Four of these steroids, Δ^4-androstene-3,17-dione, adrenosterone, 11β-hydroxy-Δ^4-androstene-3,17-dione, and 11β-hydroxyepiandrosterone have been isolated from adrenal tissue, and the fifth steroid, dehydroepiandrosterone, appears, on the basis of indirect evidence, to be present in the gland.

Acetate is a precursor of both testosterone and Δ^4-androstene-3,17-dione. Brady (21) demonstrated the conversion of acetate-C^{14} to testosterone when he incubated tissue slices derived from hog, rabbit, and human testes with carboxyl-labeled acetate and isolated C^{14}-labeled testosterone. In these experiments it was demonstrated that the synthesis of testosterone was significantly enhanced by chorionic gonadotropin. The fact that chorionic gonadotropin did not enhance the incorporation of acetate into cholesterol and that cholesterol had a lower specific activity than the formed testosterone argues for the fact that cholesterol is not a necessary intermediate between acetate and testosterone.

The results of Brady have been confirmed and extended by the perfusion studies of Savard et al. (269). In these studies, acetate-1-C^{14} was perfused through the human testis, with the result that C^{14}-labeled testosterone and Δ^4-androstene-3,17-dione were formed.

Adrenal cancer patients, who frequently excrete enormous quantities of 17-ketosteroids, have been treated with acetate-1-C^{14} (134, 305). Dehydroepiandrosterone, Δ^5-androstene-3β,17β-diol, androsterone, and 3α-hydroxyetiocholan-17-one (etiocholanolone) containing C^{14} have been isolated from the urine. The presence of the labeled androgen, dehydroepiandrosterone, in the urine indicated that acetate is readily converted to this adrenal androgen. The presence of labeled androsterone in the urine indicates the synthesis of Δ^4-androstene-3,17-dione or of 11-deoxycortisol and 17-hydroxyprogesterone. Since labeled androsterone and etiocholanolone were present in equal quantities and had specific activities equal to that of the isolated dehydroepiandrosterone, it is most likely that the ring A saturated steroids were derived from dehydroepiandrosterone; the two C_{21} steroids are metabolized predominantely to the 5β stereoisomer (etiocholanolone) (p. 633).

Perfusion of the bovine adrenal with acetate-1-C^{14} and added ACTH resulted in the detection of C^{14}-labeled adrenosterone, 11β-hydroxy-Δ^4-androstene-3,17-dione, and Δ^4-androstene-3,17-dione (15).

The steroid fractions isolated from the urine of an adrenal cancer patient following the oral administration of cholesterol-3-C^{14} contained C^{14} radio-activity.   No positive statement can be made regarding the origin of the steroid carbon content.   Although a sample of cholesterol isolated from the urine had a specific activity approximately equal to that of the blood cholesterol, androsterone and etiocholanolone isolated during this period had only $\frac{1}{10}$ the specific activity of the cholesterol.   Thus, the 17-keto-steroids could arise from breakdown products of the administered chole-sterol as well as from cholesterol directly.   The fact that the specific activity of the isolated androsterone and etiocholanolone was distinctly lower than that of the urine or blood cholesterol is consistent also with the idea that cholesterol is not an obligatory intermediate in the bio-genesis of the C_{19} androgens (305).   Hellmann *et al.* (134) concluded from their studies that dehydroepiandrosterone could arise directly from acetate.

The incubation of pregnenolone with testicular interstitial cells resulted in the formation of testosterone (288).   This may represent a pathway for biosynthesis of androgens.   The steps in biosynthesis are considered to be oxidation of pregnenolone to progesterone followed by 17α-hy-droxylation to 17α-hydroxyprogesterone, which in turn could yield Δ^4-androstene-3,17-dione.   Reduction of the 17-ketone group to the 17β-hydroxyl group would result in the formation of testosterone.

B. CATABOLISM OF ANDROGENS

1. *Testosterone, Δ^4-Androstene-3,17-dione, and Dehydroepiandrosterone*

The metabolism of these $C_{19}O_2$ androgens is illustrated in Fig. 6.   In this series of compounds some 12 steroids have been isolated from natural sources, and 24 reactions have been studied either by *in vitro* or *in vivo* techniques.   The details are indicated in the figure and the references are included in Table VIII.   Two points of interest deserve mention.   In the human being particularly, and perhaps in most mammals, although relatively great numbers of possible reactions can take place and a rather large number of metabolites are present, the two 17-ketosteroids, andro-sterone and etiocholanolone, are quantitatively the most important me-tabolites of all three $C_{19}O_2$ androgens in tissues.   Dehydroepiandrosterone is unique amongst these three $C_{19}O_2$ steroids in that it is excreted to a reasonable extent unchanged.   A second important point is the fact that although a remarkable amount of interconvertibility has been demon-strated, certain reactions proceed exclusively in one direction.   Thus, dehydroepiandrosterone may be converted to Δ^4-androstene-3,17-dione, but the reverse of this reaction has never been demonstrated by mam-malian tissue.   The reduction of the double bonds at carbons 4 and 5 to yield a saturated group, either of the androstane (5α) or etiocholane (5β) type, is adequately documented, but the reverse reactions have not been

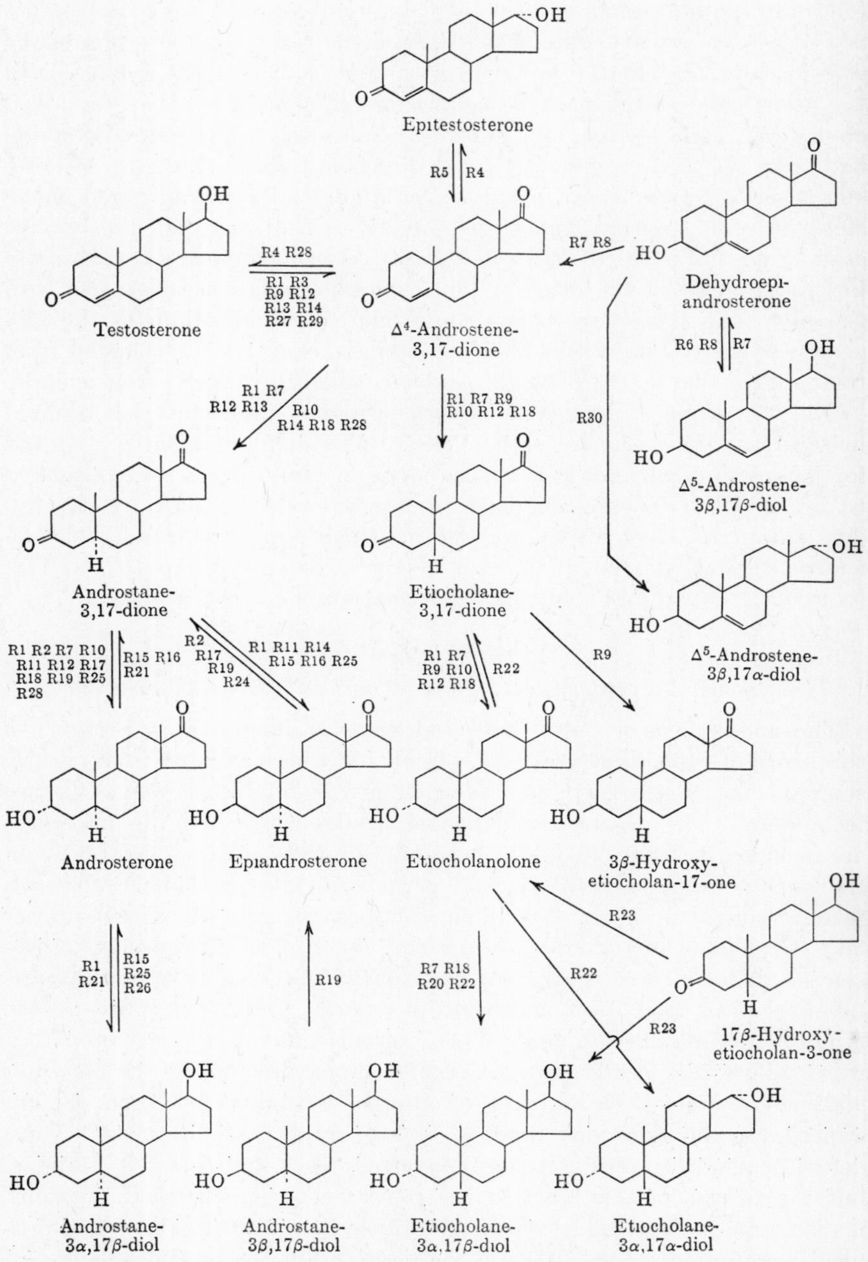

Fig. 6. Metabolism of Δ^4-androstene-3,17-dione, testosterone, and related steroids.

TABLE VIII

REFERENCES FOR FIGURE 6

Isolations

Δ^4-Androstene-3,17-dione	Beef adrenal	von Euw and Reichstein (315)
	Human urine	Lieberman et al. (170)
		Miller et al. (212)
	Dog spermatic vein blood	West et al. (316)
	Human testis	Savard et al. (269)
	Human fetal adrenal	Bloch et al. (14)
	Beef adrenal perfusate	Bloch et al. (15)
Testosterone	Bull testis	David et al. (59)
	Stallion testis	Tagmann et al. (297)
	Human testis	Brady (21)
	Dog spermatic vein blood	West et al. (316)
Dehydroepiandrosterone	Human urine	Butenandt (36)
		Engel et al. (86)
		Callow and Callow (45)
		Hirschmann (137)
	Cow urine, pregnancy	Marker (182)
	Bull urine	Marker (182)
	Steer urine	Marker (183)
	Mare urine, pregnancy	Oppenauer (216)
Δ^5-Androstene-3β,17β-diol	Human urine	Hirschmann and Hirschmann (139)
		Schiller et al. (275)
		Mason and Kepler (197)
Androstane-3,17-dione	Human urine	Lieberman et al. (170)
Etiocholane-3,17-dione	Human urine	Lieberman et al. (170)
Androsterone	Human urine	Butenandt (37)
		Butenandt and Dannenbaum (38a)
		Engel et al. (86)
		Callow (43)
		Callow and Callow (44)
	Human urine, female castrate	Hirschmann (137)
	Cow urine, pregnancy	Marker (182)
	Bull urine	Marker (182)
	Steer urine	Marker (183)
Epiandrosterone	Human urine	Pearlman (218)
	Mare urine, pregnancy	Oppenauer (216)
Etiocholanolone	Human urine	Callow (43)
		Callow and Callow (44)
	Human urine, male castrate	Callow and Callow (45)
	Human urine, female castrate	Hirschmann (137)

TABLE VIII—(*Continued*)

Isolations

3β-Hydroxyetiocholan-17-one	Human urine	Dobriner and Lieberman (66)
Etiocholane-3α,17β-diol	Human urine	Miller and Dorfman (210a)
Etiocholane-3α,17α-diol	Ox bile	Pearlman (220)

Reactions

R1	Human	(*In vivo*)	Testosterone	→ Androsterone Etiocholano-lone Etiocholane-3α,17β-diol Androstane-3α,17β-diol	Dorfman *et al.* (75) Dorfman (69, 70) Gallagher *et al.* (99, 100) West *et al.* (316) Callow (43) Schiller *et al.* (274)
R2	Rat liver	(*In vitro*)	Androstane-3,17-dione	→ Androsterone Epiandroster-one	Ungar and Dorfman (308)
R3	Rabbit liver	(*In vitro*)	Testosterone	→ Δ⁴-Andros-tene-3,17-dione	Clark and Kochakian (51) Sweat *et al.* (296)
R4	Rabbit liver	(*In vitro*)	Δ⁴-Andros-tene-3,17-dione	→ Testosterone Epitestoster-one	Clark *et al.* (52)
R5	Rabbit liver	(*In vitro*)	Epitestoster-one	→ Δ⁴-Andros-tene-3,17-dione	Kochakian *et al.* (156)
R6	Human	(*In vivo*)	Dehydroepi-androster-one	→ Δ⁵-Andros-tene-3β,17β-diol	Mason and Kepler (196) Miller *et al.* (211)
	Rabbit liver	(*In vitro*)	Dehydroepi-androster-one	→ Δ⁵-Andros-tene-3β,17β-diol	Schneider and Mason (281) Ungar *et al.* (311)
R7	Guinea pig	(*In vivo*)	Δ⁵-Andros-tene-3β,17β-diol	→ Dehydroepi-androster-one	Miller and Dorfman (209)

TABLE VIII—(*Continued*)

Reactions

R7 con't.	Human	(*In vivo*)	Δ^5-Andros-tene-3β, 17β-diol	→ Dehydroepi-androster-one Androsterone Etiocholano-lone Etiocholane-3α,17β-diol	Ungar *et al.* (311)
R8	Rat liver	(Perfusion)	Dehydroepi-androster-one	→ Δ^4-Andros-tene-3,17-dione Δ^5-Andros-tene-3β,17β-diol	Ungar *et al.* (311)
R9	Chicken liver	(*In vitro*)	Testosterone	→ Etiocholano-lone 3β-Hydroxy-etiocholan-17-one	Samuels (264) Samuels *et al.* (266)
R10	Human	(*In vivo*)	Δ^4-Andros-tene-3,17-dione	→ Androsterone Etiocholano-lone	Dorfman and Hamilton (77) Dorfman *et al.* (81) Gallagher *et al.* (100)
R11	Human	(*In vivo*)	Androstane-3,17-dione	→ Androsterone Epiandroster-one	Dorfman and Hamilton (77) Dorfman *et al.* (81) Gallagher *et al.* (100)
R12	Chimpan-zee	(*In vivo*)	Testosterone	→ Androsterone Etiocholano-lone	Fish and Dorf-man (94)
R13	Monkey	(*In vivo*)	Testosterone	→ Androsterone	Horwitt *et al.* (145)
R14	Guinea pig	(*In vivo*)	Testosterone	→ Androsterone Epiandroster-one	Dorfman and Fish (76) Burstein *et al.* (34)
R15	Human	(*In vivo*)	Androstane-3α,17β-diol	→ Androsterone Epiandroster-one	Dorfman and Hamilton (77) Dorfman *et al.* (81)

TABLE VIII—(Continued)

Reactions

			Reactions		
R16	Guinea pig	(*In vivo*)	Androsterone	→ Epiandrosterone	Schiller and Dorfman (273)
R17	Human	(*In vivo*)	Epiandrosterone	→ Androsterone	Dorfman *et al.* (79)
R18	Human	(*In vivo*)	Dehydroepiandrosterone	→ Androsterone Etiocholanolone Etiocholane-3α,17β-diol	Mason and Kepler (196) Miller *et al.* (211)
R19	Human	(*In vivo*)	Androstane-3β,17β-diol	→ Androsterone Epiandrosterone	Ungar *et al.* (309)
R20	Human	(*In vivo*)	Etiocholanolone	→ Etiocholane-3α,17β-diol	Gallagher *et. al.* (100)
R21	Rabbit liver	(*In vitro*)	Androsterone	→ Androstane-3,17-dione Androstane-3α,17β-diol	Schneider and Mason (282)
R22	Rabbit liver	(*In vitro*)	Etiocholanolone	→ Etiocholane-3,17-dione Etiocholane-3α,17β-diol Etiocholane-3α,17α-diol	Schneider and Mason (282)
R23	Human	(*In vivo*)	17β-Hydroxy-etiocholan-3-one	→ Etiocholanolone Etiocholane-3α,17β-diol	Ungar *et al.* (309)
R24	Bovine adrenal	(Perfusion)	Epiandrosterone	→ Androstane-3,17-dione	Meyer *et al.* (206)
R25	Rabbit liver	(*In vitro*)	Δ⁴-Androstene-3,17-dione	→ Androstane-3,17-dione Androsterone Epiandrosterone	Kochakian and Aposhian (155)
R26	Guinea pig liver and kidney	(*In vitro*)	Androstane-3α,17β-diol	→ Androsterone	Kochakian and Aposhian (155)
R27	Human prostate	(*In vitro*)	Testosterone	→ Δ⁴-Androstene-3,17-dione	Wotiz and Lemon (327) Lemon *et al.* (163)
R28	Guinea pig liver and kidney	(*In vitro*)	Δ⁴-Androstene-3,17-dione	→ Testosterone Androsterone	Kochakian *et al.* (157)

TABLE VIII—(*Continued*)

Reactions

| R29 | Guinea pig liver | (*In vitro*) | Testosterone $\rightarrow \Delta^4$-Androstene-3,17-dione | Kochakian *et al.* (157) |
| R30 | Rabbit liver | (*In vitro*) | Dehydroepi-androster-one $\rightarrow \Delta^5$-Andros-tene-3β,17α-diol | Rosenkrantz and Dorf-man (253, 254) |

demonstrated.   These limitations in steroid metabolism involving mam-malian tissues are general and have been observed for androgens, proges-terone, and adrenocortical steroids.

2. *Adrenosterone and 11β-Hydroxy-Δ⁴-androstene-3,17-dione (71, 268)*

These two androgens of the $C_{19}O_3$ series, produced exclusively by the adrenal cortex, are metabolized in a manner similar to that for the $C_{19}O_2$ series, as discussed in the preceding section.   Quantitatively, it is most likely that of the two $C_{19}O_3$ steroids produced, 11β-hydroxy-Δ⁴-androstene-3,17-dione is the most important.   This comes from consideration of the manner in which the 11-oxygen function is inserted into the nucleus as well as from isolation studies on adrenal venous blood.   An 11β-hydrox-

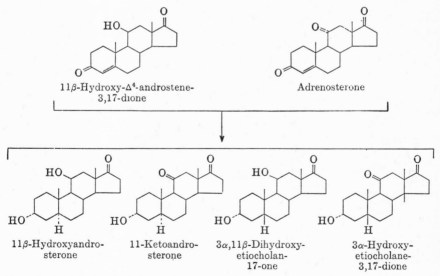

FIG. 7.   Metabolism of 11β-hydroxy-Δ⁴-androstene-3,17-dione and adrenosterone.

TABLE IX
MICROBIOLOGICAL REACTIONS OF ANDROGENS

Reaction	Organism	Substrate	Product	Reference
Δ^1-Group → saturated group	Yeast	Δ^1-Androstene-3,17-dione	Androstane-3β,17β-diol	Butenandt et al. (39)
17-Ketone → 17β-hydroxyl	Yeast	Androstane-3,17-dione	Androstane-3β,17β-diol	
		Adrenosterone	17β-Hydroxy-Δ^4-androstene-3,11-dione	Herzog et al. (136)
3-Ketone → 3β-hydroxyl	Yeast	Androstane-3,17-dione	Androstane-3β,17β-diol	Butenandt et al. (39)
17β-Hydroxyl → 17-ketone	Proactinomyces erythropolis	Δ^5-Androstene-3β,17β-diol	Δ^4-Androstene-3,17-dione	Turfitt (299)
Δ^5-3β-Hydroxyl → Δ^4-3-ketone		Δ^5-Androstene-3β,17β-diol	Δ^4-Androstene-3,17-dione	
	Corynebacterium mediolanum	Dehydroepiandrosterone	Δ^4-Androstene-3,17-dione	Mamoli and Vercellone (178)
6β-Hydroxylation	Cunninghamella blakesteena	Δ^4-Androstene-3,17-dione	6β-Hydroxy-Δ^4-androstene-3,17-dione	Murray and Peterson (214)
11α-Hydroxylation	Rhizopus nigricans	Testosterone	11α,17β-Dihydroxy-Δ^4-androsten-3-one	
		Δ^4-Androstene-3,17-dione	11α-Hydroxy-Δ^4-androstene-3,17-dione	
16α-Hydroxylation	Actinomycetes	Δ^4-Androstene-3,17-dione	16α-Hydroxy-Δ^4-androstene-3,17-dione	Perlman et al. (232)

TABLE IX—(*Continued*)

Reaction	Organism	Substrate	Product	Reference
Formation of Δ^1- group	*Fusarium solani*	Δ^4-Androstene-3,17-dione	$\Delta^{1,4}$-Androsta-diene-3,17-dione	Vischer and Wettstein (314)
		Dehydroepian-drosterone	$\Delta^{1,4}$-Androsta-diene-3,17-dione	
		Androstane-3,17-dione	$\Delta^{1,4}$-Androsta-diene-3,17-dione	
Formation of Δ^4- group	*Fusarium solani*	Androstane-3,17-dione	$\Delta^{1,4}$-Androsta-diene-3,17-dione	

ylase has been described which is active in the C_{19} series as well as in the C_{21}, resulting in the formation of 11β-hydroxyl derivatives. A relatively small quantity of the 11-keto derivatives are produced in the adrenal, most likely from the corresponding 11β-hydroxy compounds (Fig. 7).

Adrenosterone and 11β-hydroxy-Δ^4-androstene-3,17-dione are converted to the diketo-hydroxy and triketo derivatives and in turn reduced to the four 3α-hydroxy 17-ketosteroids, 11β-hydroxyandrosterone, 11-ketoandrosterone, 3α-hydroxyetiocholane-11,17-dione, and $3\alpha,11\beta$-dihydroxyetiocholan-17-one.

3. *Proandrogens*

Since these are exclusively adrenocortical steroids, they will be discussed as members of that group of steroids in another section of this chapter (see p. 632).

C. Metabolism of Testosterone in Rodents

Gallagher *et al.* (100) were unable to detect $C^{14}O_2$ in the expired air of mice treated intraperitoneally with testosterone-4-C^{14}. When this labeled steroid was administered to rats, within 24 hours 7% to 12% of the C^{14} was found in the urine, 31% to 40% in the feces, and about 35% in the gastrointestinal tract. In another series of experiments, Ashmore *et al.* (3) studied the same steroid in rats and found one-third of the C^{14} in the urine and about two-thirds in the feces. When animals bearing bile canulas were employed, significant amounts of radioactive material were excreted in the bile and resorbed from the intestinal tract. No radioactivity could be found in the expired air.

Testosterone-3-C^{14} administered intraperitoneally to a male guinea pig resulted in 83 % of the C^{14} being detected in the crude urine within 17 hours and only 3 % in an alcoholic extract of the feces collected during the same period. C^{14}-Labeled etiocholanolone and epiandrosterone were isolated from urinary extracts (34).

D. Microbiological Reactions of Androgens

Table IX summarizes the reactions which have been reported for androgens using various microorganisms. Of the eight reactions noted, two, the saturation of the Δ^1 group and 11α-hydroxylation, have not been observed for mammalian tissues. The remaining six reactions have all been noted in mammalian tissues, including 6β-and 16α-hydroxylation.

VI. Adrenocortical Hormones

A. Steroids of the Adrenal Cortex

The isolation and identification of adrenocortical steroids has been reviewed (Volume I, p. 549). Recently, aldosterone, a highly active

TABLE X
ADRENOCORTICAL STEROIDS (247, 286, 287)
(Excluding androgens, estrogens, and progesterone)

Biologically Active Steroids
    Cortisol
    Cortisone
    Corticosterone
    11-Dehydrocorticosterone
    11-Dehydrocortisol
    Deoxycorticosterone
    17α-Hydroxyprogesterone
    Aldosterone
Biologically Inactive Steroids
    Allopregnane-3β,11β,17α,20,21-pentol
    3β,11β,17α,21-Tetrahydroxyallopregnan-20-one
    3α,11β,17α,21-Tetrahydroxyallopregnan-20-one
    3β,17α,21-Trihydroxyallopregnane-11,20-dione
    11β,17α,20β,21-Tetrahydroxy-Δ^4-pregnen-3-one
    17α,20β,21-Trihydroxy-Δ^4-pregnene-3,11-dione
    Allopregnane-3β,17α,20β,21-tetrol
    3β,17α,21-Trihydroxyallopregnan-20-one
    3β,11β,20-Trihydroxyallopregnan-20-one
    3β,21-Dihydroxyallopregnane-11,20-dione
    20β,21-Dihydroxy-Δ^4-pregnene-3,11-dione
    Allopregnane-3β,17α,20β-triol
    Allopregnane-3β,17α,20α-triol
    3β,17α-Dihydroxyallopregnan-20-one
    3β-Hydroxyallopregnan-20-one

steroid, particularly with respect to electrolyte metabolism, has been isolated and identified from adrenal tissue. The chemistry and biological action are discussed in Chapters XI and XIV, respectively. Table X lists the adrenocortical steroids other than androgens, estrogens, and progesterone. The steroids are also subdivided into biologically active and inactive substances.

B. Biosynthesis of Neutral Adrenocortical Hormones

The discovery that the perfused adrenal gland can synthesize adrenocortical steroids from endogeneous precursors, that this production can be significantly enhanced by the addition of ACTH to the perfusing medium, and that a variety of individual biosynthetic reactions can be demonstrated by employing proper substrates was an important stimulus to the study of adrenocortical hormone biosynthesis (133). A variety of biosynthetic reactions that have been demonstrated by the perfusion technique are summarized in Table XI and include the oxidation of the Δ^5-3β-hydroxyl group to the Δ^4-3-ketone, 6β-hydroxylation, 11β-hydroxylation, 17α-hydroxylation, and 21-hydroxylation.

In place of the whole isolated bovine adrenal using a perfusion method, Haynes et al. (121, 122), Saffran et al. (260, 260a), and Brady (22) have employed adrenal slices which may be stimulated by ACTH to produce cortisol and other adrenocortical steroids. Bloch et al. (15) have also shown that C_{19} steroids may similarly arise from carboxyl-labeled acetate.

Hayano et al. (117) incubated deoxycorticosterone with adrenal slices and homogenates and produced glycogenic material which indicated the C-11 oxygenation of the substrate. This approach to the problem of biosynthesis of adrenocortical hormones has since been developed as summarized in Table XII. In addition to the oxidation reaction of the Δ^5-3β-hydroxyl group to the Δ^4-3-ketone, it has been possible to demonstrate 6α-, 6β-, 11β-, 17α-, and 21-hydroxylation reactions by adrenal enzyme preparations.

C. A Scheme of Adrenocortical Steroid Biogenesis

Large gaps in our knowledge still exist, but enough reproducible facts are available to propose a system of adrenocortical biogenesis which involves both the anterior pituitary and adrenal cortex and to indicate how a continuous system for the production of adrenocortical hormones is possible. The reader is referred to a review by Hechter and Pincus (131) in which a scheme for the biogenesis of C_{21} adrenocortical steroids is presented. The scheme presented here has many features in common with that presented in this extensive review.

Figure 8 will be used in the presentation of the scheme for adrenocortical

TABLE XI

Biosynthetic Reactions Demonstrated by Perfusion (Bovine Adrenal)

Reaction	Substrate	Product(s)	References
Δ^5-3β-Hydroxyl group → Δ^4-3-ketone	3β-Hydroxy-Δ^5-pregnen-20-one	Progesterone Corticosterone Cortisol	Levy et al. (167)
	Dehydroepiandrosterone	11β-Hydroxy-Δ^4-androstene-3,17-dione Δ^4-Androstene-3,17-dione	Meyer et al. (205) Ungar et al. (311)
6β-Hydroxylation	Progesterone	6β-Hydroxyprogesterone	Levy et al. (166)
	Δ^4-Androstene-3,17-dione	6β-Hydroxy-Δ^4-androstene-3,17-dione	Meyer et al. (204)
11β-Hydroxylation	11-Deoxycorticosterone	Corticosterone	Hechter et al. (133) Levy et al. (168) Ungar et al. (303)
	11-Deoxycortisol	Cortisol	Hechter et al. (133) Ungar et al. (303)
	Δ^4-Androstene-3,17-dione	11β-Hydroxy-Δ^4-androstene-3,17-dione	Jeanloz et al. (150, 151)
	Progesterone	11β-Hydroxyprogesterone Corticosterone Cortisol	Levy et al. (167) Hechter et al. (133)
	17α-Hydroxyprogesterone	Cortisol	Levy et al. (167) Hechter et al. (133)
	3β-Hydroxy-Δ^5-pregnen-20-one	Corticosterone Cortisol	Levy et al. (167) Hechter et al. (133)
	Epiandrosterone	11β-Hydroxyandrostane-3,17-dione 11β-Hydroxyepiandrosterone	Meyer et al. (205)

TABLE XI—(*Continued*)

Reaction	Substrate	Product(s)	References
11β-Hydroxyl- ation (*Con't.*)	21-Hydroxyallo- pregnane-3,20- dione	11β,21-Dihydroxy- allopregnane-3,20- dione	Meyer (203)
	Testosterone	11β-Hydroxytestos- terone	Axelrod and Miller (5)
17α-Hydrox- ylation	Progesterone	11-Deoxycortisol	Levy *et al.* (166)
		17α-Hydroxyproges- terone Cortisol	Levy *et al.* (167) Hechter *et al.* (133) Ungar *et al.* (303)
	3β-Hydroxy-Δ⁵- pregnen-20-one	Cortisol	Levy *et al.* (167) Hechter *et al.* (133)
21-Hydroxyl- ation	Progesterone	11-Deoxycortisol Corticosterone Cortisol	Levy *et al.* (166) Levy *et al.* (167) Hechter *et al.* (133) Ungar *et al.* (303)
	21-Deoxycortisone	Cortisone	Meyer *et al.* (202) Ungar *et al.* (303)
	17α-Hydroxypro- gesterone	Cortisol	Hechter *et al.* (133)
	3β-Hydroxy-Δ⁵- pregnen-20-one	Corticosterone Cortisol	

biogenesis. Letter designations (*A* through *G*) of the headings in the text will refer to portions of the scheme illustrated in Fig. 8.

1. *Influence of Adrenocorticotropic Hormone (ACTH) (A) (Fig. 8)*

The fact that the anterior pituitary exerts a dual effect on the adrenal cortex is well recognized. Through the medium of ACTH (either single or multiple entities) the size and structure of the adrenal gland is maintained. This effect may be considered to be a relatively slow effect in contrast to the fast reactions which are concerned with steroid production. It is the latter effect that will be emphasized in this section. Stone and Hechter (292a) have studied the production of labeled cortisol and corticosterone when C¹⁴-labeled acetate, cholesterol, and progesterone are

TABLE XII

BIOSYNTHETIC REACTIONS DEMONSTRATED BY *In Vitro* INCUBATION WITH ADRENAL TISSUE PREPARATIONS

Reaction	Substrate	Product	References
Δ^5-3β-Hydroxyl group → Δ^4-3-Ketone	3β-Hydroxy-Δ^5-pregnen-20-one	Progesterone	Plager and Samuels (241)
6α-Hydroxylation	Δ^4-Androstene-3,17-dione	6α-Hydroxy-Δ^4-androstene-3,17-dione	Meyer *et al.* (204)
6β-Hydroxylation	11-Deoxycorticosterone	6β,21-Dihydroxy-Δ^4-pregnene-3,20-dione	Haines (106)
	Δ^4-Androstene-3,17-dione	6β-Hydroxy-Δ^4-androstene-3,17-dione	Meyer *et al.* (204)
11β-Hydroxylation	11-Deoxycorticosterone	Corticosterone	McGinty *et al.* (200) Savard *et al.* (270) Haines (106)
	11-Deoxycortisol	Cortisol	Hayano and Dorfman (114)
	Δ^4-Androstene-3,17-dione	11β-Hydroxy-Δ^4-androstene-3,17-dione	Hayano and Dorfman (114) Meyer *et al.* (204)
	21-Hydroxyallopregnane-3,20-dione	11β,21-Dihydroxyallopregnane-3,20-dione	Hayano and Dorfman (114)
	6β,17α,21-Trihydroxy-Δ^4-pregnene-3,20-dione	6β,11β,17α,21-Tetrahydroxy-Δ^4-pregnene-3,20-dione	Hayano and Dorfman (115)
17α-Hydroxylation	Progesterone	Cortisol	Dorfman *et al.* (78) Plager and Samuels (241)
	Deoxycorticosterone	Cortisol	Dorfman *et al.* (78)
21-Hydroxylation	21-Deoxycortisone	Cortisone	Hayano and Dorfman (113)
	17α-Hydroxyprogesterone	Cortisol	
	Progesterone	Corticosterone	Plager and Samuels (241)

point of interest in the formation of aldosterone is the fact that Venning (313a) was unable to demonstrate an increased urinary excretion of the compound after ACTH administration to human beings but found that treatment with growth hormone did result in a significant increased excretion.

D. Catabolism of Adrenocortical Hormones

1. *General Aspects*

Important differences have been demonstrated by *in vitro* and *in vivo* experiments dealing with metabolism of adrenocortical steroids. When adrenocortical hormones were administered to human subjects, the preponderance of reduced metabolites isolated from the urine were in the 5β or pregnane (C_{21}) and etiocholane (C_{19}) series. This has not been true when Δ^4-3-keto adrenocortical steroids have been incubated with tissue preparations or perfused through animal glands. Under these *in vitro* conditions the reduced metabolites have been of the 5α or allopregnane (C_{21}) and androstane (C_{19}) series. The reason for this discrepancy is, at the moment, unexplained, and since most of the *in vivo* experiments have been done on human subjects and practically all of the *in vitro* experiments done with animals, usually rodent tissue, it is tempting to suggest a species difference. That this is not the whole explanation is indicated by the fact that progesterone administered to rabbits was converted to, and excreted in the urine as, the 5β steroid, pregnane-3α,20α-diol (124). Two other observations that argue against simple species differences are the findings by Tompkins and Isselbacher (298) that cortisone may be reduced to the 5β type compound by a rat liver preparation and the finding of Horwitt and Segaloff (146) that rabbit liver converts progesterone to pregnane-3α,20α-diol. In view of these recent findings, it is suggested that the tissues contain individual reducing enzyme systems capable of producing both 5α and 5β reduced steroids. The products obtained (5α and/or 5β) are probably dependent on the type of tissue preparation employed in an individual experiment. For example, in the experiments of Tompkins and Isselbacher it is possible that their fractionation procedure specifically removes the Δ-5β-hydrogenase from the Δ-5α-hydrogenase system.

A second aspect of steroid metabolism of interest is the question of 6-oxygenated compounds. Thus far, all *in vitro* 6-hydroxylations involving either the corpus luteum, the adrenal, or liver have yielded steroid predominately containing the 6β-hydroxy group. In only one instance has a 6α-hydroxy derivative been demonstrated. That was the case when 6α-hydroxy-Δ^4-androstene-3,17-dione was isolated after incubation of Δ^4-androstene-3,17-dione with a bovine adrenal homogenate (204). In one experiment involving the guinea pig, the administration of cortisol resulted in the excretion of significant amounts of 6β-hydroxycortisol. Further, two urinary steroids isolated from human pregnancy urine containing the 6-hydroxy grouping were in the α-series, namely 3α,6α-dihydroxyallopregnan-20-one and 3α,6α-dihydroxypregnan-20-one (170, 260b). The explanation for these facts might lie in the possibility that 6β-hydroxylation is in fact the physiological route and that the 6β-hydroxy group is inverted to the 6α-hydroxy group in the course of metabolism when ring A is reduced. This could explain the observed facts, including the fact that the hydroxy group was still β in the urinary metabolite after cortisol administration in the guinea pig. The recent finding of Meyer et al. (204), however, that 6α-hydroxylation does actually occur with adrenal tissue indicates that both 6-hydroxylations are possible and no inversion need take place to explain the facts.

Differences in metabolism between in vitro and in vivo experiments have been observed with respect to the reduction of the C-20 ketone group (80). In vivo experiments in man have led exclusively to the formation of the C-20α-hydroxy derivatives of progesterone, deoxycorticosterone, 11-dehydrocorticosterone, 3β-hydroxy-Δ5-pregnen-20-one, and Δ4,16-pregnadiene-3,20-dione. In vitro studies involving cortisone and cortisol perfused through rat livers, deoxycorticosterone and 11-deoxycortisol incubated with rat liver tissue preparations, and progesterone incubated with bovine corpus luteum or perfused through bovine adrenals, have yielded C-20β-hydroxy derivatives. That this is not due simply to species difference or to in vitro versus in vivo technique is illustrated by these additional findings: progesterone incubated with rabbit liver tissue resulted in the formation of pregnane-3α,20α-diol, progesterone administered to rabbits resulted in the excretion of pregnane-3α,20α-diol, and the administration of cortisol to guinea pigs resulted in the excretion of both the C-20α-hydroxy and C-20β-hydroxy derivatives.

2. Catabolism in Human Subjects (In Vivo)

The metabolism of certain adrenocortical steroids has already been discussed, including estrone and $C_{19}O_2$ and $C_{19}O_3$ androgens as well as progesterone. The metabolism of progesterone has been discussed both from the point of view of reductive changes that occur at carbon atoms 3, 4, 5, and 20 and from that of the various types of hydroxylations that are possible. It is therefore unnecessary at this point to further detail the metabolism of these biologically active substances.

The two adrenocortical hormones, 17α-hydroxyprogesterone and 11-deoxycortisol, undergo specific catabolic changes involving essentially two pathways. These substances yield C_{19} metabolites of the 17-ketosteroid

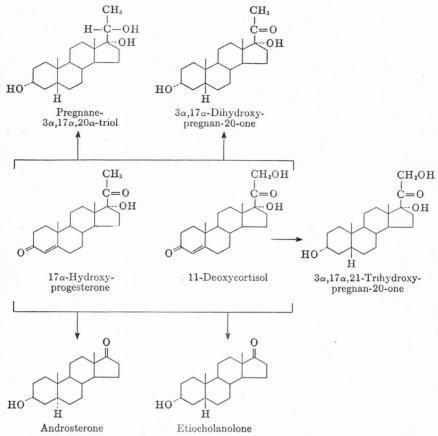

Fig. 9. Metabolism of 17α-hydroxyprogesterone and 11-deoxycortisol (human *in vivo*).

type as well as certain specific metabolites in the C_{21} series. Both 17α-hydroxyprogesterone and 11-deoxycortisol may be converted to androsterone and etiocholanolone, the latter 17-ketosteroid being formed in by far the greater amount (12, 12b, 72, 99) (Fig. 9). Three C_{21} metabolites, including pregnane-3α,17α,20α-triol, 3α,17α-dihydroxypregnan-20-one, and 3α,17α,21-trihydroxypregnan-20-one, have been observed (80, 173). The evidence for the presence of these compounds is still indirect rather than direct; that is, two of these metabolites, pregnanetriol and the tetrahydro derivative (5β) have been definitely demonstrated to arise after the administration of the dihydro derivative (5β) (303). Since C_{21} compounds are known to be reduced preferentially to the 3α-pregnane form in human

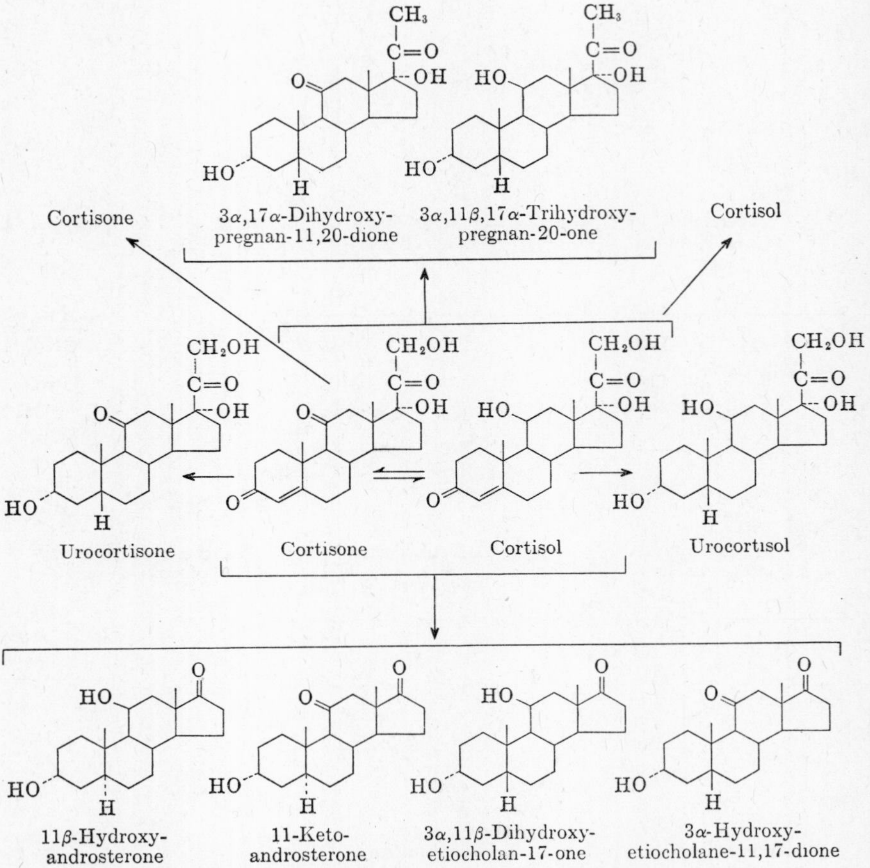

FIG 10.   Metabolism of cortisone and cortisol (human *in vivo*).

metabolism, there is a reasonable certainty that this compound is actually a true intermediate in the reaction.   Richardson *et al.* (248) have presented evidence in man for the relationship between 11-deoxycortisol and the tetrahydro derivative, $3\alpha,17\alpha,21$-trihydroxypregnan-20-one.

Cortisol and cortisone yield three types of metabolic products when studied by *in vivo* methods (Fig. 10).   Since the 11-keto group and 11β-hydroxy group are interchangeable in metabolism, both steroids yield essentially the same metabolic products.   Quantitatively there are some differences, but qualitatively no differences are expected to occur.   The first group of *in vivo* metabolites consist of cortisol and cortisone themselves, which are invariably excreted in human urine (31–33, 54, 198, 276, 277, 330).

A second group of metabolites include those derivatives in which reduction has occurred at carbons 3, 4, 5, and/or 21. Urocortisone, a metabolite involving the reduction of carbons 3, 4, and 5, is quantitatively the most important metabolite of this group. A tetrahydro derivative of cortisol, urocortisol, also appears in the urine but in concentrations decidedly less than those found for urocortisone. Two additional C_{21} ring A reduced steroids are possible, but only one of these compounds has as yet been isolated, this being $3\alpha,17\alpha$-dihydroxypregnane-11,20-dione (31–33, 35, 54, 171, 248, 276, 277).

A third major class of cortisol and cortisone metabolites is the 17-ketosteroids. These consist of the same array of 11-oxygenated-17-ketosteroids that are produced from adrenosterone and 11β-hydroxy-Δ^4-androstene-3,17-dione, the difference being that the 17-ketosteroids derived from cortisone and cortisol are primarily of the etiocholane series; that is, 3α, 11β-dihydroxyetiocholan-17-one and 3α-hydroxyetiocholane-11,17-dione. The two 17-ketosteroids in the androstane series, 11β-hydroxyandrosterone and 11-ketoandrosterone, are also formed and are considered to be the minor constituents (12a, 31–33, 171). However, it is the androstane derivatives that are responsible for the androgenic properties of cortisol and cortisone when these steroids are administered in high concentrations.

As in the case of cortisol and cortisone, the metabolites of corticosterone and 11-dehydrocorticosterone appear to be interchangeable. One *in vivo* metabolism study demonstrated that 11-dehydrocorticosterone can be converted to $3\alpha,20$-dihydroxypregnan-11-one (194). In a second experiment, 11-dehydrocorticosterone was metabolized to the tetrahydro derivative $3\alpha,21$-dihydroxypregnane-11,20-dione (248). Corticosterone is metabolized to the same steroid (85) and to two tetrahydro derivatives of corticosterone, namely, $3\alpha,11\beta,21$-trihydroxypregnan-20-one (248) and $3\alpha,11\beta,21$-trihydroxyallopregnan-20-one (85). These latter workers point out that in contrast to progesterone, cortisone, and other C_{21} steroids, corticosterone yields a major ketonic metabolite in the 5α series. These two adrenocortical steroids do not yield 17-ketosteroids in metabolism, since, as in the case of progesterone or deoxycorticosterone, the side chain cannot be oxidatively removed, owing to the absence of the 17-hydroxy group (Fig. 11).

Fukushima *et al.* (98a) synthesized tritium containing cortisone so that 70 % of the radioactivity was located at C-16. Certain difficulties arose when the compound was used for metabolic studies (99). Removal of the side chain with the formation of a 17-ketosteroid resulted in metabolites capable of exchange with hydrogen of the medium by way of the enol form at carbons 16, 17.

Deoxycorticosterone administered to human subjects is known to give

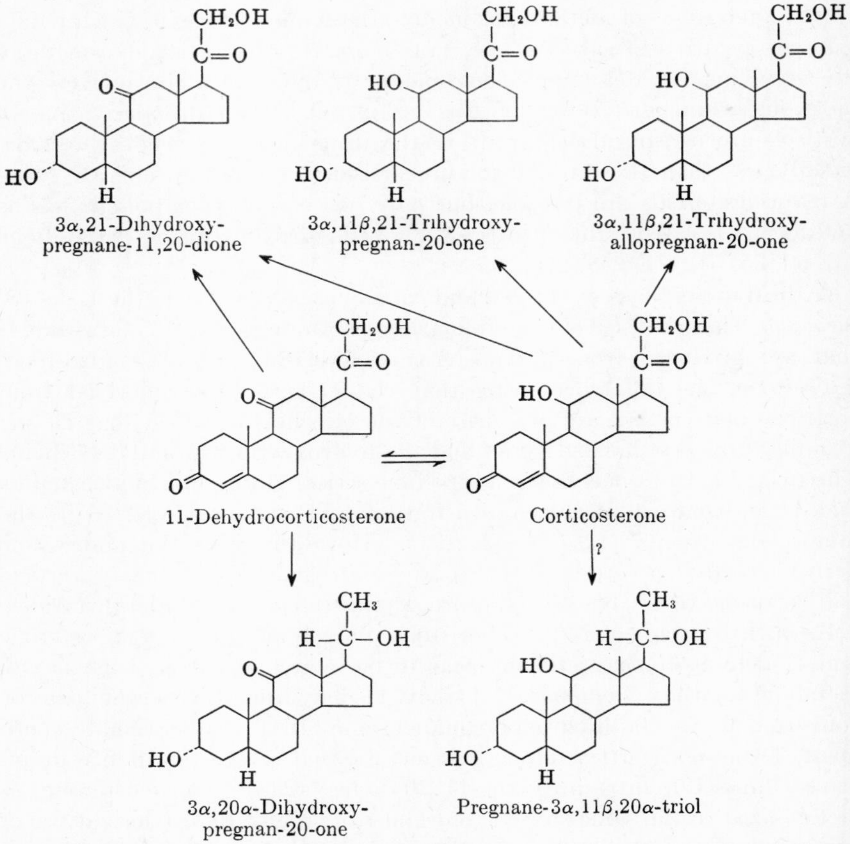

FIG. 11. Metabolism of 11-dehydrocorticosterone and corticosterone (human *in vivo*).

rise to pregnane-$3\alpha,20\alpha$-diol (144) as well as to a tetrahydro derivative, $3\alpha,21$-dihydroxypregnan-20-one (248).

Deoxycorticosterone-21-C^{14} was administered intravenously to a woman, and 83 % of the total radioactivity contained in the urine was found in the neutral fraction. This neutral fraction was obtained by glucuronidase hydrolysis followed by adjustment of the pH of the urine to 1 prior to ether extraction (99).

3. *Catabolism in Various Species (In Vivo)*

In vivo studies of cortisol in the guinea pig have not revealed the presence of any detectable ring A C_{21}-reduced steroids in the urine. Rather, all of the steroid metabolites thus far isolated still possessed the Δ^4-3-

ketone grouping.   These studies involved the extraction of the urine with ethyl acetate at pH 6 so that only unconjugated metabolites were studied. Further studies employing glucuronidase for the possible isolation of conjugated steroids, and perhaps ring A reduced steroids, are indicated. After cortisol feeding, in addition to unchanged cortisol, 6β-hydroxycortisol, 20α and 20β reduced derivatives were isolated (29, 30).   Other highly polar Δ^4-3-ketones have been detected by paper chromatographic techniques but not as yet identified.   The oral administration of cortisone to the guinea pig produced an array of urinary metabolites similar to those found after cortisol feeding, including the presence of cortisol and no detectable quantities of the administered cortisone.

Deoxycorticosterone administered to chimpanzees (144), rabbits (143), and mice (233) was converted to and excreted in the urine in part as pregnane-3α,20α-diol.

Deoxycorticosterone-21-C^{14} (233) when administered to mice was excreted in the urine, feces, and expired air, and 5 % remained fixed in the tissues.   In a typical experiment extending over a 6-day period, 11.7 % of the label appeared in the expired air.   The urine contained 33 %, and the feces a total of 28.9 %.

In a second experiment, deoxycorticosterone-21-C^{14} acetate was administered subcutaneously, and the excreta collected for a 7-day period.   In addition to crystalline pregnane-3α,20α-diol being identified, it was found that 57.3 % of the C^{14} was excreted in the urine and 13.7 % in the feces. A second steroid, as yet unidentified, appeared to arise as a direct metabolite of the administered steroid since the specific activity was 41,000 c./min./mg. as compared to a count of 48,000 for the deoxycorticosterone-21-C^{14}.

11-Dehydrocorticosterone-21-C^{14} was synthesized by Hsia et al. (147) and studied in two spayed adult rats.   In this preliminary paper it was reported that no appreciable amount of radioactivity could be detected in the expired air and that the bulk of radioactivity was recovered in the feces.

4. In Vitro Studies

In vitro studies by Schneider (278) with deoxycorticosterone have yielded four C_{21} metabolites.   These experiments were done with rat liver slices, and the ring A reduction products were of the (5α) allopregnane series.   The diketone, 21-hydroxyallopregnane-3,20-dione, considered to be the first reduced intermediate, has been isolated.   Both the 3α and 3β hydroxy derivatives were identified.   In another study the transformation of deoxycorticosterone to the same diketone and to the 3β-hydroxy derivative has been realized, using the perfusion technique and the bovine adrenal

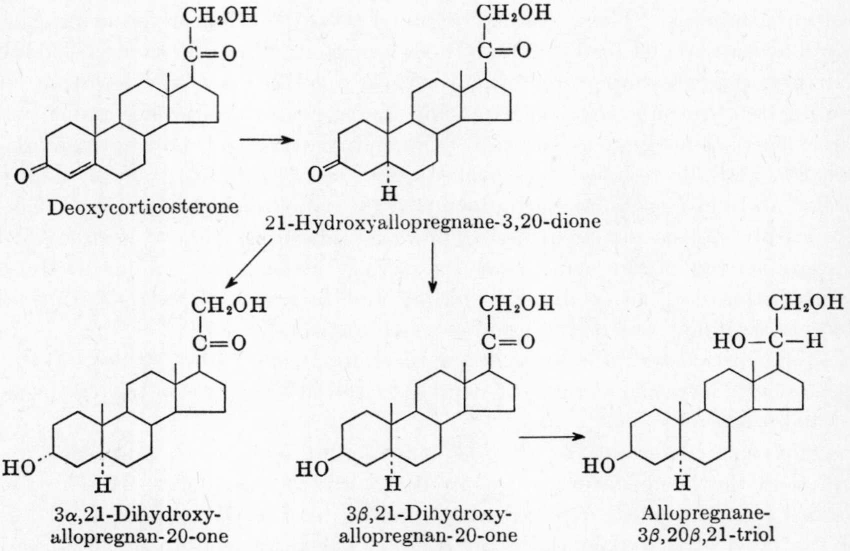

FIG. 12.   Metabolism of deoxycorticosterone (rat liver *in vitro*).

(166, 203).   The fourth *in vitro* metabolite, a triol, allopregnane-$3\beta,20\beta$-21-triol, was obtained after rat liver incubation (278) (Fig. 12).

A possible intermediate (human *in vivo* metabolism) in the metabolism of 11-deoxycortisol, $17\alpha,21$-dihydroxypregnane-3,20-dione, was incubated with a rat liver homogenate and converted to the 3α-hydroxy derivative, $3\alpha,17\alpha,21$-trihydroxypregnane-3,20-dione (306).

11-Deoxycortisol incubated with rat liver homogenates did not yield any 5β reduced products, as would be expected from human *in vivo* studies, but instead, all the isolated products were of the 5α series.   These metabolites included $3\beta,17\alpha,21$-trihydroxyallopregnan-20-one, $3\alpha,17\alpha,21$-trihydroxyallopregnan-20-one, $17\alpha,20\beta,21$-trihydroxy-Δ^4-pregnen-3-one, $17\alpha,21$-dihydroxyallopregnane-3,20-dione, and androsterone (96). (Fig. 13).

Caspi *et al.* (47, 48) have perfused cortisone and cortisol through rat livers and isolated a series of reduced metabolites as well as 17-ketosteroids.   With cortisone, the reduction products $17\alpha,20\beta,21$-trihydroxy-Δ^4-pregnene-3,20-dione and cortisol were isolated and identified.   Reduction of the ring A yielded two tetrahydro derivatives, $3\alpha,17\alpha,21$-trihydroxyallopregnane-11,20-dione and $3\beta,17\alpha,21$-trihydroxyallopregnane-11,20-dione, and reduction at C-11 as well as ring A yielded the two corresponding 11β-hydroxytetrahydro derivatives.   Two 17-ketosteroids, adrenosterone and 11-ketoandrosterone, were isolated.   Two tetrols,

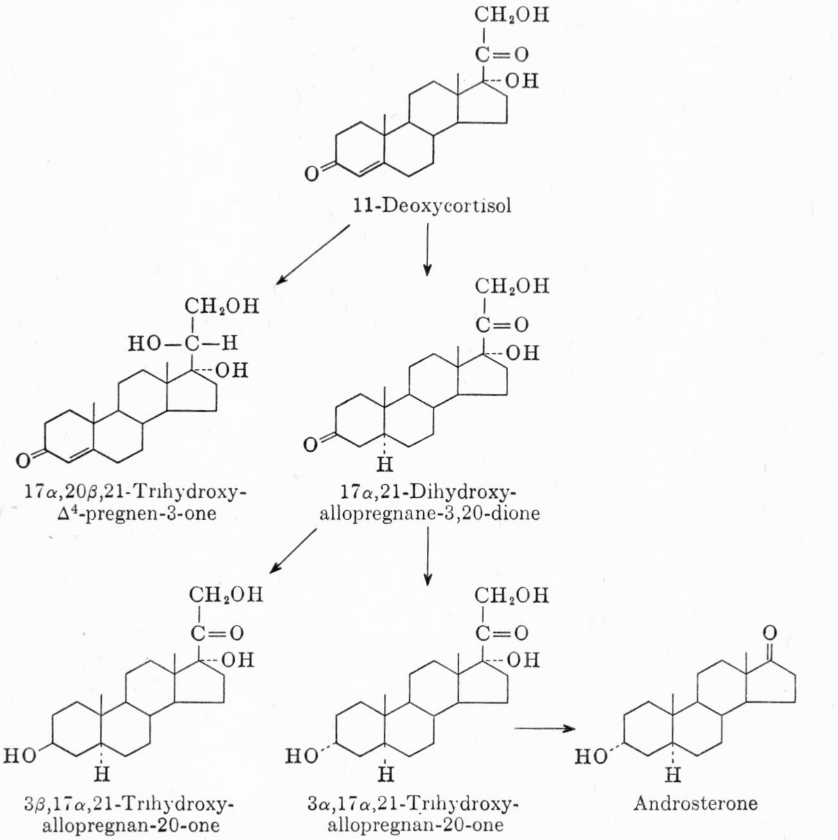

FIG. 13.   Metabolism of 11-deoxycortisol (rat liver *in vitro*).

$3\beta,17\alpha,20\beta,21$-tetrahydroxyallopregnan-11-one and $11\beta,17\alpha,20\beta,21$-tetra-hydroxy-$\Delta^4$-pregnen-3-one, were also isolated.   These studies involving cortisone show similar transformation (particularly reduction to the 5α form) to those found in the deoxycorticosterone and 11-deoxycortisol studies but are quite different from those of Tompkins and Isselbacher (298), who used a purified liver preparation and found only 5β-reduction of the cortisone molecule (Fig. 14).

Cortisol perfused through rat livers gave rise to five metabolites including three C_{21} reduction products, $17\alpha,20\beta,21$-trihydroxy-Δ^4-pregnene-3,11-dione, allopregnane-$3\beta,11\beta,17\alpha,20\beta,21$-pentol, and $3\beta,11\beta,17\alpha,21$-tetrahydroxyallopregnan-20-one together with two 17-ketosteroids, 11β-hydroxy-Δ^4-androstene-3,17-dione and $3\beta,11\beta$-dihydroxyandrostan-17-one (47).

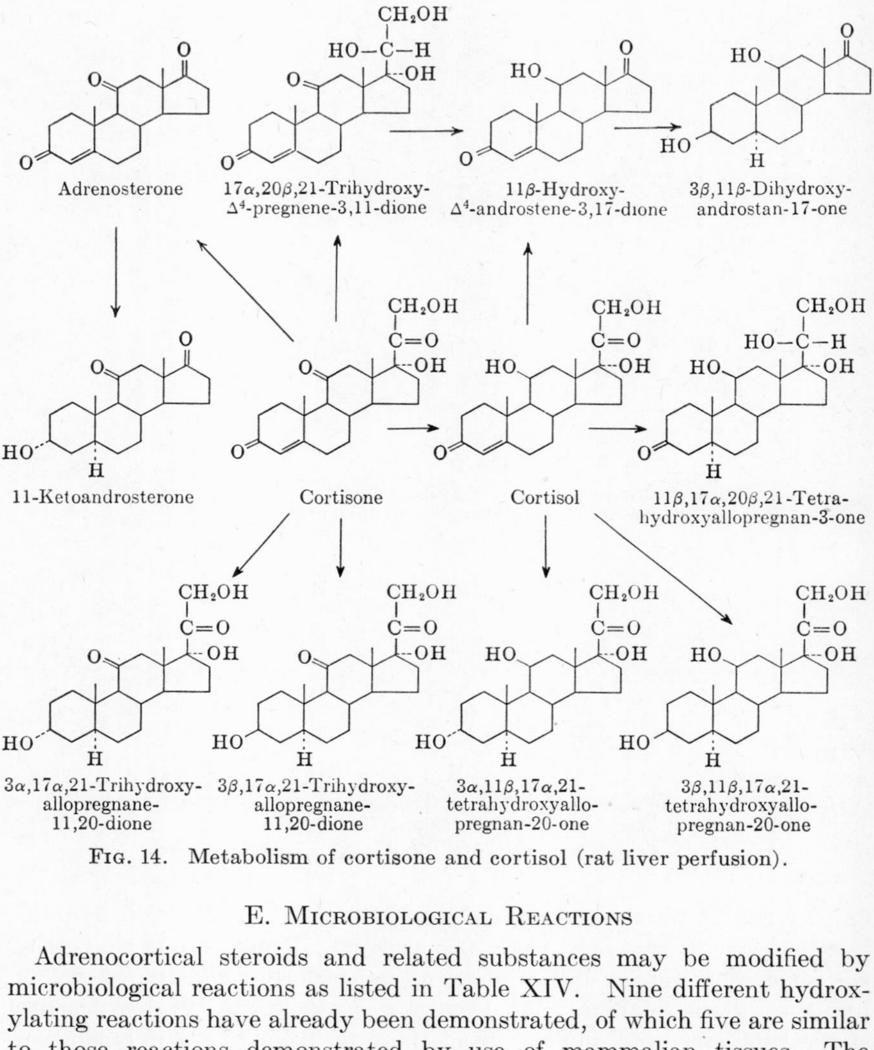

FIG. 14. Metabolism of cortisone and cortisol (rat liver perfusion).

E. MICROBIOLOGICAL REACTIONS

Adrenocortical steroids and related substances may be modified by microbiological reactions as listed in Table XIV. Nine different hydroxylating reactions have already been demonstrated, of which five are similar to those reactions demonstrated by use of mammalian tissues. The hydroxylating reactions probably represent the pathways leading to the disruption of the steroid rings. Introduction of the hydroxy groups can be considered to provide rupture points for C—C bonds.

In addition to the hydroxylating reactions and relatively simple oxidative and reductive changes, three reactions stand out as particularly unique. Two involve dehydrogenations in ring A at positions α,β to the C-3 oxygen function. These reactions result in the formation of the

TABLE XIV

Microbiological Reaction of Adrenocortical Steroids and Related
Compounds
(Reactions of progesterone listed in Table V)

Reaction	Organism	Substrate	Product	Reference
6β-Hydrox-ylation	*Rhizopus arrhizus*	17α-Hydroxy-progesterone	6β,17α-Dihydroxy-progesterone	Meister *et al.* (207)
		Deoxycorti-costerone	6β,21-Dihydroxy-Δ⁴-pregnene-3, 20-dione	Murray and Peterson (214) Eppstein *et al.* (88)
		11-Deoxycor-tisol	6β,17α,21-Trihy-droxy-Δ⁴-preg-nene-3,20-dione	Murray and Peterson (214) Peterson *et al.* (234)
	Cunning-hamella blakes-teena	11-Deoxycor-tisol	6β,17α,21-Trihy-droxy-Δ⁴-preg-nene-3,20-dione	Murray and Peterson (214)
	Helicosty-lum piri-forme	11-Deoxycor-tisol	6β,17α,21-Trihy-droxy-Δ⁴-preg-nene-3,20-dione	
7β-Hydrox-ylation	*Rhizopus arrhizus*	3β,21-Dihy-droxyallo-pregnan-20-one	3β,7β,21-Trihy-droxyallopreg-nan-20-one	Kahnt *et al.* (152) Murray and Peterson (214)
8-Hydroxyl-ation	*Helicosty-lum piri-forme*	11-Deoxycor-tisol	8,17α,21-Trihy-droxy-Δ⁴-preg-nene-3,20-dione	Murray and Peterson (214)
11α-Hydrox-ylation	*Rhizopus nigri-cans*	Deoxycorti-costerone	Epicorticosterone	Murray and Peterson (214) Eppstein *et al.* (88)
		17α-Hydroxy-progesterone	11α,17α-Dihy-droxyprogester-one	Murray and Peterson (214) Meister *et al* (201)

TABLE XIV—(*Continued*)

Reaction	Organism	Substrate	Product	Reference
11α-hydroxylation (*con't.*)	*Helicostylum piriforme*	11-Deoxycortisol	Epicortisol	Murray and Peterson (214)
	Cunninghamella blakesteena	11-Deoxycortisol	Epicortisol	
	Rhizopus arrhizus	17α-Hydroxyprogesterone	11α,17α-Dihydroxyprogesterone	Murray and Peterson (214)
		Deoxycorticosterone	Epicorticosterone	Kahnt *et al.* (152)
		11-Deoxycortisol	Epicortisol	
	Aspergillus niger	17α-Hydroxyprogesterone	11α,17α-Dihydroxyprogesterone	Fried *et al.* (98)
		Deoxycorticosterone	Epicorticosterone	
		11-Deoxycortisol	Epicortisol	
11β-Hydroxylation	*Streptomyces fradiae*	11-Deoxycortisol	Cortisol	Collingsworth *et al.* (53)
	Cunninghamella blakesteena	11-Deoxycortisol	Cortisol	Murray and Peterson (214) Hanson *et al.* (108)
14-Hydroxylation	*Helicostylum piriforme*	11-Deoxycortisol	14,17α,21-Trihydroxy-Δ⁴-pregnene-3,20-dione	Murray and Peterson (214)
16α-Hydroxylation	*Actinomycetes*	Progesterone	16α-Hydroxyprogesterone	Perlman *et al.* (232)
17α-Hydroxylation	*Cephalothecium roseum*	11-Dehydrocorticosterone	Cortisone	Meister *et al.* (201A)
	Trichothecium	Corticosterone	Cortisol	Meystre *et al.* (206A)

TABLE XIV—(*Continued*)

Reaction	Organism	Substrate	Product	Reference
21-Hydroxylation	*Ophiobolus* (*Scolecosporae*)	11-Keto-progesterone	11-Dehydrocorticosterone	Meystre *et al.* (206A)
		17α-Hydroxy-progesterone	11-Deoxy-cortisol	
Δ⁵-3β-Hydroxy → Δ⁴-3-ketone	*Rhizopus arrhizus*	3β-Hydroxy-Δ⁵-pregnen-20-one	Progesterone	Murray and Peterson (214)
Δ⁴-Group → 5α-Saturated group	*Rhizopus nigricans*	11-Deoxycortisol	11α,17α,21-Trihydroxyallopregnane-3,20-dione	
11β-Hydroxy group → 11-ketone	*Cunninghamella blakesteena*	Cortisol	Cortisone	
Formation of ring D lactone	*Aspergillus flavus*	17α-Hydroxy-progesterone	Testololactone	Peterson *et al.* (235)
Formation of Δ¹-group	*Fusarium solani*	Deoxycorticosterone	Δ¹,⁴-Androstadiene-3,17-dione	Vischer and Wettstein (314)
		3β-Hydroxy-Δ⁵-pregnen-20-one	Δ¹,⁴-Androstadiene-3,17-dione	
		3β-Acetoxy-allopregnan-20-one	Δ¹,⁴-Androstadiene-3,17-dione	
		Allopregnan-3,20-dione	Δ¹,⁴-Androstadiene-3,17-dione	
C₂₁ → C₁₉-17-ketone	*Fusarium solani*	Deoxycorticosterone	Δ¹,⁴-Androstadiene-3,17-dione	Vischer and Wettstein (314)
		3β-Hydroxy-Δ⁵-pregnen-20-one		
		Allopregnan-3,20-dione		

TABLE XIV—(*Continued*)

Reaction	Organism	Substrate	Product	Reference
$C_{21} \rightarrow C_{19}$-17-ketone (*con't.*)	*Fusarium solani*	3β-Acetoxy-allopregnan-20-one		Vischer and Wettstein (314)
		3β-Hydroxy-Δ^5-pregnen-20-one	Dehydroepian-drosterone	
5$\beta \rightarrow \Delta^4$-group	*Fusarium solani*	Allopregnan-3,20-dione	$\Delta^{1,4}$-Androsta-diene-3,17-dione	
		3β-Acetoxy-allopregnan-20-one		
3β-Hydroxy group $\rightarrow$ 3-ketone group	*Fusarium solani*	3β-Acetoxy-allopregnan-20-one	$\Delta^{1,4}$-Androsta-diene-3,17-dione	

Δ^1 and Δ^4 groups from saturated compounds and are not known to occur in mammalian tissues. The third reaction, the removal of the two carbon side chains in the absence of a 17-hydroxyl group, has not been reported for mammalian tissues, and the possibility exists that the reaction proceeds by way of a 17α-hydroxy intermediate.

VII. Mammalian Enzymes Influencing Steroid Reactions

It is anticipated that steroid metabolism involves a great number of diverse enzyme systems. When one contemplates the many biosynthetic steps between acetate and a steroid nucleus or even conversion of a complex molecule such as cholesterol to either a C_{21} or C_{19} steroid, numerous enzyme systems are expected to participate. Studies to date have taught us little concerning these biosynthetic enzymes leading to the steroid nucleus and/or steroid nucleus plus the characteristic ethyl side chain. Some progress, however, has been made in the elucidation of those systems which are concerned with steroid metabolic changes involving the intact steroid nucleus.

Steroid enzymes involving certain biosynthetic and catabolic reactions have been reviewed recently, and general class names have been suggested (80). Those associated with mammalian tissues may be listed in the following manner:

1. Hydroxylases—the enzyme systems that selectively introduce hydroxyl groups at specific points in the nucleus or side chain.

2. Hydrogenases—enzyme systems that reduce ketonic groups to secondary alcohols having specific stereoisomeric configurations. The reactions catalyzed by these enzyme systems are probably reversible, and the enzymes indicated in this group are most likely the same as those listed under dehydrogenases except for the state of oxidation of the cofactors.

3. Dehydrogenases—enzyme systems that oxidize secondary alcohols having specific stereoisomer configurations to ketones. (See discussion under (*2*) above.)

4. Δ-Hydrogenase—enzyme systems that reduce double bonds in the nucleus possessing, in some cases, stereo specificity.

5. Desmolases—enzyme systems that rupture carbon to carbon linkages.

6. Deoxylases—enzyme systems that reduce alcoholic groups to corresponding hydrocarbon.

A. Hydroxylases

1. 6β-Hydroxylase.
2. 6α-Hydroxylase.
3. 11β-Hydroxylase.
4. 16α-Hydroxylase.
5. 17α-Hydroxylase.
6. 21-Hydroxylase.

In 1949, Hayano *et al.* (117) incubated deoxycorticosterone with adrenocortical slices and adrenal homogenates and demonstrated the formation of material which possessed glycogenic activity when tested in the fasting-adrenalectomized mouse. The conclusion was reached that 11β-hydroxylation had occurred and that deoxycorticosterone was converted to corticosterone. This conclusion was justified, as seen from subsequent reports containing definitive isolation of the 11β-hydroxy derivatives of deoxycorticosterone, 11-deoxycortisol, Δ^4-androstene-3,17-dione, and progesterone, after incubating the proper substrates with adrenal tissue preparations (24, 114, 153, 200, 270, 295). This enzyme system has been studied in some detail.

Adrenal homogenates are active as are mitochondrial residues prepared by centrifugation at 5000 × g. Active acetone powders of this adrenal residue have been prepared. The optimum pH is 7.4, and fumarate and TPN are requirements along with an oxygen atmosphere (114).

The mechanism of hydroxylation does not appear to proceed by way of the $\Delta^{9(11)}$ or $\Delta^{11(12)}$ intermediate, since the incubation of these two intermediates did not lead to satisfactory yields of 11β-hydroxylated products. $17\alpha,21$-Dihydroxy-$\Delta^{4,9(11)}$-pregnadiene-3,20-dione, 21-hydroxy-$\Delta^{4,9(11)}$-pregnadiene-3,20-dione, and $\Delta^{4,11}$-pregnadiene-3,20-dione were so studied, and in each case the yield of 11β-hydroxy derivative was lower than that from the corresponding ring A saturated compound. To further rule out the unsaturated intermediate, 11-deoxycortisol was subjected to the 11β-hydroxylating enzyme preparation in the presence of deuterium oxide. No significant uptake of deuterium oxide could be detected. Miescher *et al.* (207) reported approximately 20 % 11β-hydroxylation of $17\alpha,21$-dihydroxy-$\Delta^{9(11)}$-pregnene-3,20-dione and suggest that this $\Delta^{9(11)}$-steroid is a possible intermediate in the hydroxylating reaction. The results of Hayano and Dorfman (116) do not agree with such a conclusion.

A possible mechanism of 11β-hydroxylation involving the introduction of the hydroxyl group as a free radical has been proposed by Levy *et al.* (168). Experimental proof for or against this idea is not available.

Brownie and Grant (24) prepared a mitochondrial 11β-hydroxylating preparation which showed a "concurrent requirement for oxidative phosphorylation" in which various members of the citric acid cycle could participate readily. These investigators reported that the reaction is dependent upon a coupled phosphorylation mechanism—a finding which is at variance with the report of Hayano and Dorfman (114, 116).

Studies by Hayano and Dorfman (114) have reported that an 11β-hydroxylating enzyme preparation can perform the reaction on a variety of steroids, but the percentage yields varied with the structure. The order of efficiency follows:

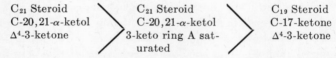

C_{21} Steroid		C_{21} Steroid		C_{19} Steroid
C-20,21-α-ketol		C-20,21-α-ketol		C-17-ketone
Δ^4-3-ketone		3-keto ring A saturated		Δ^4-3-ketone

6α- and 6β-hydroxylases are indicated in adrenal tissue (204, 106) and 6β-hydroxylase in the corpus luteum (120). Although the reactions have been established by isolations and identifications of the expected products, enzymological studies are yet to be done.

Rabbit liver slices contain an enzyme which can perform 16α-hydroxylation on dehydroepiandrosterone (281). No details as to the characteristics or the requirements of this enzyme have as yet been reported.

A mitochondrial adrenal preparation performs, in the presence of ATP and DPN, 21-hydroxylation. Hayano and Dorfman (113) described the presence of this enzyme, 21-hydroxylase, in an adrenal homogenate but neither purified the enzyme nor studied the requirements. The supernatant of adrenal homogenates (20,000 × g) contains both 17α-hydroxylase and 21-hydroxylase which require ATP and DPN or TPN (241, 240).

B. Hydrogenases

The hydrogenases and dehydrogenases are discussed in this chapter on the basis that they are individual enzyme systems, although it is recognized that the reductions and oxidations may well be reversible.   Actually, one such system has been described (298).   In this system, $17\alpha,21$-dihydroxypregnane-$3,11,20$-trione is converted to urocortisone in the presence of reduced TPN or DPN and the urocortisone reversibly oxidized to $17\alpha,21$-dihydroxypregnane-$3,11,20$-trione in the presence of TPN or DPN.

On the basis of steroid reactions already described in the literature it appears that many ketones on the steroid molecule may be reduced.   In all instances two stereoisomeric forms of the resulting hydroxyl group are possible, and in fact evidence is at hand for both.   If we assume that for each reduction a separate enzyme is possible, then the present experimental evidence would indicate a 3α-hydrogenase (48, 96, 278, 306), a 3β-hydrogenase (48, 238, 278, 306), an 11β-hydrogenase (89), a 16α-hydrogenase (293), a 17α-hydrogenase (51), a 17β-hydrogenase (257, 258, 282), a 20β-hydrogenase (30, 48, 96, 120), and a 20α-hydrogenase (30, 146).

Few enzymological studies of the steroid hydrogenases have been reported.   Ungar and Dorfman (306) have shown the presence of 3α-hydrogenase in rabbit liver and kidney homogenates, with the latter source being the richer.   With rat liver the major 3α-hydrogenase activity was found in a cell-free homogenate supernatant.   The enzyme activity was retained in the supernatant of an acetone powder which on dialysis gives a severely decreased activity but which could be restored (to 95%) by the addition of 0.002 M DPN.

Tompkins and Isselbacher (298) appear to be working with the same enzyme system as that reported by Ungar and Dorfman (306).   The former workers found the activity in the particle-free supernatant of a sucrose or phosphate rat liver homogenate.   The activity was precipitated between 55% and 70% saturation with ammonium sulfate.   The reaction, reduction of the 3-ketone to the 3α-hydroxy group, required DPNH or TPNH.   The reaction was found to be completely inhibited by p-chloromercuribenzoate (5×10^{-4} M) and the inhibition could be relieved by cysteine or glutathione (5×10^{-3} M).

The supernatant fraction obtained by centrifuging rat liver homogenate preparations at $5000 \times$ g contained the 11β-hydrogenase, and an acetone powder of whole homogenate supplemented with DPN was active (89). Using paper chromatographic procedures, Amelung et al. (2) demonstrated the presence of 11β-hydrogenase in rat, pork, and beef liver and also reported that the activity was associated with the structural elements (microsomes) of the cell.

C. Dehydrogenases

Six steroid dehydrogenases are indicated on the basis of *in vitro* and *in vivo* studies. Each of these enzyme systems is most likely identical with the corresponding hydrogenases. These include a 3α-dehydrogenase (282, 298), a 3β-dehydrogenase (265), an 11β-dehydrogenase (31), a 17β-dehydrogenase (50, 51, 267), a 17α-dehydrogenase (156), and a 20α-dehydrogenase (104). Of these, the 17β-dehydrogenase has been studied in the greatest detail by Samuels and his co-workers.

The 17β-dehydrogenase was found in the supernatant fraction (steer liver) after centrifuging for 1 hour at 20,000 $\times$ g. The enzyme could be precipitated by complete saturation with ammonium sulfate. A study of the kinetics of the reaction indicated a Michaelis constant, $Km = 3.3 \times 10^{-5}$ mole per liter (296). The same enzyme appears to be present in kidney tissue (158, 163, 317). Wotiz *et al.* (328) have reported the presence of 17β-dehydrogenase in a variety of human tissues including skin, prostate, and mammary cancer, as opposed to the negative finds of Samuels (263, 264), who was unable to detect significant concentrations of the enzyme in such tissues as rabbit uterus, rat prostate and seminal vesicles, and mouse mammary tumor. Species differences may explain the findings.

The C_{21} aldehyde group of 17α-dihydroxy-3,20-dione-Δ^4-pregnen-21-al has been reduced to the C_{21}-alcohol group yielding cortisone. A liver acetone powder preparation contained the enzyme system which required reduced DPN or TPN (279). In another study both 17α-hydroxy-3,11,20-trione-Δ^4-pregnen-21-al and 11β,17α-dihydroxy-3,20-dione-Δ^4-pregnen-21-al yielded cortisone and cortisol, respectively, when incubated with bovine adrenal slices and homogenates (112).

D. Δ-Hydrogenases

Only three Δ-hydrogenases have been demonstrated in mammals by *in vivo* studies or by *in vitro* studies employing their tissues. These include a Δ^4-5β-hydrogenase (146, 264, 266, 298) and a Δ^4-5α-hydrogenase (48, 96, 151, 255, 280).

Samuels and his group (267) have reported a series of investigations on the disappearance of the Δ^4-3-ketone group in testosterone and progesterone. With respect to testosterone, two systems appeared to be present, one requiring DPN and the other requiring citrate. It is quite likely that one of these systems represents either a Δ-5α- or Δ-5β-hydrogenase or both, perhaps requiring citrate, while the second system, requiring DPN, is either the 3α- or 3β-hydrogenase. Certain variations may also occur depending upon the tissue studied and the species. Samuels and West (267) make the point that "the enzyme reducing ring A in progesterone does not require oxygen while that reducing this ring in testosterone does."

The enzyme system reducing ring A of progesterone was stimulated by the presence of one of the tricarboxylic acids but not by DPN or dicarboxylic acids. The authors speculate that the action of the tricarboxylic acid "was due to their ability to form complexes with metal ions since cysteine and cyanide increased the metabolism of progesterone by liver tissue to a similar extent" (325).

These experiments, reduction of ring A, will require further study, since in the disappearance of the Δ^4-3-ketone four stereoisomeric forms are possible and four different enzymes may participate. In such experiments it will be necessary to quantitate and identify each product so that mechanisms and precise pathways may be established. Actually, one such definitive experiment has been reported in which cortisone has been converted to $17\alpha,21$-dihydroxypregnane-3,11,20-trione by a cell-free supernatant from rat liver. The activity could be precipitated by 70 % saturation of ammonium sulfate but not by 55 % saturation. The hydrogen donor is TPNH, and DPNH was found to be inactive. The reduction could be coupled to the oxidation of d-isocitrate by TPN and isocitrate dehydrogenase or to the oxidation of glucose-6-phosphate by TPN with glucose-6-phosphate dehydrogenase. The reaction proceeded faster in nitrogen than air.   Although other Δ^4-3-ketosteroids could act as substrates, the authors pointed out that the question of one or more enzymes was still open (298).

E. Miscellaneous Enzyme Systems

Three desmolases and one deoxylase have been indicated. A 21-deoxylase (143, 144); a 17,20-desmolase (46–48); a 20,21-desmolase (166, 237); and a 20,22-desmolase (175, 259) have been reported. Lynn et al. (175) incubated cholesterol with aqueous particle-free extracts of beef adrenals, ovary, and testis and rat liver with ATP and DPN, and isolated the isocaproic acid in yields up to 5 %. When cholesterol-4-C^{14} was incubated with adrenal extracts, neither progesterone nor pregnenolone could be demonstrated. On the other hand, Saba et al. (259), using a bovine adrenal homogenate and C^{14}-labeled cholesterol, C^{14}-pregnenolone was isolated from the incubate, indicate the presence of 20,22-desmolase.

VIII. Generalizations

The availability of a mass of facts on steroid metabolism has led, naturally, to the possibility of suggesting working hypotheses to bring at least some of the information into a cohesive framework so that further theoretical and applied advances can be efficiently realized. One such hypothesis has been published (72, 80). This is concerned with the *in vivo* reduction of neutral steroid hormones and states in brief that the type of reduction product (from the Δ^4-unsaturated group) formed in metabolism is dependent upon the kind of functional groups (at carbons 11 and 17) present on the steroid nucleus. A second hypothesis, described in a following section of this chapter, is concerned with the physiological-biochemical changes causing certain types of adrenal hyperfunction. These two hypotheses or generalizations may help to unify the field and group the isolated facts in such a manner that the intimate changes in steroid production by specialized tissues can be better understood. These generalizations, at least in some instances, also focus our attention on the fact that specific biochemical changes or defects may be responsible for various syndromes associated with changes in the production of steroid hormones.

A. Nuclear Substitution and Reduction Products of Neutral Steroid Hormones

Detailed arguments have been published (71, 72) for the idea that the Δ^4-3-ketone, which is characteristically present in all neutral steroid hormones, is reduced in the organism to both 5α and 5β stereoisomeric forms and that the ratio of the 5β form to the 5α form is not a chance occurrence but rather determined by the type of substitutions on the nucleus. We may outline the general facts here which indicate (1) that the presence of only an oxygen function at carbon 17, in addition to the Δ^4-3-ketone in ring A (C_{19} steroid), causes the reduction to occur in such a manner that the ratio of 5β-stereoisomers to that of 5α-stereoisomers is approximately 2:1. This has been demonstrated for a variety of compounds in this series, including testosterone, Δ^4-androstene-3,17-dione, dehydroepiandrosterone (easily converted to Δ^4-androstene-3,17-dione), Δ^5-androstene-3β,17β-diol (converted to testosterone and/or Δ^4-androstene-3,17-dione). (2) If a side chain is present at carbon 17, such as in progesterone, without oxygen at carbon 11, the reduction of the Δ^4-3-ketone is such that the ratio of 5β- to 5α-stereoisomers is approximately 20:1. (3) If, instead of a side chain, the modification consists merely of an oxygen function at carbon 11, the reduction of the Δ^4-group is so oriented that the ratio of the 5β to the 5α form is 1:2. (4) When both oxygen substitution at carbon 11 and a side chain are present in the steroid nucleus, the orientation is essentially that of the influence of the side chain alone, and, thus, there is a preponderance of the 5β form.

On the basis of these generalizations concerning the influence of nuclear substitutions on the reduction of the Δ^4-group it is further suggested that when substances like cortisone, cortisol, 17α-hydroxyprogesterone, and 11-deoxycortisol are converted to 17-ketosteroids, they are converted by the mechanism of preliminary reduction of the double bond at carbons 4 and 5 followed by oxidative removal of the side chain. This appears to be the predominating mechanism in the intact organism, since the 17-ketosteroids formed under these conditions are primarily of the etiocholane (5β) type. The fact that 17-ketosteroids derivable from cortisone and cortisol have a ratio of 5β to 5α forms of approximately 9:1 instead of a ratio of 20:1 for the reduction products of a compound like progesterone strongly indicates that at least part of the 17-ketosteroids are derivable through a pathway involving, as a first step, the removal of the side chain and the formation of a Δ^4-3-keto-17-ketosteroid. This latter compound in turn yields two parts of the 5α form to one part of the 5β form, so that the net result of 5β-stereoisomer to 5α-stereoisomer could be 9:1 as the mean figure arising from a 20:1 and 1:2 ratio. If one accepts these figures, then it is calculable that the 17-ketosteroids arising from C_{21}-11-oxygenated steroids arise approximately 92 % by way of the dihydro- or tetrahydro-C_{21} steroids and approximately 8 % by way of the Δ^4-3-keto-17-ketosteroids. Since these ratios are known and since certain values for individual 17-ketosteroids are derivable from direct analysis, it is possible in any one urine to calculate that portion of the 17-ketosteroids which is derived from the various precursors. Sample calculations have been published (71).

B. Hypotheses Concerning Adrenocortical Hyperactivity

A number of well-defined clinical conditions are known to be due to adrenocortical hyperactivity. This section is concerned with the possible biochemical and physiological changes in the adrenal cortex and anterior pituitary which cause the specific types of dysfunction leading to specific clinical states. The discussions will be limited to three types of adrenal hyperactivity. The first type of adrenal hyperactivity represents the Cushing's disease patient and is definable in simplest terms as a set of clinical symptoms due to increased blood concentrations of corticoids such as cortisone and cortisol. These patients exhibit metabolic defects including diabetes, hypertension, moon face, stria, and in the "pure form" no symptoms attributable to excessive androgen production. Adrenal cancer is the second type of hyperactivity that will be considered, and this condition may be characterized by the presence of a malignant tumor coupled with excessive androgen production but no metabolic changes attributable to increased concentration of cortisol. The third type of adrenal hyperactivity will be described under the adrenogenital syndrome characterized by excessive androgen production and the absence of increased cortisol production.

It is recognized that it is not unusual for mixed types of adrenal hyperactivity to exist. Thus, patients have been observed in whom the Cushing's disease can coexist with definite signs of masculinization due to adrenal cancer.

The basic assumptions that will be employed in presenting hypotheses concerning adrenal hyperactivity rest on the plan of adrenal hormone biogenesis presented in another section of this chapter. Essentially, it is considered that normally ACTH stimulates the adrenal to produce C_{21} steroids leading to such steroids as cortisol and corticosterone. By way of an independent pathway, ACTH also stimulates the adrenal to produce C_{19} steroids leading to such steroids as Δ^4-androstene-3,17-dione and 11β-hydroxy-Δ^4-androstene-3,17-dione. Important in this scheme is the idea that the pituitary production of ACTH is dependent upon the concentration of cortisol and that the production of androgens is dependent upon the ACTH production but that androgens do not significantly influence the ACTH concentrations.

Discussions of hypotheses concerning adrenal hyperactivity have been published (73, 73a). In this chapter only an outline is presented, and for complete documentation the original article should be consulted.

In Cushing's disease due to abnormally high concentrations of cortisol it is postulated that the following changes from normal are evident:

1. Increased ACTH production by anterior pituitary.

2. ACTH stimulation of Cushing's adrenal causes disproportionate increased production of C_{21} steroids such as cortisol.

3. Anterior pituitary is relatively refractory to the inhibitory effect of cortisol, so that in spite of increased concentration of this steroid, ACTH level remains increased and high production of cortisol continues producing the disease picture.

Adrenal cancer resulting in masculinization with no cortisol disease, can be visualized as involving the following changes from normal:

1. Adrenal cortex produces steroids autonomously; pituitary ACTH not a factor.

2. C_{19} steroid production tends to be greater than C_{21} steroid production.

3. Bulk of C_{19} and C_{21} are of the Δ^5-3β-hydroxyl type owing to relative lack of enzyme system (3β-dehydrogenase). This causes the excessive excretion of dehydroepiandrosterone, which has been known to be increased as much as 700 times. The predominant concentration of C_{21} steroids are of the Δ^5-3β-hydroxy type.

The adrenogenital syndrome consisting of masculinization of the female or precocious puberty in the male can be summarized as follows:

1. An increased production of pituitary ACTH causes in turn an increased production of both C_{19} and C_{21} steroids by the adrenal.

2. Although the quantity of C_{21} steroids produced by the adrenal is increased, the concentration of cortisol and corticosterone remain relatively low. Since progesterone, 17-hydroxylated, and 11-hydroxylated steroids are increased, whereas cortisol and corticosterone are not proportionately increased, it is suggested that the 21-hydroxylating system is relatively decreased.

3. Because of the situation described in point *2*, the ACTH production of pituitary remains high and the high production of C_{19} steroids continues, leading to excessive androgen stimulation.

The extent of the lack of 21-hydroxylase determines the type of symptoms that are observed. If the lack of 21β-hydroxylase is relatively small, enough cortisol can be produced to maintain the organism against stress, and enough deoxycorticosterone and aldosterone can be produced to maintain proper electrolyte balance. Under these conditions, only virilism and masculinization are observed. On the other hand, if 21-hydroxylation is severely impaired, these patients may actually show severe masculinization with adrenal insufficiency owing to the fact that the cortisol and corticosterone lack may become critical for stress needs and the concentration of deoxycorticosterone and aldosterone may become so limiting that electrolyte metabolism cannot be properly maintained. This condition is typical of that seen in children with the salt-losing syndrome (320).

Of particular importance in the adrenogenital syndrome is the fact that although the principal defect appears to lie at the level of the biosynthesis of the C_{21} steroids, that is, relative inability to 21-hydroxylate steroids, the most pressing symptoms that are usually seen involve the by-product, the increase in androgen production. Thus, it is not unusual that the clinician sees and attempts to treat the by-product of the disease without getting at the primary defect. Wilkins and his group (321) made the important discovery that cortisol or cortisone can alleviate the common symptoms of this disease; this method is a direct treatment of the cause, and the results are entirely in accord with the hypothesis presented here. The administration of exogenous hormone in the form of cortisol and cortisone makes up for the relative lack in 21-hydroxylation by supplying materials which can adequately suppress the hyperactive anterior pituitary with respect to ACTH production. Once the ACTH production is decreased, the stimulation of the adrenal cortex is proportionately decreased; this is then mirrored in a decreased production of the by-products, the androgens, which are the cause of the clinical symptoms. The production of these compounds, in turn, when decreased over sufficient periods of time, causes a reverting of the masculinized individual to a normal state.

Various investigators have speculated on the biochemical and physiological defects leading to the adrenogenital syndrome including Sayers (271), Jailer (149), and Morris (213). Sayers suggested that the syndrome may be a result of aberrant secretory activity of the adrenal cortex or that it may be an "abnormality" in the mechanism concerned with the degradation of the hormone in the liver or other tissues such that the conversion of cortical hormone to androgens proceeds at an abnormally high rate. The second suggestion is unlikely, since cortisone and cortisol cause an amelioration of the disease and not an intensification as would be indicated by conversion of the corticoids to androgens. The adrenogenital syndrome is characterized by high amounts of urinary 11β-hydroxyandrosterone which arises primarily from $C_{19}O_3$ steroids, not the corticoids (254a).

Jailer (149) has discussed the defects concerned with adrenal steroid biogenesis in the adrenogenital syndrome in the following manner:

"It is possible that the enzyme system which is normally responsible for the hydroxylation at the C-11 and C-21 position in the synthesis of Compound F (cortisol) may be deficient. Thus, the synthesis of Compound F would stop at the 17α-hydroxyprogesterone state. Consequently, this normal intermediary in the synthesis of Compound F may be the steroid which is secreted by these adrenals, and is converted by the liver to an androgen. Since insufficient quantities of "F" (cortisol) would be secreted, the pituitary would now secrete excessive amounts of ACTH, cause an hypertrophy of the gland, which would now secrete a normal amount of Compound F (cortisol) for homeostasis. In order to achieve this, excessive amounts of 17α-hydroxyprogesterone would be elaborated. This may be the androgen responsible for the virilism. We have obtained further circumstantial evidence for this hypothesis which is beyond the scope of this discussion."

Jailer's suggestion that there is a relative lack of 21-hydroxylase so that insufficient cortisol is produced to effectively inhibit the ACTH production and/or release is reasonable. The suggestion that 17α-hydroxyprogesterone is the steroid which in metabolism is converted to the offending causative androgen appears to be unreasonable, since this steroid in metabolism in the human being is converted principally to a nonandrogenic 17-ketosteroid, etiocholanolone and in minor quantities to the relatively weak androgen, androsterone. Actually, except for weak androgenic activity when fed to chicks, 17α-hydroxyprogesterone does not possess significant androgenic activity. It is also unlikely that 11β-hydroxylase is relatively deficient, as suggested by Jailer, since in four cases of adrenogenital syndrome tenfold increases of 11β-hydroxyandrosterone (metabolite of 11β-hydroxy-Δ^4-androstene-3,17-dione and adrenosterone)were found in the urine of such patients (254a).

Morris has suggested that the adrenogenital syndrome is characterized by high ACTH production which selectively stimulates the adrenal to produce C_{19} steroids (androgens), and that impaired corticoid production is "due to defects in the later stages; 17α- or 11β-hydroxylation, etc." Morris further points out that the production of ACTH is maintained at a high rate owing to insufficient quantities of endogenous corticoids to inhibit the pituitary. The author agrees with a portion of the thesis of Morris but feels that both the 11β- and 17α-hydroxylating mechanisms are functioning at increased rates and that the true defect is in the 21-hydroxylating mechanism.

REFERENCES

1. Albert, S., Heard, R. D. H., Leblond, C. P., and Saffran, J. *J. Biol. Chem.* **177**, 247 (1949).
2. Amelung, D., Hübener, H. J., Roka, L., and Meyerheim, G. *J. Clin. Endocrinol. and Metabolism* **13**, 1126 (1953).
3. Ashmore, J., Elliott, W. H., Doisy, E. A., Jr., and Doisy, E. A. *J. Biol. Chem.* **200**, 661 (1953).
4. Axelrod, L. R., and Arroyare, G. *J. Am. Chem. Soc.* **75**, 5729 (1953).
5. Axelrod, L. R., and Miller, L. *Arch. Biochem. and Biophys.* **49**, 248 (1954).
6. Barry, M. C., Eidinoff, M. L., Dobriner, K., and Gallagher, T. F. *Endocrinology* **50**, 587 (1952).
7. Beall, D. *Biochem. J.* **32**, 1957 (1938).
8. Beall, D. *Nature* **144**, 76 (1939).
9. Beall, D. *Biochem. J.* **34**, 1293 (1940).
10. Beall, D., and Reichstein, T. *Nature* **142**, 479 (1938).
11. Berger, M., Daudel, R., and Buu-Hoï, N. P. *J. Radiol. électrol.* **28**, 238 (1947), (through Twombly, G. H. *Vitamins and Hormones* **9**, 260 (1951)).
12. Birke, G., and Plantin, L. O. *Science* **118**, 751 (1953).
12a. Birke, G., and Plantin, L. O. *Acta Endocrinol.* **15**, 61 (1954).
12b. Birke, G. *Acta Endocrinol.* **15**, 17 (1954).
13. Bischoff, F., Gray, C. L., and Katherman, R. E. *Endocrinology* **53**, 321 (1953).
14. Bloch, E., Benirschke, K., and Dorfman, R. I. *J. Clin. Endocrinol. and Metabolism,* **15**, 379 (1955).
15. Bloch, E., Dorfman, R. I., and Pincus, G. *Proc. Soc. Exptl. Biol. Med.* **85**, 106 (1954).
16. Bloch, K. *J. Biol. Chem.* **157**, 661 (1945).
17. Bloch, K. *Harvey Lectures* **48**, 68 (1952).
18. Bloch, K., Borek, E., and Rittenberg, D. *J. Biol. Chem.* **162**, 441 (1946).
19. Bocklage, B. C., Nicholas, H. J., Doisy, E. A., Jr., Elliott, W. H., Thayer, S. A., and Doisy, E. A. *J. Biol. Chem.* **202**, 27 (1953).
20. Bonner, J., and Arreguin, B. *Arch. Biochem. and Biophys.* **21**, 109 (1949).
21. Brady, R. O. *J. Biol. Chem.* **193**, 145 (1951).
22. Brady, R. O. *Endocrinology* **52**, 49 (1953).
23. Brooks, R. V., Klyne, W., and Miller, E. *Biochem. J.* **49**, xl (1951).
24. Brownie, A. C., and Grant, J. K. *Biochem. J.* **56**, 25 (1954).
25. Brownie, A. C., and Grant, J. K. *Biochem. J.* **57**, 255 (1954).
26. Bucher, N. L. R. *J. Am. Chem. Soc.* **75**, 498 (1953).
27. Bucher, N. L. R., McGovern, N. H., Kingston, R., and Kennedy, M. H. *Federation Proc.* **12**, 184 (1953).
28. Burstein, S., and Dorfman, R. I. *Proc. Am. Chem. Soc., New York* p. 27C (1954).
29. Burstein, S., and Dorfman, R. I. *J. Biol. Chem.,* **213**, 581 (1955).
30. Burstein, S., Dorfman, R. I., and Nodel, E. M. *J. Biol. Chem.* **213**, 597 (1955).
31. Burstein, S., Savard, K., and Dorfman, R. I. *Endocrinology* **52**, 448 (1953).
32. Burstein, S., Savard, K., and Dorfman, R. I. *Endocrinology* **53**, 88 (1953).

656   RALPH I. DORFMAN

33. Burstein, S., Savard, K., and Dorfman, R. I. *Endocrinology* **53**, 267 (1953).
34. Burstein, S., Ungar, F., Gut, M., and Dorfman, R. I. *Endocrinology* **56**, 267 (1955).
35. Burton, R. B., Keutmann, E. H., and Waterhouse, C. *J. Clin. Endocrinol. and Metabolism* **13**, 48 (1953).
36. Butenandt, A. *Z. angew. Chem.* **44**, 905 (1931).
37. Butenandt, A. *Z. angew. Chem.* **45**, 655 (1932).
38. Butenandt, A. *Wien. Klin. Wochschr.* **47**, 936 (1934).
38a. Butenandt, A., and Dannenbaum, H. *Z. physiol. Chem.* **229**, 192 (1934).
39. Butenandt, A., Dannenbaum, H., and Suranyl, L. *Ber.* **73**, 818 (1940).
40. Butenandt, A., and Westphal, U. *Z. physiol. Chem.* **67**, 1140 (1934).
41. Butler, G. C., and Marrian, G. F. *J. Biol. Chem.* **119**, 565 (1937).
42. Buxton, C. L., and Westphal, U. *Proc. Soc. Exptl. Biol. Med.* **41**, 1284 (1938).
43. Callow, N. H. *Biochem. J.* **33**, 559 (1939).
44. Callow, N. H., and Callow, R. K. *Biochem. J.* **33**, 931 (1939).
45. Callow, N. H., and Callow, R. K. *Biochem. J.* **34**, 276 (1940).
46. Caspi, E., and Hechter, O. *Arch. Biochem. and Biophys.*, **52**, 478 (1954).
47. Caspi, E., Thesis, Ph.D. Dept. of Chemistry Clark U. 1955.
48. Caspi, E., Levy, H., and Hechter, O. *Arch. Biochem. and Biophys.* **45**, 169 (1953).
49. Channon, H. J. *Biochem. J.* **20**, 400 (1926).
50. Clark, L. C., Jr., and Kochakian, C. D. *Endocrinology* **35**, 222 (1944).
51. Clark, L. C., Jr., and Kochakian, C. D. *J. Biol. Chem.* **170**, 23 (1947).
52. Clark, L. C., Jr., Kochakian, C. D., and Lobotsky, J. *J. Biol. Chem.* **171**, 493 (1947).
53. Collingsworth, D. R., Brunner, M. P., and Haines, W. J. *J. Am. Chem. Soc.* **74**, 2382 (1952).
54. Cope, C. L., and Hurloch, B. *Clinical Sci.* **13**, 69 (1954).
55. Cornforth, J. W., Hunter, C. D., and Popjak, G. *Arch. Biochem. and Biophys.* **42**, 481 (1953).
56. Cornforth, J. W., Hunter, G. D, and Popjak, G. *Biochem. J.* **54**, 597 (1953).
57. Daudel, P., Apelgot, S., Buu-Hoï, N. P., Costerousse, O., and Lacassagne, A. *Bull. soc. chim. biol.* **32**, 264 (1950).
58. Daudel, P., Berger, M., Buu-Hoï, N. P., and Lacassagne, A. *Experentia* **2**, 107 (1946).
59. David, K., Dingemanse, E., Freud, J., and Laqueur, E. *Z. physiol. Chem.* **233**, 281 (1935).
60. DeJongh, S. E., Kober, S., and Laqueur, E. *Biochem. Z.* **240**, 247 (1931).
61. Deulofeu, V., and Ferrari, J. *Z. physiol. Chem.* **226**, 192 (1934).
62. Diczfalusy, E. *Acta Endocrinol.* **15**, 317 (1954).
63. Dingemanse, E., Laqueur, E., and Mühlboch, O. *Nature* **141**, 927 (1938).
64. Dobriner, K. Steroids in Experimental and Clinical Practice. Blakiston, Philadelphia, 1951, p. 130.
65. Dobriner, K., Katzenellenbogen, E. R., and Schneider, R. *Arch. Biochem. and Biophys.* **48**, 167 (1954).
66. Dobriner, K., and Lieberman, S. *Ciba Colloq. Endocrinol.* **2**, 381 (1952).
67. Dobriner, K., Rhoads, C. P., Lieberman, S., Hill, B. R., and Fieser, L. F. *Science* **99**, 494 (1944).
68. Doisy, E. A., Thayer, S. A., Levin, L., and Curtis, J. M. *Proc. Soc. Exptl. Biol. Med.* **28**, 88 (1930).

69. Dorfman, R. I.   *Proc. Soc. Exptl. Biol. Med.* **45,** 739 (1940).
70. Dorfman, R. I.   *Proc. Soc. Exptl. Biol. Med.* **46,** 351 (1941).
71. Dorfman, R. I.   *Recent Progr. Hormone Research* **9,** 5 (1954).
72. Dorfman, R. I.   *J. Clin. Endocrinol. and Metabolism* **14,** 318 (1954).
73. Dorfman, R. I.   *Ciba Colloquia Endocrinol.* **8,** 112 (1955).
73a. Dorfman, R. I.   *Trans 5th Josiah Macy, Jr., Conf. on Adrenal Cortex* p. 27 (1953).
74. Dorfman, R. I., Bloch, E., and Rubin, B. L.   To be published (1955).
75. Dorfman, R. I., Cook, J. W., and Hamilton, J. B.   *J. Biol. Chem.* **130,** 285 (1939).
76. Dorfman, R. I., and Fish, W. R.   *J. Biol. Chem.* **135,** 349 (1940).
77. Dorfman, R. I., and Hamilton, J. B.   *J. Biol. Chem.* **133,** 753 (1940).
78. Dorfman, R. I., Hayano, M., Haynes, R., and Savard, K.   *Ciba Colloquia Endocrinol.* **7,** 191 (1953).
79. Dorfman, R. I., Ross, E., and Shipley, R. A.   *Endocrinology* **42,** 77 (1948).
80. Dorfman, R. I., and Ungar, F.   Metabolism of Steroid Hormones. Burgess, Minneapolis, 1953.
81. Dorfman, R. I., Wise, J., and Shipley, R. A.   *Endocrinology* **46,** 127 (1950).
82. Dorfman, R. I., Wise, J., and VanWagenen, G.   *Endocrinology* **36,** 347 (1945).
83. Eidinoff, M. L., Knoll, J. E., Marano, B. J., Kvanne, E., Rosenfeld, R. S., and Hellman, L.   *Proc. Am. Chem. Soc., New York,* p. 26C (1954).
84. Engel, L. L.   *In* F. Homburger and W. H. Fishman, The Physiopathology of Cancer. Hoeber, New York, 1953, p. 687.
85. Engel, L. L., Carter, P., and Springer, J. J.   *Federation Proc.* **13,** 204 (1954).
86. Engel, L. L., Thorn, G. W., and Lewis, R. A.   *J. Biol. Chem.* **137,** 205 (1941).
87. Engel, L. L., Wilson, R., Slaunwhite, W. R., Jr., Carter, P., Olmsted, P. C., and Nathanson, I. T.   *Ciba Colloquia Endocrinol.* **2,** 104 (1952).
88. Eppstein, S. H., Meister, P. D., Peterson, D. H., Murray, H. C., Leigh, H. M., Lyttle, D. A., Reineke, L. M., and Weintraub, A.   *J. Am. Chem. Soc.* **75,** 408 (1953).
89. Fish, C. A., Hayano, M., and Pincus, G.   *Arch. Biochem. and Biophys.* **42,** 480 (1953).
90. Fish, W. R., and Dorfman, R. I.   *Science* **91,** 388 (1940).
91. Fish, W. R., and Dorfman, R. I.   *J. Biol. Chem.* **135,** 349 (1940).
92. Fish, W. R., and Dorfman, R. I.   *J. Biol. Chem.* **140,** 83 (1941).
93. Fish, W. R., and Dorfman, R. I.   *J. Biol. Chem.* **143,** 15 (1942).
94. Fish, W. R., and Dorfman, R. I.   *Endocrinology* **35,** 22 (1944).
95. Fish, W. R., Dorfman, R. I., and Young, W. C.   *J. Biol. Chem.* **143,** 715 (1942).
96. Forchielli, E., Rosenkrantz, H., and Dorfman, R. I.   *J. Biol. Chem.,* in press, (1955).
97. Fried, J.   *Recent Progr. Hormone Research,* **11,** 149 (1955).
97a. Fried, J., Thoma, R. W., and Klingsberg, A.   *J. Am. Chem. Soc.* **75,** 5764 (1953).
98. Fried, J., Thoma, R. W., Gerke, J. R., Herz, J. F., Donin, M. N., and Perlman, D.   *J. Am. Chem. Soc.* **74,** 3962 (1952).
98a. Fukushima, D. K., Kritchevsky, T. H., Eidinoff, M. L., and Gallagher, T. F.   *J. Am. Chem. Soc.* **74,** 487 (1952).
99. Gallagher, T. F., Bradlow, H. L., Fukushima, D. K., Beer, C. T., Kritchevsky, T. H., Stokem, M., Eidinoff, M. L., Hellman, L., and Dobriner, K.   *Recent Progr. Hormone Research* **9,** 411 (1954).
100. Gallagher, T. F., Fukushima, D. K., Barry, M. C., and Dobriner, K.   *Recent Progr. Hormone Research* **6,** 131 (1951).

101. Girard, A., Sandulesco, G., Fridenson, A., Gaudefroy, C., and Rutgers, J. J.
     Compt. rend. **194**, 1020 (1932).
102. Girard, A., Sandulesco, G., Fridenson, A., and Rutgers, J. J. *Compt. rend.*
     195, 981 (1932).
103. Goldzieher, J. W., and Roberts, I. S. *J. Clin. Endocrinol.* **12**, 143 (1952).
104. Grant, J. K. *Biochem. J.* **51**, 358 (1952).
105. Green-Armytage, V. B., Silberstein, F., and Wechtel, G. E. *J. Obstet. Gynaecol.
     Brit. Empire* **54**, 324 (1947).
106. Haines, W. J. *Recent Progr. Hormone Research* **7**, 255 (1952).
107. Haines, W. J., Johnson, R. H., Goodwin, M. P., and Kuizenga, M. H. *J. Biol.
     Chem.* **174**, 925 (1948).
108. Hanson, F. R., Mann, K. M., Nielson, E. D., Anderson, H. V., Brunner, M. P.,
     Karnemaat, J. N., Collingsworth, D. R., and Haines, W. J. *J. Am. Chem.
     Soc.* **75**, 5369 (1953).
109. Hartmann, M., and Locher, F. *Helv. Chim. Acta* **18**, 160 (1935).
110. Hartmann, M., and Wettstein, A. *Helv. Chim. Acta* **17**, 878 (1934).
111. Haussler, E. P. *Helv. Chim. Acta* **17**, 531 (1934).
112. Hayano, M., and Dorfman, R. I. Unpublished results.
113. Hayano, M., and Dorfman, R. I. *Arch. Biochem. and Biophys.* **36**, 237 (1952).
114. Hayano, M., and Dorfman, R. I. *J. Biol. Chem.* **201**, 175 (1953).
115. Hayano, M., and Dorfman, R. I. *Arch. Biochem. and Biophys.* **50**, 218 (1954).
116. Hayano, M., and Dorfman, R. I. *J. Biol. Chem.*, **211**, 227 (1954).
117. Hayano, M., Dorfman, R. I., and Prins, D. A. *Proc. Soc. Exptl. Biol. Med.* **72**,
     700 (1950).
118. Hayano, M., Lindberg, M. C., Wiener, M., Rosenkrantz, H., and Dorfman, R. I.
     Endocrinology **55**, 316 (1954).
119. Hayano, M., Wiener, M., and Lindberg, M. C. *Federation Proc.* **12**, 216 (1953).
120. Hayano, M., Wiener, M., Lindberg, M. C., and Dorfman, R. I. *J. Biol. Chem.*,
     in press.
121. Haynes, R., Savard, K., and Dorfman, R. I. *J. Biol. Chem.* **207**, 925 (1953).
122. Haynes, R., Savard, K., and Dorfman, R. I. *Proc. Soc. Exptl. Biol. Med.* **82**,
     608 (1953).
123. Heard, R. D. H. *In* G. Pincus and K. V. Thimann, The Hormones. Academic
     Press, New York, 1948, Vol. 1, p. 549.
124. Heard, R. D. H., Bauld, W. S., and Hoffman, M. M. *J. Biol. Chem.* **141**, 709
     (1941).
125. Heard, R. D. H., and Hoffman, M. M. *J. Biol. Chem.* **138**, 651 (1941).
126. Heard, R. D. H., and Hoffman, M. M. *J. Biol. Chem.* **141**, 329 (1941).
127. Heard, R. D. H., Jacobs, R., O'Donnell, V., Peron, F., Saffran, J., Solomon, S.
     S., Thompson, L. M., Willoughby, H., and Yates, C. H. *Recent Progr. Hor-
     mone Research* **9**, 383 (1954).
128. Heard, R. D. H., and O'Donnell, V. J. *Endocrinology* **54**, 209 (1954).
129. Hechter, O. *Ciba Colloquia Endocrinol.* **7**, 176 (1953).
130. Hechter, O., Jacobsen, R. P., Jeanloz, R. W., Levy, H., Marshall, C. W., Pincus,
     G., and Schenker, V. *Arch. Biochem. and Biophys.* **25**, 457 (1950).
131. Hechter, O., and Pincus, G. *Physiol. Revs.* **34**, 459 (1954).
132. Hechter, O. *Trans. 3rd Josiah Macy, Jr., Conf. on Adrenal Cortex* p. 115 (1951).
133. Hechter, O., Zaffaroni, A., Jacobsen, R. P. Levy, H., Jeanloz, R. W., Schenker,
     V., and Pincus, G. *Recent. Progr. Hormone Research* **6**, 215 (1951).
134. Hellman, L., Rosenfeld, R. R., Fukushima, D. K., Gallagher, T. F., and Do-
     briner, K. *J. Clin. Endocrinol. and Metabolism* **12**, 934 (1952).

135. Helmreich, M. L., Lasater, M. B., and Samuels, L. T.   *Federation Proc.* **11,** 228 (1952).

136. Herzog, H. L., Jevnik, M. A., Perlman, P. L., Mobile, A., and Hershberg, E. B. *J. Am. Chem. Soc.* **75,** 266 (1953).

137. Hirschmann, H.   *J. Biol. Chem.* **136,** 483 (1940).

138. Hirschmann, H.   *J. Biol. Chem.* **150,** 363 (1943).

139. Hirschmann, H., and Hirschmann, F.   *J. Biol. Chem.* **157,** 601 (1945).

140. Hirschmann, H., and Hirschmann, F.   *J. Biol. Chem.* **167,** 7 (1947).

141. Hirschmann, H., and Hirschmann, F.   *J. Biol. Chem.* **187,** 137 (1950).

142. Hirschmann, H., and Wintersteiner, O.   *J. Biol. Chem.* **122,** 303 (1937–38).

143. Hoffman, M. M., Kazmin, V. E., and Browne, J. S. L.   *J. Biol. Chem.* **147,** 259 (1943).

144. Horwitt, B. N., Dorfman, R. I., Shipley, R. A., and Fish, W. R.   *J. Biol. Chem.* **155,** 213 (1944).

145. Horwitt, B. N., Dorfman, R. I., and VanWagenen, G.   *Endocrinology* **34,** 352 (1944).

146. Horwitt, B. N., and Segaloff, A.   *Federation Proc.* **13,** 232 (1954).

147. Hsia, R. S.-L., Elliott, W. H., Doisy, E. A., Jr., and Thayer, S. A.   *Federation Proc.* **11,** 232 (1952).

148. Huffman, M. M., Thayer, S. A., and Doisy, E. A.   *J. Biol. Chem.* **133,** 567 (1940).

149. Jailer, J. W.   *Bull. N. Y. Acad. Med.* **29,** 377 (1953).

150. Jeanloz, R. W., Levy, H., Jacobsen, R. P., Hechter, O., Schenker, V., and Pincus, G.   *Abstr. 118th Meeting Am. Chem. Soc., Chicago,* p. 29C (1950).

151. Jeanloz, R. W., Levy, H., Jacobsen, R. P., Hechter, O., Schenker, V., and Pincus, G. *J. Biol. Chem.* **203,** 453 (1953).

152. Kahnt, F. W., Meystre, C., Neher, R., Vischer, E., and Wettstein, A.   *Experientia* **8,** 42 (1952).

153. Kahnt, F. W., and Wettstein, A.   *Helv. Chim. Acta* **34,** 1790 (1951).

154. Katznan, P. A., Straw, R. F., Buehler, H. J., and Doisy, E. A.   *Recent Progr. Hormone Research* **9,** 45 (1954).

155. Kochakian, C. D., and Aposhian, H. V.   *Arch. Biochem. and Biophys.* **37,** 442 (1952).

156. Kochakian, C. D., Nall, D. M., and Parente, N.   *Federation Proc.* **11,** 442 (1952).

157. Kochakian, C. D., Nall, D. M., and Stidworthy, G.   *Federation Proc.* **12,** 232 (1953).

158. Kochakian, C. D., Parente, N., and Aposhian, H. V.   *Federation Proc.* **8,** 214 (1949).

159. Kyle, T. I., and Marrian, G. F.   *Biochem. J.* **49,** 80 (1951).

160. Langdon, R. G., and Bloch, K.   *J. Am. Chem. Soc.* **74,** 1869 (1952).

161. Langdon, R. G., and Bloch, K.   *J. Biol. Chem.* **200,** 129 (1953).

162. Ledogar, J. A., and Jones, H. W., Jr.   *Science* **112,** 536 (1953).

163. Lemon, H. M., Wotiz, H. H., and Robitschen, T.   *J. Clin. Endocrinol. and Metabolism* **13,** 948 (1953).

164. Levin, L.   *J. Biol. Chem.* **158,** 725 (1945).

165. Levy, L., and Fish, C. A.   To be published.

166. Levy, H., *et al.* To be published (1955).

167. Levy, H., Jeanloz, R. W., Jacobsen, R. P., Hechter, O., Schenker, V., and Pincus, G.   *Abstr. 118th Meeting Am. Chem. Soc., Chicago,* p. 29C (1950).

168. Levy, H., Jeanloz, R. W., Marshall, C. W., Jacobsen, R. P., Hechter, O., Schenker, V., and Pincus, G.   *J. Biol. Chem.* **203,** 433 (1953).

169. Lieberman, S., and Dobriner, K.   *Recent Progr. Hormone Research* **3,** 71 (1948).

170. Lieberman, S., Dobriner, K., Hill, B. R., Fieser, L. F., and Rhoads, C. P. *J. Biol. Chem.* **172,** 263 (1948).
171. Lieberman, S., Katzenellenbogen, E. R., Schneider, R., Studer, P. E., and Dobriner, K. *J. Biol. Chem.* **205,** 87 (1953).
172. Lieberman, S., Mond, B., and Smyles, E. *Recent Progr. Hormone Research* **9,** 113 (1954).
173. Lieberman, S., and Teich, S. *Pharmacol Revs.* **5,** 285 (1953).
174. Little, H. N., and Bloch, K., *J. Biol. Chem.* **183,** 33 (1950).
175. Lynn, W. S., Jr., Staple, E., and Gurin, S. *J. Am. Chem. Soc.* **76,** 4048 (1954).
176. MacCorquodale, D. W., Thayer, S. A., and Doisy, E. A. *J. Biol. Chem.* **115,** 435 (1936).
177. Maddock, W. O., Epstein, M., and Nelson, W. O. *Ann. N. Y. Acad. Sci.* **55,** 657 (1952).
178. Mamoli, L., and Vercellone, A. *Ber.* **71,** 154 (1938).
179. Mancera, O., Zaffaroni, A., Rubin, B. L., Sondheimer, F., Rosenkranz, G., and Djerassi, C. *J. Am. Chem. Soc.* **74,** 3711 (1952).
180. Marker, R. E. *J. Am. Chem. Soc.* **60,** 2442 (1938).
181. Marker, R. E. *J. Am. Chem. Soc.* **60,** 2931 (1938).
182. Marker, R. E. *J. Am. Chem. Soc.* **61,** 944 (1939).
183. Marker, R. E. *J. Am. Chem. Soc.* **61,** 1287 (1939).
184. Marker, R. E., and Kamm, O. *J. Am. Chem. Soc.* **59,** 1373 (1937).
185. Marker, R. E., Kamm, O., Crooks, H. M., Jr., Oakwood, T. S., Lawson, E. J., and Whittle, E. L. *J. Am. Chem. Soc.* **59,** 2297 (1937).
186. Marker, R. E., Kamm, O., and McGrew, R. V. *J. Am. Chem. Soc.* **59,** 616 (1937).
187. Marker, R. E., Lawson, E. J., Whittle, E. L., and Crooks, H. J., Jr. *J. Am. Chem. Soc.* **60,** 1559 (1938).
188. Marker, R. E., and Rohrmann, E. *J. Am. Chem. Soc.* **60,** 1565 (1938).
189. Marker, R. E., and Rohrmann, E. *J. Am. Chem. Soc.* **61,** 2537 (1939).
190. Marker, R. E., and Rohrmann, E. *J. Am. Chem. Soc.* **61,** 2719 (1939).
191. Marker, R. E., and Rohrmann, E. *J. Am. Chem. Soc.* **61,** 3476 (1939).
192. Marrian, G. F. *J. Soc. Chem. and Ind.* **49,** 515 (1930).
193. Marrian, G. F. *Nature* **154,** 19 (1944).
194. Mason, H. L. *J. Biol. Chem.* **172,** 783 (1948).
195. Mason, H. L. *Recent Progr. Hormone Research* **9,** 267 (1954).
196. Mason, H. L., and Kepler, E. J. *J. Biol. Chem.* **160,** 255 (1945).
197. Mason, H. L., and Kepler, E. J. *J. Biol. Chem.* **161,** 235 (1945).
198. Mason, H. L., and Sprague, R. G. *J. Biol. Chem.* **175,** 451 (1948).
199. McCullagh, E. P., and Schaffenburg, C. A. *J. Clin. Endocrinol.* **11,** 1403 (1951).
200. McGinty, D. A., Smith, G. N., Wilson, M. L., and Worrel, C. S. *Science* **112,** 506 (1950).
201. Meister, P. D., Peterson, D. H., Murray, H. C., Spero, G. B., Eppstein, S. H., Weintraub, A., Reineke, L. M., and Leigh, H. M. *J. Am. Chem. Soc.* **75,** 416 (1953).
201a. Meister, P. D., Reineke, L. M., Meeks, R. C., Murray, H. C., Eppstein, S. H., Osborn, M. M. L., Weintraub, A., and Peterson, D. H. *J. Am. Chem. Soc.* **76,** 4050 (1954).
202. Meyer, A. S., Rodgers, O. G., and Pincus, G. *Acta Endocrinol.* **16,** 293 (1954).
203. Meyer, A. S. *Science* **118,** 101 (1953).
204. Meyer, A. S., Hayano, M., Lindberg, M. C., and Rodgers, O. G. *Acta Endocrinol.* **18,** 148 (1955).
205. Meyer, A. S., Jeanloz, R. W., and Pincus, G. *J. Biol. Chem.* **203,** 463 (1953).
206. Meyer, A. S., Rodgers, O. G., and Pincus, G. *Endocrinology* **53,** 245 (1953).

206a. Meystre, C., Vischer, E., and Wettstein, A. *Helv. Chim. Acta* **37**, 1548 (1954).
207. Miescher, K., Wettstein, A., and Kahnt, F. W. *Acta Physiol. Latinoamer.* **3**, 144 (1953).
208. Migeon, C. J., and Plager, J. E. *Recent Progr. Hormone Research* **9**, 243 (1954).
209. Miller, A. M., and Dorfman, R. I. *Endocrinology* **37**, 217 (1945).
210. Miller, A. M., and Dorfman, R. I. *Endocrinology* **46**, 514 (1950).
210a. Miller, A. M., and Dorfman, R. I. *Endocrinology* **46**, 105 (1950).
211. Miller, A. M., Dorfman, R. I., and Miller, M. *Endocrinology* **46**, 105 (1950).
212. Miller, A. M., Rosenkrantz, H., and Dorfman, R. I. *Endocrinology* **53**, 238 (1954).
213. Morris, C. J. O. R. *Ciba Colloquia Endocrinol.* **4**, 372 (1952).
214. Murray, P. L., and Peterson, D. H. U. S. Patent 2,602,769, July 8, 1952.
215. Nicholas, N. J., Thayer, S. A., Doisy, E. A., Jr., Elliott, W. H., Bocklage, B. C., and Doisy, E. A. *Federation Proc.* **9**, 209 (1950).
216. Oppenauer, R. *Z. physiol. Chem.* **270**, 97 (1941).
217. Patterson, E., Gilbert, C. W., and Gallagher, U. M. *Nature* **163**, 801 (1949).
218. Pearlman, W. H. *Endocrinology* **30**, 270 (1942).
219. Pearlman, W. H. *J. Biol. Chem.* **166**, 473 (1946).
220. Pearlman, W. H. *Federation Proc.* **7**, 178 (1948).
221. Pearlman, W. H., and Cerceo, E. *J. Biol. Chem.* **176**, 847 (1948).
222. Pearlman, W. H., and Cerceo, E. *J. Biol. Chem.* **198**, 79 (1952).
223. Pearlman, W. H., and DeMeio, R. H. *J. Biol. Chem.* **179**, 1141 (1949).
224. Pearlman, W. H., Pearlman, M. R. J., and Rakoff, A. E. *Federation Proc.* **11**, 268 (1952).
225. Pearlman, W. H., Pearlman, M. R. J., and Rakoff, A. E. *J. Clin. Endocrinol.* **13**, 847 (1953).
226. Pearlman W. H., Pearlman, M. R. J., and Rakoff, A. E. *J. Biol. Chem.* **209**, 803 (1954).
227. Pearlman, W. H., and Pincus, G. *J. Biol. Chem.* **144**, 569 (1942).
228. Pearlman, W. H., and Pincus, G. *Federation Proc.* **5**, 79 (1946).
229. Pearlman, W. H., Pincus, G., and Werthessen, N. T. *J. Biol. Chem.* **142**, 649 (1942).
230. Pearlman, W. H., Rakoff, A. E., Cantarow, A., and Paschkis, K. E. *J. Biol. Chem.* **170**, 173 (1947).
231. Pearlman, W. H., Rakoff, A. E., Paschkis, K. E., Cantarow, A., and Walkling, A. A. *J. Biol. Chem.* **173**, 175 (1948).
232. Perlman, D., Titus, E., and Fried, J. *J. Am. Chem. Soc.* **74**, 2126 (1952).
233. Peron, F., and Heard, R. D. H. *Rev. can. biol.* **11**, 76 (1952).
234. Peterson, D. H., Eppstein, S. H., Meister, P. D., Magerlein, B. J., Murray, H. C., Leigh, H. M., Weintraub, A., and Reineke, L. M. *J. Am. Chem. Soc.* **75**, 412 (1953).
235. Peterson, D. H., Eppstein, S. H., Meister, P. D., Murray, H. C., Leigh, H. M., Weintraub, A., and Reineke, L. M. *J. Am. Chem. Soc.* **75**, 5768 (1953).
236. Peterson, D. H., Murray, H. C., Eppstein, S. H., Reineke, L. M., Weintraub, A., Meister, P. D., and Leigh, H. M. *J. Am. Chem. Soc.* **74**, 5933 (1952).
237. Picha, G. M., Saunders, F. J., and Green, D. M. *Science* **115**, 704 (1952).
238. Pincus, G. *In* P. Kallos, Progress in Allergy, S. Karger p. 199, 1954 Basel Vol. 4.
239. Pincus, G., and Romanoff, E. B. Private communication (1953).
240. Plager, J. E. Private communication (1953).
241. Plager, J. E., and Samuels, L. T. *Federation Proc.* **11**, 383 (1952).

242. Popjak, G.   *Arch. Biochem. and Biophys.* **48**, 102 (1954).

243. Prelog, V., and Meister, P.   *Helv. Chim. Acta* **32**, 2435 (1949).

244. Prelog, V., Tagmann, E., Lieberman, S., and Ruzicka, L.   *Helv. Chim. Acta* **30**, 1080 (1947).

245. Rabinovitch, M., and Greenberg, D. M.   *Arch. Biochem. and Biophys.* **40**, 472 (1952).

246. Rabinowitz, J. L., and Gurin, S.   *Biochim. et Biophys. Acta* **10**, 345 (1953).

247. Reichstein, T., and Shoppee, C. W.   *Vitamins and Hormones* **1**, 346 (1943).

248. Richardson, E. M., Touchstone, J. C., and Dohan, F. C.   *Federation Proc.* **13**, 118 (1954).

249. Riegel, B., Hartop, W. L., Jr., and Kittinger, G. W.   *Endocrinology* **47**, 311 (1950).

250. Riisfeldt, O.   *Acta Endocrinol.* **1**, 217 (1948).

251. Rittenberg, D., and Schoenheimer, R.   *J. Biol. Chem.* **121**, 235 (1937).

252. Robinson, R.   *J. Soc. Chem. Ind.* (*London*) **53**, 1062 (1934).

253. Rosenkrantz, H., and Dorfman, R. I.   Unpublished (1953).

254. Rosenkrantz, H., and Dorfman, R. I.   *Proc. 19th Intern. Physiol. Congr.*, Montreal, p. 713 1953.

254a. Rubin, B. L., Dorfman R. I., and Pincus, G.   *Recent Progr. Hormone Research* **9**, 213 (1954).

255. Rubin, B. L., and Dorfman, R. I.   Unpublished (1954).

256. Ruzicka, L., and Prelog, V.   *Helv. Chim. Acta* **26**, 975 (1943).

257. Ryan, K. J., and Engel, L. L.   *Endocrinology* **52**, 277 (1953).

258. Ryan, K. J., and Engel, L. L.   *Endocrinology* **52**, 287 (1953).

259. Saba, N., Hechter, O., and Stone, D.   *J. Am. Chem. Soc.* **76**, 3863 (1954).

260. Saffran, M., Bayliss, M. J., and Webb, J. L.   *Federation Proc.* **10**, 116 (1951).

260a. Saffran, M., Grad, B., and Bayliss, M. J.   *Endocrinology* **50**, 639 (1952).

260b. Salamon, I. I., and Dobriner, K.   *J. Biol. Chem.* **207**, 323 (1954).

261. Salhanick, H. A., Noall, M. W., Zarrow, M. X., and Samuels, L. T.   *Science* **115**, 708 (1952).

262. Salmon, U. J., Geist, S. H., and Salmon, A. A.   *Proc. Soc. Exptl. Biol. Med.* **47**, 279 (1941).

263. Samuels, L. T.   *J. Biol. Chem.* **168**, 471 (1947).

264. Samuels, L. T.   *Recent Progr. Hormone Research* **4**, 56 (1949).

265. Samuels, L. T., Helmreich, M. L., Lasater, M. B., and Reich, H.   *Science* **113**, 490 (1951).

266. Samuels, L. T., Sweat, M. L., Levedahl, B. H., Pottner, M. N., and Helmreich, M. L.   *J. Biol. Chem.* **183**, 231 (1950).

267. Samuels, L. T., and West, C. D.   *Vitamins and Hormones* **10**, 251 (1952).

268. Savard, K., Burstein, S., Rosenkrantz, H., and Dorfman, R. I.   *J. Biol. Chem.* **202**, 717 (1953).

269. Savard, K., Dorfman, R. I., and Poutasse, E.   *J. Clin. Endocrinol. and Metabolism* **12**, 935 (1952).

270. Savard, K., Green, A. A., and Lewis, L. A.   *Endocrinology* **47**, 418 (1950).

271. Sayers, G.   *Physiol. Revs.* **30**, 241 (1940).

272. Sayers, G., and Sayers, M. A.   *Recent Progr. Hormone Research* **2**, 81 (1948).

273. Schiller, S., and Dorfman, R. I.   *Endocrinology* **42**, 476 (1948).

274. Schiller, S., Dorfman, R. I., and Miller, M.   *Endocrinology* **36**, 355 (1945).

275. Schiller, S., Miller, A. M., Dorfman, R. I., Sevringhaus, E. H., and McCullough, E. P.   *Endocrinology* **27**, 262 (1945).

276. Schneider, J. J. *J. Biol. Chem.* **183,** 365 (1950).
277. Schneider, J. J. *J. Biol. Chem.* **194,** 337 (1952).
278. Schneider, J. J. *J. Biol. Chem.* **199,** 235 (1952).
279. Schneider, J. J. *J. Am. Chem. Soc.* **75,** 2024 (1953).
280. Schneider, J. J., and Horstmann, P. M. *J. Biol. Chem.* **191,** 327 (1951).
281. Schneider, J. J., and Mason, H. L. *J. Biol. Chem.* **172,** 771 (1948).
282. Schneider, J. J., and Mason, H. L. *J. Biol. Chem.* **175,** 231 (1948).
283. Schwenk, E., and Werthessen, N. T. *Arch. Biochem. and Biophys.* **40,** 334 (1952).
284. Serchi, G. *Chimica (Milan)* **8,** 9 (1953).
285. Simpson, S. A., Tait, J. F., Wettstein, A., Neher, R., von Euw, J., Schindler, O., and Reichstein, T. *Experientia* **10,** 132 (1954).
286. Simpson, S. A., Tait, J. F., Wettstein, A., Neher, R., von Euw, J., Schindler, O., and Reichstein, T. *Helv. Chim. Acta* **37,** 1163 (1954).
287. Simpson, S. A., Tait, J. F., Wettstein, A., Neher, R., von Euw, J., Schindler, O., and Reichstein, T. *Helv. Chim. Acta* **37,** 1200 (1954).
288. Slaunwhite, W. R., Jr., and Samuels, L. T. *J. Biol. Chem.,* in press.
289. Slotta, K. H., Ruschig, H., and Fels, E. *Ber.* **67,** 1270 (1934).
290. Smith, G. V. S., Smith, O. W., Huffman, M. N., MacCorquodale, D. W., Thayer, S. A., and Doisy, E. A. *J. Biol. Chem.* **130,** 431 (1939).
291. Solomon, S., Lenz, A. L., VandeWiele, R., and Lieberman, S. *Proc. Am. Chem. Soc., New York,* p. 29C (1954).
292. Stone, D., and Hechter, O. *Arch. Biochem. and Biophys.* **51,** 246 (1954).
292a. Stone, D., and Hechter, O. *Arch. Biochem. and Biophys.,* **51,** 457 (1954).
293. Stimmel, B. F., Grollman, A., and Huffman, M. N. *J. Biol. Chem.* **184,** 677 (1950).
294. Stroud, S. W. *J. Endocrinol.* **1,** 201 (1939).
295. Sweat, M. L. *J. Am. Chem. Soc.* **73,** 4056 (1951).
296. Sweat, M. L., Samuels, L. T., and Lumry, R. *J. Biol. Chem.* **185,** 75 (1950).
297. Tagmann, E., Prelog, V., and Ruzicka, L. *Helv. Chim. Acta* **29,** 440 (1946).
298. Tompkins, G., and Isselbacher, K. J. *J. Am. Chem. Soc.* **76,** 3100 (1954).
299. Turfitt, G. E. *Biochem. J.* **40,** 79 (1946).
300. Twombly, G. H. *Vitamins and Hormones* **9,** 260 (1951).
301. Twombly, G. H., McClintock, L., and Engelman, M. *Am. J. Obstet. Gynecol.* **56,** 260 (1948).
302. Twombly, G. H., and Schoenewaldt, E. F. *Cancer* **3,** 601 (1950).
303. Ungar, F., Davis, J. W., Rosenkrantz, H., and Dorfman, R. I. *J. Biol. Chem.* **207,** 375 (1954).
304. Ungar, F., and Dorfman, R. I. *Science* **115,** 115 (1952).
305. Ungar, F., and Dorfman, R. I. *J. Biol. Chem.* **205,** 125 (1953).
306. Ungar, F., and Dorfman, R. I. *J. Am. Chem. Soc.* **76,** 1197 (1954).
307. Ungar, F., and Dorfman, R. I. *Proc. Am. Chem. Soc., New York,* (1954).
308. Ungar, F., and Dorfman, R. I. Unpublished (1954).
309. Ungar, F., Dorfman, R. I., and Prins, D. A. *J. Biol. Chem.* **189,** 11 (1951).
310. Ungar, F., Dorfman, R. I., Stecher, R. M., and Vignos, P. J., Jr. *Endocrinology* **49,** 400 (1951).
311. Ungar, F., Miller, A. M., and Dorfman, R. I. *J. Biol. Chem.* **206,** 597 (1954).
312. Venning, E. H., and Browne, J. S. L. *Endocrinology* **21,** 711 (1937).
313. Venning, E. H., and Ripstein, M. P. *Proc. Can. Physiol. Soc.,* p. 34 (1947).
313a. Venning, E. H. *Ciba Colloquia Endocrinol.,* in press (1955).
314. Vischer, E., and Wettstein, A. *Experientia* **9,** 371 (1953).

315. von Euw, J., and Reichstein, T.   *Helv. Chim. Acta* **24**, 879 (1941).
316. West, C. D., Hollander, V. P., Kritchevsky, T. H., and Dobriner, K.   *J. Clin. Endocrinol. and Metabolism* **12**, 915 (1952).
317. West, C. D., and Samuels, L. T.   *J. Biol. Chem.* **190**, 827 (1951).
318. Westerfeld, W. W., Thayer, S. A., MacCorquodale, D. W., and Doisy, E. A.   *J. Biol. Chem.* **126**, 181 (1938).
318a. Wettstein, A.   *Helv. Chim. Acta* **22**, 250 (1939).
319. Wettstein, A.   *Ciba Colloq. Endocrinol.*, in press (1955).
320. Wilkins, L., Fleishman, W., and Howard, J. E.   *Endocrinology* **26**, 385 (1940).
321. Wilkins, L., Lewis, R. A., Klein, R., Gardner, L. I., Crigler, J. F., Jr., Rosemberg, E., and Migeon, C. L.   *J. Clin. Endocrinol.* **11**, 1 (1951).
322. Wintersteiner, O., and Allen, W. M.   *J. Biol. Chem.* **107**, 321 (1934).
323. Wintersteiner, O., and Pfiffner, J. J.   *J. Biol. Chem.* **111**, 599 (1935).
324. Wintersteiner, O., Schwenk, E., Hirschmann, H., and Whitman, B.   *J. Am. Chem. Soc.* **58**, 2652 (1936).
325. Wiswell, J. G., and Samuels, L. T.   *J. Biol. Chem.* **201**, 155 (1951).
326. Woodward, R. B., and Bloch, K.   *J. Am. Chem. Soc.* **75**, 2023 (1953).
327. Wotiz, H. H., and Lemon, H. M.   *J. Biol. Chem.* **206**, 525 (1954).
328. Wotiz, H. H., Lemon, H. M., and Voulgaropoulos, A.   *J. Biol. Chem.* **209**, 437 (1954).
329. Wüerch, J., Huang, R. L., and Bloch, K.   *J. Biol. Chem.* **195**, 439 (1952).
330. Zaffaroni, A., Burton, R. B., and Keutmann, E. H.   *Science* **111**, 6 (1950).
331. Zaffaroni, A., Hechter, O., and Pincus, G.   *J. Am. Chem. Soc.* **73**, 1390 (1951).
332. Zondek, B.   *Skand. Arch. Physiol.* **70**, 133 (1934).

Chapter XIII

The Physiology of Ovarian and Testis Hormones

By GREGORY PINCUS

CONTENTS

I. Introduction

Any report of contemporary developments in a field characterized by intensive research activity may be motivated by a wish for objectivity, but balanced assessment, when all the evidence is obviously not at hand, is not easy. The chance observation made today may be the basis for the significant developments of tomorrow. Nonetheless the gonadal hormones are sufficiently well established as chemical and physiological entities to enable one to accept as well established certain broad functional activities. We may accept as the normal state of affairs the secretion of estrogen and progestin by ovaries and of androgen by testes. Again the characteristic effects of these secretory products upon accessory organs of the reproductive tracts and upon secondary sexual characteristics are common knowledge.

When, however, one ventures beyond characteristic specific functions of these hormones the assessment of observed physiological effects is complicated indeed. First of all, there is the need to distinguish between direct and indirect effects; as a simple example we cite the adrenocorticomimetic effects of estrogens in sheep, quail, and guinea pigs which depend upon stimulation of pituitary adrenocorticotropin secretion leading, via adrenocortical secretion, to the observed phenomena (220, 271, 274). Secondly, there is the recurring problem of dosage relationships; often quite opposite effects are observed at two dosage levels, e.g., pituitary inhibition at one and pituitary stimulation at another (48). Thirdly, there is the question of species differences in response to gonadal hormones; consider, for example, the repeated observations of the effectiveness of androgens as inhibitors of cortisone-induced atrophy in the rat (264, 94) and their ineffectiveness for this purpose in the monkey (142). This, indeed, is one of the most grievous aspects of endocrine research, for the tendency to generalize clearly established relationships is well nigh irresistible. Fourthly, the facts of gonad hormone interaction must be considered in any attempt at functional analysis; for example, unless one excludes the possibility of circulating androgen or estrogen from any source (*e.g.*, from the food or the adrenal cortex), the possibility of unexpected synergisms or antagonisms cannot be excluded. Finally, one must be continually alert to the possibility of multiple activities of a presumed single entity; thus progesterone is not merely a progestin—it is also a weak androgen (270, 202) and effective in electrolyte regulation (250, 12). In fact, the days of ascribing to a given steroid molecule a simple functional activity are gone by. Not only do the acknowledged gonad hormones have multiple physiological effects, but there are now available numerous substances determined by standard bio-assays to be estrogens or progestins or androgens which multiply these multiple effects. Steroid physiology is now in large part steroid pharmacology, and there is no disentangling the two.

If one recognizes these limitations on critical interpretation of the experimental facts, one may still come to the recognition of certain cardinal physiological realms in which the sexagens are at work. In this chapter we shall concentrate on those realms most readily bounded. If, in so doing, we overlook certain shadowy borders, it is not for lack of interest; it is either because we feel that a second look is needed or because our comprehension is too limited.

II. The Assay of Ovarian and Testis Hormones

Methods for the assay of estrogen, progestin, and androgen have been developed for two major purposes: (*1*) the measurement of these hormones and their metabolites in various body tissues and fluids, particularly in blood and urine, and (*2*) the determination of relative biological potencies of a large number of substances of either natural or synthetic origin. For (*2*) bio-assay has been essential; for (*1*) microchemical and/or microphysical techniques have been sought wherever possible, bio-assay being used as an ancillary method or because high sensitivity makes it "super-micro." Since the last publication of assay methods in this book, major advances have been made in the chemical and physical methods of assay for the sexagens and their metabolites. These advances have involved first of all the development of methods for the separation and isolation of the steroids present in biological media by means of partitioning between solvents or paper chromatographic partitioning. Secondly, microcolorimetric or microspectrophotometric methods to supplement the partitioning have been improved. In Table I we list recent advances in estrogen, progestin, and

TABLE I

SOME RECENT ANALYTICAL METHODS FOR OVARIAN AND TESTIS HORMONES AND SOME OF THEIR METABOLITES

Compound(s)	Where measured[a]	Method of extraction	Method of purification	Method of measurement
Progesterone	B and U and placenta	By organic solvents especially ethyl ether	Partitioning between petroleum ether and aqueous alcohols (190), column chromatography (49)	Ultraviolet absorption of free steroid and its thiosemicarbazide (190, 191) and polarographic analysis of Girard ketone derivative (49)
Pregnanediol	U	Acid hydrolysis (237), or glucuronidase hydrolysis (96), followed by toluene extraction (237, 96)	Filtration thru absorbent (237, 96)	Colorimetric by method of Talbot et al. (247)
Estrogens	U	Acid hydrolysis or enzymic hydrolysis (163, 135, 186) followed by organic solvents.	Pigments removed by anion-exchange resins (13), solvent partition (135, 78), or column (241, 29) and paper (13, 109) chromatography.	Ultraviolet absorption (50), various modifications of the Kober reaction (cf. 16), and fluorescence reactions with sulfuric acid (16) and phosphoric acid (98)
Androgens (17-ketosteroids)	U & B	Acid or enzymic hydrolysis (153, 134) followed by organic solvent extraction.	Separation of α- and β-keto-steroids by digitonin precipitation (197), column (65, 213, 124, 171) or paper (225, 221) chromatography.	Application of various color reactions (177, 196, 176).

[a] B = blood, U = urine.

androgen analytical methods. Fairly comprehensive reviews of current methods will be found in the paper by Engel (77), and in a symposium on steroid analytical methods published as Volume IX of *Recent Progress in Hormone Research* (198).

The statistical requirements for valid sexagen bio-assay have been detailed by Emmens (76). His book summarizes a number of methods, and since its publication improvements have been concerned with increasing specificity and sensitivity.

The standard tests for estrogen continue to be the Allen-Doisy method in spayed rats or mice or the uterine weight hypertrophy in immature mice or rats. Steeper dose-response curves in the mouse assay may be obtained in animals made hypothyroid by methylthiouracil or treatment with I[131] (28). The highly sensitive intravaginal assay in the mouse has been well standardized by Emmens (75), and the effects of various solvents for the estrogens on sensitivity and accuracy have been delineated (26, 27).

Although the Corner-Allen and Clauberg tests continue to be standard assay methods for progesterone, a notable development has been the extremely sensitive local-application method of Hooker and Forbes (117). In the ovariectomized mouse, the injection into a uterine segment of as little as 0.0002 μg. of progesterone leads to a detectable response which appears to be highly specific (272), excluding most progestins (87). In a study of local uterine reactions to common progestational steroids, Robson and Sharaf (215) have confirmed the fact that the mouse uterus responds only to progesterone; they observed too that the cat uterus responds to progesterone and 11-deoxycorticosterone acetate, whereas the rabbit endometrium shows even less specificity, reacting to these two and to Δ[5]-pregnenolone and to ethinyl and methyl testosterone with pseudopregnant proliferation.

The standard androgen bio-assays continue to be the response of the capon's comb or, for greater sensitivity and accuracy, the response of the baby chick comb (66). The androgen-stimulated weight increase of the seminal vesicles and the ventral prostate in the castrate rat has been developed as an accurate, moderately sensitive mammalian assay (121, 111). In the same test animal the myotrophic effect of androgen may be quantitatively assessed by measuring the hypertrophy of the levator ani (230, 111). An androgen assay which appears to be accurately quantifiable involves the measurement of fructose and citric acid in the castrate rat seminal vesicles and prostate after the administration of varying dosages of testosterone (160).

III. A Synopsis of the Physiological Effects of Ovarian Hormones

In presenting below (Table II) a summary of recently reported physiological effects of estrogen and progestin, no attempt has been made to be

TABLE II

SYNOPSIS OF EFFECTS OF ESTROGEN (E) AND PROGESTIN (P)[a]

Ovary, direct action

Stimulation of ovarian tissue by massive doses of E (61, 212)

Stimulation of follicle growth and ovocytogenesis in hypophysectomized animals by E (265)

E pellets implanted into rabbit corpora lutea (I) maintain I beyond normal life span in intact and hypophysectomized animals (105)

Mating behavior

Induced by E in adrenalectomized female rats and in ovariectomized cows (232, 92)

Induced by P into lateral ventricles and by DOC into golden hamster (138, 120)

May be abolished by hypothalamic obesity in rats (39)

Vagina

Vaginal cycles evident after spaying in rats, guinea pigs, and women (157, 8, 255)

Shows lower response threshold than uterus to E in women, but higher threshold in guinea pigs (276, 9)

Shows 5-day cycles on constant dose of E along with androgen or DOC (257)

E increases content of H_2O, P decreases it in rats (279)

Cyclic changes in alkaline phosphatase and β-glucuronidase of rat and human epithelium suggest E increases these enzymes (210, 85)

Behavior of orthophosphate, labile phosphate, and stable phosphate in vaginal mucous membrane of E-injected rabbits suggests initial increase in permeability to phosphate plus increased intracellular phosphate metabolism (21)

Increase of esterase in castrated mouse reversed by E; P decreases E-induced increase of β-glucuronidase (107)

Concentrates S^{35} after E in rats and rabbits (35)

Uterus

Traumatic deciduomata in spayed rat most "normal" when E, P, and vitamin E are injected together (136)

P-conditioned deciduomata in rats and rabbits inhibited by E, but also by pregnanediol, T, DOC, cortisone, or ACTH, and not by pregnanedione or Δ^5-pregnenolone (192, 114, 52, 115)

E, P, and chorionic gonadotropin all needed to maintain decidua in nonpregnant women (for 5 months) (72)

Aminopterin (I) inhibits P-conditioned rat deciduomata; effect of I overcome by citrovorum factor or folic acid (253)

Cyclic increase (at 4 hrs.), decrease, increase (at 20 hrs.) of water content after E shown in castrate or immature rats (279, 245)

E-stimulated H_2O content increase (I) in rats is inhibited by partial hepatectomy (II), cortisone and hydrocortisone (III); I is unaffected by P, T, or pregnenolone; neither I, II, nor III is affected by hypophysectomy; nor is I affected by aminopterin (245, 231)

E-induced increase in O consumption (I) of rat uterus maximal during growth phase is accompanied by increased glucose utilization (II) and anaerobic glycolysis, and these effects are inhibited by hydrocortisone administration (245)

I and II involve both lactate production and adenosine triphosphate phosphorylation (260)

E increases O consumption of human endometrium *in vitro*, especially glucose and pyruvate metabolism, and E reverses somewhat iodoacetate inhibition of O consumption with pyruvate as substrate (102)

E induces glycogen increase in rat uterus, whereas P does this in human endometrium (31, 275)

E-stimulated glycogen formation due to increase in hexokinase reaction which is unaffected by P, T, epinephrine, or adrenal extract (259, 258)

Large uptake of isotopic P^{32}-labeled phosphate shown in E-injected immature and castrated rats and rabbits (200, 261, 32, 33, 34)

E-induced P^{32} uptake inhibited by hydrocortisone during growth phase in rats (245)

P also increases P^{32}, but activates phosphorylation of slowly hydrolyzable organic phosphates, whereas E promotes phosphorylation of easily hydrolyzable organic phosphates (32)

E stimulates nucleic acid synthesis in rat and human uteri and P alters pattern of synthesis in deciduomata (248, 95)

E-stimulated incorporation of C^{14}-alanine *in vivo* in rat uteri inhibited by hydrocortisone administration (245)

E-stimulated rat uteri increase *in vitro* the incorporation of C^{14}-glycine (I) and C^{14}-tryptophane but not C^{14}-alanine. I uptake inhibited by serine, formate, DOC, and P; T increases I uptake (175)

Alkaline phosphatase changes in estrus and menstrual cycles suggest E-control (210, 10)

E-induced increase in alkaline phosphatase in guinea pig and human endometrium counteracted by P and T (90, 188)

In mice, rats, and rabbits E increases β-glucuronidase (107, 83, 141)

E-induced β-glucuronidase increase is inhibited by progesterone, not by corticoids (245, 83, 24)

In rat preputial gland E-stimulated β-glucuronidase not inhibited by P, T, DOC, or pregnenolone, but by hydrocortisone (25)

P induces endometrial histaminase increase in castrate or intact rabbits' endometria, but has no effect on uterine histaminase in rats; E has no effect in either species (3, 211)

E stimulates ATP-ase activity and restores actomyosin concentration in castrate rabbit uteri; P affects uterus probably by varying potassium content of muscle (60, 58)

E stimulates S^{35} incorporation into rat and rabbit endometrium, in part as ester-bound sulfate (35)

Oviducts

E stimulation of chick and toad oviducts requires folic acid (6, 193)

E and P may antagonize or synergize (depending on dose) in effects on pullet oviduct weight (165)

Pregnant uterus

10 mg./day P maintains pregnancy in goat, 25–75 mg. in heifers, and 4 mg. and 1 μg. estrone in pyridoxine-deficient rats (169, 205, 92, 183)

P causes fetal death on days 16–20 in the mouse and is toxic to newborn mice (132)

E administration increases placental and infant weight in man (238)

Uterine contraction

E and P synergize to sensitize cat's uterus to oxytocins (56)

Rat uterine sensitivity to serotonin diminished by castration is restored by E but not by P, T, or certain corticoids (216)

E and P more effective than E in restoring ability of castrate rat's uterus to utilize various substrates for contraction energy, but P relaxes E-stimulated human uterus (262, 144)

Menstrual cycle

Menstrual bleeding in women precipitated by either continuous E, various E's on withdrawal, P withdrawal, or by androgen (145, 166, 167, 168)

"With the exception of the glucocorticoids, any steroid with physiological action may inhibit uterine bleeding in normal monkeys, or induce it in spayed ones" (278)

P maintains uterine growth inhibited by E, but after withdrawal of any combination of E and P bleeding occurs in women and monkeys (37, 113)

Of all steroids, E has lowest threshold to induce withdrawal bleeding, but E esters have longer latent period than free E (278, 82)

Anterior pituitary

A cholinergic neurohumor induces the release of an adrenergic neurohumor which induces pituitary LH release; P and E (like picrotoxin) act on the nervous mechanism; copper acts on the pituitary tissue to release LH directly; E and P synergize in lowering the hypothalamic threshold to an "ovulating" stimulus (161, 162)

P effect on LH-release mechanism demonstrated by P-induced: (1) ovulation from ovaries in castrate male rats' ears, (2) ovulation in the fowl, (3) ovulation in anovulatory monkeys and sheep, (4) ovulation in heifers, (5) ovulation in estrogenized rabbits, and (6) testicular weight increases in pigeons (137, 182, 194, 70, 214, 106, 226, 129)

P administered early in the estrus cycle inhibits ovulation in pigs and heifers, and when administered to rabbits or rats at any time in adequate dose (251, 251a, 199, 234)

In immature female rats low E doses inhibit LH and high E doses stimulate FSH (187)

In women E causes LH release, but has no effect on FSH (91)

In monkeys E and P doses ineffective alone discharge pituitary gonadotropin completely (224)

In men and women, as judged by 17-KS output, E and P both markedly depress pituitary gonadotropin (104)

E stimulates ACTH release in sheep, guinea pigs, quail (220, 274, 271)

E stimulates ACTH release in sheep, guinea pigs, quail, and rats, but decreases adrenal weight and carbonyl lipid in the hamster and enzymic activity in pigeon adrenal cortex (178, 208, 5, 130)

Other extragenital organs

A cycle in epidermal mitosis in the mouse parallels the estrus cycle, and the mitotic activity decreased by castration is stimulated and accelerated by E, provided a sufficient amount of energy-rich substrates are present in the epidermal cell (41, 42, 44, 43)

In vivo E in female rats causes thinning of epidermis and diminishment in sebaceous gland size independent of the mitosis-stimulating effect; in growing male rats it inhibits growth and wound healing, but in vitro E causes swelling of pig skin (71, 154, 146)

In rats large doses of E inhibit hair growth in intact or adrenalectomized adrenal-extract–maintained animals, but E is relatively ineffective in adrenalectomized animals (119, 14)

E destroys lymphocytes independent of the pituitary adrenal system, but it synergizes with ACTH in involuting rat thymus (68, 86)

P (also DOC, T, and pregnenolone) increases circulating eosinophils in adrenalectomized rats, and inhibits phagocytosis of neutrophil leucocytes stimulated by E (59, 45)

E increases total plasma proteins in men and women, P has no effect, and a similar E-induced increase in the fowl is prevented by DL-thyroxin administration (180, 181, 243)

P increases serum cholinesterase activity in man and dogs, and E depresses it in female rabbits (101, 172)

P reduces blood heparin concentrations increased by irradiation or liquemin, and acutely increases blood iron in intact and ovariectomized bitches (2, 4)

E is alkalosis producing, causes hemodilution, increases serum precipitable iodine in men and women (150, 268, 79)

E causes an increase in blood biotin in immature chicks, and prevents or delays advent of biotin deficiency in rats (112, 185)

E increases liver weight, total protein and nucleic acid of liver in immature pullets (unaffected by P), but depresses guinea pig liver methionine, cholesterol synthesis in rat livers, and fat deposit in livers of high-fat–choline-deficient rats (195, 51, 218, 74)

E increases kidney weight in immature pullets and this effect is augmented by P; in rats it increases the enzyme content of the proximal tubules of the kidney (195, 239)

E prevents pancreatic hyperglycemia in cats and the hyperglycemia of force-fed rats; E and P increase pancreatic islet weight in castrate rats, E enhances cortisone-induced weight loss and glycosuria in force-fed rats (1, 217, 139, 118)

P, which lowers the excitability threshold of cat papillary muscle, reduces by 20–30% the ATP-ase of heart and skeletal muscle and of muscle fibrils (179, 174)

E and P decrease chronaxie of rabbit cervical sympathetics and inhibit audiogenic seizures of inbred mice; both effects appear to be nonspecific since T, cortisone, and other steroids act similarly (54, 256)

E inhibits goitrogenic action of antithyroid drugs in rats and thyroxin-induced metamorphosis in axolotls (P and T in very high dose also effective in axolotls) (53, 235)

Miscellaneous effects include: (1) tumorigenic and fibromogenic action of E inhibited by P, (2) ineffectiveness of P (and T) and effectiveness of E pretreatment in increasing survival time of mice receiving lethal doses of X-ray, (3) restoration of jejunal loss of alkaline phosphatase due to castration, (4) failure of E or P to prevent cortisone-induced adrenal atrophy, and (5) the demonstration that the thermogenic effect of P in men is not thyroid-mediated (155, 189, 254, 273, 219)

---

[a] Other abbreviations are: T = testosterone; DOC = 11-deoxycorticosterone; ACTH = pituitary adrenocorticotropic hormone; LH = luteinizing hormone or interstitial cell-stimulating hormone; FSH = follicle-stimulating hormone.

comprehensive. The purpose of the table is to indicate typical experimental findings in this very wide field of investigation and to group these findings in mildly logical order. Omission of relaxin effects from this table is purposeful, in view of the excellent review by Frieden and Hisaw (89) and a recent summary by Leathem (148).

IV. A Synopsis of the Physiological Effects of Testis Hormones

The table (III) of recently reported physiological effects of androgen again is intended as an accounting of types of investigation, not as a comprehensive presentation.

TABLE III

A SYNOPSIS OF THE PHYSIOLOGICAL EFFECTS OF ANDROGENS (A)[a]

Testis, direct action
A increases testis hyaluronidase in rats, and maintains testes in high dose (223, 156)
Mating behavior
A induces increased mating behavior in male hamsters, rabbtis, and men; its stimu-
lating effect in the rat is due to increased tactile sensitivity of the glans penis
(18, 55, 233, 17)
Although degree of induced sex drive is proportional to A in rats, in guinea pigs A
restores castrate males only to precastration level regardless of dose (126, 99, 209)
Reproductive tract organs
A maintenance and E stimulation of male accessory genital system in rabbits, mice,
rats, guinea pigs, hamsters, swine, cats, ferrets, monkeys, and men reviewed (249)
In castrate rats and guinea pigs, prostate and seminal vesicle weights are most stimulated by T propionate (I), moderately so by Δ^5-androstenedione (II), but, except in the guinea pig, affected little or not at all by II diproprionate (III); II
and III are estrogenic and I progestational in castrate rats; in the hamster A and
E synergize to increase seminal vesicle anterior and middle, but not ventral,
prostate lobe weights; A-stimulated seminal vesicle and prostate weights in castrate rats inhibited by 11-alpha-hydroxyprogesterone, and in hypophysectomized
mice A effect on seminal vesicle secretion inhibited by E (80, 122, 46, 81)
Substances present in seminal vesicle and prostate secretions include citric acid (I),
fructose (II), phosphorylcholine, various lipids, certain "unusual" proteins,
phosphatase, beta-glucuronidase, amylolytic and proteolytic enzymes; I and
II are definitely increased by A, especially in castrates (158, 159)
Although A restores castration-induced nitrogen and acid and alkaline phosphatase
loss in the rat seminal vesicles and prostate, A (also P) decreases alkaline phosphatase of all accessory organs of the guinea pig (240, 201, 131)
A (and E) *in vitro* inhibits O consumption of rat ventral prostate brie, and does not
restore marked drop in Q_{O_2} of prostate tissue taken from castrate rats (23)
Aspartic and alanine transaminase activity of the ventral prostate (but not of the
dorsal prostate or seminal vesicles) is decreased by castration in rats and restored
by A; similarly reversible by A is the decrease in ventral prostate aconitase and
fumarase and the increase in lactic dehydrogenase activity; unaffected by castration or A are isocitric dehydrogenase, glucose-6-phosphate dehydrogenase, and
enolase, and no system is affected *in vitro* by A (11, 263)
In rat ventral prostate acetate conversion to long-chain fatty acids more depressed
than respiration by castration, and both restored by A; P^{32} uptake not affected
by castration or A (184)
Neither pteroylglutamic acid nor cortisone inhibits A effects on the prostate in
various species, but both inhibit effects of E (38, 97, 246)
Seminal fructose (I) and various amino acids (II) disappear from bull semen on
castration and I is completely and II partly restored by A replacement therapy;
in hypogonadal men I is low and increased by A treatment (93, 147)
A stimulated chick oviduct growth requires pteroylglutamic acid, but not nicotinic
acid or riboflavin (140)
Anterior pituitary
Pituitary-inhibiting effects of T propionate (not of androstenediol or its dipropio-
nate) observed in intact male rats by testis damage, also in prairie dog (80, 156, 7)

Other extragenital organs

A increases hexosamine-containing mucopolysaccharide in the chick comb, and is maximally stimulating to comb growth in combination with E and P (227, 30)

A in rats stimulates mitosis in resting epithelium (inhibited by cortisone) (242)

Tubular portion of submaxillary gland A-labile in intact, castrate, or hypophysectomized mice and in rats; effect antagonized by E in rats but not in mice (81, 206, 229)

Weight gain induced by A appears to be a specific protein anabolic phenomenon, since it occurs in castrate, hypophysectomized, and adrenalectomized rats and in phlorizin or alloxan diabetic rats without concomitant improvement in the diabetes; the effect in steers and heifers may be due to thyroid activation (228, 222, 133, 269, 47)

Bitches receiving anabolic doses of A retained nicotinic acid, riboflavin, and ascorbic acid, showed no change in allantoin excretion and a drop of blood vitamin A (19)

A increased resistance of rats to starvation, but reduced weight gain·of rats recovering from starvation (252, 203)

Renotrophic effect of A in rats and mice involves increase in cell protoplasmic mass not cell multiplication; note that in the pullet A decreases kidney weight, and in the dog it is renotrophic and induces a large net secretory transport of thiosulfate (103, 204, 195, 88)

Castration-depletion of rat liver D-amino oxidase reversed by A with no effects of either on L-amino oxidase; hepatic (and renal) lesions caused by high-fat–low-choline diet aggravated by A, but A overcomes inability of fasted immature and castrate male rats to mobilize liver fat during fasting (164, 74, 152)

A restores skeletal muscle glycogen (I) in castrate rats, increases I in intact and hypophysectomized rats, does not synergize with growth hormone (151, 36)

T and adrenosterone acidosis-inducing in rats, other androgens (e.g., androsterone, trans-dehydroandrosterone) alkalosis-inducing (150, 149)

A decreases all blood proteins in men, reduces blood heparin, and in rabbits increases serum lysozyme (180, 181, 2, 22)

Audiogenic seizures of inbred mice most markedly inhibited by A, which also decreases chronaxie of cervical sympathetic fibers in rabbits (256, 54)

Miscellaneous A effects include: (1) increasing the severity of biotin avitaminosis in rats, (2) decreasing liver and lung histamine in castrate guinea pigs (increased by E), (3) inhibition of lymphoma formation with irradiation in mice, (4) stimulation of respiration of adrenal cortex slices, (5) reducing the granuloma reaction to turpentine in intact (but not adrenalectomized or hypophysectomized) rats, and (6) hypotensive action in post-DOC hypertension (185, 110, 128, 40, 69, 244)

---

[a] Abbreviations used in this table are as in Table II.

V. Gonad Hormones in Embryogeny

A symposium (57) on sex differentiation in vertebrates reviews *in extenso* experimental data on various species. The two outstanding hormone problems involve the role of gonad hormones in: (1) gonad differentiation and (2) the differentiation of secondary sexual structures. The first is by far the most difficult. Although there is general acceptance of the thesis that the medullary portions of the embryonic gonad segregate male potencies and cortical rudiments, female potencies, the role of the sex hormones in their differentiation is incompletely established.   Thus, in certain lower vertebrates it would appear that androgens selectively inhibit cortical differentiation and estrogens' medullary differentiation so completely as to cause genuine sex reversal (266), but estrogens in large dose may paradoxically masculinize frog gonads (267).   Furthermore, sex reversal in frogs is not necessarily accomplished by all estrogens (*e.g.*, stilbestrol and other synthetic estrogens are ineffective) and progestins may act as stimulants of testis differentiation.

The relative ease of sex reversal with steroids in amphibia is not duplicable in birds, though undoubted instances are cited (57).   When one considers the data on mammals there are no convincing evidences of sex reversal, although certain alterations in gonad development may be accepted as steroid-induced (125).   A curious obstacle to experimental work on gonad differentiation in the intact young embryo is the toxicity to fetuses of steroids quite nontoxic to adults (132, 277).

It appears generally agreed that in embryo development the gonad hormones affect homologous rudiments of the accessory tract organs, *i.e.*, testosterone stimulates Wolffian duct derivatives development while suppressing Müllerian duct derivatives, and estrogens may act in a reverse manner (57).   Nonetheless, in the oppossum, differentiation of these rudiments appears to be independent of gonad hormones (173).   In placental mammals direct approaches to this problem have been described in detail by Jost (125), and the role of testis hormone appears to be substantiated. Furthermore, pituitary influence on gonad development is observable in the fetus, although the interactions so evident in adult animals are not indicated.

VI. Sexagens and Enzyme Systems

In considering the diverse effects of the sex hormones and their derivatives, there is a natural desire for an explanation of these phenomena on the basis of a biochemical mechanism of action.   Since the phenomena are taken logically as manifestations of the behavior of enzyme systems, much attention has been given to hormone-enzyme interrelationships.   In an excellent review on steroid hormones and enzymes, Dorfman (67) has pointed out that effects of hormones on enzyme systems may be due to: (*1*) changes in tissue-enzyme concentration, (*2*) the hormones' functioning as components of enzyme systems, as coenzymes or cofactors, (*3*) the inhibition or acceleration of enzyme activity, or (*4*) direct or indirect effects on accelerators or inhibitors of enzyme systems.

When one examines the data available for the resolution of these possibilities, one is struck by the fact that two major types of experimentation are employed. The first involves an examination of the effects of castration, replacement therapy, or sexagen administration to intact animals on the concentrations (or activities) of a diversity of tissue enzymes. Such studies of the effects of the administration of the hormones *in vivo* have been exemplified in Tables II and III. These data may be taken as fundamental to the role of the hormones as regulators of tissue enzyme concentrations, and on the face of it the tissue concentrations of arginase, ATP-ase, cholinesterase, and other esterases, enolase, β-glucuronidase, hexokinase, histaminase, D-amino oxidase, the phosphatases, and other known enzymes are significantly altered by sex hormone administration. Furthermore, there is a degree of specificity to the hormone effect even in nongenital organs; thus androgen administration will increase kidney β-glucuronidase with no concomitant alteration in the enzyme concentration in the liver, whereas estrogen administration effects an increase in liver but not in kidney β-glucuronidase (84). This specificity of action extends to species also, for example, increase in D-amino oxidase activity is stimulated by androgen in the kidneys of castrate mice but only in the liver of castrate rats (20). A simple explanation invoking the synthesis of additional tissue enzyme based on the general protein anabolic activity of sexagens on tissues is clearly excluded. A synthesis of specific enzymes, perhaps by the redistribution of tissue nitrogen (20), is indicated.

When one comes to consider the possible role of the hormones as components of enzyme systems or as inhibitors or accelerators of enzyme systems, the data from experiments involving their *in vivo* administration are not very illuminating, since indirect effects on known enzyme systems are difficult to exclude. Thus increased respiration and activity of uterine enzyme systems following estrogen administration may not involve direct action of estrogen but may be secondary to alterations in cellular permeability or in uterine vascularity effected by the estrogens (245).

Studies of sexagen effects *in vitro* presumably give more direct indications of hormone-enzyme relationships. Most of the data for *in vitro* systems indicate inhibitory actions of sexagens. Thus the respiration of surviving liver and kidney slices of several mammals is inhibited by both androgen (73, 108, 143, 236) and estrogen (108). Furthermore when such inhibitory action is traced to specific enzyme systems, there appears to be no hormonal specificity involved. For example, the cytochrome oxidase activity of kid heart muscle is inhibited by estradiol, testosterone, and progesterone (15); various hormonally active and inactive 3-ketosteroids inhibit α-glycerophosphate dehydrogenase *in vitro* (116). Dirscherl *et al.* (62) have indeed reported that impure catalase preparations are inhibited by estradiol and stimulated by testosterone (with no effect exerted by progesterone), but no steroid effect is observed with crystalline catalase preparations. One suspects these and other inhibitory effects (*e.g.*, estrogen inhibition of malic and fumarate dehydrogenases and of succinoxidase (207, 170, 127)) to be nonspecific effects of the steroids acting, perhaps, as surface-active agents. It has been suggested also that the metabolism of certain substrates may be inhibited owing to competition for coenzyme by steroid transforming enzymes (100).

The few instances in which stimulative action of sexagens *in vitro* are reported also afford no great evidence of specificity. Thus both estrogens and androgens stimulate mouse diaphragm respiration and both appear to do so by activating enolase, hexokinase, and carboxylase (63, 64). Here some difference in rates of action of estrogen and androgen are observed, but nonspecific effects offer plausible explanations of the common diverse qualitative activations observed. Similar activation by estrogens of the enolase and phosphomonoesterase of neutrophilic leucocytes (45) appears to be inhibited by progesterone. Here again one is faced by a paradoxical inhibition with large concentrations of stilbestrol not observed with estradiol. The suggestion of a specific effect of progesterone is perhaps reenforced by the observation that progesterone *in vitro* increases the release of phosphate from adenosine triphosphate added to rat liver homogenates (123).

Regardless of the degree of specificity involved, the physiological significance of observed effects of sexagens on enzyme systems is not assessable. The inhibitory effects observed *in vitro* are effected by rather large concentrations of steroid which presumably do not normally occur *in vivo*. Furthermore Kochakian (143) has pointed out that surviving liver and kidney slices taken from androgen-treated animals respire at normal rates, indicating that the respiration inhibition observed when androgen is added *in vitro* is probably not a normal physiological event. Certainly investigation aimed at correlating enzymic effects with known functional activities of the sexagens is very much needed, but this writer doubts that such correlations will be easily established. The nature of sex hormone action is not a special department—it is part of the general problem of hormone action, and to the general problem we have, as yet, no single definitive answer. The reader is referred to a most illuminating discussion of the mechanism of hormone action by Hechter (108a).

REFERENCES

1. Acevedo, D., and Migone, A. *Anales fac. med. Univ. nacl. mayor San Marcos Lima* **35,** 261 (1952).
2. Agolini, G., Libretti, A., and Tusini, G. *Boll. soc. ital. biol. sper.* **28,** 381 (1952).
3. Ahlmark, A., and Swanberg, H. *Acta Endocrinol.* **12,** 279 (1953).
4. Allegra, G., and Pace, M. *Ormonology* **11,** 297 (1950).
5. Alpert, M. *Endocrinology* **46,** 166 (1950).

6. Andrus, M., and Zarrow, M. X. *Proc. Soc. Exptl. Biol. Med.* **72,** 714 (1949).
7. Anthony, A. *J. Morphol.* **93,** 331 (1953).
8. Aron, C., Marescaux, J., and Isaac, J. P. *Compt. rend. soc. biol.* **145,** 764 (1951).
9. Aron, C., Marescaux, J., and Petrovitch, A. *Compt. rend. soc. biol.* **146,** 938 (1952).
10. Atkinson, W. B. Menstruation and Its Disorders. Charles C Thomas, Springfield, Ill., 1950.
11. Awapara, J. *Endocrinology* **51,** 75 (1952).
12. Axelrad, B. J., Cates, J. E., Johnson, B. B., and Luetscher, J. A., Jr. *Endocrinology* **55,** 568 (1954).
13. Axelrod, L. R. *Recent Progr. Hormone Research* **9,** 69 (1954).
14. Baker, B. L., and Whitaker, W. L. *Am. J. Physiol.* **159,** 118 (1949).
15. Bargoni, N., and Di Bella, S. *Boll. soc. ital. biol. sper.* **26,** 1095 (1950).
16. Bates, R. W. *Recent Progr. Hormone Research* **9,** 95 (1954).
17. Beach, F. A., and Levinson, G. E. *J. Exptl. Zool.* **114,** 159 (1950).
18. Beach, F. A., and Pauker, R. S. *Endocrinology* **45,** 211 (1949).
19. Beher, W. T., and Gaebler, O. H. *J. Nutrition* **41,** 447 (1950).
20. Van Bekkum, G., and Kasenaar, A. A. H. *Acta Endocrinol.* **15,** 9 (1954).
21. Bengtsson, L. P. *Acta Endocrinol.* Suppl. 13 (1953).
22. Berengo, A., Manicardi, E., and Bussinello, E. *Rev. ist. sieroterap. ital.* **26,** 319 (1951).
23. Bern, H. A. *J. Endocrinol.* **9,** 312 (1953).
24. Beyler, C. A., and Szego, C. M. *Endocrinology* **54,** 232 (1954).
25. Beyler, C. A., and Szego, C. M. *Endocrinology* **54,** 334 (1954).
26. Biggers, J. D. *J. Endocrinol.* **9,** 136 (1953).
27. Biggers, J. D. *J. Endocrinol.* **9,** 145 (1953).
28. Biggers, J. D., and Claringbold, P. J. *Australian J. Biol. Sci.* **6,** 305 (1953).
29. Bitman, J., and Sykes, J. F. *Science* **117,** 356 (1953).
30. Bolton, W. *J. Endocrinol.* **9,** 440 (1953).
31. Bo, W. J. *Anat. Record* **112,** 313 (1952).
32. Borell, U. *Acta Endocrinol.* **7,** 17 (1951).
33. Borell, U. *Acta Endocrinol.* **8,** 131 (1951).
34. Borell, U. *Acta Endocrinol.* **9,** 141 (1952).
35. Bostrom, H., and Odeblad, E. *Acta Endocrinol.* **10,** 89 (1952).
36. Bowman, R. H. *Am. J. Physiol.* **172,** 157 (1953).
37. Bradbury, J. T., Brown, W. E., and Gray, L. A. *Recent Progr. Hormone Research* **5,** 151 (1950).
38. Brendler, H. *Science* **110,** 119 (1949).
39. Bruce, H. M., and Kennedy, G. C. *Proc. Soc. Study Fertility* **3,** 24 (1952).
40. Brummel, E., Halkerston, I. D. K., and Reiss, M. *J. Endocrinol.* **10,** 111 (1954).
41. Bullough, W. S. *J. Endocrinol.* **6,** 340 (1950).
42. Bullough, W. S. *J. Endocrinol.* **6,** 350 (1950).
43. Bullough, W. S. *Biol. Revs.* **27,** 133 (1952).
44. Bullough, W. S., and Van Oordt, J. *Acta Endocrinol.* **4,** 291 (1950).
45. Burger, H., and Leonhardt, K. *Arch. Gynäkol.* **181,** 300 (1952).
46. Burnes, W. W., Stafford, R. O., and Olson, K. J. *Proc. Soc. Exptl. Biol. Med.* **82,** 243 (1953).
47. Burris, M. J., Bogart, R., and Krueger, H. *Proc. Soc. Exptl. Biol. Med.* **84,** 181 (1953).
48. Burrows, H. Biological Actions of Sex Hormones. Cambridge Univ. Press, New York, 1949, pp. 61–70.

49. Butt, W. R., Morris, P., Morris, C. J. O. R., and Williams, D. C.   *Biochem. J.*
    49, 434 (1950).
50. Carol, J., and Rotondaro, F. A.   *J. Am. Pharm. Assoc.* **35,** 176 (1946).
51. Castellani, L., and Adezati, L.   *Boll. soc. ital. biol. sper.* **28,** 420 (1952).
52. Chambon, Y.   *Compt. rend. soc. biol.* **143,** 1528 (1949).
53. Chamorro, A.   *Compt. rend. soc. biol.* **143,** 1540 (1949).
54. Chauchard, B., and Chauchard, P.   *Compt. rend. soc. biol.* **145,** 655 (1951).
55. Cheng, P., Ulberg, L. C., Christian, R. E., and Casida, L. E.   *Endocrinology* **46,**
    447 (1950).
56. Clary, M. L., Cameron, A., and Craver, B. N.   *Proc. Soc. Exptl. Biol. Med.* **77,**
    778 (1951).
57. Colloquium on Sex Differentiation in Vertebrates.   *Arch. anat. microscop. et
    morphol. exptl.* **39** (1950).
58. Corner, G. W., and Csapo, A.   *Brit. Med. J.* **481,** 687 (1953).
59. Coste, F., Laurent, F., and Delabarre, F.   *Compt. rend. soc. biol.* **145,** 838 (1951).
60. Csapo, A.   *Am. J. Physiol.* **162,** 406 (1950).
61. Desclin, L.   *Compt. rend. soc. biol.* **143,** 1004 (1949).
62. Dirscherl, W., Bergmeyer, H. U., and Krüsenkemper, W.   *Biochem. Z.* **322,** 263
    (1952).
63. Dirscherl, W., and Hauptmann, K. H.   *Biochem. Z.* **320,** 199 (1950).
64. Dirscherl, W., and Knüchel, W.   *Biochem. Z.* **320,** 228 (1950).
65. Dobriner, K., Lieberman, S., and Rhoads, C. P.   *J. Biol. Chem.* **172,** 241 (1948).
66. Dorfman, R. I.   *In* C. W. Emmens, Hormone Assay.   Academic Press, New
    York, 1950, p. 291.
67. Dorfman, R. I.   *Vitamins and Hormones* **10,** 331 (1952).
68. Dougherty, T. F.   *Physiol. Revs.* **32,** 379 (1952).
69. Ducommun-Lehmann, S., Ducommun, P., and Salgado, E.   *Rev. can. biol.* **11,**
    300 (1952).
70. Dutt, R. H.   *J. Animal Sci.* **11,** 792 (1952).
71. Ebling, F. S.   *J. Endocrinol.* **9,** xxxi (1953).
72. Eichner, E., Goler, G. G., Reed, J., and Gordon, M. B.   *Am. J. Obstet. Gynecol.*
    61, 253 (1951).
73. Eisenberg, E., Gordon, O. S., and Elliott, H. W.   *Endocrinology* **45,** 113 (1949).
74. Emerson, W. J., Zamecnik, P. C., and Nathanson, I. T.   *Endocrinology* **48,** 548
    (1951).
75. Emmens, C. W.   *J. Endocrinol.* **6,** 302 (1950).
76. Emmens, C. W.   (Ed.)   Hormone Assay.   Academic Press, New York, 1950.
77. Engel, L. L.   *Recent Progr. Hormone Research* **5,** 335 (1950).
78. Engel, L. L., Slaunwhite, W. R., Jr., Carter, P., and Nathanson, I. T.   *J. Biol.
    Chem.* **185,** 255 (1950).
79. Engstrom, W. W., Markhardt, B., and Liebman, A.   *Proc. Soc. Exptl. Biol. Med.*
    81, 582 (1952).
80. Ercoli, A., and Koller, M.   *Farm. sci. e tec. (Pavia)* **7,** 20 (1952).
81. Ferguson, D. J., and Visscher, M. B.   *Endocrinology* **52,** 463 (1953).
82. Ferin, J.   *J. Clin. Endocrinol.* **12,** 28 (1952).
83. Fishman, W. H.   *Vitamins and Hormones* **9,** 213 (1951).
84. Fishman, W. H.   *Ann. N. Y. Acad. Sci.* **54,** 548 (1951).
85. Fishman, W. H., Kasdon, S. C., Bonner, C. D., Fishman, L. W., and Homburger,
    F.   *J. Clin. Endocrinol.* **11,** 1425 (1951).
86. Foglia, V. G., and Pinto, R. M.   *Compt. rend. soc. biol.* **146,** 1986 (1952).
87. Forbes, T. R.   *Endocrinology* **55,** 704 (1954).

88. Foulks, J., Brazeau, P., Koille, E. S., Gilman, A., and Senger, G. *Am. J. Physiol.* **168,** 77 (1952).
89. Frieden, E. H., and Hisaw, F. L. *Recent Progr. Hormone Research* **8,** 333 (1953).
90. Fuenzalida, F. *Endocrinology* **45,** 231 (1949).
91. Funnel, J. W., Keaty, C., and Hellbaum, A. *J. Clin. Endocrinol.* **11,** 98 (1951).
92. Gassner, F. X. *Recent Progr. Hormone Research* **7,** 165 (1952).
93. Gassner, F. X., and Hopwood, M. L. *Proc. Soc. Exptl. Biol. Med.* **81,** 37 (1952).
94. Gaunt, R., Tuthill, C. H., Antonchak, N., and Leathem, J. H. *Endocrinology* **52,** 407 (1953).
95. Gold, N. I., and Sturgis, S. H. *J. Biol. Chem.* **206,** 51 (1954).
96. Goldfine, M. M., and Cohen, S. L. *Endocrinology* **52,** 597 (1953).
97. Goldsmith, E. D., Black, H. M., and Nigrelli, R. F. *Nature* **164,** 62 (1949).
98. Goldzieher, J. W., Bodenchuk, J. M., and Nolan, P. *J. Biol. Chem.* **199,** 621 (1952).
99. Grunt, J. A., and Young, W. C. *Endocrinology* **51,** 237 (1952).
100. Guidry, M. A., Segaloff, A., and Altschul, A. M. *Federation Proc.* **19,** 356 (1951).
101. Habbe, K., and Pfoertner, W. *Deut. med. Wochschr.* **76,** 269 (1951).
102. Hagerman, D. D., and Villee, C. A. *J. Biol. Chem.* **203,** 425 (1953).
103. Halpern, B. N., and Cournot, L. *Arch. sci. physiol.* **7,** 111 (1953).
104. Hamburger, C., and Sprechler, M. *Acta Endocrinol.* **7,** 167 (1951).
105. Hammond, J., Jr., and Robson, J. M. *Endocrinology* **49,** 384 (1951).
106. Hansel, W., and Trimberger, G. W. *J. Dairy Sci.* **35,** 65 (1952).
109. Harris, R. S., and Cohen, S. L. *Endocrinology* **48,** 264 (1951).
108. Hayano, M., Schiller, S., and Dorfman, R. I. *Endocrinology* **46,** 387 (1950).
108a. Hechter, O. *Vitamins and Hormones,* in press, 1955.
109. Heftmann, E. *J. Am. Chem. Soc.* **73,** 851 (1951).
110. Herschberg, A. D., and Hindobro, H. *Compt. rend. soc. biol.* **146,** 1850 (1952).
111. Hershberger, L. G., Shipley, E. G., and Meyer, R. K. *Proc. Soc. Exptl. Biol. Med.* **83,** 175 (1953).
112. Hertz, R., Dhyse, F. G., and Tullner, W. W. *Endocrinology* **45,** 451 (1949).
113. Hisaw, F. L. *Anat. Record* **112,** 344 (1952).
114. Hisaw, F. L., and Velardo, J. T. *Endocrinology* **49,** 530 (1951).
115. Hisaw, F. L., and Velardo, J. T. *Endocrinology* **49,** 732 (1951).
116. Hochster, R. M., and Quastel, J. H. *Ann. N. Y. Acad. Sci.* **54,** 626 (1951).
117. Hooker, C. W., and Forbes, T. R. *Endocrinology* **45,** 71 (1949).
118. Ingle, D. J. *Am. J. Physiol.* **172,** 115 (1953).
119. Ingle, D. J., and Baker, B. L. *Endocrinology* **48,** 764 (1951).
120. Isaacson, J. E., Jr. *Endocrinology* **45,** 558 (1949).
121. Ito, Y., Tamaoki, B., and Egusa, M. *J. Pharm. Soc. Japan* **72,** 54 (1952).
122. Ito, Y., Tamaoki, B., and Sakamoto, H. *J. Pharm. Soc. Japan* **72,** 756 (1952).
123. Jones, H. W., Jr., and Wade, R. *Science* **118,** 103 (1953).
124. Jones, J. K. N., and Stitch, S. R. *Biochem. J.* **53,** 679 (1953).
125. Jost, A. *Recent Progr. Hormone Research* **8,** 379 (1953).
126. Kagan, J., and Beach, F. A. *J. Comp. and Physiol. Psychol.* **46,** 204 (1953).
127. Kalman, M. *Endocrinology* **50,** 361 (1952).
128. Kaplan, H. S., and Brown, M. B. *Cancer Research* **12,** 445 (1952).
129. Kar, A. B. *Endocrinology* **45,** 346 (1949).
130. Kar, A. B. *Endocrinology* **46,** 363 (1950).
131. Kar, A. B., and Ghosh, A. *Proc. Natl. Inst. Sci. India* **18,** 197 (1952).
132. Karnofsky, D. A., Hambre, P. J., and Hysom, G. *Proc. Soc. Exptl. Biol. Med.* **79,** 641 (1952).

133. Kassenaar, A. A. H. *Acta Endocrinol.* **14**, 130 (1953).
134. Katzman, P. A., Kinsella, R. A. Jr., and Doyle, L. M. *Science* **116**, 524 (1952).
135. Katzman, P. A., Straw, R. F., Buehler, H. J., and Dorsey, E. A. *Recent Progr. Hormone Research* **9**, 45 (1954).
136. Kehl, R., Donard, T., and Lanfranshi, J. *Compt. rend. soc. biol.* **145**, 1161 (1951).
137. Kempf, R. *Compt. rend. soc. biol.* **143**, 1006 (1949).
138. Kent, C. C., Jr., and Liberman, M. J. *Endocrinology* **45**, 29 (1949).
139. Kerr, E. H., Stears, J. C., MacDougall, I., and Haist, R. E. *Am. J. Physiol.* **170**, 448 (1952).
140. Kline, I. T., Dorfman, R. I., and McCreery, P. *Endocrinology* **48**, 39 (1951).
141. Knobil, E. *Endocrinology* **50**, 16 (1952).
142. Knobil, E., Hofmann, F. G., and Greep, R. O. *Endocrinology* **53**, 242 (1953).
143. Kochakian, C. D. *Ann. N. Y. Acad. Sci.* **54**, 534 (1951).
144. Krantz, S. C., Jr. *Surg. Gynecol. Obstet.* **90**, 372 (1950).
145. Krohn, P. L. *Endocrinology* **45**, 537 (1949).
146. Kulonen, E. *Acta Endocrinol.* **12**, 147 (1953).
147. Landau, R. L., and Loughead, R. *J. Clin. Endocrinol.* **11**, 1411 (1951).
148. Leathem, J. H. *Ann. Rev. Physiol.* **16**, 445 (1954).
149. Lecoq, R. *Compt. rend.* **236**, 975 (1953).
150. Lecoq, R., Chauchard, P., and Mazoné, H. *Compt. rend.* **233**, 830 (1951).
151. Leonard, S. L. *Endocrinology* **90**, 199 (1952).
152. Levin, L., and Farber, R. K. *Recent Progr. Hormone Research* **7**, 399 (1952).
153. Lieberman, S., Mond, B., and Smyles, E. *Recent Progr. Hormone Research* **9**, 113 (1954).
154. Light, A. E., and Tornbean, J. A. *J. Nutrition* **49**, 51 (1953).
155. Lipschutz, A. Steroid Hormones and Tumors. Williams & Wilkins, Baltimore, 1950.
156. Ludwig, D. J. *Endocrinology* **46**, 453 (1950).
157. Mandl, A. M. *J. Exptl. Biol.* **28**, 585 (1951).
158. Mann, T., and Lutwak-Mann, C. *Physiol. Revs.* **31**, 27 (1951).
159. Mann, T., and Parsons, U. *Nature* **160**, 294 (1947).
160. Mann, T., and Parsons, U. *Biochem. J.* **46**, 440 (1950).
161. Markee, J. E. *Ann. Rev. Physiol.* **13**, 367 (1951).
162. Markee, J. E., Everett, J. W., and Sawyer, C. H. *Recent Progr. Hormone Research* **7**, 139 (1952).
163. Marrian, G. F., and Bauld, W. S. *Acta Endocrinol.* **7**, 240 (1951).
164. Marsili, G., and Branzi, G. *Sperimentale* **103**, 15 (1953).
165. Mason, R. C. *Endocrinology* **51**, 510 (1952).
166. Masters, W. H., and Magallon, D. T. *Proc. Soc. Exptl. Biol. Med.* **73**, 672 (1950).
167. Masters, W. H., and Magallon, D. T. *Am. J. Obstet. Gynecol.* **59**, 970 (1950).
168. Masters, W. H., and Magallon, D. T. *Am. J. Obstet. Gynecol.* **58**, 308 (1950).
169. Meites, J., Webster, H. D., Young, F. W., Thorp, F., and Hatch, R. N. *J. Animal Sci.* **10**, 411 (1951).
170. Meyer, R. K., and McShan, W. H. *Recent Progr. Hormone Research* **5**, 464 (1950).
171. Migeon, C. J., and Plager, J. *Recent Progr. Hormone Research* **9**, 235 (1954).
172. Milani, L. *Boll. soc. ital. biol. sper.* **29**, 106 (1953).
173. Moore, C. R. *Arch. anat. microscop. et morphol. exptl.* **39**, 484 (1950).
174. Mor, M. A. *Experientia* **9**, 342 (1953).
175. Mueller, G. C. *J. Biol. Chem.* **204**, 77 (1953).
176. Munson, P. L., Jones, M. E., McCall, P. J., and Gallagher, T. F. *J. Biol. Chem.* **176**, 73 (1948).

177. Munson, P. L., and Kenny, A. D. *Recent Progr. Hormone Research* **9**, 135 (1954).
178. Nadel, E., Josephson, E. S., and Mulay, A. S. *Endocrinology* **46**, 255 (1950).
179. Nahum, L. H., Geller, H. M., Levine, H., and Sikand, R. S. *In* A. White, Symposium on Steroids in Experimental and Clinical Practice. The Blakiston Co., Phila., 1951, pp. 33–49.
180. Nava, G., and Zilli, E. *Arch. "E. Maragliano" patol. e clin.* **5**, 637 (1950).
181. Nava, G., and Zilli, E. *Arch. "E. Maragliano" patol. e clin.* **5**, 649 (1950).
182. Neher, B. H., and Fraps, R. M. *Endocrinology* **46**, 482 (1950).
183. Nelson, M. M., Lyons, W. R., and Evans, H. M. *Endocrinology* **48**, 726 (1951).
184. Nyden, S. J., and Williams-Ashman, H. G. *Am. J. Physiol.* **172**, 588 (1953).
185. Okey, R., Pencharz, R., and Lepovsky, S. *Am. J. Physiol.* **161**, 1 (1950).
186. Oneson, I. B., and Cohen, S. L. *Endocrinology* **51**, 173 (1952).
187. Paesi, F. S. A. *Acta Endocrinol.* **11**, 251 (1952).
188. Page, E. W., Glendening, M. B., and Parkinson, D. *Am. J. Obstet. Gynecol.* **62**, 1100 (1951).
189. Patt, H. M., Straube, R. L., Tyree, E. B. Swift, M. N., and Smith, D. E. *Am. J. Physiol.* **159**, 269 (1949).
190. Pearlman, W. H. *Recent Progr. Hormone Research* **9**, 27 (1954).
191. Pearlman, W. H., and Cerceo, E. *J. Biol. Chem.* **203**, 127 (1953).
192. Peckham, B. M., and Greene, R. R. *Endocrinology* **46**, 489 (1950).
193. Penhos, J. C., and Cardeza, A. F. *Rev. soc. argentina biol.* **28**, 125 (1952).
194. Pfeiffer, C. A. *Anat. Record* **106**, 233 (1950).
195. Phillips, W. E. J., Common, R. H., and Maw, W. A. *Can. J. Zool.* **30**, 201 (1952).
196. Pincus, G. *Endocrinology* **32**, 176 (1943).
197. Pincus, G. *J. Clin. Endocrinol.* **5**, 291 (1945).
198. Pincus, G. (ed.) *Recent Progr. Hormone Research* **9**, (1954).
199. Pincus, G., and Chang, M. C. *Acta Physiol. Latinoamer.* **3**, 177 (1953).
200. Plaice, C. H. J. *J. Endocrinol.* **9**, xxxvii (1953).
201. Porter, J. C., and Melampy, R. M. *Endocrinology* **51**, 412 (1952).
202. Price, D., Mann, T., and Lutwak-Mann, C. *Nature* **104**, 950 (1949).
203. Quimby, F. H., Bartlett, R. G., and Artress, J. L. *Am. J. Physiol.* **166**, 566 (1951).
204. Rabinovitch, M., and Valeri, V. *Rev. brasil. biol.* **12**, 417 (1952).
205. Raeside, I. J., and Turner, C. W. *J. Dairy Sci.* **34**, 496 (1951).
206. Raynaud, J. *Bull. soc. hist. nat. Toulouse* **86**, 226 (1951).
207. Reilly, J., and Prisament, M. *Arch. Biochem. and Biophys.* **43**, 25 (1953).
208. Rennels, E. G., Hess, M., and Finerty, J. C. *Proc. Soc. Exptl. Biol. Med.* **82**, 304 (1953).
209. Riis, W., and Young, W. C. *Endocrinology* **54**, 232 (1954).
210. Ring, J. *Anat. Record* **107**, (1950).
211. Roberts, M., and Robson, J. B. *J. Physiol.* (*London*) **119**, 286 (1953).
212. Robertson, G. G. *Proc. Soc. Exptl. Biol. Med.* **71**, 542 (1949).
213. Robinson, A. M. *Recent Progr. Hormone Research* **9**, 163 (1954).
214. Robinson, T. J. *J. Endocrinol.* **10**, 117 (1954).
215. Robson, J. M., and Sharaf, A. A. *J. Physiol.* (*London*) **115**, 313 (1951).
216. Robson, J. M., Trounce, J. R., and Didcock, K. A. H. *J. Endocrinol.* **10**, 129 (1954).
217. Rodriguez, R. D. *Proc. Soc. Exptl. Biol. Med.* **73**, 317 (1950).
218. Rosenman, R. H., Friedman, M., and Byers, S. O. *Endocrinology* **51**, 142 (1952).
219. Rothchild, I., and Rapport, R. L. *Endocrinology* **50**, 580 (1952).

220. Roy, A., Jarnik, Y. R., and Blattacharya, P. *Indian J. Physiol. and Allied Sci.* **5**, 113 (1951).

221. Rubin, B. L., Dorfman, R. I., and Pincus, G. *Recent Progr. Hormone Research* **9**, 213 (1954).

222. Rupp, J., and Paschkis, K. E. *Metabolism* **2**, 268 (1953).

223. Rüsfeldt, O. *Endocrinology* **45**, 622 (1949).

224. Salhanick, H. A., Hisaw, F. L., and Zarrow, M. X. *J. Clin. Endocrinol. and Metabolism* **12**, 310 (1952).

225. Savard, K. *Recent Progr. Hormone Research* **9**, 185 (1954).

226. Sawyer, C. H., Everett, J. W., and Markee, J. E. *Proc. Soc. Exptl. Biol. Med.* **74**, 185 (1950).

227. Schiller, S., Benditt, E. P., and Dorfman, A. *Endocrinology* **50**, 504 (1952).

228. Scow, R. O. *Endocrinology* **51**, 42 (1952).

229. Shafer, W. G., and Muhler, J. C. *J. Dental Research* **32**, 262 (1953).

230. Shemano, I., Gordan, G. S., and Eisenberg, E. *Proc. Soc. Exptl. Biol. Med.* **78**, 612 (1951).

231. Silver, M. *J. Endocrinol.* **10**, 95 (1954).

232. Simpson, S. A., and Williams, P. C. *J. Endocrinol.* **6**, 169 (1949).

233. Simpson, S. L. *Brit. Med. J.* **7**, 692 (1950).

234. Slechta, R. F., Pincus, G., and Chang, M. C. *Fertility and Sterility* **5**, 282 (1954).

235. Sluczewski, A., and Roth, P. *Gynécol. et obstét.* **47**, 164 (1948).

236. Smith, T. C., Kochakian, C. D., and Fondal, E. *Am. J. Physiol.* **174**, 247 (1953).

237. Somerville, I. F., Gough, N., and Marrian, G. F. *J. Endocrinol.* **5**, 247 (1953).

238. Sommers, S. C., Lawley, T. B., and Hertig, A. T. *Am. J. Obstet. Gynecol.* **58**, 101 (1949).

239. Soulaviac, A., Desclaux, P., and Teysseyre, J. *Ann. Endocrinol.* **10**, 535 (1949).

240. Stafford, R. O., Rubenstein, I. N., and Meyer, R. K. *Proc. Soc. Exptl. Biol. Med.* **71**, 353 (1949).

241. Stimmel, B. F. *J. Biol. Chem.* **153**, 237 (1944).

242. Studer, A., and Frey, J. R. *Dermatologica* **104**, 1 (1952).

243. Sturkie, P. D., and Newman, H. J. *Endocrinology* **49**, 565 (1951).

244. Sturtevant, F. M., Jr. *Proc. Soc. Exptl. Biol. Med.* **84**, 262 (1953).

245. Szego, C. M., and Roberts, S. *Recent Progr. Hormone Research* **8**, 419 (1953).

246. Talalay, P., Dobson, M. M., Ebersole, C. M., and Huggins, C. *Endocrinology* **50**, 574 (1952).

247. Talbot, N. B., Berman, R. A., MacLachlan, E. A., and Wolfe, J. K. *J. Clin. Endocrinol.* **1**, 668 (1941).

248. Telfer, M. E. *Arch. Biochem. and Biophys.* **44**, 111 (1953).

249. Thorborg, J. V. *Acta Endocrinol.* Suppl. 2, 1 (1948).

250. Thorn, G. W., and Engel, L. L. *J. Exptl. Med.* **68**, 299 (1938).

251. Ulberg, L. C., Grummer, R. H., and Casida, L. E. *J. Animal Sci.* **16**, 665 (1951).

251a. Ulberg, L. C., Grummer, R. H., and Casida, L. E. *J. Animal Sci.* **16**, 752 (1951).

252. Usuelli, F., Piana, G., and Moinardi, C. *Boll. soc. ital. biol. sper.* **25**, 82 (1949).

253. Velardo, J. T., and Hisaw, F. L. *Am. J. Physiol.* **172**, 535 (1953).

254. Verne, J., and Hébert, S. *Ann. endocrinol. (Paris)* **10**, 460 (1950).

255. Veziris, C. D. *Ann. endocrinol. (Paris)* **12**, 917 (1951).

256. Vicari, E. M., Tracy, A., and Jongbloed, A. *Proc. Soc. Exptl. Biol. Med.* **80**, 47 (1952).

257. Vimeaux, J. *Compt. rend. soc. biol.* **145**, 1747 (1951).

258. Walaas, O. *Acta Endocrinol.* **10**, 175 (1952).

259. Walaas, O., Walaas, E., and Löken, F. *Acta Endocrinol.* **10,** 201 (1952).
260. Walaas, O., Walaas, E., and Löken, F. *Acta Endocrinol.* **11,** 61 (1952).
261. Walaas, O., and Walaas, E. *Acta Physiol. Scand.* **21,** 18 (1950).
262. West, T. C., Jones, D. M., and Loomis, T. A. *Am. J. Physiol.* **172,** 541 (1953).
263. Williams-Ashman, H. G. *Endocrinology* **54,** 121 (1954).
264. Winter, C. A., Hollings, H. L., and Stebbins, R. B. *Endocrinology* **52,** 123 (1953).
265. de Wit, J. C. *Acta Endocrinol.* **16,** 123 (1953).
266. Witschi, E. *Recent Progr. Hormone Research* **6,** 1 (1951).
267. Witschi, E. *J. Clin. Endocrinol.* **13,** 366 (1953).
268. Witten, C. L., and Bradbury, J. T. *Proc. Soc. Exptl. Biol. Med.* **78,** 626 (1951).
269. Wright, P. M., and Kochakian, C. D. *Am. J. Physiol.* **173,** 217 (1953).
270. Zahler, H. *Arch. Pathol. Anat. Physiol.* **320,** 374 (1951).
271. Zarrow, M. X., and Baldini, J. T. *Endocrinology* **50,** 555 (1952).
272. Zarrow, M. X., and Naber, G. H. *J. Clin. Endocrinol.* **13,** 203 (1953).
273. Zizine, A. *Compt. rend. soc. biol.* **146,** 910 (1952).
274. Zondek, B., and Burstein, S. *Endocrinology* **50,** 419 (1952).
275. Zondek, B., and Hestrin, S. *Am. J. Obstet. Gynecol.* **54,** 173 (1947).
276. Zondek, B., Toaff, R., and Rozin, S. *J. Clin. Endocrinol.* **10,** 615 (1950).
277. Zuckerman, S. *Arch. anat. microscop. et morphol. exptl.* **39** (1950).
278. Zuckerman, S. *Acta Endocrinol.* **7,** 378 (1951).
279. Zuckerman, S., Palmer, A., and Hanson, D. A. *J. Endocrinol.* **6,** 261 (1950).

CHAPTER XIV

Physiology of the Adrenal Cortex

BY R. L. NOBLE

CONTENTS

I. Introduction

The previous publication of this chapter coincided with the first preliminary report in 1949 from the Mayo Clinic of the beneficial action of Compound E on patients suffering from rheumatoid arthritis (823). Since that time, with the increasing availability of adrenocorticotropic hormone (ACTH) and cortisone, the world medical literature has been saturated with papers concerning the functions of the adrenal cortex. It has been impossible, therefore, to refer to many of these references, appearing at the rate of perhaps three every day for the past five years. As a result, the present chapter has been designed to supplement rather than to replace the original, and an attempt has been made to bring up to the present (January, 1954) changing concepts and to expand some of the newer foci of attention. Many of the older and generally accepted aspects of adrenal physiology, therefore, are not discussed in this chapter, even though additional recent publications have been made. It is perhaps symbolic of the future expansion of knowledge on adrenal physiology that the publication of this second chapter coincides with the announced structural formula of aldosterone (1029), the physiological hormone of the adrenal cortex affecting electrolyte and other metabolic processes.

As far as possible, the same order of contents has been followed and new subjects incorporated in their logical place according to the original outline. In some sections a summary which seems to the author to explain best the experimental data at the present time has been included. References to clinical papers have of necessity been limited, and usually only the earlier reports have been included. The response of various diseases to adrenal steroid therapy has received limited consideration, and usually only when physiological effects have been noted. The actions of such steroids on already altered metabolic processes have been left for the consideration of other authors in this book. Similarly, papers concerned chiefly with the effects of ACTH may be found in other chapters. Additional sources of reference may be found in a recent series of papers by Thorn and associates which includes most clinical references to cortisone (1151). "The Cortisone Investigator" (768) summarizes publications on ACTH or adrenal steroids and contains thousands of references. The conferences on ACTH (795, 796) contain much interesting preliminary information, but this has not been used in this chapter unless published elsewhere.

To attempt to decide how much of the newer information concerning the adrenal cortex can be considered of strictly physiological importance is difficult at this time. A great deal of the newer knowledge concerns the actions of adrenal hormones on normal or pathological tissue, and in most cases the doses used are well above physiological levels. It is probably profitable, therefore, at this point to outline the various aspects of adrenal function as they have been considered in this chapter, in an attempt to understand the possible roles which the adrenal cortex normally may play in body functions. The alterations occurring in adrenal insufficiency serve as an accurate index of those functions which are normally maintained by physiological amounts of secreted adrenal steroids. These functions can conveniently be divided for descriptive purposes into those concerned chiefly with electrolyte and water metabolism which are related essentially to a disturbed kidney function. Similarly, changes in carbohydrate, protein, and fat metabolism may be grouped together, although the basic mechanism underlying such disturbances is still not clear. The division of adrenal steroids into those affecting these two types of function is justified by the predominant types of actions of such steroids. However, in most cases the dividing line is not clear-cut, and most adrenal steroids possess all types of activity to some degree. The finding that aldosterone, the most highly active steroid affecting electrolytes, has in addition potentially powerful actions on other metabolic processes, emphasizes the artificiality of too stringent an attempt to divide adrenal activities. The effects of adrenal insufficiency may all be restored to normal by replacement therapy, although this may necessitate the use of more than a single adrenal steroid. Such physiological functions of the adrenals and the actions of the various adrenal steroids were discussed for the main part in the original chapter.

The adrenal cortex is also indirectly influenced by innumerable extraneous stimuli which cause the liberation of pituitary ACTH. Such a response was originally believed by Selye to result in a protective release of adrenal steroids against the stress of the stimulus. Although adrenal stimulation and a release of hormones do occur under such circumstances, the normal function of the released hormones is still not understood. It seems clear that such hormones per se do not increase the normal tolerance of the animal against the particular stress, although they may be necessary for normal adaptation or protective reactions to such stimuli to occur at a maximal rate.   That they increase the various protein defense mechanisms of the body no longer appears tenable.   The decreased tolerance to any form of stress shown by the adrenalectomized animal may be restored by suitable treatment with O^{11} adrenal steroids.   An increased dosage or duration of treatment, however, does not further improve the response of the adrenalectomized or the intact animal above normal.   On the contrary, in many cases the effect may be deleterious.   In most instances the treatment of the adrenal-deficient animal with a basal dose level of steroid now allows such a preparation to respond to stimuli by the same manifestations as shown by an intact animal.   Such "permissive" treatment apparently allows other cellular reactions to take place in a normal fashion.   The evidence at present, therefore, would indicate that with deficient adrenal function the normal homeostatic mechanisms of the body are impaired. Thus the adrenal stimulation which occurs as a response to ACTH liberation would seem to assure the optimal conditions to obtain homeostasis.

The possible function of an increased adrenal steroid secretion above normal physiological levels in response to stimuli remains an unsettled problem.   That such an increased secretion may serve as a physiological control of abnormal processes in the body is at once suggested by the therapeutic use of adrenal steroids in disease.   The theory of Selye that a continued increased secretion of DCA-like adrenal steroids may in itself be the etiological factor leading to those diseased states which respond to steroid therapy, still requires proof by direct methods.   Although lesions may be produced in animals under certain conditions by deoxycorticosterone acetate (DCA), and although the cardiovascular system and kidneys are primarily affected, there is not agreement that these effects have their counterparts in the human collagen diseases.   Whatever may be the initiating factors in such human conditions, cortisone and hydrocortisone appear to control the manifestations of the disease rather than its cause, and in no way to act as a replacement type of therapy.   Presumably the adrenal cortex does not produce quantities of steroids equal to the amounts required for therapeutic responses under the stimulus exerted by the disease process.   It would seem improbable that the normal adrenal can liberate such quantities of steroids in response to exogenous stimuli, since only under the abnormal conditions found in Cushing's disease do the effects of adrenal secretion approximate those seen after prolonged exogenous adrenal steroid therapy.   The actions of larger doses of cortisone or hydrocortisone have been considered in Sections XXI, XXII, and XXIII of this chapter.   Although the ultimate result of such effects can logically be categorized as being generally harmful to the welfare of the organism, certain of these actions have proved to be of considerable therapeutic benefit in disease.

It is difficult to envision these harmful actions as being even an exaggerated physiological response to adrenal steroids, although it is tempting to speculate that they all result from a common interference with the synthesis of some essential protein.   In such a case a normal physiological role in protein metabolism might be envisioned.   The exact physiological role of all these possible functions of the adrenal hormones obviously awaits future clarification and is a challenge to the investigator.   Because of the existing faults in our knowledge it was thought advisable to review all of the above aspects of adrenal action in this chapter.

Hormones. Terminology and Abbreviations Used.   Throughout this chapter the following abbreviations have been used: Compound A or 11-dehydrocorticosterone; Compound B or corticosterone; Compound E, or cortisone, or 17-hydroxycorticosterone; Compound F, or cortisol, or hydrocortisone, or 17-hydroxy-11 dehydrocorticosterone; 11-deoxycorticosterone or DOC—(the acetate, DCA); Compound S or 11-deoxy-17-hydrocorticosterone; aldosterone or electrocortin; aqueous adrenocortical extract (beef) or ACE; lipo adrenocortical extract (pig) or lipo ACE.   The anterior pituitary hormones have been abbreviated to STH or somatotropic or growth hormone; TSH or thyroid-stimulating hormone or thyreotropic hormone; ACTH or adrenocorticotropic hormone.

II. Morphology and Control of the Adrenal Cortex

The cytology and cytochemistry of the adrenal cortex may be found in a comprehensive review by Greep and Deane in 1949 (430).   Some of the more relevant and newer data on this subject are abbreviated into the following summary.

A. Cytological Localization of Adrenal Ketosteroids

A detailed review of this subject has recently been made by Deane and Seligman (212).   Starting from the original reports of Bennett in 1939 (70, 71) on the localization of ketosteroids by histochemical methods, this subject has now been advanced to a point where many techniques have been described in attempts to localize the different hormones in the gland. Although much valuable information has resulted and although many of the changes found may be considered typical for different responses to hormones or deficiency states, it should be realized that none of the histochemical techniques is specific enough actually to identify any particular adrenal hormone (212).

1. *Relation of the Zones of the Cortex to Hormone Production*

From a correlation of histological observations and the physiological status of hypophysectomized rats, Swann in 1940 (1118) suggested that the relatively normal appearance of the zona glomerulosa indicated its functional relationship to producing salt hormones, and from converse changes that the zona fasciculata produced O^{11} steroids. Greep and Deane (430) have reviewed their own extensive studies and those of others which have tended to confirm the original hypothesis of Swann. The zona glomerulosa of the rat showed histochemical evidence of stimulation after sodium deprivation or potassium administration, and it was depressed by potassium deprivation or DCA administration.

The zona fasciculata, on the other hand, could be stimulated by ACTH or induced hyperthyroidism or by alarming stimuli. It was depressed in hypothyroidism and after the administration of O^{11} steroids. A large series of papers confirm these findings in the rat. In the mouse, guinea pig, and dog, there is less agreement that the glomerulosa is not under pituitary control; these findings have been reviewed recently (212). In man, for example, ACTH stimulates all three zones of the cortex (831). It is of some interest that the adrenals of cattle, sheep, pig, and hamster possess little or no demonstrable lipid (212), and that a number of the 250 species examined by Bourne (107) have no distinguishable adrenal cortical zones. Ascorbic acid is apparently present in low concentrations in the zona glomerulosa, but in greater quantities in the inner zones (389, 400). Alkaline phosphatase persists in the glomerulosa but disappears from the zona fasciculata after hypophysectomy in the rat (225). The distinct vascular zoning of the adrenal cortex of the rat has recently been restudied by Lever (690), and the effect of cortisone described (207).

A number of histological studies on human adrenals from persons receiving ACTH or cortisone have been reported (76, 832, 1053). In addition, cytological studies of the pituitaries have shown degenerative changes in the basophiles, especially following ACTH therapy (77).

2. Effect on Adrenal Cortex of DDD

The action of the compound 2,2-bis-para-dichlorophenyl-1,1-dichloroethanol(DDD), closely related to the insecticide DDT, on the adrenal, is of considerable interest. In the dog at least, the action of DDD is to cause desctruction of the O^{11}-secreting zones of the adrenal cortex (811, 820). Treated animals show evidence of insufficiency such as increased insulin sensitivity (819, 820), but normal electrolyte response (820). The response to ACTH as measured by an increased oxygen consumption of slices of the adrenal cortex does not take place in DDD-treated animals (818). The rat, although much more resistant than the dog, shows an eosinopenia following ACTH or cold stress which was reduced after DDD treatment, and the sensitivity to insulin was increased. No change in salt or water metabolism was found (114). In a human case of Cushing's disease, no alleviation

of symptoms was found following massive doses of DDD (1014).   Anethole
has also been reported to affect steroid metabolism in the adrenal (279).

3. *Effect on Adrenal Cortex of Amphenone B and Erucic Acid*

Amphenone-B (1,2-*bis*-(*p*-aminophenyl)-2-methylpropanone-1 dihydro-
chloride) has been shown by Hertz and associates to cause, in addition to
other endocrine changes, hypertrophy of the adrenals in rats, the cortex
showing a marked increase in lipid and cholesterol (506, 977).   Cortisone
administered simultaneously prevented such hypertrophy (507).   Erucic
acid, a fatty acid component of rapeseed oil, has also been found to cause a
slight adrenal hypertrophy in the rat, associated with a marked increase in
cholesterol (132, 133, 626).   The response of animals treated with these
compounds will be discussed later in a consideration of adrenal cholesterol.

B. CONTROL OF ADRENAL CORTEX

A large number of studies have concerned the mechanism whereby the
pituitary releases ACTH to stimulate adrenocortical function.   Evidence
has indicated that the posterior hypothalamic nuclei and mammillary body
may be closely related to anterior pituitary function and probably act
through a chemical release into a portal circulation.   Although grafts of
pituitary tissue in the eye of the hypophysectomized rat respond directly
to epinephrine (740), those in the temporal lobe of the brain may show a
reduced response to stress.   These studies have been discussed in a recent
review (875).   The level of circulating adrenal cortical hormones, as studied
extensively by Sayers (960), would appear to be the major factor influencing
ACTH action, since exogenous O^{11} steroids will effectively block all forms of
pituitary ACTH stimuli.   Conversely, evidence has been presented that
ACTH is increased after adrenalectomy.   The content in the gland may be
increased by 1-$\frac{1}{2}$ times, but the increase in ACTH in body fluids amounted
to some 30 times the normal (380).   The role of epinephrine and the response to stress are more problematical and have been reviewed by Long
(706).   Exogenous epinephrine may cause some effects apparently due to
the release of ACTH, but these can be prevented by cortisone administration (960).   On the other hand, epinephrine stimulation does not increase
the blood 17-hydroxycorticoids or the urinary corticoids or 17-ketosteroids,
and initial adrenal stimulation is followed by a period of pituitary blockade.
Blood levels of epinephrine do not increase when discharge of the adrenal
pituitary system occurs (875).   Since there is experimental evidence that
the release of ACTH is triggered by a stimulus acting only for a few seconds
(423), it is probable that the momentary stimulation from epinephrine
would be difficult to demonstrate directly in the intact animal, and under

physiological conditions may not act long enough per se to induce changes associated with more prolonged adrenocortical stimulation (710).

1. *Effect of Age*

a. Premature and Newborn Infants.   The adrenal of the newborn responds to ACTH, and an increased excretion of urinary corticoids is found (899). The premature infant responds in the same fashion (666).   The low urinary corticoid value at birth increases with age.   Similarly, eosinopenia follows ACTH treatment, and the response is increased during the second week of life (899); 37 % of cases under 7 days old and 82 % at 7 days responded (641).   Urinary 17-ketosteroids are relatively high immediately after birth and then fall off, but respond by an increase to ACTH injection (899).

The response to epinephrine is present 24 hours after birth in approximately half full-term infants.   Premature infants did not respond to epinephrine before the 9th day of life, but all responded to ACTH (591).

b. Old Age.   Epinephrine-induced eosinopenia was found to be less in elderly individuals.   Similarly a reduced response in uric acid excretion and uric acid–creatine ratio, and a reduced rise in potassium excretion and potassium–creatine ratio indicated a lowered activity of the adrenal cortex (1054).   Where debility is not marked, however, the adrenal of the aged preserves relatively well its functional capacity (101, 874).

c. Rats.   The response of the embryo adrenal to ACTH has been reviewed by Kitchell and Wells (638).   They described unilateral adrenalectomy in the fetal rat which was followed by compensatory hypertrophy of the remaining adrenal.   This effect was inhibited by implanted cortisone pellets (638).   Additional information on the fetal adrenal is contained in a review by Jost (601).

2. *Transplantation of Adrenals*

The successful autotransplantation of adrenal glands to the spleen or mesentery without functional impairment has been described (80, 81, 124). Fetal homologous transplants of adrenal to the anterior chamber of the eye have been reported in the guinea pig, rabbit, and dog (197).   ACTH did not exert a beneficial effect on survival of adrenalhomotransplants in the rat (1233).   It is of interest that Parkes and Smith have found that frozen adrenals may, after storage, be successfully implanted and become functional in adrenalectomized rats (849).

C. ADRENAL HORMONES IN BLOOD

The measurement of adrenal steroid activity in the venous blood from the adrenal gland has been improved from the original assays for total activity, as described by Vogt, to present methods in which isolation and identifica-

tion of individual steroids is possible.   The method has been extended to
studies of the effluent of the isolated perfused adrenal of various species.
Extensive variations in the different steroid patterns have been found, both
as to the relative proportions and as to the individual components, when
different species were compared.   Perhaps the most striking feature of these
reports is the absence in many species of the production of cortisone.   Hydrocortisone and corticosterone appear to be the predominant hormones
found, with occasionally 11-dehydrocorticosterone.   A substance of high
electrolyte activity, presumably aldosterone, and other unidentified substances, are normally secreted.   Details of these experiments may be seen
in recent reviews by Vogt (1179), Bush (123), and Pincus and Elmadjian
(875).

The study of peripheral blood has led to somewhat similar findings,
although metabolic transformations make this method a less accurate indication of the actual secretory products of the adrenal.   Nelson and Samuels
(281, 814) have applied their method to studies on human blood.   A normal value for 17-hydroxycorticosteroids in peripheral blood of 4 to 10 μg.
per 100 ml. whole blood was found; the same figures were obtained by others
(122).   Plasma from children averaged 10 μg. per 100 ml. (122).   There
was no significant arteriovenous difference nor any change in patients with
rheumatic fever or rheumatoid arthritis.   In Addison's disease no hormone
was found.   ACTH caused an increased level.   Very high levels were also
found in patients *in extremis*.   Predominantly, hydrocortisone, but no
cortisone, was found (814, 815).   Others have found corticosterone values
to average 4.9 μg. and hydrocortisone to average 11.0 μg. per 100 ml. in
normal human peripheral blood.   The values were sharply increased by
ACTH and conditions associated with hyperadrenal function (1119), and
reduced by adrenalectomy in man (381).

The peripheral blood of a number of different species of animals has been
studied by Bush and others.   The dog and cat adrenals secreted mainly
hydrocortisone with some corticosterone.   In the guinea pig mainly hydrocortisone was noted, but also cortisone and 11-dehydrocortisone.   The
ferret shows approximately equal amounts of hydrocortisone and corticosterone, whereas the rat and rabbit exhibited nearly all corticosterone (122).
Others have confirmed the negligible amounts of cortisone, hydrocortisone,
and 11-deoxy-17-hydroxy-corticosterone in the blood of rats and rabbits.
Furthermore, ACTH treatment did not cause these substances to appear in
peripheral blood (244).

The application of the methods for measuring blood steroids in order to
assess adrenalcortical activity would seem to be a milestone in adrenal
physiology.   It is hoped that many of the former methods using indirect
and often variable secondary actions may now be happily abandoned.   The

actual formation of steroids by adrenal tissue and the metabolic utilization and urinary secretion of products of adrenal origin will be considered by other authors in this volume.

III. Adrenocortical Insufficiency

A. SURVIVAL AFTER ADRENALECTOMY

The effects of adrenalectomy on survival and other relevant changes on species not commonly used for experimental purposes, which were omitted from the previous volume, are described. In addition, reference is made to the operation on human subjects.

1. *Hamster*

The golden hamster (*Mesocricetus auratus*) shows an unusual sex dimorphism in adrenal size in that the adrenals are larger in the male, whereas the opposite is found in most other mammals. Gonadectomy causes equalization in adrenal weight with changes in both sexes (629, 861). Following adrenalectomy, the average survival was found to be 6.7 days for males and 10.2 days for females. Previously ovariectomized females survived the same length of time as males. Progesterone appeared to be more effective than DCA in maintaining life and body weight (1048).

2. *Sheep*

Observations have been made on five adrenalectomized sheep. Death occurred from 34 to 60 hours after removal of the second adrenal. The postoperative course was associated with low blood sugar and lactic acid and increased inorganic phosphate (1090).

3. *Goat*

A series of 19 animals were adrenalectomized by Cowie and Stewart and all but 2 were dead in 7 days (185), confirming observations made many years ago (786). Blood changes included a marked increase in nonprotein nitrogen (NPN), potassium, phosphate, and magnesium (in the longest survivors). Sodium and chloride were decreased. Very little change took place in hemoglobin or blood sugar levels (185).

4. *Monkey* (*Macaca mulatta*)

A careful, detailed study of adrenalectomy of this species has been reported by Greep and collaborators. The average length of survival was 13 days (10 to 16 days). Blood changes showed increasing NPN, potassium, and inorganic phosphate, and declining sodium and chloride; marked hypoglycemia was a prominent feature. Detailed post-mortem findings are also described (431).

5. *Man*

The use of bilateral adrenalectomy as a treatment of certain forms of hypertension or cancer in man has led to increasing reports on the effects of this operation. Huggins and Bergenstal have described some of the particular pre- and post-operative problems created by this procedure (542, 543). The results of bilateral adrenalectomy have also been described by others (472, 473, 544, 860, 1201). Subtotal adrenalectomy has also been used in the treatment of Cushing's disease and hypertension (884, 1258).

B. METHODS OF ADMINISTRATION OF CORTICAL HORMONES

Certain changes in the method of administration have been related to the use of different chemical preparations of adrenal steroids. In some cases one method of administration has been found to be particularly effective, especially in the case of human beings. The following is a brief summary of some of the more relevant observations. Complete details may be found in the review by Thorn and associates (1151).

Adrenal stimulation by ACTH is most marked when continuous intravenous administration is used. In man the intravenous dose (slow infusion) may be as much as 10 to 20 times more effective than intramuscular injection (725, 815, 1119). It should be appreciated that an increasing amount of direct evidence indicates that a number of components may be separated from ACTH and that these may possess varying degrees of activity when assayed for different types of activity (875).

Variations are apparent in the response to different methods of administration of the adrenal steroids. As would be expected from earlier experimental studies, both cortisone and hydrocortisone are highly active orally (350). The alcohol and acetate of cortisone and hydrocortisone, however, may show different oral activities. From a comparison of the therapeutic effects on human beings, free cortisone and the acetate were equally effective orally. Free hydrocortisone was about 1-1/3 times as active as cortisone acetate, but hydrocortisone acetate was even less effective than cortisone acetate (95). In studies of metabolic effects for a normal subject both forms of hydrocortisone were equally effective when taken orally. However, the acetate was much less active when administered by intramuscular injections, in contrast to the alcohol, which retained its expected potency (24, 172). It is perhaps not surprising that variations occur in different preparations administered by different routes, since the rates of absorption and individual response must be variables affecting the optimal level of circulating hormone which exerts the most beneficial actions. The alcohols, being more soluble than the acetates, have been administered intravenously with marked effectiveness (158). Deoxycorticosterone glucoside, a water-soluble DCA-like substance, also may be administered intravenously (1121). Cortisone may be administered effectively as pellets. In one report the absorption from 50 mg. pellets averaged 0.5 mg. per day per pellet (341). The rate of absorption from pellets in animals has been reviewed (365).

Intraarticular injections of hydrocortisone are much more effective than cortisone, although both steroids appear equally active in other forms of topical application (527, 528).

C. TREATMENT OF ADRENAL INSUFFICIENCY

1. *Addison's Disease*

The actions of cortisone on patients with Addison's disease were investigated by many clinical groups as soon as the steroid became generally available. Initial reports emphasized its beneficial action. Some of the effects of daily doses of 50 to 100 mg. were as follows: small but definite retention of Na and Cl; decreased excretion of urinary inorganic phosphate and creatine; increased excretion of uric acid and 17-ketosteroids; small increase in blood sugar; a significant transitory rise in fasting blood ketones; depression of circulating eosinophils; return to normal of the electroencephalogram (74, 341, 1079) and electrocardiogram (1057). Because of the relatively slight effect of cortisone on electrolytes, the hormone treatment of adrenal insufficiency is best accomplished by both DCA and cortisone. An average dose level of 1 to 2 mg. daily and 12-½ mg. twice daily, respectively, has been recommended. Hydrocortisone and corticosterone (170) are also effective forms of therapy. Details on this subject may be found in the comprehensive reviews published in 1951 and 1953 by Thorn and his collaborators (1150, 1151). The beneficial action of licorice extract and glycyrrhizic acid in adrenal insufficiency has been described by Groen and others (434, 435, 541).

2. *Adrenalectomized Human Subjects—Corticosterone Therapy*

A detailed discussion on the management of patients for bilateral adrenalectomy has been omitted. However, it should be strongly emphasized that vigorous treatment with adrenal steroids in large doses must be started before operation and maintained throughout the postoperative course to compensate for the sudden cessation of endogenous hormone production. Following recovery from the operative procedures, the management of the patient is essentially similar to that of the Addisonian (542, 1150).

a. Corticosterone Therapy. The effect of replacement therapy by corticosterone on a number of adrenalectomized patients has been described in a paper by West, Pearson, and Kappas. An oral dose of 100 to 200 mg. per

698 R. L. NOBLE

day maintained one patient satisfactorily for 9 days. Withdrawal of the steroid was followed by prompt clinical collapse, which was rapidly controlled by 100 mg. daily as the only form of therapy. Doses of 100 to 800 mg. daily by mouth for 24 days were followed by a profound retention of NaCl and water, but no changes in carbohydrate or protein metabolism. The intravenous administration of 300 to 600 mg. daily for 6 days caused a slight increase in nitrogen, phosphate, and K excretion and a marked retention of NaCl and water; again, no effect was noted on blood glucose (1200). These changes are similar to those described by Conn and associates for normal persons or Addisonians treated with corticosterone (170).

3. Effectiveness of Less Common Steroids in Adrenalectomized Animals

a. *9 α Halogen Derivatives of Cortisone.* Substituted chloro or fluoro derivatives have been reported to be considerably more active than cortisone (350a). The more recent findings have indicated that in addition the the action of such compounds differs qualitatively from that of cortisone in that a marked action on electrolytes occurs. Life maintenance activity may be 10 to 20 times that of DCA (350b).

b. *Δ¹ Deoxycorticosterone Acetate.* Daily doses of 0.25 and 0.5 mg. administered to young adrenalectomized rats maintained life and caused a weight increase over 20 days, averaging 1 and 2 gm. daily, respectively. The activity was from one-eighth to one-tenth that of DCA (676).

c. *Δ⁴⁻⁶ Dehydrocortisone (Diene Compound).* This substance was obtained from the partial synthesis of cortisone and was found to have a similar activity in maintaining adrenalectomized rats but was better tolerated (512).

d. *Deoxycorticosterone Glucoside.* This compound is suitable for intravenus use and exerts a DCA-like activity (753). Intravenously, it was found to be most effective in reviving adrenalectomized dogs from crises. When administered as single daily intramuscular doses it was one-sixth to one-seventh as active as DCA in maintaining adrenalectomized dogs. The low activity was probably due to its rapid excretion or inactivation (1121).

e. *17-Hydroxy 11-Deoxycorticosterone (Compound S).* In adrenalectomized rats this compound exerted a weak DCA-like action (377).

f. *Deoxycorticosterone Esters.* These compounds show a DCA-like activity, but of more prolonged duration. This is true of the benzoate and palmitate (773), the trimethylacetate in rats and dogs (441, 1207), and the phenylacetate and β-cyclopentylpropionate in dogs (1120) and rats (376). The trimethylacetate has the longest action (377). The ability of these compounds to cause toxic effects on the cardiovascular system has been recorded (453), and clinical trials with some of these esters have been reported (345).

D. Some Untoward Actions of Adrenal Steroids

Although the last sections of this chapter consider the action of large doses of adrenal steroids which may be considered as causing undesirable or toxic manifestations, certain other toxic effects which do not logically come into the future contents have been grouped in this section for consideration.

1. Human Subjects

The more serious toxic effects of chronic cortisone therapy, which on occasion have been described as possible dangers from this form of treatment, may be summarized as follows: the development of symptoms and findings associated normally with Cushing's disease; hyperglycemic effects leading to a form of diabetes mellitus; elevation of blood pressure; sodium retention and edema; depletion of potassium; mild or severe mental disturbances; development or aggravation of peptic ulcer; suppression of antibodies and resistance to various infections; osteoporosis; masking of disease by suppression of symptoms; adrenal atrophy resulting in a hypoadrenal state with a reduced tolerance to anesthetics, surgery, etc., if therapy is inadvertently discontinued.

The acute toxicity of cortisone in man is apparently low, since doses of 2000 mg. given in the first 2 days, 200 mg. on the third day, and 100 mg. for 6 days, were not found to cause toxic symptoms (65).

2. Toxic Effects on Embryos and Pregnancy

a. Chicks. ACE was first shown by Landauer in 1947 to retard the growth of chick embryos (665). Karnofsky and associates extended these observations to show that chicken embryos and newly hatched chicks showed modifications of development and growth inhibition following treatment. Hydrocortisone acetate was 100 times more potent than cortisone in this respect, and corticosterone was almost as active as hydrocortisone. DCA also showed similar effects (610, 611). Chick embryos injected with 0.25 mg. of DCA or 0.5 mg. of cortisone into the yolk sac on day 6 showed retarded growth, but no morphological changes were encountered with such doses (956).

b. Mice. Pregnant mice received 2.5 mg. of cortisone daily for 2 days. When treated on days 7 to 8 ante partum, fetal death occurred. When treated 3 to 5 days ante partum, the young were born alive but died in 2 to 5 days. Treatment of the mothers 4 to 6 days post partum caused death of young in 3 to 5 days. The mammary glands of the mothers were distended with milk (398, 399).

c. Rats. DCA and salt administered to rats in doses producing hyper-

tension had no effect on conception, implantation, or normal delivery (845).
Cortisone, 2 mg. daily, was found to act as replacement therapy in the pregnant, adrenalectomized rat and to prevent interruption of pregnancy (208).

   d. Rabbits.   Pregnant rabbits receiving 25 mg. cortisone daily after day
15 were found to show abnormal gestations (183).   Extensive studies on
rabbits treated with 15 mg. of cortisone daily have been made by De Costa
and Abelman.   Such dosage had no effect on ovulation or sexual receptivity.   If given before mating, fertility was reduced, with only 7.1 % pregnancies occurring, whereas controls showed 65.9 %.   If cortisone was given
48 hours post coitum 48.8 % pregnancies were observed.   Cortisone disrupted pregnancy, causing fetal death or abortion, and sensitivity appeared
to increase as pregnancy progressed.   Gestation was sometimes prolonged,
but only one fetal anomaly was noted.   Lactation was normal (218, 219).
DCA and salt treatment of pregnant rabbits led to marked changes associated with death and retention of the fetuses (735).

   e. Human Pregnancy.   Cortisone in therapeutic doses has been well
tolerated by pregnant women, with no adverse effects noted (218, 242).

3. *Inhibition of Body Growth*

   Many reports have included the inhibiting effect of adrenal steroids on
body growth and may be noted in Ingle's review (560).

   a. Rats.   In newborn rats cortisone, 0.3 mg. daily for 3 days, caused
death in a few days.   DCA, 0.25 mg. daily, was nontoxic.   Growth was
inhibited by even single injections of 0.25 mg. of cortisone, but tooth eruption and opening of the eyes were speeded.   DCA also had the same action
on the teeth and eye opening (850).

   With continuous subcutaneous injections of cortisone and hydrocortisone
for 10 days, the latter substance was twice as effective in affecting weight.
A negative nitrogen balance, glycosuria, stomach ulcers, and renal damage
were also observed (566).

   In 1940 Wells and Kendall noted that immature rats receiving 1 mg. of
cortisone daily by mouth weighed 30 gm. less than controls after 10 days
treatment (1195).   Young rats receiving 3 mg. cortisone daily for six weeks
showed cessation of growth, although they consumed 47 % more food than
paired controls to remain at the same weight.   The associated adrenal
atrophy of 50 % was confined to the inner zones of the adrenal cortex (1219).
Cortisone, 2 mg. daily, stopped growth and was followed by cardiac and
kidney hypertrophy.   DCA in the same dose had no effect on growth or
heart weight but caused moderate kidney enlargement (452).   The growth
of young rats was not affected in doses of cortisone up to 20 mg. per kilogram; from 20 to 50 mg. per kilogram some decreased growth was observed;
and with doses above 50 mg. per kilogram growth impairment was marked

(336). Hydrocortisone was found to be two to four times more active than cortisone (338).

b. Adrenalectomized Rats. Cortisone at any dose level does not allow a normal growth rate to occur in the young adrenalectomized animal (560). Daily treatment with cortisone was followed by a greater weight loss in adrenalectomized than in intact animals. The former also showed a greater excretion of glucose, increased incidence of pathological changes in the kidneys, and stomach ulcers (562).

c. Other Species. Similar inhibition of growth has been noted after cortisone in many species. Inhibition of the growth of mice, guinea pigs, and rabbits was found after cortisone (23, 337). The toxic effects of cortisone on mice were enhanced by an increased environmental temperature (966).

4. *Adrenal Atrophy*

The atrophy of the adrenal cortex associated with adrenal steroid therapy has been noted in numerous papers. Such atrophy after cortisone does not affect the zona glomerulosa (1070). The adrenal atrophy caused by DCA is much less than that caused by cortisone (452, 960). In the rat adrenal atrophy can be counteracted by the simultaneous administration of testosterone propionate, dihydrotestosterone, and methylandrostenediol (378, 1158, 1218), but such an action was not found in the monkey (645a). The latter substance did not counteract the antiinflammatory action of cortisone (1218). Such combined therapy has been used clinically (534). Further atrophy of the adrenal glands in the hypophysectomized rat does not occur following cortisone injections, indicating that the action in the intact animal is by suppression of ACTH (1092). Similarly, if the adrenal of the hypophysectomized rat is maintained by daily ACTH, simultaneous cortisone treatment does not affect the adrenal size (697). In human panhypopituitarism treated with ACTH, cortisone did not diminish the function of the adrenal cortex (1078), but, on the other hand, cortisone in normal patients diminished the response to ACTH (745). Cortical atrophy follows cortisone therapy in man (1077). The reactions of the adrenals to stress have been reviewed by Sayers and Sayers (961).

IV. Adrenal Steroid Assay Procedures

In the previous volume many assay methods which had been used for adrenal steroids were mentioned during a discussion of the various mechanisms to which they were related. During the past few years a number of modifications have been suggested, new methods advocated, and older ones discarded. These changes will be discussed together in this section, but the detailed procedures and statistical evaluation may be found in the recent complete review by Dorfman (250).

1. *Electrolyte Changes*

The influence of adrenal steroids on the urinary excretion of Na and/or K in adrenalectomized rats or mice is the basis of the most satisfactory methods. Measurement of the salts has been facilitated by the use of the flame photometer, and the use of the radioactive elements is well suited to this method. Dorfman *et al.*, using radioactive sodium excretion in adrenalectomized male rats, found that giving a preliminary load of sodium to the animals increased the sensitivity of the test. DCA was active at a dose level of 0.98 μg. (251); hydrocortisone showed no activity at 25 μg., and at 50 μg. an increased sodium excretion occurred; at 200 μg. no effect on excretion or retention was observed. 11-Dehydrocorticosterone acetate (100 μg.) and corticosterone (400 μg.) were inactive (248). A similar method has been used by Singer and Venning (1031). Others have used similar methods but determined the electrolytes by the flame photometric or chemical technique in adrenalectomized rats (222, 727) or mice (604, 1073). Marcus (727) and associates found DCA at a dose level of 2.4 μg. to cause a slight (9 %) retention of sodium, which increased to 78 % retention with doses of 60 μg. K behaved in the inverse manner. All dose levels of DCA produced retention of Na and increased excretion of K. 11-Dehydrocorticosterone, on the other hand, caused retention of Na at 10 μg. but had no effect on K. At dose levels of 50 μg. and 200 μg. there was no Na retention but marked K excretion. This action of increasing K excretion, but without Na retention, was also noted for corticosterone (50 μg. to 400 μg.) and low doses of cortisone (10 μg. and 50 μg.). Larger doses of cortisone (200 μg.) caused increased excretion of both Na and K. Hydrocortisone showed no effect at 10 μg. and 50 μg., but 200 μg. caused only K excretion (727). Simpson and Tait reduced the time of the test to 2 hours instead of 6 hours, (as have others (604)). They measured both urinary radioactive Na and K and used the ratio as an index of electrolyte activity (1026). A more recent modification using the potassium and sodium ratio has been described; this allows greater differentiation in activity of the various steroids (596).

Because of the clinical importance of the effects of the different steroids on Na and K, and since apparently paradoxical actions depend on dose, it should be noted that the sodium-retaining action of compounds other than DCA is comparatively poor and large doses may even increase sodium loss. Increased excretion of K is caused by all compounds and is not necessarily related to any action on Na. Such results clearly show the need for combined steroid therapy in the adequate treatment of adrenal insufficiency.

2. *Electroshock Threshold*

The electroshock threshold (EST) in the rat is increased by DCA and lowered by cortisone, the effect apparently being related to the action of these substances on the concentration of extracellular sodium in the body and brain (1228, 1229, 1232).   Adrenalectomized, salt-maintained rats were used for assay purposes.   The EST control value was determined from three tests before steroid treatment was started.   Decreasing EST values were induced by daily doses of cortisone from 25 μg. to 750 μg. (532).

3. *Liver Glycogen Deposition*

The adrenalectomized mouse or rat, primed by glucose, is extensively used for the assay of the O^{11} steroids and urine extracts causing glycogen deposition.   Attempts to eliminate variability in the control animals by dietary measures (339) and the appreciation of variation due to impure strains of mice (821, 822) have been stressed in recent papers.   When compared with cortisone, hydrocortisone shows up to double the activity, whereas corticosterone and 11-dehydrocorticosterone are approximately half as active (252, 843).   Dose levels of 5 μg. to 10 μg. of cortisone are required for the mouse and 125 μg. to 300 μg. for the rat for accurate assay.

4. *Eosinophil Depression*

The eosinopenia secondarily induced following the injection of ACTH or epinephrine as used as an index of adrenal or pituitary responsiveness will be discussed later in the chapter.

The fall in the number of circulating eosinophils in the adrenalectomized male mouse has been developed by Speirs and Meyer into an accurate assay for O^{11} steroids (1072).   Certain strains of mice having greater sensitivity for the assay may be selected (1241).   Pretreatment with epinephrine is used to render nonsensititive any extraadrenal tissue remaining after adrenalectomy.   Assays require a dose of from 0.5 μg. to 3 μg. of cortisone or hydrocortisone, whereas 11-dehydrocorticosterone was about one-eighth as active.   Bibile has found the relative order of potencies for different steroids as follows: when cortisone = 100; hydrocortisone = 78; corticosterone = 38; and 11-dehydrocorticosterone = 24.   This test was sensitive to 1 μg. of cortisone (85).   The eosinophil-depression assay method has recently been used extensively for extracts of blood and urine and its merits discussed (940).

5. *Lymphocyte Destruction—in Vitro*

Techniques have been described so that the direct cytocidal action of adrenal steroids was studied on rabbit lymphocytes *in vitro*.   The effective doses required for assay were very small, being 0.025 μg. for hydrocortisone and 0.1 μg. for cortisone, corticosterone, and 11-dehydrocorticosterone (316, 974–976).

6. *Anti-Inflammation*

The inhibitory action of O^{11} steroids on the cellular reaction to inflammatory agents may be used for assay purposes. Inflammation has been induced in the adrenalectomized mouse by initial sensitization to foreign protein followed by local injection of protein into the skin (257) or by the injection of histamine (971). From mounts of the surrounding tissue differential cell counts were made on fibroblasts and the various leucocytes. When histamine was used the steroid exerted an inhibitory action when injected mixed with the histamine. (Similar findings have been reported when the steroid was mixed with turpentine (1135).) Hydrocortisone was reported as 20 times as effective as cortisone in the assay using histamine (971).

7. *Stress*

Traumatic stress may be quantitatively applied to rats by the drum-shock method (825, 826). Schenker has used this method to assay adrenal steroids on adrenalectomized rats. Mortality was reduced by pretreatment with 25 μg. of hydrocortisone. Corticosterone was more active, whereas cortisone was less than half as effective as hydrocortisone. It is possibly of some interest that this is the only assay procedure described where the greatest activity has been shown by the naturally secreted O^{11} adrenal steroids in the species studied (965).

8. *Other Methods*

The following newer tests described for assay purposes may be listed: involution of the thymus gland (183, 249), typhoid vaccine test (695, 696), inhibition of various inflammatory reactions (754, 995), the granuloma pouch (1001), and *in vitro* effects on tissue swelling (292) and on mammary tissue (50). The evaluation of these and of survival and growth methods, blood NPN, muscle work tests, and the cold test, may be found in Dorfman's reviews (247, 250).

V. Adrenal Cortex and Kidney Function

Considerable clinical interest has been shown by the numerous reports on the action of ACTH and adrenal steroids on kidney disease, particularly the nephrotic syndrome. A discussion of these papers is beyond the scope of this chapter, but some of the references to this work may be found in a recent paper by Farnsworth (315; see also reference 1151).

A. Sodium and Chloride

a. Man. The effects of cortisone on electrolyte metabolism have been reviewed by Sprague (1076). In most cases at least transitory retention of sodium, chloride, and water are observed, and edema may occur.   Similar findings have been reported for hydrocortisone (172).   After prolonged therapy the reverse picture may be presented (1080).   The sodium retention after cortisone apparently could be diminished or abolished by treatment with supplemental K (73).   Cortisone had no effect on fecal electrolytes or nitrogen, whether salt was added to the diet or not (201).

The effects of different steroids have been compared on four cases of chronic leukemia.   Cortisone (100 to 200 mg. daily) caused a positive balance of Na and Cl, but hydrocortisone in doses up to 400 mg. daily did not have this effect.   11-Dehydrocorticosterone (100 mg. daily) caused retention of Na and Cl, and Compound S (200 mg. daily) caused a slight retention (857).   Others, however, noted a marked Na and Cl retention with hydrocortisone (400 mg. daily) (177).   Corticosterone also causes typical Na, Cl, and water retention (170).

Observations have been made on infants of three weeks of age or under. Cortisone, 25 mg., in one case caused sodium retention but was ineffective in another at double the dose.   ACTH caused a negative sodium balance. DCA, 1 to 5 mg., gave the expected retention of sodium (640).

The effects of prolonged treatment with DCA on sodium, chloride, and water retention, and potassium loss in man, may prove different from the well-known actions following shorter treatment of normal persons or following treatment of patients with Addison's disease.   Thus, reports of sodium and water loss, as well as K loss, during continued hormone administration in high doses have been reported (744, 1253).   Recent studies have confirmed the observations that Na and Cl loss may replace the initial retention on prolonged DCA therapy.   Associated with the Na loss was a marked increase in calcium excretion, possibly suggesting that Na from bone was being mobilized (714).   Similar changes were observed after continued combined cortisone and DCA therapy (1034).   These changes have not been found in corresponding experiments in the dog (206).   Following DCA administration in Cushing's syndrome there was either no effect or an increased excretion of salt rather than the retention typically observed in normal persons (1050).   The effects of deoxycorticosterone glucoside given intravenously have been described.   Despite a marked continued increase in urinary output, Na output was rapidly decreased and retention occurred (426).

b. Addison's Disease.   Two patients were maintained on constant DCA and cortisone therapy but showed wide changes in Na balance similar to those shown by normal patients in response to varied stimuli.   It was concluded that variations in Na retention or excretion do not require changes in adrenal activity per se but that the adrenal plays a permissive role in such effects (941).

   c. *Adrenalectomized Human Subjects.* When such patients were maintained on approximately 50 mg. of cortisone daily, withdrawal of therapy
caused a prompt antidiuresis with low blood Na and Cl and no urinary
loss of salt. Blood and urinary K were normal. There was an associated
marked gain in weight. The return of cortisone therapy caused a prompt
diuresis and weight loss. Such changes were believed to be due to water
retention associated with a low sodium balance (859, 860).
   d. *Dogs.* The treatment with cortisone, 5 mg. per kilogram, and DCA,
½ mg. per kilogram, was compared in the adrenalectomized and in
the normal animal. The increase in plasma Na and Cl produced by
cortisone was greater in the adrenalectomized animal. DCA did not affect
chloride and caused a slight Na increase in the normal dogs (205). Intravenous cortisone, when administered to adrenalectomized dogs, decreased the renal excretion of Na and restored plasma electrolytes towards
normal. The additional treatment with DCA increased the effect (920).
Deoxycorticosterone glucoside caused a marked excretion of urine and a
reduction in urinary Na concentration (425).
   e. *Mice.* Sodium excretion may be increased in adrenalectomized mice
after a sodium load and critical doses of DOC below those causing Na
retention (342).
   f. *Rabbits.* In this species 4 mg. of cortisone daily led to a decreased
concentration of plasma sodium for approximately one week; thereafter
both Na and K retention were found associated with water retention. Cessation of therapy led to a prompt weight loss, diuresis, and negative Na
balance. With a dose of 25 mg. daily a marked loss of K occurred (11).
   g. *Rats.* The initial increased excretion of Na, Cl, and K following
cortisone or hydrocortisone in the rat (571, 1146) is a transitory effect
lasting from 1 to 3 days despite continuous treatment. Thereafter a normal balance was restored, although the excretion of K was more prolonged
(584).
   h. *NaCl-Deficient Rats.* Hartroft and Hartroft have described granules
in the renal juxtaglomerular cells, which showed degranulation on the
administration of NaCl. This was enhanced by DCA treatment, although
DCA had no effect alone. They suggest that these cells may be involved
in Na metabolism (475). Salt depletion in rats was found to be followed
by a temporary increase in 17-ketosteroid secretion, and the terminal
adrenal hypertrophy was associated with a reduced adrenal ascorbic acid
content (198).

1. *Aldosterone*

   The very recent chemical identification of the natural adrenal steroid
predominantly responsible for maintenance of electrolyte metabolism must

rank as a major chemical achievement, and has been described by Simpson, Tait, Wettstein, Neber, von Euw, Schindler and Reichstein (1029).   This followed the reported isolation of the active material from beef adrenals by the same collaborating groups (1028).   Other groups working on the chemical isolation of apparently the same substance had made major achievements in this direction (645, 737).   Grundy and associates had previously described the finding of a fraction separated by chromatography from adrenal extracts which possessed very high mineralocorticoid activity (444, 1131).   It was also shown that the same substance was secreted into the adrenal vein blood of a monkey and a dog in biologically significant amounts (1027).   The biological activity of aldosterone is from 30 to 100 times (depending on the type of assay) that of DCA on electrolyte metabolism.   It now seems clear that activities formerly ascribed to the amorphous fraction were due to its aldosterone content.   From preliminary data available at this time various workers using aldosterone-containing fractions or the pure compound have intimated that it may possess approximately 30 times the activity of DCA on glycogen deposition tests in the mouse (979) and in the maintenance of the adrenalectomized dog and rat (229, 440). Tentative results discussed at a recent conference (1026a) indicated that aldosterone is orally active.   Following ACTH there was only a slight increase in the aldosterone content of adrenal effluent blood when compared with the increase in other O^{11} steroids.   Conversely, hypophysectomy caused only a small decline in aldosterone, suggesting that this hormone is under only partial control by the pituitary.   This might suggest its possible origin from the zona glomerulosa.   The physiological and pathological changes induced by this compound and its estimation in biological fluids will greatly aid in determining the possible role of the adrenal in the etiology of various diseases of man.

B. POTASSIUM

The effects of cortisone on man are somewhat variable but usually lead to a negative potassium balance (1076, 1080), which in chronic treatment may lead to dangerous potassium depletion.   A rebound retention of K usually follows cessation of steroid therapy (343, 714).   When rheumatoid patients were treated with cortisone it was found that supplemental K did not modify the therapeutic action or other effects such as increased urinary uric acid, nitrogen, and 17-ketosteroids, but it did prevent or decrease the usual sodium retention (73).   Cortisone and hydrocortisone (100 to 200 mg. daily) caused a negative K balance.   11-Dehydrocorticosterone, up to doses of 800 mg. daily, had no effect on K.   Compound S (200 mg.) also showed no action on K (857).   Hydrocortisone, 400 mg. daily, was also reported by others to cause a marked K diuresis (177), and corticosterone had a similar action (170).   The loss of K after DCA would appear to be mainly of intracellular origin, since other metabolic changes, such as protein breakdown, which could explain the loss of potassium, were not found (714).   After cortisone, however, K was derived from both intra- and extracellular fluids.   The negative potassium balance was almost equivalent to the negative nitrogen balance (713, 1080).

    a. Dogs.   The reduction in plasma K by cortisone was found to be greater in adrenalectomized than in normal dogs.   DCA showed the same degree of action on both groups of animals (205).   It was suggested that the condition similar to diabetes insipidus produced in dogs by treatment with DCA was related to the induced potassium loss, since K deficiency per se has been shown by Smith and Lasater to induce the same condition in dogs. Urinary volume as high as 1710 ml. per day and typical paralytic attacks were observed (1045).   Swingle and colleagues made the interesting observations that adrenalectomized dogs could be maintained in an active, vigorous, and symptom-free condition by cortisone treatment at a dose level of 0.93 mg. per kilogram per day.   However, such animals showed a progressive decline in serum Na and Cl and marked elevation of K, until they suddenly collapsed and cardiac failure occurred.   Doubling the dose of cortisone restored the animal and maintained normal electrolyte values; this was at least 60 times the requisite dose of DCA in oil (1122, 1123). Whitney and Bennett have shown that an increased intake of K in rats may inhibit the usual nitrogen excretion after ACTH (1205).

1. *Epinephrine and Potassium*

    The possibility that K may also be markedly influenced by the adrenal medulla has received recent consideration.   Serum K in dogs can be diminished by intravenous epinephrine given in physiological doses, and the increased K of adrenalectomized dogs can be corrected by the same procedure.   No changes were noted in Na (936).   Similarly, in normal and adrenalectomized rats epinephrine caused a fall in plasma K (272).   Demedullated rats also showed a reduction in plasma K after epinephrine (273).   Dury also cites experiments which indicated that the toxicity of hypertonic glucose in the adrenalectomized animal may be due to the increased blood K, which can be counteracted with injections of epinephrine, with resulting prevention of mortality (271).   Similarly, the fall in plasma K after insulin can be prevented by demedullation in the rat (273).

C. AMMONIA AND TITRATABLE ACID

    A reinvestigation of this problem has been published by Sartorius *et al.* (959).   The adrenalectomized rat was shown to have a reduced capacity to excrete ammonia and titratable acid, amounting to 50 % and 80 %, respectively, of the normal. This was associated with a lowering of bicarbonate reserves. ACE and DCA effectively reversed such changes. The adrenalectomized rat, therefore, even though maintained on NaCl, suffers mild-to-moderate acidosis. It was believed that the kidney mechanism for such regulation of acid-base balance was independent of that controlling electrolyte concentrations. In the adrenalectomized dog, however, few changes in titratable acid were observed. When such animals were given a phosphate load, the changes in acid excretion did not differ from controls, nor was the response modified by cortisone (921).

In man ACTH or cortisone administration frequently results in alkalosis (885, 1080). DCA also induced an increased CO_2-combining capacity of the plasma and an increase in urinary pH (1034). Such changes were not found in the dog after similar treatment (206).

D. CLEARANCE TESTS

1. *Human Subjects*

That the Addisonian shows a decreased glomerular filtration rate (GFR), renal blood flow (RBF), maximal tubular transfer of diodone, and decreased water diuresis has been confirmed in a more recent paper (1035); the subject has been reviewed by Heller (488).

Normal patients on a salt-free diet treated with cortisone showed a gradual increase, then a decrease, in GFR (693). Clearance studies in patients with rheumatoid arthritis studied before and after treatment with 100 mg. of cortisone daily showed a GFR which was greatly increased; the RPF was increased slightly or unchanged. Water resorption by the tubules was increased (954). In patients with normal renal and adrenal function, cortisone was found to alter the rate of excretion of uric acid, phosphorus, Na, and K; this alteration is independent of the serum concentrations and rates of kidney filtration (557). In man, therefore, it would appear that cortisone and DCA (and ACTH) increase the GFR and RPF and the filtration fraction (FF). A direct action on the renal tubular transport of electrolytes, however, occurs independent of the rates of kidney filtration and serum concentrations of electrolytes. Water resorption by the tubules may be increased. The opposite changes occurring in adrenal insufficiency are reversed by adrenal steroid therapy.

2. *Adrenalectomized Dog*

The low GFR and RPF following adrenalectomy (as described in older papers and reviewed by Heller (488)) was found to be restored towards normal by intravenous cortisone. An increased effect was found by the addition of DCA in treatment (920). The GFR was reduced by conditions of acute adrenal insufficiency (704), but may be essentially normal when the animal is well hydrated and in good condition (934).

3. *Normal Dogs*

Cortisone, and DCA were found to cause an increased GFR and RPF with an increased water exchange, but not to effect the FF (differing from man). The increased water exchange produced by DCA, however, differs from that caused by cortisone, since the level of water exchange caused by the former is a function of salt intake in the dog (802) and also in the rat (909), but this is not so in the case with cortisone (206). The reabsorption capacity of the renal tubules for phosphates was depressed by cortisone, but not by DOC (921).

4. *Adrenalectomized Rats*

When maintained on normal saline such animals showed essentially normal rates of glomerular filtration (105, 360, 709) and renal blood flow (360). An increased tubular resorption of water caused a reduced urine output (709).

5. *Normal Rats*

The effects of ACE and DCA were found to be an increased urinary excretion without increased glomerular filtration or renal plasma flow. It was concluded that alterations in urinary electrolyte levels are largely independent of GFR or RPF, and that ACE acts primarily on the renal tubular reabsorption of water and electrolytes (106, 360).

E. INTRACELLULAR FLUID AND ELECTROLYTES

Davis, Bass, and Overman, in a study of plasma and tissue electrolytes, found that after cortisone, 5 mg. per kilogram, there was a greater increase in Na concentration and a greater loss of K in the muscle of normal dogs than in that of the adrenalectomized animal (205). Earlier results showed that in adrenal insufficiency changes in the diminution in extracellular water volume and increase in the intracellular fluid were greater than alterations in plasma volume or in the total body water (90, 373).

1. *Rat*

The water retained by the untreated adrenalectomized animal after a water load was shown to be almost all intracellular. The loss of NaCl from the extracellular fluid during adrenal insufficiency has been suggested by Frost and Talmage as the primary cause of the increased cellular hydration (362). Cole has made detailed studies of the changes in electrolytes in various tissues of adrenalectomized rats and the corrective influence of DCA treatment. He concluded that the water and electrolyte changes were secondary to changes in the plasma sodium level and in the nondiffusible molecule concentration within the cells (161, 162). Cole also has shown that the loss of skeletal muscle sodium and increase in K were due to independent processes in the adrenalectomized rat and that DCA chiefly affected the latter (163). From studies of the change in balance and the sodium loss during adrenal insufficiency and retention during recovery, it has been suggested that some labile store of Na and Cl is present in the body, possibly in the bone (327).

2. *Man*

Levitt and Bader found that cortisone given to normal persons on a salt-free diet resulted in a shift from intracellular fluid to a 20 % to 40 % increase in extracellular volume, reaching a maximum in 8 to 9 days and then decreasing to normal despite continued treatment. The fluid shift occurred without a concomitant Na and Cl retention, but this was probably related to the prior salt depletion of the patients (693), as such changes were not found with cortisone and DCA in persons on a normal diet (714, 1034).

F. WATER EXCRETION

1. *Human Subjects*

In one patient with Addison's disease cortisone, 30 mg. daily, restored to normal the diuretic response to a water load. DCA, 10 mg. daily, did not show this effect (954). Similar findings were reported in Addison's disease and in six cases of panhypopituitarism, with cortisone treatment restoring the diuretic response to normal (142). In adrenalectomized patients, the withdrawal of cortisone therapy led to marked water retention. Restitution of cortisone therapy led to a marked diuresis and alleviation of symptoms (859, 860).

2. *Adrenalectomized Rat*

The 48-hour adrenalectomized nontreated rat, after two doses of water, retains greater than twice as much fluid as controls owing to the delayed diuresis, the unexcreted water being almost all intracellular (362). Combined hypophysectomy and adrenalectomy further reduces water excretion (523). The impaired diuretic response after adrenalectomy was partially restored by cortisone, but not by DCA. Combined therapy led to a complete restoration of normal diuresis (790). Cortisone acetate was more effective by intraperitoneal injection than by the subcutaneous route in restoring water diuresis in the adrenalectomized rat (429). Bristol and Drill showed that when hydrating saline solutions of varying concentration were used instead of water, normal urinary excretion could be found in adrenalectomized rats, indicating that a NaCl deficit was primarily responsible for the inability to excrete a water load (110).

3. *Diabetes Insipidus—Human*

In a classical case neither cortisone nor deoxycorticosterone glucoside had any effect on water excretion or on the action of pitressin therapy (304, 675).

4. *Polyuria in Dogs*

Normal dogs, when treated with cortisone, 50 to 300 mg. daily for 4 to 14 days, were shown to develop a marked polydipsia and polyuria (up to 6200 ml. and 5790 ml. per day, respectively). Curiously, there were no associated changes in fasting blood sugar or in glucose tolerance tests (1032). In the adrenalectomized dog cortisone (10 mg. per kilogram daily) induced similar changes in water metabolism, and this could be controlled by pitressin (1124). Deoxycorticosterone glucoside administration is also followed by increased water excretion of from 50 % to 200 % above control levels (425).

5. *Antidiuretic Activity*

The antidiuretic activity of the hypothalamus or neurohypophysis was not altered in donor rats by treatment with NaCl, cortisone, or DCA nor by adrenalectomy (235).

6. *Relationship of Adrenal Cortex and Posterior Pituitary to Water Metabolism*

This subject has been reviewed by Gaunt (374) and others (375, 824). The effects of adrenal steroids on salt exchange and the influence of blood osmotic changes on posterior-lobe secretion would indicate a close relationship between these two endocrine organs. This is further suggested by the finding that a moderate dose of pitressin or a large water load will cause depletion of adrenal ascorbic acid. Stimulation of adrenal secretion, therefore, may be associated with an increased diuresis after a water load (and related to suppression of activity of the neurohypophysis (808)).

VI. Influence of the Adrenal Cortex on Sweat and Saliva

1. *Sweat*

The investigations by Conn and his associates on human beings have been published in a series of papers. ACTH and DCA were found to cause a progressive decrease in Na and Cl in thermal sweat. In Addison's disease the sweat contained increased NaCl, and conversely, in hypercorticalism the NaCl was low (167, 169, 171, 174). This action of DCA was confirmed by others (928). It has also been shown that DCA caused an increase in sweat Cl concentration relative to the rate of sweating. Cortisone had a similar but smaller effect (703). The adrenal gland would appear to play an important role during acclimatization to humid heat. During this period there is a marked reduction in NaCl of the excreted sweat and evidence of adrenal stimulation such as increased urinary 17-ketosteroids. If an acclimatized subject is treated with DCA and then such therapy is stopped abruptly, there is a temporary loss of acclimatization (167, 169, 171).

2. Saliva

In four patients treated with ACTH the saliva showed a reduced Na and increased K concentration. These correlated with a decreased circulatory eosinophil count and increased urinary 17-ketosteroid excretion (417). Similar findings were reported by Frawley (345).

VII. Influence of the Adrenal Cortex on the Cardiovascular System

A. Heart

1. Electrocardiogram

a. Addison's Disease. Changes in the electrocardiogram due to adrenal insufficiency were shown to improve after cortisone treatment (1056). An extensive study of 90 patients showed that 52 % had an abnormal electrocardiogram (ECG). It was believed that the level of serum K might be a major factor in causing such changes. Cortisone had no effect on 4 cases with a normal ECG, but caused improvement in 10 of 12 showing abnormal ECG (1057).

b. Hamster. Adrenal insufficiency in this species was associated with a marked increase in serum K, decreased Na, and changes in the electrocardiogram (1245).

c. Rabbit. Cortisone injections in normal rabbits were found to cause changes in the ECG, including an increased amplitude, QRS complexes, T waves (with ST segment elevation), and P waves. In some cases showing such changes the serum K was normal (3).

2. Cardiac Damage

a. Dog. Adrenalectomized dogs maintained on cortisone (0.93 mg. per kilogram per day) for long periods remained active, vigorous, and symptom-free until sudden collapse and death occurred owing to cardiac failure. The ECG at this time showed abnormalities typical of hyperpotassemia. Doubling the dose of cortisone corrected the electrolyte and cardiac defects.

714 R. L. NOBLE

In these experiments the dose of cortisone to maintain electrolytes and prevent cardiac changes was at least 60 times greater than that required with DCA in oil (1122, 1123, 1126).

b. Rat. The myocardial necrosis caused by DCA overdosage in rats was believed to be related directly to a potassium effect and not to resemble rheumatic fever heart lesions (870).

B. Blood Pressure and Hypertension

1. *Steroid Hypertension*

a. Man. The occurrence of hypertension has been noted by many workers in a small percentage of patients receiving cortisone (24). Patients with renal involvement were more susceptible to the hypertensive effects of cortisone, irrespective of their original blood pressure (863). Cases of hypertension associated with congenital adrenal hyperplasia, however, may show a fall in blood pressure after cortisone due to adrenal depression (1212). Patients treated with cortisone showed a marked potentiation of the pressor action of nor-epinephrine (660). Subtotal or complete adrenalectomy has been performed on human subjects for hypertension with beneficial results, and such studies may be found in the following references (472, 884, 1258).

b. Hydrocortisone Hypertension. In the rat this compound has been found to be as active as DCA, or more so, in causing an increased systolic and diastolic blood pressure. This was associated with an increased size of the heart and kidneys (359).

c. DCA Hypertension. Chronic treatment with DCA, especially with an increased intake of NaCl, results in hypertension, changes in fluid and electrolyte distribution, and varied renal and other lesions (734, 1006, 1007). Such hypertension persists after nephrectomy (451) and disappears promptly on removal of pellets of DCA (361), indicating that the changes in blood pressure are not directly related to kidney damage (109). However, a persistence of the hypertension after the natural disappearance of DCA pellets in rats has been reported, indicating a possible renal action (427). Rats and dogs chronically treated with DCA do not show any increased pressor response to epinephrine, renin, or angiotonin (736). Hypertension, similar to that induced by DCA, has been reported to follow the ingestion of hypertonic saline by normal rats (958). Excess NaCl given to dogs caused a transitory increase in blood pressure. On withdrawal a lowering of blood pressure occurred, but no signs of adrenal insufficiency (1208). Masson has reported that the zona glomerulosa of the adrenal is hyperplastic in hypertensive rats. Renin injections are also followed by hypertrophy of this zone. Since renin also causes salt diuresis, it is suggested that its action on the adrenal may be secondary to the loss of NaCl, inducing an hypertrophy of the zona glomerulosa and so producing DCA-like hormones (733).

In the rat cortisone was found to inhibit the hypertensive effects of DCA, but it did not alter the increased weight of heart and kidneys. An additive effect was shown on the renal glomerular lesions (358). Cortisone and 11-deoxy-17-hydrocorticosterone acetate were not hypertensive per se (733).

Lipo-adrenal extract also inhibited DCA hypertension and increased heart weight but not the kidney enlargement. Neither 11-deoxy-17-hydroxycorticosterone acetate nor 11-dehydrocorticosterone acetate had any effect on the hypertension or other changes (357). Potassium, when given as a 1 % solution in the drinking water to old rats, was found to cause a persistence of the hypertensive action of DCA (4 mg. subcutaneously three times a week). A 1 % solution of NaCl did not show a similar effect. Conversely, the induction of K deficiency abolished the pressor action of DCA (944). The importance of K in DCA hypertension has recently been emphasized in a recent review by Freed *et al.* (347).

2. *Renal Hypertension*

Rats and dogs with renal hypertension, when treated with cortisone at dose levels of 1 to 2 mg. and 50 mg. per day, respectively, did not show any specific changes in blood pressure (437).

a. Adrenalectomy. Since Goldblatt found that adrenalectomy in the dog eliminated the response to renal artery constriction (404), others have confirmed this finding (89, 846). A similar effect has been shown in the rat (372). However, in some dogs hypertension may persist or only gradually decrease following adrenalectomy (166, 935). It has been suggested that it is difficult to maintain such adrenalectomized animals in a satisfactory state of nutrition for hypertension to develop, and such a factor may be involved in the varied effects of adrenalectomy reported (647). More recently, renal hypertension in dogs was found to be markedly reduced following adrenalectomy. This could be restored by combined cortisone and DCA therapy (1214). Similar replacement therapy was affected by 1.6 mg. of 11-dehydrocorticosterone acetate combined with 1 mg. DCA daily. The DCA could be replaced by 18 mg. NaCl and 4 g. $NaHCO_3$ daily. DCA alone was only temporarily effective because of developing hypoglycemia (847).

3. *Other Types of Hypertension*

Antikidney serum hypertension in normal or adrenalectomized rats was not prevented by 5 mg. daily of cortisone, nor was the degree of nephritis affected (646). In the case of adrenalectomized animals it was necessary to maintain a satisfactory state of nutrition (which proved difficult) for hypertension to develop (647). Following subtotal nephrectomy in the rat, high- but not low-protein diets caused hypertension. Cortisone treatment of the low-protein–fed animals was followed by hypertension (466). Adrenalectomized-nephrectomized dogs have been maintained for 40 days by intraperitoneal lavage and terramycin injections. Such animals developed hypertension as well as typical arteriolar and myocardial lesions despite the absence of the adrenals (1159).

4. *Vasomotor Response in Adrenal Insufficiency*

The pressor response to epinephrine and other drugs was decreased in adrenalectomized dogs maintained in good health on small doses of ACE (157). The vasomotor response to central sciatic stimulation was reduced in acute adrenal insufficiency and restored by ACE (985).

C. Capillaries

In human subjects, capillary resistance was found to increase after various forms of nonspecific stress or after ACTH. DCA caused a decreased resistance (930, 931). In the rat, however, similar changes have been noted after acute stress, but in long-standing adrenal insufficiency capillary resistance is decreased and can be restored to normal by cortisone (656). The changes in circulation in the transilluminated cheek pouch of the hamster after adrenalectomy and cortisone treatment have been described (1244, 1245). The actions of cortical hormones and adrenalectomy on capillaries have recently been reviewed by Zweifach *et al.* (1263).

D. Atherosclerosis

1. *Human Beings*

In children suffering from leukemia and treated with cortisone an increased deposition of lipid was observed in both the intima and media of the aorta in those under 11 years of age (309). In adults, short- or long-term cortisone therapy was not found to be associated with significant changes in total serum cholesterol or in lipoproteins (92).

2. *Chicks*

Chicks fed a high-cholesterol diet and treated with cortisone, 1.5 mg. daily, increasing to 5 mg. daily, showed after 12 weeks a significant increase in the incidence and severity of aortic and coronary atherosclerosis. No change was detected in the degree of hypercholesterolemia or phospholipemia or in the cholesterol–lipid-phosphorus ratio. Whereas the cortisone group showed a decreased body weight and a slight increase in blood pressure and in size of comb and testis, there was no difference in thyroid or adrenal weight, in fluid intake, or in plasma Na, K, or glucose (1089).

Hydrocortisone, 2.5 to 5.0 mg. daily, also enhances hyperlipemia, but without influencing atherogenesis in cholesterol-fed cockerels. Increased blood cholesterol and lipid phosphorus and blood sugar also occurred when the birds were fed a normal diet, and no aortic lesions were noted (871). In elderly chickens the number of foci of coronary arterial disease was reduced to half by cortisone treatment (853).

3. *Rabbits*

Cook and associates found that rabbits fed cholesterol for 112 days showed an increase in all lipoproteins. The increased concentrations of lipoproteins and total serum cholesterol correlated with the severity of the atherosclerosis produced. Cortisone in normal rabbits caused similar blood changes but no atherosclerosis. When cortisone was given to those fed cholesterol, no significant changes were found (DCA gave the same results) (179). Oppenheim and Bruger, on the other hand, found essentially similar results with normal rabbits but believed that in cholesterol-fed animals cortisone inhibited aortic atherosclerosis, even though it did not alter the blood changes (838).

4. *Guinea Pig*

The atherosclerotic lesions induced by Vitamin C deficiency were not inhibited by cortisone treatment (1215).

VIII. Influence of the Adrenal Cortex on the Nervous System

A. MAN

Extensive observations have frequently been reported on the effects of cortisone treatment on various diseases of the nervous system (395, 764). The effects on myasthenia gravis are of some physiological interest, but both temporary remissions and exacerbation have been described in this disease as a result of cortisone treatment (433, 577, 764). A detailed discussion of the actions of adrenal steroids on the various nervous diseases has been omitted from this article. Similarly, the state of adrenocortical function, with its etiological significance in various psychotic disorders, has not been considered here but is reviewed by others (156, 494, 515, 516, 906). It is of interest to note that because of the suggested involvement of the adrenal mechanism in schizophrenia, suitable patients have been adrenalectomized. The removed adrenals were studied by perfusion techniques to determine if the steroid output were abnormal. The detailed results of these observations should tend to clarify the state of adrenal function in such mental disorders (517). The development of psychotic reactions in patients under treatment with ACTH or cortisone may occasionally be of a serious magnitude and necessitate cessation of therapy.

Many individuals show minor reactions of euphoria or depression. The various changes have been frequently reported and reviewed (112, 153, 246, 394, 694).

1. Cerebral Blood Flow and Metabolism

Measurements on patients receiving ACTH or cortisone therapy have indicated that the psychotic reactions produced were not related to changes in cerebral blood flow (967). On the other hand, such treatment decreased cerebral blood flow by 18 % and was associated with an increased cerebral vascular resistance of 32 %. The arterial blood pressure increased 9 %, but the cerebral utilization of oxygen and glucose was unchanged (967). Others found somewhat similar changes but no marked variation in cerebral blood flow (1009, 1010).

The action of deoxycorticosterone glucoside on the rate of cerebral blood flow and rate of O_2 and sugar utilization and CO_2 production has been described (78). The most striking change was found in sugar values, where the steroid apparently caused a release of sugar (possibly galactose) from brain tissue. The effects of deoxycorticosterone in causing *in vitro* glyco- genolysis from brain and other tissues are fully discussed in a review by Gordon *et al.* (414).

2. Electroencephalogram

Changes of abnormally slow waves occur in the electroencephalogram in Addison's disease and may be of diagnostic significance. Successful therapy induces a return to normal findings (302, 303, 341, 522, 1150). The administration of ACTH or cortisone in children caused modification of the electroencephalogram in approximately half the cases. These changes were not related to the size of the dose administered (217). In adults receiving ACTH or cortisone various changes occur in certain individuals (94, 355, 432, 521, 878, 1188). Changes have also been described in a case of adrenal cortical hyperplasia (59).

3. Pain

The marked alleviation of pain which occurs in patients in whom the associated disease responds to adrenal steroid therapy would appear not to be due to a direct action on sensory nerves. Cutaneous, dental, and visceral pain assessed in patients with rheumatoid arthritis before and after ACTH or cortisone treatment, were not changed in intensity nor was the pain threshold altered (436, 1169). Similarly, in normal trained sub- jects neither ACTH nor cortisone altered the threshold to heat or electrical tooth stimulation. 11-Deoxy-17-hydrocorticosterone, however, did ap- parently lower tooth sensitivity to pain (681).

B. Experimental Animals

1. *Brain Lesions*

In the rat, Castor and associates have reported that ACTH injections were followed by chromatolysis of the cells of the paraventricular nuclei of the hypothalamus. Cortisone, 10 mg. daily for 10 days, besides causing the same effect, induced more widespread chromatolysis and vacuolation of both thalamic and hypothalamic cells (138). Laqueur studied dogs and rats but could not demonstrate any effects of cortisone on the ganglion cells or on the Gomori substance in the hypothalamus. Following adrenalectomy, however, Gomori-positive granules were absent, but they were restored by cortisone therapy (667).

2. *Brain Excitability*

The electroshock threshold (EST) was found to be elevated, indicating a decreased brain excitability, in the adrenalectomized DCA-salt–maintained rat. Treatment with cortisone, 1 mg. twice daily, causing a lowering of the EST (1232). In intact rats DCA was shown by Woodbury and Davenport to increase markedly the EST (492, 1228, 1231), and cortisone, hydrocortisone, or corticosterone have been shown to reduce this effect or to reduce the EST in untreated animals (492, 1229, 1232). Changes in EST appear to be related to the predictable concentration of extracellular sodium concentration, affecting brain excitabliity. An increasing elevation of the EST occurred in the following order of conditions: intact rats; intact on water, DCA-treated; adrenalectomized on water, DCA-treated; adrenalectomized on salt, DCA-treated (1232). Phenobarbital or dilantin has been found to counteract the effect of cortisone in decreasing the EST in the rat (322), whereas dilantin, but not phenobarbital or tridione, increased the action of DCA in raising the EST (1227). These results are of interest in view of clinical observations that DCA may exert anticonvulsive activity when administered to epileptics (13, 642, 748). Repeated electroconvulsive shocks caused adrenal hypertrophy in the rat, but this could be inhibited if the shocks were given when the animal was under anesthetic (947). The problem of whether electrical shock treatment stimulates the pituitary directly to release ACTH or whether indirectly through a stress mechanism, has been studied in the rat (493).

a. EEG. Changes in the electroencephalogram (EEG) of adrenalectomized rats were associated with a markedly reduced blood flow through the head and decreased tissue oxygen consumption. Restoration to normal was accomplished by ACE or pregnenelone, but not by DOC (518), and paralleled the increase in blood flow and oxygen consumption (517).

3. *Peripheral Nerves*

The adrenalectomized rat has been found to show an increased conduction time and decreased excitability of the sciatic nerve. Both conditions could be restored to normal by lipo ACE (1036). Changes in thermoanalgesic sensitivity have been reported in the adrenalectomized animal, in which cortisone caused an increase in sensitivity (587). The adrenalectomized rat showed a marked fatigue on repetitive nerve stimulation, which could be reversed by cortisone treatment. Synthesis of acetylcholine was little affected but was found to be reduced in the hypophysectomized animal. The defective nerve function in such animals was restored in part by cortisone (1155).

4. *In Vitro Studies*

The reported anesthetic activity of certain steroids by Selye (993, 994) suggested that *in vitro* studies of brain might increase the understanding of this action. It has been found that the respiration of brain homogenates using a glucose substrate is inhibited by various steroids in direct relation to their potency as anesthetics (diethylstilbestrol being an exception). DCA was the most active steroid (284, 413, 480, 1153). It appeared that this inhibition of the utilization of carbohydrate was at the level of the dehydrogenases rather than at the cytochrome level, as is found with other anesthetics (414).

IX. Adrenal Cortex and Muscle Function

Further studies on the work performance of the adrenalectomized rat have been reported by Ingle and his associates, who used the adrenalectomized-nephrectomized preparation in which the electrically stimulated muscle pulls against a weight load until exhausted. With continuous intravenous treatment in doses from 0.1 to 1.0 mg. per rat per 24 hours, hydrocortisone was found to be about twice as effective as cortisone (577). However, with the same technique and method of administration, adrenocortical extract, 20 ml. per 24 hours (equivalent to 2 mg. of hydrocortisone by liver glycogen assay), allowed a considerably greater amount of work to be done than did optimal doses of cortisone (4 mg. per 24 hours) or hydrocortisone (2 to 4 mg. per 24 hours) (578). In nonadrenalectomized rats ACE or cortisone (4 to 6 mg. per 24 hours, by continuous intravenous injection) sustained or increased the work output 22.4 % above the average (567, 574). Previous results not showing this action (576) were due to to insufficient dosage to maintain high blood glucose levels (574). The diminished work output of hypophysectomized rats similarly could be restored to normal by continuous intravenous ACTH (579). The diene compound ($\Delta^{4\text{-}6}$dehydrocortisone acetate) showed about one-half the ac-

tivity of cortisone acetate on the work test and glycogen deposition (573).
The stiffness syndrome in guinea pigs, which responds to ergostanyl acetate,
was not improved by cortisone, DCA, or ACE (835).   The response to
cortisone of certain human diseases and disorders of muscle function has
been reviewed by McEachern (743).

X. Adrenal Cortex and Carbohydrate Metabolism

A. Blood Sugar and Glycogen

The role of the adrenal cortex in the various metabolic processes in the
body is still an unsettled problem.   Whereas the various actions on gross
biochemical changes are now wellknown and predictable, the fundamental
changes induced in the cellular physiology are still a challenge to further
investigations.   The actions of cortisone and hydrocortisone result in an
increased carbohydrate reserve of the body.   Newer research tends to support the view that not only is gluconeogenesis from protein necessary to
attain this effect but also glucose formation from fat must take place.
Recent investigators have returned their attention to the inhibition of
some phase of carbohydrate utilization which is also stimulated by oxyster-
oids.   The various mechanisms which will be discussed appear to be essentially cellular ones which are usually affected only *in vivo* by the adrenal
hormones.   The action of the hormones in many cases appears to concern
mainly the speed of various enzymatic reactions.

1. *Blood Sugar*

The effective use of cortisone, hydrocortisone, and corticosterone as
replacement therapy for the carbohydrate defects in Addison's disease has
been reviewed in many clinical papers (1151).   Of some clinical interest
is the contraindication to the use of the intravenous glucose tolerance test
in cases of Addison's disease, since it is frequently followed by severe
febrile reactions (1150).   The chronic use of cortisone or hydrocortisone
for therapeutic reasons may be followed by glycosuria (172, 177, 1080),
and may lead in approximately 0.5 % of patients to diabetes mellitus.
Such occurrences have been reviewed (103).   The renal threshold to glucose may be reduced (343).

The metabolic effects on carbohydrates and protein of adrenal steroids
in experimental animals are contained in a review by Ingle (559).   It has
been suggested that the acute toxicity of oral 50 % glucose in adrenalectomized rats is related to the secondary high blood K.   This and mortality
can be prevented by pretreatment with epinephrine (271).   ACE was
found to cause gluconeogenesis and moderate hyperglycemia in normal
chicks (405).   Adrenalectomized or normal dogs showed little or no change

in blood sugar following treatment with large doses of deoxycorticosterone glucoside (1125).

2. *Glucose Utilization*

Experiments studying glucose oxidation have been reported by Wick, Dury, and McKay, using the eviscerated rabbit. In such preparations adrenalectomy does not result in any change in glucose oxidation. Large doses of ACE may cause a slight increase in the oxidation of glucose in the nonadrenalectomized animal, but the changes are small. These results indicate, therefore, that the actions of adrenal hormones on glucose oxidation must be primarily on the liver (1206). Similarly, adrenalectomy did not alter the extrahepatic utilization of glucose in the dog (160). Recent studies on adrenalectomized rats have supported the older observations that glucose oxidation by peripheral tissue was decreased, but could be increased, after cortisone injections (160). Using the glucose uptake of the isolated rat diaphragm, Huisman has found that the *in vitro* addition of cortisone in large doses markedly inhibited the disappearance of glucose from the medium. This was greater when diaphragms of adrenalectomized rats were used. Since the oxygen consumption, lactic acid formation, and glycogen deposition were not appreciably altered from control values, it seems unlikely that this represented an inhibiting effect on glucose utilization. Glucose from extracarbohydrate sources may have formed, or the steroid may have rendered the tissue more resistant to the penetration of glucose (546).

3. *Glycogen*

Older reports have shown a decreased liver gluconeogenesis after adrenalectomy. Using liver slices Chiu and Needham more recently have found that ACE, DCA, or cortisone inhibited glycogenolysis and enhanced the new formation of total carbohydrate (148, 149).

In adrenalectomized mice hydrocortisone caused glycogen deposition. Epihydrocortisone (a stereoisomer of hydrocortisone) had much less action but did not inhibit the action of hydrocortisone (986). $\Delta^{4\text{-}6}$Dehydrocortisone acetate was about one-half as active as cortisone in causing glycogen deposition in the adrenalectomized rat (573). Marked glycogen deposition in the liver and kidneys of rabbits was noted after large doses of cortisone (1137), and up to 11.8 % of liver glycogen has been produced in the rat by doses of 20 mg. daily of cortisone (572). Cortisone therapy given to 25 patients did not produce any demonstrable changes in a complete study of various liver function tests (531).

4. *Phosphorylase*

Kerppola, in studies on the increase in both muscle (3 to 4 times normal) and liver (20 to 30 times normal) glycogen of rabbits after cortisone (up to 20 mg. daily), showed this to parallel a depression of phosphorylase activity in these tissues.   The largest doses completely inactivated phosphorylase.   Cortisone was believed to retard the action of phosphorylase and strongly inhibit glycogenolysis, but this action could be restored by treatment with epinephrine.   Epinephrine alone stimulated phosphorylase activity (627).   In fasted adrenalectomized rats epinephrine resulted in a loss of muscle glycogen double that of controls, but little or no increase was found in liver glycogen.   ACE treatment allowed the normal pattern of changes in carbohydrate metabolism to occur after epinephrine.   The disappearance of carbohydrate in the adrenalectomized animals could not be accounted for by the accumulation of glucose or lactic acid in the body fluids (1220).   The action of epinephrine on phosphorylase has been reviewed by Sutherland (1117).

Verzár has reviewed his studies on phosphorylation.   Minced tissues of muscle and of liver from adrenalectomized animals both showed a depressed phosphorylase activity *in vitro*.   Treatment of the adrenalectomized animal with deoxycorticosterone maintained glycogen phosphorylation at normal levels.   *In vitro* restoration of decreased phosphorylation was reported with deoxycorticosterone and also with glutathione.   In other studies it was found that the *in vitro* glycogen production from glucose by surviving muscle (from either normal or adrenalectomized rats) was completely inhibited by deoxycorticosterone and somewhat less by cortisone—possibly by activation of glycogen phosphorylase (1176).

5. *Alkaline Phosphatase*

Verzár and Sailer have confirmed older studies that adrenalectomy in the guinea pig is followed by diminished alkaline phosphatase in the intestinal mucosa.   Restoration of normal values followed treatment of the animal with DCA, ACE, or cortisone.   No *in vitro* actions of these steroids were found.   Similar results were found with the alkaline phosphatase in the kidney (1176).   Alkaline phosphatase in serum and bone has been found to increase in the adrenalectomized rat (117) or after cortisone injections in intact rats (1219).

6. *Other Enzyme Studies*

The oxidative metabolism was studied by Sourkes and Heneage in homogenates of atrophied adrenals removed from rats after cortisone (3 mg. daily for 6 days) treatment.   Such homogenates showed a decreased endogenous respiration as well as a greatly reduced absolute rate of oxidation of various intermediates of the Krebs cycle (1059). Further studies of normal adrenal homogenates and tissue slices showed that intermediates of the tricarboxylic acid cycle and of fat oxidation (acetate, butyrate) were metabolized by both preparations. The *in vitro* addition of cortisone and DCA markedly increased the rate of metabolism, indicating the exertion of a specific action on enzymes catalyzing oxidations. Cardiac muscle and kidney homogenates were also affected (1060). Umbreit, however, could not demonstrate any effect of adrenalectomy or cortisone treatment on phosphocreatine of muscle, kidney, or liver, upon adenosine triphosphate (ATP), or upon the ability of homogenates to generate energy-rich phosphate (14, 1161).

a. RNA and DNA.   The livers of rabbits treated with cortisone (25 mg. per day) for 1 to 6 days showed a decreased nitrogen and increased carbohydrate content. Both pentose nucleic acid (RNA) and deoxypentose nucleic acid (DNA) per gram liver decreased, but the ratio RNA:DNA rose steadily with increasing duration of treatment. All constituents had returned to normal 9 days after cessation of treatment. The nucleic acid composition of the kidneys was not affected (711). The livers of rats after treatment with cortisone showed an increase in size and increased RNA content, but no change occurred in DNA (1025). The protein content of whole chick embryos was reduced by injections of cortisone and was associated with decreased growth. The RNA synthesis was particularly affected (141).

B. Glutathione

Interest in glutathione was stimulated by the observations of Conn and associates on patients receiving ACTH. They noted that the diminished glucose tolerance and glycosuria were associated with a diminished blood glutathione (GSH) and increasing urinary uric acid (174, 176). This was confirmed in one patient (616), but little change in blood GSH was noted in patients by other workers (597, 1080). More recently, however, in a study of 11 patients treated with ACTH, and 11 with cortisone, a fall in blood GSH was noted with both agents (508). This has also been confirmed by others (410). Glutathione administered to a normal person showing hyperglycemia and glycosuria following ACTH caused a dramatic but transitory reduction of the deranged carbohydrate metabolism (173, 175). Blood glutathione showed no consistent pattern in patients with rheumatoid arthritis, nor were any changes related to clinical improvement after cortisone therapy (1187).

1. *Rats*

Studies on rats have been made by Lazarow. It was shown that cortisone treatment led to a decrease in blood GSH which appeared to correlate with the extent of glycosuria (674). However, glutathione injections in rats on a high-carbohydrate diet led to glycosuria, which gradually decreased. Cortisone treatment (10 mg. daily) was followed by a persistence of the glycosuria and a potentiation of up to 10 times in sugar output. High blood sugars were associated. Other reducing agents were less effective than GSH, and it was suggested that such substances protect cortisone from destruction in the body (673). Others, however, could not demonstrate any action of ACTH on the blood glutathione of rats (558). Using modified technique for measurement, recent observers have again confirmed the transitory drop in blood sulfhydryl following ACTH (410). The various theories relating to the actions of glutathione, alloxan, and ascorbic acid on adrenal function and diabetes, are discussed in a review by Meiklejohn (755), and by others (410).

C. DIABETES AND INSULIN
1. *Human Subjects*

In a case of Addison's disease associated with diabetes, cortisone, 30 mg. daily, caused a marked increase in urinary glucose excretion despite a fourfold increase in insulin dosage (1079). From studies on 3 diabetics given ACTH or cortisone, it was suggested that the increased carbohydrate came from fatty acids (636). About 1 in 500 normal cases developed diabetes after cortisone therapy, and some predisposing factors were described. Such diabetes was not associated with ketonemia and responded well to insulin (103). ACTH may cause glycosuria which is renal in origin (616). A number of papers on this general subject have been reviewed by Conn and Fajans (168).

2. *Insulin Insensitivity*

In eight of nine cases of insensitivity to insulin, DCA treatment (4 to 10 mg. per day), changed the glucose-insulin tolerance test to a susceptible type. This reverted to the resistant type 1 to 3 weeks after the cessation of treatment. DCA did not show this effect on 6 cases normally sensitive to insulin (1255, 1256). In the rat DCA was also found to increase the sensitivity to insulin, probably by causing inhibition of ACTH output from the pituitary (146, 960).

3. *Hyperinsulinism*

A case of islet adenoma associated with hypoglycemia was described in which cortisone maintained normal fasting blood sugar levels preopera-

R. L. NOBLE

tively (±15). In four other patients similar beneficial effects of cortisone were noted, but none became asymptomatic and the effect was transitory, diminishing with continued treatment (100 mg. daily) (841).

D. ADRENAL-PITUITARY-PANCREAS RELATIONSHIP

1. *Dogs*

Dogs were administered cortisone (10 to 25 mg. per day) for 3 days, and at this time were found to be irresponsive to insulin ($\frac{1}{10}$ unit per kilogram intravenous). Following evisceration and nephrectomy the distribution of galactose, with or without insulin, was not changed. Adrenalectomized animals also showed no difference. It was believed that the peripheral effects of insulin, therefore, were not affected by cortisone or adrenalectomy, and the observations support the view that the antagonism between the adrenal steroids and insulin is not located in the extrahepatic tissue (409). "This conclusion is at variance with much evidence in the literature indicating that the response of muscle to insulin in the presence of excess cortisone, or in the adrenalectomized animal, is not the same as that in normal animals" (1083).

De Bodo and collaborators have made extensive studies on the response of dogs to insulin and on the influence of the adrenals and pituitary. These findings have been reviewed (213). The adrenalectomized dog maintained in excellent condition by DCA therapy showed an increased sensitivity to insulin injections, but this was less than that shown by the hypophysectomized animal (215). In the latter preparation cortisone or hydrocortisone, given at the dose levels of 0.83 and 1.2 mg. per kilogram per day, respectively, (sufficient to restore carbohydrate metabolism to normal in the adrenalectomized dog) also abolished insulin hypersensitivity; the secondary hypoglycemia of the glucose tolerance test and epinephrine resistance were also abolished. This dose level did not cause insulin resistance, diabetes, or an augmented response to epinephrine. The additional treatment with pituitary growth hormone STH (1.5 mg. per kilogram per day) did not alter the above picture. STH alone, however, caused insulin resistance and diabetes (214, 216).

2. *Mechanism of Action*

The interaction of insulin with anterior pituitary and adrenal hormones and the resulting influence on hexokinase and carbohydrate metabolism were described in a series of fundamental papers by the Coris and associates. More recently a number of workers have questioned the conclusions from these observations and have failed to confirm certain of the original experiments. Broh-Kahn and Mirsky could not detect significant differences between the hexokinase of muscle extracts of alloxan-diabetic rats and that of normal rats.   Inhibition of hexokinase by diabetogenic extracts of the pituitary and reversal by insulin was inconsistent and not related to the diabetogenic activity of the extracts.   Inhibitory effects were also found with extracts of other organs (113).   Others have also found that the action of the pituitary factor was not related to diabetogenic activity (903, 1041).   Stadie and Haugaard failed to show any alteration of the hexokinase reaction in muscle or kidney extract, with the addition of ACE or ACE plus insulin, from diabetic rats when compared with controls (1084).   In addition, the same absence of effect was found using extracts of tissues from depancreatized cats (1085).   Stadie (1083), in a recent review of this complex field, concludes that: "On the basis of the summation of this evidence it seems reasonable to conclude that an effect of hormones on the hexokinase reaction in structureless tissue extracts is not proven."   There would possibly appear to be stronger support to the hexokinase theory in *in vitro* experiments using intact cells, such as studies using liver slices (1138) or rat diaphragm (1086, 1087, 1177), but conclusions as to the precise mechanism still remain equivocal and are discussed in various reviews (655, 1082).

XI. Adrenal Cortex and Protein Metabolism

Most of the recent work has concerned the mode of action of the O^{11} steroids on protein, and the changes following cortisone in various clinical conditions.   Although cortisone and hydrocortisone usually induce a negative nitrogen balance, the results are variable and partly depend on dosage (1077, 1151).   The negative nitrogen balance induced by cortisone in elderly patients has been studied (653).

A. Amino Acids

1. *Excretion in Human Beings*

Following ACTH (919, 937) or cortisone, there is a characteristic increase in free amino acids in the urine.   The actual increase of the separate acids has been determined in many cases.   Urinary histidine was markedly increased by ACTH or cortisone (1099) and may be associated with clinical remission of rheumatoid arthritis.   Urinary threonine and tyrosine are also increased by cortisone, and lysine by ACTH (111).   Corticosterone (200 mg. per day) also caused a similar increase in urinary amino acids, but had no beneficial action on rheumatoid arthritis (929).   In the Addisonian, infused amino acids tend to be retained for a longer time than in normal patients (127).

2. *Amino Acid Metabolism*

The administration of cortisone and C^{14} glycine to normal and adrenal-ectomized rats caused a marked increase in urinary nitrogen, and this was greater in the adrenalectomized animals (151). In the eviscerated or eviscerated-adrenalectomized rat maintained on intravenous saline, glucose, and insulin, ACE and cortisone (5 or 10 mg. per day) caused a significant increase in plasma amino acids, indicating an extrahepatic action on protein (96, 581). Significant increases in free amino acids were found in the liver and kidney of the rat 2 hours after cortisone or ACTH. In the latter case a similar finding on the adrenal glands was made (680). Kline observed a decreased rate of release of nitrogen from the diaphragm of adrenalectomized rats *in vitro*, and this could be restored to normal by pretreatment with ACE (644).

The interesting observation was made on developing chick embryos that cortisone injection markedly increased free hydroxyproline and occasionally glycine, but no other alterations in free amino acids took place (918). Cortisone not only increased the glycogen content of the livers of rats but caused an associated decrease in concentration of dicarboxylic amino acids and an increased alanine content. It was suggested that cortisone stimulated the synthesis of carbohydrate through utilization of dicarboxylic acids (33). Lee and Williams found that fed adrenalectomized rats showed a reduced incorporation of cystine S^{35} into protein, but this could be restored to normal by treatment with ACE, DCA, or cortisone. This may represent a turnover rate in protein rather than an indication of protein catabolism or anabolism. ACTH in the intact rat increased the incorporation of S^{35} into protein (679). Similar results with ACTH have been reported in the intact mouse in that the incorporation of C^{14} histidine into visceral and muscle protein was increased (829). Other workers have shown the opposite, however, in fasted mice. They showed that C^{14} glycine or S^{35} methionine increased in the tissues following adrenalectomy. 11-Dehydrocorticosterone suppressed such incorporation, as did ACTH administered to the hypophysectomized animal (352, 729, 1203). The incorporation of C^{14} alanine into rat diaphragm was inhibited by 30 % on the *in vitro* addition of cortisone (1030).

Further discussion of the anabolic and catabolic effects of the adrenal hormones on protein has been given by Russell (952), and she particularly considers the observations of Hoberman, who used N^{15} glycine as an index of protein metabolism (519). It appeared that in fasting rats adrenalectomy caused perhaps a slight decrease in synthesis and breakdown of body protein. Cortisone, conversely, increased catabolism, and the amount of synthesis was unchanged. Similar results were reported for a patient with Cushing's disease given S^{35} methionine. The excretion was normal and uptake into plasma proteins somewhat increased.   The over-all persistent negative nitrogen balance was therefore attributed to increased catabolism of tissue protein (728).   Roberts has reviewed some aspects of catabolic processes which were increased by O^{11} steroids, particularly the mobilization of protein from the liver and spleen following ACE treatment (922). Clark has found that the adrenalectomized animal incorporated more C^{14} amino acids into the tissues and excreted less in the urine than did normal animals.   Hydrocortisone increased the urinary excretion of such amino acids (152).   In the adrenalectomized mouse C^{14} glycine was not catabolized in the liver.   When ACE was given prior to the glycine the incorporation into liver protein was inhibited and the catabolism of glycine was increased both in the normal and adrenalectomized animals (58).   Similarly, hydrocortisone may inhibit the rate of C^{14} amino acid incorporation into lymphatic cells (639).   It perhaps may be added that even though a markedly negative nitrogen balance and weight loss can follow cortisone treatment, in the rat certain organs may at the same time show an anabolic process.   It is probable that changes in protein anabolism or catabolism may have to be referred to individual organs rather than assessed from over-all balance studies (651, 1025).

The majority of reports, therefore, suggest that adrenalectomy is followed by an increased uptake of amino acids and that O^{11} steroids exert a converse action.   Some amino acids, such as cysteine, may behave differently, however.   It has been suggested that the dietary state of the animal may have an important influence on such actions and might explain the divergent results described.   When protein loss is high, as in starvation, the process may be exaggerated by adrenal steroids.   On the other hand, when nitrogen metabolism is properly supported by adequate metabolism of carbohydrate or perhaps by nitrogen replacement, the O^{11} steroids have little effect (570, 952).   In the case of adrenalectomized animals steroids such as DCA might exert an indirect action by improving the appetite and nutritional status.

3. Nephrectomized Rats

Extensive studies have been made by Engel and associates using the nephrectomized animal to show changes in protein metabolism (296).   The basal rate of urea formation was greatest in ACTH-treated, and lowest in adrenalectomized, animals, when compared with controls.   The administration of 500 mg. of glucose per 100 gm. reduced the rate of urea formation (297).   In early experiments following the intravenous injection of amino acids, neither ACE nor adrenalectomy caused any change in blood urea (97, 301), and it was concluded that the action of adrenal steroids must be at the whole protein level.   Under changed technical conditions, however, when urea formation was measured at 1 and 2 hours after intravenous amino acids, some differences were observed. In the adrenalectomized animal there was a decreased urea formation in the first hour when compared with controls (or after ACTH treatment, which did not give results differing from the control values). Administered glucose decreased the amount of urea formed in the control and adrenalectomized animals, but not in the ACTH-treated group, and the blood amino nitrogen was higher in the glucose-treated adrenalectomized rats. It is suggested from these results that adrenal steroids act at some step in the utilization of carbohydrate, possibly in the Krebs cycle, and that other metabolic changes are secondary (297). Acute stress was also found to increase urea formation in the intact, but not in the adrenalectomized, rat maintained on salt and DCA. The adrenalectomized rat maintained on cortisone, however, responded with an increase in urea. Intact rats treated with ACE and subjected to mild stress, showed an increased urea not found in the uninjected controls (298).

B. ENZYMES

1. *Aminopeptidase*

Serum peptidase in mice has been reported to be markedly increased following ACTH or ACE treatment (530), but others could not confirm this observation in mice or rats (982). Similarly, various tissue homogenates from ACTH-treated animals did not show increased peptidase activity (299). In normal human beings a small increase was observed in plasma peptidase following ACTH injections (962). In cases of rheumatoid arthritis a high plasma value was obtained, and this dropped to normal with clinical remissions induced by ACTH or cortisone. Cases not responding to cortisone treatment showed no effect on plasma peptidase. One case of Cushing's disease and Addison's disease showed normal values. However, a case of Addison's disease showing arthritis had high values. From these results it was concluded that the plasma aminopeptidase level was a reflection of the clinical status of the disease rather than an index of adrenal activity (983).

2. *Oxidases*

The amino acid oxidase activity of liver and kidney homogenates was found to be reduced in the adrenalectomized rat. The activity could be restored to normal by ACE treatment or by the *in vitro* addition of ACE (126). The question has been raised whether these changes were a reflection of cardiovascular failure in the adrenalectomized animal (297).

a. D-*Amino-Acid Oxidase.* This enzyme has been shown by Umbreit to be reduced in the liver of the adrenalectomized rat but not in the kidney.

Cortisone treatment of the animal restored the enzyme levels in the liver and had no effect on the kidney. No *in vitro* action of cortisone was found. Since the enzyme in the liver shows alterations related to nutritional factors, the effects of cortisone could be indirect; however, if such were the case, one would expect to find comparable changes in other enzymes such as succinoxidase, but this was not the case (1161). Deoxycorticosterone, on the other hand, apparently exerts an *in vitro* inhibitory effect on oxidation of many substrates, including hexoses, phosphorylated intermediates, Krebs cycle components, and amino acids, and has been extensively studied by Hayano and Dorfman. Thus the oxidations of DL-alanine, DL-methionine, and DL-isoleucine, were all inhibited by deoxycorticosterone and the more active glucoside. The less water-soluble steroids had some, but less, activity. In addition to inhibiting D-amino acid oxidase, deoxycorticosterone also inhibited tyrosinase, urease, ascorbic acid oxidase, lipase, and transaminase (478, 479).

Oxidative deamination has also been studied by Jensen and Gray (593). Using DL-alanine they found that the liver of adrenalectomized rats showed a decreased amino acid dehydrogenase activity which could be restored by ACE treatment. Such treatment of normal rats increased the enzyme activity in liver. The oxidase activity of the normal animals could also be increased by the *in vitro* addition of ACE. The same results were obtained using kidney homogenates as for liver, and were in accord with the older observations of Russell and Wilhelmi (953). Umbreit has pointed out that the kidney of the adrenalectomized rat (7 days postoperatively) required an increased amount of adenylic acid to maintain a maximum rate of oxidation; this effect probably explains the decreased oxidation of α-ketoglutarate previously shown by others in such preparations (1161).

b. Proline Oxidase. Proline and hydroxyproline oxidation by rat kidney homogenates were found by Umbreit to be markedly reduced 72 hours after adrenalectomy. Cortisone treatment of the adrenalectomized animal restored the low values to normal, but in *in vitro* tests cortisone was ineffective. Glutamate, the oxidation product of proline, and other amino acids were not oxidized by kidney homogenates from adrenalectomized rats, untreated or treated with cortisone. No effects of cortisone on liver proline oxidation were demonstrated. It was suggested from these experiments, therefore, that cortisone acted on the kidney specifically at the level of the proline-oxidizing enzyme in the whole animal, probably in the formation of the enzyme rather than in its activation (1161–1163).

3. *Arginase*

A decrease in arginase after adrenalectomy has been shown in rat liver, kidney, and mammary gland (334, 335, 344, 652). Cortisone was more effective than DCA in restoring arginase under such conditions. Lactating rats when adrenalectomized showed similar changes (335). Cortisone caused an immediate increase in arginase in the kidney of castrated mice and a delayed increase in the liver (650). Cortisone treatment for 7 days in the mouse produced a decrease in the aspartic-glutamic transaminase activity of the liver, but an increase in that of the kidney and heart (282). These changes have been discussed in relation to protein metabolism by Kochakian (649).

C. Purines

The marked effect of O^{11} steroids and ACTH in increasing the urinary excretion of uric acid has been noted by many observers; it has been used as an index of adrenal activity in man and has been the suggested explanation for the beneficial action of these substances on gout (172, 177, 341, 491, 929, 1080), although exacerbation of gouty arthritis can occur from cortisone therapy. From studies using isotopic uric acid in a patient with gout, the response to ACTH appeared to be due to an increased renal clearance of uric acid (68). Others have found in addition to changes in renal function an increased endogenous production of uric acid (982). Studies on rats also suggested a primary action on the kidney as the cause of the uricosuria (356). Conn and Fajans, however, found in studying the action of ACTH on Dalmatian and mongrel dogs, that an increased production as well as an increased renal clearance accounted for the increased urinary excretion of uric acid. In mongrel dogs the predominant increase was in allantoin (168). Hunter noted that liver slices from rats treated with ACTH showed an increased guanidoacetic acid methylation. Formation of tyrosine from phenylalanine and of uric acid from xanthine was inhibited (554).

XII. Adrenal Cortex and Fat Metabolism

A. Man

Aldersberg and associates have reported in a series of papers the changes produced by cortisone (60 to 200 mg. daily, total dose 0.5 to 7.2 gm. over 6 to 105 days) in blood lipids in 22 patients with various diseases. Serum total or ester cholesterol increased 19 % to 23 % and phospholipid increased 24 %. Serum neutral fat fell 43 %. Phospholipid and cholesterol increased in 2 patients even when on a fat-free diet. Turbidity of the blood sera was noted in some cases, although there was no increase in neutral fat (5–9). Other workers did not detect significant changes in total serum cholesterol (92). The hypercholesterolemia when present may be related to the hypothyroid function induced by cortisone. The treatment of 4 patients with idopathic steatorrhea with cortisone (100 mg. daily) decreased fat excretion but did not abolish the steatorrhea (41). Fasting blood ketone bodies in patients with Addison's disease rose significantly after cortisone therapy but returned to normal despite continued therapy (74, 341). On the other hand, cortisone was found to suppress completely or partially the hyperketonemia and ketonuria after fasting in normal subjects. 11-Dehydrocorticosterone (600 mg.) did not show this effect (637). One patient with rheumatoid arthritis on cortisone excreted less 17-ketosteroid when on a pure fat diet. On return to a mixed diet Cushing-like symptoms rapidly appeared (635).

B. Blood Lipids in Animals

1. Rabbit

After treatment with cortisone (7.5 mg. daily) rabbits showed grossly turbid or milky sera containing stainable fat droplets. The serum total fatty acids and cholesterol was increased, and the plasma proteins were unchanged (911). Various reports by others have indicated that serum cholesterol may be little affected, but that serum phospholipids are definitely increased (179, 237, 648, 838, 911). Cortisone (20 mg. daily) and stress caused an increase in serum lipids and also swelling and hydropic changes in the pancreatic islets, with the production of a diabetic condition (648).

2. Rat

The serum cholesterol and lipid phosphorus was increased by cortisone in intact rats but not in adrenalectomized animals maintained on DCA (770).

3. Dog

The adrenalectomized dog showed increased changes in phospholipids when maintained on DCA, a marked decrease in plasma phospholipid concentrations and total circulating plasma phospholipid being noted (1254).

C. Liver Fat

Recent papers have confirmed earlier work showing that the adrenals are necessary for the action of pituitary extracts in increasing liver fat (691, 854). Szego and White, however, reported an increase in liver fat in both normal and adrenalectomized mice in response to impure STH (1129). Levin and Farber have shown that normal mice treated with cortisone (0.5 mg. twice daily) showed only a very slight increase in liver fat. The DCA-maintained adrenalectomized mouse lost 26% liver fat, and this could be prevented by cortisone treatment. The adrenalectomized animal did not respond to anterior pituitary extract, although the normal animal

showed a 44 % increase in liver fat.   If the former preparation were treated
with cortisone and pituitary extract together, an increase of 87 % occurred.
ACTH and STH showed activity similar to that of the pituitary extract.
It appeared, therefore, that fat mobilization required two factors: adequate
adrenal steroids and an unknown pituitary factor (692, 854).   Adrenal
steroids given to the intact animal may cause an increase in liver size and
total fat in the rat (1025) and guinea pig (468).

D. Body Fat

In fully fed rats Stoerk and Porter found that adrenal insufficiency had
no influence on body or testicular fat.   When the diet was limited to one-
third of the normal, the adrenalectomized animal lost twice as much fat as
did intact controls, and four times as much as when treated with cortisone
(2 mg. twice daily).   DCA had no effect.   Parallel changes occurred in
neutral fat of the carcass and liver.   Recovery occurred rapidly in adipose
tissue when the animal was starved before adrenalectomy and then restored
to an adequate diet (1109).   The authors noted the apparent similarity in
partial starvation of the behavior of fat and carbohydrate in adrenalectomized rats.   In both cases excessive utilization took place, and, conversely,
adrenal steroids had an opposing action.   They suggest that the increased
utilization may be secondary in both cases to compensate for the decreased
utilization of amino acids (1109).   Welt and Wilhelmi had also presented
evidence that the rate of fatty acid synthesis was increased by adrenalectomy (1196).   Schiffer and Wertheimer, however, had previously reported
that the adrenalectomized rat lost body fat more rapidly than sham-
operated controls, independently of their general condition, and that DCA
(2 mg. daily) was more effective in preventing fat loss than ACE.   DCA
had no effect on normal rats.   Experiments with elaidic acid showed normal incorporation into adipose tissue after adrenalectomy (968).   Cortisone
pretreatment was found to diminish the incorporation of C^{14} into fatty acids
of the mammary gland of lactating rats (51).

1. Brown Fat

The interscapular brown fat of the rat showed a greater increase in the
deposition of fat after treatment with cortisone and thyroxine combined
than with either alone.   Changes induced by adrenalectomy were corrected
by cortisone alone but not by DCA (663).   Cortisone had a similar tropic
effect on the brown fat in mice and hamsters (25, 1178).   This fat deposit
has been used by Engel to study possible changes in glycogen formation,
as influenced by adrenal hormones and insulin.   No changes in glycogen
content of the fat body occurred in adrenalectomized rats or after adrenal
steroid treatment alone (295, 300).

E. Adrenals

1. *Phospholipids*

The metabolism of phosphorus in the adrenal glands of the rat has been studied using P^{32}. Gemzell and Samuels found that hypophysectomy reduced the specific activity of inorganic phosphorus of the adrenal relative to that of plasma. A single injection of ACTH restored the value to normal (379). Similar findings were also reported (907), and similar changes were found in the total acid-soluble phosphorus fraction of the adrenals (907). Riedel and associates have shown that the concentration of lipid phosphorus and incorporation of P^{32} into it are decreased by hypophysectomy and restored to approximately normal by a single dose of ACTH (915). It is suggested that these results are due to a slowing in the passage of inorganic phosphorus from extracellular to intracellular spaces and a slowing in the formation of lipid phosphorus from intracellular inorganic phosphorus. Both changes could arise from the decrease in over-all energy metabolism of the adrenal cells after hypophysectomy (914).

2. *Cholesterol*

Following cortisone (1.25 mg. daily for 20 days) the adrenals of female rats atrophied 32%. The cholesterol content ratio increased by 40% (697). With larger doses of cortisone causing 50% atrophy, the total adrenal cholesterol was greatly reduced (1219). Rapeseed oil fed to rats increased the adrenal cholesterol (mainly esterified) by three to four times normal, whereas the total phosphorus and ascorbic acid were unchanged. Such changes were not found in the hypophysectomized rat (132, 133). The expected fall in adrenal ascorbic acid and cholesterol occurred in such treated animals following ACTH or unilateral adrenalectomy (134). Amphenone-B also caused a marked increase in total cholesterol, limited to the adrenal glands in the rat (493, 525, 977). Acute stress in such rats did not diminish adrenal cholesterol, but ascorbic acid was reduced (977), as were the eosinophil count and thymus weight (524).

F. Ketogenesis

The role of the adrenal cortex on the effects of pituitary extracts in inducing increased production of ketone bodies and the inhibiting effect of hypophysectomy have been reviewed by Tepperman and Tepperman (1139) and Scott and Engel (984). Both purified growth hormone and ACTH have been described as enhancing ketonemia, and some synergism in action was noted (75). Bondy and Wilhelmi described ketogenic defects in liver slices obtained from hypophysectomized rats (prolonged deficiency), but these were not corrected by treatment of the animal with growth hormone

(99). Tepperman and Tepperman confirmed the increasing failure of ketogenesis after hypophysectomy but found that growth hormone injections would restore ketogenesis at 15 days postoperatively, but not at 30 days. If the latter group of animals were treated with both growth hormone and cortisone, a marked stimulation of ketogenesis occurred in the removed liver slices. Cortisone alone had little effect but apparently acted in a permissive role (1139). Lipsett and Moore found that liver slices of adrenalectomized mice showed a slowed rate of production of ketone bodies from octanoic acid; this was restored to normal by cortisone treatment (700, 701). In the fasting phlorizinized rat, Segaloff and Many found adrenalectomy to completely suppress ketone body secretion. This could be restored and raised above normal by lipo ACE, cortisone, hydrocortisone, and 11-dehydrocorticosterone (987). The adrenalectomized dog shows increased blood ketones after ACTH treatment (72). Treatment with ACTH or cortisone of rats force-fed a high-fat diet has been found to cause a transient ketosis (580, 582). More recently, however, Scott and Engel have found that cortisone or hydrocortisone (5 or 10 mg. daily) inhibited ketosis (and increased the blood sugar) in the rat during a 5-day fast. Furthermore, such treatment depressed the ketosis found after exposure of the animals to stress by cold. They concluded, therefore, that the effect of O^{11} steroids was to inhibit ketosis (984). Experiments on human beings by Kinsell and associates and others have also indicated that cortisone may suppress fasting ketosis. It was believed that acceleration of ketolysis occurs, but also decreased ketone formation (reviewed in 168, 313).

XIII. Adrenal Cortex and Vitamins

A. Caloric Restriction

Diverse changes have been described in adrenal cortical function in man following malnutrition; these have been reviewed by Zubiran and Gomez-Mont (1261).

1. *Starvation—Rats*

Whereas acute starvation results in adrenal hypertrophy, as is common with other forms of stress, the chronic condition may lead to adrenal atrophy (128, 586, 801). The degree of change varies, however, as the increase after acute starvation was found to be relative rather than absolute (200); others, however, have reported an increase in absolute weight in completely starved rats (800). The ratio of protein in isocaloric but restricted diets did not alter the extent of relative hypertrophy of the adrenals, the absolute weights remaining unchanged (917).

In the past few years there has been particular interest in the relationships of certain vitamins to the adrenal function, particularly pantothenic acid, pyridoxine, ascorbic acid, and B_{12} ; these will be discussed in detail. Following adrenalectomy in the rat the concentrations in the liver of pantothenic acid, biotin, riboflavin, niacin, pyridoxine, and folic acid were not significantly altered, nor were they by injections of cortisone (234). Similarly, following cold stress no changes were found in the content of adrenal biotin, folic acid, niacin, or riboflavin (978).

B. Pantothenic Acid

Coenzyme A, the functional form of pantothenic acid, is present in large amounts in the adrenal cortex of the rat (606). Deficiency of pantothenic acid causes pathological changes in the adrenals of the rat (195, 792) and also in other species. Such changes have been reviewed by Ralli and Dumm (891).

1. *Histology of Adrenals*

Deficiency of pantothenic acid causes characteristic lesions in the adrenal cortex, as observed by many and described in detail by Deane and McKibbin. These may appear after a one-week deficiency, before other symptoms are apparent, and affect chiefly the inner zones of cortex (211). Such effects may be reversed by giving pantothenic acid, provided the changes are not too advanced (891). In deficient mice the hypertrophied adrenals showed a gradual depletion of lipid and ketosteroid material from the zona fasciculata, the glomerulosa remaining normal (760). In deficient rats the total measured cholesterol of the adrenals was markedly reduced (211, 791), whereas the serum cholesterol was normal (1223). Changes in adrenal ascorbic acid were questionable (868, 891). After stress in the deficient rat the normally rapid resynthesis of cholesterol in the adrenals was not complete for 7 days (268).

2. *ACTH*

Young rats, pantothenic-acid–deficient, showed greatly increased adrenal damage by ACTH treatment. Cortisone, 2 mg. daily, prevented this and also histological changes of the deficiency alone. There was no alleviation by cortisone of the signs of depletion of the vitamin in the peripheral tissues. Histologically, the ACTH-treated deficient animals showed practically no adrenal cholesterol, but cortisone restored the amount and distribution to normal (981). Cortisone was not found to alter the pantothenic acid content of the tissues of normal rats (261).

3. *Blood Picture*

Deficient rats showed the expected eosinopenia and lymphopenia in response to cortisone, but no significant changes were found after ACTH or epinephrine.   It was suggested, therefore, that coenzyme A functions in the adrenal cortex in the biosynthesis of O^{11} steroids (267, 1221).

4. *Carbohydrate Metabolism*

Most reports indicate that the deficient animal can maintain an average normal fasting blood sugar level (891).   The most direct evidence described of abnormal carbohydrate metabolism was that deficient rats showed an increased sensitivity to insulin and decreased ability to deposit liver glycogen.   These changes were corrected by cortisone but not by ACTH. After phlorizin less glucose and nitrogen were excreted than by normal controls; this change could be restored to normal by cortisone, but not by ACTH (1222).

5. *Stress*

The effects of pantothenic acid in stress may be found in the review by Ralli and Dumm (891).   In some cases the effects may be attributable to an affected function of the adrenal cortex.

6. *Survival*

When rats previously subjected to a period of pantothenate deficiency were adrenalectomized, it was found that large doses of the vitamin prolonged survival (893, 899).   This was also demonstrated in rats not previously deficient (890).

It would appear that pantothenic acid has a normal function in maintaining the structure and function of the adrenal cortex.   The former action can be readily demonstrated, but changes in function are more difficult to interpret.   The function of coenzyme A may be directly related to adrenal steroid formation as well as to carbohydrate and fatty acid metabolism.

C. Pyridoxine

1. *Deficiency—Mice*

When deficiency was induced by the injection of the competitive deoxypyridoxine, mice showed granulocytosis, lymphopenia, and myeloid metaplasia in the spleen.   These changes were the same as could be induced with cortisone (1190, 1191).   However, it was found that the same changes could be produced by pyridoxine deficiency in adrenalectomized mice (799). The vitamin deficiency and cortisone treatment together, however, caused an augmented response, and such an effect could not be blocked by large doses of pyridoxine (799).

2. *Rats*

Pyridoxine deficiency was found to cause adrenal enlargement mainly affecting the zona fasciculata.   Microscopically, this zone showed a progressive loss of sudanophilic lipoid and cholesterol, but ascorbic-acid–like substance was not reduced. Administration of a single dose of pyridoxine was followed by a rapid restoration of such changes to normal (1091). The deficient rat showed a normal eosinophil response to stimuli (125).

3. Dogs and Monkeys

Pyridoxine deficiency was shown to cause some of the histological changes in the inner zones of the adrenals that were noted in rats (806).

4. Survival

Cortisone had no effect on pyridoxine excretion or on the survival time of pyridoxine-deficient rats (261).

D. VITAMIN B_{12}

Meites has shown that following large doses of cortisone B_{12}-deficient rats were found to show an inhibition of body growth and hair growth. The addition of B_{12} to the diet counteracted the inhibition of body growth. When B_{12} and aureomycin were fed, the thymus atrophy, but not the adrenal atrophy, following cortisone treatment was inhibited. It was suggested that cortisone increased the animals' requirement for B_{12} (756–759). This has also been suggested from experiments on young pigs on a B_{12}-deficient diet. Cortisone (20 mg. daily) increased the state of deficiency (1181). The weight loss and death of immature rats fed a diet containing 100 mg. of cortisone per kilogram, were reported to be prevented by the addition of 10 % desiccated liver to the diet (305, 306).

E. ASCORBIC ACID

1. Findings in Scorbutic Animals

Giroud and collaborators in older papers emphasized that most of the symptoms of scurvy could be related to adrenal insufficiency. The asthenia, weight loss, edema, alterations in potassium, decreased liver glycogen, and increased blood NPN were believed related to the reduced adrenal activity in scurvy (390, 392, 393). In addition, it was noted that many of these symptoms could be corrected by the administration of ACE (388, 391) but not by DCA (897). Further interest was aroused by the resemblance in scurvy of changes in the collagen and joint tissue and the arthritis, resembling rheumatoid arthritis in human beings. It has been pointed out, however, that although ascorbic acid has an essential role in the normal formation of collagen and intracellular substance, it has no apparent relation to fibrinoid—the abnormal material present in the connective tissues of the rheumatoid group of diseases. Fibrinoid has only a questionable relation to collagen, since it does not contain hydroxyproline, an unusually high amino acid constituent of collagen (85a, 622).

Many recent reports on experimental findings relating ascorbic acid to adrenal function have been reviewed by Meiklejohn (755). In the scorbutic guinea pig the concentration of adrenal ascorbic acid and cholesterol is reduced (52, 469, 895). At certain stages of deficiency the adrenal cholesterol level may be high, yet associated with a low ascorbic acid (833). With a totally deficient diet a marked reduction in adrenal ascorbic acid and cholesterol was found, together with histological evidence of decreased cortical steroids. After two to three weeks a rapid fall in liver glycogen occurred. The administration of $\frac{1}{2}$ mg. daily of ascorbic acid markedly reduced such changes (1100). The adrenal content of O^{11} steroids decreased with the development of scurvy (887). Similarly, the excretion of formaldehydogenic substances in the urine of guinea pigs on a scorbutic diet became depressed but then rose to very high levels as scurvy developed. Urine extracts at this time caused an increased liver glycogen deposition when compared with extracts of normal guinea pig urine (807). Similarly, the scorbutic animal excreted less 17-ketosteroids in the urine than did normal animals (54). Clayton and Prunty, however, reported an increase in the 17-ketosteroid excretion of scorbutic guinea pigs, but this may possibly be explained by the preceding findings of differences related to the degree of avitaminosis (154). A decreased blood sodium, and increased blood potassium with diminished urinary excretion of potassium, were also associated with scurvy (53). As ascorbic acid depletion increased in the guinea pig, a gradual increase in pituitary ACTH was found (1101).

2. Effects of Cortisone and ACTH on Scurvy

a. *Guinea Pigs.* Cortisone has been shown to cause a transitory prevention of weight loss and to inhibit many of the manifestations of scurvy, capillary hemorrhages being an exception. DCA, on the other hand, aggravated scorbutic symptoms (963). However, this effect of DCA has not been found by others (896). Similar findings with ACTH and cortisone have been noted and also a prolongation of life with some reduction in hemorrhagic manifestations (555, 556). When groups of guinea pigs were given diets containing graded contents of ascorbic acid, the adrenal weight was found to vary inversly with the vitamin content. With progressive depletion there was a progressive decrease in blood eosinophils. The onset of scurvy and mortality were delayed by ACTH (286). The rapid death and bone changes of scorbutic animals also were delayed or prevented by 5 mg. of cortisone daily, but no beneficial action was noted on changes in the joints or testes (504). Others have not found any beneficial effect on experimental scurvy (154, 1168). In a detailed study Walbach and Maddock could not detect any action of cortisone in preventing the loss of intercellular substances nor any effect on healing of the scorbutic lesions in guinea pigs (1182). The adrenalectomized guinea pig, when deprived of ascorbic acid, died rapidly (155).

b. *ACTH.* Despite the very low level of ascorbic acid in the adrenal glands of the scorbutic animal, a still further depression can be elicited by exogenous ACTH (155, 286, 705, 1168).

3. *Ascorbic Acid and Stress*

Dugal and associates have described the beneficial action of ascorbic acid on adrenal cortex activity related to stress (265, 266). The eosinopenia following epinephrine and also adrenal steroid depletion was prevented by ascorbic acid (38, 285). The eosinophilia characteristic of stress in the adrenalectomized rat was delayed by similar treatment (39). Apparently the eosinophil was the only type of leucocyte affected (34). Dogs and rats on a constant ascorbic acid intake when treated with cortisone or DCA showed a reduced urinary excretion of the vitamin. The former steroid was more effective in the rat, whereas the latter was more active in the dog. Plasma ascorbic acid was increased by steroid treatment (102). Pretreatment of mice with ascorbic acid was found to prevent the eosinopenia following epinephrine but not that after ACTH. It was suggested that the vitamin might act by depressing the release of pituitary ACTH (37).

a. *Human Stress.* The markedly increased catabolism of ascorbic acid in human beings after burns and fractures (22) and in active rheumatoid arthritis (454), requiring large amounts of ascorbic acid to restore blood levels, is not readily explained. There seems little evidence to support the use of ascorbic acid as a routine procedure to facilitate wound healing (188, 755). In an interpretation of the effects of ascorbic acid on stress it should be noted that in both man and the rat the oral ingestion of large doses of the vitamin is followed by an increased corticoid excretion, but decreased 17-ketosteroid in the urine, indicating a direct action on the adrenal cortex (621). In children this effect was found to be less constant (1081).

4. *Human Scurvy*

In scorbutic patients the eosinophil response to ACTH was found to be normal and was not changed after treatment with ascorbic acid. An increased 17-ketosteroid excretion was observed in one scorbutic patient (1156). Metabolic studies have been made on normal human subjects with a fixed dietary regimen and fixed analyzed ascorbic acid intakes. In classical scurvy the typical findings of eosinopenia and increased urinary 17-ketosteroids were noted after ACTH injection. Ascorbic acid levels in whole blood, urine, and feces were unchanged. After saturation of the individual with ascorbic acid a marked increase in urinary ascorbic acid occurred following treatment with ACTH or cortisone. Whole blood, plasma, and fecal values were unchanged. In no case was retention of ascorbic acid observed, as has been shown to follow severe damage (608). In two reports, patients on high dosage of cortisone have been noted to develop ascorbic acid deficiency associated with a low blood level and retention of administered ascorbic acid. A return to normal values followed ascorbic acid therapy (529, 1094).

5. *Adrenal Ascorbic Acid*

In the Sayer's test extremely minute doses of ACTH have been found to give a paradoxical increase in adrenal ascorbic acid (462).

a. Birds. Following ACTH or stress the adrenal glands of chicks hypertrophy and show depleted sudanophilic material, but this is not associated with a fall in adrenal ascorbic acid (588). This is apparently also true for the duck (1250) and quail (1248).

b. Hamster. This species was reported to show relatively small changes or none in adrenal ascorbic acid after ACTH (18).

c. Man. In persons dying after continuous stress, the enlarged adrenals were found to be depleted to about 50% of the normal ascorbic acid and cholesterol content (1167).

XIV. Influence of the Adrenal Cortex on Lymphoid Tissue; Reticuloendothelial and Mast Cells

A. THYMUS AND LYMPH NODES

Many observers have commented on the atrophy of lymphoid tissue after cortisone treatment. Cortisone and 11-dehydrocorticosterone in the rat have been found to cause a marked decrease in thymus and lymph node weight. Hydrocortisone did not show this action on the thymus and had less effect on lymph nodes (781). The decreased weight of the thymus gland of the normal mouse 14 hours after a single dose of adrenal steroid has been suggested as the basis of an assay method of adrenal steroids. The minimal effective dose of injected cortisone was found to be 0.2 mg., some 15 times less than that obtained by oral administration. Adrenalectomized mice were not more sensitive (209). Others have found, however, that when daily doses of 0.25 mg. were administered orally for 5 days cortisone caused a 53% weight loss of the thymus. When given subcutaneously in the same dose the weight loss was 85%. Intrasplenic injections were less effective, indicating portal inactivation. The same total dose given in a single administration was much less effective (209).

The thymus atrophy following fasting or stress was not found to be associated with significant effects on its total nitrogen content (4, 864), but atrophy induced by steroids reduced the nitrogen content (864). The importance of pyridoxine for the maintenance of normal lymphoid tissue has been emphasized, and its relationship with adrenal function has been described (1105).

B. Spleen

Splenic atrophy has similarly been frequently reported after cortisone injections (1065, 1066). Cortisone, 2 mg. daily intraperitoneally, administered to *Bartonella*-free mice caused a marked atrophy of the spleen to 21 % the size of that of the controls (779).

C. Reticuloendothelial System

Gordon and Katsh have studied extensively the uptake of thorium in the reticuloendothelial system (RES) of the rat. A significantly decreased uptake in the spleen took place after adrenalectomy. Cortisone, but not DCA, restored the accumulation. Degenerative changes in the macrophages and a decrease in their number in some organs followed adrenal insufficiency. It was concluded that the adrenal cortex exerted a regulatory influence on the structure and functional activity of the macrophagic cells (411). More recently the activity of the RES has been measured in the rat by isotope studies using colloidal chromium phosphate (Cr $P^{32}O_4$) as an indicator. Cortisone, 20 mg. daily for 3 days, was found to cause a depression in the functional capacity of the RES, amounting to 50 % (489). Others have also found a depressed ability of the RES to dispose of foreign substances deposited in the tissues of rabbits (617), and have favored such an action to explain the deterimental action of adrenal steroids on infection (1142). Heller has recently reported that either choline or vitamin B_{12} will overcome the depression of the reticuloendothelial system induced by cortisone (490).

D. Mast Cells

From extensive histological studies of connective tissue, Asboe-Hansen has reported that cortisone produces alterations in, and diminishes the number of, mast cells in man, rabbits, guinea pigs, and mice (27, 29). Such changes have been found to be associated with a decreased hyaluronic acid content of connective tissue (26, 139), and also of sulfomucopolysaccharide (29a). Cortisone, 100 mg. daily, administered to a dog with multiple malignant mast-cell tumors, caused a rapid regression and disappearance of the tumors by the 9th day of treatment (91). Other workers have not found a consistent change in mast cells in all tissues after cortisone injections in normal rats (230, 973) or in the hamster (366, 623). The conflicting views on the behavior of mast cells in relation to the adrenal cortex have been reviewed by Baker (44).

XV. Influence of the Adrenal Cortex on Blood and Bone Marrow

A. LYMPHOCYTES

Circulating lymphocytes show a periodic rhythm in numbers as do eosinophils (293). Six hours following a single dose of ACTH or ACE the bone marrow of guinea pigs showed a significant increase in the lymphocyte content, with no destructive action on lymphocytes occurring in the marrow (1247); repeated injections of extract caused a similar picture (540). In both normal and hypophysectomized rats a 10-mg. dose of hydrocortisone was followed in 4 hours by a marked lymphocytopenia in the thoracic duct lymph. This effect was more marked in the hypophysectomized animal and was associated with a decreased lymph flow. Hydrocortisone was more effective than cortisone in reducing lymphocytes (551). The lymphocytosis normally following adrenalectomy in the mouse was found by Kumagai and Dougherty to be suppressed by 0.05 mg. per 20 gm. body weight per day of cortisone (659). Two to twelve hours after adrenalectomy, stress caused a marked increase in circulatory lymphocytes in untreated mice, indicating that the adrenal cortex did not have an active participation in this reaction (256).

1. *In Vitro Effects*

The lymphotoxic action of adrenal steroids was demonstrated by Schrek on unstained cell counts of viable cells of incubated rabbit thymus. Corticosterone, cortisone, and 11-dehydrocorticosterone showed comparable activity, and hydrocortisone was four times more active. DCA showed no effect (976). This and other *in vitro* methods (975) have also shown that corticosterone, hydrocortisone, and ACE have a cytocidal action on rabbit lymphocytes (974, 975), as do ACE and 11-dehydrocorticosterone (316). In some reports using varied techniques lipo ACE was particularly active in affecting lymphocytes, whereas some adrenal steroids were inactive (316, 484, 774, 974).

B. EOSINOPHILS

An extensive number of papers has been published on studies concerning the response of the eosinophil leucocyte to adrenal steroids in both man and animals, and many applications of such tests have been reported (902, 1147). It should be noted, however, that the reliability of this response as an indication of adrenal function has been seriously challenged (84, 223, 765, 1224, and see below).

1. *Man*

The eosinopenia following ACTH is dependent upon functioning adreno-cortical tissue and may be used in the diagnosis of adrenal insufficiency. In normal individuals 25 units of ACTH evokes a drop of 50 % or more in circulating eosinophils in 4 hours time (usually 70 % and more). In 50 patients with Addison's disease the average drop was 7 %, and one-third of the cases actually showed an increase. Cases of hypopituitarism fall between the above two levels, averaging a 30 % drop (1150). Both cortisone and hydrocortisone cause eosinopenia, which parallels approximately their blood level (624). A series of other chemically related substances had no effect on eosinophils (1074), nor did the local application of cortisone ointment (202). Cortisone treatment causes a refractiveness to the effects of ACTH on circulating eosinophils, which may persist for some weeks after cessation of therapy (24). During observations on circulating eosinophils of some hours duration, the normal 24 hour periodic rhythm in counts must be considered. This occurs in man as well as in animals (448) and is not related to caloric intake (449). Such a rhythm is not found in adrenal-ectomized patients, in Addisonians, or in early infancy (447, 450) but coincides with other indications of rhythmic adrenal activity in normal individuals (293, 873, 876). The interpretation and clinical value of the eosinopenia following the injections of epinephrine have been questioned (607, 624, 798, 957, 960, 1150, 1183). The response of normal subjects to nor-epinephrine is very much less than to epinephrine (87, 549, 719, 862). The response to intravenous insulin was reported to be more constant than that to epinephrine (865). Because of the various factors influencing the eosinopenia of stress or epinephrine injections and making interpretations unreliable, it would seem logical that future alterations in the blood picture should be correlated with the direct measurement of blood 17-hydroxy-steroids (1145, 1148).

2. *Mice*

The adrenalectomized mouse showed an increase in total count and in absolute numbers of eosinophils and mononuclear leucocytes in the circulating blood. The effect was greater at two to three weeks than 4 to 5 days postoperatively. The number of mitoses in the bone marrow was reduced and the ratio of myeloid to erythroid elements increased. This eosinophilia was considered to be related to the decreased rate of maturation of marrow cells and increased survival of eosinophils in the blood (1098). A regular diurnal variation of large magnitude was found to occur in the eosinophil count in five strains of mice. The midnight count was only one-third of the morning level (448). The eosinopenic response of the adrenalectomized

DCA-maintained mouse treated with cortisone was shown by Wragg and Speirs to vary according to the genetic strain of the animals. Sensitive strains may respond to 1 μg. of cortisone, whereas 16 μg. is necessary to evoke a comparable response in resistant strains. Male animals proved to be more reliable (1241). The degree of eosinopenia is directly related to the dose of steroid. Cortisone induced a response at 3 μg., whereas 11-dehydrocorticosterone required 25 μg. (939, 1071). Speirs and Meyer have described in detail the use of the induced eosinopenia of the adrenalectomized mouse to assay adrenal steroids. Cortisone and hydrocortisone may be effective in susceptible strains in doses from 0.5 to 6 μg., the latter dose causing an 80 % or more decrease in eosinophils. Pretreatment with epinephrine renders insensitive any adrenal-rest tissue which may remain after adrenalectomy (1072). A single application of cortisone ointment was also effective in a total dose of 3 μg. (1070). Large doses of DCA (150 μg.) were reported to cause a partial eosinopenia in adrenalectomized mice (1071).

3. *ACTH Response in Animals*

Hungerford, Reinhardt, and Li have reported that the degree of eosinopenia produced in normal or hypophysectomized rats by ACTH was not always comparable. The extent of eosinopenia did not correlate with the amount of fall in adrenal ascorbic acid when various ACTH preparations were compared (552). The release of ACTH and stimulation of the release of adrenal steroids in the rat has been shown by Love to occur even though the animals were adrenalectomized 10 minutes after the inciting injection of epinephrine. A progressive typical fall in eosinophils then occurred in the absence of the adrenals (710). In dogs, repeated daily treatment with epinephrine resulted in a progressively diminished eosinopenic response (668). The fall in blood sugar in dogs following insulin injection was accompanied by a significant rise in circulating eosinophils. Since this also was observed in demedullated, adrenalectomized, or hypophysectomized animals, it was not related to an adrenal mechanism (1180). Pregnant guinea pigs did not show a consistent degree of eosinopenia after ACTH (274). Cortisone treatment of adrenalectomized dogs exerted a permissive action so that epinephrine caused eosinopenia (501).

4. *Mechanism of Eosinopenia*

This subject has been recently reviewed (307). Experimental evidence at present would indicate that the eosinopenia induced via adrenal steroids results from increased destruction of eosinophils in the tissues (not in the spleen), or less likely in the blood, rather than from accumulation in certain organs. Bone marrow is stimulated either secondarily or directly, but prolonged treatment may lead to exhaustion of eosinophil-producing elements. Many workers have studied the bone marrow changes associated with the eosinopenia in the blood induced acutely by various means in man and animals. Such studies consistently failed to show any increased destruction of eosinophilic cells in the marrow, and in most cases an increase in number was observed (83, 319, 402, 540, 600, 886, 945, 946). Therapy with ACTH in man or with ACE in adrenalectomized mice may stimulate, or be followed by, predominantly immature forms of eosinophils in the marrow (269, 443). Prolonged cortisone treatment of the adrenalectomized mouse or rat has led to marrow eosinopenia (412, 1098). The eosinopenia in the blood after cortisone, hydrocortisone, or stress, was reported not to be associated with a fall in eosinophils in peritoneal fluid in the mouse (848). In the rat, however, Padawer and Gordon found changes in the peritoneal fluid to parallel directly those of the blood after ACTH or cortisone (844). Higgins also reported an eosinopenia in the peritoneal fluid of the normal rat after epinephrine, and adrenalectomy abolished this response. 11-Dehydrocorticosterone, hydrocortisone, and ACE were all effective in the adrenalectomized animal, but corticosterone was less active (510). Many observers have found that the eosinophils are not removed from the circulation by migration to the spleen, since splenectomy does not affect the eosinopenia in the mouse, rat, or dog (270, 741, 1071). Similarly, no arteriovenous difference was found in the splenic blood of dogs after ACTH or epinephrine injections (1104). No accumulation of eosinophils was noted in the spleen of rats (363), but migration of eosinophils to the spleen of mice has been reported (1064). Evidence of degenerative changes in eosinophils, followed by macrophagocytosis, has been noted following administration of cortisone (364, 844). Blockade of the reticuloendothelial system prevented the eosinopenic action of cortisone (307). The destructive effects of cortisone and hydrocortisone in vitro have been described (403, 797), but others did not find evidence of an increased in vitro destruction of eosinophils (49, 131, 181). A recent detailed study on the in vitro action of cortisone and hydrocortisone on the eosinophils of citrated or defibrinated blood failed to demonstrate any effect (308). The eosinophila associated with infestation by Trichina responds to ACE (1097).

C. NEUTROPHILS

Changes occur in the number of neutrophil leucocytes following adrenal steroid treatment, but these have received less attention than those occurring in the other blood cells. Particular interest, however, has centered around leukemic states, and these will be discussed later. Usually the neutrophil count in peripheral blood shows the opposite change to the lymphocyte and eosinophil count. Such changes have been frequently reported and may be found in mice, rats, guinea pigs, dogs, and man (258, 514, 722, 905). The possible functional changes in these cells in response to adrenal steroids is considered later under "inflammation."

In vitro studies of human peripheral leucocytes failed to demonstrate any cytotoxic effects of cortisone, and cellular migration was not inhibited (49). The leucopenia induced in rabbits by treatment with mustard (HN2) was increased by cortisone or stress (1192).

1. *Bone Marrow*

Extensive studies of the bone marrow of rats have shown that adrenalectomy is followed by an increase in granulocytes and that ACE or cortisone treatment prevents such a change (412). The recovery of the bone marrow of rats from the effects of radiation was retarded by cortisone treatment (1141), although Burkell has used cortisone in leukemic patients to prevent severe depression of the leucocyte count following irradiation (121).

D. Red Blood Cells

The use of cortisone in the treatment of acquired hemolytic anemia in human subjects has not been considered in this chapter. Following adrenalectomy, in the salt-maintained rat, anemia developed and the R.B.C. was reduced by 25% in three weeks time, associated with a reticulocytosis and decreased fragility of the corpuscles. Whereas the bone marrow showed an increase in most components, the nucleated erythroid elements were decreased. ACE or cortisone ($\frac{1}{2}$ to 1 mg. daily), but not DCA or 11-dehydrocorticosterone, prevented the development of anemia and restored the altered marrow to normal (412, 872). The red cells of adrenalectomized rats were found to exhibit an increased resistance to hypotonic lysis, but this could be abolished by using washed cells. It appeared, therefore, that a factor was present in plasma which inhibited such lysis and was increased by adrenal removal (752). The anemia following phenylhydrazine in the rat could be prevented by ACTH. Conversely, the anemia was increased in the adrenalectomized animal. Cortisone treatment resulted in decreased red cell destruction (317). ACTH treatment of guinea pigs was reported to stimulate erythroid cells in the bone marrow (540).

1. *Iron*

Adrenalectomized rats showed a significant decrease in the level of plasma iron; this was prevented by ACE or cortisone, but not by DCA, confirming previous experiments in dogs. Normal animals, however, also showed hypoferremia following treatment with ACE, cortisone, or DCA (463).

E. PLATELETS AND COAGULATION

1. *Man*

An extensive series of measurements of factors influencing coagulation were reported by Monto and associates on normal and diseased persons after cortisone or ACTH therapy. Although no consistent change was found, many alterations did occur in different individuals. No significant change occurred in platelets. A decreased clotting time was found in 60 % of cases, and an increased protamine titration was frequently encountered. Plasma accelerator globulin, two-stage prothrombin, and antifibrinolysin values showed an alteration in some cases (784). Others have reported the clotting time after cortisone or ACTH to be unchanged (312), shortened (180), or prolonged (1044). The use of cortisone in patients who had suffered from thrombotic phenomena in the heart or brain did not occasion any new thrombotic or embolic episodes (951). Others, however, were impressed with the number of thromboembolic episodes after ACTH or cortisone (180). Platelets in the peripheral blood of 19 normal subjects were found to be significantly but only temporarily reduced after 50 to 100 mg. of ACTH. Similarly, in one splenectomized patient ACTH produced a slight thrombocytopenia (670). The increase in blood platelets which may occur after the use of cortisone in the treatment of idiopathic thrombocytopenic purpura has been discussed in many clinical papers and is omitted in this chapter.

2. *Animals*

In rats a form of thrombocytopenic purpura was induced by the use of antiplatelet serum. In these animals cortisone did not prevent the decrease in platelets nor did it influence the prolonged bleeding or other pathological manifestations of purpura (1068). In the normal guinea pig, but not after splenectomy, ACTH or cortisone (but not DCA or corticosterone) increased the antifibrinolytic activity of the serum. Cortisone treatment of the normal animal had no effect on the amount of fibrinolysin resulting from the activation of profibrinolysin by peptone (1166).

F. FIBRINOGEN AND SEDIMENTATION RATE

Many clinical papers contain observations on the sedimentation rate since it was first noted to return to normal in many of the diseases treated with cortisone. Although a raised sedimentation rate is usually decreased by cortisone treatment, the response may be paradoxical and not necessarily related to changes in clinical symptoms (42). Such a fall is normally associated with a lowering of blood fibrinogen and γ-globulin (328, 1174).

The sedimentation rate in the rat has been found to be slightly increased by DCA treatment and markedly reduced by cortisone (1005).   Plasma fibrinogen was reduced by cold stress in normal rats.   Although adrenalectomy diminished this response of fibrinogen to injury, it was not abolished (499, 500).

G. Blood Proteins

In man cortisone (since it became available for clinical study) has been consistently found to cause a decrease in globulins.   It is particularly effective were increased γ-globulin levels are found.   Decreased levels of β- and γ-globulins, at first, and later of α-globulins, have been observed (836). Albumin levels tend to be increased.

In adrenalectomized dogs the decrease in plasma albumin occurred irrespective of changes in blood pressure and even after certain forms of replacement therapy.   All globulin fractions increased during insufficiency (847).

Young rats tested with cortisone (3 mg. daily) showed a decreased serum α-globulin, but an increased γ-globulin (1219).

Guinea pigs show an increased albumin-globulin ratio after cortisone (722).

XVI. Influence of the Adrenal Cortex on Malignancy

Interest in the relationship of the adrenal cortex to malignancy has mainly centered around: (1) the beneficial effects of surgical removal of the adrenals in certain forms of endocrine cancer in man as a supplementary procedure to the removal of all endogenous steroid hormones; (2) the action of O^{11} steroids in favorably affecting some forms of leukemia and malignancy of lymphoid tissue; and (3) the action of adrenal steroids on various experimental tumors and in the reduction of antigenic processes to remove factors resisting successful tumor transplantation.

A. Adrenalectomy in Man

Although this field of interest is mainly beyond the scope of this chapter, reference can be found to the original work of Huggins and others on the effects of adrenalectomy in malignant disease in the following papers (473, 543–545, 1201).   It may be noted that in many of the cases reported a striking subjective improvement was found, and in some, at least temporary regression of the primary and secondary lesions may occur.   Adenocarcinoma and papillary carcinoma of the breast and adenocarcinoma of the prostate responded most satisfactorily, whereas mammary duct carcinoma, undifferentiated growths, and malignancy of other organs were not affected favorably.

B. Steroid Therapy in Human Malignancy

An extensive review and bibliography on the hormone treatment of cancer was published in 1952 by Nathanson and Kelley.   They concluded that such therapy with ACTH or cortisone should be limited to carefully selected neoplasms of the lymphoid and hemopoietic systems, and that in most cases such therapy should be considered only as a supplement to established therapeutic measures (809).   An earlier review of such treatment was made by Pearson and Eliel (856).   Acute leukemia (855, 858, 908, 980, 1047, 1075, 1102), chronic lymphatic leukemia (288, 855), and follicular lymphosarcoma (288, 855, 1047, 1075), Hodgkin's disease (855, 908, 1102), may all respond to ACTH or cortisone, but no response in chronic myelogenous or acute monocytic or monocytoid leukemias was noted (287, 855). 11-Dehydrocorticosterone and Compound S were not found to be active (857).   Remissions were usually only temporary and a second course of treatment gave less satisfactory effects.   The developed refractiveness to hormone therapy was not necessarily related to refractiveness to other different types of therapy (855, 980, 1102).   Patients showing the various malignant diseases sensitive to cortisone therapy were reported to have an increased blood antihyaluronidase.   This was found to decrease with clinical response to therapy.   Cases of myelocytic leukemia showed an exacerbation after cortisone, and this was associated with an increased titer of antihyaluronidase (503).   Various changes in hyaluronidase and related enzymes induced by cortisone are discussed in other sections of this chapter.

C. Experimental Cancer

1. *Tumor Growth*

The growth response of a large number of transplanted and spontaneous experimental tumors to ACTH or large doses of adrenal steroids has been investigated.

a. Mice.   Sarcoma 37 (241, 1113); lymphosarcoma (487, 1113); osteogenic sarcoma (1113); rhabdomyosarcoma (511); spontaneous or transplanted mammary carcinoma (415, 731); were all reported in most cases to be inhibited by cortisone.   Lymphoid tumors were also affected by hydrocortisone, 11-dehydrocorticosterone, and corticosterone (1238, 1239). Adenoma K7 showed inhibited growth by cortisone, but such treatment also caused multiple metastases to appear—an occurrence never noted in untreated mice (10).   An increased number of metastases after cortisone treatment has also been noted by others, even though the growth of the primary tumor was unaffected (60a).   Erlich's ascites tumor responded to both cortisone and hydrocortisone (1112).   A slight effect only was demon-

strated on Sarcoma T 241 (1113). No effect was usually observed with
Sarcoma 180; adenocarcinoma EO 771; Harding-Passey melanoma (113);
or an ascitic tumor (415). The induction of lymphosarcoma in C_{57} mice
following irradiation could be reduced from 82 % to 26 % by cortisone treatment, but this effect depended on the time of the start of treatment (605).
Cortisone was found to increase the tolerance of mice to toxic substances
which caused damaging effects on Sarcoma 37. However, such treatment
also counteracted the damaging effect on the tumor to the same extent (62,
63).

b. *Rat.* In this species cortisone also has been shown to cause a significant inhibition of Sarcoma R-39 (1113); Walker 256 (583); and lymphosarcoma (568). No effect was reported on Flexner-Jobling carcinoma or on
Walker 256 (1113).

c. *Hamster.* Cortisone treatment inhibited a mixed-cell sarcoma (186).

d. *Dog.* A spontaneous malignant mast-cell tumor (mastocytoma)
showed rapid regression and disappearance with cortisone (100 mg. daily)
treatment (91).

e. *Adrenalectomy.* Relatively few recent studies have been reported on
the effect of adrenal insufficiency on tumor growth (545). In initial studies
Murphy and Sturm showed that adrenalectomy increased the susceptibility
of the rat to their transplantable lymphosarcoma (leukemia), and cortisone
exerted an opposing action (243, 803, 804). Growth of Walker carcinoma
256 in the adrenalectomized rat was retarded when compared with the
normal animal, even though force-feeding maintained nutrition. The
Murphy lymphosarcoma showed a similar but less marked change (563).
Adrenalectomy increased the susceptibility of C_{57} mice to irradiation
induced lymphosarcoma (605).

f. *Pyridoxine.* The growth of transplanted lymphosarcoma in pyridoxine-deficient rats was retarded. Cortisone (2 mg. per day) also retarded tumor growth, and the two effects on the tumor were additive, although the animals died more rapidly (1107).

2. Leukemia in Mice

The early reports of benefit of ACE on leukemia (671) have been confirmed. The periodic treatment of the high-leukemic AKR mice throughout life with cortisone prolonged the length of survival from a mean of
9.3 months for untreated controls to 14.3 months (1240a). Similarly,
11-dehydrocorticosterone was shown to prolong the life of mice with transplantable leukemia (1238); others reported that cortisone (30 to 100 mg.
per kilogram two to eight times daily) did not prolong life after transplantation with leukemia AK4, although a definite lowering of blood counts was
observed (119). A mouse leukemia resistant to aminopterin treatment

was found to respond to cortisone treatment (120). Mice of a strain resistant to leukemia were found to exhibit induced susceptibility after radiation or cortisone injections. The two effects were also found to be additive. No effect was caused by such methods of treatment on mice made resistant to leukemia by active immunization (1198).

3. *Cortisone and Host Resistance*

Because of the action of cortisone in depressing antibody formation, as discussed elsewhere in this article, it offered a new approach to the possibility of reducing the resistance of animals and allowing the successful growth of transplanted tumors not otherwise possible. Following treatment with large doses of cortisone, successful heterologous transplantation of human tumors to the subcutaneous tissues of rats has been reported by Toolan and others (520, 1154). Similar treatment improves the chances of successful transplantation into the brain (147). The resistance of alien strains of mice to certain tumors of mice of different strains may be markedly decreased by cortisone, allowing successful transplantation and tumor growth (332, 536). This effect is apparently restricted to certain tumors and certain strains of mice, and is therefore not necessarily related to a general breakdown of natural barriers to tumor transplantation (331). Transplantation of the Murphy lymphosarcoma to Sprague-Dawley rats was followed by early rapid growth and then regression. Plasma sulfhydryl levels decreased with the rapid growth of the tumor and then increased. Cortisone was found to delay the accelerated phase of growth and prevent the fall in sulfhydryl levels. It was suggested that the effect of cortisone on the tumor might be secondary to its inhibition of the utilization of sulfhydryl groups (1011). The effects of cortisone on immunity to homogeneous tissue has been recently discussed by Stoerck (1108).

4. *Cortisone and Carcinogenesis*

Engelbreth-Holm and Asboe-Hansen have made the interesting observation that cortisone treatment had a marked inhibiting action on the carcinogenic action of 9,10-dimethyl-1,2-benzanthracene on the skin of mice (303a). The same inhibiting action of cortisone has also been reported by Baserga and Shubik, using skin applications of methylcholanthrene (60a). These results would appear to be of considerable interest in a consideration of the mechanism of carcinogenesis.

XVII. Influence of the Adrenal Cortex on Bone

The use of cortisone or hydrocortisone as a chronic therapeutic procedure may be associated with an increased loss of calcium, phosphorus, and nitrogen (177, 221, 343, 857, 1080). 11-Dehydrocorticosterone or Compound S had little effect (857).   As a result of prolonged therapy in human beings, marked osteoporosis and pathological fractures may occur (221). In one case this occurred despite simultaneous treatment with testosterone and a high calcium intake (1136).   Severe toxic reactions to Vitamin D_2 in a patient responded dramatically to cortisone therapy (236).   The increased density of the growing ends of bones in the rat described by Follis following cortisone or hydrocortisone (336, 338) was not found in mice, guinea pigs, or rabbits (337).   In the rabbit cortisone caused a decreased blood calcium and citrate and increased inorganic phosphate (877).   The tubular resorption of phosphate in the kidney was decreased following cortisone treatment of intact and adrenalectomized dogs, causing a negative phosphate balance (921).

XVIII. Influence of the Adrenal Cortex on Skin and Hair

1. *Skin*

In rats the prolonged local application of cortisone was found to lead to a general thinning of the skin in the treated area, with an atrophy of the sebaceous glands and a cessation in hair growth.   On microscopic examination there were fewer collagenous fibers and fibroblasts but no change in elastic fibers.   Such changes did not persit, and a return to normal occurred even though treatment was continued for 180 days (137).   A similar atrophy of sebaceous glands in rats has been observed after cortisone injections (48, 476).   Mitotic activity of the epidermis was decreased by adrenal steroid treatment (118).   In human patients, cortisone or hydrocortisone has been used topically or parenterally in a large number of skin diseases. Such diseases as dermatomyositis, pemphigus, exfoliative dermatitis, and acute lupus erythematosus may respond to treatment (239), as do certain other dermatoses (69, 1114, 1115).   The altered skin sensitivity to ultraviolet light reported after cortisone (592) has not been found by others (311).

a. *Pigmentation.* In human beings hyperpigmentation is frequently encountered following ACTH administration; it may also occur after cortisone (406, 438, 739).   In Addison's disease cortisone may decrease pigmentation, and DCA treatment be followed by increased pigment deposition (739). Hall, McCraken, and Thorn, from spectrophotometric analysis of the skin, concluded that the increased pigment in Addison's disease was due to an increased content of melanin and melanoid material as well as to a decreased content of blood and oxyhemoglobin.   Cortisone tended to reverse such changes towards normal.   Pigmentation, as in Addison's disease, was observed to develop after bilateral adrenalectomy despite adequate cortisone therapy.   The various theories on skin pigmentation have been reviewed in the light of the above observations (455).   The skin sulfhydryl content was found to be increased in depigmented areas, whereas it was decreased in hyperpigmented areas in cases of pemphigus following ACTH therapy.   In rabbits, however, the hyperpigmentation induced by ACTH was not associated with changes in sulfhydryl content (1173).

2. Hair

Cortisone has been reported to cause a regrowth of hair in cases of human alopecia (238, 239, 948).

The growth of hair has been reviewed by Chase (144) and Baker (43). In the rat, adrenalectomy has been shown to be followed by accelerated hair growth (46, 1252).   In such a preparation estrogen does not cause inhibition of hair growth as it does in the intact rat.   The estrogen action apparently required permissive amounts of adrenal steroids to operate (564).   Cortisone and ACE suppressed hair growth, particularly in adult rats (45, 1219).   In black rats showing greying of the hair induced by pantothenic acid deficiency, adrenalectomy was first shown by Ralli and Graef to cause a return of black hair (892).   These results have been discussed by Ralli and Dumm (891).   Grey hair has also been induced in black rats by a copper-deficient diet.   Adrenalectomy caused blackening of the grey hair or prevented its development in most cases (550).

XIX. Influence of the Adrenal Cortex on Appetite and the Stomach

1. Appetite

A stimulation of appetite is one of the earliest and most striking effects of the response to cortisone therapy in patients suffering from disease.   In children, the caloric intake may rise to five times the basal requirement if the diet is not restricted.   This effect has been considered to be secondary to the increased sense of well-being or decreased sense of illness experienced, or to the actual remission of the disease (1172).   In normal individuals, ACTH did not cause an improvement in appetite (104).   Experiments on normal and traumatized rats did not indicate that cortisone treatment was followed by an increase in food intake (1172).

2. Gastric Ulceration

In human patients on ACTH or cortisone therapy gastric disturbances may occur.   The development of peptic ulcer or reactivation of a dormant ulcer with secondary complications has been frequently noted (725).   Such effects are probably directly related to the changes which occur in gastric secretion.   In rats, both cortisone and hydrocortisone treatment for 10 days resulted in some cases in ulceration of the stomach (566).   Adrenalectomized animals similarly treated showed a greater incidence of gastric lesions (398, 847).

3. Gastric Secretion

In human beings with normal stomachs, cortisone (200 to 500 mg. daily for 4 to 18 days), was found to increase the concentration of both free and total HCl and pepsin concentration in the gastric juice (422). An increased uropepsin excretion in the urine paralleled these changes (275, 420, 421). The basal and nocturnal secretion of acid and pepsin was increased up to 200% (421). Increased gastric acidity after cortisone also occurred in previously vagotomized patients (949).

a. Dogs. Studies on dogs have indicated that cortisone caused a hypersecretion by a direct action on the gastric glands (1260). The adrenalectomized animal was found to show a reduction in gastric secretion, acidity, and enzyme content, which could be restored with ACE (1157).

b. Rats. In pylorus-tied rats the acid secretion was found to be reduced after adrenalectomy; this could be restored to normal by cortisone treatment (718, 1157, 1194). Cortisone in normal rats tended to reduce acid secretion (1194).

c. Mice. No effects on gastric secretion were found with cortisone or after adrenalectomy (204).

XX. Adrenal Cortex and Resistance to Damage

Papers on various aspects of this problem continue to be published. As in older references, it is usually shown that adrenalectomy reduces the tolerance to any form of damage, and replacement therapy by the O^{11} steroids, but not DCA, restores the resistance to normal. In the adrenalectomized animal, treatment with a basal dose level of adrenal steroids acts in a permissive role, allowing the metabolic phenomena which accompany stress to take place in a normal fashion. It logically follows, therefore, that such effects of stress are not due to adrenal steroid secretion per se (827). The treatment of normal animals does not increase their tolerance to damaging stimuli above normal levels, with the exception of those where the limiting factor is related to a lack of glucose. In such cases as in anoxia or muscle exhaustion the O^{11} steroids, by increasing gluconeogenesis, may permit a supernormal tolerance to be demonstrated. The damaging effects exhibited by DCA continue to be studied by Selye and collaborators, and their findings have been reviewed (561, 997, 1004). That the pituitary may be implicated in such damage has been described. Some, but not all, of the sensitizing actions by DCA to damage may be antagonized by the O^{11} steroids. Many authors have also commented on the opposing action of the two types of adrenal steroids in numerous diverse actions. The possible role of a hypersecretion of a DCA-like hormone in the etiology of the human diseases which respond to steroid therapy, still remains theoretical and without proof (561, 1004). The discovery of aldosterone may aid in a rapid solution of this controversy. The role of the adrenal cortex in stress has been reviewed in an extensive paper by Sayers (960).

A. Toxic Substances

1. *Egg White*

The injection of egg white into the rat is followed by massive edema of the nose and paws. Selye has found this reaction in the adrenalectomized rat to be inhibited by cortisone but exaggerated by DCA (996). In adrenalectomized rats hydrocortisone was about 1-½ times more active than cortisone in preventing acute toxicity, whereas cortisone was 2-½ times more active than 11-dehydrocorticosterone (145).

2. *DCA damage*

Selye has shown in various experiments that pituitary STH augments the damaging effects of DCA. It was also found to cause adrenal enlargement and prevent the compensatory atrophy which normally follows DCA treatment (999).

3. *Histamine Toxicity*

The relationship of histamine to allergic disease and the effects of cortisone have been reviewed by Rose (938).

a. Rabbits. No protective action of cortisone against histamine could be demonstrated in this species (664).

b. Rats. In rats, Ingle and Nezamis have compared the effects of continuously administered intravenous histamine alone or with cortisone, added to the solution in a daily dose of 4 mg. No difference in resistance or survival could be demonstrated (569).

c. Mice. In adrenalectomized mice either cortisone or epinephrine increased the animal's tolerance to 5 to 10 times the minimum lethal dose of histamine. However, if given together, the tolerance was increased to 50 to 100 times. Such an effect did not occur in intact animals (460).

d. In Vitro. Using rabbit's blood, cortisone was not found to affect histamine liberation during *in vitro* hemolytic reactions (136), nor did it affect histamine liberation from serum or blood in either sensitized or normal rabbits (1062). The effect of histamine on the response of isolated artery diminished to 10 % of the control level when cortisone was added *in vitro*. This was believed to represent a direct antihistamine action (1037).

4. *Bacterial Toxins*

Massive bilateral cortical necrosis of the kidney of rabbits and Syrian hamsters has been reported following simultaneous treatment with large doses of cortisone (25 mg. per kilogram per day and 10 mg. per day, respectively) and the intravenous injection of the toxin of meningococcus or *S. marcescens*. No lesions were observed when either agent was given singly. Blood cultures were negative (1143). Cortisone and ascorbic acid exerted no protective action in guinea pigs against diphtheria and other toxins (805). Parabiosis "intoxication" was not affected by cortisone treatment (321).

5. *Choline Deficiency*

Rats fed a diet low in choline and its precursors eventually show a kidney lesion characterized by kidney enlargement and hemorrhage. Treatment with cortisone resulted in partial protection, with the result that the renal lesions were less severe (992).

B. Tissue Damage
1. *Frostbite*

In rabbits, cortisone 2-½ mg. twice daily, did not modify the extent of skin or muscle necrosis after exposure of the hind leg to cold (698).

2. *Fractures*

In rats fractures were followed by urinary retention of Na and Cl, but with a loss in nitrogen and K. Since the same picture was found in adrenalectomized animals maintained on a permissive dose level of ACE such changes were not caused by stimulation of the adrenal cortex (575).

3. *Hepatectomy*

Adrenalectomy caused impaired regeneration of liver protein after partial hepatectomy. ACE, DCA, or 11-Dehydrocorticosterone caused a restoration to normal and were more effective than cortisone (353).

4. *Myocardial Infarction*

Myocardial infarction was produced in dogs by ligation of a branch of a coronary artery. Cortisone therapy was not followed by any deleterious effects on the resulting infarct or on myocardial healing (although some delay in early healing was noted) (143, 595). After cortisone doses of 12 to 20 mg. twice daily, the infarcts were found to be only one-seventh the size of those in control animals; pericardial adhesions were reduced to one-fourth, and a marked improvement in regaining normal activity was noted in the treated animals (594). Interarterial coronary anastomosis was found to be increased by cortisone (even if no ligation). The mortality was reduced from 52.9 % to 21.5 % by such treatment (595).

5. *Burns*

In rats, survival was not increased by cortisone treatment and was decreased by pretreatment. DCA pretreatment afforded some protection (810).

6. *Intestinal Trauma*

In rats, shock produced by intestinal trauma was favorably affected by the immediate injection of 25 mg. per kilogram of cortisone. The duration of survival was increased by 40 % (1038).

7. *Wild Rats*

Wild rats apparently endure various stresses, which affect the domesticated variety, without depletion of adrenal ascorbic acid or stainable lipids. ACTH was effective in wild rats, but comparatively large doses were required (1226).

C. IRRADIATION

The effects of radiation on adrenal function are of considerable interest. It was shown by Leblond and Segal in 1942 that the effects may be twofold. Local irradiation may result in generalized thymolymphoid atrophy through pituitary-adrenal stimulation, since adrenalectomy abolishes this action. On the other hand, adrenalectomy does not prevent the atrophy of lymphoid tissue exposed to direct irradiation (678).

Acute whole-body irradiation of the dog results in a marked immediate increase in blood 17-oxycorticosteroids, indicating pituitary-adrenal stimulation. These blood findings were found to parallel the degree of severity of anorexia, vomiting, and lassitude of the animal, rather than the histopathological changes (108). Adrenalectomized mice have been shown to be more sensitive to irradiation, as might be expected from their decreased resistance to general damaging agents (190). The various effects of treatment before or after irradiation of normal animals have been described. Cortisone, 0.2 mg. intraperitoneally, has been reported to have no effect on mortality or survival time of mice (1046), but others have found an increased mortality and decreased survival time with similar dosage (291, 1197). DCA treatment was reported to reduce mortality (289), but others did not observe this effect (419, 1111). Following head radiation, both cortisone and DCA have been found to afford protection, possibly by counteracting pituitary-adrenal insufficiency (775). The discrepancy in

results of the various workers may be explained by strain differences in the
mice used and the different effects of treatment when the head is primarily
irradiated (775). Radiation has been shown to cause an increased susceptibility to virus and other infections similar to that induced by cortisone
injections. The combined action was found to be more effective than
either agent used separately (290, 1127).

XXI. Adrenal Steroids and the Cellular Reaction to Inflammation and Injury

INTRODUCTION TO SECTIONS XXI, XXII, XXIII

The following three sections of this chapter concern the influence of adrenal steroids on the cellular response to inflammatory reactions and injury,
on hypersensitivity states and related antigen-antibody responses, and on
spontaneous and induced infections by varied organisms. In all these
actions the effects of cortisone and hydrocortisone appear to be detrimental
to the host, although some actions such as depression of inflammation or
fibroblastic proliferation may be of therapeutic benefit. Usually, large
doses have been used to cause such detrimental effects, and the magnitude
of the response appears directly related to the dose. Because of the
doses required, similar types of reactions are not so frequently encountered
in man. In many of the actions to be described ACTH appears to be a
much less effective agent, even in large doses, than cortisone or hydrocortisone. It is tempting to try to find a common factor which is affected by
adrenal steroids and so explain these related actions. Many theories have
been suggested implicating various systems, as will be seen from the data
to be listed later. Some of these may be mentioned. Depression of inflammation and wound healing involves most tissue, cellular, and vascular elements as well as a depression in margination, diapedesis and migration of
leucocytes, and a diminished number of all types of leucocytes in the reactive area, together with a reduction in antifibrinolysin. The diminished
response in fibroblastic multiplication and differentiation has been particularly noted, and a direct inhibition of mitosis suggested. In the presence
of infection, the paucity of cellular reaction allows rapid bacterial multiplication and enhances blood stream penetration. The phagocytic activity
of the leucocytes present may be impaired, and a reduced capacity of the
fixed macrophages of the reticuloendothelial system to destroy bacteria
aids in the fulmination of such infections. In addition, the synthesis of
specific antibodies is inhibited (although already established circulatory
antibodies may be less affected), with the result that the natural immunity
responses fail to function. In a consideration of a possible common factor
for these effects, the apparent failure of adrenal steroids to produce the

expected inhibitory response in *in vitro* tissue culture experiments should be noted.　Whereas the results on infection might be anticipated from the effects of the adrenal steroids on the cellular responses and antibody formation, the other actions cannot readily be focused to a single primary action.　Early results tended to implicate hyaluronidase, but this has not been established by later work.　It is possible, since the effects are essentially on the response of the host, that some chemical mechanism initiates the inflammatory response and is essential for antigen-antibody union, and that the action of such a tissue substance is primarily blocked by adrenal steroids.　Detailed discussions of the above generalizations may be found in the following references (189, 245, 253–255, 324, 326, 384, 411, 428, 442, 617, 706a, 762, 898, 900, 923, 926, 991, 1110, 1133, 1142, 1165).

A. Inflammation

This subject has been reviewed by Cameron (129) and Rebuck and Mellinger (900).

1. *Effects of Steroids*

a. Rabbits.　When inflammatory reactions were induced in the skin by scratching or the application of croton oil, cortisone given intravenously (12-$\frac{1}{2}$ mg. daily) delayed all the tissue components of the earliest inflammatory response.　This included an inhibition of the vascular margination of leucocytes, of the migration of leucocytes from blood vessels, and of the formation of edema and fibrin (767).　Using the ear chamber technique for *in vitro* studies of inflammatory reactions to various stimuli, Ebert (276–278) showed that cortisone treatment (5 to 25 mg. a day) was followed by a better maintenance of arteriolar tone; the integrity of the vascular endothelium was preserved with less damage to arteriolar and venule endothelium; the sticking of leucocytes to the endothelium was diminished, as was the endothelial swelling; and the diapedesis of leucocytes and formation of exudate were reduced.　The increased capillary permeability, associated with the inflammatory response to "leukotaxine," was found by Menkin to be suppressed by cortisone (762).

b. Guinea Pigs.　In this species cortisone has been shown to reduce diapedesis, capillary hemorrhage and edema, hyperemia, and leucocytic infiltration.　Such effects were believed to be related to an increased resistance of the capillary walls (785).

c. Rats.　Granulomatous reactions in the rat have been studied by Selye (1002, 1003).　Cortisone and hydrocortisone inhibited the inflammatory reactions and granuloma development following croton oil application to a granuloma pouch (1003).　Cortisone was also found to inhibit granulation tissue around abscesses produced by turpentine injection in intact and

hypophysectomized rats. Pituitary STH stimulated granulation tissue
(1134). When cortisone was suspended in turpentine, it inhibited the
development of granulation tissue locally. On the other hand, control
turpentine injections elsewhere in the animal were unaffected (1135). Denervation or ischemia did not counteract the effects of cortisone (1013).
Estradiol was also found to show the same local inhibiting action of granulation tissue, but DCA apparently counteracted the effects of cortisone
(1135).

   d. Mice. Following the application of croton oil to the skin of mice,
cortisone was not found to alter the hyperplasia, although a slight increase
in mitotic rate in the epidermis was noted. Similarly, no alteration in
response to a carcinogenic hydrocarbon applied prior to croton oil was
observed (916).

   The use of adrenalectomized mice to assay antiphlogistic potency has
been advocated by Schneebeli and Dougherty (971). Inflammation follows
the subcutaneous injection of histamine, but this may be prevented for 6
hours by *in vitro* mixing with adrenal steroids. Differential counts on
fibroblasts, polymorphonuclear cells, lymphocytes, and eosinophils on
stained spreads of the affected areolar tissue indicated the extent of the
reaction. Cortisone inhibited such an inflammatory reaction, and hydrocortisone was found to be 20 times as active as cortisone. DCA had no
action alone but would suppress the effects of cortisone (971). Others
have reported the suppression of skin reactions to histamine by cortisone
in mice (55). Cortisone treatment of inflammation in mice has been followed by the appearance of acidophilic (azurophilic) inclusions in macrophages and fibroblasts. Since these changes also follow injection of the
vehicle of cortisone, they are not necessarily related to the steroid. The
possible effect on connective tissue and fibroblasts in tissue repair of this
nonspecific reaction in relation to cortisone action has been discussed
(972, 984). Vacuolated or "foam" cells around the wound edge of rats
treated with cortisone have also been noted (483, 1135) and may represent
the same reaction.

   e. Monkey. The acute encephalomyelitis which follows the injection of
brain emulsion and adjuvants was markedly affected by cortisone in doses
from 10 to 40 mg. daily. The larger doses completely inhibited the granulomatous reaction and prevented all symptoms (603).

   f. Antifibrinolysin. Ungar found that antifibrinolysin was decreased
following cortisone at the same time that inflammation was decreased.
From this and other observations it was postulated that the primary function of adrenal steroids in influencing the inflammatory process might be
through the action on antifibrinolysin (1165).

   g. Reaction of Blood Cells to Inflammation. The inhibiting action of adrenal steroids on the blood-contributed defense cellular units in inflammation has been commented upon by many workers and recently reviewed (900). Decreased margination, diapedesis, and migration by cortisone treatment have been noted after varied stimuli inciting inflammation (182, 278, 385, 397, 486, 767, 785, 926, 1067).

2. Permeability—Hyaluronidase

The action of cortisone on mast cells which are concerned with the production of hyaluronic acid has been discussed previously. Various studies have been reported on the effects of steroids on the action of hyaluronidase in increasing the spread of injected dyes. Opsahl, in a number of papers, showed that O^{11} steroids would inhibit the intradermal spreading of India ink induced by hyaluronidase in mice, and similar findings have been reported by others (60, 66, 1019). 11-Dehydrocorticosterone was less effective than cortisone (839). Similarly in rats, intravenous hyaluronidase increased the rate of disappearance of Evans blue from the circulation. Pretreatment with 5 mg. daily of cortisone counteracted the effects of hyaluronidase (66). It has been reported, however, that purified hyaluronidase has no demonstrable effects on the permeability of blood vessels except in the rat (294). The inhibiting action of cortisone on hyaluronidase in mice can be counteracted by glutathione, but not by oxidized glutathione. It was suggested, therefore, that cortisone inhibited hyaluronidase by removing SH groups (21). Adrenalectomy in mice was found to increase the spread of the dye T1824 with or without hyaluronidase (1216). When hyaluronidase-containing staphylococci were injected, ACE was found to inhibit the expected infection both in intact and adrenalectomized animals. When hyaluronidase-free bacteria were used, protection was found only in the adrenalectomized ACE-treated animal. It was suggested that the susceptibility to infection after adrenalectomy might be due to the removal of adrenal inhibition of hyaluronidase (1039). In the adrenalectomized rat, the spreading of T1824 was also increased, but the animals had to be depleted of electrolytes to show such an action. Cortisone strongly inhibited the spreading, but testosterone propionate and other steroids were also active (1216). The prolonged local or parenteral treatment of rats with ACE has been shown to cause the reverse of the previous findings, in that the spreading action of hyaluronidase was markedly accelerated and extended (28, 482, 483). However, if an acute increase in ACE dosage was given, there still followed a marked inhibition (482). It was suggested from these experiments that prolonged treatment may alter the physical state of the ground substance, allowing an increased action of hyaluronidase. The acute action, however, may be interpreted as a direct inhibitory action on the enzyme (482). Prolonged treatment of rats with corticosterone is apparently ineffective in affecting hyaluronidase spreading (481). In dogs, repeated wounding was followed by an increase in the serum anti-hyaluronidase activity, which gradually returned to normal as healing progressed. Cortisone treatment (2 mg. per kilogram), was not found to affect the antihyaluronidase activity of the serum (164).

3. Joint Permeability

Seifter and collaborators have shown that following the injection of phenolsulfophthalein into the talocrural joint cavity of the rabbit, the substance is excreted in the urine, allowing a calculation of the rate of absorption and permeability of synovial membranes. (The use of other species and other joint cavities of the rabbit has yielded conflicting results.) A marked increase in permeability was found to be produced by hyaluronidase or DCA. In the rabbit, ACE or cortisone decreased permeability and also antagonized the action of hyaluronidase. Cortisone treatment, 1 mg. per kilogram, was followed by only 25 % to 30 % excretion of the dye in 4 hours time. This action was not specific for O^{11} steroids, since estrone also depressed permeability and 21-acetoxypregnelolone was more active than cortisone (988–991). No effect on normal joint permeability in rabbits was caused by cortisone in doses of 10 to 25 mg. per kilogram or by ACE or ACTH. The increased effect of hyaluronidase was confirmed, and this was inhibited by ACTH treatment (509).

In a recent review it has been suggested that the adrenal steroids affect directly the mucopolysaccharides that are depolymerized by hyaluronidase. Cortisone depresses or inhibits such an action, whereas DCA causes augmentation. The action probably does not involve inactivation of the enzyme, but an alteration of the substrate, and can take place in the absence of the adrenals. It was concluded that the therapeutic effects of cortisone in collagen disease do not depend entirely on the inhibition of hyaluronidase or DCA actions (991).

4. Joint Inflammation

Various procedures have been developed to induce inflammatory changes in joint tissue. How far the pathology or etiology of such conditions can be compared with the various forms of arthritis in man is yet unsettled, but conservative opinion prefers simply to describe the lesions as joint inflammation, without the implications connected with the term arthritis.

a. Hyaluronidase. Repeated daily injection of this substance into the knee joint in rats is followed by a proliferation of fibroblasts and endothelial cells, associated with a leucocyte infiltration and exudation of fibrin. Cortisone was found to be effective in preventing such changes, particularly the fibrinous exudation into the synovial cavity (228).

b. Formalin. The injection of this substance into tissues near a joint is followed by a marked swelling and inflammatory changes in the joint. Using this method, Selye showed that the lesion could be inhibited by ACTH or cortisone and that it was aggravated by DCA or anterior pituitary extract (995). Other results have been reported confirming the deleterious action of DCA in increasing mesenchymal proliferation, and the improvement of the formalin lesion by cortisone treatment through the action in reducing fibroblastic proliferation and deposition of collagen (136, 1024). The report by Brownlee that protection against the reaction to formalin in rats was afforded by the separate simultaneous injections of DCA and ascorbic acid (116) was soon refuted (349). It has been stated that ascorbic acid hastens recovery in the intact rat (35) but has no effect in the adrenalectomized rat, although cortisone reduces the inflammatory swelling in this preparation (36).

c. Other Agents. Following infection with pleuropneumonia-like organisms (L-4 strain) in the rat, multiple joint swellings may be observed. These responded to terramycin therapy, but were not prevented or improved by cortisone. Large doses caused aggravation of the lesions (662). An arthritis of unknown etiology in pigs has been found in some cases to be improved by cortisone or ACTH therapy (260). Following the treatment of adrenalectomized, ovariectomized rats with growth hormone, joint inflammation was induced which responded to treatment with hydrocortisone, possibly through hormone antagonism (904).

5. Rheumatoid Arthritis

The alleviation of pain, swelling, and inflammation of affected joints of persons suffering from rheumatoid arthritis and the resulting increase in movement were among the dramatic changes first observed in the response to cortisone treatment by Hench *et al.* (495). This has now become a characteristic action attributed to cortisone or hydrocortisone, and has been confirmed and extended in large numbers of patients (496, 497, 625, 883, 1080, 1149, 1151, 1186). It is of some interest to note that neither 11-dehydrocorticosterone nor corticosterone has been found to be active in this respect, although the latter compound may induce changes in electrolyte and organic metabolism comparable with those induced by cortisone (496, 929). Other ineffective compounds tested included Compound S, deoxycortisone, 21-deoxycortisone, 21-deoxy 11-dehydrocorticosterone, dihydrocortisone acetate, 6-dehydrocortisone acetate, DOC, 17-hydroxyprogesterone, and pregnenetriolone (882). In addition, Kendall's ACE given intravenously, and lipo-adrenal extract given intramuscularly, had no effect in the doses used (882). Even massive doses of Compound S, hydrocortisone, and pregnenetriolone caused no objective improvement

(1140). Large doses of concentrated ACE had some effect in one of three patients (882). When given orally, cortisone was effective (350, 882, 883, 1186), and free hydrocortisone was slightly more effective than cortisone acetate, but hydrocortisone acetate was inferior to both. Cortisone-free alcohol was about equally as effective as the acetate (95).

a. Intraarticular Injection. The local action of hydrocortisone on the inflammatory process has been repeatedly demonstrated by the injection into affected joints in many patients with rheumatoid arthritis. This action is not specific for rheumatoid arthritis, since inflammatory processes involving the joints but due to many other etiologic factors also respond to such therapy. The injection of 25 mg. of hydrocortisone is usually followed by a rapid symptomatic improvement due to a local action (527, 528). Cortisone, even in large doses, when injected into a joint cavity shows a much less effective action than does hydrocortisone (263, 527, 528, 1151).

b. Changes in Rheumatoid Tissue. Histopathological studies of rheumatoid lesions in human patients have been made after cortisone treatment. In general an acceleration of the involutional changes which occur spontaneously in such lesions and a more rapid regression due to prevention of further activity have been described (262, 318, 828, 1018).

B. Wound Healing

1. *Skin*

a. Rabbits. Cortisone in large doses, 12½ mg. twice daily, caused a marked delay in the healing of wounds of the skin and the development of granulation tissue (55, 537, 669, 880, 881, 888).

b. Mice. Cortisone, 1 mg. daily, caused a suppression of all the cellular elements in skin wound healing. When cortisone was given 48 hours after wounding, such effects were not found (1065, 1066).

c. Rats. The granulation tissue and fibroplasia after wounding were delayed by cortisone (16, 55, 669, 672, 747, 750, 964). The appearance of all the cellular elements of mesenchymal origin was retarded (16). *Local application* of ACE to cutaneous wounds of the rat was followed by a delayed closure of wounds and an interference with the formation of granulation tissue (47). The tensile strength of the wounds was also reduced (16, 537). *Adrenalectomy* did not affect wound healing (16), nor did treatment with DCA (750).

d. Guinea Pig. Cortisone had no effect on wound healing in this species (55), and DCA increased the granulation tissue in the wound (879).

e. Dog. Wound healing by primary intention (sutured) was not affected by cortisone treatment (2 mg. per kilogram) (165).

f. Chicken. Large doses of cortisone, 25 mg. per kilogram, showed no effect on wound healing (672).

Part of the deleterious effects on wound healing which have been described may be related to the general weight loss, since protein depletion and starvation in rabbits have been shown to interfere with wound healing. These conditions also intensify the deleterious effects of low doses of cortisone on wound healing (320). Similar findings have been reported in rats (750).

2. Bones

a. Fractures—Rabbits. The healing of experimental fractures in rabbits was delayed by cortisone (93, 537, 1033). With cortisone, 12½ mg. twice daily, the healing and absorption of the hematoma were greatly delayed, and a failure of connective tissue regeneration was seen (93).

b. Rats. Experimental fractures (some pinned) showed no difference between cortisone (2 to 4 mg. daily) treated and control animals in gross or histological changes (628).

c. Mice. ACTH was found to inhibit the healing and callus formation of fractures (1017).

d. Monkeys. In two monkeys, cortisone, 10 mg. daily, did not delay osteogenesis, with experimental ear fenestration healing rapidly as in control animals (894).

3. Eye

a. Perforating Wounds—Rabbit. The conjunctival injection of large doses of cortisone completely prevented healing. Smaller doses inhibited the formation of the fibrinous coagulum, cellular infiltration, fibroplastic repair, and endothelial regeneration (30).

b. Chemical or Thermal Burns, etc.—Rabbit. The growth of capillaries and vascularization were inhibited by cortisone or hydrocortisone (742) by subconjunctival injections (599, 687, 702, 742, 768, 769), or by parenteral administration (439, 702, 840). A less dense scarring of the treated eyes resulted (687, 688).

c. Rat. Re-epithelialization of the traumatized cornea was slightly inhibited by cortisone (585). Autogenous red blood cells injected into the vitreous humor were more rapidly absorbed after cortisone treatment, possibly owing to increased macrophagocytosis (585), but the opposite effect has been described in rabbits when cells were injected into the anterior chamber (67).

d. Rabbit. Following cortisone eye drops, penetration of the steroid into the anterior chamber occurred, and it also was detected in the vitreous humor. Higher steroid levels were reached earlier with subconjunctival injection than with systemic treatment and lasted 24 hours (687, 688). The blood-aqueous barrier to fluorescein was not affected, or slightly lowered, by cortisone treatment in animals and man (178, 585, 689, 742).

e. Monkeys. Following trephine-induced defects of the cornea the local application of cortisone slowed healing and the formation of granulation tissue (585).

f. Guinea Pigs. When subjected to nonperforating wounds of the cornea guinea pigs showed a reduced infiltration by cells following cortisone, and this was also observed when the animals were rendered scorbutic. Cortisone treatment of the scorbutic animal increased fibroblastic proliferation and also delayed the onset of symptoms of scurvy (56).

g. Human Being. Many conditions associated with inflammatory reactions of the eye have been reported benefited by cortisone or hydrocortisone (498, 742, 794, 1095, 1096, 1234, 1243). The clinical assessment of treatment in the various disorders may be found in the following reviews (689, 1043, 1151, 1235).

C. Fibrosis

1. *Silicotic Nodules*

The collagen induced in the peritoneal cavity of rabbits by silica was not reduced by cortisone treatment, but further fibroblastic proliferation was retarded (720). Other experimental studies also showed a modification by cortisone in the amount and distribution of the nodular reaction (471, 969).

2. *Beryllium*

Poisoning in man with this substance has been described by a number of workers. The beneficial actions of treatment with ACTH or cortisone are most likely associated with the inhibitory action of inflammatory changes. The clinical effects of treatment of this condition have been reviewed by Van Ordstrand (1171).

In mice treated with ACTH no direct effect on the distribution or retention of radio beryllium was demonstrated, and survival was not influenced (1204).

3. *Strictures and Adhesions*

In rabbits, esophageal strictures were produced by the local applications of caustics. Cortisone, 6 to 10 mg. per kilogram, reduced the severity of the strictures and the number of animals showing final strictures, but a marked increase in infection and spontaneous perforation caused an increased mortality (942, 943).

4. *Adhesions—Dog*

The application of talc sprinkled over the bowel results in dense matted adhesions. Cortisone, 10 mg. twice daily, resulted in an estimated 75% fewer adhesions, and these were thin and readily separated (964). However, when adhesions follow denudation of the small bowel, cortisone has been shown to have much less effect, although some diminution in extent and denseness was found. It was pointed out that in contrast to surgical denudation, the application of talc is followed by a much more intense granulomatous inflammatory reaction, which might be expected to show a greater response to cortisone (538). A similar beneficial effect was noted with talc-induced pleural adhesions (964), and on pericardial adhesions after experimental myocardial infarction (594).

5. *Rats*

Cortisone, 2 mg. daily, markedly lessened talc abdominal adhesions and had no effect on wound healing; however, 3 mg. daily also delayed wound healing (628, 964).

6. *Liver Fibrosis*

Hepatic fibrosis, which follows the damage produced by the injection of carbon tetrachloride in the rat, was inhibited by the simultaneous injection of cortisone (31).

D. TISSUE CULTURE

In view of the marked effects of cortisone on the cellular response to inflammation, it is of interest to note the effects in tissue culture. Steen has found that fibroblasts and epithelial growth of chick embryo are unaffected even by large doses of cortisone, normal mitosis being observed (1093). High concentrations of cortisone did not affect the migration of fibroblasts during the first 72 hours, but rapid degeneration of fibroblasts occurred after the third day. The pulsation of heart tissue continued for more than two weeks (672). Negative effects on tissue culture of skin fibroblasts for cortisone (free or acetate) and DCA, were also reported by Evans of Dr. Earle's laboratory (310). Others have reported that cortisone and hydrocortisone had an inhibiting effect *in vitro* on migration and growth of fibroblasts (49, 526, 619). When rats were subjected to high doses of cortisone and then tissues removed for culture, it was found that fibroblasts and striated and cardiac muscle all showed normal growth (17). Layton has found that cortisone inhibits the synthesis of chondroitin sulfate by chick embryonic and wound tissues *in vitro*, the response being proportional to the dose of steroid. Inhibition of the synthesis of soluble organic sulfates by heart and skeletal muscle was also noted. It was suggested that the action of cortisone on connective tissues may be due to this inhibition of the chondroitin sulfate moiety of the ground substance (672).

XXII. Adrenal Steroids and Sensitivity. Antigen-Antibody Reactions

A. SENSITIVITY

1. *Skin*

a. Man. ACTH and cortisone have been found to depress the degree of skin sensitivity to pneumococcal polysaccharides (776). Similarly, cortisone, 100 to 200 mg. daily for 3 to 30 days, obliterated the reaction to β hemolytic streptococci in 19 of 34 patients, and all of the others showed milder reactions (707).

Tuberculin. In man tuberculin sensitivity was obliterated in 13 of 34 individuals by cortisone, 100 to 200 mg. daily for 3 to 30 days. A positive test returned in one to four weeks after cessation of treatment (707). The tuberculin reaction was also found to be inhibited by the intradermal injection of hydrocortisone (407).

Dermatitis. Poison Oak (*Rhus diversiloba*) contact dermatitis was markedly improved by cortisone therapy, 100 to 200 mg. daily (314). The effects of the intradermal injection of cortisone and hydrocortisone on reactions to various irritants have been reviewed. The latter steroid was more effective. No beneficial effect on poison ivy was noted (407). The local application of hydrocortisone, but not cortisone, was reputed to cause a sustained inhibition of the local reaction to mosquito bites (408). Such effects were not immediate, but delayed (933). Various sensitivity dermatoses have been described as responding to cortisone and are reviewed (1242).

Penicillin. The symptoms of severe sensitivity reactions to penicillin were relieved by cortisone, 200 to 350 mg. daily. They may recur when treatment is stopped. This was believed to represent a suppression of the manifestations of hypersensitivity rather than an alteration of the hypersensitive state (502).

b. Guinea Pigs. The cutaneous tuberculin reaction in infected animals with virulent tubercle was modified but not abolished by cortisone, 10 to 20 mg. per day, and a quantitative diminution of the inflammatory exudate has been noted (192, 227, 1015). Even daily treatment for 50 days did not entirely suppress the reactions (1015). Cortisone in doses of 11 mg. per day, however, was reported to cause suppression of dermal reactivity, the test becoming positive again 4 days after the last injection (470, 1106).

c. Rabbits. Adrenalectomy was found to enhance slightly, whereas cortisone inhibited, the cutaneous sensitivity to antigen (233). Large doses of cortisone, 34 mg. per day, were found to inhibit tuberculin sensitivity (470).

Schwartzman phenomena. This reaction has been described as being either modified (1144), or prevented (548), by cortisone. ACTH is also effective in preventing the phenomena (1052). The degree of suppression is proportional to the dose of cortisone, and greater effects are found if pretreatment is given (726).

2. *Isolated Organs*

Guinea pigs were sensitized to rabbit antisera. The bowel from animals treated with cortisone, 5 mg. daily, before or after sensitization, showed an inhibited *in vitro* response to antigen. The uterus was unaffected (816). However, little *in vitro* action of large doses of cortisone on the ileum was noted in experiments using animals sensitized to horse serum (424).

B. HYPERSENSITIVITY—ANAPHYLAXIS

1. *Rat*

The nephrotoxic nephritis following the injection of rabbit anti-rat kidney serum was not prevented by ACTH or cortisone (445, 646). Adrenalectomy caused enhancement of anaphylaxis owing in part to enhancement of sensitization. When cortisone was given just prior to the challenging dose in the adrenalectomized rat, there was an increased resistance to anaphylaxis, although severe reactions occurred. If cortisone was given during sensitization, the reaction was greatly reduced (233).

2. *Rabbit*

Cortisone treatment was found to prevent the arteritis in 8 of 9 animals after injection of horse serum, but the glomerular nephritis was not affected (990). Arteritis and cardiac lesions were noted in 17 of 20 controls, whereas only 4 of 20 cortisone-treated animals showed such changes. The typical kidney lesion (diffuse glomerulonephritis with cellular proliferation of glomerular tufts) was inhibited but was replaced by a different type of kidney damage (particularly hemorrhage) (910, 912). The inhibiting effects of cortisone on foreign protein, with complete suppression of arterial and cardiac lesions, including the above kidney lesions (746), were also noted by others (382). The progressive rise in serum globulin seen in control animals was inhibited by treatment (746). γ-Globulin–induced coronary arteritis was also prevented by cortisone (788). Adrenalectomy was found to increase the hypersensitivity to bovine γ-globulin, and cortisone inhibited the fall in serum complement, antibody formation, and glomerular lesions (778). Germuth also found the cardiovascular and renal lesions following intravenous bovine albumin less extensive after cortisone treatment, although the percentage of affected animals was the same in the treated animals as in the controls. Intravenous administration had no effect on the elimination of antigen or on the appearance of circulating antibodies. The beneficial action of cortisone appeared to be by protection against the damaging effect of antigen-antibody union (383). Cortisone, 10 mg. twice daily, tended to prevent the cardiac and vascular lesions and diminish the intensity of the lesions of glomerulonephritis induced by bovine globulin and Freund's adjuvant, but the alteration was not found to be statistically singificant (789). Anaphylactic uveitis induced by horse serum in the eye was modified by hydrocortisone injected subconjunctivally (1178).

3. Guinea Pig. Anaphylactic Shock

This species would appear to be much more resistant to the action of adrenal steroids. Sensitization to various proteins such as sheep serum, horse serum, anti-human rabbit serum, and egg white has been used. Neither ACTH (354, 682) nor cortisone in daily doses up to 34 mg. (232, 274, 470, 664) was shown to prevent mortality from anaphylactic shock in such animals. Similarly, no effect was noted against passive anaphylaxis (386, 416). Others, however, have noted partial protection by cortisone (191), and apparently the intensity of the shock reaction can be reduced especially when treatment is given during active immunization (386, 1164)'

4. Rat

The sensitization of rats by γ-globulin and nephrotoxic sera was modified by cortisone (699).

5. Mouse

Nelson, Fox, and Freeman found in mice sensitized with horse serum that 28 of 34 controls died. Of those treated, with 0.75 mg. to 3 mg. of cortisone, 18 hours before the challenging dose, the mortality observed was only 4 of 42 (78% of the survivors died 11 days later on a rechallenging dose). The complete protection from 3 mg. of cortisone occurred as early as 6 hours after injection and lasted 48 hours. At 92 hours only about half of the animals were protected (812, 813).

6. Man—Untoward Reactions

Untoward sensitivity reactions in human beings to ACTH and cortisone were found to occur in about 8% of cases (226).

a. Allergic Rhinitis. Patients have been treated by the submucosal injection of 2 to 5 mg. of cortisone under the inferior turbinates.   A favorable response was obtained in 80% of cases.   The injection of 25 mg. by this route in two patients led to an unusual and rapid constitutional reaction consisting of flushing of the skin over the body, substernal pain, dyspnea, and fall in blood pressure (1184).

b. Hay fever and Asthma.   A number of conflicting clinical reports have been published on the effects of cortisone on pollen sensitivity.   In extensive tests on patients with ragweed sensitivity, it was found that large doses of cortisone were of value for brief periods only (1103).   A discussion of the beneficial effects reported for cortisone in the treatment of asthma has been omitted from this chapter.

C. ANTIGEN-ANTIBODY REACTIONS

1. *Human Beings*

No effect of ACTH or cortisone, when administered in clinical doses, was found on antibody production to pneumococcal-capsule polysaccharides.   A drop in γ-globulin was noted in 6 of the 12 cases on cortisone, even though the antibody titer was rising (776).   Schick-negative patients receiving ACTH or cortisone were given diphtheria toxoid.   No change was found in the expected amount of circulating antitoxin.   Similarly, no effect of cortisone was noted when it was administered when the antitoxin titer was declining.   (ACTH, however, reduced the antibody titer when treatment was started at this time) (477).   Similar negative effects were noted in patients suffering from acute hepatitis (280).

2. *Arthus' Reaction*

a. Rabbits.   Cortisone, 10 mg. daily, was found to inhibit the sensitization of rabbits to egg albumin, owing to the suppression of antibody formation (384, 387).   A dose of 4 mg. twice daily completely depressed the skin reaction.   DCA also showed some effect (990).   The reaction may be present but was less intense after 10 mg. twice daily of cortisone (789).   Others have reported little effect (470).   ACTH has been found to be less effective than cortisone (384).

The passive phenomena in rabbits produced by intracutaneous antibody and antigen were not found to be affected by cortisone (384).   However, a dose of ½ to 2 mg. per kilogram modified the lesion and prevented edema at the site of the passive Arthus' reaction (548).

b. Guinea Pigs.   Cortisone, 5 mg. per kilogram daily, did not abolish the reaction in guinea pigs, but a diminished intensity was noted (424).   The effects of cortisone are apparently not so pronounced in this species as in the rabbit (386)

3. Antibody Formation

The action of cortisone or ACTH given to experimental animals during immunization would appear to result in low levels of circulating antibodies. Once immunization is established, such treatment may cause a diminished antibody level. It would seem, however, that antibody synthesis is primarily affected (88, 324, 384, 1110).

a. Rabbits. Antibody formation to a variety of antigens was found to be diminished by ACTH or cortisone treatment (187, 323, 723). Circulating antibodies were reduced when cortisone was given at the start or after immunization was well advanced (88, 326). The relationship of the suppression of antibody formation to the negative nitrogen balance and synthesis of antibody has been discussed (88). After sensitization with ovalbumin the antibodies were higher in cortisone-treated animals than in controls during the first 48 hours, but thereafter they were lower than in controls (461). Dews and Code showed that in both intact and adrenalectomized animals circulating antibodies in response to daily intracutaneous injections of antigen were greatly lowered by cortisone treatment (233). In rabbits showing enhanced mortality and severity of infection from streptococcal-induced infection following cortisone treatment, it was noted that this action could be counteracted by immunization with live streptococci, the time of appearance and titer of antistreptolysin-O being unaffected by cortisone (777).

b. Response to Antigen Mixtures. Some interesting observations have been reported by Hanan and Overman (464, 842) on the effects of cortisone in rabbits when immunization is attempted by the simultaneous administration of two antigens. When bovine albumin and mumps vaccine were used, cortisone, 4 mg. daily, suppressed the formation of antibody to the albumin, but not to the mumps vaccine (842). Similarly, when bovine albumin and sheep red cells or stroma were given together, again the antibody formation to albumin was suppressed, but hemolysin or agglutinin was produced in normal amounts (464). Other experiments indicate that the antibody response to an antigen of small particle size is inhibited relatively more by cortisone than is the antibody response to an antigen of larger size. This finding probably explains the above observations (465).

4. Passive Immunization

In the rabbit antipneumococcus globulin concentrations were unaffected by cortisone, 10 mg. daily. The rate of disappearance of antibodies was unaffected (325). Cortisone treatment was not found to interfere with anti-gonadotrophic hormone effectiveness in the rat (505).

a. Hemolysin. The concentrations of hemolysins, as shown by Dews and Code, in response to injected rabbit red blood cells were slightly re-

duced by cortisone in normal or adrenalectomized rats but were not changed
in normal guinea pigs (233).   In the mouse the effects are more clear-cut
and may serve as a method of assessing the activity of various adrenal
steroids (817).

b. Rh Erythroblastosis.   In an early report cortisone was administered
for long periods to two immunized Rh-negative pregnant women to block
anti-Rh agglutinin.   No effect, however, was noted, and such treatment
did not prevent the hemolytic syndrome in the infants.   The hormone
was well tolerated during pregnancy with no untoward effects (242).
Others, however, have subsequently found cortisone to be of value as both
a prophylactic (70 patients) and therapeutic agent (12 patients) (553).
Such treatment resulted in fewer than the expected number of erythro-
blastotic infants (1012).

D. Tissue and Organ Grafts

1. *Corneal Grafts*

In rabbits, cortisone decreased the duration and severity of ocular reactions, including vascularization, and allowed an increased percentage of
clear corneal grafts (738, 834).

2. *Skin*

In rabbits, the life of skin homografts was found to be at least doubled
by cortisone treatment (86, 657).   This has been confirmed in rabbits
(793), guinea pigs (1069), and chicks (130).   In guinea pigs, young pigs, and
human beings, cortisone and ACTH treatment did not interfere with successful autotransplantation of skin, but guinea pigs were more resistant to
the effect of the steroids (1069).   No prolongation of survival of homologous skin grafts was noted (1193).

3. *Bone*

In a study in dogs, using homogenous bone grafts and autogenous fresh
bone grafts, the injection of cortisone (1 mg. per pound), was found to
inhibit early healing of both kinds of grafts; after two to four weeks no
effect was noted (194).

4. *Aorta*

In dogs, cortisone treatment did not exert any beneficial action on homologous aortic grafts.   On the other hand, a decreased fibrous tissue
reaction and inhibited healing of the wound and graft site were noted.
Increased susceptibility to infection was also encountered (57).

5. *Kidney*

Cortisone, 75 to 100 mg. daily, did not increase the survival of functional homogenous kidney transplants in dogs (869).

6. *Adrenal*

Cortisone and ACTH had no effect on the survival of adrenal homo-transplants in dogs (620).

XXIII. Adrenal Steroids and Susceptibility to Infection

A. SPONTANEOUS INFECTION

Following large doses of cortisone over periods of 10 days and longer, animals develop spontaneous infections from various organisms. Selye noted in rats receiving 10 mg. daily of cortisone the development of septicemia and multiple abscesses, particularly of lungs, kidneys, spleen, liver, due to organisms normally present but usually nonpathogenic. He also found that the simultaneous treatment with pituitary STH (2 mg. twice daily) counteracted the onset of infections and the weight loss associated with cortisone injections (998, 1000). Antopol's original observations on the occurrence of spontaneous infections in mice (23) have been confirmed, and such effects have been observed after treatment with 0.75 or 1.25 mg. of cortisone daily for 28 days. It was found that 41 of 167 animals so treated died of bacteremia, from gastrointestinal organisms (*E. coli, Proteus,* and *Pseudomonas*) (79). Antopol also observed that the toxicity of cortisone, 1.25 mg. per day, was associated with positive blood cultures for *Corynebacterium* (23). Spontaneous infections have frequently been reported in other species (384). The development of fulminating pseudotuberculosis in rats given large doses of cortisone, but not after massive doses of ACTH, is of experimental interest because of the frequency of this latent infection in rats used for experimental purposes (684, 685). It has been suggested, from the effects of cortisone on the removal of injected bacteria in the rabbit, that the steroid prevents localization of infection in the tissues (730). Similarly, the phagocytic activity of human leucocytes for pneumococci was markedly depressed following cortisone treatment of patients (189).

B. SPECIFIC INFECTIONS

General reviews by Robinson (925) and others (900, 926) contain additional references to the many papers on this subject. Cortisone has been shown to increase the susceptibility to, or the severity of, many types of infection. In general, it is apparent that ACTH is less effective than is cortisone in producing these adverse actions. Such an effect may occur in human patients and contraindicates the use of cortisone in the presence of infection unless this can be controlled by antibiotics (1151). In severely toxic patients, however, the temporary use of cortisone may improve the response to antibiotics.

1. *Tuberculosis*

a. Mice. Cortisone, $\frac{1}{4}$ to $\frac{1}{2}$ mg. daily, markedly exacerbated the infection, with a resulting high mortality (474), and increased the susceptibility to tubercle strains of low virulence (1055). The beneficial effects of previous vaccination with high-virulence strains of tubercle were nullified by cortisone (1055). Pituitary STH antagonized the sensitizing action of cortisone (686).

b. Guinea Pig. Cortisone injections, 5 mg. daily, were followed by more extensive and less well localized tubercular lesions (1063). In animals examined 14 days after infection, organ involvement was less frequent in the treated animals, and only half as many had developed nodules. However, at 28 days there was no difference from the control animals and no evidence of enhanced spread of the infection (683). Cortisone did not interfere with the beneficial effects of streptomycin when given simultaneously (609). Others have not found deterimental effects of cortisone on tubercle infections in this species of animal (1189).

c. Rats. Cortisone treatment, 5 mg. daily, induced tubercular lesions which were more diffuse and contained fewer inflammatory cells (766). The natural resistance of this species was lowered by cortisone, so that all animals died or developed progressive lesions which contained increased numbers of organisms (685, 766, 932). The exacerbation in infection caused by cortisone diminished the therapeutic effects of streptomycin (193).

d. Rabbits. Cortisone caused a fourfold increase in the number of tubercles in the lungs, but these were smaller than in untreated controls and showed increased caseation. The high susceptibility of a special strain of rabbits was reduced to that of a resistant type by cortisone treatment. Although an increased number of tubercles was found, the actual dissemination of the disease was reduced (717). *Ocular tuberculosis* in the rabbit was not controlled by cortisone or hydrocortisone but was made more severe (1236).

In 1952 the American Trudeau Society reviewed 39 papers on the effects of cortisone on experimental tuberculosis. They concluded that further work was required to clarify the conflicting reports (19). The action of adrenal steroids on experimental tuberculosis has been more recently reviewed (716).

e. Man. The same Society also reviewed the data on 81 human cases of tuberculosis treated with cortisone. Of these 46 showed unfavorable effects from the following causes: (*1*) exacerbation of active or inactive tuberculous infection; (*2*) reduction of the inflammatory response with resulting poor localization and widespread dissemination; (*3*) the frequent development or progression of excavation in pulmonary lesions; (*4*) possible reduction of the signs and symptoms of the disease but with harmful net effects. The conclusion was reached that cortisone was contraindicated in the treatment of tuberculosis (20).

f. Leprosy. The effect of cortisone therapy on leprosy has been reviewed by Lowe (712).

2. *Streptococcus, Staphylococcus, and Pneumococcus*

a. Rats. Pneumonia was induced by the intrabronchial inoculation of streptococci or pneumococci. Cortisone treatment reduced the survival rate after infection. Histologically, the lesions contained more bacteria and showed excessive amounts of relatively acellular edema fluid. Control tests showed that cortisone did not exert any growth stimulation per se on the bacteria, nor did it interfere with phagocytosis once leucocytes had appeared. The effect, however, might have been related to the observed delayed diapedesis of leucocytes (396, 446).

b. Rabbits. Cortisone, 6 mg. per kilogram daily, increased the lethal action of experimental infection with group A streptococci, with the result that 71 of 76 animals showed bacteremia and died; with half this dose of cortisone 6 of 9 animals died. Of 86 infected control animals, 6 showed bacteremia and only 3 died. No difference in the phagocytic activity of leucocytes could be observed in the different groups of animals (777). Cortisone and hydrocortisone were also found to lower resistance to pneumococcal infection, but no effect on the pneumococcus per se was noted (926). Others also noted that pneumococcal infections were exaggerated after cortisone (924).

c. Guinea Pigs. Infections induced by staphylococci were increased by cortisone treatment (643).

d. Mice. Induced streptococcal cervical adenitis infection was more severe following cortisone treatment and was associated with an increased mortality (396).

e. Beneficial Effects of Cortisone. Contrary to most reports, Robinson, Mason, and Smith have recently found an optimal dose of cortisone (2.5 to 3.0 mg. per day) in the intact or adrenalectomized rat, which will enhance survival after experimental infection with *D. pneumoniae*. Smaller or larger doses of cortisone allowed increased mortality (927). Such observations, if applicable to other infections, would alter the present concept of the deleterious actions of O^{11} steroids on infections.

3. *Viruses*

a. Poliomyelitis. Shwartzman found that cortisone, 5 mg. daily, increased the susceptibility of mice and hamsters to poliomyelitis infection (1020). The dose of cortisone was important, since 2 mg. daily was ineffective. DCA, progesterone, and stilbestrol, did not cause this effect (1021, 1023, 1058). Other reports, however, have not shown a similar effect of cortisone on this infection in mice and monkeys (12, 1022).

b. West Nile, Ilheus, Bunyamwera Viruses. Cortisone-treated mice with these infections showed a greatly increased susceptibility. DCA, testosterone, progesterone, estradiol, or adrenalectomy did not alter susceptibility. Cortisone did not affect the virus *in vitro* (1061).

c. Influenza. ACTH was not found to exert any favorable effect on Type A infection in ferrets (547), but showed an unfavorable effect on the course of the disease in mice (708). Cortisone and hydrocortisone had a similar deleterious action (69, 614). The concentration of B virus in chick embryos tissue culture was significantly greater following the addition of cortisone (631, 632).

d. Mumps. An increased concentration of the virus was found in the allantoic fluid of eggs injected with cortisone (also observed with influenza virus) (631).

e. Mouse Pneumonia Virus. Cortisone enhanced the infection and multiplication of the virus but ACTH was less active. Adrenalectomized mice showed a slightly lowered susceptibility and retarded virus growth (1040).

f. Infectious Hepatitis. Cortisone-treated rats, in contrast to controls, were reported to develop hepatitis after inoculation with serum from human infectious hepatitis cases (761).

g. Coxsackie Virus. In a strain of mice in which the virus is normally avirulent, cortisone was shown to enhance pathogenicity (418, 630).

h. Vaccinia. Rabbits with induced keratoconjunctivitis were unfavorably affected by cortisone treatment (633), as were intradermally infected guinea pigs (643).

i. Herpes Virus Keratitis. In rabbits, cortisone has little or no beneficial effect on the experimental disease process and may be harmful in large doses. Vascularization may, however, be reduced (456, 840, 1152).

4. *Other Infections*

a. Brucella. Cortisone treatment has been shown to increase the death rate and cause wider distributions of the lesions, with necrosis of the granuloma, in mice infected with three different strains of *Brucella* (1). The normal mild course of the disease was altered by cortisone into a fulminating fatal illness (2).

b. Trypanosoma cruzi. Experimental infection in normal baby rats was mild and transient. Cortisone-treated animals, however, all died of parasitemia, and the organism increased in virulence (1008).

c. Syphilis. ACTH was found not to alter the course of experimental infection in rabbits, although delayed healing and large ulcers were noted (1016). Cortisone treatment in chickens and rabbits has resulted in the presence of more numerous organisms and in the occurrence of a peculiar degenerative process in the tubular cells and blood vessels (220, 1160).

d. Trichinella spiralis. Guinea pigs were infested experimentally and treated with ACTH. No difference was observed in the reactions of the host or anatomically in the larvae. The hormone therapy, however, reduced the general toxic effects and caused a temporary diminution of circulating eosinophils. The study included three human patients suffering from trichinosis; they responded well to ACTH, with a fall in fever and eosinophils (715).

e. Malaria. The primary and developed infections of primate malaria were studied in monkeys treated with cortisone. At a dose level of 10 mg. per kilogram daily given during a primary attack, a striking intensification of the peripheral blood infection during the postcrisis phase of the disease was noted. Cortisone, 10 to 50 mg. per kilogram, given during the chronic latent stage, was followed by a recrudescence of marked severity, similar to that induced by splenectomy. It was believed that the effects of cortisone might be caused by a reduction in the supply of macrophages rather than by the inhibition of phagocytic action (970). In three human subjects with induced benign tertian malaria ACTH was found to cause higher parasite counts (613).

C. FEVER

The use of cortisone in clinical cases showing a fever is frequently followed by a fall in temperature as well as by a general improvement and sense of well-being. Such changes may be misleading in cases of infection, since the disease agent is unaffected (615). In rabbits, after experimental infections or the injection of bacterial toxins, the associated fever has been found to be reduced by cortisone treatment (264, 612, 901). Small doses of cortisone, however, have been observed to augment the febrile and systemic response (264).

XXIV. Adrenal-Thyroid Relationship

Early interest in the relationship of the thyroid to the adrenal gland has been recorded since the administration of thyroid substance or hyperthyroid states were found to be associated with an increased adrenal size (159, 210, 565, 751, 1185). Conversely, thyroidectomy, myxedema, or the use of antithyroid drugs was followed by a decrease in the adrenal size and histological changes of reduced activity (61, 196, 210, 401, 654, 677, 721, 749, 760, 1249). Thyroid administration was also found to affect the adrenal ascorbic acid content (1116, 1185).

A. MAN

There is considerable clinical evidence that chronic hypothyroidism results in a decreased adrenocortical function and also that adrenal hyperactivity is capable of diminishing the function of the thyroid gland (168).

1. *Myxedema*

Patients on cortisone, 100 to 200 mg. daily, were found to show an increase in basal metabolic rate (B.M.R.), but the I^{131} uptake was unchanged. The B.M.R. had returned to the preinjection level 5 days after cessation of treatment (64). The response to ACTH was similarly inadequate, and the increased B.M.R. after cortisone was believed to be due to a direct calorigenic action (513).

2. *Euthyroidism*

Euthyroid patients showed an increase in B.M.R. after treatment by cortisone, also owing to a direct calorigenic action (1225). With chronic cortisone treatment hypothyroidism may develop owing to decreased pituitary TSH (513, 1225). In normal patients treated with cortisone the B.M.R. was found to vary, but the I^{131} pickup and protein-bound iodine (PBI) were usually depressed (82, 467, 513). Thyroid function may also be depressed by ACTH, hydrocortisone, DCA, and progesterone (535, 1257). Serum cholesterol may increase (346). In Cushing's disease normal thyroid function was found, but this was markedly depressed by exogenous adrenal steroids (513). An increased excretion of I^{131} after cortisone has been noted, but the serum cholesterol levels and B.M.R. were unaffected in these patients (658).

3. *Hyperthyroidism*

In severe thyrotoxic crisis of hyperthyroidism a number of patients were found to respond successfully to ACTH therapy (1130).

4. *Malignant Exopthalmos*

Improvement in nine cases was reported following cortisone therapy (634). In the rat, however, cortisone has been stated to cause exophthalmos (32).

5. *Thyroiditis*

Cortisone, 100 to 200 mg. daily, has been found to cause a prompt and consistent suppression of fever and pain. The effects, however, were symptomatic, since the disease recurred after cessation of treatment (150, 955, 1199).

B. Animals

1. I^{131} Pickup

a. Rat. In normal animals treatment with ACTH or cortisone has been found by many investigators to decrease I^{131} uptake and in some cases to cause a decrease in weight of the thyroid (15, 782, 866, 1049). DCA, 11-dehydrocorticosterone, and other steroids have also been shown to decrease I^{131} pickup (780, 783). Other workers did not find such effects of cortisone in rats when the diet contained 1.2 mg. of iodine per 100 gm. (772). Stress or epinephrine injections also caused a decreased I^{131} uptake and reduced the weight of the thyroid (852, 1051).

b. Adrenalectomized Rat. Such animals, after ACTH treatment, showed a depressed I^{131} uptake, indicating a suppression of pituitary TSH (1049). Epinephrine, on the other hand, was reported to induce an increased uptake; this could be prevented by cortisone (1051). Cortisone was found to diminish the I^{131} uptake of DCA-maintained animals, and also to increase the blood I^{131} and to diminish the urinary and fecal excretion of radioactive iodine (772).

c. Hypophysectomized Rat. In such a preparation the injection of TSH causes an increased I^{131} uptake. On the administration of cortisone this uptake was diminished, indicating a direct antagonistic action on the TSH-thyroid mechanism (851, 1230).

2. Thyroid Cell Height

In hypophysectomized and in normal rats, prolonged cortisone therapy has been found to enhance slightly the effect of TSH on the cell height of the thyroid (457, 458, 512).

a. Tadpole. Cortisone injections did not affect thyroid function as judged by tadpole metamorphosis (661).

3. Protein-Bound Iodine

a. Rat. The blood level of protein-bound iodine (PBI) in the rat was reduced by cortisone injections or after exposure to stress (98). After prolonged cortisone treatment the plasma PBI was found to be increased (458).

b. Thyroidectomized Rat. In such animals, whether maintained on thyroxine or not, cortisone increased the plasma PBI, apparently by decreasing the rate of thyroxine metabolism (98). Stress caused a reduced PBI, owing to an increased disappearance of thyroxine. Cortisone prevented the effects of stress on PBI. It was suggested that cortisone acted by reducing the rate of removal of thyroxine from the plasma (98).

c. Dog. The lowered PBI of the hypophysectomized dog was increased by TSH. The magnitude and duration of such an effect was not changed by cortisone treatment (837).

4. *Antithyroid Drugs*

In the rat, prolonged treatment with thiouracil, propylthiourea, or other antithyroid drugs, is followed by adrenal atrophy. Such glands may have a low ascorbic content but show a normal response to eoxgenous ACTH (367, 1251) or epinephrine injection (367). Adrenal hypertrophy in such animals also followed exogenous ACTH therapy (1251). Thyroidectomy was followed by a less pronounced adrenal atrophy and terminal decrease in ascorbic acid (348). The above evidence indicates that endogenous ACTH is depressed by the excessive production of TSH induced by antithyroid drugs or thyroidectomy, although the ACTH content of rat pituitaries was not found to be significantly changed following thyroidectomy (459). The adrenal cholesterol is apparently increased by thiourea or propylthiouracil treatment, even though the ascorbic acid content is reduced (867, 950). The increase in weight of the thyroid after propylthiourea treatment in the rat was reduced by ACTH, but not by cortisone or DCA (368, 369).

It would seem that all of the complex reactions considered in this section on adrenal-thyroid relationship, can be explained, at least in the rat, by assuming that the following evidence is correct. Pituitary TSH (and therefore any mechanism increasing it) depressed ACTH with resulting adrenal atrophy. Whereas ACTH depresses the secretion, cortisone directly antagonizes the action of TSH. (The latter action may be reciprocal.) Cortisone decreases either the metabolic destruction or removal from the plasma of thyroxine and also exerts a direct calorigenic action on the tissues.

XXV. Adrenal-Gonad Relationship. Lactation

A. CONGENITAL ADRENAL HYPERPLASIA

Considerable clinical interest has been shown in the action of cortisone in cases of adrenal hyperfunction. In cases of congenital hyperplasia the high 17-ketosteroid level of the urine is markedly depressed by cortisone treatment (59, 539, 589, 771, 830, 1209, 1211, 1213). Hydrocortisone acts in a similar fashion (589). ACTH treatment of such cases causes an increased 17-ketosteroid excretion, but little change in urinary corticoids (370, 590, 732). Cases of virilism associated with adrenal cortical malignancy, however, do not usually respond to cortisone by a fall in urinary 17-ketosteroids (589, 771). Others, however, have reported that some decrease may occur and have cautioned against the interpretation of this response for diagnostic purposes (1175). Dehydroisoandrosterone excretion may aid in the differential diagnosis of adrenal hyperfunction (370). Similarly, increased urinary pregnanediol and pregnanetriol, in cases of adrenal hyperplasia, has been reduced by cortisone therapy (100), and urinary estrogens may also be reduced (371, 771). The therapeutic use of cortisone to depress adrenal secretion in nonmalignant cases has been encouraging.

Adrenal tumors in the mouse have been discussed in a review by Woolley (1237), and the adrenal-genital relationship reviewed by Zuckerman (1262).

B. Ovarian Disturbances

The use of cortisone in various ovarian disturbances and its use in cases of sterility have been described (598). ACTH caused a two- to eight-fold increase in urinary output of gonadotropins in eight of nine patients treated (1042). From the studies on adrenalectomized patients, it appears that the adrenals normally produce estrogens (203). In rats, cortisone caused a slight augmentation of the increase in ovarian weight after administration of chorionic gonadotrophin (330). Cortisone alone did not exert any sex hormone or gonadotrophic activity (787). Szego found that the acute stimulation of the uterus by estrogens could be antagonized by cortisone or hydrocortisone but not by DCA. Such action was independent of pituitary function (1128). Others observed a similar action using ovariectomized rats (1132). In castrated male guinea pigs cortisone in small doses exerted a stimulating estrogen-like action on nipple growth. Larger doses, however, inhibited nipple growth (1202). The correlation between ovarian and adrenal cyclic function in guinea pigs has been suggested as related to the estrogen stimulation of the anterior pituitary to release ACTH (1259). In the dog cortisone did not exert androgenic effects, nor did it antagonize the action of testosterone propionate on the prostate (1132). A recent detailed review containing extensive experimental data on the influence of the adrenals on the reproductive system has been published by Moore (787).

C. Maintenance of Lactation

The controversy over the effectiveness of DCA or cortisone, and 11-dehydrocortisone in maintaining lactation in adrenalectomized rats, has been reinvestigated by Cowie. Whereas no agent alone was completely effective, it was found that in the rat cortisone pellets (2 of 11 mg.) and DCA (1 of 50 mg.) allowed complete restoration of lactation (184). The relationship between the adrenal cortex and the mammary gland has been reviewed by Folley (333).

REFERENCES

1. Abernathy, R. *J. Clin. Invest.* **30,** 626 (1951).
2. Abernathy, R., and Spink, W. W. *J. Clin. Invest.* **31,** 947 (1952).

3. Abrams, W. B., and Harris, T. N. *Am. Heart J.* **42,** 876 (1951).
4. Adams, E., and White, A. *Proc. Soc. Exptl. Biol. Med.* **75,** 590 (1950).
5. Adlersberg, D., Schaefer, L. E., and Drachman, S. R. *J. Am. Med. Assoc.* **144,** 909 (1950).
6. Adlersberg, D., Schaefer, L. E., and Drachman, S. R. *J. Clin. Endocrinol.* **11,** 67 (1951).
7. Adlersberg, D., Schaefer, L. E., and Dritch, R. *Proc. Soc. Exptl. Biol. Med* **74,** 877 (1950).
8. Adlersberg, D., Schaefer, L. E., and Dritch, R. *J. Clin. Endocrinol.* **10,** 814 (1950).
9. Adlersberg, D., Drachman, S. R., Schaefer, L. E., and Dritch, R. *J. Clin. Invest.* **30,** 626 (1951).
10. Agosin, M., Christen, R., Badinez, O., Gasic, G., Neghme, A., Pizarro, O., and Jarpa, A. *Proc. Soc. Exptl. Biol. Med.* **80,** 128 (1952).
11. Aikawa, J. K. *Proc. Soc. Exptl. Biol. Med.* **82,** 105 (1953).
12. Ainslie, J. D., Francis, T., and Brown, G. C. *J. Lab. Clin. Med.* **38,** 344 (1951).
13. Aird, R. B., and Gordan, G. S. *J. Am. Med. Assoc.* **145,** 715 (1951).
14. Albaum, H. G., Hirshfeld, A. I., Tonhazy, N. E., and Umbreit, W. W. *Proc. Soc. Exptl. Biol. Med.* **76,** 546 (1951).
15. Albert, A., Tenney, A., and Ford, E. *Endocrinology* **50,** 324 (1952).
16. Alrich, E. M., Carter, J. P., and Lehman, E. P. *Ann. Surg.* **133,** 783 (1951).
17. Alrich, E. M., Carter, J. P., and Lehman, E. P. *Surgery* **32,** 326 (1952).
18. Alpert, M. *Endocrinology* **46,** 166 (1950).
19. American Trudeau Society Committee on Medical Research, *Am. Rev. Tuberc.* **66,** 257 (1952).
20. American Trudeau Society Committee on Therapy, *Am. Rev. Tuberc.* **66,** 254 (1952).
21. Anderson, G. E., Wiesel, L. L., Hillman, R. W., and Stumpe, W. M. *Proc. Soc. Exptl. Biol. Med.* **76,** 825 (1951).
22. Andreae, W. A., and Browne, J. S. L. *Can. Med. Assoc. J.* **55,** 423 (1946).
23. Antopol, W. *Proc. Soc. Exptl. Biol. Med.* **73,** 262 (1950).
24. Appel, S. B., and Orr, K. D. *U. S. Armed Forces Med. J.* **3,** 207 (1952).
25. Aronson, S. M., Teodoru, C. V., Adler, M., and Shwartzman, G. *Proc. Soc Exptl. Biol. Med.* **85,** 214 (1954).
26. Asboe-Hansen, G. *Ann. Rheumatic Diseases* **9,** 149 (1950).
27. Asboe-Hansen, G. *Scand. J. Clin. & Lab. Invest.* **2,** 271 (1950).
28. Asboe-Hansen, G. *Acta Endocrinol.* **9,** 29 (1952).
29. Asboe-Hansen, G. *Proc. Soc. Exptl. Biol. Med.* **80,** 677 (1952).
29a. Asboe-Hansen, G. *Cancer Research.* **14,** 94 (1954).
30. Ashton, N., and Cook, C. *Brit. J. Ophthalmol.* **35,** 708 (1951).
31. Aterman, K. *Lancet* ii, 517 (1950).
32. Aterman, K., and Greenberg, S. M. *Endocrinology* **52,** 510 (1953).
33. Awapara, J., Marvin, H. N., and Wells, B. B. *Endocrinology* **44,** 378 (1949).
34. Bacchus, H. *Proc. Soc. Exptl. Biol. Med.* **77,** 167 (1951).
35. Bacchus, H. *Endocrinology* **49,** 789 (1951).
36. Bacchus, H. *Endocrinology* **51,** 576 (1952).
37. Bacchus, H., and Altszuler, N. *Endocrinology* **51,** 1 (1952).
38. Bacchus, H., and Toompas, C. A. *Science* **113,** 269, 367 (1951).
39. Bacchus, H., Altszuler, N., and Heiffer, M. H. *Proc. Soc. Exptl. Biol. Med.* **80,** 88 (1952).

786   R. L. NOBLE

40. Bacchus, H., Heiffer, M. H., and Altszuler, N. *Proc. Soc. Exptl. Biol. Med.* **79,** 648 (1952).

41. Badenoch, J. *Brit. Med. J.* **i,** 356 (1952).

42. Bagnall, A. W. *Can. Med. Assoc. J.* **65,** 125 (1951).

43. Baker, B. L. *Ann. N. Y. Acad. Sci.* **53,** 690 (1951).

44. Baker, B. L. *Ann. N. Y. Acad. Sci.* **56,** 684 (1953).

45. Baker, B. L., and Schairer, M. A. *Proc. Soc. Exptl. Biol. Med.* **82,** 235 (1953).

46. Baker, B. L., and Whitaker, W. L. *Am. J. Physiol.* **159,** 118 (1949).

47. Baker, B. L., and Whitaker, W. L. *Endocrinology* **46,** 544 (1950).

48. Baker, B. L., Ingle, D. J., Li, C. H., and Evans, H. M. *Anat. Record* **102,** 313 (1948).

49. Baldridge, G. D., Kligman, A. M., Lipnik, M. J., and Pillsbury, D. M. *Arch. Pathol.* **51,** 593 (1951).

50. Balmain, J. H., and Folley, S. J. *Arch. Biochem.* **39,** 188 (1952).

51. Balmain, J. H., Folley, S. J., and Glascock, R. F. *Nature* **169,** 447 (1952).

52. Banerjee, S., and Deb, C. *J. Biol. Chem.* **190,** 177 (1951).

53. Banerjee, S., and Deb, C. *Endocrinology* **51,** 572 (1952).

54. Banerjee, S., and Deb, C. *J. Biol. Chem.* **194,** 575 (1952).

55. Bangham, A. D. *Brit. J. Exptl. Pathol.* **32,** 77 (1951).

56. Barber, A., and Nothacker, W. G. *Arch. Pathol.* **54,** 334 (1952).

57. Barberio, J. R., Pate, J. W., Sawyer, P. N., and Hufnagel, C. A. *Surgery* **33,** 827 (1953).

58. Barton, A. D. *Federation Proc.* **10,** 160 (1951).

59. Bartter, F. C., Albright, F., Forbes, A. P., Leaf, A., Dempsey, E., and Carroll, E. *J. Clin. Invest.* **30,** 237 (1951).

60. Baschiere, L., and Rossi, A. *Folia Endocrinol.* **3,** 57 (1950).

60a. Baserga, R., and Shubik, P. *Cancer Research* **14,** 12 (1954).

61. Baumann, E. J., and Marine, D. *Endocrinology* **36,** 400 (1945).

62. Beck, L. V. *Cancer Research* **11,** 235 (1951).

63. Beck, L. V., and Voloshin, T. *Am. J. Physiol.* **163,** 696 (1950).

64. Beierwaltes, W. H., Wolfson, W. Q., Jones, J. R., Knorpp, C. T. and Siemienski, J. S. *J. Lab. Clin. Med.* **36,** 799 (1950).

65. Bell, G. I., Bell, R. E., and Wilson, D. R. *Can. Med. Assoc. J.* **63,** 63 (1950).

66. Benditt, E. P. Schiller, S., Wong, H., and Dorfman, A. *Proc. Soc. Exptl. Biol. Med.* **75,** 782 (1950).

67. Benedict, W. H., and Hollenhorst, R. W. *Am. J. Ophthalmol.* **36,** 247 (1953).

68. Benedict, J. D., Forsham, P. H., Roche, M., Soloway, S., and Stetten, D., Jr. *J. Clin. Invest.* **29,** 1104 (1950).

69. Benjamin, F. B., Cornbleet, T., and Grossman, M. I. *J. Invest. Dermatol.* **19,** 109 (1952).

70. Bennett, H. S. *Proc. Soc. Exptl. Biol. Med.* **42,** 786 (1939).

71. Bennett, H. S. *Am. J. Anat.* **67,** 151 (1940).

72. Bennett, L. L., Garcia, J. F., and Li, C. H. *Proc. Soc. Exptl. Biol. Med.* **69,** 52 (1948).

73. Bennett, L. L., Liddle, G. W., and Bentinck, R. C. *J. Clin. Endocrinol. and Metabolism* **13,** 392 (1953).

74. Bennett, L. L., Slessor, A., and Thorn, G. W. *J. Clin. Endocrinol. and Metabolism* **9,** 675 (1949).

75. Bennett, L. L., Kreiss, R. E., Li, C. H., and Evans, H. M. *Am. J. Physiol.* **152,** 210 (1948).

76. Bennett, W. A. *Am. J. Pathol.* **27,** 704 (1951).
77. Bennett, W. A., and Kilby, R. A. *Am. J. Pathol.* **29,** 586 (1953).
78. Bentinck, R. C., Gordan, G. S., Adams, J. E., Arnstein, L. H., and Leake, T. B. *J. Clin. Invest.* **30,** 200 (1951).
79. Berlin, B. S., Johnson, C., Hawk, W. D., and Lawrence, A. G. *J. Lab. Clin. Med.* **40,** 82 (1952).
80. Bernstein, D. E. *Proc. Soc. Exptl. Biol. Med.* **73,** 175 (1950).
81. Bernstein, D. E. *Proc. Soc. Exptl. Biol. Med.* **75,** 847 (1950).
82. Berson, S. A., and Yalow, R. S. *J. Clin. Endocrinol. and Metabolism* **12,** 407 (1952).
83. Best, W. R., and Samter, M. *Blood* **6,** 61 (1951).
84. Best, W. R., Muehrcke, R. C., and Kark, R. H. *J. Clin. Invest.* **31,** 733 (1952).
85. Bibile, S. W. *J. Endocrinol.* **9,** 357 (1953).
85a. Bien, E. J., and Ziff, M. *Proc. Soc. Exptl. Biol. Med.* **78,** 327 (1951).
86. Billingham, R. E., Krohn, P. L., and Medawar, P. B. *Brit. Med. J.* ii, 1049 (1951).
87. Bisso, A. *J. Clin. Endocrinol. and Metabolism* **13,** 1226 (1953).
88. Bjørneboe, M., Fischel, E. E., and Stoerk, H. C. *J. Exptl. Med.* **93,** 37 (1951).
89. Blalock, A., and Levy, S. E. *Ann. Surg.* **106,** 826 (1937).
90. Bloodworth, J. M. B. *Endocrinology* **50,** 174 (1952).
91. Bloom, F. *Proc. Soc. Exptl. Biol. Med.* **79,** 651 (1952).
92. Bloom, B., and Pierce, F. T. *Metabolism, Clin. and Exptl.* **1,** 155 (1952).
93. Blunt, J. W., Plotz, C. M., Lattes, R., Howes, E. L., Meyer, K., and Ragan, C. *Proc. Soc. Exptl. Biol. Med.* **73,** 678 (1950).
94. Boland, E. W., and Headley, N. E. *J. Am. Med. Assoc.* **141,** 301 (1949).
95. Boland, E. W., and Headley, N. E. *J. Am. Med. Assoc.* **148,** 981 (1952).
96. Bondy, P. K. *Endocrinology* **45,** 605 (1949).
97. Bondy, P. K., Engel, F. L., and Farrar, B. *Endocrinology* **44,** 476 (1949).
98. Bondy, P. K., and Hagewood, M. A. *Proc. Soc. Exptl. Biol. Med.* **81,** 328 (1952).
99. Bondy, P. K., and Wilhelmi, A. E. *J. Biol. Chem.* **186,** 245 (1950).
100. Bongiovanni, A. M. *Bull. Johns Hopkins Hosp.* **92,** 244 (1953).
101. Bonner, C. D., Fishman, W. H., and Homburger, F. *Geriatrics* **5,** 203 (1950).
102. Booker, W. M., Dent, F. M., Hays, R. L., Harris, W., and Green, S. *Proc. Soc. Exptl. Biol. Med.* **78,** 170 (1951).
103. Bookman, J. J., Drachman, S. R., Schaefer, L. E., and Adlersberg, D. *Diabetes* **2,** 100 (1953).
104. Borden, A. L., Brodie, E. C., Wallraff, E. B., Holbrook, W. P., Hill, D. F., Stephens, C. A. L., Johnson, R. B., and Kemmerer, A. R. *J. Clin. Invest.* **37,** 375 (1952).
105. Boss, W. R., Birnie, J. H., and Gaunt, R. *Endocrinology* **46,** 307 (1950).
106. Boss, W. R., Osborn, C. M., and Renzi, A. A. *Endocrinology* **51,** 66 (1952).
107. Bourne, G. H. *J. Anat.* **83,** 70 (1949).
108. Bowers, J. Z., Nelson, D. H., Bay, R., and Samuels, L. T. *J. Clin. Endocrinol. and Metabolism* **12,** 921 (1952).
109. Braun-Menandez, E., and Covian, M. R. *Rev. soc. argentina biol.* **24,** 31 (1948).
110. Bristol, W. R., and Drill, V. A. *Endocrinology* **50,** 677 (1952).
111. Brodie, E. C., Wallraff, E. B., Borden, A. L., Holbrook, W. P., Stephens, C. A. L., Hill, D. F., Kent, L. J., and Kemmerer, A. R. *Proc. Soc. Exptl. Biol. Med.* **75,** 285 (1950).

112. Brody, S. *Psychosom. Med.* **14,** 94 (1952).
113. Broh-Kahn, R. H., and Mirsky, I. A. *Science* **106,** 148 (1947).
114. Brown, J. H. U. *Federation Proc.* **12,** 21 (1953).
115. Brown, H., Hargreaves, H. P., and Tyler, F. H. *Arch. Intern. Med.* **89,** 951 (1952).
116. Brownlee, G. *Lancet* **i,** 157 (1950).
117. Buchwald, K. W., Hudson, L., and Bellanca, J. *Endocrinology* **47,** 228 (1950).
118. Bullough, W. S. *J. Endocrinol.* **8,** 264 (1952).
119. Burchenal, J. H., Stock, C. C., and Rhoads, C. P. *Cancer Research* **10,** 209 (1950).
120. Burchenal, J. H., Webber, L. F., and Johnston, S. F. *Proc. Soc. Exptl. Biol. Med.* **78,** 352 (1951).
121. Burkell, C. C. *J. Can. Assoc. Radiologists* **3,** 30 (1952).
122. Bush, I. E. *J. Physiol.* **115,** 12 (1951).
123. Bush, I. E. *J. Endocrinol.* **9,** 95 (1953).
124. Butcher, E. O. *Endocrinology* **43,** 30 (1948).
125. Butler, L. C., and Morgan, A. F. *Proc. Soc. Exptl. Biol. Med.* **83,** 655 (1953).
126. Cagan, R. N., Gray, J. L., and Jensen, H. *J. Biol. Chem.* **183,** 11 (1950).
127. Cagan, R. N., Klein, R. L., and Loewe, L. *J. Clin. Endocrinol. and Metabolism* **13,** 429 (1952).
128. Cameron, A. T., and Carmichael, J. *Can. J. Research* **24,** 37 (1946).
129. Cameron, G. R. *In* J. M. Yoffey, The Suprarenal Cortex. Academic Press, New York, 1953, p. 155.
130. Cannon, J. A., and Longmire, W. P. *Ann. Surg.* **135,** 60 (1952).
131. Cape, R. D. T., Thomas, J. W., and Palmer, R. A. *Can. Med. Assoc. J.* **66,** 441 (1952).
132. Carroll, K. K. *Endocrinology* **48,** 101 (1951).
133. Carroll, K. K. *J. Biol. Chem.* **200,** 287 (1953).
134. Carroll, K. K., and Noble, R. L. *Endocrinology* **51,** 476 (1952).
135. Carroll, K. K., McAlpine, H. T., and Noble, R. L. *Can. Med. Assoc. J.* **65,** 363 (1951).
136. Carryer, H. M., and Code, C. F. *J. Allergy* **21,** 258, 310 (1950).
137. Castor, C. W., and Baker, B. L. *Endocrinology* **47,** 234 (1950).
138. Castor, C. W., Baker, B. L., Ingle, D. J., and Li, C. H. *Proc. Soc. Exptl. Biol. Med.* **76,** 353 (1951).
139. Cavallero, C., and Braccun, C. *Proc. Soc. Exptl. Biol. Med.* **78,** 141 (1951).
140. Cavallero, C., and Sala, G. *Lancet* **i,** 175 (1951).
141. Cavallero, C., Di Marco, A., Fuoco, L., and Sala, G. *Proc. Soc. Exptl. Biol. Med.* **81,** 619 (1952).
142. Chalmers, T. M., and Lewis, A. A. G. *Lancet* **ii,** 1158 (1951).
143. Chapman, D. W., Skaggs, R. H., Thomas, J. R., and Greene, J. A. *Am. J. Med. Sci.* **223,** 41 (1952).
144. Chase, H. B. *Physiol. Revs.* **34,** 113 (1954).
145. Chen, G., and Wickel, A. *Endocrinology* **51,** 21 (1952).
146. Cheng, C. P., and Sayers, G. *Endocrinology* **44,** 400 (1949).
147. Chesterman, F. C. *Lancet* **i,** 1253 (1953).
148. Chiu, C. Y. *Biochem.* **46,** 120 (1950).
149. Chiu, C. Y., and Needham, D. M. *Biochem. J.* **46,** 114 (1950).
150. Clark, D. E., Nelson, T. S., and Raiman, R. J. *J. Am. Med. Assoc.* **151,** 551 (1953).

151. Clark, I. *Federation Proc.* **9**, 161ᵃ(1950).
152. Clark, I. *J. Biol. Chem.* **200**, 69 (1952).
153. Clark, L. D., Quarton, G. C., Cobb, S., and Bauer, W. *New Engl. J. Med.* **249**, 178 (1953).
154. Clayton, B. E., and Prunty, F. T. G. *Brit. Med. J.* **ii**, 927 (1951).
155. Clayton, B. E., and Prunty, F. T. G. *J. Endocrinol.* **9**, 370 (1953).
156. Cleghorn, R. A. *J. Clin. Endocrinol. and Metabolism* **13**, 1291 (1953).
157. Cleghorn, R. A., Fowler, J. L. A., Greenwood, W. F., and Clarke, A. P. W. *Am. J. Physiol.* **161**, 21 (1950).
158. Cochrane, G. C., Jahn, J. P., Foreman, N., and Kinsell, L. W. *J. Clin. Endocrinol. and Metabolism* **13**, 993 (1953).
159. Cohen, R. S. *Am. J. Anat.* **56**, 143 (1935).
160. Cohn, C., Katz, B., Huddlestun, B., Kolinsky, M., and Levine, R. *Am. J. Physiol.* **170**, 87 (1952).
161. Cole, D. F. *J. Endocrinol.* **6**, 245 (1950).
162. Cole, D. F. *J. Endocrinol.* **6**, 251 (1950).
163. Cole, D. F. *Acta. Endocrinol.* **14**, 245 (1953).
164. Cole, J. W., and Holden, W. D. *Proc. Soc. Exptl. Biol. Med.* **77**, 363 (1951).
165. Cole, J. W., Orbison, J. L., Holden, W. D., Hancock, T. J., and Lindsay, J. F. *Surg. Gynecol. Obstet.* **93**, 321 (1951).
166. Collins, D. A., and Wood, E. H. *Am. J. Physiol.* **123**, 224 (1938).
167. Conn, J. W. *Arch. Intern. Med.* **83**, 416 (1949).
168. Conn, J. W., and Fajans, S. S. *Ann. Rev. Physiol.* **14**, 453 (1952).
169. Conn, J. W., and Louis, L. H. *J. Clin. Endocrinol. and Metabolism* **10**, 12 (1950).
170. Conn, J. W., Fajans, S. S., Louis, L. H., and Johnson, B. *J. Lab. Clin. Med.* **36**, 813 (1950).
171. Conn, J. W., Johnston, M. W., and Louis, L. H. *J. Clin. Invest.* **25**, 912 (1946).
172. Conn, J. W., Louis, L. H., and Fajans, S. S. *Science* **113**, 713 (1951).
173. Conn, J. W., Louis, L. H., and Johnston, M. W. *Science* **109**, 279 (1949).
174. Conn, J. W., Louis, L. H., and Johnston, M. W. *J. Lab. Clin. Med.* **34**, 255 (1949).
175. Conn, J. W., Louis, L. H. and Johnston, M. W. *J. Clin. Invest.* **28**, 775 (1949).
176. Conn, J. W., Louis, L. H., and Wheeler, C. E. *J. Lab. Clin. Med.* **33**, 651 (1948).
177. Conn, J. W., Louis, L. H., Fajans, S. S., Johnson, B. J., Barott, G. W., Hogg, L. W., Blood, J. P., and Weiss, M. *J. Lab. Clin. Med.* **38**, 799 (1951).
178. Cook, C., and MacDonald, R. K. *Brit. J. Ophthalmol.* **35**, 730 (1951).
179. Cook, D. L., Ray, R., Davisson, E., Feldstein, L. M., Calvin, L. D., and Green, D. M. *J. Exptl. Med.* **96**, 27 (1952).
180. Cosgniff, S. W., Diefenbach, A. F., and Vogt, W., Jr. *Am. J. Med.* **9**, 752 (1950).
181. Coste, F., Delbarre, F., and Bassett, G. *Rev. rhumat.* **19**, 327 (1952).
182. Coste, F., Piquet, B., Gomiche, P., and Cayala, J. *Ann. méd.* **52**, 747 (1951).
183. Courrier, R., and Collonge, A. *J. Am. Med. Assoc.* **146**, 493 (1951).
184. Cowie, A. T. *Endocrinology* **51**, 217 (1952).
185. Cowie, A. T., and Stewart, J. *J. Endocrinol.* **6**, 197 (1949).
186. Crabb, E. D., and Kelsall, M. A. *J. Natl. Cancer Inst.* **12**, 91 (1951).
187. Craig, J. M. *Am. J. Pathol.* **28**, 629 (1952).
188. Crandon, J. H., Lund, C. C., and Dill, D. B. *New Engl. J. Med.* **223**, 353 (1940).

189. Crepea, S. B., Magnin, G. E., and Seastone, C. V. *Proc. Exptl. Biol. Med.* **77,** 704 (1951).
190. Cronkite, E. P., and Chapman, W. H. *Proc. Soc. Exptl. Biol. Med.* **74,** 337 (1950).
191. Cummings, M. M., and Hudgins, P. C. *Diseases of the Chest* **22,** 289 (1952).
192. Cummings, M. M., and Hudgins, P. C. *J. Immunol.* **69,** 331 (1952).
193. Cummings, M. M., Hudgins, P. C., Wharton, M. C., and Sheldon, W. H. *Am. Rev. Tuberc.* **65,** 596 (1952).
194. Curtiss, P. H., and Wilson, P. D. *Surg. Gynecol. Obstet.* **96,** 155 (1953).
195. Daft, F. S., and Sebrell, W. H. *Public Health Repts.* (*U.S.*) **54,** 2247 (1939).
196. Dalton, A. J., Morris, H. P., and Dubnik, C. S. *J. Natl. Cancer Inst.* **5,** 451 (1945).
197. Dameron, J. T. *Proc. Soc. Exptl. Biol. Med.* **73,** 343 (1950).
198. Danford, P. A., and Danford, H. G. *Am. J. Physiol.* **164,** 690 (1951).
199. Danford, H. G., and Danford, P. A. *Am. J. Physiol.* **166,** 524 (1951).
200. D'Angelo, S. A., Gordon, A. S., and Charipper, H. A. *Proc. Soc. Exptl. Biol. Med.* **68,** 527 (1948).
201. Danowski, T. S., Tarail, R., Peters, J. H., Weigand, F. A., Mateer, F. M., and Greenman, L. *Proc. Soc. Exptl. Biol. Med.* **81,** 445 (1952).
202. Danto, J. L., and Maddin, S. *J. Invest. Dermatol.* **18,** 381 (1952).
203. Dao, T. L-Y. *Science* **118,** 21 (1953).
204. Davenport, H. W., and Chavre, V. J. *Endocrinology* **47,** 193 (1950).
205. Davis, A. K., Bass, A. C., and Overman, R. R. *Am. J. Physiol.* **166,** 493 (1951).
206. Davis, J. O., and Howell, D. S. *Endocrinology* **52,** 245 (1953).
207. Davis, M. E., Plotz, E. J., and Plotz, E. *Endocrinology* **52,** 164 (1953).
208. Davis, M. E., and Plotz, E. J. *Endocrinology* **54,** 384 (1954).
209. De Andino, A. M., Rivero-Fontan, J. L., and Paschkis, K. E. *Proc. Soc. Exptl. Biol. Med.* **77,** 700 (1951).
210. Deane, H. W., and Greep, R. O. *Endocrinology* **41,** 243 (1947).
211. Deane, H. W., and McKibbin, J. M. *Endocrinology* **38,** 385 (1946).
212. Deane, H. W., and Seligman, A. M. *Vitamins and Hormones* **11,** 173 (1953).
213. DeBodo, R. C., and Sinkoff, M. W. *Recent Progr. Hormone Research* **8,** 511 (1953).
214. DeBodo, R. C., Kurtz, M., Sinkoff, M. W., and Kiang, S. P. *Proc. Soc. Exptl. Biol. Med.* **80,** 345 (1952).
215. DeBodo, R. C., Sinkoff, M. W., and Kiang, S. P. *Proc. Soc. Exptl. Biol. Med.* **80,** 350 (1952).
216. DeBodo, R. C., Sinkoff, M. W., Kiang, S. P., and Den, H. *Proc. Soc. Exptl. Biol. Med.* **81,** 425 (1952).
217. Debre, R., Mozziconacci, P., and Nekhorocheff, I. *Presse méd.* **60,** 502 (1952).
218. DeCosta, E. J., and Abelman, M. A. *Am. J. Obstet. Gynecol.* **64,** 746 (1952).
219. DeCosta, E. J., and Abelman, M. A. *Obstet. and Gynecol.* **1,** 269 (1953).
220. DeLamater, E. D., Saurino, V. R., and Urbach, F. *Am. J. Syphilis, Gonorrhea, Venereal Diseases* **36,** 127 (1952).
221. Demartini, F., Grokoest, A. W., and Ragan, C. *J. Am. Med. Assoc.* **149,** 750 (1952).
222. Deming, Q. B., and Luetscher, J. A., Jr. *Proc. Soc. Exptl. Biol. Med.* **73,** 171 (1950).
223. DeMowbray, R. R., and Bishop, P. M. F. *Brit. Med. J.* **i,** 17 (1953).
224. DeMoor, P. *Ann. Endocrinol.* **12,** 1073 (1952).

225. Dempsey, E. W., Greep, R. O., and Deane, H. W. *Endocrinology* **44**, 88 (1949).
226. Derbes, V. J., and Weiss, T. *Quart. Rev. Allergy and Appl. Immunol.* **5**, 153 (1951).
227. Derbes, V. J., Dent, J. H., Weaver, N. K., and Vaughn, D. D. *Proc. Soc. Exptl. Biol. Med.* **75**, 423 (1950).
228. Dervinis, A., Seifter, J., and Ehrich, W. E. *Federation Proc.* **11**, 338 (1952).
229. Desaulles, P., Tripod, J., and Schuler, W. *Schweiz. med. Wochschr.* **83**, 1088 (1953).
230. Devitt, J. E., Pirozynski, W. J., and Samuels, P. B. *Proc. Soc. Exptl. Biol. Med.* **83**, 335 (1953).
231. DeVries, J. A. *J. Immunol.* **65**, 1 (1950).
232. Dews, P. B., and Code, C. F. *Proc. Soc. Exptl. Biol. Med.* **77**, 141 (1951).
233. Dews, P. B., and Code, C. F. *J. Immunol.* **70**, 199 (1953).
234. Dhyse, F. G., Fisher, G. R., Tullner, W. W., and Hertz, R. *Endocrinology* **53**, 447 (1953).
235. Diamond, M. C. *Am. J. Physiol.* **171**, 719 (1952).
236. Dickel, H. *Münch. med. Wochschr.* **93**, 1 (1951).
237. Diczfalusy, E., and Westman, A. *Lancet* **ii**, 541 (1950).
238. Dillaha, C. J., and Rothman, S. *J. Invest. Dermatol.* **18**, 5 (1952).
239. Dillaha, C. J., and Rothman, S. *Am. Practitioner* **3**, 646 (1952).
240. Dillaha, C. J., and Rothman, S. *J. Am. Med. Assoc.* **150**, 546 (1952).
241. Diller, I. C., Beck, L. V., and Blanch, B. *Cancer Research* **8**, 581 (1948).
242. Doerner, A. A., Naegele, C. F., Regan, F. D., Shanaphy, J. F., and Edwards, W. B. *J. Am. Med. Assoc.* **147**, 1099 (1951).
243. Donald, T. C., and Higgins, G. M. *Cancer Research* **11**, 937 (1951).
244. Done, A. K., Ely, R. S., Raile, R. B., and Kelley, V. C. *Proc. Soc. Exptl. Biol. Med.* **81**, 667 (1952).
245. Dorfman, A. *Ann. N. Y. Acad. Sci.* **56**, 698 (1953).
246. Dorfman, A., Apter, N. S., Smull, K., Bergenstal, D. M., and Richter, R. B. *J. Am. Med. Assoc.* **146**, 25 (1941).
247. Dorfman, R. I. *Ann. N. Y. Acad. Sci.* **50**, 556 (1949).
248. Dorfman, R. I. *Proc. Soc. Exptl. Biol. Med.* **70**, 732 (1949).
249. Dorfman, R. I. *Recent. Progr. Hormone Research* **8**, 87 (1953).
250. Dorfman, R. I. *Physiol. Revs.* **34**, 138 (1954).
251. Dorfman, R. I., Potts, A. M., and Feil, M. S. *Endocrinology* **41**, 464 (1947).
252. Dorfman, R. I., Ross, E., and Shipley, R. A. *Endocrinology* **38**, 178 (1946).
253. Dougherty, T. F. *Am. J. Pathol.* **27**, 714 (1951).
254. Dougherty, T. F. *Recent Progr. Hormone Research* **7**, 307 (1952).
255. Dougherty, T. F. *Ann. N. Y. Acad. Sci.* **56**, 748 (1953).
256. Dougherty, T. F., and Kumagai, L. F. *Endocrinology* **48**, 691 (1951).
257. Dougherty, T. F., and Schneebeli, G. L. *Proc. Soc. Exptl. Biol. Med.* **75**, 854 (1950).
258. Dougherty, T. F., and White, A. *Endocrinology* **35**, 1 (1944).
259. Dougherty, T. F., Chase, J. H., and White, A. *Proc. Soc. Exptl. Biol. Med.* **58**, 135 (1945).
260. Doyle, L. P., Andrews, F. M., and Hutchings, L. M. *Proc. Soc. Exptl. Biol. Med.* **74**, 373 (1950).
261. Draper, H. H., and Johnson, B. C. *Proc. Soc. Exptl. Biol. Med.* **82**, 73 (1953).
262. Drury, M. I., Hickey, M. D., and Malone, J. P. *Brit. Med. J.* **ii**, 1487 (1951).

263. Duff, I. F., Robinson, W. D., and Smith, E. M. *J. Lab. Clin. Med.* **38**, 805 (1951).
264. Duffy, B. J., and Morgan, H. R. *Proc. Soc. Exptl. Biol. Med.* **78**, 687 (1951).
265. Dugal, L. P., and Leblanc, J. *Rev. can. biol.* **8**, 440 (1949).
266. Dugal, L. P., and Therien, M. *Endocrinology* **44**, 420 (1949).
267. Dumm, M. E., and Ralli, E. P. *Metabolism, Clin. and Exptl.* **2**, 153 (1953).
268. Dumm, M. E., Gerschberg, H., Beck, E. M., and Ralli, E. P. *Proc. Soc. Exptl. Biol. Med.* **82**, 659 (1953).
269. Durgin, M. L., and Meyer, R. K. *Endocrinology* **48**, 518 (1951).
270. Dury, A. *Am. J. Physiol.* **160**, 75 (1950).
271. Dury, A. *Proc. Soc. Exptl. Biol. Med.* **77**, 199 (1951).
272. Dury, A., and Johnston, T. N. *Proc. Soc. Exptl. Biol. Med.* **78**, 425 (1951).
273. Dury, A., and Moss, L. D. *Proc. Soc. Exptl. Biol. Med.* **80**, 199 (1952).
274. Dworetzky, M., Code, C. F., and Higgins, G. M. *Proc. Soc. Exptl. Biol. Med.* **75**, 201 (1950).
275. Eastcott, H. H. G., Fawcett, J. K., and Rob, C. G. *Lancet* **i**, 1068 (1953).
276. Ebert, R. H. *J. Clin. Invest.* **30**, 636 (1951).
277. Ebert, R. H. *Am. Rev. Tuberc.* **65**, 64 (1952).
278. Ebert, R. H., and Barclay, W. R. *Ann. Internal Med.* **37**, 506 (1952).
279. Edelmann, A. *Federation Proc.* **12**, 37 (1953).
280. Eichman, P. L., Havens, W. P., Jr., and Miller, R. W. *J. Clin. Endocrinol. and Metabolism* **13**, 648 (1953).
281. Eik-Nes, K., Nelson, D. H., and Samuels, L. T. *J. Clin. Endocrinol. and Metabolism* **13**, 1280 (1953).
282. Eischeid, A. M., and Kochakian, C. D. *Proc. Soc. Exptl. Biol. Med.* **85**, 339 (1954).
283. Eisen, H. N., Mayer, M. M., Moore, D. H., Tarr, R., and Stoerk, H. C. *Proc. Soc. Exptl. Biol. Med.* **65**, 301 (1947).
284. Eisenberg, E., Gordan, G. S., Elliott, H. W., and Talbot, J. *Proc. Soc. Exptl. Biol. Med.* **73**, 140 (1950).
285. Eisenstein, A. B., and Boniface, J. *Federation Proc.* **11**, 207 (1952).
286. Eisenstein, A. B., and Shank, R. E. *Proc. Soc. Exptl. Biol. Med.* **78**, 619 (1951).
287. Eliel, L. P., and Pearson, O. H. *N. Y. State J. Med.* **51**, 1839 (1951).
288. Eliel, L. P., Pearson, O. H., Katz, B., and Kraintz, F. W. *Federation Proc.* **9**, 168 (1950).
289. Ellinger, F. *Proc. Soc. Exptl. Biol. Med.* **64**, 31 (1947).
290. Ellinger, F. *Proc. Soc. Exptl. Biol. Med.* **80**, 215 (1952).
291. Ellinger, F. *Proc. Soc. Exptl. Biol. Med.* **80**, 214 (1952).
292. Elliott, K. A. C., and Yrarrazaval, S. *Nature* **169**, 416 (1952).
293. Elmadjian, F., and Pincus, G. *J. Clin. Endocrinol. and Metabolism* **6**, 286 (1946).
294. Elster, S. K., and Lowry, E. L. *Proc. Soc. Exptl. Biol. Med.* **73**, 49 (1950).
295. Engel, F. L. *Endocrinology* **49**, 127 (1951).
296. Engel, F. L. *Recent Progr. Hormone Research* **6**, 277 (1951).
297. Engel, F. L. *Endocrinology* **49**, 538 (1951).
298. Engel, F. L. *Endocrinology* **50**, 462 (1952).
299. Engel, F. L., and Schwartz, T. B. *Proc. Soc. Exptl. Biol. Med.* **77**, 615 (1951).
300. Engel, F. L., and Scott, J. L., Jr. *Endocrinology* **48**, 56 (1951).
301. Engel, F. L., Schiller, S., and Pentz, E. I. *Endocrinology* **44**, 458 (1949).
302. Engel, G. L., and Margolin, S. *Arch. Internal Med.* **70**, 236 (1942).

303. Engel, G. L., and Romano, J. *Arch. Neurol. Psychiat.* **51,** 378 (1944).
303a. Engelbreth-Holm, J., and Asboe-Hansen, G. *Acta Pathol. Microbiol. Scand.* **32,** 560 (1953).
304. Engstrom, W. W., and Liebman, A. *Am. J. Med.* **15,** 180 (1953).
305. Ershoff, B. H. *Proc. Soc. Exptl. Biol. Med.* **78,** 836 (1951).
306. Ershoff, B. H. *Metabolism, Clin. and Exptl.* **2,** 59 (1953).
307. Essellier, A. F., and Wagner, K. F. *Acta Haematol.* **8,** 63 (1952).
308. Essellier, A. F., Jenneret, P., Kopp, E., and Morandi, L. *Endocrinology* **54,** 477 (1954).
309. Etheridge, E. M., and Hoch-Ligeti, C. *Am. J. Pathol.* **28,** 315 (1952).
310. Evans, V. J. *J. Natl. Cancer Inst.* **14,** 741 (1953).
311. Everall, J., and Fisher, L. *J. Invest. Dermatol.* **19,** 97 (1952).
312. Fahey, J. L. *Proc. Soc. Exptl. Biol. Med.* **77,** 491 (1951).
313. Fajans, S. S., Louis, L. H., and Conn, J. W. *J. Clin. Endocrinol. and Metabolism* **11,** 455 (1951).
314. Falk, M. S., Allende, M. F., and Bennett, J. H. *J. Invest. Dermatol.* **18,** 307 (1952).
315. Farnsworth, E. B. *J. Clin. Endocrinol. and Metabolism* **13,** 1169 (1953).
316. Feldman, J. D. *Endocrinology* **46,** 552 (1950).
317. Feldman, J. D., Rachmilewitz, M., Stein, O., and Stein, Y. *Blood* **8,** 342 (1953).
318. Fienberg, R., and Colpoys, F. L. *Am. J. Pathol.* **27,** 925 (1951).
319. Finch, S. C., Crockett, C. L., Ross, J. F., and Bayles, T. B. *Blood* **6,** 1034 (1951).
320. Findlay, C. W., and Howes, E. L. *New Engl. J. Med.* **246,** 597 (1952).
321. Finerty, J. C., and Panos, T. C. *Proc. Soc. Exptl. Biol. Med.* **76,** 833 (1951).
322. Fingal. E., Olsen, L. J., Harding, E. W., Cockett, A. T., and Goodman, L. S. *J. Pharmacol. Exptl. Therap.* **105,** 37 (1952).
323. Fischel, E. E. *Bull. N. Y. Acad. Med.* **26,** 255 (1950).
324. Fischel, E. E., LeMay, M., and Kabat, E. A. *J. Immunol.* **61,** 89 (1949).
325. Fischel, E. E., Stoerk, H. C., and Bjørneboe, M. *Proc. Soc. Exptl. Biol. Med.* **77,** 111 (1951).
326. Fischel, E. E., Vaughan, J. H., and Photopoulos, C. *Proc. Soc. Exptl. Biol. Med.* **81,** 344 (1952).
327. Flanagan, J. B., Davis, A. K., and Overman, R. R. *Am. J. Physiol.* **160,** 89 (1950).
328. Fletcher, A. A., Dauphinee, J. A., and Ogryzlo, M. A. *J. Clin. Invest.* **31,** 561 (1952).
329. Flink, E. B., and Thorn, G. W. *J. Clin. Endocrinol. and Metab.* **9,** 660 (1949).
330. Fluhmann, C. F. *Proc. Soc. Exptl. Biol. Med.* **80,** 507 (1952).
331. Foley, E. J. *Proc. Soc. Exptl. Biol. Med.* **80,** 669 (1952).
332. Foley, E. J., and Silverstein, R. *Proc. Soc. Exptl. Biol. Med.* **77,** 713 (1951).
333. Folley, S. J. *In* J. M. Yoffey, The Suprarenal Cortex. Academic Press, New York, 1953, p. 85.
334. Folley, S. J., and Greenbaum, A. L. *Biochem. J.* **60,** 40, 46 (1946).
335. Folley, S. J., and Watson, S. C. *Proc. Soc. Exptl. Biol. Med.* **78,** 473 (1951).
336. Follis, R. H. *Proc. Soc. Exptl. Biol. Med.* **76,** 722 (1951).
337. Follis, R. H. *Proc. Soc. Exptl. Biol. Med.* **78,** 723 (1951).
338. Follis, R. H. *Bull. Johns Hopkins Hosp.* **90,** 337 (1952).

339. Forbes, A. P., Griswold, G. C., and Albright, F. J. *J. Clin. Endocrinol. and Metabolism* **10**, 230 (1950).
340. Forsham, P. H., Thorn, G. W., Prunty, F. T. G., and Hills, A. G. *J. Clin. Endocrinol. and Metabolism* **8**, 15 (1948).
341. Forsham, P. H., Bennett, L. L., Roche, M., Reiss, R. S., Slessor, A., Flink, E. B., and Thorn, G. W. *J. Clin. Endocrinol. and Metabolism* **9**, 660 (1949).
342. Forsyth, B. T. *Endocrinology* **52**, 65 (1953).
343. Fourman, P., Bartter, F. C., Albright, F., Dempsey, E., Carroll, E., and Alexander, J. A. *J. Clin. Invest.* **29**, 1462 (1950).
344. Fraenkel-Conrat, H., Simpson, M. E., and Evans, H. M. *J. Biol. Chem.* **147**, 99 (1943).
345. Frawley, T. F., and Forsham, P. H. *J. Clin. Endocrinol. and Metabolism* **11**, 772 (1951).
346. Fredrickson, D. S., Forsham, P. H., and Thorn, G. W. *J. Clin. Endocrinol. and Metabolism* **12**, 541 (1952).
347. Freed, S. C., Rosenman, R. H., and Friedman, M. *Ann. N. Y. Acad. Sci.* **56**, 637 (1953).
348. Freedman, H. H., and Gordon, A. S. *Proc. Soc. Exptl. Biol. Med.* **75**, 729 (1950).
349. Frenk, S., Wolfe, S., and Paschkis, K. E. *Endocrinology* **47**, 386 (1950).
350. Freyberg, R. H., Traeger, C. T., Adams, C. H., Kuscu, T., Wainerdi, H., and Bonomo, I. *Science* **112**, 429 (1950).
350a. Fried, J., and Sabo, E. F. *J. Am. Chem. Soc.* **76**, 1455 (1954).
350b. Fried, J., Thoma, R. W., Perlman, D., Herz, J. E., and Borman, A. *Recent Progr. Hormone Research* **11**, 149 (1955).
351. Friedberg, F. *Euclides (Madrid)* **10**, 116 (1950).
352. Friedberg, F., and Greenberg, D. M. *Arch. Biochem.* **17**, 193 (1948).
353. Friedgood, C. E., Vars, H. M., and Zerbe, J. W. *Am. J. Physiol.* **163**, 354 (1950).
354. Friedlaender, S., and Friedlaender, A. S. *J. Allergy* **21**, 303 (1950).
355. Friedlander, W. J., and Rottger, E. *J. Electroenceph. and Clin. Neurophysiol.* **3**, 311 (1951).
356. Friedman, M., and Byers, S. O. *Am. J. Physiol.* **163**, 684 (1950).
357. Friedman, S. M., and Friedman, C. L. *Endocrinology* **49**, 318 (1951).
358. Friedman, S. M., Friedman, C. L., and Nakashima, M. *Am. J. Physiol.* **163**, 319 (1950).
359. Friedman, S. M., Friedman, C. L., and Nakashima, M. *Endocrinology* **51**, 401 (1952).
360. Friedman, S. M., Mackenzie, K. R., and Friedman, C. L. *Endocrinology* **43**, 123 (1948).
361. Friedman, S. M., Polley, J. R., and Friedman, C. L. *J. Exptl. Med.* **87**, 329 (1948).
362. Frost, R. C., and Talmage, R. V. *Endocrinology* **49**, 606 (1951).
363. Fruhman, G. J., and Gordon, A. S. *Federation Proc.* **11**, 51 (1952).
364. Fruhman, G. J., and Gordon, A. S. *Proc. Soc. Exptl. Biol. Med.* **82**, 162 (1953).
365. Fuenzalida, F., and Lipschutz, A. *J. Clin. Endocrinol. and Metabolism* **13**, 1201 (1953).
366. Fulton, G. P., and Maynard, F. L. *Proc. Soc. Exptl. Biol. Med.* **84**, 259 (1953).
367. Gabrilove, J. L., and Soffer, L. J. *Endocrinology* **47**, 461 (1950).
368. Gabrilove, J. L., and Soffer, L. J. *J. Clin. Invest.* **29**, 814 (1950).

XIV. PHYSIOLOGY OF THE ADRENAL CORTEX 795

369. Gabrilove, J. L., Dorrance, W. R., and Soffer, L. J. *Am. J. Physiol.* **169**, 565 (1952).
370. Gardner, L. I., and Migeon, C. J. *J. Clin. Endocrinol. and Metabolism* **12**, 1117 (1952).
371. Gastineau, C. F., Logan, G. B., Albert, A., and Mason, H. L. *J. Clin. Endocrinol. and Metabolism* **13**, 724 (1953).
372. Gaudino, N. M. *Rev. soc. argentina biol.* **20**, 470 (1944).
373. Gaudino, N. M., and Levitt, M. F. *J. Clin. Invest.* **28**, 1487 (1949).
374. Gaunt, R. *Recent Progr. Hormone Research* **6**, 247 (1951).
375. Gaunt, R., Birnie, J. H., and Eversole, W. J. *Physiol. Revs.* **29**, 281 (1949).
376. Gaunt, R., Leathem, J. H., Howell, C., and Antonchak, N. *Federation Proc.* **11**, 53 (1952).
377. Gaunt, R., Leathem, J. H., Howell, C., and Antonchak, N. *Endocrinology* **50**, 521 (1952).
378. Gaunt, R., Tuthill, C. H., Antonchak, N., and Leathem, J. H. *Endocrinology* **52**, 407 (1953).
379. Gemzell, C. A., and Samuels, L. T. *Endocrinology* **47**, 48 (1950).
380. Gemzell, C. A., Van Dyke, D. C., Tobias, C. A., and Evans, H. M. *Endocrinology* **49**, 325 (1951).
381. Gemzell, C. A., Birke, G., Hellström, J., Franksson, C. E., and Plantin, L. O. *Acta Endocrinol.* **12**, 1 (1953).
382. Germuth, F. G. *Am. J. Pathol.* **28**, 565 (1952).
383. Germuth, F. G. *J. Exptl. Med.* **98**, 1 (1953).
384. Germuth, F. G., and Ottinger, B. *Proc. Soc. Exptl. Biol. Med.* **74**, 815 (1950).
385. Germuth, F. G., Ottinger, B., and Oyama, J. *Bull. Johns Hopkins Hosp.* **91**, 22 (1952).
386. Germuth, F. G., Ottinger, B. and Oyama, J. *Proc. Soc. Exptl. Biol. Med.* **80**, 188 (1952).
387. Germuth, F. G., Nedzel, G. A., Ottinger, B., and Oyama, J. *Proc. Soc. Exptl. Biol. Med.* **76**, 177 (1951).
388. Giroud, A. *Presse méd.* **48**, 841 (1940).
389. Giroud, A., and Leblond, C. P. *Arch. anat. microscop.* **31**, 111 (1935).
390. Giroud, A., and Ratsimamanga, A. R. *Presse méd.* **48**, 449 (1940).
391. Giroud, A., and Ratsimamanga, A. R. *Paris méd.* **30**, 356 (1940).
392. Giroud, A., and Santa, N. *Compt. rend. soc. biol.* **131**, 1176 (1939).
393. Giroud, A., Santa, N., and Martinet, M. *Compt. rend. soc. biol.* **134**, 23, 100 (1940).
394. Glaser, G. H. *Psychosomat. Med.* **15**, 280 (1953).
395. Glaser, G. H., and Merritt, H. H. *J. Am. Med. Assoc.* **148**, 898 (1952).
396. Glaser, R. J., Berry, J. W., Loeb, L. H., and Wood, W. B. *J. Clin. Invest.* **30**, 640 (1951).
397. Glaser, R. J., Berry, J. W., Loeb, L. H., Wood, W. B., and Hamlin, A. *J. Lab. Clin. Med.* **38**, 363 (1951).
398. Glaubach, S. *J. Mt. Sinai Hosp. N. Y.* **19**, 84 (1952).
399. Glaubach, S., Antopol, W., and Graff, S. *Bull. N. Y. Acad. Med.* **27**, 398 (1951).
400. Glick, D., and Biskind, G. R. *J. Biol. Chem.* **115**, 551 (1936).
401. Glock, G. E. *Nature* **158**, 518 (1945).
402. Godlowski, Z. Z. *Brit. Med. J.* **i**, 46 (1948).
403. Godlowski, Z. Z. *J. Endocrinol.* **8**, 102 (1952).
404. Goldblatt, H. *Ann. Internal Med.* **11**, 69 (1937).

796   R. L. NOBLE

405. Golden, W. R. C., and Long, C. N. H. *Endocrinology* **30,** 675 (1942).
406. Goldman, L., and Richfield, D. F. *J. Am. Med. Assoc.* **147,** 941 (1951).
407. Goldman, L., Preston, R., and Rockwell, E. *J. Invest. Dermatol.* **18,** 89 (1952).
408. Goldman, L., Rockwell, E., and Richfield, D. F. *Am. J. Trop. Med. Hyg.* **1,** 514 (1952).
409. Goldstein, M. S., Mendel, B., and Levine, R. *Am. J. Physiol.* **163,** 714 (1950).
410. Goldzieher, J. W., Epstein, P. R., Rawls, W. B., and Goldzieher, M. A. *J. Clin. Endocrinol. and Metabolism* **13,** 662 (1953).
411. Gordon, A. S., and Katsch, G. F. *Ann. N. Y. Acad. Sci.* **52,** 1 (1949).
412. Gordon, A. S., Piliero, S. J., and Landau, D. *Endocrinology* **49,** 497 (1951).
413. Gordan, G. S., and Elliott, H. W. *Endocrinology* **41,** 517 (1947).
414. Gordan, G. S., Bentinck, R. C., and Eisenberg, E. *Ann. N. Y. Acad. Sci.* **54,** 575 (1951).
415. Gottschalk, R. G., and Grollman, A. *Cancer Research* **12,** 651 (1952).
416. Grabar, P., Benacerraff, B., and Biozzi, G. *Ann. inst. Pasteur* **81,** 187 (1951).
417. Grad, B. *J. Clin. Endocrinol. and Metabolism* **12,** 708 (1952).
418. Graham, A. B., Werder, A. A., Syverton, J. T., and Friedman, J. *Federation Proc.* **11,** 470 (1952).
419. Graham, J. B., Graham, R. M., and Graffeo, A. J. *Endocrinology* **46,** 434 (1950).
420. Gray, S. J., Benson, J. A., and Reifenstein, R. W. *Proc. Soc. Exptl. Biol. Med.* **78,** 338 (1951).
421. Gray, S. J., Benson, J. A., Reifenstein, R. W., and Ramsey, C. *J. Clin. Invest.* **31,** 633 (1952).
422. Gray, S. J., Benson, J. A., Reifenstein, R. W., and Spiro, H. M. *J. Am. Med. Assoc.* **147,** 1529 (1951).
423. Gray, W. D., and Munson, P. L. *Endocrinology* **48,** 471 (1951).
424. Gray, W. D., Pedrick, L., and Winne, R. *Proc. Soc. Exptl. Biol. Med.* **78,** 679 (1951).
425. Green, D. M., Farah, A., and Klemperer, W. W. *Endocrinology* **47,** 281 (1950).
426. Green, D. M., Johnson, A. D., Bridges, W. E., Lehmann, J. H., and Gray, F. *Endocrinology* **47,** 102 (1950).
427. Green, D. M., Saunders, F. J., Wahlgren, N., and Craig, R. L. *Am. J. Physiol.* **170,** 94 (1952).
428. Green, H. N. *Brit. Med. J.* **i,** 1165 (1950).
429. Greenspan, F. S., Gifford, H., and Deming, Q. B. *Endocrinology* **52,** 638 (1953).
430. Greep, R. O., and Deane, H. W. *Ann. N. Y. Acad. Sci.* **50,** 596 (1949).
431. Greep, R. O., Knobil, E., Hofmann, F. G., and Jones, T. L. *Endocrinology* **50,** 664 (1952).
432. Grenell, R. G., and McCrawley, E. L. *Federation Proc.* **6,** 116 (1947).
433. Grob, D., and Harvey, A. M. *Bull. Johns Hopkins Hosp.* **91,** 124 (1952).
434. Groen, H., Pelser, H., Frenkel, M., Kaminga, C. E., and Willebrands, A. F. *New Engl. J. Med.* **244,** 471 (1951).
435. Groen, H. *J. Clin. Invest.* **31,** 87 (1952).
436. Grokoest, A. W., Vaillancourt, deG., Gattsegen, R., and Ragan, C. *J. Clin. Invest.* **30,** 644 (1951).
437. Grollman, A., and Konnerth, A. *Endocrinology* **48,** 213 (1951).
438. Grolnick, M. *J. Allergy* **23,** 416 (1952).
439. Gross, F. *Schweiz. med. Wochschr.* **80,** 697 (1950).
440. Gross, F., and Gysel, H. *Acta. Endocrinol.* **15,** 199 (1954).

441. Gross, F., and Tschopp, T. *Experientia* **8,** 75 (1952).

442. Gross, J. *Ann. N. Y. Acad. Sci.* **56,** 674 (1953).

443. Gross, R., and Siecke, V. *Klin. Wochschr.* **30,** 456 (1952).

444. Grundy, H. M., Simpson, S. A., and Tait, J. F. *Nature* **169,** 795 (1952).

445. Hackel, D. B., Portfolio, A. G., and Kinney, T. D. *Proc. Soc. Exptl. Biol. Med.* **74,** 458 (1950).

446. Hahn, E. O., Houser, H. B., Rammelkamp, C. H., Denny, F. W., and Wannamaker, L. W. *J. Clin. Invest.* **30,** 274 (1951).

447. Halberg, F., and Ulstrom, R. A. *Proc. Soc. Exptl. Biol. Med.* **80,** 747 (1952).

448. Halberg, F., and Visscher, M. B. *Proc. Soc. Exptl. Biol. Med.* **75,** 846 (1950).

449. Halberg, F., and Visscher, M. B. *Endocrinology* **51,** 329 (1952).

450. Halberg, F. Cohen, S. L., and Flink, E. B. *J. Lab. Clin. Med.* **38,** 817 (1951).

451. Hall, C. E., and Hall, O. *Proc. Soc. Exptl. Biol. Med.* **71,** 690 (1949).

452. Hall, C. E., and Hall, O. *Proc. Soc. Exptl. Biol. Med.* **79,** 536 (1952).

453. Hall, C. E., and Hall, O. *Endocrinology* **52,** 157 (1953).

454. Hall, M. G., Darling, R. C., and Taylor, F. H. L. *Ann. Internal Med.* **13,** 415 (1939).

455. Hall, T. C., McCracken, B. H., and Thorn, G. W. *J. Clin. Endocrinol. and Metabolism* **13,** 243 (1953).

456. Hallett, J. W., Leopold, I. H., and Steinmetz, C. G. *Arch. Ophthalmol.* **46,** 268 (1951).

457. Halmi, N. S. *Proc. Soc. Exptl. Biol. Med.* **80,** 175 (1952).

458. Halmi, N. S., and Barker, S. B. *Endocrinology* **51,** 127 (1952).

459. Halmi, N. S., and Bogdanove, E. M. *Proc. Soc. Exptl. Biol. Med.* **77,** 518 (1951).

460. Halpern, B. N., Benacerraff, B., and Briot, M. *Proc. Soc. Exptl. Biol. Med.* **79,** 37 (1952).

461. Halpern, B. N., Mauric, G., Holtzer, A., and Briot, M. *J. Allergy* **23,** 303 (1952).

462. Hamburger, C. *Acta Endocrinol.* **14,** 325 (1953).

463. Hamilton, L. D., Gubler, C. J., Ashenbrucker, H., Cartwright, G. E., and Wintrobe, M. M. *Endocrinology* **48,** 44 (1951).

464. Hanan, R., and Overman, J. R. *Proc. Soc. Exptl. Biol. Med.* **84,** 420 (1953).

465. Hanan, R., and Oyama, J. *Proc. Soc. Exptl. Biol. Med.* **85,** 373 (1954).

466. Handler, P., and Bernheim, F. *Federation Proc.* **10,** 194 (1951).

467. Hardy, J. D., Riegel, C., and Erisman, E. P. *Am. J. Med. Sci.* **219,** 582 (1950).

468. Harris, L. J., Bland, M. U., Hughes, R. E., and Constable, B. J. *Lancet* **i,** 1021 (1953).

469. Harris, L. J., and Ray, S. N. *Biochem. J.* **27,** 303 (1933).

470. Harris, S., and Harris, T. N. *Proc. Soc. Exptl. Biol. Med.* **74,** 186 (1950).

471. Harrison, C. U., King, E. H., Dole, J. C., and Sichel, R. *Brit. J. Ind. Med.* **9,** 165 (1952).

472. Harrison, J. H., Thorn, G. W., and Criscitiello, M. G. *J. Urol.* **67,** 405 (1952).

473. Harrison, J. H., Thorn, G. W., and Jenkins, D. *New Engl. J. Med.* **248,** 86 (1953).

474. Hart, P. D., and Rees, R. J. W. *Lancet* **ii,** 391 (1950).

475. Hartroft, P. M., and Hartroft, W. S. *J. Exptl. Med.* **97,** 415 (1953).

476. Haskin, D., Lasher, N., and Rothman, S. *J. Invest. Dermatol.* **20,** 207 (1953).

477. Havens, W. P., Jr., Shaffer, J. M., and Hopke, C. J. *J. Immunol.* **68,** 389 (1952).

478. Hayano, M., and Dorfman, R. I. *Ann. N. Y. Acad. Sci.* **54,** 608 (1951).

479. Hayano, M., Dorfman, R. I., and Yamada, E. Y. *J. Biol. Chem.* **186,** 603 (1950).
480. Hayano, M., Schiller, S., and Dorfman, R. I. *Endocrinology* **46,** 387 (1950).
481. Hayes, M. A. *Endocrinology* **52,** 646 (1953).
482. Hayes, M. A., and Baker, B. L. *Endocrinology* **49,** 379 (1951).
483. Hayes, M. A., Reed, T. G., and Baker, B. L. *Proc. Soc. Exptl. Biol. Med.* **75,** 357 (1950).
484. Hechter, O., and Johnson, S. *Endocrinology* **45,** 351 (1949).
485. Heidelberger, M., and Kendall, F. E. *J. Exptl. Med.* **62,** 697 (1935).
486. Heilman, D. N. *Proc. Staff Meetings Mayo Clinic* **20,** 310 (1945).
487. Heilman, F. R., and Kendall, E. C. *Endocrinology* **34,** 416 (1944).
488. Heller, H. *In* J. M. Yoffey, The Suprarenal Cortex. Academic Press, New York, 1953, p. 187.
489. Heller, J. H. *Federation Proc.* **12,** 65 (1953).
490. Heller, J. H. *Federation Proc.* **13,** 69 (1954).
491. Hellman, L. *Science* **109,** 280 (1949).
492. Heming, A. E., Holtkamp, D. E., and Mansor, L. F. *J. Clin. Endocrinol. and Metabolism* **12,** 961 (1952).
493. Heming, A. E., Holtkamp, D. E., Kerwin, J. F., Mansor, L. F., and Dacanay, J. G. *Proc. Soc. Exptl. Biol. Med.* **80,** 154 (1952).
494. Hemphill, R. E. *In* J. M. Yoffey, The Suprarenal Cortex. Academic Press, New York, 1953, p. 135.
495. Hench, P. S., Kendall, E. C., Slocumb, C. H., and Polley, H. F. *Proc. Staff Meetings Mayo Clinic* **24,** 181 (1949).
496. Hench, P. S., Kendall, E. C., Slocumb, C. H., and Polley, H. F. *Arch. Intern. Med.* **85,** 545 (1950).
497. Hench, P. S., Slocumb, C. H., Barnes, A. R., Smith, H. L., Polley., H F., and Kendall, E. C. *Proc. Staff Meetings Mayo Clinic* **24,** 277 (1949).
498. Henderson, J. W., and Hollenhorst, R. W. *Proc. Staff Meetings Mayo Clinic* **25,** 459 (1950).
499. Henriques, O. B., Henriques, S. B., and Selye, H. *Proc. Soc. Exptl. Biol. Med.* **73,** 611 (1950).
500. Henriques, S. B., Henriques, O. B., and Mattos, L. *Endocrinology* **47,** 457 (1950).
501. Henry, W. L., Oliver, L., and Ramey, E. R. *Federation Proc.* **12,** 66 (1953).
502. Hensler, N. M., Wurl, O. A., and Gillespie, J. O. *U. S. Armed Forces Med. J.* **3,** 199 (1952).
503. Hentstell, H. H., and Freedman, R. I. *Proc. Soc. Exptl. Biol. Med.* **76,** 238 (1951).
504. Herrick, E. H., Mead, E. R., Egerton, B. W., and Hughes, J. S. *Endocrinology* **50,** 259 (1952).
505. Hertz, R., and Tullner, W. W. *Proc. Soc. Exptl. Biol. Med.* **78,** 737 (1951).
506. Hertz, R., Allen, M. J., and Tullner, W. W. *Proc. Soc. Exptl. Biol. Med.* **75,** 627 (1950).
507. Hertz, R., Tullner, W. W., and Allen, M. J. *Proc. Soc. Exptl. Biol. Med.* **77,** 480 (1951).
508. Hess, W. C., Kyle, L. H., and Doolan, P. D. *Proc. Soc. Exptl. Biol. Med.* **76,** 418 (1951).
509. Hidalgo, J., McClure, C. D., Henderson, J. B., Whitehead, R. W., and Smyth, C. J. *Proc. Soc. Exptl. Biol. Med.* **80,** 97 (1952).

510. Higgins, G. M. *Am. J. Clin. Pathol.* **23,** 775 (1953).
511. Higgins, G. M., Woods, K. A., and Bennett, W. A. *Cancer Research* **10,** 203 (1950).
512. Higgins, G. M., Woods, K. A., and Kendall, E. C. *Endocrinology* **48,** 175 (1951).
513. Hill, S. R., Reiss, R. S., Forsham, P. H., and Thorn, G. W. *J. Clin. Endocrinol. and Metabolism* **10,** 1375 (1950).
514. Hills, A. G., Forsham, P. H., and Finch, C. A. *Blood* **3,** 755 (1948).
515. Hoagland, H. *Psychosomat. Med.* **12,** 142 (1950).
516. Hoagland, H. *Intern. Record of Med.* **166,** 183 (1953).
517. Hoagland, H. *In* J. M. Yoffey, The Suprarenal Cortex. Academic Press, New York, 1953, p. 125.
518. Hoagland, H., Bergen, J. R., Slocombe, A. G., and Hunt, C. *Ann. N. Y. Acad. Sci.* **56,** 659 (1953).
519. Hoberman, H. D. *Yale J. Biol. and Med.* **22,** 341 (1950).
520. Hoch-Ligeti, C., and Hsu, Y. T. *Am. J. Pathol.* **29,** 614 (1953).
521. Hoefer, P. F. A., and Glaser, G. H. *J. Am. Med. Assoc.* **143,** 620 (1950).
522. Hoffman, W. C., Lewis, R. A., and Thorn, G. W. *Bull. Johns Hopkins Hosp.* **70** 335 (1942).
523. Hofmann, F. G. *Endocrinology* **50,** 206 (1952).
524. Hogness, J. R., Lee, N. D., and Williams, R. H. *Endocrinology* **52,** 378 (1953).
525. Hogness, J. R., Williams, R. H., and Lance, M. *Proc. Soc. Exptl. Biol. Med.* **79,** 43 (1952).
526. Holden, M., Seegal, B. C., and Ryby, I. *Am. J. Pathol.* **27,** 748 (1951).
527. Hollander, J. L., Brown, E. M., Jessar, R. A., and Brown, C. Y. *J. Clin. Invest.* **30,** 650 (1951).
528. Hollander, J. L., Brown, E. M., Jessar, R. A., and Brown, C. Y. *J. Am. Med. Assoc.* **147,** 1629 (1951).
529. Holley, H. L., and McLester, J. S. *Arch. Internal Med.* **88,** 760 (1951).
530. Holman, H. R., White, A., and Fruton, J. S. *Proc. Soc. Exptl. Biol. Med.* **65,** 196 (1947).
531. Holmes, J. H., and Percefull, S. C. *Ann. Internal Med.* **35,** 608 (1951).
532. Holtkamp, D. E., Mansor, L. F., and Heming, A. E. *Federation Proc.* **11,** 358 (1952).
533. Homburger, F., and Bonner, C. D. *Geriatrics* **8,** 385 (1953).
534. Homburger, F., Dart, R. M., Bonner, C. D., Branche, G., Kasdon, S. C., and Fishman, W. H. *J. Clin. Endocrinol. and Metabolism* **13,** 704 (1953).
535. Houssay, A. B. *Rev. assoc. méd. argentina* **66,** 132 (1952).
536. Howes, E. L. *Yale J. Biol. and Med.* **23,** 454 (1951).
537. Howes, E. L., Plotz, C. M., Blunt, J. W., and Ragan, C. *Surgery* **28,** 177 (1950).
538. Hubay, C. A., Weckesser, E. C., and Holden, W. D. *Surg. Gynecol. Obstet.* **96,** 65 (1953).
539. Hubble, D. *Lancet* **ii,** 464 (1952).
540. Hudson, G., Herdan, G., and Yoffey, J. M. *Brit. Med. J.* **i,** 999 (1952).
541. Hudson, P. B., Mittleman, A., and Mann, P. *J. Clin. Endocrinol. and Metabolism* **13,** 1064 (1953).
542. Huggins, C., and Bergenstal, D. M. *J. Am. Med. Assoc.* **147,** 191 (1951).
543. Huggins, C., and Bergenstal, D. M. *Proc. Natl. Acad. Sci. U. S.* **38,** 73 (1952).
544. Huggins, C., and Dao, T. L-Y. *J. Am. Med. Assoc.* **151,** 1388 (1953).

545. Huggins, C., Bergenstal, D. M., and Cleveland, A. S. *Recent Progr. Hormone Research* **8**, 273 (1953).
546. Huisman, T. H. J. *Acta Endocrinol.* **13**, 55 (1953).
547. Hull, R. B., and Loosli, C. G. *J. Lab. Clin. Med.* **37**, 603 (1951).
548. Humphrey, J. H. *Brit. J. Exptl. Pathol.* **32**, 274 (1951).
549. Humphreys, R. J., and Raab, W. *Proc. Soc. Exptl. Biol. Med.* **74**, 302 (1950).
550. Hundley, J. M., and Ing, K. B. *Endocrinology* **48**, 482 (1951).
551. Hungerford, G. F., Reinhardt, W. O., and Li, C. H. *Blood* **7**, 1125 (1952).
552. Hungerford, G. F., Reinhardt, W. O., and Li, C. H. *Proc. Soc. Exptl. Biol. Med.* **81**, 320 (1952).
553. Hunter, O. B., and Ross, J. B. *Southern Med. J.* **45**, 732 (1952).
554. Hunter, S. F. *Proc. Soc. Exptl. Biol. Med.* **82**, 14 (1953).
555. Hyman, G. A., Ragan, C., and Turner, J. C. *Proc. Soc. Exptl. Biol. Med.* **75**, 470 (1950).
556. Hyman, G. A., Ragan, C., and Turner, J. C. *Trans. N. Y. Acad. Sci.* **13**, 167 (1951).
557. Ingbar, S. H., Kass, E. H., Burnett, C. H., Relman, A. S., Burrows, B. A., and Sisson, J. H. *J. Lab. Clin. Med.* **38**, 533 (1951).
558. Ingbar, S. H., Otto, J. F., and Kass, E. H. *Proc. Soc. Exptl. Biol. Med.* **77**, 20 (1951).
559. Ingle, D. J. *Ann. N. Y. Acad. Sci.* **50**, 576 (1950).
560. Ingle, D. J. *J. Clin. Endocrinol. and Metabolism* **10**, 1312 (1950).
561. Ingle, D. J. *Recent Progr. Hormone Research* **7**, 375 (1952).
562. Ingle, D. J. *Proc. Soc. Exptl. Biol. Med.* **79**, 184 (1952).
563. Ingle, D. J., and Baker, B. L. *Endocrinology* **48**, 313 (1951).
564. Ingle, D. J., and Baker, B. L. *Endocrinology* **48**, 764 (1951).
565. Ingle, D. J., and Kendall, E. C. *Am. J. Physiol.* **122**, 585 (1938).
566. Ingle, D. J., and Meeks, R. C. *Am. J. Physiol.* **170**, 77 (1952).
567. Ingle, D. J., and Nezamis, J. E. *Am. J. Physiol.* **156**, 365 (1949).
568. Ingle, D. J., and Nezamis, J. E. *Endocrinology* **48**, 484 (1951).
569. Ingle, D. J., and Nezamis, J. E. *Endocrinology* **52**, 361 (1953).
570. Ingle, D. J., and Prestrud, M. C. *Endocrinology* **45**, 143 (1949).
371. Ingle, D. J., and Thorn, G. W. *Am. J. Physiol.* **132**, 670 (1941).
572. Ingle, D. J., Meeks, R. C., and Beary, D. F. *Proc. Soc. Exptl. Biol. Med.* **84**, 334 (1953).
573. Ingle, D. J., Morley, E. H., and Nezamis, J. E. *Proc. Soc. Exptl. Biol. Med.* **78**, 220 (1951).
574. Ingle, D. J., Morley, E. H., and Nezamis, J. E. *Endocrinology* **51**, 487 (1952).
575. Ingle, D. J., Meeks, R. C., and Thomas, K. E. *Endocrinology* **49**, 703 (1951).
576. Ingle, D. J., Nezamis, J. E., and Jeffries, J. W. *Am. J. Physiol.* **157**, 99 (1949).
577. Ingle, D. J., Nezamis, J. E., and Morley, E. H. *Proc. Soc. Exptl. Biol. Med.* **78**, 79 (1951).
578. Ingle, D. J., Nezamis, J. E., and Morley, E. H. *Endocrinology* **50**, 1 (1952).
579. Ingle, D. J., Nezamis, J. E., and Morley, E. H. *Am. J. Physiol.* **171**, 378 (1952).
580. Ingle, D. J., Prestrud, M. C., and Li, C. H. *Am. J. Physiol.* **166**, 165 (1951).
581. Ingle, D. J., Prestrud, M. C., and Nezamis, J. E. *Proc. Soc. Exptl. Biol. Med.* **75**, 801 (1950).
582. Ingle, D. J., Prestrud, M. C., and Nezamis, J. E. *Am. J. Physiol.* **166**, 171 (1951).
583. Ingle, D. J., Prestrud, M. C., and Rice, K. L. *Endocrinology* **46**, 510 (1950).

584. Ingle, D. J., Sheppard, R., Oberle, E. A., and Kuizenga, M. H. *Endocrinology* **39**, 52 (1946).

585. Ivon Sallmann, L., Jones, I. S., Wiggins, R. L., and Locke, B. D. *Wien. klin. Wochschr.* **63**, 684 (1951).

586. Jackson, C. M. *Am. J. Anat.* **21**, 321 (1917).

587. Jacob, J., and Szerb, J. *Arch. intern. pharmacodynamie* **90**, 301 (1952).

588. Jailer, J. W., and Boas, N. F. *Endocrinology* **46**, 314 (1950).

589. Jailer, J. W., Louchart, J., and Cahill, G. F. *J. Am. Med. Assoc.* **150**, 575 (1952).

590. Jailer, J. W., Louchart, J., and Cahill, G. F. *J. Clin. Invest.* **31**, 883 (1955).

591. Jailer, J. W., Wong, A. S. H., and Engle, E. T. *J. Clin. Endocrinol. and Metabolism* **11**, 186 (1951).

592. Järvinen, K. A. J. *Brit. Med. J.* ii, 1377 (1951).

593. Jensen, H., and Gray, J. L. *Ann. N. Y. Acad. Sci.* **54**, 619 (1951).

594. Johnson, A. S., Scheinberg, S. R., Gerisch, R., and Saltzstein, H. C. *Harper Hosp. Bull.* **9**, 187 (1951).

595. Johnson, A. S., Scheinberg, S. R., Gerisch, R., and Saltzstein, H. C. *Circulation* **7**, 224 (1953).

596. Johnson, B. B. *Endocrinology* **54**, 196 (1954).

597. Joiner, C. L. *Brit. Med. J.* ii, 642 (1952).

598. Jones, G. E. S., Howard, J. E., and Langford, H. *Fertility and Sterility* **4**, 49 (1953).

599. Jones, I. S., and Meyer, K. *Proc. Soc. Exptl. Biol. Med.* **74**, 102 (1950).

600. Josey, A. I., and Lawrence, J. S. *Folia Haematol.* **48**, 303 (1952).

601. Jost, A. *Recent. Progr. Hormone Research* **8**, 379 (1953).

602. Kabat, E. A., and Heidelberger, M. *J. Exptl. Med.* **66**, 229 (1937).

603. Kabat, E. A., Wolf, A., and Bezer, A. E. *J. Immunol.* **68**, 265 (1952).

604. Kagawa, C. M., Shipley, E. G., and Meyer, R. K. *Proc. Soc. Exptl. Biol. Med.* **80**, 281 (1952).

605. Kaplan, H. S., Brown, M. B., and Marder, S. N. *Cancer Research* **11**, 262 (1951).

606. Kaplan, N. O., and Lipmann, F. *J. Biol. Chem.* **174**, 37 (1948).

607. Kark, R. M., and Muehrcke, R. C. *Lancet* i, 1189 (1952).

608. Kark, R. M., Chapman, R. E., Consolazio, C. F., and Nesby, C. *J. Lab. Clin. Med.* **40**, 817 (1952).

609. Karlson, A. G., and Gainer, J. H. *Proc. Staff Meetings Mayo Clinic* **27**, 465 (1952).

610. Karnofsky, D. A., Ridgway, L. P., and Patterson, P. A. *Endocrinology* **48**, 596 (1951).

611. Karnofsky, D. A., Ridgway, L. P., and Stock, C. C. *Federation Proc.* **10**, 204 (1951).

612. Kass, E. H., and Finland, M. *New Engl. J. Med.* **243**, 693 (1950).

613. Kass, E. H., Geiman, Q. M., and Finland, M. *New Engl. J. Med.* **245**, 1000 (1951).

614. Kass, E. H., Lundgren, M. M., and Finland, M. *Ann. N. Y. Acad. Sci.* **56**, 765 (1953).

615. Kass, E. H., Ingbar, S. H., and Finland, M. *Ann. Internal Med.* **33**, 1081 (1950).

616. Kass, E. H., Ingbar, S. H., and Finland, M. *Proc. Soc. Exptl. Biol. Med.* **73**, 669 (1950).

617. Kass, E. H., Kendrick, M. I., and Finland, M. *Ann. N. Y. Acad. Sci.* **56,** 737 (1953).

618. Kass, E. H., Ingbar, S. H., Lundgren, M. M., and Finland, M. *J. Lab. Clin. Med.* **37,** 780 (1951).

619. Kaufman, N., Mason, E. J., and Kinney, T. D. *Am. J. Pathol.* **29,** 761 (1953).

620. Kay J. H. *Surgery* **32,** 686 (1952).

621. Kayahan, S. *J. Endocrinol.* **8,** 211 (1952).

622. Kellgren, J. H. *Brit. Med. J.* **i,** 1093 (1952).

623. Kelsall, M. A., and Crabb, E. D. *Anat. Record* **115,** 331 (1953).

624. Kelley, V. C., Ely, R. S., Raile, R. B., and Bray, P. F. *Proc. Soc. Exptl. Biol. Med.* **81,** 611 (1952).

625. Kendall, E. C. *Science* **111,** 457 (1950).

626. Kennedy, T. H., and Purves, H. D. *Brit. J. Exptl. Pathol.* **22,** 241 (1941).

627. Kerppola, W. *Endocrinology* **51,** 192 (1952).

628. Key, J. A., Odell, R. T., and Taylor, L. W. *J. Bone and Joint Surgery* **34,** 665 (1952).

629. Keyes, P. H. *Endocrinology* **44,** 274 (1949).

630. Kilbourne, E. D., and Horsfall, F. L. *Proc. Soc. Exptl. Biol. Med.* **77,** 135 (1951).

631. Kilbourne, E. D., and Horsfall, F. L. *Proc. Soc. Exptl. Biol. Med.* **76,** 116 (1951).

632. Kilbourne, E. D., and Tateno, I. *Proc. Soc. Exptl. Biol. Med.* **82,** 274 (1953).

633. Kimura, S. J., Thygeson, P., and Geller, H. O. *Am. J. Ophthalmol.* **36,** 116 (1953).

634. Kinsell, L. W., Partridge, J. W., and Foreman, N. *Ann. Internal Med.* **38,** 913 (1953).

635. Kinsell, L. W., Partridge, J. W., Boling, L., and Margen, S. *Ann. Internal Med.* **37,** 921 (1952).

636. Kinsell, L. W., Michaels, G. D., Margen, S., Boling, L., and Partridge, J. W. *Am. J. Med.* **13,** 96 (1952).

637. Kinsell, L. W., Margen, S., Michaels, G. D., Reiss, R., Frantz, R., and Carbone, J. *J. Clin. Invest.* **30,** 1491 (1951).

638. Kitchell, R. L., and Wells, L. J. *Endocrinology* **50,** 83 (1952).

639. Kit, S., and Guzman Barron, E. S. *Endocrinology* **52,** 1 (1953).

640. Klein, R. *J. Clin. Invest.* **30,** 318 (1951).

641. Klein, R., and Hanson, J. *Pediat.* **6,** 192 (1950).

642. Klein, R., and Livingstone, S. *J. Pediat.* **37,** 733 (1950).

643. Kleigman, A. M., Baldridge, G. D., Rebell, G., and Pillsbury, D. M. *J. Lab. Clin. Med.* **37,** 615 (1951).

644. Kline, D. L. *Endocrinology* **45,** 596 (1949).

645. Knauff, R. E., Nielson, E. D., and Haines, A. J. *J. Am. Chem. Soc.* **75,** 4869 (1953).

645a. Knobil, E., Hofmann, F. G., and Greep, O. *Endocrinology* **53,** 242 (1953).

646. Knowlton, A. I., Loeb, E. N., Stoerk, H. C., and Seegal, B. C. *Proc. Soc. Exptl. Biol. Med.* **72,** 722 (1949).

647. Knowlton, A. I., Loeb, E. N., Seegal, B. C., Stoerk, H. C., and Berg, J. L. *Proc. Soc. Exptl. Biol. Med.* **74,** 661 (1950).

648. Kobernick, C. D., and More, R. H. *Proc. Soc. Exptl. Biol. Med.* **74,** 602 (1950).

649. Kochakian, C. D. *Ann. N. Y. Acad. Sci.* **54,** 534 (1951).

650. Kochakian, C. D., and Robertson, E. *J. Biol. Chem.* **190,** 481 (1951).

651. Kochakian, C. D., and Robertson, E. *J. Biol. Chem.* **190,** 495 (1951).
652. Kochakian, C. D., and Vail, V. N. *J. Biol. Chem.* **169,** 1 (1947).
653. Kountz, W. B., Ackermann, P. G., and Kheim, T. *J. Clin. Endocrinol. and Metabolism* **13,** 534 (1953).
654. Kowalewski, K., and Bastenie, P. A. *Acta Endocrinol.* **11,** 284 (1950).
655. Krahl, M. E. *Ann. N. Y. Acad. Sci.* **54,** 649 (1951).
656. Kramar, J., and Simay-Kramar, M. *Endocrinology* **52,** 453 (1953).
657. Krohn, P. L. *In* J. M. Yoffey, The Suprarenal Cortex. Academic Press, New York, 1953, p. 167.
658. Kuhl, W. J., and Ziff, M. *J. Clin. Endocrinol. and Metabolism* **12,** 554 (1952).
659. Kumagai, L. F., and Dougherty, T. F. *Am. J. Physiol.* **167,** 804 (1951).
660. Kurland, G. S., and Freedberg, A. S. *Proc. Soc. Exptl. Biol. Med.* **78,** 28 (1951).
661. Kuusisto, A. N., and Telkkä, A. *Acta Endocrinol.* **13,** 61 (1953).
662. Kuzell, W. C., and Mankle, E. A. *Proc. Soc. Exptl. Biol. Med.* **74,** 677 (1950).
663. Lachance, J. P., and Page, E. *Endocrinology* **52,** 57 (1953).
664. Landau, W. W., Nelson, W. A., and Gay, L. N. *Bull. Johns Hopkins Hosp.* **88,** 395 (1951).
665. Landauer, W. *Endocrinology* **41,** 489 (1947).
666. Lanman, J. T. *Pediatrics* **12,** 62 (1953).
667. Laqueur, G. L. *Am. J. Pathol.* **28,** 521 (1952).
668. Last, J. H., Jordan, P. H., Pitesky, I., and Siegel, B. M. *Proc. Soc. Exptl. Biol. Med.* **74,** 96 (1950).
669. Lattes, R., Blunt, J. W., Rose, H. M., Jessar, R. A., Vaillancourt, de G., and Ragan, C. *Am. J. Pathol.* **29,** 1 (1953).
670. Lauridsen, J., Belko, J. S., and Warren, R. *Proc. Soc. Exptl. Biol. Med.* **79,** 709 (1952).
671. Law, L. W., and Speirs, R. S. *Proc. Soc. Exptl. Biol. Med.* **66,** 226 (1947).
672. Layton, L. L. *Proc. Soc. Exptl. Biol. Med.* **76,** 598 (1951).
673. Lazarow, A. *Proc. Soc. Exptl. Biol. Med.* **74,** 702 (1950).
674. Lazarow, A., and Berman, J. *Anat. Record* **106,** 215 (1950).
675. Leaf, A., Mamby, A. R., Rasmussen, H., and Marasco, J. P. *J. Clin. Invest.* **31,** 914 (1952).
676. Leathem, J. H. *Proc. Soc. Exptl. Biol. Med.* **74,** 855 (1950).
677. Leblond, C. P., and Hoff, H. E. *Endocrinology* **35,** 229 (1944).
678. Leblond, C. P., and Segal, G. *Am. J. Roentgenol. Radium Therapy* **47,** 302 (1942).
679. Lee, N. D., and Williams, R. H. *Endocrinology* **51,** 451 (1952).
680. Lee, N. D., and Williams, R. H. *Proc. Soc. Exptl. Biol. Med.* **79,** 669 (1952).
681. Lee, R. E., and Pfeiffer, C. C. *Proc. Soc. Exptl. Biol. Med.* **77,** 752 (1951).
682. Leger, J., Leith, W., and Rose, B. *Proc. Soc. Exptl. Biol. Med.* **69,** 465 (1948).
683. LeMaistre, C., and Tompsett, R. *Am. Rev. Tuberc.* **64,** 295 (1951).
684. LeMaistre, C., and Tompsett, R. *J. Exptl. Med.* **95,** 393 (1952).
685. LeMaistre, C., Tompsett, R., and McDermott, W. *Ann. N. Y. Acad. Sci.* **56,** 772 (1953).
686. Lemonde, P., Panisset, M., Dobija, M., and Selye, H. *J. Clin. Endocrinol. and Metabolism* **12,** 973 (1952).
687. Leopold, I. H., and Maylath, F. R. *Am. J. Ophthalmol.* **35,** 1125 (1952).
688. Leopold, I. H., and Maylath, F. R. *Arch. Ophthalmol.* **48,** 115 (1952).
689. Leopold, I. H., Purnell, J. E., Cannon, E. J., Steinmetz, C. G., and McDonald, P. R. *Am. J. Ophthalmol.* **34,** 361 (1951).

690. Lever, J. D. *J. Endocrinol.* **10,** 133 (1954).
691. Levin, L. *J. Clin. Endocrinol. and Metabolism* **9,** 657 (1949).
692. Levin, L., and Farber, R. K. *Proc. Soc. Exptl. Biol. Med.* **74,** 758 (1950).
693. Levitt, M. F., and Bader, M. E. *J. Clin. Invest.* **30,** 655 (1951).
694. Lewin, E., and Wassèn, E. *Lancet* **ii,** 993 (1949).
695. Lewis, L. A., and Page, I. H. *Endocrinology* **43,** 415 (1948).
696. Lewis, L. A., and Page, I. H. *Ann. N. Y. Acad. Sci.* **50,** 547 (1949).
697. Lewis, R. A., Rosemberg, E., and Wilkins, L. *Endocrinology* **47,** 414 (1950).
698. Lewis, R. B., and Freytag, E. *Proc. Soc. Exptl. Biol. Med.* **77,** 816 (1951).
699. Lippman, R. W., and Marti, H. U. *Proc. Natl. Acad. Sci. U. S.* **37,** 447 (1951).
700. Lipsett, M. N., and Moore, F. J. *J. Biol. Chem.* **192,** 743 (1951).
701. Lipsett, M. N., and Moore, F. J. *J. Biol. Chem.* **197,** 303 (1952).
702. Lister, A., and Greaves, D. P. *Brit. J. Ophthalmol.* **35,** 725 (1951).
703. Locke, W., Talbot, N. B., Jones, H. S., and Worcester, J. *J. Clin. Invest.* **30,** 325 (1951).
704. Lockett, M. F. *J. Physiol.* **109,** 250 (1949).
705. Long, C. N. H. *Federation Proc.* **6,** 461 (1947).
706. Long, C. N. H. *Science* **111,** 458 (1950).
706a. Long, D. A. *Lancet* **i,** 529 (1954).
707. Long, J. B., and Favour, C. B. *Bull. Johns Hopkins Hosp.* **87,** 186 (1950).
708. Loosli, C. G., Hull, R. B., Berlin, B. S., and Alexander, E. R. *J. Lab. Clin. Med.* **37,** 464 (1951).
709. Lotspeich, W. D. *Endocrinology* **44,** 314 (1949).
710. Love, W. D. *Proc. Soc. Exptl. Biol. Med.* **75,** 639 (1950).
711. Lowe, C. U., Williams, W. L., and Thomas, L. *Proc. Soc. Exptl. Biol. Med.* **78,** 818 (1951).
712. Lowe, J. *Brit. Med. J.* **ii,** 746 (1952).
713. Luft, R., and Sjörgen, B. *Acta Endocrinol.* **7,** 211 (1951).
714. Luft, R., and Sjörgen, B. *Acta Endocrinol.* **10,** 49 (1952).
715. Luongo, M. A., Reid, D. H., and Weiss, W. W. *New Engl. J. Med.* **245,** 757 (1951).
716. Lurie, M. B., Zappasodi, P., Dannenburg, A. M., Jr., and Cardona-Lynch, E. *Ann. N. Y. Acad. Sci.* **56,** 779 (1953).
717. Lurie, M. B., Zappasodi, P., Dannenburg, A. M., Jr., and Swartz, I. B. *Science* **113,** 234 (1951).
718. Madden, R. J., and Ramsburg, H. H. *Endocrinology* **49,** 82 (1951).
719. Madison, L. L. *J. Clin. Invest.* **29,** 789 (1950).
720. Magarey, F. R., and Gough, J. *Brit. J. Exptl. Pathol.* **33,** 510 (1952).
721. Maqsood, M. *J. Endocrinol.* **7,** 82 (1950).
722. Malkiel, S. *Proc. Soc. Exptl. Biol. Med.* **77,** 333 (1951).
723. Malkiel, S., and Hargis, B. J. *J. Immunol.* **69,** 217 (1952).
724. Mancini, R. E., and de Lustig, E. S. *J. Natl. Cancer Inst.* **13,** 247 (1952).
725. Mandel, W., Singer, M. J., Gudmundson, H. R., Meister, L., and Modern, F. W. S. *J. Am. Med. Assoc.* **146,** 546 (1951).
726. Marcus, S., and Donaldson, D. M. *J. Immunol.* **69,** 101 (1952).
727. Marcus, F., Romanoff, L. P., and Pincus, G. *Endocrinology* **50,** 286 (1952).
728. Margen, S., Kinsell, L. W., Flanagan, E. K., Suiter, L. E., and Rapaport, E. *J. Clin. Endocrinol. and Metabolism* **9,** 662 (1949).
729. Marshall, L. M., and Friedberg, F. *Endocrinology* **48,** 113 (1951).
730. Martin, S. P., and Kerby, G. P. *Proc. Soc. Exptl. Biol. Med.* **81,** 73 (1952).

731. Martinez, C., Visscher, M. B., King, J. T., and Bittner, J. J.   *Proc. Soc. Exptl. Biol. Med.* **80,** 81 (1952).
732. Mason, A. S., and Morris, C. J. O. R.   *Lancet* **i,** 116 (1953).
733. Masson, G. M. C.   *Am. J. Pathol.* **27,** 717 (1951).
734. Masson, G. M. C., Corcoran, A. C., and Page, I. H.   *J. Lab. Clin. Med.* **34,** 1416 (1949).
735. Masson, G. M. C., Lewis, L. A., Corcoran, A. C., and Page, I. H.   *J. Clin. Endocrinol. and Metabolism* **13,** 300 (1953).
736. Masson, G. M. C., Page, I. H., and Corcoran, A. C.   *Proc. Soc. Exptl. Biol. Med.* **73,** 434 (1950).
737. Mattox, V. R., Mason, H. L., Albert, A., and Code, C. F.   *J. Am. Chem. Soc.* **75,** 4869 (1953).
738. Maumenee, A. E.   *Am. J. Ophthalmol.* **34,** 142 (1951).
739. McCracken, B. H., and Hall, T. C.   *J. Clin. Endocrinol. and Metabolism* **12,** 923 (1952).
740. McDermott, W., Fry, E. G., Brobeck, J. R., and Long, C. N. H.   *Proc. Soc. Exptl. Biol. Med.* **73,** 609 (1950).
741. McDermott, W., Fry, E. G., Brobeck, J. R., and Long, C. N. H.   *Yale J. Biol. and Med.* **23,** 52 (1950).
742. McDonald, P. R., Leopold, I. H., Vogel, A. W., and Mulberger, R. D.   *Arch. Ophthalmol.* **49,** 400 (1953)
743. McEachern, D.   *Bull. N. Y. Acad. Med.* **27,** 3 (1951).
744. McGavack, T. T., Saccone, A., Vogel, M., and Harris, R.   *J. Clin. Endocrinol. and Metabolism* **6,** 776 (1946).
745. McIntosh, H. W., and Holmes, C. B.   *Lancet* **ii,** 1061 (1951).
746. McLean, C. R., Hamilton, J. D., and Fitzgerald, J. D. L.   *Am. J. Pathol.* **27,** 711 (1951).
747. McManus, J. F. A., Cash, J. R., Carter, J. P., Alrich, E. M., and Lehman E. P.   *Federation Proc.* **10,** 364 (1951).
748. McQuarrie, I., Anderson, J. A., and Ziegler, M. R.   *J. Clin. Endocrinol. and Metabolism* **2,** 406 (1942).
749. McQuillan, M. T., and Trikojus, V. M.   *Brit. J. Exptl. Pathol.* **27,** 247 (1946).
750. Meadows, E. C., and Prudden, J. F.   *Surgery* **33,** 841 (1953).
751. Means, J. H.   *Lancet* **ii,** 543 (1949).
752. Megel, H., and Gordon, A. S.   *Endocrinology* **48,** 391 (1951).
753. Meier, R., Gysel, H., and Muller, R.   *Schweiz. Méd. Wochschr.* **74,** 93 (1944).
754. Meier, R., Schuler, W., and Desaulles, P.   *Experientia* **6,** 469 (1950).
755. Meiklejohn, K. P.   *Vitamins and Hormones* **11,** 62 (1953).
756. Meites, J.   *Proc. Soc. Exptl. Biol. Med.* **78,** 692 (1951).
757. Meites, J.   *Metabolism* **1,** 58 (1952).
758. Meites, J.   *Proc. Soc. Exptl. Biol. Med.* **81,** 307 (1952).
759. Meites, J., and Feng, Y. S. L.   *Proc. Soc. Exptl. Biol. Med.* **85,** 341 (1954).
760. Melampy, R. M., Cheng, D. W., and Northrop, L. C.   *Proc. Soc. Exptl. Biol. Med.* **76,** 24 (1951).
761. Melcher, G. W., Blunt, J. W., and Ragan, C.   *J. Clin. Invest.* **31,** 649 (1952).
762. Menkin, V.   *Am. J. Physiol.* **166,** 518 (1951).
763. Merck and Co.   *The Cortisone Investigator* **1–10,** Published by Merck and Co. (1950–54.)
764. Merritt, H. H.   *Yale J. Biol. and Med.* **24,** 466 (1952).
765. Meyer, R. J.   *J. Clin. Endocrinol. and Metabolism* **13,** 123 (1953).

766. Michael, M., Cummings, M. M., and Bloom, W. L.   *Proc. Soc Exptl. Biol. Med.* **75,** 613 (1950).

767. Michael, M., Jr., and Whorton, C. M.   *Proc. Soc. Exptl. Biol. Med.* **76,** 754 (1951).

768. Michaelson, I. C.   *Arch. Ophthalmol.* **47,** 459 (1952).

769. Michaelson, I. C.   *Arch. Ophthalmol.* **48,** 144 (1952).

770. Migeon, C. J.   *Proc. Soc. Exptl. Biol. Med.* **80,** 571 (1952).

771. Migeon, C. J., and Gardner, L. I.   *J. Clin. Endocrinol. and Metabolism* **12,** 1513 (1952).

772. Migeon, C. J., Gardner, L. I., Crigler, J. F., Jr., and Wilkins, L.   *Endocrinology* **51,** 117 (1952).

773. Miescher, K., Fischer, W. H., and Tschopp, T.   *Nature* **142,** 435 (1938).

774. Miller, Z.   *Endocrinology* **54,** 431 (1954).

775. Mirand, E. A., Reinhard, M. C., and Goltz, H. L.   *Proc. Soc. Exptl. Biol. Med.* **81,** 397 (1952).

776. Mirick, G. S.   *Bull. Johns Hopkins Hosp.* **88,** 332 (1951).

777. Mogabgab, W. J., and Thomas, L.   *J. Lab. Clin. Med.* **39,** 271 (1952).

778. Moll, F. C., and Hawn, C. van Z.   *J. Immunol.* **70,** 441 (1953).

779. Molomut, N., Spain, D. M., and Haber, A.   *Proc. Soc. Exptl. Biol. Med.* **73,** 416 (1950).

780. Money, W. L., Fager, J., Lucas, V., and Rawson, R. W.   *Endocrinology* **51,** 87 (1952).

781. Money, W. L., Fager, J., and Rawson, R. W.   *Cancer Research* **12,** 206 (1952).

782. Money, W. L., Kirschner, L., Kraintz, L., Merrill, P., and Rawson, R. W.   *J. Clin. Endocrinol. and Metabolism* **10,** 1282 (1950).

783. Money, W. L., Kraintz, L., Fager, J., Kirschner, L., and Rawson, R. W.   *Endocrinology* **48,** 682 (1951).

784. Monto, R. W., Brennan, M. J., Margulis, R. R., and Smith, R. W.   *J. Lab. Clin. Med.* **36,** 1008 (1950).

785. Moon, V. H., and Tershakovec, G. A.   *Proc. Soc. Exptl. Biol. Med.* **79,** 63 (1952).

786. Moore, B., and Purinton, C. O.   *Am. J. Physiol.* **5,** 182 (1901).

787. Moore, C. R.   *J. Clin. Endocrinol. and Metabolism* **13,** 339 (1953).

788. Moore, D. F., Lowenthal, J., Fuller, M., and Jaques, L. B.   *Am. J. Clin. Pathol.* **22,** 936 (1952).

789. More, R. H., and Kobernick, S. D.   *Am. J. Pathol.* **27,** 708 (1951).

790. Morel, F.   *Compt. rend. soc. biol.* **146,** 202 (1952).

791. Morgan, A. F., and Lewis, E. M.   *Federation Proc.* **11,** 451 (1952).

792. Morgan, A. F., and Simms, H. D.   *Science* **89,** 565 (1939).

793. Morgan, J. A.   *Surgery* **30,** 506 (1951).

794. Mosher, H. A.   *Arch. Ophthalmol.* **45,** 317 (1951).

795. Mote, J. R. (ed.)   *Proc. 1st Clin. ACTH Conf., Phila.* (1950).

796. Mote, J. R. (ed.)   *Proc. 2nd. Clin. ACTH Conf., Phila.* (1951).

797. Muehrcke, R. C., Lewis, J. L., and Kark, R. M.   *Science* **115,** 377 (1952).

798. Muehrcke, R. C., Staple, T. W., and Kark, R. M.   *J. Lab. Clin. Med.* **40,** 169 (1952).

799. Mueller, J. F. Weir, D. R., and Heinle, R. W.   *Proc. Soc. Exptl. Biol. Med.* **77,** 312 (1951).

800. Mulinos, M. G., and Pomerantz, L.   *J. Nutrition* **19,** 493 (1940).

801. Mulinos, M. G., and Pomerantz, L.   *Am. J. Physiol.* **132,** 368 (1941).

802. Mulinos, M. G., Spingarn, C. L., and Lojkin, M. E. *Am. J. Physiol.* **135,** 102 (1941).
803. Murphy, J. B., and Sturm, E. *Science* **99,** 303 (1944).
804. Murphy, J. B., and Sturm, E. *Cancer Research* **10,** 191 (1950).
805. Murray, R., and Branham, S. E. *Proc. Soc. Exptl. Biol. Med.* **78,** 750 (1951).
806. Mushett, C. W., Stebbins, R. B., and Barton, M. N. *Trans. N. Y. Acad. Sci.* **9,** 291 (1947).
807. Nadel, E. M., and Schneider, J. J. *Endocrinology* **51,** 5 (1952).
808. Nagareda, C. S., and Gaunt, R. *Endocrinology* **48,** 560 (1951).
809. Nathanson, I. T., and Kelley, R. M. *New Engl. J. Med.* **246,** 135, 180 (1952).
810. Neal, W. B., Jr., Woodward, E. R., Kark, A. E., Zubiran, J. M., and Montalbetti, J. A. *Arch. Surg.* **65,** 774 (1952).
811. Nelson, A. A., and Woodward, C. *Arch. Pathol.* **48,** 387 (1949).
812. Nelson, C. T., Fox, C. L., and Freeman, E. B. *Proc. Soc. Exptl. Biol. Med.* **75,** 181 (1950).
813. Nelson, C. T., Fox, C. L., and Freeman, E. B. *J. Invest. Dermatol.* **18,** 113 (1952).
814. Nelson, D. H., and Samuels, L. T. *J. Clin. Endocrinol. and Metabolism* **12,** 519 (1952).
815. Nelson, D. H., Samuels, L. T., Willardson, D. G., and Tyler, F. H. *J. Clin. Endocrinol. and Metabolism* **11,** 1021 (1951).
816. Nelson, R. J. *Proc. Soc. Exptl. Biol. Med.* **77,** 589 (1951).
817. Newsom, S. W., and Darrach, M. *Can. J. Physiol. & Biochem.*, **32,** 372 (1954).
818. Nichols, J., and Davis, C. *Federation Proc.* **12,** 103 (1953).
819. Nichols, J., and Gardner, L. I. *J. Lab. Clin. Med.* **37,** 229 (1951).
820. Nichols, J., and Sheehan, H. L. *Endocrinology* **51,** 362 (1952).
821. Nissim, J. A. *J. Endocrinol.* **8,** 10 (1952).
822. Nissim, J. A. *Endocrinology* **52,** 611 (1953).
823. Noble, R. L., The Hormones, Vol. 2. Academic Press, New York, 1950, p. 65.
824. Noble, R. L. *Can. J. Physiol. & Biochem.* **33,** in press (1955).
825. Noble, R. L., and Collip, J. B. *Quart. J. Exptl. Physiol.* **31,** 200 (1942).
826. Noble, R. L., and Crispin, E. J. *Rev. can. biol.* **11,** 57 (1952).
827. Noble, R. L., and Toby, C. G. *J. Endocrinol.* **5,** 303 (1948).
828. Norcross, B. M., Lockie, L. M., Constantine, A. G., Talbott, J. H., and Stein, R. H. *Ann. Internal Med.* **36,** 751 (1952).
829. Novack, A. *Am. J. Physiol.* **168,** 121 (1952).
830. Nowakowski, H. K., and Puschel, L. *Acta Endocrinol.* **11,** 320 (1952).
831. O'Donnell, W. M., and Fajans, S. S. *Univ. Mich. Med. Bull.* **16,** 169 (1950).
832. O'Donnell, W. M., Fajans, S. S., and Weinbaum, J. G. *Arch. Internal Med.* **88,** 28 (1951).
833. Oesterling, M. J., and Long, C. N. H. *Science* **113,** 241 (1951).
834. Ojers, G. W., Yasuna, J. M., and Scheie, H. G. *Am. J. Ophthalmol.* **36,** 120 (1953).
835. Oleson, J. J. *Arch. Biochem.* **29,** 449 (1950).
836. Olhagen, B. *Nord. Med.* **43,** 798 (1950).
837. O'Neal, L. W., and Heinbecker, P. *Endocrinology* **53,** 60 (1953).
838. Oppenheim, E., and Bruger, M. *Circulation* **6,** 470 (1952).
839. Opsahl, J. C. *Yale J. Biol. and Med.* **22,** 115 (1949).
840. Ormsby, H. L., Dempster, G., and van Rooyen, C. E. *Am. J. Ophthalmol.* **34,** 1687 (1951).

841. Osnes, M., and Thorsen, R. K. *Acta Med. Scand.* **145**, 44 (1953).
842. Overman, J. R., and Hanan, R. *Proc. Soc. Exptl. Biol. Med.* **82**, 427 (1953).
843. Pabst, M. L., Sheppard, R., and Kuizenga, M. H. *Endocrinology* **41**, 55 (1947).
844. Padawer, J., and Gordon, A. S. *Endocrinology* **51**, 52 (1952).
845. Page, E. W., and Glendening, M. B. *Proc. Soc. Exptl. Biol. Med.* **82**, 466 (1953).
846. Page, I. H. *Am. J. Physiol.* **122**, 352 (1938).
847. Page, I. H., and Lewis, L. A. *Am. J. Physiol.* **164**, 61 (1951).
848. Panzenhagen, H., and Speirs, R. S. *Blood* **8**, 536 (1953).
849. Parkes, A. S., and Smith, A. U. *J. Physiol.* **124**, 13 (1954).
850. Parmer, L. G., Katonach, F., and Angust, A. A. *Proc. Soc. Exptl. Biol. Med.* **77**, 215 (1951).
851. Paschkis, K. E., Epstein, D., Cantarow, A., and Friedler, G. *J. Clin. Endocrinol. and Metabolism* **12**, 939 (1952).
852. Paschkis, K. E., Cantarow, A., Eberhard, T., and Boyle, D. *Proc. Soc. Exptl. Biol. Med.* **73**, 116 (1950).
853. Paterson, J. C., and Mitchell, C. A. *Arch. Pathol.* **52**, 260 (1951).
854. Payne, R. W. *Endocrinology* **45**, 305 (1949).
855. Pearson, O. H. and Eliel, L. P. *J. Am. Med. Assoc.* **144**, 1349 (1950).
856. Pearson, O. H., and Eliel, L. P. *Recent Progr. Hormone Research* **6**, 373 (1951).
857. Pearson, O. H., Eliel, L. P., and Hollander, V. P. *J. Clin. Invest.* **30**, 665 (1951).
858. Pearson, O. H., Eliel, L. P., and Talbot, T. R. *Cancer Research* **10**, 235 (1950).
859. Pearson, O. H., Mendelsohn, M. L., and West, C. D. *J. Clin. Endocrinol. and Metabolism* **13**, 841 (1953).
860. Pearson, O. H., Hollander, V. P., West, C. D., Whitmore, W. F., and Randall, H. T. *J. Clin. Invest.* **31**, 653 (1952).
861. Peczenik, O. *Proc. Roy. Soc. Edinburgh* **B 62**, 59 (1944).
862. Pellegrino, P. C., Morris, G. M., and Trubowitz, S. *Proc. Soc. Exptl. Biol. Med.* **74**, 330 (1950).
863. Perera, G. A. *Proc. Soc. Exptl. Biol. Med.* **76**, 583 (1951).
864. Perlman, P. L., and Cassidy, J. W. *Proc. Soc. Exptl. Biol. Med.* **77**, 232 (1951).
865. Perlmutter, M., and Mufson, M. *J. Clin. Endocrinol. and Metabolism* **11**, 277 (1951).
866. Perry, W. F. *Endocrinology* **49**, 284 (1951).
867. Perry, W. F. *Can. J. Med. Sci.* **30**, 36 (1952).
868. Perry, W. F., Hawkins, W. W., and Cumming, G. R. *Am. J. Physiol.* **172**, 259 (1953).
869. Persky, L., and Jacob, S. *Proc. Soc. Exptl. Biol. Med.* **77**, 66 (1951).
870. Peschel, E., Black-Schaffer, B., and Schlayer, C. *Endocrinology* **48**, 399 (1951).
871. Pick, R., and Stamler, J. *Federation Proc.* **13**, 112 (1954).
872. Piliero, S. J., Landau, D., and Gordon, A. S. *Science* **112**, 559 (1950).
873. Pincus, G. *J. Clin. Endocrinol. and Metabolism* **3**, 195 (1943).
874. Pincus, G. *Psychosomat. Med.* **12**, 225 (1950).
875. Pincus, G., and Elmadjian, F. *Ann. Rev. Physiol.* **16**, 403 (1953).
876. Pincus, G., Romanoff, L. P., and Carlo, J. *J. Clin. Endocrinol. and Metabolism* **8**, 221 (1948).
877. Pincus, J. B., Natelson, S., and Lugovoy, J. K. *Proc. Soc. Exptl. Biol. Med.* **78**, 24 (1951).
878. Pine, I., Engel, F. L., and Schwartz, T. B. *J. Electroenceph. and Clin. Neurophysiol.* **3**, 301 (1951).

879. Pirani, C. L., Stepto, R. C., and Sutherland, K. *J. Exptl. Med.* **93,** 217 (1951).
880. Plotz, C. M., Howes, E. L., Blunt, J. W., Meyer, K., and Ragan, C. *Arch. Dermatol. and Syphilol.* **61,** 919 (1950).
881. Plotz, C. M., Howes, E. L., Meyer, K., Blunt, J. W., Lattes, R., and Ragan, C. *Am. J. Pathol.* **26,** 709 (1950).
882. Polley, H. F., and Mason, H. L. *J. Am. Med. Assoc.* **143,** 1474 (1950).
883. Polley, H. F., Ward, L. E., Slocumb, C. H., and Hench, P. S. *J. Lab. Clin. Med.* **38,** 937 (1951).
884. Priestley, J. T., Walters, W., Sprague, R. G., and Salassa, R. M. *Ann. Surg.* **134,** 464 (1951).
885. Prunty, F. T. G., Forsham, P. H., and Thorn, G. W. *Clin. Sci.* **7,** 109 (1948).
886. Quittner, H., Wald, N., Sussmann, L. N., and Antopol, W. *Blood* **6,** 513 (1951).
887. Rabinowicz, M., and Ratsimamanga, A. R. *Compt. rend. soc. biol.* **144,** 1466 (1950).
888. Ragan, C., Howes, E. L., Plotz, C. M., Meyer, K., and Blunt, J. W. *Proc. Soc. Exptl. Biol. Med.* **72,** 718 (1949).
889. Ralli, E. P. *Endocrinology* **39,** 225 (1946).
890. Ralli, E. P., and Dumm, M. E. *Endocrinology* **51,** 135 (1952).
891. Ralli, E. P., and Dumm, M. E. *Vitamins and Hormones* **11,** 133 (1953).
892. Ralli, E. P., and Graef, I. *Endocrinology* **32,** 1 (1943).
893. Ralli, E. P., and Graef, I. *Endocrinology* **37,** 252 (1945).
894. Rambo, J. H. T. *Arch. Otolaryngol.* **55,** 554 (1952).
895. Randoin, L., and Michaux, A. *Compt. rend.* **183,** 1055 (1926).
896. Ratsimamanga, A. R. *Compt. rend. soc. biol.* **138,** 19 (1944).
897. Ratsimamanga, A. R., and Giroud, A. *Compt. rend. soc. biol.* **138,** 19 (1944).
898. Rawlins, A. G. *Ann. Allergy* **10,** 440 (1952).
899. Read, C. H., Venning, E. H., and Ripstein, M. P. *J. Clin. Endocrinol. and Metabolism* **10,** 845 (1950).
900. Rebuck, J. W., and Mellinger, R. C. *Ann. N. Y. Acad. Sci.* **56,** 715 (1953).
901. Recant, L., Ott, W. H., and Fischel, E. E. *Proc. Soc. Exptl. Biol. Med.* **75,** 264 (1950).
902. Recant, L., Hume, D. M., Forsham, P. H., and Thorn, G. W. *J. Clin. Endocrinol. and Metabolism* **10,** 187 (1950).
903. Reid, E., Smith, R. H., and Young, F. G. *Biochem. J.* **42,** xix (1948).
904. Reinhardt, W. O., and Li, C. H. *Science* **117,** 295 (1953).
905. Reinhardt, W. O., Aron, H., and Li, C. H. *Proc. Soc. Exptl. Biol. Med.* **57,** 19 (1944).
906. Reiss, M. *Intern. Record of Med.* **166,** 196 (1953).
907. Reiss, M., and Halkerston, J. M. *J. Endocrinol.* **6,** 369 (1950).
908. Rhoads, C. P. *Cancer* **2,** 943 (1949).
909. Rice, K. K., and Richter, C. P. *Endocrinology* **33,** 106 (1943).
910. Rich, A. R., Berthrong, M., and Bennett, I. L. *Bull. Johns Hopkins Hosp.* **87,** 549 (1950).
911. Rich, A. R., Cochran, T. H., and McGoon, D. C. *Bull. Johns Hopkins Hosp.* **88,** 101 (1951).
912. Rich, A. R., Bennett, I. L., Cochran, T. H., Griffith, P. C., and McGoon, D. C. *Bull. Johns Hopkins Hosp.* **88,** 189 (1951).
913. Richards, J. B., and Sayers, G. *Proc. Soc. Exptl. Biol. Med.* **77,** 87 (1951).
914. Riedel, B. E., and Rossiter, R. J. *Can. J. Physiol. & Biochem.* **32,** 261 (1954).

915. Riedel, B. E., Logan, J. E., Deluca, H. A., and Rossiter, R. J. *Endocrinology*, **55**, 219 (1954).
916. Ritchie, A. C., Shubik, P., Lane, M., and Leroy, E. P. *Cancer Research* **13**, 45 (1953).
917. Rivero-Fontan, J., Paschkis, K. E., West, E., and Cantarow, A. *Endocrinology* **51**, 100 (1952).
918. Roberts, E., Karnofsky, D. A., and Frankel, S. *Proc. Soc. Exptl. Biol. Med.* **76**, 289 (1951).
919. Roberts, E., Ronzoni, E., and Frankel, S. *Cancer Research* **11**, 275 (1951).
920. Roberts, K. E., and Pitts, R. F. *Endocrinology* **50**, 51 (1952).
921. Roberts, K. E., and Pitts, R. F. *Endocrinology* **52**, 324 (1953).
922. Roberts, S. *J. Biol. Chem.* **200**, 77 (1952).
923. Roberts, S., and White, A. *Endocrinology* **48**, 741 (1951).
924. Robinson, H. J. *Federation Proc.* **10**, 332 (1951).
925. Robinson, H. J. *In* J. M. Yoffey, The Suprarenal Cortex. Academic Press, New York, 1953, p. 105.
926. Robinson, H. J., and Smith, A. L. *Ann. N. Y. Acad. Sci.* **56**, 757 (1953).
927. Robinson, H. J., Mason, R. C., and Smith, A. L. *Proc. Soc. Exptl. Biol. Med.* **84**, 312 (1953).
928. Robinson, S., Kinkaid, R. C., and Rhamy, R. K. *J. Appl. Physiol.* **2**, 399 (1950).
929. Robinson, W. D., Wolfson, W. Q., and Duff, I. F. *Ann. Rheumatic Diseases* **11**, 313 (1952).
930. Robson, H. N., and Duthie, J. J. R.: *Brit. Med. J.* **ii**, 971 (1950).
931. Robson, H. N., and Duthie, J. J. R. *Brit. Med. J.* **i**, 994 (1952).
932. Roche, P., Cummings, M. M., and Hudgins, P. C. *Am. Rev. Tuberc.* **65**, 603 (1952).
933. Rockwell, E. M., and Johnson, P. *J. Invest. Dermatol.* **19**, 137 (1952).
934. Roemmelt, J. C., Sartorius, O. W., and Pitts, R. F. *Am. J. Physiol.* **159**, 124 (1949).
935. Rogoff, J. M., Nixon, E. N., and Stewart, G. N. *Proc. Soc. Exptl. Biol. Med.* **41**, 57 (1939).
936. Rogoff, J. M., Quashnock, J. M., Nixon, N., and Rosenberg, A. W. *Proc. Soc. Exptl. Biol. Med.* **73**, 163 (1950).
937. Ronzoni, E., Roberts, E., Frankel, S., and Ramasarma, G. B. *Proc. Soc. Exptl. Biol. Med.* **82**, 496 (1953).
938. Rose, B. *Recent. Progr. Hormone Research* **7**, 375 (1952).
939. Rosemberg, E., and Lewis, R. A. *J. Appl. Physiol.* **3**, 164 (1950).
940. Rosemberg, E., Cornfield, J., Bates, R. W., and Anderson, E. *Endocrinology* **54**, 363 (1954).
941. Rosenbaum, J. D., Papper, S., and Ashley, M. M. *J. Clin. Invest.* **31**, 657 (1952).
942. Rosenberg, N., Kunderman, P. J., Vroman, L., and Moolten, S. E. *Arch. Surg.* **63**, 1 (1951).
943. Rosenberg, N., Kunderman, P. J., Vroman, L., and Moolten, S. E. *Arch. Surg.* **66**, 593 (1953).
944. Rosenman, R. H., Freed, S. G., and Friedman, M. *Proc. Soc. Exptl. Biol. Med.* **78**, 77 (1951).
945. Rosenthal, R. L., Etess, A. D., and Litwins, J. *Acta. Haematol.* **6**, 174 (1951).
946. Rosenthal, R. L., Wald, N., Yager, A., and Litwins, J. *Proc. Soc Exptl. Biol. Med.* **75**, 740 (1950).

947. Rosvold, H. E., Kaplan, S. J., and Stevenson, J. A. F. *Proc. Soc. Exptl. Biol. Med.* **80,** 60 (1952).
948. Rothman, S., and Dillaha, C. J. *Arch. Dermatol. and Syphilol.* **65,** 749 (1952).
949. Rowe, C. R., Grimson, K. S., Flowe, B. H., Lyons, C. K., Longino, F. H., and Taylor, H. M. *Surgery* **32,** 226 (1952).
950. Roy, A. C., Kar, A. B., and Sur, R. N. *Acta Endocrinol.* **14,** 254 (1953).
951. Russek, H. I., Russek, A. S., Doerner, A. A., and Zohman, B. L. *Arch. Internal Med.* **91,** 487 (1953).
952. Russell, J. A. *Ann. Rev. Physiol.* **13,** 327 (1951).
953. Russell, J. A., and Wilhelmi, A. E. *J. Biol. Chem.* **137,** 713 (1941).
954. Sala, G., Sereni, F., and Ballabio, C. B. *Lancet* **ii,** 1090 (1951).
955. Salassa, R. M. *J. Clin. Endocrinol. and Metabolism* **13,** 857 (1953).
956. Sames, G. L., and Leathem, J. H. *Proc. Soc. Exptl. Biol. Med.* **78,** 231 (1951).
957. Sandberg, A. A., Nelson, D. H., Palmer, J. G., Samuels, L. T., and Tyler, F. H. *J. Clin. Endocrinol. and Metabolism* **13,** 629 (1953).
958. Sapirstein, L. A., Brandt, W. L., and Drury, D. R. *Proc. Soc. Exptl. Biol. Med.* **73,** 82 (1950).
959. Sartorius, O. W., Calhoon, D., and Pitts, R. F. *Endocrinology* **51,** 444 (1952).
960. Sayers, G. *Physiol. Revs.* **30,** 241 (1950).
961. Sayers, G., and Sayers, M. A. *Ann. N. Y. Acad. Sci.* **50,** 522 (1950).
962. Sayers, G., Burns, T. W., Tyler, F. H., Jager, B. V., Schwartz, T. B., Smith, E. L., Samuels, L. T., and Davenport, H. W. *J. Clin. Endocrinol. and Metabolism* **9,** 593 (1949).
963. Schaffenburg, C., Masson, G. M. C., and Corcoran, A. C. *Proc. Soc. Exptl. Biol. Med.* **74,** 358 (1950).
964. Scheinberg, S. R., and Saltzstein, H. C. *Arch. Surg.* **63,** 413 (1951).
965. Schenker, V. *Endocrinology* **53,** 345 (1953).
966. Scherr, G. H. *Science* **116,** 685 (1952).
967. Schieve, J. F., Scheinberg, P., and Wilson, W. P. *J. Clin. Invest.* **30,** 1527 (1951).
968. Schiffer, F., and Wertheimer, E. J. *J. Endocrinol.* **5,** 147 (1947).
969. Schiller, E. *Brit. J. Ind. Med.* **10,** 1 (1953).
970. Schmidt, L. H., and Squires, W. L. *J. Exptl. Med.* **94,** 501 (1951).
971. Schneebeli, G. L., and Dougherty, T. F. *Am. J. Physiol.* **167,** 825 (1951).
972. Schneebeli, G. L., Dougherty, T. F., and Loewe, S. *Proc. Soc. Exptl. Biol. Med.* **77,** 407 (1951).
973. Schoch, E. P., and Glick, D. *J. Invest. Dermatol.* **20,** 119 (1953).
974. Schrek, R. *Endocrinology* **45,** 317 (1949).
975. Schrek, R. *Proc. Soc. Exptl. Biol. Med.* **76,** 557 (1951).
976. Schrek, R. *Proc. Soc. Exptl. Biol. Med.* **77,** 709 (1951).
977. Schricker, J. A., Fisher, G. R., Tullner, W. W., and Hertz, R. *Endocrinology* **51,** 394 (1952).
978. Schricker, J. A., Hertz, R., and Tullner, W. W. *Proc. Soc. Exptl. Biol. Med.* **78,** 522 (1951).
979. Schuler, W., Desaulles, P., and Meier, R. *Experientia* **10,** 142 (1954).
980. Schulman, I., Lanman, J. T., Laxdal, O. E., and Holt, L. E. *Pediatrics* **8,** 34 (1951).
981. Schultz, R. B., Winters, R. W., and Krehl, W. A. *Endocrinology* **51,** 336 (1952).
982. Schwartz, T. B., and Engel, F. L. *J. Biol. Chem.* **180,** 1047 (1949).
983. Schwartz, T. B., and Engel, F. L. *Proc. Soc. Exptl. Biol. Med.* **74,** 82 (1950).
984. Scott, J. L., Jr., and Engel, F. L. *Endocrinology* **53,** 410 (1953).

985. Secker, J. *J. Physiol.* **109,** 49 (1949).
986. Segaloff, A., and Horwitt, B. N. *Science* **118,** 220 (1953).
987. Segaloff, A., and Many, A. S. *Endocrinology* **49,** 390 (1951).
988. Seifter, J., Baeder, D. H., and Begany, A. J. *Proc. Soc. Exptl. Biol. Med.* **72,** 277 (1949).
989. Seifter, J., Worter, P. J., and Fitch, D. R. *Proc. Soc. Exptl. Biol. Med.* **73,** 131 (1950).
990. Seifter, J., Ehrich, W. E., Begany, A. J., and Warren, G. H. *Proc. Soc. Exptl. Biol. Med.* **75,** 337 (1950).
991. Seifter, J., Ehrich, W. E., Baeder, D. H., Butt, A. J., and Hauser, E. A. *Ann. N. Y. Acad. Sci.* **56,** 693 (1953).
992. Sellers, E. A., You, R. W., Ridout, J. H., and Best, C. H. *Nature* **166,** 514 (1950).
993. Selye, H. *J. Immunol.* **41,** 259 (1941).
994. Selye, H. *Endocrinology* **30,** 437 (1942).
995. Selye, H. *Brit. Med. J.* **ii,** 1129 (1949).
996. Selye, H. *Can. Med. Assoc. J.* **61,** 553 (1949).
997. Selye, H. *In* Stress. Acta Inc., Montreal, 1950.
998. Selye, H. *Can. Med. Assoc. J.* **64,** 489 (1951).
999. Selye, H. *Proc. Soc. Exptl. Biol. Med.* **76,** 510 (1951).
1000. Selye, H. *Federation Proc.* **11,** 144 (1952).
1001. Selye, H. *Proc. Soc. Exptl. Biol. Med.* **82,** 328 (1953).
1002. Selye, H. *J. Am. Med. Assoc.* **152,** 1207 (1953).
1003. Selye, H. *Abstr. 19th Intern. Physiol. Congr.,* Montreal, p. 750 (1953).
1004. Selye, H. *Recent Progr. Hormone Research* **8,** 117 (1953).
1005. Selye, H., and Carey, N. *J. Clin. Endocrinol. and Metabolism* **10,** 824 (1950).
1006. Selye, H., Hall, C. E., and Rowley, E. M. *Can. Med. Assoc. J.* **49,** 88 (1943).
1007. Selye, H., Hall, O., and Rowley, E. M. *Lancet* **i,** 301 (1945).
1008. Seneca, H., and Rockenbach, J. *Science* **116,** 14 (1952).
1009. Sensenbach, W., and Madison, L. *Am. J. Med.* **13,** 652 (1952).
1010. Sensenbach, W., Madison, L., and Ochs, L. *J. Clin. Invest.* **32,** 372 (1953).
1011. Shacter, B., Entenman, C., and Shimkin, M. B. *J. Natl. Cancer Inst.* **13,** 647 (1952).
1012. Shanaphy, J. F. *Am. J. Obstet. Gynecol.* **64,** 1261 (1952).
1013. Shapiro, R., Taylor, B., and Taubenhaus, M. *Proc. Soc. Exptl. Biol. Med.* **76,** 854 (1951).
1014. Sheehan, H. L., Summers, V. K., and Nichols, J. *Lancet* **i,** 312 (1953).
1015. Sheldon, W. H., Cummings, M. M., and Evans, L. D. *Proc. Soc. Exptl. Biol. Med.* **75,** 616 (1950).
1016. Sheldon, W. H., Heyman, A., and Evans, L. D. *Am. J. Syphilis, Gonorrhea, Veneral Diseases* **36,** 77 (1952).
1017. Shepanek, L. A. *Surg. Gynecol. Obstet.* **96,** 200 (1953).
1018. Shick, R. M., Baggenstoss, A. H., and Polley, H. F. *Proc. Staff Meetings Mayo Clinic* **25,** 135 (1950).
1019. Shuman, C. R., and Finestone, A. J. *Proc. Soc. Exptl. Biol. Med.* **73,** 248 (1950).
1020. Shwartzman, G. *Proc. Soc. Exptl. Biol. Med.* **75,** 835 (1950).
1021. Shwartzman, G. *Am. J. Pathol.* **27,** 714 (1951).
1022. Shwartzman, G., and Aronson, S. M. *Ann. N. Y. Acad. Sci.* **56,** 793 (1953).
1023. Shwartzman, G., and Fisher, A. *J. Exptl. Med.* **95,** 347 (1952).
1024. Siebenmann, R. *Schweiz. Z. Pathol. u. Bakteriol.* **15,** 174 (1952).

1025. Silber, R. H., and Porter, C. C.   *Endocrinology* **52**, 518 (1953).
1026. Simpson, S. A., and Tait, J. F.   *Endocrinology* **50**, 150 (1952).
1026a. Simpson, S. A., and Tait, J. F.   *Recent Progr. Hormone Research* **11**, 183 (1955).
1027. Simpson, S. A., Tait, J. F., and Bush, I. E.   *Lancet* **ii**, 226 (1952).
1028. Simpson, S. A., Tait, J. F., Wettstein, A., Neher, R., von Euw, J., and Reichstein, T.   *Experientia* **9**, 333 (1953).
1029. Simpson, S. A., Tait, J. F., Wettstein, A., Neher, R., von Euw, J., Schindler, O., and Reichstein, T.   *Experientia* **10**, 132 (1954).
1030. Sinex, F. M.   *Federation Proc.* **10**, 247 (1951).
1031. Singer, B., and Venning, E. H.   *Endocrinology* **52**, 623 (1953).
1032. Sirek, O. V., and Best, C. H.   *Proc. Soc. Exptl. Biol. Med.* **80**, 594 (1952).
1033. Sissons, H. A., and Hadfield, C. J.   *Brit. J. Surg.* **39**, 172 (1951).
1034. Sjögren, B.   *Acta Endocrinol.* **10**, 40 (1952).
1035. Slessor, A.   *J. Clin. Endocrinol. and Metabolism* **11**, 700 (1951).
1036. Slocombe, A. G., Hoagland, H., and Praglin, J.   *Federation Proc.* **2**, 149 (1952).
1037. Smith, D. J.   *Federation Proc.* **10**, 249 (1951).
1038. Smith, D. L., and d'Amour, F. E.   *J. Pharmacol. Exptl. Therap.* **106**, 429 (1952).
1039. Smith, G. H., and Opsahl, J. C.   *Yale J. Biol. and Med.* **23**, 361 (1951).
1040. Smith, J. M., Murphy, J. S., and Mirick, G. S.   *Proc. Soc. Exptl. Biol. Med.* **78**, 505 (1951).
1041. Smith, R. H.   *Biochem. J.* **44**, xlii (1949).
1042. Smith, R. W.   *Proc. Soc. Exptl. Biol. Med.* **78**, 868 (1951).
1043. Smith, R. W., and Steffensen, E. H.   *New Engl. J. Med.* **245**, 972, 1007 (1951).
1044. Smith, R. W., Morgulis, R. R., Brennan, M. J., and Monto, R. W.   *Science* **112**, 295 (1950).
1045. Smith, S. G., and Lasater, T. E.   *Proc. Soc. Exptl. Biol. Med.* **74**, 427 (1950).
1046. Smith, W. W., Smith, F., and Thompson, E. C.   *Proc. Soc. Exptl. Biol. Med.* **73**, 529 (1950).
1047. Snelling, C. E., Donohue, W. L., Laski, B., and Jackson, S. H.   *Pediatrics* **8**, 22 (1951).
1048. Snyder, J. G., and Wyman, L. C.   *Endocrinology* **49**, 205 (1951).
1049. Soffer, L. J., Gabrilove, J. L., and Dorrance, W. R.   *Proc. Soc. Exptl. Biol. Med.* **76**, 763 (1951).
1050. Soffer, L. J., Gabrilove, J. L., and Jacobs, M. D.   *J. Clin. Invest.* **28**, 1091 (1949).
1051. Soffer, L. J., Gabrilove, J. L., and Jailer, J. W.   *Proc. Soc. Exptl. Biol. Med.* **71**, 117 (1949).
1052. Soffer, L. J., Schwartzman, G., Schneierson, S. S., and Gabrilove, J. L.   *Science* **111**, 303 (1950).
1053. Sokoloff, L., Sharp, J. T., and Kaufman, E. H.   *Am. J. Pathol.* **27**, 706 (1951).
1054. Solomon, D. H., and Shock, N. W.   *J. Gerontol.* **5**, 302 (1950).
1055. Solotorovsky, M., Gregory, F. J., and Stoerk, H. C.   *Proc. Soc. Exptl. Biol. Med.* **76**, 286 (1951).
1056. Somerville, W.   *Brit. Med. J.* **ii**, 860 (1950).
1057. Somerville, W., Levine, H. D., and Thorn, G. W.   *Medicine* **30**, 43 (1951).
1058. Sommers, S. C., Wilson, J. C., and Hartman, F. W.   *J. Exptl. Med.* **93**, 505 (1951).
1059. Sourkes, T. L., and Heneage, P.   *Endocrinology* **49**, 601 (1951).
1060. Sourkes, T. L., and Heneage, P.   *Endocrinology* **50**, 73 (1952).
1061. Southam, C. M., and Babcock, V. I.   *Proc. Soc. Exptl. Biol. Med.* **78**, 105 (1951).

1062. Spain, D. C., Fontant, B. J., and Strauss, M. B. *J. Allergy* **23**, 242 (1952).
1063. Spain, D. M., and Molomut, N. *Am. Rev. Tuberc.* **62**, 337 (1950).
1064. Spain, D. M., and Thalhimer, W. *Proc. Soc. Exptl. Biol. Med.* **76**, 320 (1951).
1065. Spain, D. M., Molomut, N., and Haber, A. *Am. J. Pathol.* **26**, 710 (1950).
1066. Spain, D. M., Molomut, N., and Haber, A. *Science* **112**, 335 (1950).
1067. Spain, D. M., Molomut, N., and Haber, A. *J. Lab. Clin. Med.* **39**, 383 (1952).
1068. Spait, T. H., and Mednicoff, I. *Bull. New Engl. Med. Center* **13**, 201 (1951).
1069. Sparrow, E. M. *J. Endocrinol.* **9**, 101 (1953).
1070. Speirs, R. S. *Science* **113**, 621 (1951).
1071. Speirs, R. S., and Meyer, R. K. *Endocrinology* **45**, 403 (1949).
1072. Speirs, R. S., and Meyer, R. K. *Endocrinology* **48**, 316 (1951).
1073. Spencer, A. G. *Nature* **166**, 32 (1950).
1074. Spies, T. D., and Stone, R. E. *Lancet* ii, 890 (1949).
1075. Spies, T. D., Stone, R. E., Garcia-Lopez, G., Milanes, F., Lopez Toca, R., and Reboredo, A. *Lancet* ii, 241 (1950).
1076. Sprague, R. G. *Am. J. Med.* **10**, 567 (1951).
1077. Sprague, R. G., Mason, H. L., and Power, M. H. *Recent Progr. Hormone Research* **6**, 315 (1951).
1078. Sprague, R. G., Power, M. H., and Mason, H. L. *J. Am. Med. Assoc.* **144**, 1341 (1950).
1079. Sprague, R. G., Power, M. H., Mason, H. L., and Cluxton, H. E. *J. Clin. Invest.* **28**, 812 (1949).
1080. Sprague, R. G., Power, M. H., Mason, H. L., Albert, A., Mathieson, D. R., Hench, P. S., Kendall, E. C., Slocumb, C. H., and Polley, H. F. *Arch. Internal Med.* **85**, 199 (1950).
1081. Sprechler, M., and Vesterdal, J. *Acta Endocrinol.* **12**, 207 (1953).
1082. Stadie, W. C. *Ann. N. Y. Acad. Sci.* **54**, 671 (1951).
1083. Stadie, W. C. *Physiol. Revs.* **34**, 52 (1954).
1084. Stadie, W. C., and Haugaard, N. *J. Biol. Chem.* **177**, 311 (1949).
1085. Stadie, W. C., Haugaard, N., and Hills, A. G. *J. Biol. Chem.* **184**, 617 (1950).
1086. Stadie, W. C., Haugaard, N., and Marsh, J. B. *J. Biol. Chem.* **198**, 785 (1952).
1087. Stadie, W. C., Haugaard, N., and Vaughan, M. *J. Biol. Chem.* **199**, 729 (1952).
1088. Stamler, J., and Pick, R. *Proc. Soc. Exptl. Biol. Med.* **75**, 803 (1950).
1089. Stamler, J., Pick, R., and Katz, L. N. *Circulation* **4**, 461 (1951).
1090. Stand, R., Anderson, W., and Allcroft, W. M. *Biochem. J.* **28**, 642 (1934).
1091. Stebbins, R. B. *Endocrinology* **49**, 25 (1951).
1092. Stebbins, R. B. *Endocrinology* **49**, 671 (1951).
1093. Steen, A. S. *Brit. J. Ophthalmol.* **35**, 741 (1951).
1094. Stefanini, M., and Rosenthal, M. C. *Proc. Soc. Exptl. Biol. Med.* **75**, 806 (1950).
1095. Steffensen, E. H., Ivy, H. B., and Nagle, F. O. *Am. J. Ophthalmol.* **35**, 933 (1952).
1096. Steffensen, E. H., Olson, J. A., Margulis, R. R., and Smith, R. W. *Am. J. Ophthalmol.* **33**, 1033 (1950).
1097. Stein, K. F. *Proc. Soc. Exptl. Biol. Med.* **71**, 225 (1949).
1098. Stein, K. F., and Martin, C. *Proc. Soc. Exptl. Biol. Med.* **78**, 513 (1951).
1099. Stephens, C. A. L., Wallraff, E. B., Borden, A. L., Brodie, E. C., Holbrook, W. P., Hill, D. F., Kent, L. J., and Kemmerer, A. R. *Proc. Soc. Exptl. Biol. Med.* **74**, 275 (1950).
1100. Stepto, R. C., Pirani, C. L., Consolazio, C. F., and Bell, J. H. *Endocrinology* **49**, 755 (1951).

1101. Stepto, R. C., Pirani, C. L., Fisher, J. D., and Sutherland, K. *Federation Proc.* **11,** 429 (1952).
1102. Stickney, J. M., Heck, F. J., and Watkins, C. H. *Proc. Staff Meetings Mayo Clinic* **25,** 488 (1950).
1103. Stier, R. A., Feinberg, S. M., Malkiel, S., and Werle, M. D. *J. Allergy* **23,** 395 (1952).
1104. Solomon, D. H., and Humphreys, S. R. *Blood* **6,** 824 (1951).
1105. Stoerk, H. C. *Proc. Soc. Exptl. Biol. Med.* **62,** 90 (1946).
1106. Stoerk, H. C. *Federation Proc.* **9,** 345 (1950).
1107. Stoerk, H. C. *Proc. Soc. Exptl. Biol. Med.* **74,** 798 (1950).
1108. Stoerk, H. C. *Ann. N. Y. Acad. Sci.* **56,** 742 (1953).
1109. Stoerk, H. C., and Porter, C. C. *Proc. Soc. Exptl. Biol. Med.* **74,** 65 (1950).
1110. Stoerk, H. C., and Solotorovsky, M. *Am. J. Pathol.* **26,** 708 (1950).
1111. Straube, R. L., Patt, H. M., Tyree, E. B., and Smith, D. E. *Proc. Soc. Exptl. Biol. Med.* **71,** 539 (1949).
1112. Suguira, K. *Cancer Research* **13,** 431 (1953).
1113. Suguira, K., Stock, C. C., Dobriner, K., and Rhoads, C. P. *Cancer Research* **10,** 244 (1950).
1114. Sulzberger, M. B., and Witten, V. H. *J. Invest. Dermatol.* **19,** 101 (1952).
1115. Sulzberger, M. B., Witten, V. H., and Smith, C. C. *J. Am. Med. Assoc.* **151,** 468 (1953).
1116. Sure, B., and Theis, R. M. *Endocrinology* **24,** 673 (1939).
1117. Sutherland, E. W. *Ann. N. Y. Acad. Sci.* **54,** 693 (1951).
1118. Swann, H. G. *Physiol. Revs.* **20,** 493 (1940).
1119. Sweat, M. L., Abbott, W. E., Jefferies, W. McK., and Bliss, E. L. *Federation Proc.* **12,** 141 (1953).
1120. Swingle, W. W., Collins, E., Barlow, G., and Fedor, E. J. *Am. J. Physiol.* **168,** 118 (1952).
1121. Swingle, W. W., Perlmutt, J., Seay, P., and Collins, E. *Am. J. Physiol.* **169,** 278 (1952).
1122. Swingle, W. W., Barlow, G., Collins, E., Fedor, E. J., Welch, W. J., and Rampona, J. M. *Endocrinology* **51,** 353 (1952).
1123. Swingle, W. W., Collins, E., Barlow, G., Fedor, E. J., Ben, M., and Maxwell, R. *Proc. Soc. Exptl. Biol. Med.* **81,** 52 (1952).
1124. Swingle, W. W., Fedor, E. J., Ben, M., Maxwell, R., Baker, C., and Barlow, G. *Proc. Soc. Exptl. Biol. Med.* **82,** 571 (1953).
1125. Swingle, W. W., Perlmutt, J., Collins, E., Seay, P., Fedor, E., and Barlow, G. *Proc. Soc. Exptl. Biol. Med.* **78,** 865 (1951).
1126. Swingle, W. W., Barlow, G., Fedor, E., Ben, M., Maxwell, R., Collins, E., and Baker, C. *Am. J. Physiol.* **173,** 4 (1953).
1127. Syverton, J. T., Werder, A. A., Friedman, J., Roth, F. J., Graham, A. B., and Mira, O. J. *Proc. Soc. Exptl. Biol. Med.* **80,** 123 (1952).
1128. Szego, C. M. *Endocrinology* **50,** 429 (1952).
1129. Szego, C. M., and White, A. *Endocrinology* **44,** 150 (1949).
1130. Szilagyi, D. E., McGraw, A. B., and Smyth, N. P. D. *Ann. Surg.* **136,** 555 (1952).
1131. Tait, J. F., Grundy, H. M., and Simpson, S. A. *Lancet* i, 122 (1952).
1132. Talalay, P., Dobson, M. M., Ebersole, C. M., and Huggins, C. *Endocrinology* **50,** 574 (1952).
1133. Taubenhaus, M. *Ann. N. Y. Acad. Sci.* **56,** 666 (1953).

1134. Taubenhaus, M., and Amromin, G. D. *J. Lab. Clin. Med.* **36,** 7 (1950).
1135. Taubenhaus, M., Taylor, B., and Morton, J. B. *Endocrinology* **51,** 183 (1952).
1136. Teicher, R., and Nelson, C. T. *J. Invest. Dermatol.* **19,** 205 (1952).
1137. Teilum, G., Enbaek, H. C., and Simonsen, M. *Acta Endocrinol.* **5,** 181 (1950).
1138. Teng, C., Sinex, F. M., Deane, H. W., and Hastings, A. B. *J. Cellular Comp. Physiol.* **39,** 73 (1952).
1139. Tepperman, J., and Tepperman, H. M. *Ann. N. Y. Acad. Sci.* **54,** 707 (1951).
1140. Terry, L. L., and London, F. *Proc. Soc. Exptl. Biol. Med.* **73,** 251 (1950).
1141. Thiersch, J. B., Conroy, L., Stevens, A. R., and Finch, C. A. *J. Lab. Clin. Med.* **40,** 174 (1952).
1142. Thomas, L. *Ann. N. Y. Acad. Sci.* **56,** 799 (1953).
1143. Thomas, L., and Good, R. A. *Proc. Soc. Exptl. Biol. Med.* **76,** 604 (1951).
1144. Thomas, L., and Mogabgab, W. J. *Proc. Soc. Exptl. Biol. Med.* **74,** 829 (1950).
1145. Thorn, G. W. *J. Clin. Endocrinol. and Metabolism* **13,** 614 (1953).
1146. Thorn, G. W., Engel, L. L., and Lewis, R. A. *Science* **94,** 348 (1941).
1147. Thorn, G. W., Jenkins, D., and Laidlaw, J. C. *Recent Progr. Hormone Research* **8,** 171 (1953).
1148. Thorn, G. W., Goetz, F. C., Streeten, D. H. P., Dingman, J. F., and Arons, W. L. *J. Clin. Endocrinol. and Metabolism* **13,** 604 (1953).
1149. Thorn, G. W., Forsham, P. H., Frawley, T. F., Hill, F. R., Roche, M., Staehelin, D., and Wilson, D. L. *New Engl. J. Med.* **242,** 783, 824, 865 (1950).
1150. Thorn, G. W., Forsham, P. H., Frawley, T. F., Wilson, D. L., Renold, A. E., Fredrickson, D. S., and Jenkins, D. *Am. J. Med.* **10,** 595 (1951).
1151. Thorn, G. W., Jenkins, D., Laidlaw, J. C., Goetz, F. C., Dingman, J. F., Arons, W. L., Streeten, H. P., and McCracken, B. H. *New Engl. J. Med.* **248,** 232, 284, 323, 369, 414, 588, 632 (1953).
1152. Thygeson, P., Geller, H. O., and Schwartz, A. *Am. J. Ophthalmol.* **34,** 885 (1951).
1153. Tipton, S. R. *Am. J. Physiol.* **127,** 710 (1938).
1154. Toolan, H. W. *Proc. Am. Assoc. Cancer Research* **1,** 56 (1953).
1155. Torda, C., and Wolff, H. G. *Am. J. Physiol.* **163,** 755 (1950).
1156. Treager, H. S., Gabuzda, G. J., Zamcheck, N., and Davidson, C. S. *Proc. Soc. Exptl. Biol. Med.* **75,** 517 (1950).
1157. Tuerkischer, E., and Wertheimer, E. *J. Endocrinol.* **4,** 143 (1945).
1158. Turiaf, J., Zizine, L., Jeanjean, Y., and Depraiter, M. *Presse méd.* **61,** 817 (1953).
1159. Turner, L. B., and Grollman, A. *Am. J. Physiol.* **167,** 462 (1951).
1160. Turner, T. B., and Hollander, D. H. *Bull. Johns Hopkins Hosp.* **87,** 505 (1950).
1161. Umbreit, W. W. *Ann. N. Y. Acad. Sci.* **54,** 569 (1951).
1162. Umbreit, W. W., and Tonhazy, N. E. *J. Biol. Chem.* **191,** 249 (1951).
1163. Umbreit, W. W., and Tonhazy, N. E. *J. Biol. Chem.* **191,** 257 (1951).
1164. Ungar, G. *Am. J. Physiol.* **167,** 833 (1951).
1165. Ungar, G. *Lancet* **ii,** 742 (1952).
1166. Ungar, G., and Damgäard, E. *J. Exptl. Med.* **93,** 89 (1951).
1167. Uotila, U., and Pekkarinen, A. *Acta Endocrinol.* **6,** 23 (1951).
1168. Upton, A. C., and Coon, W. W. *Proc. Soc. Exptl. Biol. Med.* **77,** 153 (1951).
1169. Vaillancourt, de G., Grokoest, A. W., and Ragan, C. *Proc. Soc. Exptl. Biol. Med.* **78,** 383 (1951).
1170. Van der Scheer, J., Bohnel, E., Clarke, F. H., and Wyckoff, R. W. G. *J. Immunol.* **44,** 165 (1942).

1171. Van Ordstrand, H. S. *Ann. Internal Med.* **35,** 1203 (1951).
1172. Van Putten, L. M., Van Bekkum, D. W., and Querido, A. *Acta Endocrinol.* **12,** 159 (1953).
1173. Van Scott, E. J., Rothman, S., and Greene, C. R. *J. Invest. Dermatol.* **20,** 111 (1953).
1174. Vaughan, J. H., Bayles, T. B., and Favour, C. B. *Proc. Soc. Exptl. Biol. Med.* **76,** 274 (1951).
1175. Venning, E. H., Pattee, C. J., McCall, F., and Browne, J. S. L. *J. Clin. Endocrinol. and Metabolism* **12,** 1409 (1952).
1176. Verzár, F. *Ann. N. Y. Acad. Sci.* **54,** 716 (1951).
1177. Villee, C. A., and Hastings, A. B. *J. Biol. Chem.* **179,** 673 (1949).
1178. Vogel, A. W., and Leopold, I. H. *Am. J. Ophthalmol.* **36,** 690 (1953).
1179. Vogt, M. *In* J. M. Yoffey, The Suprarenal Cortex. Academic Press, New York, 1953, p. 59.
1180. Volk, B. W., Lazarus, S. S., and Tui, C. *Proc. Soc. Exptl. Biol. Med.* **80,** 1 (1952).
1181. Wahlstrom, R. C., and Johnson, B. C. *Proc. Soc. Exptl. Biol. Med.* **78,** 112 (1951).
1182. Walbach, S. B., and Maddock, C. L. *Arch. Pathol.* **53,** 54 (1952).
1183. Waldenström, J. *Acta Endocrinol.* **5,** 235 (1950).
1184. Wall, J. W., and Shure, N. *Arch. Otolaryngol.* **56,** 172 (1952).
1185. Wallach, D. P., and Reineke, E. P. *Endocrinology* **45,** 75 (1949).
1186. Ward, L. E., Slocumb, C. H., Polley, H. F., Lowman, E. W., and Hench, P. S. *Proc. Staff Meetings Mayo Clinic* **26,** 361 (1951).
1187. Watson, D., Bidmead, D. S., and Kersley, G. D. *Ann. Rheumatic Diseases* **11,** 292 (1952).
1188. Wayne, H. L., and Bayle, J. *J. Clin. Endocrinol. and Metabolism* **13,** 1070 (1953).
1189. Weimer, H. W., Boak, R. A., Bogen, E., Drusch, H. E., Miller, J. N., Moshin, J. R., and Carpenter, C. M. *Am. Rev. Tuberc.* **68,** 31 (1953).
1190. Weir, D. R., and Heinle, R. W. *Proc. Soc. Exptl. Biol. Med.* **75,** 655 (1950).
1191. Weir, D. R., Heinle, R. W., and Welch, A. D. *Proc. Soc. Exptl. Biol. Med.* **72,** 457 (1949).
1192. Weisberger, A. S., and Levine, B. *J. Clin. Invest.* **31,** 671 (1952).
1193. Weisman, P. A., Wight, A., Quinby, W. C., and Cannon, B. *Plastic and Reconstr. Surg.* **8,** 417 (1951).
1194. Welbourn, R. B., and Code, C. F. *Gastroenterology* **23,** 356 (1953).
1195. Wells, B. B., and Kendall, E. C. *Proc. Staff Meetings Mayo Clinic* **15,** 324 (1940).
1196. Welt, I., and Wilhelmi, A. E. *Yale J. Biol. and Med.* **23,** 99 (1950).
1197. Wentworth, J. H., and Billows, J. A. *Radiology* **59,** 559 (1952).
1198. Werder, A. A., Friedman, J., MacDowell, E. C., and Syverton, J. T. *Cancer Research* **13,** 158 (1953).
1199. Werner, S. C. *J. Clin. Endocrinol. and Metabolism* **13,** 1332 (1953).
1200. West, C. D., Pearson, O. H., and Kappas, A. *J. Clin. Endocrinol. and Metabolism* **13,** 841 (1953).
1201. West, C. D., Hollander, V. P., Whitmore, W. F., Randall, H. T., and Pearson, O. H. *Cancer* **5,** 1009 (1952).
1202. Wheeler, C. E., Cawley, E. P., and Curtis, A. C. *J. Invest. Dermatol.* **20,** 385 (1953).

1203. White, A., Hoberman, H. D., and Szego, C. M.   *J. Biol. Chem.* **174**, 1049 (1948).
1204. White, M. R., Finkel, A. J., and Schubert, J.   *Proc. Soc. Exptl. Biol. Med.* **80**, 603 (1952).
1205. Whitney, J. E., and Bennett, L. L.   *Endocrinology* **50**, 657 (1952).
1206. Wick, A. N., Drury, D. R., and Mackay, E. M.   *Ann. N. Y. Acad. Sci.* **54**, 684 (1951).
1207. Weiland, P., Heer, J., Schmidlin, J., and Miescher, K.   *Helv. Chim. Acta* **34**, 354 (1951).
1208. Wilhelmj, C. M., Walderman, E. B., and McGuire, T. F.   *Proc. Soc. Exptl. Biol. Med.* **77**, 379 (1951).
1209. Wilkins, L., Lewis, R. A., Klein, R., and Rosemberg, E.   *Helv. Paediat. Acta* **5**, 418 (1950).
1210. Wilkins, L., Lewis, R. A., Klein, R., and Rosemberg, E.   *Bull. Johns Hopkins Hosp.* **86**, 249 (1950).
1211. Wilkins, L., Lewis, R. A., Klein, R., and Rosemberg, E.   *Am. J. Diseases Children* **80**, 883 (1950).
1212. Wilkins, L., Crigler, J. F., Silverman, S. H., Gardner, L. I., and Migeon, C. J.   *J. Clin. Endocrinol. and Metabolism* **12**, 1015 (1952).
1213. Wilkins, L., Lewis, R. A., Klein, R., Gardner, L. I., Crigler, J. F., Jr., Rosemberg, E., and Migeon, C. J.   *J. Clin. Endocrinol. and Metabolism* **11**, 1 (1951).
1214. Williams, W., Whismant, C., and Fitts, W. T.   *Am. J. Physiol.* **170**, 57 (1952).
1215. Willis, G. C.   *Can. Med. Assoc. J.* **69**, 17 (1953).
1216. Winter, C. A., and Flataker, L.   *Federation Proc.* **9**, 137 (1950).
1217. Winter, C. A., and Flataker, L.   *J. Pharmacol. Exptl. Therap.* **105**, 358 (1952).
1218. Winter, C. A., Hollings, H. L., and Stebbins, R. B.   *Endocrinology* **52**, 123 (1953).
1219. Winter, C. A., Silber, R. H., and Stoerk, H. C.   *Endocrinology* **47**, 60 (1950).
1220. Winternitz, W. W., and Long, C. N. H.   *Proc. Soc. Exptl. Biol. Med.* **81**, 683 (1952).
1221. Winters, R. W., Schultz, R. B., and Krehl, W. A.   *Endocrinology* **50**, 377 (1952).
1222. Winters, R. W., Schultz, R. B., and Krehl, W. A.   *Endocrinology* **50**, 388 (1952).
1223. Winters, R. W., Schultz, R. B., and Krehl, W. A.   *Proc. Soc. Exptl. Biol. Med.* **79**, 695 (1952).
1224. Wolfson, W. Q.   *J. Clin. Endocrinol. and Metabolism* **13**, 125 (1952).
1225. Wolfson, W. Q., Beierwaltes, W. H., Robinson, W. D., Duff, I. F., Jones, J. R., Knorpp, C. T., and Eya, M.   *J. Lab. Clin. Med.* **36**, 1005 (1950).
1226. Wood, J. W.   *Federation Proc.* **12**, 159 (1953).
1227. Woodbury, D. M.   *J. Pharmacol. Exptl. Therap.* **105**, 46 (1952).
1228. Woodbury, D. M., and Davenport, V. D.   *Am. J. Physiol.* **157**, 234 (1949).
1229. Woodbury, D. M., and Sayers, G.   *Proc. Soc. Exptl. Biol. Med.* **75**, 398 (1950).
1230. Woodbury, D. M., Ghosh, B. N., and Sayers, G.   *J. Clin. Endocrinol. and Metabolism* **11**, 761 (1951)
1231. Woodbury, D. M., Cheng, C. P., Sayers, G., and Goodman, L. S.   *Am. J. Physiol.* **160**, 217 (1950).
1232. Woodbury, D. M., Emmett, J. W., Hinckley, G. V., Jackson, N. R., Newton, J. D., Bateman, J. H., Goodman, L. S., and Sayers, G.   *Proc. Soc. Exptl. Biol. Med.* **76**, 65 (1951).
1233. Woodruff, M. F. A., and Boswell, T.   *J. Endocrinol.* **10**, 86 (1953).
1234. Woods, A. C.   *Am. J. Ophthalmol.* **33**, 1325 (1950).
1235. Woods, A. C.   *Am. J. Ophthalmol.* **34**, 945 (1951).
1236. Woods, A. C., and Wood, R. M.   *Arch. Ophthalmol.* **47**, 477 (1952).

1237. Woolley, G. W.   *Ann. N. Y. Acad. Sci.* **50,** 616 (1949).
1238. Woolley, G. W.   *Proc. Soc. Exptl. Biol. Med.* **74,** 286 (1950).
1239. Woolley, G. W.   *Cancer Research* **11,** 291 (1951).
1240. Woolley, G. W., and Little, C. C.   *Cancer Research* **5,** 193 (1945).
1240a. Woolley, G. W., and Peters, B. A.   *Proc. Soc. Exptl. Biol. Med.* **82,** 286 (1953).
1241. Wragg, L. E., and Speirs, R. S.   *Proc. Soc. Exptl. Biol. Med.* **80,** 680 (1952).
1242. Wrong, N. M., and Smith, R. C.   *Can. Med. Assoc. J.* **68,** 50 (1952).
1243. Wyman, G. J.   *Am. J. Ophthalmol.* **35,** 1206 (1952).
1244. Wyman, L. C., Fulton, G. P., and Shulman, M. H.   *Ann. N. Y. Acad. Sci.* **56,** 643 (1953).
1245. Wyman, L. C., Fulton, G. P., Sudak, F. N., and Patterson, G. N.   *Proc. Soc. Exptl. Biol. Med.* **84,** 280 (1953).
1246. Yoffey, J. M. (ed.)   *In* The Suprarenal Cortex. Academic Press, New York, 1953, p. 31.
1247. Yoffey, J. M., Metcalf, W. K., Herdan, G., and Nairn, V.   *Brit. Med. J.* **i,** 660 (1951).
1248. Zarrow, M. X., and Baldini, J. T.   *Endocrinology* **50,** 555 (1952).
1249. Zarrow, M. X., and Money, W. L.   *Endocrinology* **44,** 345 (1949).
1250. Zarrow, M. X., and Zarrow, I. G.   *Anat. Record* **108,** 112 (1950).
1251. Zarrow, M. X., and Zarrow, I. G.   *Proc. Soc. Exptl. Biol. Med.* **76,** 620 (1951).
1252. Zeckwer, I. T.   *Endocrinology* **52,** 39 (1953).
1253. Zierler, K. L., and Lilienthal, J. L., Jr.   *Am. J. Med.* **4,** 186 (1948).
1254. Zilversmit, D. B., Stern, T. N., and Overman, R. R.   *Am. J. Physiol.* **164,** 31 (1951).
1255. Zimmerman, H. J., Parrish, A. E., and Alpert, L. K.   *Proc. Soc. Exptl. Biol. Med.* **73,** 81 (1950).
1256. Zimmerman, H. J., Parrish, A. E., and Alpert, L. K.   *Am. J. Med.* **10,** 235 (1951).
1257. Zingg, W., and Perry, W. F.   *J. Clin. Endocrinol. and Metabolism* **13,** 712 (1953).
1258. Zintel, H. A., Wolferth, C. C., Jeffers, W. A., Hafkenschiel, J. H., and Lukens, F. D. W.   *Ann. Surg.* **134,** 351 (1951).
1259. Zondek, B., and Burstein, S.   *Endocrinology* **50,** 419 (1952).
1260. Zubiran, J. M., Kark, A. E., Montalbetti, J. A., Morel, C. J. L., and Dragstedt, L. R.   *Arch. Surg.* **65,** 809 (1952).
1261. Zubirán, S., and Gómez-Mont, F.   *Vitamins and Hormones* **11,** 97 (1953).
1262. Zuckerman, S.   *In* J. M. Yoffey, The Suprarenal Cortex. Academic Press, New York, 1953, p. 69.
1263. Zweifach, B. W., Shorr, E., and Block M. M.   *Ann. N. Y. Acad. Sci.* **56,** 626 (1953).

CHAPTER XV

Clinical Endocrinology

BY K. E. PASCHKIS AND A. E. RAKOFF

CONTENTS

I. Introduction

The task of reviewing, within the framework of this book, recent progress in clinical endocrinology, is not easy. In view of the extensive literature, we had to impose upon ourselves certain limitations. It would hardly appear likely that the student or the practicing physician would turn, for detailed practical guidance, to a book dealing quite predominantly with the chemistry and physiology of the hormones. Rather, the biochemist and physiologist would seek here information on the clinical applications of the scientific achievements in his field. In fact, the line between physiological and clinical investigations is being reduced almost to the vanishing point. We are therefore presenting advances in principles and approaches rather than details of procedures or of therapeutic results.

II. Anterior Pituitary Gland

A. General Remarks

In the not so distant past, the anterior pituitary was supposed to secrete some twenty different hormones. For every and any effect of crude pituitary extracts a separate hormone entity was postulated and a name coined. Chemical isolation procedures have yielded six hormones, and a better knowledge of metabolic interrelations has led to an understanding of multiple effects of individual single hormones.

The anterior pituitary then produces six hormones, growth hormone (also called somatotropic hormone), thyrotropic hormone (TSH), adrenocorticotropic hormone (ACTH), and the three gonadotropic hormones: follicle-stimulating hormone (FSH), luteinizing or interstitial-cell-stimulating hormone (LH, ICSH), and luteotropic hormone (LTH), identical with lactogenic hormone.

At present the trend appears to reverse itself. Observations have been recorded suggesting the existence of two adrenocorticotropic hormones (one responsible for adrenocortical growth, another for secretory function) (8, 125), as well as of two thyrotropic hormones (73). Regarding growth hormone, a separation of the diabetogenic factor from the protein anabolic growth hormone has been reported (169). These problems are under current investigation and cannot as yet be evaluated from the standpoint of the physiologist or clinician. Even if the fractionations and chemical separations mentioned above should be borne out by further work, the question will have to be answered whether the pituitary gland at any time secretes these factors separately or whether it secretes a complex hormone with different actions residing in different parts of the molecule, parts which could be separated *in vitro*.

Regarding ACTH, various preparations have been made and have be-

come available for clinical use.   The action of these preparations is qualitatively identical.   A highly purified preparation, designated ACTX (Corticotropin A), is much less subject to destruction than is ACTH (the crude
preparation), when administered intramuscularly.   Actide corticotropin
(Corticotropin B) is a preparation obtained by peptic hydrolysis of ACTH.
It evidently represents the active peptides of the larger ACTH molecule.
It is readily inactivated or destroyed in the extravascular tissues, and at
present appears to offer little advantage for clinical use (239).

As far as the six hormone entities are concerned, it appears that their
secretion is to a large extent independent and that the gland does not function as a unit.   There is no "panhyperpituitarism," hyperfunction of the
entire anterior pituitary, nor is there a concerted hypofunction, panhypopituitarism, except that due to destruction of the glandular tissue.   As a
matter of fact, interrelations of secretion of individual pituitary hormones
appear to be the result of retrograde action upon the pituitary from secretions of the secondary glands.   Examples of this type of interrelation may
be the dependence of growth hormone secretion upon thyroid hormone
secretion, and the release of LH through changes in estrogen levels.

The independence of secretion of individual pituitary hormones has
become more intelligible through the discovery of individual cell types
responsible for elaboration of the individual hormones.   Traditionally, the
hormone-secreting cells of the anterior pituitary are classified, on the basis
of the staining properties of their granules and of the morphologic characteristics of the Golgi apparatus, as acidophilics (eosinophilics) and basophilics.
The elaboration of FSH, TSH, and ACTH is tentatively ascribed to the
basophilics, and that of the other three hormones to the eosinophilics.
It has, however, become evident, that basophilic staining is the common
property of specialized cells, differentiated by histochemical reactions.   A
basophilic FSH-producing cell is different from the basophilic TSH-produc-
ing cell (78, 79, 165, 166).   No similar recent differentiations have been
reported within the eosinophilic cells; but an older observation of carmino-
philic cells in the cat pituitary, believed responsible for LH production,
points in the same direction (60).

B. Acromegaly and Gigantism

The clinical picture of gigantism and acromegaly was outlined in *The
Hormones*, Volume II.   More information has accumulated regarding the
natural history of acromegaly.   The excessive secretion of growth hormone
by the eosinophilic cells occurs periodically.   Periods of excessive secretion
are followed by periods of relative quiescence.   Such cycles may be repeated several times in the course of years.   It is of more than academic
interest to recognize the active phase of the disease earlier than in retro-

spect by increased growth phenomena, such as enlargement of feet or separation of teeth. Bio-assay of growth hormone in the blood has been reported in one case (115), but assay methods which would lend themselves readily to clinical work have yet to be developed. Increased levels of serum inorganic phosphate have been found in the active phase of acromegaly; the levels return to normal under treatment with sex steroids, as well as with radiation therapy (115).

Diabetes has long been known to be a frequent complication of acromegaly. In many respects it appears to be the human equivalent to the growth-hormone–induced diabetes of dogs. Even the reversibility of early stages of growth-hormone–induced diabetes in dogs has been paralleled in diabetes of acromegaly: in an acromegalic, observed and studied repeatedly for several years, a diabetic glucose tolerance made its appearance and reverted to normal following intensive roentgen irradiation of the pituitary (152). It has been pointed out that diabetes in acromegaly is more frequent in acromegalics in whose families non-acromegalic members have diabetes. This would tentatively suggest that an inherited "vulnerability" of the islets ("doglike" islets) is a prerequisite for the growth hormone to exert its diabetogenic effect. The bearer of "nonvulnerable" islets would respond much like those species (e.g., the rat) in whom diabetes cannot readily be induced by growth hormone.

It has long been known that goiter is a frequent occurrence in acromegalics. Also, in many cases a high BMR is recorded (39). In view of the well-known stimulation of the thyroid by anterior-pituitary TSH, the obvious assumption was that in this type of hyperpituitarism an increased secretion of TSH was associated with the increased secretion of growth hormone, and that the former caused goiter and increased function of the thyroid. The situation is undoubtedly more complicated and the whole story has yet to be told. Cushing and his collaborators pointed out early that the histologic appearance of goiters of acromegalics differed markedly from that in thyrotoxicosis; also thyroidectomy caused regression of the elevated BMR and of other manifestations only in exceptional cases of acromegaly (39). More recently it has been found that the I-131 uptake of the thyroid gland of acromegalics was normal, regardless as to whether there was a goiter or whether the BMR was elevated or normal (136). These observations have suggested, as did the older clinical observations of Cushing and associates that the high BMR of many acromegalics may be due to factors other than increased thyroid function (136). TSH levels in the serum of acromegalics have been found elevated, regardless of the presence or absence of goiter, and of the levels of the BMR (42). Neither the significance of this finding in the pathophysiology of acromegaly nor the cause of excessive secretion of TSH (believed to be secreted by the basophilic anterior-pituitary cells) is at present understood.

Treatment. In the opinion of most clinicians, indication for surgical treatment is not the demonstrable evidence for presence of an adenoma, but rather a rapidly progressive encroachment of the optic nerves.   Other cases should be subjected to roentgen ray treatment; its effectiveness has been greatly improved with the use of higher doses of radiation than were previously employed (112).   If there is no evidence of increased hormonal activity, nor evidence of expansive growth of an adenoma, treatment should be withheld.   Treatment with androgens or with androgens and estrogens has been tried in an attempt to suppress growth hormone secretion through the suppressive action of the steroid hormones upon the anterior pituitary. With this form of therapy return of the elevated serum inorganic phosphorus levels to normal, as well as improvement of the diminished carbohydrate tolerance, has been observed, but it is as yet too early to judge the practical usefulness of steroid hormone therapy in acromegaly (115).

C. Hypopituitarism

Destruction of the anterior pituitary, resulting from tumor (chromophobe adenoma, parapituitary tumors, *e.g.*, craniopharyngioma) or postpartum necrosis, causes panhypopituitarism.   Depending on the amount of pituitary tissue destroyed, the severity of the disorder may vary from complete loss of pituitary function to milder forms.   It is interesting that in the incomplete forms not all pituitary functions are diminished or abolished in the same proportions (151).   It is our impression that the gonadotropin secretion is most sensitive and is usually lost first.   The various combinations of functional deficiencies seen in tumor cases, in which the nontumorous part of the gland is exposed to compression from the tumor, cannot be explained readily by topographic arrangement of the cells responsible for the respective hormone secretion, but perhaps rather by differences of vulnerability of these cells to the pressure exerted on all.

The essential findings are described in Volume II.   It should be added that sodium loss, evidently due to adrenocortical "salt hormone deficiency," is found in severe cases (151); this is of interest because it has been stated that in rodents "salt hormone" function of adrenal cortex is not governed by the anterior pituitary.   The lack of response of the adrenal cortex to ACTH, mentioned in Volume II, pertains only to single intramuscular injections.   With repeated injections, and especially with intravenous drip infusion, the atrophic adrenal can be stimulated, and evidence of function be obtained (rise of 17-ketosteroid and 11-oxysteroid excretion, eosinopenia).   We have been able to stimulate the adrenal cortex 18 years after post-partum necrosis (152).   The therapeutic regime as outlined in Volume II now includes cortisone and hydrocortisone.

1. *Single-Hormone Hypopituitarism*

In contradistinction to panhypopituitarism due to destruction of the anterior pituitary, the secretion of individual single hormones may be deficient, in the presence of normal secretion of the others.

Hypogonadotropism occurs both in males and females and causes clinical pictures indistinguishable from that due to primary gonadal failure.   The distinction is made chiefly by assay of urinary levels of gonadotropin excretion, which is high in primary gonadal failure and absent in hypogonadotropism.   This will be further discussed in the chapters on Testes (VII) and Ovaries (V).

Hypothyrotropism is indistinguishable clinically from hypothyroidism due to primary thyroid failure.   A distinction based on thyrotropin assay, analogous to the gonadotropin studies mentioned above, can be attempted only in laboratories equipped for TSH assays.   In view of the difficulties of this assay procedure the two types of hypothyroidism are usually differentiated by the response to injections of TSH (102, 159).   An increase of I-131 uptake, protein-bound iodine (PBI), or BMR can be expected only if the thyroid gland is intact, and can therefore be accepted as evidence of hypothyrotropism.

There is at present no information as to whether these single-hormone deficiencies of the anterior pituitary are the result of an anatomical derangement or whether the lack of secretion of the respective hormones is due only to a functional disturbance.

The growth-hormone deficiency causing pituitary dwarfism of the Lorain-Levy type does not belong strictly in the category of single-hormone deficiencies, because in this disorder growth-hormone deficiency is usually associated with gonadotropin deficiency and consequent hypogonadism In exceptional cases, however, gonadal structure and function are normal (88, 180), and these cases legitimately can be considered under the heading of single-hormone deficiencies.   As is discussed below under the heading of pituitary dwarfism, there is evidence for morphological changes in the eosinophilic cells of the anterior pituitary.

2. *Pituitary Dwarfism*

Dwarfism due to lack of growth hormone secretion is seen in children in whom the anterior pituitary is destroyed or encroached upon by tumors, in most instances craniopharyngiomas.   Almost always the growth deficiency in these cases is associated with deficiencies of the tropic hormones; in other words, the growth deficiency is part of panhypopituitarism.   In cases of pituitary dwarfism without clinically or radiologically demonstrable pituitary lesion (Lorain-Levy type) the diagnosis is difficult. In most cases hypogonadism is present (but of course recognizable only after the age of puberty), but normal sexual development and even fertility have been recorded in exceptional cases (88, 180). Delayed closure of the epiphyses appears to be typical. Increased insulin sensitivity might be expected in view of the "anti-insulin action" of growth hormone; however, few observations are available, and it would appear far from certain whether a normal insulin sensitivity would rule out growth-hormone deficiency in the presence of normal adrenocortical function. The pituitary dwarfism of the Lorain-Levy type may be compared with the dwarfism of the dwarf Silver mouse. In the latter dwarfism and hypogonadism occur as a recessive hereditary trait (188, 189). The pituitary shows absence of eosinophilic cells. A marked diminution of the number of eosinophilic cells and degenerative changes in those present have been reported in a case of pituitary dwarfism in a woman (88).

Whereas most growth-hormone preparations have been found to be entirely ineffective in man, inducing neither N-retention nor growth in length (in spite of good potency in the rat assay), positive results have been obtained recently by several investigators (114, 184). These active growth hormone preparations are not yet commercially available.

II. Thyroid Gland

A. Diagnostic Procedures

A considerable amount of work during the last several years has been concerned with diagnostic methods based on the role of the thyroid gland in iodine metabolism. The interest in these aspects has overshadowed that in the older procedures, especially in the determination of the BMR. Conditions other than those of abnormal thyroid function are known to effect the oxygen consumption. In clinical diagnostic use, one of the most common, and most disturbing, factors is that of emotional unrest, causing high oxygen consumption probably by release of epinephrine. Techniques have been introduced for performing the test in barbiturate-induced sleep or anesthesia; under such conditions the high oxygen consumption resulting from nervous factors is reduced to normal values, whereas the high BMR due to hyperthyroidism is not appreciably affected (13, 172).

The use of I-131 tracer studies and PBI determinations has added materially to the knowledge of the pathophysiology of thyroid disease, and these procedures have proved invaluable as diagnostic tools. Obviously, a study of these parameters of thyroid function gives no information regarding the "target" response of the body tissues. This is highlighted by the unexplained syndrome of "hypometabolism" in which the basal oxygen consumption may be as low as in severe hypothyroidism, but in which the manufacture and release of thyroid hormone is entirely normal, as are all other body functions dependent on thyroid hormone.

1. *Tracer Studies*

The physiological basis for the diagnostic use of I-131 tracers has been discussed in Volume II. In many clinics the uptake is determined 24 hours after an oral tracer dose by measuring the radiation over the thyroid region; it has generally been confirmed that the uptake is high (more than 40%) in hyperthyroidism, and low (less than 10%) in hypothyroidism. The tracer dose employed depends largely upon the sensitivity of the measuring instruments, and of course on the particular parameters to be studied. With the use of scintillation counters the dose can be as low as 1 to 10 microcuries (3). Urinary excretion studies can supplement the measurements over the thyroid, being inversely related to the latter. Most of the iodine not taken up by the gland is rapidly excreted in the urine. It should be remembered that conditions other than thyrotoxicosis cause increased uptake of I-131; the high uptake of iodine-deficiency goiter, long postulated on the basis of animal experiments, has now been demonstrated in an endemic goiter population not exposed to iodine prophylaxis, such as the use of iodized table salt (198). The high uptake in some goitrous cretins is discussed on page 837. Drug-induced situations of internal iodine starvation also may cause a temporary rise of uptake considerably above normal. This is the case in individuals in whom the iodine-trapping mechanism was blocked by thiocyanate with development of goiter. Following withdrawal of thiocyanate the uptake by the iodine-starved goitrous gland is very high. A similar situation occurs after withdrawal of thiouracils in experimental animals but has not been definitley observed in man (41).

Conversely, low uptakes occur in conditions other than hypothyroidism. Antithyroid drugs (thiourea derivatives, imidazoles) as well as thiocyanate block the "uptake," though in different ways. Thiocyanate truly blocks iodide uptake under ordinary conditions; only the presence of very large amounts of iodide would force the latter into the gland through the block. The antithyroid drugs do not materially interfere with the iodide-concentrating mechanism but inhibit incorporation of molecular iodine into the amino acid. Since, 24 hours after the tracer dose, mainly the protein-bound moiety remains, the result at this time interval is one of decreased "uptake." Low uptake values are also obtained during, and for several weeks after, medication with thyroid hormone, evidently through suppression of TSH secretion from the anterior pituitary. Administration of large amounts of iodine, either as iodide, or as organically bound compound (as used in roentgenographic studies of cholecystograms, uterosalpingo-grams, urograms, bronchograms, encephalograms) also causes low tracer uptakes. Two factors may be involved. The iodide may cause a real block, perhaps by inactivating TSH. Furthermore, if the iodide pool (circulating and extracellular) is considerably increased, the tracer is di-luted much more than in an average pool; the uptake of the tracer may thereby be smaller owing to dilution. In renal disease the urinary excretion of iodide is diminished, both because of impaired glomerular filtration and increased tubular reabsorption. Tracer studies based on urinary excretion of I-131 would give erroneous results. The increased I-127 pool also causes a greater dilution of the administered tracer, and the accumulation of I-131 in the thyroid is delayed. However, values obtained by direct measurement over the thyroid at 26 hours are within normal range (157).

These physiological and pharmacological factors influencing I-131 uptake are of interest not only because of the light they throw on the pathophysi-ology of thyroid disease, but also because they are pitfalls in diagnostic interpretation of the results of such studies. Another interesting finding is the almost complete obliteration of I-131 uptake in acute thyroiditis, without other evidence of hypothyroidism.

Several procedures, using I-131 tracers, have been introduced, which add materially to the information obtained by determining the "uptake" after 24 hours. By repeated measuring of activity over the neck following a tracer dose, the concentration of I-131 in the thyroid is found to be a linear function of the square root of time. The slope of this curve is called the accumulation gradient (9, 74).

The mathematical relationship is simple, but rather obscure in terms of biological significance. The linear relationship just mentioned is found in euthyroid and hypothyroid individuals, but not in hyperthyroidism. The method is valuable inasmuch as it establishes the accumulation gradient within 1 to 2 hours after administration of the tracer and permits study of factors influencing the iodine accumulation of the thyroid (168). For example, the activity of antithyroid drugs has been screened by this method (200).

Determination of thyroidal and renal plasma I-131 clearance rates has been recommended as a routine diagnostic test. Whereas determinations of the 24-hour uptake fail to correlate with the clinical condition in 7 % to 10 % of cases, the claim is made that the clearance rates show no overlapping of values in normal and hyperthyroid individuals (17). It will be interest-ing to see whether such a sharp dividing line between euthyroid and hyper-thyroid individuals will be confirmed on a larger material which will include mild cases of hyperthyroidism. It may appear questionable to some whether there is biologically a sharp line of demarcation between a thyroid gland with "top normal" function and that functioning slightly in excess of normal.

Another parameter of thyroid function which can be studied by the use of I-131 tracers is that of release of thyroid hormone from the gland. By daily direct determination of the radiation over the thyroid for several days, a measure for the secretion of thyroid hormone can be obtained (9). This is also referred to as "physiological decay," and the time during which the gland loses 50% of its activity (corrected for physical decay) is called the biological half life. For more precise determinations, it is necessary to administer antithyroid drugs (thiouracil derivatives or imidazole derivatives) after the tracer dose in order to block uptake of that iodide moiety originating from the secreted thyroid hormone (9). Because of the necessary length of observation period, this method is not generally used in clinical practice. Measurements of protein-bound iodine I-131 following a tracer dose reflect the secretory activity of the thyroid (186). Under certain circumstances the values of PBI_{131} do not correlate with the clinico-physiological status of the individual. In some cases of postoperative myxedema the PBI_{131} values have been found high in the presence not only of clinical manifestations of hypothyroidism but also of low PBI_{127} values. This has been thought to indicate a very small but very active thyroid remnant with rapid turnover rate but small total output (19). By determining total plasma I-131 and protein-bound plasma I-131, a conversion ratio has been calculated by the formula conversion ratio = $\dfrac{PBI_{131}}{\text{total plasma I-131}} \times 100$. This ratio is believed to be related to the rate at which the gland utilizes iodine for hormone synthesis and release. There is some doubt as to the validity of such a simple formula on physiological grounds; correlation with the clinical condition has been found only in hyperthyroidism, whereas the "conversion ratio" of hypothyroid and euthyroid individuals did not differ materially (183).

A further application of the tracer technique, made possible through the introduction of the highly sensitive scintillation counter, is the scanning procedure (68, 69). One or several scintillation counters are moved, by a motor-driven device, across the thyroid region: the impulses are transmitted to a stylus which records them on graph paper. Such "scintigrams" record the outlines of the thyroid gland and have been used for determining thyroid weight as a basis for calculating therapeutic doses (69). Inactive and hyperactive nodules can be demonstrated, inasmuch as the scintigram will show regions of diminished or absent density or regions of increased density (68). The procedure has furthermore been used as an aid in differential diagnosis of masses of the neck, and by scanning body regions other than the neck, for detection of thyroid cancer metastases (10, 195).

2. *Protein-Bound Iodine (PBI) (207)*

Methods for determination of PBI have been improved; a discussion of these methods is beyond the scope of this review. In interpreting PBI values as indicative of abnormal thyroid function, sources of error, other than those of a technical nature, must be kept in mind. The most important error results from the presence in the body fluids of large amounts of nonhormonal iodine. This may be the result of ingestion of large amounts of iodide; organic iodine compounds used as contrast media in various diagnostic procedures (cholecystography, pyelography, bronchography encephalomyelography, uterosalpingography) cause even greater and more prolonged spuriously high PBI values. It appears that in the presence of large amounts of iodide in the serum some iodine will come down with the protein-precipitate, causing high yields in this fraction. High PBI levels are regularly found in pregnancy (129). This finding poses an intriguing question. Evidently the normal pregnant woman exhibits no signs of hyperthyroidism. Is this because the body "needs" more thyroid hormone in pregnancy? Spuriously low PBI levels have been obtained during the use of mercurial diuretics; during the technical procedures of digestion insoluble mercuric iodates or iodides are formed (139).

B. Thyrotoxicosis

No progress has been made regarding the etiology of thyrotoxicosis.

Advances in diagnostic methods are discussed on page 827. Diagnosis is not difficult in fairly typical cases; certain types of patients pose a more difficult diagnostic problem, in which the use of the newer procedures outlined above are of particular value. One is the "thyrocardiac" individual, presenting cardiac failure, frequently without a history typical of thyrotoxicosis; nor are the clinical manifestations unequivocal. Frequently a failure to respond to digitalis first arouses suspicion. Signs and symptoms such as auricular fibrillation, tachycardia, and nervousness can be the result of the cardiac condition and therefore help little in establishing the diagnosis of thyrotoxicosis. In the presence of cardiac failure and passive congestion a true basal metabolic rate cannot be determined. PBI and tracer studies have been of great diagnostic value in these cases. Control of the thyrotoxicosis will improve the cardiac condition significantly. Whether thyrotoxicosis can cause failure, and consequent passive congestion, of an otherwise entirely normal heart, is debatable. The fact that the majority of "thyrocardiac" patients are in the older age group would lend support to the assumption that thyrotoxicosis causes failure only of a damaged heart. The argument loses practical significance if one keeps in mind that the pre-existing cardiac damage (most frequently arteriosclerotic in origin) may be "subclinical," and may revert to a symptomless stage after the thyrotoxic component is controlled.

Another group of thyrotoxic patients in whom the diagnosis can be established only with the aid of the tests described, is that of certain severely agitated psychoneurotics. It is generally believed that psychic factors can precipitate or aggravate thyrotoxicosis; equally thyrotoxicosis is apt to aggravate, or bring into the open, psychoneurotic tendencies. Regardless of what is cause or effect in an individual case, control of thyrotoxicosis, if present, is of greatest importance. Sleeping BMR, PBI, and tracer studies will help to establish the presence or absence of thyrotoxicosis.

Therapy. No basically new approach in the treatment of thyrotoxicosis has evolved. However, a great amount of experience has accumulated with the use of the methods outlined in Volume II.

Numerous antithyroid drugs have been tested. Those which have proved most useful, and are generally used, are two thiouracil derivatives, propylthiouracil and methylthiouracil, and an imidazole derivative, 1-methyl-2-mercaptoimidazole (trade name Tapazole). They can be used in preparation for surgery or for definitive medical treatment. If given preoperatively, the increased vascularity and friability of the hyperplastic gland may cause technical difficulties at operation. Iodide (*e.g.*, in the form of liquor iodi comp., Lugol's solution) causes "involution" of the hyperplastic gland, with decreased vascularity and friability; iodide is therefore administered, together with the antithyroid drug, for a few days prior to operation. The mechanism of action of iodide under these conditions is but poorly understood. It may enter the gland but is not oxidized, and rapidly leaves the gland again. It may possibly inactivate endogenous TSH. If the antithyroid drugs are used for definitive medical treatment, they should be administered for long periods of time. It is advisable to continue maintenance doses for 8 to 12 months after a euthyroid condition has been attained. Then treatment is discontinued. Fifty to sixty per cent of the patients remain in remission; the others relapse. It has been possible in some instances to keep up maintenance treatment for several years, if for any reason the other forms of therapy, surgery or radiation, were inadvisable.

Toxic reactions are observed in a small number of cases both with propyl- and methyl-thiouracil, and with Tapazole. The total incidence is less than 2%; in a few instances agranulocytosis has occurred.

Experience with radioactive iodine has also been greatly extended. There still is considerable difficulty in determining the dose which will reduce thyroid activity to normal but not cause hypothyroidism (see also p. 830). In many cases there occurs an exacerbation of the thyrotoxicosis during the first two to three weeks following the administration of I-131, owing to the liberation of stored hormone incident to the destruction of thyroid tissue. This exacerbation is rarely serious, but thyroid crisis has been observed. We have seen the most gratifying results of I-131 therapy in the thyrocardiac patient, but the temporary exacerbation of the thyrotoxicosis may cause the patient to go through a period of more severe cardiac failure.

The possibility, that the radiation from therapeutic doses of I-131 may be carcinogenic is considered remote by most investigators. However, thyroid cancer has been observed in rats treated with I-131 (65). Furthermore, the possibility of late development of radiation-induced fibrosis has to be considered. Many clinics therefore prefer not to treat thyrotoxicosis with I-131 in individuals younger than 35 to 40 years.

1. *Ophthalmopathy*

Interest in the ophthalmopathic facet of Graves' disease continues. There appears to be no question that the severe ophthalmopathy is caused by a pituitary factor, as outlined in Volume II. In the older experiments, in which exophthalmos had been induced in experimental animals with pituitary extracts, this action had been ascribed to TSH or to a pituitary factor closely allied to TSH. Dobyns and Steelman have succeeded in separating the exophthalmos-producing principle from the thyroid-stimulating hormone (49). This still leaves open the question whether the pituitary actually secretes the two factors separately, or whether the separation is a chemical one only. The most severe forms of ophthalmopathy are usually observed following thyroidectomy for thyrotoxicosis; occasionally they occur during treatment with antithyroid drugs. As long as the thyrotoxicosis is uncontrolled the ophthalmic picture is usually less severe; in exceptional cases the dissociation of thyrotoxicosis and ophthalmopathy is complete, the latter occurring in euthyroid individuals or in spontaneous myxedema, in either case without any indication of a preceding hyperthyroid episode.

The early changes in the retrobulbar tissue, both in exophthalmos produced experimentally by injections of TSH and in human cases, are those of edema; the edema fluid is rich in mucopolysaccharides (127). The muscle changes are swelling, edema, and lymphocytic infiltration (pseudohypertrophy). Whereas these muscular changes occur quite predominantly in the extrinsic muscles of the eye, they are demonstrable to a minor extent also in skeletal muscles.

Occasionally severe ophthalmopathy occurs simultaneously with pretibial, localized myxedema (38, 224). The cutaneous localized infiltration shows the same chemical characteristics as the retrobulbar tissue (227). Injection of hyaluronidase into such lesions has been reported to cause resolution, evidently owing to the specific depolymerizing action of this enzyme on the mucopolysaccharides (77, 142); in one case of our own

observation we were not able to show any changes following local hyaluronidase injection (152). Similarly, hyaluronidase has been injected into the
retrobulbar tissue in cases of severe ophthalmopathy, but results have been
unsatisfactory (77, 107). Because TSH was believed to be the active
factor from the anterior pituitary, several investigators have studied the
TSH levels in blood or the urinary excretion of TSH in ophthalmopathic
cases (5, 42, 164). In most instances high blood levels or high urinary
excretion was found (5), but this appears not to be invariably the case (42
164). If the *in vitro* separation of an exophthalmos-inducing factor from
the thyroid-stimulating moiety is confirmed, the TSH studies just described
would suggest that TSH secretion usually, but not invariably, parallels
that of exophthalmos-inducing factor.

The question whether the ophthalmopathy associated with Graves' disease is always and in all cases due to a pituitary factor (so-called "thyrotropic ophthalmopathy") can as yet not be definitely answered. Most
investigators favor a unitarian etiology for both the severe ophthalmopahty
and the ocular manifestations of "classical" Graves' disease. However,
the occurrence of two etiologically different types of ophthalmopathy has
been suggested, "thyrotropic" and "thyrotoxic" in nature (143). In the
latter the ocular changes are supposed to be the direct effect of excessive
thyroid-hormone secretion. If this type actually exists, the eye manifestation would be expected to subside after the thyrotoxicosis is brought under
control. In many instances improvement of the eyes following control of
the thyrotoxicosis is more apparent than real; the lid retraction (a definitely
"thyrotoxic" manifestation) subsides and, with weight gain, the cheeks fill
out, giving the eyes a more normal appearance, whereas the exophthalmos
may not recede, or actually increase, even if slightly. However, occasional
observations do suggest a real regression of exophthalmos and of paresis
of extrinsic ocular muscles.

It is most important to prevent the development of the most severe or
malignant forms. Since they occur mostly postoperatively, thyroidectomy
should be advised against in thyrotoxic patients in whom severe ophthalmopathy, including swelling of the lids, pain, extensive muscle paresis,
and edema of the conjunctiva, is present. In rare instances severe deterioration of the ophthalmopathy has been observed during thiouracil
therapy. In such cases the thyrotoxicosis should be brought under control
very gradually, by relatively small doses of antithyroid drugs (propylthiouracil, Tapazole) or by small, repeated doses of I-131, or by external
roentgen radiation.

The treatment of the ophthalmopathy is directed to the anterior pituitary. If at the time of treatment the patient is euthyroid or hypothyroid
(regardless of whether this was preceded by thyrotoxicosis or not), desic-

cated thyroid, given to tolerance, is frequently beneficial.   Results appear better, the earlier treatment is started.   Thyroid hormone probably acts by suppressing secretion of TSH (or an exophthalmos factor) from the anterior pituitary.   Estrogens, in large doses, have been used successfully in severe cases; they also probably act by suppressing the anterior pituitary. Roentgen ray irradiation to the pituitary was, up to recently, used mostly as an adjunct treatment of questionable value, combined with either thyroid or estrogen medication; recently, however, cases have been reported, in which roentgen radiation to the pituitary alone yielded good results (15).

2.   *Thyrotoxic Myopathy (141, 167, 240)*

It has long been known that some muscle wasting is a common occurrence in thyrotoxicosis.   The increased (endogenous) creatinuria, as well as the increased creatinuria following an exogenous creatine load (decreased "creatine tolerance"), is probably the result of the muscle dysfunction induced by the excess circulating thyroid hormone.   In rare instances of thyrotoxicosis muscle wasting is very much more pronounced, and may be the presenting feature of the disease; these cases are referred to as thyrotoxic myopathy.   Doubt has been voiced as to whether this syndrome represents only a quantitative exaggeration of the more moderate muscle involvement commonly seen in many severe thyrotoxic patients; it has been suggested that a qualitatively different, but as yet unknown, process is involved.   Good recovery is observed when the thyrotoxicosis is brought under control.   Diagnosis may be difficult, inasmuch as the myopathy can dominate the picture to the point of "masking" the thyrotoxicosis; careful history and examination and appropriate tests will aid in establishing the diagnosis.   When the presence of thyrotoxicosis and of myopathy has been established, the cases have to be differentiated from myasthenia gravis.   The latter disease is occasionally associated with thyrotoxicosis. Whether there is any causal relationship is as yet unknown.   Commonly, the response to prostigmine is used to differentiate between myasthenia gravis associated with thyrotoxicosis, and thyrotoxic myopathy.   The former does, and the latter does not, respond to the drug.   However, the specificity of the response to prostigmine has been questioned, and cases responding to a test dose of prostigmine have been reported as thyrotoxic myopathies.   This must remain a debate in terminology, until other tests characteristic for myasthenia gravis are also employed in the study of these cases (response to curare, electromyogram, etc.).   The review of clinical problems in neuromuscular physiology by Denny-Brown is helpful in understanding these complex problems (46).   In patients simultaneously afflicted with myasthenia gravis and with thyrotoxicosis, the myopathy has been reported to show improvement, deterioration, or no change after control of the thyrotoxicosis. It is trite to state that more studies of this problem are needed.

Cases are on record of simultaneous occurrence of thyrotoxicosis and periodic familial paralysis (141, 228). As far as can be judged from the reported cases, the periodic paralysis appears to be improved but not abolished following control of the thyrotoxicosis.

3. *Thyroid Crisis*

The exact nature of thyroid crisis or thyroid storm has yet to be completely unraveled. The factors most commonly precipitating crisis are (*1*) any operations performed upon untreated or incompletely controlled thyrotoxicosis cases (surgical storm), and (*2*) severe infections as well as major upsets (medical storm). Whether these factors act as "stressors" through the adrenal cortex (see below) is at present a matter for speculation. There seems, however, little doubt that thyroid crisis represents thyrotoxicosis at peak severity. Why, in this condition, the heat-regulating processes of the body break down, with the skin becoming hot and dry, rather than dripping with perspiration, is not understood. It has long been suggested that an acute adrenocortical insufficiency occurs during thyroid storm and may in part be responsible for the fatal outcome. Treatment with cortisone has been successful, and in several cases the development of post-operative, "surgical" storm was prevented by early treatment with ACTH or with cortisone, when an emergency operation became necessary in uncontrolled thyrotoxicosis (209).

C. Cretinism

Cretinism is clinically subdivided into endemic and sporadic cretinism· Prima facie this is a geographical classification of cretinism occurring in goiter areas (iodine-deficiency areas) or in nongoitrous regions. The endemic cretin is identified with the bearer of a degenerated thyroid, usually but not always goitrous, incapable of manufacturing thyroid hormone. The sporadic cretin, on the other hand, is identified with a congenital defect, a thyroid aplasia.

Tracer studies with I-131 on cretins believed to have congenital thyroid aplasia have in some instances yielded some small uptake in the region of the thyroid, indicating the presence of some thyroid tissue. This confirms old histological reports in such cases, in which small amounts of thyroid tissue rather than complete absence was reported. It will be interesting to see whether studies, including the response to TSH, of a larger material will detect early cases of TSH-hypopituitarism in "sporadic" cretins.

The occurrence of goitrous cretins outside areas of goiter endemics has been described; studies reported in some of these cases raise intriguing

problems regarding the pathophysiology.   The uptake of I-131 is rapid
and of a high order (81, 122, 137, 199) such as is usually seen in the thyrotoxic gland and has been found in endemic iodine-deficiency goiter (198).
The utilization of the iodine by the thyroid gland appears to differ in
different cases.   In Stanbury's cases the rapid purging of the gland by
thiocyanate indicates that the iodide was not oxidized, and therefore not
incorporated into organic compounds (199).   The deficiency in these
cases was similar to that induced by thiourea and imidazole compounds.
In contradistinction, in McGirr's cases thiocyanate failed to purge the
gland, suggesting oxidation of iodide with subsequent organic binding.
This was further supported by the presence of protein-precipitable I-131
in the blood.   It was assumed that this was an abnormal compound,
which was not identified (137).   In Hamilton's cases analysis of thyroid
tissue following administration of I-131 yielded radioactive fractions
corresponding to thyroxine and diiodotyrosine; these studies were done
before chromatographic analysis of these compounds had been introduced.
In these cases it was assumed that the thyroid gland was capable of synthesizing thyroid hormone but not of releasing it (81).

Hurxthal has claimed that some goitrous cretins subsequently, and
without treatment, become euthyroid or even hyperthyroid (94, 96).
These cases have not been reported in great detail, and from the data
recorded the diagnosis of cretinism may be questioned.

It is now generally recognized that treatment of cretins, even when
started early and continued uninterruptedly, frequently fails to bring
about normal mental development; mental development improves during
therapy, but in many instances does not reach normality.   The nature of
the changes underlying the lack of mental development is not known.
Recent observations indicate the presence of electroencephalographic
abnormalities in untreated cretins (43, 217); it has been suggested that
the EEG pattern becomes normal under thyroid medication only in those
cases in whom mental development is fully restored and not in those who
remain mentally deficient in spite of treatment (217).   This has not been
borne out regularly in our as yet limited experience (47a).

On the basis of the concept of a reciprocal relationship of the pituitary
tropic hormones with those of the secondary glands, one would expect a
high TSH secretion from the anterior pituitary in severe hypothyroidism
including congenital thyroaplasia (an analogy could be drawn between
the latter and ovarian agenesis, associated with high FSH excretion).
However, this is not always the case.   In a study of cretins Paschkis and
D'Angelo found absence of TSH in the blood of an untreated cretin, 11
years of age, TSH becoming detectable only after thyroid medication.
This suggests that the anterior pituitary which has not been exposed to

thyroid hormone may be incapable of manufacturing and/or secreting TSH. In untreated cretinous babies the expected high TSH levels have been found. Studies regarding secretion of hormones other than TSH by such pituitaries will be of interest.

Familial incidence of sporadic cretinism has been reported (22) (familial indicence is of course common in endemic cretinism). On the other hand, the occurrence of cretinism in one of two identical twins has been reported, unfortunately very briefly and without detailed data (175).

D. GOITER

Iodine deficiency is firmly established as the most common cause of goiter (see Chapter V, by Salter, in Volume II of *The Hormones*). Interesting historical aspects are touched upon by Salter (177). Certain aspects of the pathophysiology of human iodine-deficiency goiter had not been studied with modern methods, because iodine prophylaxis, in the form of iodized table salt, has been in general use for several decades in the goiter regions and goiter belts of Europe and North America. Recently such studies were carried out in an endemic goiter area in the Argentine Andes, where the natural conditions of the iodine-deficiency goiters had heretofore never been interfered with by administration of extra iodide. The great avidity of these goiters for iodine was demonstrated by the very high uptake of tracer doses of I-131 (198). Further results of this study will be awaited with interest.

Colloid goiters, clinically and pathologically indistinguishable from those occurring in iodine-deficiency regions, are observed sporadically in regions such as the Atlantic seaboard, where iodine supply in water and food is adequate. "Endemic" occurrence of goiter in locations not deficient in iodine has long been recorded (*e.g.*, Derbyshire goiter in England) (138). Following the observations of goitrogenic action of cabbage, brassica seeds, and other vegetable matter in rabbits and rats, Astwood isolated an active goitrogen, *l*-5-2-vinyl-thiooxazolidone, from rutabaga and studied the goitrogenic action of a great number of vegetables (6, 7). The chemical composition as well as the goitrogenic action is similar to that of thiourea and its derivatives. The subject has been reviewed by Greer (75) and by Fertman *et al.* (54). Only very few observations in human beings are recorded in whom the presence of a goiter could with great probability be traced to the ingestion of large amounts of goitrogenic vegetables (55, 138). Means has coined the term "struma cibaria" for this type of goiter (138). Careful nutritional histories should be obtained in all goiter cases, especially outside iodine-deficiency areas. However, it appears very doubtful to us that the majority of colloid goiters occurring in regions with adequate iodine supply can be explained on this basis.

The etiology of most cases is still obscure; an endogenous deficiency in iodine utilization may be thought of hypothetically (76).

In the medical treatment of colloid goiter, medication with desiccated thyroid has been revived (76). Thyroid medication evidently acts by suppressing endogenous TSH secretion. The latter was previously increased, causing enlargement of the thyroid, because the normal-size gland has, for some reason, been unable to produce adequate amounts of thyroid hormone.

E. Thyroiditis

Whereas the etiology of acute nonsuppurative thyroiditis remains obscure in most instances, an interesting physiopathologic aspect has been detected. The uptake of tracer doses of I-131 is greatly diminished or absent. No other manifestations of hypothyroidism are present; PBI values are normal or even slightly elevated. The reason for the depressed I-131 uptake is not evident; administration of TSH will increase the uptake, though to a lesser degree than in euthyroid individuals, in thyrotoxicosis factitia, or in hypopituitarism. Curiously, administration of TSH brings about an improvement, at least a temporary one, of the condition. Various hypotheses have been offered in explanation of the low I-131 uptake and the response to TSH, but none is entirely satisfactory (176).

Milder cases last only a few days; but in more severe cases fever, pain, and swelling may continue for several weeks. In the absence of any knowledge regarding the etiology (bacteriological cultures have been almost uniformly sterile), treatment is symptomatic. Antibiotics have been without effect in almost all instances. There have been reports of beneficial action of external radiation and of thiouracil therapy; more recently cortisone or ACTH has been used successfully; their beneficial action is probably due to the anti-inflammatory action of the adrenal steroids (230).

1. *Subacute Thyroiditis (36a)*

Attention has been drawn to this form of thyroiditis, which is not infrequently confused with Riedel's struma. A history of an acute phase is frequently obtained, but sometimes the onset is insidious, and fever and severe general "constitutional" manifestations are absent. The gland is enlarged and very hard; it may or may not be tender. Even in the absence of fever the sedimentation rate is elevated, and the I-131 uptake quite as low as in acute thyroiditis. Extensive fibrosis of the surrounding structures, characteristic of Riedel's struma, is absent. The histological picture (surgical or needle biopsy) is characterized by pseudotubercles and giant cells. In contradistinction to Riedel's struma, subacute thyroiditis is self-limited and responds rather well to roentgen-ray therapy; operations are unnecessary. The etiology is as obscure as that of other forms of thyroiditis.

IV. The Adrenal Gland

A. ADRENOCORTICAL HYPOFUNCTION

Chronic hypoadrenocorticalism in human beings is due to: (1) Destruction of the adrenal cortex by chronic disease (Addison's disease); (2) adrenalectomy performed for hypertension or advanced cancer of prostate or breast; (3) hypopituitarism resulting in lack of stimulation of the adrenal cortex by ACTH; (4) "salt-losing adrenogenital syndrome" (see p. 851). Acute adrenocortical insufficiency probably plays a role in Waterhouse-Friderichsen syndrome (acute fulminant bacteremia, mostly meningococcemia, with extensive hemorrhage into the adrenal cortices), and perhaps as a phenomenon of adrenocortical exhaustion in severe infection without hemorrhage into the adrenals.

B. ADDISON'S DISEASE

"Cortical atrophy," so called, and tuberculosis are the causes of Addison's disease in the vast majority of cases. The term "atrophy" is a misnomer, unfortunately ingrained in the clinical literature. The anatomical changes in the adrenal cortex in these cases are the result of cytotoxic damage, necrosis, and fibrosis. In a small number of cases histoplasmosis, involving the adrenal cortex, causes Addison's disease; cases of amyloidosis (84, 225), leucemic infiltration, and extensive tumor metastases are rare occurrences (29). It is believed that severe clinical manifestations occur only after 90% of the adrenal cortex is destroyed.

1. Diagnostic Procedures

The absence of response to ACTH has been widely employed, with ACTH given either in a single intramuscular injection or by intravenous drip infusion. The end points studied are the decrease in circulating eosinophils and the rise in urinary 17-ketosteroids and 11-oxysteroids after the more intensive stimulation by continuous infusion. The eosinophil response to epinephrine, however, cannot be used as a test for adrenal responsiveness, since it is very doubtful whether in man epinephrine in doses employed actually fires the pituitary-adrenal system (213). The most significant tests are those based on the disturbance of electrolyte metabolism. The response to NaCl deprivation combined with potassium administration (Cutler-Power-Wilder) still appears to be the most reliable and simple procedure, if it is carried out with due safeguards for the possi-

ble precipitation of a crisis (40). The deranged Na and K metabolism
can be demonstrated by testing the composition of sweat (35, 126) or
saliva (57, 226). These studies have yielded interesting results regarding
hormonal control of electrolyte balance, but they would at present appear
less suitable than urine studies for diagnostic purposes. Tests designed
to demonstrate the abnormal electrolyte metabolism are the most significant, not only because most of the clinical manifestations of Addison's
disease are due to the abnormal electrolyte metabolism, but also because
only the "salt hormone deficiency" is a constant finding in all cases of
Addison's disease. Disturbances of carbohydrate metabolism are present
in the majority of cases, in varying severity. Severe hypoglycemia after
prolonged fast and severe hypoglycemia following the hyperglycemia
induced by intravenous glucose administration are indicative of the "sugar
hormone deficiency." In many instances this deficiency is not severe
enough to be demonstrable by these procedures. Increased sensitivity
to insulin ("hypoglycemia irresponsiveness") is present in the majority of
cases. Because most Addison patients lapse into hypoglycemic coma
when tested with intravenous administration of insulin by the standard
procedures, modifications of the test have been devised; Thorn suggests
giving insulin in increasing doses with the meals (214); Engel has devised
an insulin-glucose test, in which the glucose administration prevents
severe hypoglycemic manifestations (52). Cases of "dissociated" Addison's disease are of considerable interest; in the presence of the classical
picture, with pigmentation, hypotension, weakness, and demonstrable
defect in Na and K metabolism, the response to insulin is normal, and low
normal urinary excretion of glucocorticoids is present (152). Similarly,
the very low or absent 17-ketosteroid excretion is not always found; in
some instances values in the lower range of normal excretion have been
reported (131). These "dissociated" cases cannot be adequately interpreted at this time. Even if in man the different hormones are secreted
by different zones of the cortex, as has been suggested in the rat and mouse,
it is difficult to visualize a zonal destruction in the cortex. No autopsy
reports have come to our attention which would throw light on this problem, if indeed the pathologist will hold the answer. Also follow-up studies
of such patients will be desirable in order to see whether eventually the
"dissociated" disturbance will, in later stages of the disease, embrace all
hormones, resulting in what may be called panhypocorticalism.

2. *Addison's Disease and Pregnancy*

Before adrenocortical hormones became available for treatment of
Addison's disease, the occurrence of pregnancy in Addison patients was
extremely rare and almost invariably fatal (25). With present therapy,

several women have been carried through pregnancy successfully and have given birth to viable children. The most critical periods are the first trimester, during which profuse vomiting may precipitate crisis, and the delivery, with the incident stress and blood loss. Adrenalectomized pregnant rats have been known not only to tolerate pregnancy, but to be maintained easier and better. This was ascribed to the deoxycorticosterone-like action of progesterone. However, in human beings, there is evidence that the placenta produces corticoids (and probably ACTH). These compounds are not produced in amounts sufficient for complete maintenance, but may contribute to make maintenance after the third month easier (25, 99, 150).

3. Treatment of Addison's Disease

The use of deoxycorticosterone acetate and salt was discussed in Volume II of *The Hormones*. The compound is now available in "buccal tablets"; resorption is through the mucosa of the oral cavity into the major circulation. Dosage is of necessity less accurate than with administration by injection or pellet implantation; the degree of accuracy or inaccuracy depends entirely upon the intelligent and meticulous co-operation of the patient. Recently deoxycorticosterone trimethylacetate was introduced. This is a "long-acting" preparation, permitting of maintenance by one intramuscular injection about every four weeks (215). The required dose of deoxycorticosterone and of salt must be determined empirically for every case; overdosage must be avoided because it causes hypertension, edema, and cardiac failure. Standardization is carried out with the use of body weight, blood pressure, hematocrit and serum electrolyte levels as criteria; one of the most valuable and sensitive effects is that on heart size, as determined by roentgenograms. Cortisone is used as an adjunct to the treatment with deoxycorticosterone. Even when treatment with the latter succeeds in normalizing the patient by all objective criteria, additional therapy with small doses of cortisone (12.5 to 25 mg. per day) frequently adds to the sense of well-being. Whether this is due to the action on carbohydrate metabolism or rather to the cerebral "euphorizing" action of cortisone, is not immediately apparent. Perhaps the fact may be significant in this respect that the abnormal electroencephalographic pattern of Addison's disease is corrected by cortisone therapy, but not by the use of deoxycorticosterone. Perhaps the most important place of cortisone is in prevention of crisis. Patients can be instructed to take extra cortisone if they have a sore throat or any other febrile episode, even before they report to their physician. Corticosterone (Compound B of Kendall) has been investigated as a therapeutic agent in Addison's disease, but this steroid has not been available for large-scale clinical testing (34).

The fact that glycyrrhizinic acid, the active ingredient of Liquorice, is capable of correcting the electrolyte disturbance of Addison's disease is, at this time at least, less of practical than of theoretical interest (24, 71).

Addisonian crisis is treated by intravenous infusion of glucose-saline, plasma, antibiotics, and aqueous adrenocortical extract, and by intramuscular injections of cortisone and deoxycorticosterone acetate.

C. Cushing's Syndrome

1. *Pathogenesis*

Cushing's syndrome has been recognized as a form of hyperadrenocorticalism, as was described in Volume II, page 692. The adrenals are bilaterally diffusely hyperplastic in some cases, whereas in others an adrenocortical cancer is present. In a small number of cases no morphological changes are found in the adrenals; if no ovarian tumor is present, an excessive function of adrenals of normal size and structure may be assumed. This, however, is an assumption, since it is conceivable that normal amounts of hormone might be secreted by the glands, and the picture of hyperfunction be simulated by abnormal metabolism of the hormone. The tumors of the ovary mentioned above are probably adrenal rest tumors; such tumors are rare, and most of those reported have caused adrenogenital syndrome rather than Cushing's; the occurrence of the latter, however, has been established.

Cases of hyperplasia may be the link between the newer concept of Cushing's syndrome as hyperadrenocorticalism and Cushing's original thesis that these cases were due to "basophilic" hyperpituitarism. Whether or not a basophilic adenoma is present, excessive secretion of ACTH by the pituitary basophils would explain hyperplasia and hyperfunction of the adrenal cortex. Older reports of increased ACTH levels in the blood of such patients are inconclusive because of the inadequacy of the methods employed. With the use of Sayer's method increased levels of ACTH have now been demonstrated in some instances (23, 70), but not in others (208a, 209a). Correlation with anatomical findings in adrenals and pituitary will be desirable. If the findings of increased ACTH levels in the blood of Cushing cases with adrenocortical hyperplasia are confirmed in a larger number of cases, a further problem arises. We have reason to assume that hypersecretion of cortical hormones will suppress ACTH secretion from the anterior pituitary, making endogenously caused adrenocortical hypersecretion self-limited. This would of course not apply to adrenocortical carcinomas, which may be autonomous and continue to function at high levels in spite of the retrograde suppression of ACTH secretion; the contralateral adrenal in such cases is, however, atrophic because of this mechanism. In cases of hyperplasia the question therefore arises why the excessive ACTH should persist, and not be suppressed by the liberated adrenal steroids. There is at present no answer; one could suggest the hypothesis that the control mechanism in such cases is "set" at a higher level, either in the pituitary or in the hypothalamus.

The latter has been implicated in the pathogenesis of Cushing's syndrome (83), and whereas the evidence is far from conclusive, the experimental data on hypothalamic control of ACTH secretion (26, 56, 93, 134) should stimulate further study of clinical material.

In a discussion of the pathogenesis mention should be made of the Cushing-like pictures which have been observed (1) after therapeutic administration of large doses of cortisone (197) and (2) in certain forms of hepatic cirrhosis (21). From a purely therapeutic angle, the occurrence of Cushing-like features in patients treated with cortisone is an undesirable "side effect." However, these cases are of considerable interest, inasmuch as they would seem at first sight to nullify the concepts of the pathophysiology of Cushing's syndrome as first proposed by Albright (1) and Kepler (110). According to this concept Cushing's syndrome would represent "panhypercorticalism"; some of the manifestations would be the result of excessive secretion of deoxycorticosterone-like "salt hormone" (hypertension, cardiac enlargement, edema), with others to be ascribed to the excess "sugar hormones" (diabetes, obesity, deossification, purple striae) and yet others (acne, hirsutism, plethora) to increased androgen secretion. After all these manifestations were induced by excess cortisone administration, it appeared doubtful to some investigators whether the concept of Cushing's syndrome as "multihormone excess" or "panhypercorticalism" could be upheld. In view of the fact that "single-hormone" hypersecretion as well as hyposecretion appears to occur, and in view of the fact that the adrenal gland can perform remarkable interchanges in the steroid structure, the induction of Cushing's syndrome by cortisone administration does not appear conclusively to invalidate the previous concepts.

The observation of Cushing-like pictures in certain forms of hepatic cirrhosis is of interest. This has been explained by assuming that the diseased liver is deficient in inactivating or destroying endogenous cortical hormones. The urinary excretion of formaldehydogenic steroids was found increased in these cases—a finding compatible with the explanation (21). Hepatic inactivation of cortisone has been demonstrated *in vitro* and *in vivo*.

To return to the pituitary basophils, the only constant finding in all cases of Cushing's syndrome has been that of hyalinization of many basophils; these changes are usually referred to as "Crooke's changes." The physiological significance of this finding was not apparent: the hyalinization was interpreted as possibly indicative of excessive ACTH secretion, or, as the late Dr. Kepler suggested, as an effect of the excessive adrenocortical secretion on the pituitary (109). The latter explanation may now be accepted in view of the fact that identical changes have been found in the pituitaries of subjects treated with ACTH or with cortisone for various conditions (66, 121).

2. *Hormone Secretion*

Following the development of methods for determining adrenocortical 11-17-hydroxy compounds in blood, high levels were found in cases of Cushing's syndrome (156). Urinary excretion studies have been carried out with various methods. 17-Ketosteroids have been found to be within normal range, or moderately elevated (131). This would correlate well with the moderate degree of virilizing manifestations seen in Cushing's syndrome in contradistinction to the marked degree observed in the various forms of adrenogenital syndrome. Corticoid excretion, determined by bio-assay, is elevated, and this finding correlates well with isolation studies which have yielded large amounts of 17-hydroxycorticosterone (hydrocortisone). Reports of studies using either reducing methods or formaldehyde generation are less consistent; excretion levels have been found high in some and within normal range in other cases; most of these studies were carried out without β-glucuronidase hydrolysis. On the other hand, the enzyme appears to liberate substances not related to corticosteroids which react both in the reducing and formaldehydogenic procedures. Even with technical refinements of the formaldehydogenic method (90, 237), there are still considerable sources of error in this procedure. With the use of methods based on the Porter-Silber reaction (30, 64, 173, 179, 223) more consistent results are obtained, even though (or perhaps because) this reaction determines a more limited range of compounds (17-hydroxycorticosteroids). Determination of the 17-hydroxycorticosteroids, and especially of the enzyme-liberated Porter-Silber positive compounds (17-hydroxycorticosteroids) has yielded high values in cases of Cushing's syndrome (173, 178); additional information can be obtained by separate determination of the free and the glucuronidase-liberated 17-hydroxysteroids (33).

3. *Metabolic Changes*

The retention of sodium and loss of potassium in Cushing's syndrome is a well-established fact (see Volume II). Eventually this may lead to a severe hypokalemic, hypochloremic alkalosis. To what extent the electrolyte changes are due to the action of C_{11}-oxygenated compounds alone or to a concomitant increased secretion of "salt hormone" is as yet unsettled.

Studies for the presence of aldosterone[1] will shed light on this problem. An interesting abnormality of the electrolyte metabolism pertains to the response to deoxycorticosterone acetate. Whereas in the normal individual as well as in the Addisonian injection of this compound together with intravenous administration of sodium chloride is followed by sodium and chloride retention, sodium and chloride loss occurs under these conditions in cases of Cushing's syndrome (191, 192). There is at present no adequate explanation for the paradoxical action.

The disturbance of carbohydrate metabolism is clearly the result of excess secretion of C_{11}-oxygenated steroids ("sugar hormones"). As would be expected the resulting diabetes is relatively insulin-resistant. Differences of severity of impairment of carbohydrate metabolism, ranging from severe diabetes to "latent" diabetes (impaired glucose tolerance), may in part at least be due to differences of β-cell "reserve capacity." The diabetogenic action of the C_{11}-oxygenated corticosteroids is due to increased gluconeogenesis and to decreased glucose utilization. An interesting aspect of disturbed carbohydrate metabolism in Cushing's syndrome has received some attention recently. It has been shown previously that in normal individuals the fasting blood values for glucose, lactate, and pyruvate were in the ratio of $100:10:1$; this ratio is maintained following ingestion of glucose. In diabetics the rise of blood sugar during a glucose tolerance test is not associated with a proportional rise of lactate and pyruvate; these metabolites either fail to rise or this rise lags appreciably. In contradistinction, in some cases of Cushing's syndrome the fasting levels of lactate and pyruvate were disproportionally high, and following glucose load, the diabetic glucose curve was associated with high levels of lactate and pyruvate (89, 111). This has been interpreted to indicate that in this form of "steroid diabetes" the islets respond to the glucose load with good insulin secretion, in spite of the "diabetic" shape of the glucose-tolerance curve. High blood pyruvate levels following glucose load have also been reported after administration of cortisone and ACTH (111). If the high blood levels indicate increased formation of pyruvate, this could conceivably also have some bearing on the fat formation via acetate and help to explain the obesity observed both in Cushing's syndrome and following cortisone and ACTH therapy.

[1] A number of important papers regarding the physiologic and therapeutic action of aldosterone have appeared after this manuscript was submitted. (R. Gaunt et al. Endocrinol. 55, 236 (1954); F. T. G. Prunty et al. Lancet iii, 620 (1954); G. L. Farrell et al. Proc. Soc. Exptl. Biol. Med. 87, 141 (1954); J. A. Luetscher, Jr., et al. J. Clin. Invest. 33, 276 (1954), J. A. Luetscher, Jr., et al. J. Clin. Endocrinol. and Metabolism 14, 1086 (1954).

4. *Diagnosis*

There has been no significant new contribution with regard to diagnosis. The frequency of occurrence of signs and symptoms as well as of abnormal laboratory data has been compiled by Plotz *et al.* (163).   Determination of urinary 17-ketosteroids is of limited diagnostic value because values are within normal range in many cases.   Determination of 17-hydroxysteroids promises to be of great significance.

After the diagnosis of Cushing's syndrome is made, it is obviously of greatest importance to determine presence or absence of a cortical tumor. An interesting biological test is based upon the response to exogenous cortisone.   In the normal individual, as well as in cases of adrenocortical hyperplasia, administration of cortisone suppresses 17-ketosteroid excretion, probably by suppressing ACTH secretion from the anterior pituitary, with consequent suppression of secretion of the adrenal cortex.   In cases of adrenocortical cancer, cortisone administration is not followed by a decrease of 17-ketosteroid excretion, evidently because the adrenocortical cancer is autonomous and continues to function in the absence of ACTH stimuli (97).   In a case of Cushing's syndrome, which one of us (K. E. P.) discussed in a CPC conference, injection of a test dose of insulin was followed by profound and prolonged hypoglycemia usually seen in Addison's disease and in panhypopituitarism.   This was interpreted as indicating the presence of an autonomous adrenocortical cancer, associated with the typical atrophy of the other adrenal.

The biological tests (response to cortisone, response to insulin) will have to be confirmed in a larger number of cases before the reliability and practical usefulness can be evaluated.

At present direct evidence for the presence of a tumor must still be sought in every case.   To the older methods of roentgenography following i.v. urography and periadrenal air insufflation, roentgenography following introduction of air into the retrorectal space (retroperitoneal pneumography) has been added (203).   This procedure appears to be safe and has yielded good pictures in several cases.   As before, exploratory operation has to be resorted to in doubtful cases.

5. *Course of Disease*

The natural history of Cushing's syndrome has been critically re-evaluated in a study by Plotz *et al.*, based on 33 observed cases and analysis of 189 cases reported in the literature (163).   The rare occurrence of spontaneous remissions has been re-emphasized by Knowlton (117); this may be important in trying to evaluate results of therapy.

6. *Treatment*

The treatment of choice in cases of tumor is clearly surgical removal of the tumor.

As mentioned in Volume II, treatment in cases due to adrenocortical hyperplasia had not been very satisfactory. Roentgen irradiation of the pituitary is now being carried out with much larger doses (3500 to 5000 tissue r) than were employed previously. Good results with remission of long duration have been obtained in two series of cases (51, 103). However, even these large radiation doses fail to bring about any improvement in some cases (33, 103). Partial hypophysectomy has been carried out in a few cases (128); B. Arner *et al.* report a good result following exposure and electrocoagulation of the pituitary (4). Beneficial results of subtotal and of total adrenalectomy have been reviewed (196). 2,2-*bis* (para-chlorophenyl)-1,1-dichlorethane (D.D.D.) has been found to cause atrophy of the zona fasciculata of the adrenals of dogs, rendering them insulin-sensitive (146). It is also active in rats, increasing their insulin sensitivity and alleviating alloxan diabetes but without causing adrenocortical atrophy (27, 28). Similar observations have been made in rabbits (161). However, in two cases of Cushing's syndrome this drug failed to exert any effect on corticoid excretion and on carbohydrate metabolism (33, 182).

D. THE ADRENOGENITAL SYNDROME

As indicated in Volume II, the clinical manifestations are due to increased secretion of androgenic 17-ketosteroids from the adrenal cortex. The anatomical change in the latter is either diffuse bilateral hyperplasia or tumors of one cortex. The picture will differ depending on the age and sex of the individual, as summarized in Table I.

Excretion of 17-ketosteroids is increased above the levels normal for the respective age group. Higher values are found in tumor cases, but there is some overlap. However, excretion of more than 150 mg./24 hours indicates the presence of adrenocortical cancer. Tumor cases excrete proportionately more β-17-ketosteroids (mainly dehydroepiandrosterone) than do hyperplasia cases; in the latter α- and β-17-ketosteroids are increased in approximately normal ratio, the β fraction comprising up to 25% of the total. Separation into α and β fraction can be carried out by Digitonin precipitation, or with the use of color reaction based on the Pettenkofen reaction. However, cases of adrenocortical cancer with low β fractions have been recorded (62, 132) and in our experience also the differentiation of tumor and hyperplasia by determination of the α–β ratio is not reliable. Increased 17-ketosteroid values have recently also been found in blood in adrenogenital syndrome (61). Recently high urinary excretion values of pregnanetriol in adrenogenital syndrome have been

TABLE I

SYNOPSIS: ADRENOGENITAL SYNDROME

Age of onset	Anatomy of adrenal	Clinical manifestations		Remarks
		Female	Male	
1. Fetal	Diffuse hyperplasia	Female pseudohermaphrodite. Persistent urogenital sinus, large clitoris. Later in addition features like #2	Macrogenitosomia precox. Manifestations not conspicuous at birth.	Familial incidence in some instances Type 1. Effects of excess androgens only Type 2. "Salt-losing." Effects of excess androgens plus salt hormone deficiency Type 3. Effects of excess androgens plus sugar hormone deficiency
2. Childhood	Tumor or diffuse hyperplasia	Heterosexual precocious pseudopuberty. Large clitoris. Body and facial hair. Deep voice. Rapid Advanced bone age. Rapid growth in length. Amenorrhea. Absent mammary tissue.	Isosexual precocious pseudopuberty. Large penis. Small testes. Body and facial hair. Deep voice. Advanced bone age. Rapid growth in length. Azoospermia.	Tumor more frequent than hyperplasia. Similar syndrome in females from virilizing ovarian tumors; in males from Leydig cell tumors and teratomas.
3. Adult	Tumor or diffuse hyperplasia	Large clitoris, deep voice. Body and facial hair. Amenorrhea. Atrophy of breasts.		Same as #2.

found (20, 132, 140); perhaps the high pregnanediol excretion reported in earlier studies (63, 221) actually was due to the presence of the triol in the precipitate. The possibility that the pregnanetriol is a metabolite of 17-hydroxyprogesterone, probably a precursor of hydrocortisone, has been discussed (20).

The pathogenesis of the diffuse hyperplasia poses a challenging problem. There is no evidence to suggest a primary hypothalamic or pituitary disorder causing excessive secretion of ACTH. However, high blood levels of ACTH have been reported (208). It is not immediately apparent how continuous stimulation by excessive ACTH causes excess androgen secretion only, and not panhypercorticalism as seen in Cushing's syndrome. A very interesting hypothesis has been proposed by F. Bartter *et al.* (14). According to this schema the primary abnormality of the adrenal cortex in these cases is the decreased ability to produce C_{11}-oxygenated steroids ("sugar hormones") or, with other words, a low target responsiveness of 11-oxysteroid production to ACTH. It has been subsequently suggested that the "block" might be at the conversion of 17-hydroxyprogesterone to hydrocortisone and that perhaps the high excretion of pregnanetriol (probably a metabolite of 17-hydroxyprogesterone) is due to this block (20). The low levels of circulating 11-oxysteroids take the brakes off the anterior pituitary's ACTH secretion; the larger amounts of ACTH now in circulation are adequate to maintain a fair 11-oxysteroid production, but the 17-ketosteroid production now becomes excessive because the sensitivity of the processes responsible for their production is "normal"; this hypothesis assumes that the adrenal androgens are much weaker inhibitors of ACTH secretion than the C_{11}-oxysteroids. A number of observations in patients with adrenogenital syndrome would be explicable on the basis of Bartter's schema. ACTH administration fails to induce eosinopenia, nitrogen loss, and increased urinary levels of reducing steroids in cases of adrenogenital syndrome. Also, ACTH administration was not followed by Na retention or K loss (14, 124). Low blood levels of C11-17-oxygenated steroids have been reported in several cases (108); this is in apparent discrepancy with the normal urinary values of reducing or formaldehydogenic steroids found in other cases (14). The discrepancy may be more apparent than real, since methods determining reducing and formaldehydogenic steroids are not entirely specific. On the other hand, it is curious and not imediately understandable that individuals with low secretion of C_{11}-C_{17}-oxysteroids should have no manifestations referable to this deficiency. Furthermore studies indicate that these adrenals are incapable of increasing their 11-oxysteroid production under additional ACTH stimulation (14, 124); yet the individuals appear to tolerate infections and other "stresses" quite well. It would appear that the oxysteroid deficiency differs in degree in different cases, being relatively mild and "subclinical" in most instances; in others, severe deficiency with hypoglycemia has been observed (231, 235). Hypertension has been recorded in a number of cases (236).

In some cases of adrenogenital syndrome a disturbance of electrolyte metabolism similar to that present in Addison's disease is found (12, 36). In this type, designated as the "salt-losing type of adrenogenital syndrome," inability to retain sodium leads to "Addisonian" crisis. From a clinical standpoint, the most difficult cases are those occurring in very young infants; in boys there may be little in the appearance of the patient to suggest virilizing adrenocortical hyperplasia, because manifestations may not appear before the end of the first year of life. An assay of urinary 17-ketosteroid excretion will permit of early diagnosis.

In some cases an aplasia of the zona glomerulosa in addition to the hyperplasia of the inner zone of the cortex was found (18). In view of the fact that, at least in rodents, the zona glomerulosa is believed to elaborate salt hormone, it was suggested that in these cases salt loss was due to a deficiency of salt hormones (234). Another explanation was suggested based on the observation that these patients responded to ACTH injection with sodium loss instead of with the sodium retention observed in normal individuals. It is possible that these adrenals elaborate an abnormal hormone which causes Na loss. As yet such a compound has not been demonstrated. The effect of this hypothetical factor has to be overcome with large doses of deoxycorticosterone acetate and salt, until cortisone successfully suppresses its secretion (101, 124).

The familial incidence of congenital adrenocortical hyperplasia, causing pseudohermaphroditism in girls and macrogenitosomia precox in boys, has been known for some time. Bentinek and co-workers have analyzed all reported instances; they point out that in no instance has the abnormality been found in more than one generation. Generally, they believe that the evidence available militates against the assumption of a genetic factor (16).

The differentiation of cases due to adrenocortical tumor from those resulting from diffuse hyperplasia is of course of greatest practical importance. As mentioned above, neither the urinary excretion levels of total 17-ketosteroids nor the ratio of urinary alpha and beta 17-ketosteroids give reliable information. Whether pregnanetriol excretion in hyperplasia will prove a reliable differentiating feature from the tumor cases will have to await study of a larger material. Except in the congenital form, which is invariably due to hyperplasia, a tumor must always be suspected. The visualization of the adrenal glands on roentgenograms following air injections has been greatly improved by the use of "retroperitoneal pneumography" (203). Air is injected into the retrorectal space and spreads upward retroperitoneally outlining all retroperitoneal structures. This procedure appears to be technically simpler, and above all safer, than the perirenal air insufflation. If for some reason adequate visualization is not obtained, surgical exploration is necessary.

Treatment in tumor cases consists of course in surgical removal of the tumor. Treatment of hyperplasia cases was very unsatisfactory up to the introduction of cortisone therapy (232, 233, 236). Treatment with cortisone suppresses the function of the adrenal cortex, evidently by suppressing ACTH secretion from the anterior pituitary. The inhibition of androgen production causes arrest of the virilization in females, as well as of the rapid growth and bone maturation with premature closure of epiphysis. Development is normalized, and a normal female pubertal development in girls, with menarche and breast development, takes place. Evidently, exogenously administered cortisone adequately replaces the suppressed secretion of the other cortical hormones.

1. *Treatment of the "Salt-Losing Type" (36, 232)*

Treatment with cortisone alone, even with administration of extra salt, is usually inadequate for maintaining electrolyte metabolism. Deoxycorticosterone acetate (DCA) is used in combination with cortisone, the latter chiefly for suppressing androgenic 17-ketosteroid excretion, the former for correction of the inability to retain sodium. It has been found that large doses of deoxycorticosterone and NaCl are necessary. This has been tentatively considered supportive evidence for the theory that the salt loss is due not to a deficiency of "salt hormone" but to the production of a Na-losing adrenal compound, the action of which has to be overcome by DCA. The requirement for the latter is appreciably reduced after cortisone therapy has brought about suppression of adrenocortical activity.

V. Ovary

Normal cyclic function of the ovaries, with regard to both ovulation and hormone secretion, involves not only a complex but also a very labile mechanism, involving particularly (*1*) neurohumoral factors regulating the cyclic release of three gonadotropic substances (FSH, LH, and LTH); (*2*) a precise, sequential response of the germ cells to gonadotropic stimulation; and (*3*) the cyclic secretion of steroid hormones by the granulosa and theca cells in proper amounts and at the proper time to favor a self-continuing push-pull relationship between the gonad and the hypophysis. The hypothalamus is undoubtedly an important relay station in the neurohumoral control of the pituitary-ovarian axis, and present evidence suggests that gonadotropin release is mediated by a neurohumoral substance, adrenergic in nature, which passes along the portal vessels from the hypothalamus to the adenohypophysis (130).

Not only organic lesions but also various stress reactions, both physical and emotional, may influence this mechanism markedly and in at least several different ways, to produce several syndromes of pituitary-ovarian dysfunction.

A. Genetic Abnormalities

1. Ovarian Agenesis (Turner Syndrome (218), Turner-Varney Syndrome)

In this condition, there is a congenital absence of the germ cells and failure of the follicular epithelium to develop, so that the ovary consists of a thin band of fibrous tissue lined by "germinal" epithelium, lying in the mesosalpinx parallel to the Fallopian tube. It is not known whether this condition is due to failure of production of the germinal cells or to failure of the germinal cells to migrate from their site of origin in the hind-gut into the gonad.

The question has been raised (232) as to whether all of these patients are in reality females, as their external genital development denotes. Since in the male the Müllerian system appears to regress under the influence of androgen from the developing testes, is it not possible that many of these essentially agonadal individuals are genetic males?[2] On the other hand, if this were so, some other explanation would be required for the occasional "male" who presents a similar syndrome (p. 865). Experimental observations made in young rabbit embryos by Jost (106) and in mice by Wells (229), support this hypothesis.

Many other genetic and endocrine features in this syndrome require clarification. The shortness of stature is hardly to be expected in view of the congenital hypogonadism. There is a remarkable tendency for most of these people to range in height from 54 to 56 inches. The skeletal proportions are usually normal rather than "eunuchoid." The bone age is generally within the normal range, occasionally being moderately delayed. Pubic hair is present in some, but absent in other cases. Webbing of the neck is often noted. Among the other congenital defects sometimes seen are a receding chin, hypertension, coarctation of the aorta, osteoporosis with resulting orthopedic abnormalities, and polydactylism. Some patients may show no congenital defects except for the hypogonadism and shortness of stature.

Gonadotropin (FSH) excretion is uniformly elevated and indeed serves as an important point in differential diagnosis from pituitary infantilism

[2] A recent report by Wilkins et al. J. Clin. Endocrinol. and Metabolism 14, 1270 (1954) indicates that the "chromosomal sex" is male in most cases.

in questionable cases. Estrogens in the urine are very low. Despite this pattern of high gonadotropins and low estrogens, vasomotor symptoms do not occur in these patients, as they so often do in acquired types of prepubertal hypogonadism. The 17-ketosteroid excretion varies considerably; in some cases it is normal, and in others it is quite low.

As a rule, the diagnosis of this condition is not established with certainty until the postpubertal years, when the hypogonadism becomes evident. However, in instances in which it is suspected on the basis of dwarfism together with other congenital stigmata, the diagnosis can be made with certainty if there is a high urinary gonadotropic excretion, a feature distinguishing this condition from pituitary and other types of dwarfism. Wilkins (232) has noted that urinary FSH was absent or low during early childhood but rose as puberty was approached. The administration of estrogens produces a gratifying development of the breasts, secondary sex characters, and growth of the vagina suitable for sexual purposes. This should be continued in cyclic fashion to maintain development, but in moderate dosage, since otherwise marked endometrical hyperplasia with troublesome bleeding can occur. We have not noted a stimulation of skeletal growth with estrogens, even when treatment has been started in late childhood.

B. "Infantile" Ovaries with Eunuchoidism

In this syndrome, the ovaries are of the elongated ovoid (infantile) type, containing apparently normal numbers of primordial follicles. These follicles fail to grow and mature despite adequate FSH secretion as evidenced by high urinary titers. The irresponsiveness of the ovary to gonadotropic stimulation is believed to be due to a genetic defect, although the possibility of a severe childhood infection affecting the ovaries must also be considered. These patients show the characteristic stigmata of prepubertal hypogonadism: they are relatively tall, with eunuchoid proportions; the secondary sex characteristics and reproductive organs are immature; they have primary amenorrhea and hot flashes. The latter symptoms, as well as the high urinary FSH titers, distinguish them from the prepubertal, eunuchoid hypogonad, of pituitary origin. Furthermore, these patients rarely improve spontaneously, whereas the pituitary hypogonad may sometimes go into a delayed puberty in her late teems or early twenties, and may eventually attain normal reproductive function. The latter may be encouraged or hastened by the cyclic administration of gonadotropic hormones with follicle-stimulating activity, whereas the primary ovarian eunuchoid can be treated only symptomatically with estrogens or with estrogens and progesterone in cyclic fashion. The closure of the epiphyses will be hastened, the secondary sex characters will develop, as will the vagina and uterus, and the vasomotor symptoms will be controlled, but spontaneous ovarian function rarely follows the withdrawal of substitutional therapy.

C. PITUITARY HYPOGONADISM

Pituitary hypogonadism in women may be associated with pituitary dwarfism (p. 826) or may be a single gonadotropic deficiency.   The skeletal development may therefore range from marked dwarfism to eunuchoidism, depending apparently upon the degree of growth hormone deficiency.   In some instances with moderate retardation of growth, the clinical picture may resemble that of ovarian agenesis but can be distinguished from the latter by absence of FSH in the urine.   Other congenital defects are usually absent, the bone age is more markedly retarded, and the urinary 17-ketosteroids are lower (often less than 1.0 mg. per 24 hours) (232).   As indicated above, the differential diagnosis from a primary ovarian deficiency is of importance because of the possibility of a response to gonadotropic therapy.

D. NONNEOPLASTIC CYSTS OF THE OVARY

1. *Follicle Cysts of the Ovary*

The etiologic factors in follicular cystic disease of the ovary appear to be many and varied, including genetic abnormalities, inflammatory lesions of the ovary, degenerative processes, and endocrine factors.   Usually the physiologic disturbance results in a menstrual dysfunction and impairment of ovulation.   Estrogen secretion varies; the follicular fluid in some of the large follicle cysts of the ovary contains small to moderate amounts of estrogenic activity, whereas others are hormonally inactive.   Urinary excretion of estrogens also vary from diminished titers in most cases to excessive levels in occasional instances.   The endometrial pattern is likewise diverse, ranging from an early proliferative type to one of cystic hyperplasia.   A secretory pattern, with apparently normal ovulation, may occur in the patient with one or a few follicle cysts of the hormonally inactive type in which the ovaries are otherwise normal.

Little is known of the endocrine factors which may cause large follicle cysts of the ovary.   Occasionally these may be induced by too vigorous gonadotropic therapy (44), suggesting that a disturbance of the pituitary-ovarian endocrine mechanism may be the etiologic factor in some cases. In this respect, it is of interest that the use of estrogens or androgens given in full dosage for several weeks may cause rapid regression of simple follicle cysts.

2. *The Stein-Leventhal Syndrome*

A particular type of microfollicular cystosis of the ovary which is of interest because of its endocrine stigmata is that seen in the Stein-Leventhal syndrome (201, 202, 123). This condition is characterized by a menstrual dysfunction (usually amenorrhea, but sometimes irregular or excessive bleeding), infertility, and hirsutism of varying degree, together with bilateral cystic enlargement of the ovaries. The condition generally begins in the late teens or early twenties, usually after prior normal menstrual function. Although the hirsutism may become quite marked in some cases, the clitoris is rarely appreciably enlarged or the voice deepened. The 17-ketosteroid excretion is generally within the normal range, occasionally being slightly elevated (up to 20 mg. per 24 hours). A moderately high β fraction (20 % to 40 %) is often noted. Estrogens are present, but usually in moderately low titers, and the vaginal smear shows a persistent early follicular reaction. FSH is often not demonstrable in the urine, but high titers occur sporadically, especially early in the condition.

The appearance of the ovaries on exploration is quite characteristic. They are enlarged, flattened, and pale, and have a thickened gray capsule; they resemble oysters. The cut surface reveals many small cystic areas of varying size. On histologic examination, the significant abnormalities are the marked fibrous thickening of the ovarian capsule, the presence of numerous follicle cysts, with a paucity of normal growing follicles, and hyperplasia of the theca surrounding the cystic follicles. The latter finding is not consistently present.

A small type of "Stein-Leventhal ovaries" is sometimes noted, in which the ovaries are only slightly enlarged and ovoid, but have a markedly thickened capsule, microfollicular cysts, and theca hyperplasia. These patients often have excessive and irregular bleeding, rather than amenorrhea.

The etiology of this condition is not known. There is little to support an inflammatory basis for the excessive fibrosis of the capsule which could secondarily produce follicular cystosis. A genetic dysfunction likewise seems improbable in view of the previous apparently normal menstrual history and absence of other stigmata in most cases. It seems more likely that the condition is due to an endocrine dysfunction. One wonders whether the hyperplastic theca may not be secreting increased amounts of an unusual steroid, perhaps not excreted as a 17-ketosteroid, which is responsible for the mild masculinization and inhibition of FSH. In this regard, it is to be noted that hirsutism has been observed in association with ovarian hyperthecosis (162, 167, 204, 211).

This condition may be differentiated (72) from an adrenogenital syndrome on the basis of lack of true masculinization and normal 17-ketosteroids, and from a Cushing's syndrome by lack of the typical habitus, purple striae, and metabolic disturbances. A masculinizing tumor of the ovary may also be differentiated by lack of true masculinization and the fact that the ovarian enlargement is bilateral and "cystic."

Generous wedge resection of the ovaries frequently results in prompt and striking improvement of this syndrome, with return to normal ovulatory cycles, in a high percentage of cases, as indicated by basal temperature charts, endometrial biopsies, and improved fertility (202). This improvement in endocrine function following removal of ovarian tissue is difficult to explain.

Hormonal therapy is not often of help in this condition. In its early stages, occasional cases benefit from cyclic progesterone therapy or treatment with cortisone (p. 860).

E. Ovarian Deficiencies of Psychogenic Origin

It is well known that nervous or emotional disturbances may be followed by impairment of ovarian function resulting in anovulatory infertility, secondary amenorrhea, dysfunctional uterine bleeding, cystic mastitis, or other manifestations of disturbed ovarian function. The clinical findings together with hormonal and other endocrine studies of such patients indicate that there are several patterns or syndromes of ovarian hypofunction which may occur on a psychogenic basis (153, 171, 206):

1. Hypogonadotropism. Inhibition of pituitary gonadotropic secretion with secondary ovarian deficiency appears to be most common in such disturbances. In its mildest form, the menses may occur at fairly regular intervals, but there is interference with normal ovulation, causing relative infertility. This may progress to dysfunctional bleeding or to secondary amenorrhea, depending upon the degree of inhibition of the pituitary-ovarian mechanism.

2. Inhibition of gonadotropins plus other pituitary hormones. These patients generally have secondary amenorrhea with absence of gonadotropin excretion in the urine, plus clinical and metabolic evidences of mild hypothyroidism. In severe cases the clinical picture is that of anorexia nervosa with loss of weight, tiredness, hypotension, and moderately decreased 17-ketosteroids. In occasional instances, the clinical manifestations may be so marked as to require differentiation from Simmonds' disease (53).

3. Normal FSH with ovarian deficiency. This is the pattern seen in patients with so-called "hypothalamic amenorrhea," as described by Klinefelter, Albright, and Griswold (116). It has been presumed by these authors that the ovarian hypofunction results from lack of LH secretion to synergize with FSH to stimulate the ovary. The clinical manifestations are those of secondary amenorrhea with anovulatory infertility. In our experience, this group is not as commonly seen as those described under the first classification, although the clinical picture is often the same.

4. Primary ovarian deficiency with high FSH. This syndrome is characterized clinically by secondary amenorrhea and infertility and usually accompanied by hot flashes and other menopausal symptoms. It generally occurs after an acute psychic trauma and is often of long duration and highly resistant to treatment.

From the endocrine patterns which have been described above, it would appear that psychogenic factors may influence ovarian function by way of the pituitary, the hypothalamus, or the ovary directly. Unfortunately, very little is known of the intermediary mechanisms by which psychogenic factors influence these structures.

The therapeutic approach to psychogenic ovarian hypofunction is often difficult. In milder cases, readjustment of environmental factors and superficial psychotherapy may be all that is required. For this reason, many such cases eventually undergo spontaneous correction. On the other hand, in many other instances the syndrome may be prolonged and may fail to respond even to intensive psychotherapy. Such patients are also known to be very resistent to endocrine therapy of various types. The use of gonadotropic hormones in patients with low FSH only rarely results in stimulation of ovarian function. Preparations containing follicle-stimulating activity should be tried in cyclic fashion in the milder cases. In the more severe cases, substitutional therapy with estrogen followed by estrogen and progesterone may bring on cyclic bleeding. These patients seem to require much higher doses of estrogen and progesterone to obtain an endometrial response and bleeding than patients with other types of amenorrhea (67, 171). The repeated induction of cyclic bleeding is occasionally followed by resumption of spontaneous ovarian function. This approach with substitutional therapy is of course the only plan of endocrine therapy indicated in patients with a primary ovarian deficiency.

Low dosage irradiation to the pituitary or ovaries is not usually helpful in these cases of psychogenic ovarian hypofunction (170) and is reserved for cases of infertility in which all other methods of treatment have failed. Better results are obtained in patients with a gonadotropic deficiency than in those with primary ovarian failure. The effects of the irradiation therapy appear to be mediated by way of the ovary rather than the pituitary (170).

F. Metabolic Disturbances Affecting Ovarian Function

In some patients, excessive gain of weight may result in ovarian hypofunction with secondary amenorrhea or oligomenorrhea. This is usually due to inhibition of pituitary FSH secretion, although the mechanism by which this occurs is not known. It is remarkable to observe in some patients the manner in which menstrual function may return and then disappear again, depending upon their gain or loss of weight by dieting.

In this respect, it is also to be noted that some young women may develop a very severe or resistant type of secondary amenorrhea following rapid loss of weight below their usual normal by severe dietary restriction (206). In these patients there is also an FSH deficiency. Unfortunately, in some cases ovarian function does not resume spontaneously following a return to normal diet and normal weight. It is believed that diets deficient in protein and certain members of the B complex are particularly likely to cause ovarian dysfunction.

Disturbances in liver function may indirectly affect the function of the ovaries because of failure of normal inactivation of the ovarian hormones. Thus in hepatitis and in cirrhosis of the liver, disturbances of ovarian function causing menorrhagia, polymenorrhea, or cystic mastitis are sometimes encountered (98).

G. Effect of Adrenal Hyperfunction on the Ovaries

It is, of course, well known that marked degrees of adrenal cortical hyperfunction will inhibit ovarian function by depressing the gonadotropins. In the adrenogenital syndrome this may be attributed primarily to the androgens which are produced in excess. In some cases, there is also increased estrogen secretion by the adrenal (50), the effects of which are masked by the greater increase in the androgens. However, in some cases of Cushing's syndrome in which the 17-ketosteroids are not elevated and the total estrogen excretion is diminished, the inhibition of gonadotropic function may be attributed to other steroids of the adrenal cortex.

The histologic picture of the ovaries in patients with an adrenogenital syndrome due to an adrenal cortical tumor has been of particular interest to us. In two such cases in which ovarian biopsies were obtained, there was a striking resemblance of the histologic findings in the ovary to those seen in the Stein-Leventhal syndrome. Although the ovaries were not enlarged, there was marked thickening of the capsule, microfollicular cystosis, and hyperplasia of the theca cells.

Another type of ovarian dysfunction which appears to be related to a mild degree of adrenal cortical hyperfunction or dysfunction is seen in patients with mild hirsutism, anovulatory infertility, oligomenorrhea or secondary amenorrhea, and 17-ketosteroid excretion which is only slightly elevated above the normal, ranging from 15 to 22 mg. per 24 hours. Such patients will sometimes respond favorably to the administration of cortisone in a dosage of 25 to 50 mg. daily by mouth. Jones *et al.* (105) have drawn attention to the use of cortisone in stimulating greater follicular activity in patients of this type. The mechanism by which cortisone produces this favorable action would appear to be similar to that described by Wilkins in patients with congenital adrenal hyperplasia, namely, the depression of adrenal androgens by cortisone with subsequent release of FSH.

H. Ovarian Hyperfunction

The most common and the most perfect example of ovarian hyperfunction is that which is seen in early pregnancy, during which the corpus luteum is stimulated to produce maximal amounts of estrogen and progesterone by the rising titer of chorionic gonadotropin secreted by the cytotrophoblast. Even in states of anterior pituitary hyperfunction, the hypophysis is not capable of secreting sufficient luteinizing and luteotropic hormone to maintain and stimulate the corpus luteum to a degree comparable to that seen in early gestation. There are, however, several syndromes in which this may occur to a lesser extent.

I. Corpus Luteum Cysts

In some instances in which there has been excessive hemorrhage into a corpus luteum, this structure may become cystic and persist with functional activity beyond the usual two-week period so regularly noted in the human cycle. Menstruation may be delayed because of a persistently high estrogen and progesterone level. There may be signs and symptoms of early pregnancy, or the clinical picture may suggest an ectopic pregnancy. Also, in some cases, the pregnancy test may be weakly positive, suggesting increased secretion of LH and LTH.

Rare patients may often or regularly have a slightly prolonged corpus luteum phase, lasting for 16 to 18 days as indicated by basal temperature charts. This occurs occasionally in patients who are particularly anxious for pregnancy but who do not develop a true pseudocyesis syndrome.

J. Pseudocyesis

The pseudocyesis syndrome is a striking example of the influence of psychogenic factors upon the pituitary-ovarian mechanism to produce a state of ovarian hyperfunction. This condition occurs primarily in women who have a great desire to become pregnant but who have been unable to do so, or sometimes in women who have a great fear that they have become pregnant illegitimately or against their wishes. Endocrine studies (58, 59) indicate that they have persistent corpus luteum function, characterized by hyperhormonal amenorrhea, associated with a secretory endometrium, persistently good levels of estrogen and pregnanediol, plus such other evidences of ovarian hyperfunction as increased glandular tissue of the breasts, pigmentation of the nipples, softening of the cervix, and slight enlargement of the uterus.   FSH in the urine is generally absent, but assays for prolactin have been positive.   These findings explain the milky secretion which may often be expressed from the nipples of these patients.   It would seem that psychogenic factors have in some way interfered with the pituitary hypothalamic mechanism so as to favor continued secretion of LH and LTH and persistence of the corpus luteum.   The endocrine disturbance together with the other psychogenic manifestations accounts for the full-blown syndrome of pseudocyesis.   Psychiatric studies on these patients indicate that the psychosis is a type of hysteria.   Psychotherapy is only of limited value in the treatment of this condition, which also has a great tendency to be recurrent.   Testosterone is sometimes helpful, apparently by inducing regression of the corpus luteum.   This is generally followed by a menstrual flow suggesting to the patient that she is no longer pregnant.

VI. Placenta

The human placenta is a versatile and prodigious producer of both protein and steroid hormones.   There is well-documented evidence that the placenta secretes large amounts of chorionic gonadotropin, estrogens, and "progestogens."   There is also good evidence suggesting that the placenta secretes glucocorticoids (220, 100, 150).   Studies of the ketosteroids in the urine of pregnant women (48) show both qualitative and quantitative differences from those of nonpregnant women, suggesting that the placenta produces other steroid precursors or that pregnancy induces alterations in steroid metabolism, or both.   Evidence for the secretion of a protein hormone containing ACTH activity has also been presented (101).

There is increasing evidence (205, 238) that the cytotrophoblast (Langhans' layer) is the site of origin of chorionic gonadotropin, and possibly of other protein hormones, whereas histochemical studies suggest that the syncytial cells are the site of formation of the steroid hormones.

Comparatively little is known concerning the functions of the placenta in gestation.   Chorionic gonadotropin appears in the blood and urine in rapidly rising titers in the early days of pregnancy and apparently maintains the corpus luteum of pregnancy.   During the last half of pregnancy the chorionic gonadotropin levels are much lower.   The function of this hormone during the placental phase is not known; it has been suggested that it stimulates the production of estrogens and progesterone by the syncytial cells (190).   The early appearance of chorionic gonadotropin in blood and urine and its high concentration make it possible to use its assay as the basis for the more reliable pregnancy tests, including the Aschheim-Zondek, Friedman, South African frog, American male frog, and rat-ovary-hyperemia tests.

Estrogens and progesterone are secreted in increasing amounts as pregnancy progresses. It has been generally believed that during the first trimester the bulk of these steroids are of corpus luteum origin and that the corpus luteum is essential for the maintenance of pregnancy during this period. More recent studies (118) would indicate that in the human being the corpus luteum is essential for a much briefer period of time and that removal of the corpus luteum during the first weeks of pregnancy does not necessarily result in termination of the pregnancy or diminution in pregnanediol excretion, thus suggesting that the trophoblast may adequately take over this function very early.

Estrogen and progesterone appear to be essential for growth and quiescence of the uterine muscle during gestation (174). They also induce many other changes favorable for mother and fetus such as the further growth and development of the breasts, softening of the cervix, thickening of the vaginal epithelium, and increased vaginal acidity. With regard to some of these changes the action of the two hormones appears to be synergistic, whereas in others they are antagonistic.

The intermediary metabolism of estrogen and progesterone during pregnancy is discussed in Volume I of *The Hormones*.

A. PREGNANCY COMPLICATIONS

1. *Abortion*

Several patterns of hormonal imbalance have been observed (104) in patients with sporadic or habitual abortion. The latter condition has been particularly useful for such studies, since the hormonal excretion patterns have been studied from early gestation to the time of abortion. In one type the titer of chorionic gonadotropin is low from the very early days of pregnancy and progressively falls. Estrogen and pregnanediol excretion is also diminished. In these pregnancies the fetus is often resorbed and there is reason to suspect a genetic defect. In another type pregnanediol and estrogen levels are diminished, in spite of normal titers of chorionic gonadotropin, suggesting poor response by the corpus luteum or syncytiotrophoblast. In this group substitutional therapy with large doses of progesterone and estrogens appears to be particularly indicated. In a third type abortion may occur repeatedly in spite of normal urinary levels of all three hormones, suggesting a uterine factor or possibly a disturbance of other unknown hormonal factors. Diminished thyroid function must be considered; it has been suggested (158) that failure of the serum-protein-bound iodine to rise during pregnancy may be of significance in this regard.

2. *Hydatidiform Mole and Chorionepithelioma*

In many instances these conditions are associated with unusually high titers of chorionic gonadotropin which may be helpful in their diagnosis. Since hydatidiform mole is most often suspected during early pregnancy, when the titer is normally quite high, a high serum chorionic gonadotropic titer will be indicative of hydatidiform mole only if it is several times higher than the peak values for normal pregnancy, or if a moderately high level is sustained significantly beyond the period when the titer normally drops (12th to 16th weeks). A rising titer of chorionic gonadotropin following expulsion of a mole, or after an abortion or normal delivery, is presumptive evidence of chorionepithelioma, provided the possibility of another pregnancy has been ruled out. Patients who have expelled a mole or have had surgery for a chorionepithelioma should have repeated follow-up assays over a long period of time in order to detect recurrence or metastases. It should, however, be emphasized that occasionally chorionepitheliomas produce little or no chorionic gonadotropin, particularly in their early stages (212). The secretion of estrogens and progesterone by moles and chorionepitheliomas varies much more than that of chorionic gonadotropin; the assay of the former is therefore less useful from a diagnostic standpoint. Some of these tumors may secrete very large amounts of chorionic gonadotropic hormone with but little if any estrogens or progesterone, whereas others may secrete considerable amounts of all three hormones (148).

3. *Toxemias of Pregnancy*

There are many reasons to suspect a placental factor, possibly of hormonal nature, of etiologic significance in the toxemias of pregnancy, but satisfactory evidence for such an endocrine factor has not yet been obtained. Results of hormonal excretion studies in toxemias of pregnancy are quite controversial. The pattern reported by the Smiths (190) in many instances, namely increased urinary chorionic gonadotropin and diminished urinary pregnanediol and estrogen, as well as changes in the partition of the urinary estrogens, has in part been confirmed by some workers. On the other hand, these alterations are often absent in patients with severe pregnancy toxemia (155, 160, 193).

An increase in the urinary excretion of corticoids in toxemia of pregnancy has been reported (47, 148, 216); this finding has been tentatively correlated with the sodium and water retention observed in toxemia. The increase above that occurring in normal pregnancy is probably of questionable significance, especially in view of the methods employed in these studies.

Even if such an increase will be confirmed with the use of more specific methods, such as those based on the Porter-Silber reaction, the question will still remain what is cause, and what effect? The occurrence of a severe toxemia could well cause a non-specific rise of adrenocortical secretion. It has been suggested that increased production of a mineral-corticoid might play a role in this condition (147). This entire problem appears to be quite unsettled, and further advances will depend in part on better assay methods for these steroids, particularly for the "mineralocorticoids." Similarly the question of the use of cortisone or ACTH in the treatment of late pregnancy toxemias is controversial (147, 211).

VII. Testes

The hypophyseal-testicular interrelationships have been discussed in Volume II. Several problems in this sphere remain unsolved. Although FSH is believed to be primarily responsible for stimulation of spermatogenesis, it is uncertain whether this occurs without the synergism of the other gonadotropins or of androgens. It is equally uncertain whether luteotropin (LTH, prolactin) plays any role in the male, perhaps as a synergist of LH (ICSH) in stimulating Leydig cell function. The question of a "second" testicular hormone awaits final answer. The existence of such a hormone has been postulated on the basis of analogy with the female. Interstitial tissue (and corpus luteum) in the female and interstitial tissue (Leydig cells) in the male producing progesterone and testosterone, respectively, is regulated by LH (ICSH). Ovarian follicles and estrogen secretion in the female and spermatogenic tubules in the male are governed by FSH. Is there a "tubular" hormone in the male corresponding to the follicular estrogen?

In addition to such general considerations, certain clinical observations suggest the existence of a tubular hormone. In Klinefelter's syndrome (Volume II, p. 679) hyalinization of the seminiferous tubes and intact Leydig cell function are associated with excessive urinary FSH excretion. This suggests that under normal circumstances the tubules secrete a hormone the absence of which releases pituitary FSH secretion. It has been proposed that this hormone might be an estrogen. Estrogens have been extracted from the testis of human beings as well as certain animal species and are believed by some to be secreted by the Sertoli cells. This assumption is based chiefly on the findings in Sertoli cell tumors of the testis which induce feminization in dogs and in man; from Sertoli cell tumors of dogs estrogens have been extracted. However, Nelson has questioned the origin of these testicular tumors from Sertoli cells and believes them to be Leydig cell tumors (144). If androgens and estrogens are, according to

Nelson, produced in the Leydig cell, the postulated "tubular" hormone still goes begging.

A. Hypogonadism (91)

Hypogonadism is discussed in Volume II of *The Hormones*.

In view of the fact that in many instances nothing is known regarding the etiology of the various syndromes, hypogonadism may be classified, on a symptomatological basis, as follows: Failure (*1*) of both tubular (spermatogenic) and Leydig cell function, (*2*) of tubular function with intact Leydig cell function, and (*3*) of Leydig cell function with intact tubular function. All three types can, at least theoretically, be caused (*a*) by a primary testicular deficiency, and (*b*) by a testicular deficiency secondary to pituitary gonadotropic failure.

1. *Failure of Tubular and Leydig Cell Function*

This type is represented by the surgical castrate (eunuch) and by the eunuchoid in whom testicular failure is due to an anlage defect ("functional castrate" 86), or due to impaired blood supply incident to operations for cryptorchidism or hernia, or due to bilateral orchitis.

These cases may be indistinguishable in their physical appearance and in their functional deficiencies from cases of pituitary hypogonadotropism. Differentiation of primary testicular eunuchoidism and eunuchoidism secondary to hypogonadotropism is readily accomplished by assay of urinary gonadotropins ("FSH assay"), which yields very high values in the former, whereas gonadotropin excretion is absent in the latter.

The castrates and the "primary testicular" eunuchoid are treated with testosterone. In hypogonadotropic eunuchoids treatment with gonadotropic hormones (chorionic gonadotropin and FSH-containing pituitary preparations) has been successful.

Whether an anlage defect of the testis ever is associated with a syndrome analogous to that of ovarian agenesis (Turner's syndrome) is as yet uncertain. As is discussed elsewhere (p. 853), the absence of estrogen effects and of germ cells and the presence of high urinary gonadotropin (FSH) levels in ovarian agenesis are associated with features which are different from those of the prepubertal castrate: shortness of stature, frequent occurrence of other congenital malformations including webbing of the neck, usually no delay of closure of the epiphyses. None of the few cases reported as "Turner's syndrome in the male" (194) appear to us convincingly analogous to the female syndrome. The suggestion has been made (p. 853) that some patients with ovarian agenesis may, in fact, be genetic males, and thus represent instances of testicular aplasia.

2. *Impairment of Tubular Function with Intact Leydig Cell Function*

Typically these individuals are normally developed males, with normal secondary sex characteristics, normal libido and potency, and normal 17-ketosteroid excretion.   The size of the testes varies from normal to markedly diminished.   The sperm content of the ejaculate varies from oligospermia to azoospermia.   Testicular biopsy specimens show normal Leydig cells; the germinal epithelium may be well developed, with spermatogenesis progressing to the spermatide stage ("spermatocytogenesis"), but with absent sperm maturation ("spermiogenesis").   In other cases, the tubules are completely denuded, with only Sertoli cells left.   Pericanalicular fibrosis is present in varying degrees in most, but not in all cases of the latter type.   Urinary gonadotropin excretion is normal in some and very high in other cases, but a definite correlation of the FSH excretion pattern with the histological picture of the testis is as yet not possible.   There is no evidence that any of these cases is due to a pituitary gonadotropic deficiency.   The etiology is unknown.

It has been claimed that seminal failure can be recognized already in the histologic picture of the pubertal testis, by marked retardation of tubular development (31).

The Klinefelter syndrome, discussed in Volume II, characterized by hyalinization of the tubules, normal Leydig cells, gynecomastia, and high FSH excretion, would appear to be a special entity within the group of seminal failure without Leydig cell failure (45, 116).   Cases have been reported which show features of Klinefelter syndrome associated with varying degrees of Leydig cell failure (85, 87).

Treatment.   Cases with azoospermia and extensive fibrosis and/or hyalinization of the tubules, as seen in the biopsy specimen, are obviously beyond any possibility of repair.   However, results are also unsatisfactory in most instances of milder forms, with oligospermia and maturation arrest. Various gonadotropic preparations have been used on a purely empirical basis.   One would expect results, if any, from preparations containing adequate amounts of FSH such as pituitary gonadotropins or Synapoidin. Chorionic gonadotropin has also been used, and occasional good results have been claimed with any of the preparations.   Treatment with large doses of testosterone has also been suggested; complete suppression of sperm production is reported to be followed by a rise of viable sperm cells in the ejaculate to values permitting fecundation ("rebound effect") (82). Confirmation has to be awaited.

3. *Leydig Cell Deficiency with Normal Tubular Function*

Recently three reports have appeared concerning patients who had spermatogenesis in the presence of evidence for impaired Leydig cell function

(119, 135, 154). The evidence for the latter varied somewhat in individual cases; eunuchoid body proportions, sparseness or absence of pubic and axillary hair, poor beard growth, high-pitched voice, undersized penis as well as diminished urinary 17-ketosteroid values have been reported. Testicular biopsy specimens showed diminished number and pycnotic appearance of Leydig cells, and production of mature sperm in the tubules. In some instances an ejaculate could not be obtained; in one case the fructose content of the ejaculate was very low (119); the fructose content of the semen is considered to be a measure of androgen secretion (120). In other cases the ejaculate was normal, and fertility was claimed for one of these cases. McCullagh has applied in his cases an assay method believed to show LH (ICSH) in urinary extract. In three of his five cases LH was not demonstrable, suggesting a pituitary deficiency limited to this one hormone. Some response was obtained by treatment with chorionic gonadotropin; this would add further support to the assumption of a pituitary deficiency (135).

B. Testosterone as a Gonadotropin

Several older studies are on record indicating that under narrowly circumscribed experimental conditions testosterone can exert a gonadotropic function. In the male hypophysectomized rat treatment with testosterone, initiated immediately after hypophysectomy, will maintain spermatogenesis and prevent testicular atrophy, but treatment with testosterone will not repair the previously atrophied testicle nor restore spermatogenesis once the posthypophysectomy changes have taken place (145, 187).

There are for obvious reasons no observations in man which would duplicate the experimental conditions in the rat. However, in several cases of hypopituitarism sperm production occurred under treatment with testosterone (95, 113). In contradistinction to the hypophysectomized animal, the possibility cannot be ruled out in such a case that testosterone therapy induced the pituitary to secrete gonadotropins. Kinsell rejects this possibility because no rise of urinary gonadotropin titer was observed during androgen therapy (113).

C. Testicular Tumors

Tumors of the testis will be discussed briefly only with regard to endocrine aspects. Leydig cell tumors secrete large amounts of androgens and 17-ketosteroids, and androsterone sulfate has been isolated from the urine. In prepubertal boys these tumors cause precocious pseudopuberty (p. 869). It has been pointed out that, probably because of the protein anabolic action of the androgen secreted by the tumor, tumor cachexia may be absent even in advanced cases with widespread metastasis (133). It is interesting that the estrogen excretion may be increased simultaneously in such cases (222). This finding would add weight to the theory that the Leydig cell is the source of both androgens and estrogens (p. 864). However, too few cases have been adequately and completely studied to permit any generalizations or final conclusions; unfortunately reports on this rare tumor continue to appear in the literature with little information other than a histologic study of the tumor.

Tumors of the testis, believed to originate from Sertoli cells, have been found in man (210) and, more commonly, in the dog (92). These tumors secrete estrogens and cause gynecomastia. Nelson questions their origin from Sertoli cells and believes them to be a variety of the Leydig cell tumor (144) (see also p. 864).

Certain malignant tumors of the testis contain chorion-like tissue (choriocarcinoma); they are characterized by excretion of large amounts of gonadotropins which are biologically identical with chorionic gonadotropins of pregnancy. "Pregnancy tests" (Ascheim-Zondek, Friedman, rat-ovary-hyperemia test) carried out with urine of such cases are positive. Increased urinary estrogen levels and the occurrence of gynecomastia in some cases suggest that the choriocarcinoma duplicates not only the gonadotropin production but also the estrogen production of normal chorionic tissue. There is suggestive evidence that in some cases of choriocarcinoma of the testis there is increased urinary excretion not only of chorionic gonadotropin but also of FSH. Because of the technical difficulties of assaying the two gonadotropins separately in a mixture of both, the data should at present not be considered final. The presence of large amounts of urinary FSH in such cases has been tentatively explained as the result of destruction of testicular tissue ("castration by tumor"), but in view of the fact that the same hormone pattern occurs in unilateral tumors with intact second testis, this explanation is not wholly satisfactory. Similar observations of increased urinary FSH levels have been reported in other testicular tumors. Regarding the significance of this finding, the same uncertainty has to be recorded as that mentioned above in the case of choriocarcinomas. No essentially new facts have been reported recently; a good review of the subject appeared in 1946 (219).

VIII. Puberty (149)

In our population the onset of puberty normally takes place at the age of about 11 to 12 years in girls, and 12 to 13 years in boys. From this mean age of onset there occurs considerable deviation, with onset delayed up to 18 to 20 years or advanced to as early as 1 to 2 years of age (precocious puberty). The onset of pubertal changes is brought about by the beginning of the secretions of estrogens and androgens, respectively. The prepubertal gonad appears to be not completely inactive, but to secrete small amounts of the sex steroids.   These amounts are too small to induce somatic changes as evidenced by the absence of secondary sex characteristics in normal children, and by the absence of detectable somatic changes in prepubertal castrates.   However, the fact that the prepubertal castrate (80) as well as the child with ovarian agenesis (185) may secrete appreciable amounts of FSH indicates that the child's gonad is not wholly inactive.   The pubertal spurt of sex steroid secretion from the gonad is caused by a spurt of gonadotropin secretion from the anterior pituitary.   This can be shown by urinary gonadotropin assay and is evident from the fact that administration of exogenous gonadotropin causes sex hormone secretion and development of secondary sex characteristics years before the physiological onset of puberty.

The anterior pituitary probably is triggered into gonadotropin release at the time of puberty by an hypothalamic mechanism, presumably by the secretion of a neurohumeral agent which reaches the anterior pituitary by way of the portal venous system of the pituitary stalk.   Just as the gonad is capable of responding to gonadotropic stimulation long before the physiological onset of puberty, the anterior pituitary of animals (181) and human beings (11) contains appreciable amounts of gonadotropic hormones without releasing them.   The release of gonadotropic hormones from the anterior pituitary through the hypothalamic mechanism has been demonstrated for the LH release in the rabbit (130); the fact that certain organic lesions of the hypothalamus in children cause precocious puberty suggests that a similar mechanism operates in the initiation of the pubertal chain of events in the human being.

Precocious puberty is found in cases of hypothalamic lesions (tumors, encephalitis, hydrocephalus); perhaps the precocious puberty associated with polyostotic fibrous dysplasia (Albright's disease) is due to cerebral changes resulting from deformities of the base of the skull.   In the majority of cases of precocious puberty no organic lesion is present; these cases are referred to as "constitutional" precocious puberty.   It may be assumed that for some reason the intrinsic triggering mechanism in the hypothalamus is set off abnormally early in life.   Because in precocious puberty, both in that due to organic lesions and in the constitutional type, the entire physiological pubertal mechanism is duplicated, the preciocous development includes that of the gonad, involving both its endocrine secretions and maturation of ova and sperm.   Pregnancy has been reported in a girl $5\frac{1}{2}$ years old.

Tumors or hyperplasia of the adrenal cortex, tumors of the testis or ovary, and teratomas containing testicular tissue, cause precocious development of secondary sex characteristics, either isosexual or heterosexual, but not maturation of the gonad.   This type of precocity is called precocious pseudopuberty.

REFERENCES

1. Albright, F. *Harvey Lectures* (1942–43). p. 123
2. Allen, H. C., Jr., Kelly, F. J., and Greene, J. A. *J. Clin. Endocrinol.* **12,** 1356 (1952).
3. Allen, H. C., Jr., Libby, R. L., and Cassen, B. *J. Clin. Endocrinol.* **11,** 492 (1951).
4. Arner, B., Luft, R., Olivecrona, H., and Sjogren, B. *J. Clin. Endocrinol. and Metabolism* **13,** 1101 (1953).
5. Asboe-Hansen, G., Iversen, K., and Wichman, R. *Acta Endocrinol.* **11,** 376 (1952).
6. Astwood, E. B. *Ann. Internal Med.* **30,** 1087 (1949).
7. Astwood, E. B., Greer, M. A., and Ettlinger, M. G. *J. Biol. Chem.* **181,** 121 (1949).
8. Astwood, E. B., Raben, M. S., and Payne, R. W. *Recent Progr. Hormone Research* **7,** 1 (1952).
9. Astwood, E. B., and Stanley, M. M. *West. J. Surg.* **55,** 625 (1947).
10. Auger, H. O. *Am. J. Roentgenol., Radium Therapy Nuclear Med.* **70,** 605 (1953).
11. Bahn, R. C., Lorenz, H., Bennett, W. A., and Albert, A. *Endocrinology* **52,** 605 (1953).
12. Barnett, H. L., and McNamara, H. *J. Clin. Invest.* **28,** 1498 (1949).
13. Bartels, E. C. *J. Clin. Endocrinol.* **9,** 1190 (1949).
14. Bartter, F. C., Albright, F., Forbes, A. P., Leaf, A., Dempsey, E., and Carroll, E. *J. Clin. Invest.* **30,** 237 (1951).
15. Beierwaltes, W. H. *J. Clin. Endocrinol. and Metabolism* **13,** 1090 (1953).
16. Bentinek, R. C., Hinman, F., Lisser, H., and Traut, H. F. *Postgraduate Med.* **11,** 301 (1952).
17. Berson, S. A., Yalow, R. S., Sorrentino, J., and Roswitt, B. *J. Clin. Invest.* **31,** 141 (1952).
18. Blackman, S. S., Jr. *Bull. Johns Hopkins Hosp.* **78,** 180 (1946).
19. Blom, P. S., and Terpstra, J. *J. Clin. Endocrinol.* **13,** 989 (1953).
20. Bongiovanni, A. M. *Bull. Johns Hopkins Hosp.* **92,** 244 (1953).
21. Bongiovanni, A. M., and Eisenmenger, W. J. *J. Clin. Endocrinol.* **11,** 152 (1951).
22. Bornstein, I. P., Bower, L. E., and Murphy, J. *Am. J. Med. Sci.* **205,** 114 (1943).
23. Bornstein, J., and Treshella, P. *Lancet* **ii,** 678 (1950).
24. Borst, J. G. G., ten Holt, S. P., de Vries, L. A., and Molhuysen, J. A. *Lancet* **i,** 657 (1953).
25. Brant, F. *Am. J. Surg.* **79,** 645 (1950).
26. Brobeck, J. R. *Ciba Colloquia Endocrinol.* **4,** 124 (1952).
27. Brown, J. H. U. *Proc. Soc. Exptl. Biol. Med.* **83,** 59 (1953).
28. Brown, J. H. U. *Endocrinology* **53,** 116 (1953).
29. Butterly, J. M., Fishman, L., Secklen, J., and Steinberg, H. *Ann. Internal Med.* **37,** 930 (1952).
30. Carroll, K. K., McAlpine, H. T., and Noble, R. L. *Can. Med. Assoc. J.* **65,** 363 (1951).
31. Charny, C. W., Conston, A. S., and Meranze, D. S. *Fertility and Sterility* **4,** 518 (1953).
32. Chart, J. J., Shipley, E. G., and Gordon, E. S. *Proc. Soc. Exptl. Biol. Med.* **78,** 224 (1951).
33. Cloud, L. P., Schneider, J. J., and Paschkis, K. E. Unpublished observations.
34. Conn, J. W., Fajans, S. S., Louis, L. H., and Johnson, B. *Proc. 2nd Clin. ACTH Conf.* **1,** 221 (1951).

35. Conn, J. W., and Louis, L. H. *J. Clin. Endocrinol.* **10**, 12 (1950).
36. Crigler, J. F., Jr., Silverman, S. H., and Wilkins, L. *Pediatrics* **10**, 397 (1952).
36a. Crile, G., and Hazard, J. B. *J. Clin. Endocrinol.* **11**, 1123 (1951).
37. Culiner, A., and Shippel, S. *J. Obstet. and Gynaecol. Brit. Empire* **56**, 439 (1949).
38. Curtis, A. C., Cawley, E. P., and Johnwick, E. B. *Arch. Dermatol. and Syphilol.* **60**, 318 (1949).
39. Cushing, H., and Davidoff, L. M. *Arch. Internal Med.* **39**, 673 (1927).
40. Cutler, H. H., Power, M. H., and Wilder, R. M. *J. Am. Med. Assoc.* **111**, 117 (1938).
41. D'Angelo, S. A., Paschkis, K. E., Cantarow, A., Siegel, A. N., and Rivero-Fontan, J. L. *Endocrinology* **49**, 624 (1951).
42. D'Angelo, S. A., Paschkis, K. E., Gordon, A. S., and Cantarow, A. *J. Clin. Endocrinol.* **11**, 1237 (1951).
43. D'Avignon, M., and Melin, K. A. *Acta Pediat.* **40**, 368 (1951).
44. Davis, M. E. In J. V. Meigs and S. H. Sturgis, Progress in Gynecology. Grune & Stratton, New York, 1946. Vol. I.
45. de la Balze, F. A., Arrillaga, F. C., Irazu, J., and Mancini, R. E. *J. Clin. Endocrinol. and Metabolism* **12**, 1426 (1952).
46. Denny-Brown, D. *Am. J. Med.* **15**, 368 (1953).
47. Devis, R., and Devis-Vanden, E. *J. Clin. Endocrinol.* **9**, 1436 (1950).
47a. DiGeorge, A., and Paschkis, K. E. Unpublished observations.
48. Dobriner, K., Lieberman, S., Rhoads, C. P., and Taylor, H. C. In The Normal and Pathologic Physiology of Pregnancy. Williams & Wilkins, Baltimore, 1948.
49. Dobyns, B. M., and Steelman, S. L. *Endocrinology* **52**, 705 (1953).
50. Dohan, F. C., Rose, E., Eiman, J. W., Richardson, E. M., and Zintel, H. A. *J. Clin. Endocrinol. and Metabolism* **13**, 415 (1953).
51. Dohan, C. F., Rose, E., Boucot, N., and Chamberlain, R. *Trans. & Studies College Physicians Phila.* **20**, 155 (1953).
52. Engel, F. L., and Scott, J. L., Jr. *J. Clin. Invest.* **29**, 151 (1950).
53. Farquharson, R. F. Simmond's Disease. Charles C Thomas, Springfield, Ill., 1950.
54. Fertman, M. B., and Curtis, G. M. *J. Clin. Endocrinol.* **11**, 1361 (1951).
55. Fisher, G., Epstein, D., and Paschkis, K. E. *J. Clin. Endocrinol. and Metabolism* **12**, 1100 (1952).
56. Fortier, C. *Ciba Colloq. Endocrinol.* **4**, 148 (1952).
57. Frawley, T. F., and Thorn, G. W. *Proc. 2nd Clin. ACTH Conf.* **1**, 115 (1951).
58. Fried, P. H., Rakoff, A. E., Schopback, R. R., and Kaplan, A. *J. Am. Med. Assoc.* **145**, 1329 (1951).
59. Fried, P. H., and Rakoff, A. E. *J. Clin. Endocrinol.* **12**, 321 (1952).
60. Friedgood, H. B. In The Chemistry and Physiology of Hormones. Am. Assoc. Advancement of Science, Washington, D. C., 1944.
61. Gardner, L. I. *Proc. Soc. Exptl. Biol. Med.* **83**, 251 (1953).
62. Genell, S. *Acta Endocrinol.* **7**, 133 (1951).
63. Genitis, V. E., and Bornstein, I. P. *J. Am. Med. Assoc.* **119**, 704 (1942).
64. Glenn, E. M., and Nelson, D. H. *J. Clin. Endocrinol. and Metabolism* **13**, 911 (1953).
65. Goldberg, R. C., and Chaikoff, I. L. *Arch. Pathol.* **53**, 22 (1952).
66. Golden, A., Bondy, P. K., and Sheldon, W. H. *Proc. Soc. Exptl. Biol. Med.* **74**, 455 (1950).
67. Goldzieher, M. A., and Goldzieher, J. W. *J. Clin. Endocrinol.* **12**, 42 (1952).

147. Page, E. W. The Hypertensive Toxemias of Pregnancy. Charles C Thomas, Springfield, Ill., 1953.
148. Parviainen, S., Soiva, K., and Vartiainen, S. *Acta Obstet. Gynecol. Scand.* **29**, 5 (1950).
149. Paschkis, K. E. *Med. Clin. N. Amer.* **36**, 1711 (1952).
150. Paschkis, K. E., Rupp, J., and Schneider, J. J. *Trans. Studies College Physicians Phila.* **19**, 149 (1952).
151. Paschkis, K. E., and Cantarow, A. *Ann. Internal Med.* **34**, 669 (1951).
152. Paschkis, K. E., Rakoff, A. E., and Cantarow, A. Clinical Endocrinology. Hoeber, New York, 1953.
153. Paschkis, K. E., Rakoff, A. E., and Cantarow, A. Clinical Endocrinology. Hoeber, New York, 1953.
154. Pasqualini, R. Q. *Endocrinol. and Metabolism* **13**, 128 (1953).
155. Pearlman, W. H., Pearlman, M. R. J., and Rakoff, A. E. *Am. J. Obstet. Gynecol.* **66**, 370 (1953).
156. Perkoff, G. T., Sandberg, A. A., Nelson, D. H., and Tyler, F. H. *Arch. Internal Med.* **93**, 1 (1954).
157. Perry, W. F., and Hughes, J. F. *J. Clin. Invest.* **31**, 457 (1952).
158. Peters, J. P., Mann, E. P., and Heineman, M. In The Normal and Pathological Physiology of Pregnancy. Williams & Wilkins, Baltimore, 1948.
159. Pickering, D. E., and Miller, E. R. *Am. J. Diseases Children* **85**, 135 (1953).
160. Pigeaud, H., and Barthialt, R. *Gynecol. et obstet.* **50**, 341 (1951).
161. Pincus, I. J. Personal communication.
162. Plate, W. P. *Acta Endocrinol.* **8**, 17 (1951).
163. Plotz, C. M., Knowlton, A. I., and Ragan, C. *Am. J. Med.* **13**, 597 (1952).
164. Purves, H. D., and Griesbach, W. E. *Brit. J. Exptl. Pathol.* **30**, 23 (1949).
165. Purves, H. D., and Griesbach, W. E. *Endocrinology* **49**, 244 (1951).
166. Purves, H. D., and Griesbach, W. E. *Endocrinology* **49**, 427 (1951).
167. Quinn, E. L., and Worcester, R. L. *J. Clin. Endocrinol.* **11**, 1564 (1951).
168. Raben, M. S., and Astwood, E. B. *J. Clin. Invest.* **28**, 1347 (1949).
169. Raben, M. S., and Westermeyer, V. W. *Proc. Soc. Exptl. Biol. Med.* **80**, 83 (1952).
170. Rakoff, A. E. *Fertility and Sterility* **4**, 263 (1953).
171. Rakoff, A. E. *Med. Clin. N. Amer.* **32**, 1509 (1948).
172. Rapport, R. L., Curtis, G. M., and Simcox, S. J. *J. Clin. Endocrinol.* **11**, 1549 (1951).
173. Reddy, Wm. J., Jenkins, D., and Thorn, S. W. *Metabolism* **1**, 511 (1952).
174. Reynold, S. R. M. Physiology of the Uterus, 2nd ed. Hoeber, New York, 1949.
175. Reynolds, L., Corrigan, K. E., and Hayden, H. S. *Harper Hosp. Bull.* **8**, 4 (1950).
176. Robbins, J., Rall, J. E., Trunell, J. B., and Rawson, R. W. *J. Clin. Endocrinol.* **11**, 1116 (1951).
177. Salter, W. T. *Science* **109**, 453 (1949).
178. Sandberg, A. A., Nelson, D. H., Glenn, E. M., Tyler, F. H., and Samuels, L. T. *J. Clin. Endocrinol. and Metabolism* **13**, 1445 (1953).
179. Schneider, J. J. Unpublished.
180. Schwarzer, K. *Brgebn. innere Med. u. Kinderheilk.* **58**, 285 (1940).
181. Severinghaus, A. E. *Research Publ. Assoc. Research Nervous Mental Disease* **17**, 69 (1938).
182. Sheehan, H. L., Summers, V. K., and Nichols, J. *Lancet* **266**, 312 (1953).

68. Goodwin, W. E., Bauer, F. K., Barrett, T. F., and Cassen, B. *Am. J. Roentgenol., Radium Therapy Nuclear Med.* **68**, 963 (1952).
69. Goodwin, W. E., Cassen, B., and Bauer, F. K. *Radiology* **61**, 88 (1953).
70. Gray, C. H., and Parrott, D. M. *Ciba Colloq. Endocrinol.* **5**, 153 (1953).
71. Green, J., Pilser, H., Frenkel, M., Ramminga, E. E., and Willebrands, A. F. *J. Clin. Invest.* **31**, 87 (1952).
72. Greenblatt, R. B. *Postgraduate Med.* **9**, 492 (1951).
73. Greer, M. A. *J. Clin. Endocrinol.* **12**, 1259 (1952).
74. Greer, M. A. *J. Clin. Invest.* **30**, 301 (1951).
75. Greer, M. A. *Physiol. Revs.* **30**, 513 (1950).
76. Greer, M. A., and Astwood, E. B. *J. Clin. Endocrinol.* **13**, 1312 (1953).
77. Grynkewich, S. E., Laughlin, R. M., Herold, F. T., and Carmel, W. J. *Am. J. Med. Sci.* **222**, 142 (1951).
78. Halmi, N. S. *Endocrinology* **47**, 289 (1950).
79. Halmi, N. S. *Endocrinology* **50**, 140 (1952).
80. Hamilton, J. *Recent Progr. Hormone Research* **3**, 250 (1948).
81. Hamilton, J., Soley, M. H., Reilly, W. A., and Eichorn, K. B. *Am. J. Diseases Children* **66**, 495 (1943).
82. Heckel, N. J. *J. Clin. Endocrinol.* **11**, 235 (1951).
83. Heinbecker, P., and Pfeiffenberger, M., Jr. *Am. J. Med.* **9**, 3 (1950).
84. Heller, E. L., and Camarata, S. J. *Arch. Pathol.* **49**, 601 (1950).
85. Heller, C. G., and Nelson, W. O. *Recent Progr. Hormone Research* **3**, 229 (1948).
86. Heller, C. G., Nelson, W. O., and Roth, A. A. *J. Clin. Endocrinol.* **3**, 573 (1943).
87. Heller, C. G., and Nelson, W. O. *J. Clin. Endocrinol.* **8**, 345 (1948).
88. Hewer, T. F. *J. Endocrinol.* **3**, 387 (1942–1944).
89. Hills, O. W., Power, M. H., and Wilder, R. M. *Diabetes* **1**, 351 (1952).
90. Hollander, V. P., Di Mauro, S., and Pearson, O. H. *Endocrinology* **49**, 617 (1951).
91. Howard, R. P., Sniffen, R. C., Simmons, F. A., and Albright, F. *J. Clin. Endocrinol.* **10**, 121 (1950).
92. Huggins, C., and Moulder, P. V. *Cancer Research* **5**, 510 (1945).
93. Hume, D. M. *Ciba Colloq. Endocrinol.* **4**, 87 (1952).
94. Hurxthal, L. M. *Med. Clin. N. Amer.* (January 1947).
95. Hurxthal, L. M., Bruns, H. J., and Musulin, N. *J. Clin. Endocrinol.* **9**, 1245 (1949).
96. Hurxthal, L. M., and Musulin, N. *Am. J. Med.* **1**, 58 (1946).
97. Jailer, J. W. Quoted by Knowlton in reference 117.
98. Jailer, J. W. *J. Clin. Endocrinol.* **9**, 557 (1949).
99. Jailer, J. W., and Knowlton, H. I. *J. Clin. Invest.* **29**, 1430 (1950).
100. Jailer, J. W. *Proc. 2nd Clin. ACTH Conf.* **1**, 79 (1951).
101. Jailer, J. W. *Trans. N. Y. Acad. Sci.* [2] **13**, 262 (1951).
102. Jefferies, W. McK. Levy, R. P., Palmer, W. G., Storaasli, J. P., and Kelly, L. W. *New Engl. J. Med.* **249**, 876 (1953).
103. Johnson, S. G. *Acta Med. Scand.* **144**, 165 (1952).
104. Jones, G. E. S., and Delf, E. *J. Am. Med. Assoc.* **146**, 1212 (1951).
105. Jones, G. E. S., Howard, J. E., and Langford, H. *Fertility and Sterility* **4**, 49 (1953).
106. Jost, A. *Arch. anat. microscop. et morphol. exptl.* **36**, 271 (1947).
107. Kadin, M. *Am. J. Ophthalmol.* **33**, 962 (1950).
108. Kelley, V. C., Ely, R. S., and Raile, R. B. *Pediatrics* **12**, 541 (1953).

116. Klinefelter, H. F., Jr., Albright, F., and Griswold, G. C. *J. Clin. Endocrinol.* **10**, 1013 (1948).
117. Knowlton, A. I. *Bull. N. Y. Acad. Med.* **29**, 441 (1953).
118. Koff, A. K., and Tulsky, A. S. *Surg. Clin. N. Amer.* **33**, 3 (1953).
119. Landau, R. L. *J. Clin. Endocrinol. and Metabolism* **13**, 510 (1953).
120. Landau, J., and Lougheed, R. *J. Clin. Endocrinol.* **11**, 1411 (1951).
121. Laqueur, G. L. *Science* **112**, 429 (1950).
122. Lerman, J., Jones, H. W., and Calkins, E. *Ann. Internal Med.* **25**, 677 (1946).
123. Leventhal, M. L., and Cohen, M. R. *Am. J. Obstet. Gynecol.* **61**, 1034 (1951).
124. Lewis, R. A., and Wilkins, L. *J. Clin. Invest.* **28**, 394 (1949).
125. Liddle, G. W., Rinfret, A. P., Richard, J., and Forsham, P. H. *J. Clin. Endocrinol. and Metabolism* **13**, 842 (1953).
126. Locke, W., Talbot, N. B., Jones, H. S., and Worcester, J. *J. Clin. Invest.* **30**, 325 (1951).
127. Ludwig, A. W., Boas, N. F., and Soffer, L. J. *Proc. Soc. Exptl. Biol. Med.* **73**, 137 (1950).
128. Luft, R., and Olivecrona, H. *J. Neurosurg.* **10**, 301 (1953).
129. Man, E. B., Heinemann, M., Johnson, C. E., Leary, D. C., and Peters, J. P. *J. Clin. Invest.* **30**, 137 (1951).
130. Markee, J. E., Everett, J. W., and Sawyer, C. H. *Recent Progr. Hormone Research* **7**, 139 (1952).
131. Mason, H. L., and Engstrom, W. W. *Physiol. Revs.* **30**, 321 (1950).
132. Mason, H. L., and Kepler, E. J. *J. Biol. Chem.* **161**, 235 (1945).
133. Masson, P. *Rev. can. biol.* **1**, 570 (1942).
134. McCann, S. M. *Am. J. Physiol.* **175**, 13 (1953).
135. McCullagh, E. P., Beck, J. C., and Schaffenburg, C. A. *J. Clin. Endocrinol. and Metabolism* **13**, 489 (1953).
136. McCullagh, E. P., Gold, A., and McKendry, J. B. R. *J. Clin. Endocrinol.* **10**, 687 (1950).
137. McGirr, E. M., and Hutchinson, J. H. *Lancet* ii, 1117 (1953).
138. Means, J. H. The Thyroid and Its Diseases, 2nd ed. Lippincott, Philadelphia, 1948.
139. Meyers, T. H., and Man, E. B. *J. Lab. Clin. Med.* **57**, 867 (1951).
140. Miller, A. M., and Dorfman, R. I. *Endocrinology* **46**, 514 (1950).
141. Milliken, C. H., and Haines, S. F. *Arch. Internal Med.* **92**, 5 (1953).
142. Mills, E. S., and Forsey, R. R. *Trans. Assoc. Am. Physicians* **62**, 225 (1949).
143. Mulvaney, T. H. *Am. J. Ophthalmol.* **27**, 589 (1944).
144. Nelson, W. V., and Heller, G. G. *Recent Progr. Hormone Research* **3**, 197 (1948).
145. Nelson, W. O. *Anat. Record, Suppl.* **67**, 36 (1937).
146. Nichols, J., and Gardner, L. I. *J. Lab. Clin. Med.* **37**, 229 (1951).

Charles C Thomas,

183. Sheline, G. E., Moore, M. C., Kapps, A., and Clark, D. E. *J. Clin. Endocrinoi.* **11,** 91 (1951).
184. Shorr, E., Carter, A. C., Kennedy, B. J., and Smith, R. W., Jr. *Trans. Assoc. Am. Physicians* **66,** 114 (1953).
185. Silver, H. K. *Pediatrics* **8,** 368 (1951).
186. Silver, S., Fieber, M. H., and Yohalin, S. B. *Am. J. Med.* **13,** 725 (1952).
187. Simpson, M. E., and Evans, H. M. *Endocrinology* **39,** 281 (1946).
188. Smith, P. E., and MacDowell, E. C. *Anat. Record* **46,** 249 (1930).
189. Smith, P. E., and MacDowell, E. C. *Anat. Record* **50,** 85 (1931).
190. Smith, G. V., and Smith, O. W. *Physiol. Revs.* **28,** 1 (1948).
191. Soffer, L. J. Diseases of the Endocrine Glands. Philadelphia. 1951. Lea & Febiger, Philadelphia.
192. Soffer, L. J., Lesnick, G., Sorkin, S. Z., Sobotka, H. H., and Jacobs, M. *J. Clin. Invest.* **23,** 51 (1944).
193. Sommerville, I. F. *In* John Hammond, Toxemias of Pregnancy, Human and Veterinary. Blakiston, Philadelphia, 1950.
194. Sougin-Mibashan, R., and Jackson, W. P. U. *Brit. Med. J.* **2,** 371 (1953).
195. Specht, N. W., Bauer, F. K., and Adams, R. M. *Am. J. Med.* **14,** 766 (1953).
196. Sprague, R. G. *Proc. Roy. Soc. Med.* **46,** 1070 (1953).
197. Sprague, R. G., Mason, H. L., and Power, M. H. *Recent Progr. Hormone Research* **6,** 315 (1951).
198. Stanbury, J. B., Brownell, G., Riggs, D. S., Perinetti, H., del Castillo, E., and Itoiz, J. *J. Clin. Endocrinol.* **12,** 191 (1952).
199. Stanbury, J. B., and Hedge, A. N. *J. Clin. Endocrinol.* **10,** 1471 (1950).
200. Stanley, M. M., and Astwood, E. B. *Endocrinology* **41,** 66 (1947).
201. Stein, I. F., Cohen, M. R., and Elson, R. *Am. J. Obstet. Gynecol.* **58,** 267 (1949).
202. Stein, I. F., and Leventhal, M. L. *Am. J. Obstet. Gynecol.* **29,** 181 (1935).
203. Steinback, H. L., Lyon, R. P., Smith, D. R., and Miller, E. R. *Radiology* **59,** 167 (1952).
204. Sternberg, W. H., Segaloff, A., and Gaskill, C. J. *J. Clin. Endocrinol. and Metabolism* **13,** 139 (1953).
205. Stewart, L. H. *Am. J. Obstet. Gynecol.* **61,** 990 (1951).
206. Sturgis, S. H. *In* Progress in Gynecology, Grune & Stratton, New York, 1950, Vol. 2.
207. Sunderman, F. W., and Sunderman, F. W., Jr. *Am. J. Clin. Pathol.* **24,** 885 1954.
208. Sydnor, K. L., Kelley, V. C., Raile, R. B., Ely, R. S., and Sayers, G. *Proc. Soc. Exptl. Biol. Med.* **82,** 695 (1953).
208a. Sydnor, K. L., Sayers, G., Brown, H., and Tyler, F. H. *J. Clin. Endocrinol. and Metabolism* **13,** 891 (1953).
209. Szilagyi, D. E., McGraw, A. B., and Smyth, N. P. D. *Ann. Surg.* **136,** 555 (1952).
209a. Taylor, A. B., Albert, A., and Sprague, R. G. *Endocrinology* **45,** 335 (1949).
210. Teilum, G. *J. Clin. Endocrinol.* **9,** 301 (1949).
211. Tew, M. B., and McAlpins, H. T. *Can. Med. Assoc. J.* **63,** 287 (1950).
212. Thompson, R., Gross, S., and Strauss, R. *Am. J. Obstet. Gynecol.* **61,** 830 (1951).
213. Thorn, G. W. *J. Clin. Endocrinol. and Metabolism* **13,** 614 (1953).
214. Thorn, G. W., Forsham, P. H., and Emerson, K. The Diagnosis and Treatment of Adrenal Insufficiency, 2nd ed. Charles C Thomas, Springfield, Ill., 1951.
215. Thorn, G. W., Jenkins, D., Arons, W. L., and Frawley, T. F. *J. Clin. Endocrinol. and Metabolism* **13,** 957 (1953).

876 K. E. PASCHKIS AND A. E. RAKOFF

216. Tobian, L., Jr. *J. Clin. Endocrinol.* **9,** 319 (1949).
217. Topper, A. *Am. J. Diseases Children* **81,** 233 (1951).
218. Turner, H. H. *In* S. Soskin, Progress in Clinical Endocrinology. Grune & Stratton, New York, 1950.
219. Twombly, G. A. *Surgery* **16,** 181 (1944).
220. Venning, E. H. *In* "The Normal and Pathological Physiology of Pregnancy." Williams & Wilkins, Baltimore, 1948.
221. Venning, E. H., Weil, P. G., and Browne, J. S. L. *J. Biol. Chem.* **128,** cvii (1939).
222. Venning, E. H. *Rev. can. biol.* **1,** 571 (1942).
223. Vestergaard, P. *Acta Endocrinol.* **13,** 241 (1953).
224. Vilanova, X., and Canadell, J. M. *J. Clin. Endocrinol.* **9,** 883 (1949).
225. Wallach, J. B., and Scharfman, W. B. *J. Am. Med. Assoc.* **148,** 729 (1952).
226. Warming-Larsen, A., Hamburger, C., and Sprechler, M. *Acta Endocrinol.* **11,** 400 (1952).
227. Watson, E. M., and Pearce, R. H. *Am. J. Clin. Pathol.* **19,** 442 (1949).
228. Weissman, L. *J. Clin. Endocrinol. and Metabolism* **12,** 1223 (1952).
229. Wells, L. J. *Proc. Soc. Exptl. Biol. Med.* **63,** 417 (1947).
230. Werner, S. C. *J. Clin. Endocrinol.* **13,** 1332 (1953).
231. White, F. P., and Sutton, L. E. *J. Clin. Endocrinol.* **11,** 1395 (1951).
232. Wilkins, L. The Diagnosis and Treatment of Endocrine Disorders in Childhood and Adolescence. Charles C Thomas, Springfield, Ill., 1950.
233. Wilkins, L., Crigler, J. F., Jr., Silverman, S. H., Gardner, L. I., and Migeon, C. J. *J. Clin. Endocrinol. and Metabolism* **12,** 277 (1952).
234. Wilkins, L., Fleischman, W., and Howard, J. E. *Endocrinology* **26,** 385 (1940).
235. Wilkins, L., Crigler, J. F., Jr., Silverman, S. H., Gardner, L. I., and Migeon, C. J. *J. Clin. Endocrinol. and Metabolism* **12,** 1015 (1952).
236. Wilkins, L. *J. Pediat.* **41,** 860 (1952).
237. Wilson, H. *J. Clin. Endocrinol. and Metabolism* **13,** 1465 (1953).
238. Wislocki, G. B., Dempsey, E., and Fawcett, D. W. *In* The Normal and Pathological Physiology of Pregnancy. Williams & Wilkins, Baltimore, 1948.
239. Wolfson, W. Q. *Arch. Internal Med.* **92,** 108 (1953).
240. Zierler, K. L. *Bull. Johns Hopkins Hosp.* **89,** 263 (1951).

Author Index

Numbers in parentheses are reference numbers and are included to assist in locating references when the authors' names are not mentioned in the text. Numbers in italics indicate the page on which the reference is listed at the end of the chapter.

A

Abbott, W. E., 694 (1119), 696 (1119), *815*

Abderhalden, E., 475 (1), *499*

Abdon, N. O., 129 (1), *144*

Abel, J. J., 190, *195*, *425*

Abelin, I., 436 (9), 445 (2), 474 (6), 476 (3, 4, 7, 8), 483 (5), *499*, *500*

Abelman, M. A., 700 (218, 219), *790*

Abercrombie, W. F., 489 (10), *500*

Åberg, B., 11 (2, 3, 5), 12 (3), 13 (4), 14 (2, 3, 4), 15 (3, 4), 16, 25(5), *48*

Abernathy, R., 779 (1, 2), *784*

Abood, L. G., 377, *383*

Abrahams, V. C., *425*

Abramowitz, A. A., 100(2), *144*

Abrams, G. D., 258 (1), 259 (1), *296*

Abrams, M. E., 321, *379*

Abrams, W. B., 713 (3), *785*

Acevedo, D., 672 (1), *677*

Acher, R., 403 (72), 404, 414 (72), *425*, *427*

Ackermann, P. G., 727 (653), *803*

Adams, A., 221, *230*

Adams, C. H., 696 (350), 766 (350), *794*

Adams, E., 287 (2), 293 (2), *296*, 743 (4), *785*

Adams, J. E., 718 (78), *787*

Adams, R. M., 830 (195), *875*

Addicott, F. T., 29 (264), *54*

Adezati, L., 672 (51), *679*

Adler, M., 734 (25), *785*

Adlersberg, D., 721 (103), 725 (103), 732 (5-9), *785*, *787*

Adolph, E. F., *425*

Adrouny, G. A., 252 (3), *296*

Aebi, H., 477 (11), *500*

Agnello, E. J., 556 (201), *584*

Agnoletto, A., 482 (12), *500*

Agnoletto, C., 482 (12), *500*

Agolini, G., 672 (2), 674 (2), *677*

Agosin, M., 751 (10), *785*

Agrell, I., 75 (1-3), *83*

Ahlmark, A., 670 (3), *677*

Ahlquist, R. P., 134, *144*

Aikawa, J. K., 706 (11), *785*

Ainslie, J. D., 779 (12), *785*

Aird, R. B., 719 (13), *785*

Albaum, H. G., 724 (14), *785*

Albert, A., 337 (9–12), 342 (243), 343, *379*, *386*, 439 (541), 440 (14), 445 (18), 449 (21, 544), 450 (19), 451 (15, 16, 17, 328), 452 (16, 17, 61, 328), 453 (61), 454 (15, 328, 338), 455 (18, 543), 490 (446), *500*, *501* *507*, *510*, *512*, 572 (225, 226), 574 (226), *584*, 705 (1080), 707 (737, 1080), 708 (1080), 709 (1080), 721 (1080), 724 (1080), 732 (1080), 753 (1080), 765 (1080), 782 (15), 784 (371), *785*, *795*, *805*, *814*, 843 (209a), 869 (11), *870*, *875*

Albert, S., 596, *655*

Albright, E. C., 450 (144, 381), 484 (380), *503*, *508*

Albright, F., 154, 155, 160, *169*, *170*, 718 (59), 783 (59), *786*, 844, 850 (14), 857, 865 (91), 866 (116), *870*, *872*, *873*

Albright, F. J., 703 (339), *794*

Aldrich, T. B., 401 (116), 403 (116), *428*

Alexander, E. R., 779 (708), *804*

Alexander, J. A., 707 (343), 721 (343), 753 (343), *794*

Alexandrowicz, J. S., 61 (4–7), 67 (7), *83*, 109, 110, 139 (6), *144*

Alibrandi, A., 488 (22), *500*

Aliminosa, L. M., 552 (275), 554 (47), 563 (47), *579*, *586*

880 AUTHOR INDEX

Balomey, A. A., 395 (11), *425*
Bancroft, R. W., 187 (163), *199*
Bandurski, R. S., 30 (31), 39 (32), 40 (32), 41 (31), 44 (32), 45 (32), *48*
Banerjee, D. K., 537 (172), *583*
Banerjee, S., 740 (52, 53, 54), *786*
Banes, D., 542, 543 (15), 559 (14), *578, 582*
Bangham, A. D., 762 (55), 766 (55), *786*
Bannister, B., 539 (173), *583*
Bannister, J., 100 (16), *144*
Barber, A., 768 (56), *786*
Barberio, J. R., 775 (57), *786*
Barbieri, E., 485 (521), *512*
Barclay, W. R., 761 (278), 763 (278), *792*
Barger, G., 474 (283), *506*
Bargmann, W., 105, 109, *144*, 391, *426*
Bargoni, N., 676 (15), *678*
Bariety, M., 496 (41), *500*
Barker, M. H., 462 (43), 464 (42), *500*
Barker, S. B., 187 (123), *198*, 452 (402), 474 (48), 475 (45, 356), 476 (45, 46, 47, 49, 401), 490 (50, 51), 491 (51), *500, 501, 508, 509*, 782 (458), *797*
Barker-Jorgensen, C., 397, 398, 399 (15), *426*
Barkley, L. B., 539, *579*
Barlow, G., 698 (1120), 708 (1122, 1123), 712 (1124), 714 (1122, 1123, 1126), 722 (1125), *815*
Barlow, H. W. B., 2 (114), 23 (114), *50*
Barnafi, L., *426, 427*
Barnes, A. R., 765 (497), *798*
Barnes, C. S., 540 (17), 562 (17), 569 (17), *579*
Barnes, J. M., 128, *144*
Barnett, H. L., 154 (97), *172*, 851 (12), *870*
Barnicot, N. A., 158, 164, *170*
Barott, G. W., 705 (177), 707 (177), 721 (177), 732 (177), 753 (177), *789*
Barrett, G. R., 332 (172), *384*
Barrett, H. W., 254 (15), *297*, 467 (52), *501*
Barrett, T. F., 830 (68), *872*
Barrnett, R. J., 315, 324, 329, 331, 345, *379, 382, 383*
Barron, E. S. Guzman, 729 (639), *802*
Barry, A. G., 220 (78), *233*
Barry, M. C., 609, 616 (100), 618 (100), 621 (100), *655, 657*
Barry, S. R., 442 (164), *504*
Barsantini, J. C., 361, *379*, 480 (140), *503*

Bartels, E. C., 827 (13), *870*
Barthel, M., 497 (359), *508*
Barthiaalt, R., 863 (160), *874*
Bartlett, M. N., 479 (357), 480 (357), *508*
Bartlett, P. D., 243 (122), 248 (16, 17, 122), 249 (16), *297, 300*
Bartlett, R. G., 674 (203), *682*
Barton, A. D., 729 (58), *786*
Barton, D. H. R., 523, 524 (18, 19), 525, 529 (212), 540 (17), 544 (20), 562 (17), 567 (20), 569 (17), *579, 584*
Barton, M. N., 739 (806), *807*
Bartter, F. C., 153, 154 (11), *170*, 707 (343), 718 (59), 721 (343), 753 (343), 783 (59), *786, 794*, 850 (14), *870*
Baschiere, L., 763 (60), *786*
Baserga, R., 751 (60a), 753 (60a), *786*
Bass, A. C., 706 (205), 708 (205), 710 (205), *790*
Bass, A. D., 249 (90), *299*
Bassett, G., 747 (181), *789*
Bastenie, P. A., 781 (654), *803*
Bastian, J. W., 331 (266), *387*
Bateman, J. H., 703 (1232), 719 (1232), *818*
Bates, R. W., 211, *231*, 246 (312), 292 (18), *297, 305*, 373, 374, 375, *385*, 667 (16), *678*, 703 (940), *810*
Bather, R., 497 (53), *501*
Battle, F. F., 493 (424), *509*
Batres, E., 552 (270), 556 (69), *580, 586*
Batts, A. A., 251 (375), *306*
Bauchau, A. G., 63 (31), 66 (30), *84*
Bauer, F. K., 830 (68, 69, 195), *872, 875*
Bauer, W., 154 (1), *169*, 487 (39), *500*, 718 (153), *789*
Bauld, W. S., 509 (124), 606 (124), 631 (124), *658*, 667 (163), *681*
Bauman, K. L., 237 (326), *305*
Baumann, C. A., 187 (134), *198*, 488 (330), 389 (173), *504, 507*
Baumann, E. J., 436 (54, 55, 56), 461 (432), *501, 510*, 781 (61), *786*
Baxter, B., 447 (270), 473 (270), *506*
Bay, R., 759 (108), *787*
Bayle, J., 718 (1188), *817*
Bayles, T. B., 747 (319), 749 (1174), *793, 817*
Bayliss, M. J., 288 (322), 289 (321, 322), *305*, 623 (260, 260a), *662*

Britten, E. J., 17 (43), *49*
Brobeck, J. R., 281 (131), 283 (131, 241, 242), *300, 303,* 692 (740), 747 (741), *805,* 844 (26), *870*
Brock, H., 341 (31), 342 (31), *379*
Brodie, E. C., 727 (111, 1099), 755 (104), *787, 814*
Brodkin, E., 106, *145*
Brody, S., 476 (628), 488 (628), *514,* 718 (112), *788*
Broh-Kahn, R. H., 185, *195,* 484 (464), *510,* 727 (113), 752 (113), *788*
Brolin, S., 163, *170*
Brooks, R. V., 529 (36), 565 (36), *579,* 605, *655*
Brooks, V. B., 117 (32), *145*
Brophy, D., 490 (92), *502*
Brougher, J. C., 166, *170*
Brown, C. Y., 697 (527, 528), 766 (527, 528), *799*
Brown, D. H., 243 (278), 260 (278), *304*
Brown, D. M., 204 (92), *233,* 293 (135), *300*
Brown, E. F., 481 (93), *502*
Brown, E. M., 697 (527, 528), 766 (527, 528), *799*
Brown, F. A., Jr., 58 (66, 67, 68, 70), 60 (70), 61 (65, 66, 70, 75, 84, 88, 520, 525), 62 (69, 72, 76, 77, 78, 79, 80, 81, 82, 83, 84, 85, 86, 87, 89, 422, 423, 424, 521, 523, 524), 66 (71, 73), 67 (70), 78 (74), *85, 92, 94,* 116 (35), 138 (33, 34), *145*
Brown, F. C., 435 (666), *515*
Brown, G. C., 779 (12), *785*
Brown, G. L., 117(36, 37), 133, *145*
Brown, H., 726 (115), *788,* 843 (208a), *875*
Brown, J. B., 4 (45), *49,* 345, *383*
Brown, J. H. U., 691 (114), *788,* 848 (27, 28), *870*
Brown, J. W., 17 (179, 324), *52, 56*
Brown, M., *426*
Brown, M. B., 674 (128), *680,* 752 (605), *801*
Brown, R. G., Jr., 125 (195), *148*
Brown, R. W., 375, 376 (32, 33), *380*
Brown, W. E., 342, 371 (29), *379, 380,* 671 (37), *678*
Browne, J. S. L., 272 (55), 273 (55), 290 (55), *298,* 605, 606, 637 (143), 649 (143), *659, 663,* 741 (22), 784 (1175), *785, 817,* 850 (221), *876*

Brownell, G., 828 (198), 837 (198), 838 (198), *875*
Brownell, G. L., 449 (684), *516*
Browne, A. C., 645, (24), 646, *655*
Brownlee, G., 765 (116), *788*
Bruce, H. M., 220, *231,* 295 (41), *298,* 669 (39), *678*
Brücke, H. v., 101, *145*
Brückmann, G., 189 (17), *195*
Bruger, A., 488 (643), *515*
Bruger, M., 447 (333), *507,* 717, 733 (838), *807*
Brumby, P. J., 366, *380*
Brumfield, L. T., 24 (46), *49*
Brummel, E., 288 (307), 289 (307), *305,* 676 (40), *678*
Bruner, J. A., 337 (35), *380*
Brunings, K. J., 552 (200), 556 (201), *584*
Brunn, F., 396, *426*
Brunner, M. P., 642 (53, 108), *656, 658*
Bruns, H. J., 867 (95), *872*
Bryan, W. H., 42 (47), 44 (47), *49*
Bryans, F. E., 370, *380*
Buchanan, G. D., 165 (140), *173*
Bucher, N. L. R., 592, *655*
Buchholz, C., 496 (753), *517*
Buchtal, F., 120 (41), 126 (41), *145*
Buchwald, K. W., 723 (117), *788*
Bucklin, D. H., 70 (90), *85*
Budziarek, R., 556 (37, 38), *579*
Bückmann, D., 73 (92), 76 (91, 92), *85*
Bueding, E., 59 (94), *85*
Buehler, H. J., 667 (135), *659, 681*
Bülbring, E., 79 (95), 80 (95), *85,* 101 (46), 119 (44), 128 (43), 133, *145*
Bugbee, E. P., 236 (42), 270, *298,* 401 (116), 403 (116), *428*
Bullough, W. S., 421, *426,* 671 (41, 42, 43, 44), *678,* 754 (118), *788*
Bullwinkle, B., 22 (133), *51*
Bunding, I., 366 (239a), *386*
Bunding, I. M., 219, 221 (51), *232, 233*
Burchenal, J. H., 752 (119), 753 (120), *788*
Burgen, A. S. V., 117 (47), *145*
Burger, H., 671 (45), 677 (45), *678*
Burger, M., 191 (18), 193, 194, *195*
Burke, D. C., 556 (39), *579*
Burkell, C. C., 748 (121), *788*
Burkhardt, J., 319 (31), *380*
Burn, D., 574 (333a), *587*
Burn, G. P., 396 (29), *426*

(357), *508*, 616, 618, 619, 648 (50, 51, 156, 158), *656, 659*, 674 (269), 676 (143, 236), 677, *681, 683, 684*, 729 (651), 731 (652), 732, *792, 802, 803*
Kocsis, J. J., 221 (51), *232*, 377, *383*
Koechlin, B. A., 548 (191), 577 (191, 192), *583*
Koefoed-Johnsen, V., 134 (173), *148, 150*
Kögl, F., 4 (145), 10 (146), *51*
Köhler, V., 497 (359), *508*
Koelle, G. B., 119 (174), *143*
Koelling, G., 548 (171), *588*
Koenig, V., 211, 219, *232*
Koeppen, H., 487 (358), *508*
Koester, H., 537 (193), 549 (296), *584, 586*
Koff, A. K., 862 (118), *873*
Kogure, M., 142 (175), *148*
Kohler, D., 496 (41), *500*
Kohn, R. R., 81 (548), *95*
Koidsumi, K., 75 (311), *90*
Koille, E. S., 674 (88), *680*
Koivusalo, M., 487 (360), *508*
Kolinsky, M., 722 (160), *789*
Koller, F., 546 (108), *581*
Koller, G., 58 (312), 59 (313), 60 (312), 77 (314, 316), 81 (315), *90*, 138, *148*
Koller, M., 673 (80), *679*
Kollros, J. J., 77 (504), *94*
Konnerth, A., 715 (437), *796*
Konsuloff, S., 419, *428*
Konyuchenko, T. U., 496 (322), *507*
Kooistra, G., 77 (317), *90*
Kopeć, S., 71 (318), *90*
Kopp, E., 747 (308), *793*
Kordik, P., 119 (177), 123 (168), 124 (168), *148*
Koskowski, W., 107 (178), *148*
Kostial, K., 117 (166), *148*
Kountz, W. B., 727 (653), *803*
Kowalewski, K., 781 (654), *803*
Kracht, J., 442 (361), *508*
Kracht, U., 442 (361), *508*
Kraft, K., 476 (362), *508*
Krahl, M. E., 186, 188, *197*, 243 (278), 260 (278), *304*, 727 (655), *803*
Kraintz, F. W., 154 (141), 155 (142), 157 (143), 165 (140), *173*, 751 (288), *792*
Kraintz, L., 157 (143), *173*, 352, *383*, 458 (468), 459 (467, 468), 468 (702), *511, 516*, 782 (782, 783), *806*

Kramar, J., 716 (656), *803*
Kramer, H., 193, 194, *195*
Kramer, L. B., 437 (363), *508*
Kramer, M., 5 (147), 7, 10 (147), *51*
Kramer, W., 188 (8), *195*
Krantz, S. C., Jr., 670 (144), *681*
Kraychy, S., 539 (342), *588*
Krebs, H. A., 187, *197*
Krehl, W. A., 737 (981, 1223), 738 (1221, 1222), *811, 818*
Kreiss, R. E., 243 (24), 248 (24), 253 (24), *297*, 735 (75), *786*
Kribben, F. J., 32 (153), *52*
Krieger, V. I., 396, *428*
Krijgsman, B. J., 131 (179), *148*
Kretchevsky, T. H., 528 (116), 548 (191), 567 (116, 194), 568 (194, 220), 569 (194), 577 (191, 192, 194), 578 (114), *581, 583, 584*, 609 (99), 610 (316), 615 (316), 616 (316), 633 (99), 635 (98a, 99), *657, 664*
Kroc, R. L., 459 (646), *515*
Krochert, G., 492 (364), *508*
Krog, N., 3 (172), *52*
Krohn, P. L., 671 (145), *681*, 775 (86, 657), *787, 803*
Kroneberg, G., 497 (365), *508*
Kroon, D. B., 238 (119), *300*, 479 (366), 480 (366), *508*
Krough, A., *428*
Krueger, H., 674 (47), *678*
Krüsenkemper, W., 676 (62), *679*
Krupp, M. A., 470 (250), *506*
Kuang, M. H., 397 (124b), *429*
Kuehl, F. A., Jr., 222 (8, 9), 224, 226 (7, 9), *231, 232*, 279 (40), 294 (40), *298*
Kuffler, S. W., 120 (181), 126 (180, 182), *148*
Kuhl, W. J., 781 (658), *803*
Kuhl, W. J., Jr., 485 (229), *505*
Kuhn, W., 533 (195), *584*
Kuizenga, M. H., 604 (107), *658*, 703 (843), 706 (584), *801, 808*
Kulescha, Z., 28 (149a), 36 (148, 149, 150), *51*
Kulkarni, A. B., 546 (252), *585*
Kulonen, E., 671 (146), *681*
Kumagi, L. F., 243 (209), 245 (209), *302*, 744 (256), *791, 803*
Kunderman, P. J., 768 (942, 943), *810*

Marker, R. E., 528, 529 (215, 219), 540, 561 (217, 218, 219), 565 (216), 567 (214), *584*, 594, 604, 605, 615, *660*

Markhardt, B., 672 (79), *679*

Markoff, G. N., 476 (433), 478 (433), *510*

Marks, H. P., 258 (246), 262 (245, 246), 263 (246), *303*

Marois, M., 443 (599), 452 (132, 133), *503*, *514*

Maroney, S. P., 80 (347), *90*

Marrazzi, A. S., 131 (199, 200, 201), *148*

Marré, E., 24 (299), 33 (193, 195), 41 (194a), 42 (196), 46 (299), *53*, *55*

Marrian, G. F., 594, 605, *656*, *659*, *660*, 667 (163, 237), *681*, *683*

Marsh, J. B., 181 (63), 186 (131, 132), *196*, *198*, 257 (372, 373), *306*, 727 (1086), *814*

Marshall, C. W., 568 (220), *584*, 624 (168), 646 (168), *658*, *659*

Marshall, F. H. A., 317, 318, *384*

Marshall, L. M., 728 (729), *804*

Marshall, W. A., 321 (1), *379*

Marsili, G., 674 (164), *681*

Marti, H. V., 772 (699), *804*

Martin, C., 745 (1098), 747 (1098), *814*

Martin, G. J., 295 (66), *298*

Martin, P. G., 154, *172*

Martin, S. P., 776 (730), *804*

Martinet, M., *795*

Martinez, C., 751 (731), *805*

Martius, C., 477 (434, 435), *510*

Marvin, H. M., 728 (33), *785*

Marx, L., 239 (203), *302*, 485 (767), *518*

Marx, W., 202 (71), *232*, 238 (250), 239 (247), 240 (362), 241 (21, 249, 361), 242 (248), 244 (106, 248), 247 (247), 248 (247), *297*, *299*, *303*, *306*, 476 (437), 485 (436, 767), *510*, *518*

Mason, A. S., 783 (732), *805*

Mason, E. J., 769 (619), *802*

Mason, H. L., 569 (50), 572 (225, 226), 574 (226), *580*, *584*, 590 (195), 604, 605, 615, 616, 618, 634 (198), 635 (194), 646 (281), 647 (282), 648 (282), *660*, *663*, 697 (1079), 701 (1077, 1078), 705 (1080), 707 (737, 1080), 708 (1080), 709 (1080), 721 (1080), 724 (1080), 725 (1079), 727 (1077), 732 (1080), 753 (1080), 765 (882, 1080), 766 (882), 784

(371), *795*, *805*, *809*, *814*, 841 (131), 844 (110, 197), 845 (131), 848 (132), 850 (132), *873*, *875*

Mason, R. C., 670 (165), *681*, 778 (927), *810*

Masoro, E. J., 188 (22, 85), *195*, *197*

Massart, L., 121 (202), *148*

Masson, G., 361, *379*

Masson, G. M. C., 361, *384*, 700 (735), 714 (734, 736), 715 (733), 740 (963), *805*, *811*

Masson, P., 867 (133), *873*

Mast, H., 278 (166), *301*

Masters, W. H., 671 (166, 167, 168), *681*

Mateer, F. M., 705 (201), *790*

Matell, M., 11 (84, 85, 197), *50*, *53*

Mathies, J. C., *300*, 479 (438), 480 (439), *510*

Mathieson, D. R., 705 (1080), 707 (1080), 708 (1080), 709 (1080), 721 (1080), 724 (1080), 732 (1080), 753 (1080), 765 (1080), *814*

Mathiew, J. C., 250 (251), *303*

Matthews, J. D., 208, *231*

Matthews, J. I., 361, *386*

Matthews, S. A., 435 (668), *516*

Matsumoto, F., 65 (348), *90*

Matsumoto, K., 60 (350), 64 (349, 350), *90*

Mattis, P. A., 452 (290), *506*

Mattos, L., 750 (500), *798*

Mattox, V. R., 548, 571, 572 (225, 226), 574 (226), *584*, 707 (737), *805*

Maughan, G. H., 478 (175, 176), *504*

Maumenee, A. E., 775 (738), *805*

Maurer, W., 450 (440, 441), *510*

Mauric, G., 774 (461), *797*

Maw, W. A., 672 (195), 674 (195), *682*

Maxwell, R., 708 (1123), 712 (1124), 714 (1123, 1126), *815*

May, C. E., 423, *429*

May, R., 476 (442), *510*

Mayer, A. M., 27, *53*

Mayer, G., 347, 351 (184), 359, 360, 362, 363, 365, 367, 369 (185, 186), 372, *380*, *383*, *384*

Mayer, J., 202, *232*

Mayer, M. M., *792*

Maylath, F. R., 767 (687, 688), 768 (687, 688), *803*

Maynard, F. L., 743 (366), *794*

Michel, O., 438 (244), 442 (595), 443 (599), 446 (596, 597, 602, 603, 605, 606), 448 (604), *505, 514*
Michel, R., 436 (803), 438 (244), 442 (595), 443 (588, 599), 445 (461, 462, 589, 591, 593), 446 (157, 158, 461, 462, 590, 596, 597, 598, 602, 603, 605, 606), 447 (244, 461, 586, 588, 592, 600), 448 (158, 587, 601, 604), 453 (585), 454, 490 (592), *503, 505, 510, 513, 514, 519*
Micheli, R. A., 552 (65), *580*
Michie, A. J., 154 (104), *172*
Michon, J., 58 (353), *91*
Micsa, M., 164 (155), *174*
Middleton, H. H., 128 (204), *149*
Middleton, S., 128 (163, 294), *148, 149*
Midorikawa, O., 192 (71), *197*
Miescher, K., 532 (337), 533 (338), 537, 539 (339), 541 (2, 3, 4, 127, 128), 542, 567 (130, 232), *578, 582, 585, 588*, 641, 646, *661*, 698 (773, 1207), *806, 818*
Miettinen, J. K., 536 (104), *581*
Migeon, C., 286 (394), *307*
Migeon, C. J., 628 (208), *661*, 667 (171), *681*, 714 (1212), 733 (770), 782 (772), 783 (370, 771, 1213), 784 (370, 771), *795 806, 818*, 851 (235), 852 (233), *876*
Migeon, C. L., 653 (321), *664*
Migone, A., 672 (1), *677*
Milanes, F., 751 (1075), *814*
Milani, L., 672 (172), *681*
Miles, A. A., 498 (408, 409), *509*
Milkovic, S., 496 (23), *500*
Miller, A. M., 605, 615, 616, 617 (311), 618, 624 (311), *661, 663*, 850 (140), *873*
Miller, D. C., 371, *384*
Miller, E., 529 (36), 565 (36), *579*, 605 (23), *655*
Miller, E. R., 826 (159), 847 (203), 852 (203), *874, 875*
Miller, H., 489 (759), *518*
Miller, I. H., 42 (200), *53*
Miller, J. N., 777 (1189), *817*
Miller, L., 625, *655*
Miller, L. L., 443 (729), *517*
Miller, M., 604 (275), 615 (211, 275), 616 (274), 618 (211), *661, 662*
Miller, O. B., 439 (463), *510*
Miller, R. A., 278 (253, 254), *303*
Miller, R. W., 773 (280), *792*

Miller, Z., 744 (774), *806*
Millerd, A., 39 (32), 40 (32, 201), 44 (32), 45 (32), *48, 53*
Millikan, C. H., 835 (141), 836 (141), *873*
Mills, E. S., 833 (142), *873*
Mills, J. A., 536 (233, 234), *585*
Mills, L. C., 284 (196), *302*
Milman, A. E., 243 (256, 257), 246 (256), 249 (256), 252 (257), 256 (257), 256 (257), 257 (256, 257), 258 (256, 257), 260 (257), 262 (255), 265 (255), *303*
Milne, M. D., 153, 154, 160, *172*
Minnini, G., 488 (655), *515*
Minz, B., 484 (120), *503*
Mira, O. J., 760 (1127), *815*
Miramontes, L., 544 (74, 284), *580, 586*
Mirand, E. A., 759 (775), 760 (775), *806*
Mirick, G. S., 770 (776), 773 (776), 779 (1040), *806, 813*
Mirsky, I. A., 183 (57), 185, 190 (87), *195, 196, 197*, 249 (258), *303*, 331, *384*, 484 (464), *510*, 727 (113), 752 (113), *788*
Mislow, K., 528 (235), *585*
Mitchell, C. A., 717 (853), *808*
Mitchell, G. M., 358 (30), *379*, 421 (25), 422 (131), 423 (132), 424 (131, 132, 134a), *426, 429*
Mitchell, H. H., 483 (479), *511*
Mitchell, J. W., 17 (179, 202), *52, 53*
Mitchell, M. L., 246 (260), 270 (259), *303*
Mitchell, N., 479 (233), *505*
Mitolo, M., 79 (354), *91*
Mitsui, T., 10 (203, 204), *53*
Mittleman, A., 697 (541), *799*
Mobile, A., 620 (136), *659*
Modern, F. W. S., 293 (244), *303*, 696 (725), 755 (725), *804*
Moewus, F., 3 (205), *53*
Moffett, R. B., 556 (236), 568 (237), 569 (237), *585*
Mogabgab, W. J., 771 (1144), 774 (777), 778 (777), *806, 816*
Mohney, J. B., 460 (320), *507*
Moinardi, C., 674 (252), *683*
Mokia, G. G., 70 (355), *91*
Mole, R. H., 460 (465), *510*
Molhuysen, J. A., 843 (24), *870*
Molitor, H., 393 (81), *427*
Moll, F. C., 772 (778), *806*
Molomut, N., 270 (369), *306*, 743 (779,

Muller, W. H., 45 (68), 46 (68), *49*
Mullick, V., 183 (51), *196*
Mulvaney, T. H., 834 (143), *873*
Munday, K., 421 (134), 422 (134), *429*
Munroe, J. S., 243 (52, 54), 249 (54), 257 (54), 265 (52, 54), 267 (52), *298*
Munson, P. L., 153, 154 (85), 160, 165, 166, 167 (85, 106, 107), 168, 169, *172, 173*, 220, *233*, 283, 284 (39), *298, 301,* 667 (176, 177), *681, 682*, 692 (423), *796*
Mureddu, F., 169, *172*
Murlin, J. R., 190 (73), 193, *195, 197*
Murneek, A. E., 33 (195, 287), 42 (287), *53, 55*
Murphy, A. J., 485 (201), *504*
Murphy, J., 838 (22), *870*
Murphy, J. B., 752 (803, 804), *807*
Murphy, J. S., 779 (1040), *813*
Murphy, R. F. J., 395 (149), 406 (149), *429*
Murray, H., 608 (235, 236), 609 (235), 641 (234), 643 (235), *661*
Murray, H. C., 608 (201a), 641 (88, 201), 642 (201a), *657, 660*
Murray, P. L., 608, 620, 641, 642, 643, *661*
Murray, R., 758 (805), *807*
Murrill, N. M., 576 (282), *586*
Mushett, C. W., 739 (806), *807*
Mussett, M. V., 154 (37), 167 (37, 38), 168, *170*
Musulin, N., 837 (96), 867 (95), *872*
Muus, J., 445 (480), *511*
Myant, N. B., 439 (315, 481), 440 (483), 449 (482), 451 (482), 452 (482), *507, 511*
Myers, J. D., 484 (484), 491 (485), 493 (485), *511*

N

Naber, G. H., 668 (272), *684*
Nace, H. R., 525 (239), *585*
Nachimison, H., 468 (702), *516*
Nachmansohn, D., 59 (358), *91*, 106 (205, 206), 119 (205), 121 (206), *149*
Nadel, E., 637 (30), 647 (30), *655*, 671 (178), *682*, 740 (807), *807*
Naegele, C. F., 700 (242), 775 (242), *791*
Nagano, T., 62 (359, 360), 66 (359), *91*
Nagareda, C. S., 712 (808), *807*
Nagayama, T., *425*
Nagle, F. O., 768 (1095), *814*
Nahum, L. H., 672 (179), *682*

Nairn, V., 744 (1247), *819*
Najjar, V. A., 175 (90), *197*
Nakamura, K., 3 (337), 5 (337), 7, 28 (337), *56*
Nakamura, N., 64 (486), 66 (486), *93*
Nakashima, M., 714 (359), 715 (358), *794*
Nalbandov, A. V., 332, 333 (249c), 334, 335, 336, 369, 374, *383, 384, 385, 386*
Nall, D. M., 616 (156), 618 (157), 619 (157), 648 (156), *659*
Nasset, E. S., 495 (756, 757), *518*
Nastuk, W. L., 126, *149*
Natelson, S., 291 (284), *304*, 754 (877), *808*
Nathanson, I. T., 594 (87), *657*, 667 (78), 672 (74), 674 (74), *679, 751, 807*
Naurais, E., 164 (100), *172*
Nava, G., 486 (142), *503*, 672 (180, 181), 674 (180, 181), *682*
Nayar, K. K., 68 (361–363), *91*
Naylor, A. W., 22 (213), 36 (135), *51, 53*
Neal, W. B., Jr., 484 (486), *511*, 759 (810), *807*
Nebel, I., 548 (171), *583*
Nedzel, G. A., 773 (387), *795*
Needham, D. M., 722, *788*
Neely, W. B., 42 (213a), *53*
Nefores, M. N., 483 (515), *512*
Neghme, A., 751 (10), *785*
Neher, R., 572 (308, 308a), 573 (308a), 574 (308a), *587*, 622 (286, 287), 641 (152), 642 (152), *659, 663*, 671 (182), *682*, 687 (1029), 707, *813*
Nekhorocheff, I., 718 (217), *790*
Nelson, A. A., 691 (811), *807*
Nelson, C. T., 754 (1136), 772, *807, 816*
Nelson, D. H., 284 (327), 286 (32, 267), 288 (31, 265), 291 (31), *297, 304, 305,* 694 (281, 814, 815), 696 (815), 745 (957), 759 (108), *787, 792, 807, 811*, 845 (64, 156, 178), *871, 874*
Nelson, J. F., 186 (91), *197*
Nelson, J. W., 278 (266), *304*
Nelson, M. M., *385*, 670 (183), *682*
Nelson, N. A., 543, *588*
Nelson, R. J., 771 (816), *807*
Nelson, T. S., 782 (150), *788*
Nelson, W. A., 757 (664), 772 (664), *803*
Nelson, W. O., 349, 351, 361, *385*, 595 (177), *660*, 865 (86), 866 (85, 87), 867 (145), *872, 873*

O'Donnell, W. M., 691 (831, 832), *807*
O'Donovan, D. K., 251 (270), 253 (170), *304*
Oesterling, M. J., 740 (833), *807*
Östland, E., 77 (369), *91*, 103, 131 (210), *149*
Ogden, G. E., 437 (87, 135), *502, 503*
Ogilvie, A. L., 464 (498), 474 (498), *511*
Ogilvie, R. F., 257 (271), 266 (271, 272), *304*
Ogryzlo, M. A., 749 (328), *793*
Ojers, G. W., 775 (834), *807*
Okey, R., 672 (185), 674 (185), *682*
Oldham, F. K., 390 (76), *427, 429*
Oleson, J. J., 277 (264), *304,* 721 (835), *807*
Olhagen, B., 750 (836), *807*
Olivecrona, H., 848 (4, 128), *870, 873*
Oliver, L., 746 (501), *798*
Olivereau, M., 435 (395, 500), 492 (499), *509, 511*
Oliveto, E. P., 529 (243), 558 (241, 242), *585*
Ollayos, R. W., 154, *173*
Olmsted, P. C., 594 (87), *657*
Olsen, L. J., 719 (322), *793*
Olsen, N. S., 194 (92), *197*
Olson, J. A., 768 (1096), *814*
Olson, K. J., 673 (46), *678*
Oncley, J. L., 176 (93), *497*
Ondarza, R., 447 (405), *509*
O'Neal, L. W., 459 (501, 502), *511,* 783 (837), *807*
Oneson, I. B., 545 (48), *580,* 667 (186), *682*
Opdyke, D. F., 246 (312), *305*
Opienska-Blauth, J., 166, *173*
Oppenauer, R., 615, *661*
Oppenauer, R. V., 552 (244), *585*
Oppenheim, E., 717, 733 (838), *807*
Oppenheimer, E., 278 (128), *300*
Oppermann, A., 31 (117), *51*
Opsahl, J. C., 278 (273, 274), *304,* 763 (839, 1039), *807, 813*
Orbison, J. L., 766 (165), *789*
Ord, W. M., 481 (503), *511*
Ormsby, H. L., 767 (840), 779 (840), *807*
Orr, K. D., 696 (24), 714 (24), 745 (24), *785*
Ortavant, R., 339 (57b), *380*
Orten, J. M., 187 (45), *196*
Osato, R. L., 409, *431*
Osbond, J. M., 552 (56), 557 (56), *580*

Osborn, C. M., 395, *426,* 710 (106), *787*
Osborn, M. M. L., 608 (201a), 642 (201a), *660*
Osborne, D. J., 25 (221), *53*
Osborne, M. M., Jr., 154 (32), 155 (32), 162 (32), *170*
Oshry, E., 436 (56), *501*
Osnes, M., 726 (841), *808*
Osterberger, A. E., 448 (344), *508*
Oswald, A., 447 (504), *511*
Ott, I., 399 (155), *429*
Ott, W. H., 780 (901), *809*
Ottaway, J. H., 256 (275), 260 (275), *304*
Ottinger, B., 763 (385), 772 (386), 773 (384, 386, 387), 774 (384), 776 (384), *795*
Otto, G. F., 437 (431), *510*
Otto, H., 464 (505), *511*
Otto, J. F., 252 (276), 289 (276), *304,* 725 (558), *800*
Ottolenghi, A., 78 (207), *88*
Otsu, T., 65 (370), 82 (371), *91*
Oughton, D. E., 554 (31), 556 (31), *579*
Outschoorn, A. J., 102 (73), *146*
Overbeek, G. A., 295 (173), *301*
Overbeek, J. A., *304*
Overholser, M. D., 278 (426), *308*
Overman, J. R., 774 (842), *797, 808*
Overman, R. R., 489 (171), *504,* 706 (205), 708 (205), 710 (205), 711 (327), 733 (1254), *790, 793, 819*
Overton, E., *429*
Owen, E. C., 479 (110), 487 (110), 488 (109), *502*
Oyaert, W., 417 (159), *430*
Oyama, J., 763 (385), 772 (386), 773 (386, 387), 774 (465), *795, 797*
Ozeki, K., 69 (372), *91*

P

Pabst, M. L., 703 (843), *808*
Pace, M., 670 (4), *677*
Pacheco, H., 2, *53*
Padawer, J., 747 (844), *808*
Paesi, F. S. A., 671 (187), *682*
Pagan, C., 42 (185), *52*
Page, E., 375, *384,* 734 (663), *803*
Page, E. W., 670 (188), *682,* 700 (845), *808,* 864 (147), *874*
Page, I. H., 100 (276), 104 (276), 105, 135, 136, *149, 150,* 493 (128), 497 (506),

S

Saba, N., 628, 649, *662*
Sabah, D., 488 (127), *503*
Sabo, E. F., 559 (107), *581*, 698 (350a), *794*
Saccone, A., 705 (744), *805*
Sacks, J., 187 (109, 110), *198*
Sacktor, B., 75 (53, 419, 420), *84, 92*
Sadhu, D. P., 476 (628), 488 (627, 628), *514*
Saffran, J., 595 (127), 596 (1), 609 (127), *655, 658*
Saffran, M., 288 (322), 289 (321, 322), *305*, 623, *662*
Sakamoto, H., 673 (122), *680*
Sala, G., 164, *170, 172*, 709 (954), 711 (954), 724 (141), *788, 811*
Salamon, I., 527, *586*
Salamon, I. I., 632 (260b), *662*
Salassa, R. M., 696 (884), 714 (884), 782 (955), *809, 811*
Salcedo, J., Jr., 254 (376), *307*
Salgado, E., 270 (347, *306*, 674 (69), *679*
Salhanick, H. A., 334, *385*, 604, *662*, 671 (224), *683*
Salmon, A. A., 605 (262), *662*
Salmon, T. N., 239, *305*
Salmon, U. J., 605, *662*
Saloum, R., 66 (216), *88*
Salter, J. M., 238 (212, 324, 325), 239 (212, 325), *302, 305*
Salter, W. T., 439 (630), 440 (299), 445 (480, 663), 447 (289, 629), 448 (289), 449 (634), 450 (632), 474 (631, 635), 480 (639), *506, 507, 511, 515*, 838, *874*
Saltzstein, H. C., 758 (595), 759 (594, 595), 766 (964), 769 (594, 964), *801, 811*
Sames, G. L., 699 (956), *811*
Sammartino, R., 324, *383*
Samter, M., 787 (83), *787*
Samuels, L. T., 237 (326), 286 (267, 394), 287 (329), 288 (31), 291 (31), *297, 304, 305, 307*, 461 (636), 515, 600 (296), 604 (261), 606 (135), 613 (218, 288), 616 (296), 617, 626, 646 (241), 648, 649 (325), *659, 661, 662, 663*, 694 (281, 814, 815), 696 (815), 730 (962), 735 (379), 745 (957), 759 (108), *787, 792, 795, 807, 811*, 845 (178), *874*
Samuels, P. B., 743 (230), *791*
Sanborn, R. C., 75 (421), *92*

Sandberg, A. A., 284 (327), 286 (32), *297, 305*, 745 (957), *811*, 845 (156, 178), *874*
Sandeen, M. I., 61 (84, 88), 62 (80, 83, 87, 89, 422, 423, 424), *85, 92*
Sandiford, I., 481 (82), *486* (82), *502*
Sandiford, K., 481 (82), 486 (82), *502*
Sandoval, A., 544 (284), *586*
Sandulesco, G., 594 (102), *658*
Sanger, F., 177, 178 (111), 179, 180, *198*, 227, *233*, 406 (176), *430*
Santa, N., 739 (392, 393), *795*
Santamaria, L., 192 (36, 38), *196*, 261 (112), *300*
Sapirstein, L. A., 714 (958), *811*
Sarcar, U., 163 (128), *173*
Sarett, L. H., 529, 530 (286), 531 (287), 532 (286, 287), 539 (288, 290), 549 (51), 550 (51), 558 (52, 289), 567 (285), *580, 586*
Sartorius, O. W., 395 (179), *430*, 708 (959), 710 (934), *810, 811*
Satina, S., 27 (240), 35 (245), *54*
Sato, H., 497 (336), *507*
Saucy, G., 556 (150), *582*
Saunders, F. J., *661*, 714 (427), *796*
Saurino, V. R., 780 (220), *790*
Savard, K., 289 (163), *301*, 525 (291), *586*, 610, 611 (31–33), 612, 615, 619 (268), 623 (121, 122), 626, 634 (31–33), 635 (31–33), 645 (270), 648 (31), *655, 656, 657, 658, 662*, 667 (225), *683*
Savit, J., 77 (504), *94*
Sawaya, P., 61 (425), *92*
Sawyer, C. H., 322, 330, 333 (82–84), 334 (233), *381, 384, 385*, 671 (162, 226), *681, 683*, 853 (130), 869 (130), *873*
Sawyer, J., 156 (6, 7), *170*
Sawyer, M. K., 137 (240), *149, 430*
Sawyer, P. N., 775 (57), *786*
Sawyer, W. H., 137 (240), *149*, 397, 399, 398 (178), *429*
Sax, K. J., 550 (6), 552 (6), 553 (6), 560 (6), *578*
Sayers, D., *818*
Sayers, G., 166, *174*, 207 (35), 220, 221 (34, 93), *231, 233*, 276 (331, 332), 281 (328, 331), 282 (61, 62), 285 (328, 330, 331, 380, 381), 286 (44), 287 (310, 329, 382), 290 (328, 331), 293 (135, 136), *298, 300, 305, 307*, 375, 376 (32, 33), *380, 394*

848

Straube, R. L., 672 (189), *682*, 759 (1111), *815*
Strauss, E., 445 (71), *501*
Strauss, M. B., 757 (1062), *814*
Strauss, R., 863 (212), *875*
Straw, R. F., *659*, 667 (135), *681*
Street, H. E., 23, *55*
Streeten, D. H. P., 688 (1151), 696 (1151), 697 (1151), 704 (1151), 721 (1151), 727 (1151), 745 (1148), 765 (1151), 766 (1151), 768 (1151), 777 (1151), *816*
Stricker, P., 347, 351, *386*
Strickroot, F. L., 271 (334), *305*
Striganova, A. R., 164, *173*
Strisower, B., 485 (236), *505*
Strisower, E. H., 187 (34), *196*
Stroud, S. W., 599, *663*
Studer, A., 674 (242), *683*
Studer, P. E., 635 (171), *660*
Stumpe, W. M., 763 (21), *785*
Sturgis, S. H., 670 (95), *680*, 857 (206), 859 (206), *875*
Sturkie, P. D., 482 (696), *516*, 672 (243), *683*
Sturm, E., 752 (803, 804), *807*
Sturtevant, F. M., Jr., 674 (244), *683*
Stutinsky, F., 60 (478), 68 (479), 75 (480), 81 (480), *93*, 139 (262), *150*
Sudak, F. N., 713 (1245), 716 (1245), *819*
Sue, P., 438 (388), *509*
Suguira, K., 751 (1112, 1113), 752 (1113), *815*
Suiter, L. E., 729 (728), *804*
Sullivan, J., 462 (38), *500*
Sulman, F. G., 295 (378), *307*, 423 (195), *430*
Sulzberger, M. B., 754 (1114, 1115), *815*
Summers, G. H. R., 544 (304, 305), 558 (45, 273), 559 (45), *579*, *586*, *587*
Summers, V. K., 692 (1014), *812*, 848 (182), *874*
Sunderman, F. W., 831 (207), *875*
Suneson, S., 62 (119), *86*
Sung, C., 496 (697), *516*
Suomalainen, P., 81 (481, 482), *93*
Sur, R. N., 783 (950), *811*
Surányi, L. A., 544 (42), *579*
Suranyl, L., 620 (39), *656*
Sure, B., 481 (699), 489 (698), *516*, 781 (1116), *815*

Sussmann, L. N., 747 (886), *809*
Sutherland, E. W., 191 (142), 192 (144), 194, *198*, 723, *815*
Sutherland, K., 740 (1101), 766 (879), *809*, *815*
Sutton, L. E., 851 (231), *876*
Sutton, R. E., 553 (340), *588*
Svedberg, T., 448 (296), *507*
Sverdrup, A., 209 (29), *231*
Swahn, B., 486 (425), *509*
Swan, J. M., 99 (280), *150*, 404 (211), 409 (211, 211a), *431*
Swanberg, H., 670 (3), *677*
Swann, H. G., 690 (1118), *815*
Swanson, C. P., 35 (284), *55*
Swanson, E. W., 494 (700), *516*
Swartz, I. B., 777 (717), *804*
Sweat, M. L., 288 (379), *307*, 600, 616, 617 (266), 645 (295), 648 (266, 296), *662*, *663*, 694 (119), 696 (119), *815*
Swedin, B., 153 (95), *172*
Sweeney, M. J., 243 (122), 248 (122), *300*
Swenson, R. E., 442 (70), *516*
Swett, W. A., 29 (264), *54*
Swift, M. N., 672 (189), *682*
Swingle, W. W., 697 (1121), 698 (1120, 1121), 708 (1122, 1123), 712 (1124), 714 (1122, 1123, 1126), 722 (1125), *815*
Swinyard, C. A., 282 (61, 62), *298*
Sydnor, K. L., 285 (380, 381), 287 (382), *307*, 843 (208a), 850 (208), *875*
Sykes, J. F., 366, *386*, 667 (29), *678*
Syverton, J. T., 753 (1198), 760 (1127), 779 (418), *796*, *815*, *817*
Szego, C. M., 242 (383), 254 (383), *307*, 669 (245), 670 (24, 25, 245), 676 (245), *678*, *683*, 728 (1203), 733, 784 (1128), *815*, *818*
Szerb, J., 720 (587), *801*
Szilagyi, D. E., 781 (1130), *815*, 836 (209), *875*
Szmuszkovicz, J., 539 (173), *583*

T

Tagmann, E., 546 (257), *585*, 604 (244), 610, 615, *662*, *663*
Tagnon, R. F., 467 (784), *518*
Tainter, M. L., 113, *150*
Tait, J. F., 572 (121, 307, 308, 308a), 573 (308a), 574 (307, 308a), *582*, *587*, 622

Weber, R. P., 3, *50*
Webster, B., 461 (112), *502*
Webster, H. D., 670 (169), *681*
Webster, T. A., 247 (76), *299*
Webster, W. W., Jr., 20 (323), *56*
Wechtel, G. E., 595 (105), *658*
Weckesser, E. C., 769 (538), *799*
Weeks, D. C., 44 (249), *54*
Weidlich, H. A., 553 (333), *587*
Weigand, F. A., 705 (201), *790*
Weil, P. G., 850 (221), *876*
Weil, R., 243 (407), 254 (407), *307*
Weiland, P., 698 (1207), *818*
Weil-Malherbe, H., 102 (284), 150, 185, *199*
Weimer, H. W., 777 (1189), *817*
Weinbaum, J. G., 691 (832), *807*
Weinberger, H., 271 (25), *297*
Weinmann, J. P., 169 (14, 15, 79), *170, 172*
Weinstein, H. G., 498 (741), *517*
Weinstein, H. R., 187 (41), 192 (36, 38, 39, 40), 193 (37), *196*, 260 (111, 113), 261 (112), *300*
Weinstein, R. C., 260 (408), *307*
Weintraub, A., 608 (201a, 235, 236), 609 (235), 641 (88, 201, 234), 642 (201a), 643 (235), *657, 660, 661*
Weintraub, R. L., 17 (324), 28 (96), *50, 56*
Weir, D. R., 738 (799, 1190, 1191), *806, 817*
Weir, E. G., 439 (761), *518*
Weisberg, H. F., 194 (161), *199*
Weisberger, A. S., 748 (1192), *817*
Weisblat, D. I., 104 (256), *150*, 568 (237), 569 (237), *585*
Weise, C. E., 488 (762), *518*
Weisel, G. F., 398 (137a), *429*
Weisenborn, F. L., 574 (333a), *587*
Weisenfeld, S., 489 (763), 490 (763), *518*
Weisman, P. A., 775 (1193), *817*
Weiss, B., 442 (764), 447 (765), *518*
Weiss, E., *427*, 498 (766), *518*
Weiss, M., 705 (177), 707 (177), 721 (177), 732 (177), 753 (177), *789*
Weiss, P., 111, *150*
Weiss, S. B., 485 (767), *518*
Weiss, T., 560 (41), *579*, 771 (226), *791*
Weiss, W. W., 780 (715), *804*
Weissman, L., 836 (228), *876*
Weisz, P., 283 (409), *307*

Wei-Yuan Huang, 548 (99), 549 (99), 556 (98, 100), *581*
Welbourn, R. B., 756 (1194), *817*
Welch, A. D., 107, *144*, 738 (1191), *817*
Welch, J. A., 335 (156), *383*
Welch, W. J., 708 (1122), 714 (1122), *815*
Welcher, A. D., 410 (10), *425*
Weller, L. E., *56*
Wells, B. B., 700 (1195), 728 (33), *785, 817*
Wells, L. J., 278 (426), *308*, 693, *802*, 853,
Wells, P. H., 82 (527), *94*
Welsh, J. H., 60 (39–41), 61 (528), 63 (41), 66 (39), 78 (529, 530), 79 (530), *84, 94*, 98 (26, 27), 100 (291, 293), 101, 104 (295), 105 (292, 293), 106 (297, 299), 109 (26, 27), 113 (27), 116 (286, 287), 120 (300), 121, 122, 123, 124 (304), 125 (305), 126, 128 (289), 129 (289), 130, 135 (291, 292, 293), 136 (293, 294), 138 (26), 139 (26, 27), *144, 150, 151*
Welt, I., 734 (1196), *817*
Welt, I. D., 187 (139), *198*
Welt, L. G., 395 (150), *429*
Wendler, N. L., 552 (166), 558 (119, 334), 571 (168), *581, 583, 587*
Wenk, P., 68 (531), *94*
Wense, T., 103, *151*
Went, F. W., 5 (147), 7, 10 (147), 14 (329), 19, 32 (328), *51, 56*
Wentworth, J. H., 759 (1197), *817*
Werder, A. A., 753 (1198), 760 (1127), 779 (418), *796, 815, 817*
Werle, M. D., 773 (1103), *815*
Werner, S. C., 440 (769), 458 (768), *518*, 782 (1199), *817*, 839 (230), *876*
Wertheimer, E., 186 (151), 189 (17), *195, 199*, 475 (1), *499, 816*
Wertheimer, E. J., 734 (968), *811*
Werthessen, N. T., 591 (283), 594 (230), 604 (229), *661, 663*
Weslaw, W., 488 (770), *518*
Wesson, L. G., Jr., 395 (11), *425*
West, C. D., 484 (555), 486 (555), 487 (555), 490 (555), *513*, 610, 615, 616, 648, *664*, 696 (860, 1201), 698 (1200), 706 (859, 860), 711 (859, 860), *808, 817*
West, E., 736 (917), *810*
West, G. B., 102 (249), 103, *150*
West, T. C., 670 (262), *684*

Subject Index

A

ACE, see Adrenocortical extract
ACTH, see Adrenocorticotropic hormone
ACTX, see Corticotropin A
ADH, see Antidiuretic hormone
Abortion,
  hormonal imbalance and, 862
  serum protein-bound iodine and, 863
Absinthin,
  as auxin inhibitor, 26
Acetate,
  as precursor of adrenocortical steroids, 627, 628
  of Δ^4-androstene-3,17-dione, 612
  of cholesterol, 591–592, 593
  of estrogens, 596
  of testosterone, 612
3β-Acetoxyallopregnan-20-one,
  labeled, preparation, 577
  microbiological reactions, 643, 644
3α-Acetoxy-Δ^{11}-cholenic acid, methyl ester, preparation of labeled, 577
3α-Acetoxy-$\Delta^{9(11)}$-etianic acid, methyl ester, synthesis, 538
21-Acetoxy-20-ketosteroids
  conversion to etianic acid, 571
  synthesis, 569–570
3α-Acetoxypregnane-11,20-dione,
  labeled, preparation, 578
6-Acetoxyprogesterone, 547
3-Acetyl-6-methoxybenzaldehyde, as auxin inhibitor, 26
Acetylcholine, 100–101, 106–107, 119–130, 143
  action, calcium and, 126
  on cellular metabolism, 129–130
  concentration and, 127–129
  depolarizing, 126
  mechanism of, 125–127
  muscarinic, 125
  nicotinic, 125
  site of, 119–121, 133

  structure and, 122–125
  trophic, 129–130
  on vertebrate heart, 128
  adrenaline and, 131
  antagonists, 120, 125
  biosynthesis, 99, 106
  site of, 143
  blocking agents for, 124, 125
  chemical nature, 99, 143
  in crustaceans, 61
  distribution, 98, 100–101
  in insects, 77
  interaction with cholinesterases, 121
  intermedin and, 100
  in mollusks, 79, 80
  in nerve cells, 106
  as neurohumor, 142
  physiological role, 119
  reaction with acetylcholinesterase, 128
  receptors for, 120, 121–125
  cholinesterase and, 121, 122
  combination with drugs, 125
  linkage between acetylcholine and, 123, 124
  nature of, 125, 126
  reaction of acetylcholine with, 126 128
  red cell cholinesterase and, 128
  relation to cell components, 122
  release, 99, 113, 114
  chemicals affecting, 117
  mechanism, 114
  storage in nervous tissue, 107
  thyroxine and, 497
  as transmitting agent, 114
  transport, axonal, 113
  in worms, 59
Acetylcholinesterase, reaction with acetylcholine, 128
N-Acetyldiiodotyrosine, hormonal activity, 475
Acid-base balance, adrenocortical steroids and, 708–709

effect on corticotropin secretion, 281–
282
on thyroid function, 459
growth hormone and, 241
metabolism of, 589, 631–640
response of eosinophils to, 744–745
secretion, corticotropin and, 288
structure, 551
terminology, 690
Adrenocortical steroids, see also Adrenocortical hormones and individual
compounds
activity, cytocidal, 703
lymphotoxic, 744
antiinflammatory, 760, 761–766
structural requirements for, 551
orientation of side chain and, 526
ascorbic acid and, 219, 220
assay of, 701–704, 742
atherosclerosis and, 716–717
biologically active, 627
inactive, 622
biosynthesis, in adrenogenital syndrome, 652–653, 654
in blood, control of corticotropin secretion by, 281
diurnal variation in concentration,
286
brain lesions following administration
of, 719
effect on ACTH production, 281, 630
on anaphylactic reactions, 771–773
species variations in, 772
on antibody synthesis, 760
on antigen–antibody reactions, 773–
775
on bone, 753–754
on bone marrow, 746–748
on carbohydrate utilization, 730
on cellular response to infection, 760,
761
on cerebral blood flow and metabolism, 718
in chronic leukemia, 705
on electroencephalogram, 718
on experimental cancer, 751–752
on intracellular fluid and electrolytes, 710
on joint inflammation, 764–765
on purines, 732
on red blood cells, 748

on renal clearance, 709–710
species differences in, 710
on resistance to toxins, 757–758
on rheumatoid arthritis, 765–766
on stomach, 755–756
on susceptibility to infection, 776–
780
on sweat, 712–713
on tissue cultures, 769–770
on tissue damage, 758
on water excretion, 711–712
on wound healing, 766
enzymes and, 723–724, 730–732
eosinopenia following administration
of, 746
growth inhibition by, 699, 700–701
hydroxylation, enzymatic, 645–646
mechanism of, 646
hypersensitivity and, 760
insulin and, 726
maintenance of lactation and, 784
metabolic effects, 460
metabolism, differences between *in
vitro* and *in vivo*, 632
effect of anethole on, 692
microbiological reactions, 640–644
nature of, 640ff.
placenta as source of, 842
psychotic reactions following treatment with, 717–718
response to stress and, 704
secretion, in Cushing's syndrome, 845
sensitivity reactions and, 770–771
untoward effects of, 699–701, 717–718
urinary, in toxemia of pregnancy, 863
Adrenocorticotropic hormone, 687, 688,
822, see also Corticotropin(s)
activity, 822
adrenal ascorbic acid-depleting, 423,
424, 425, 742
galactopoietic, 365
mode of administration and, 696
adrenogenital syndrome and, 602, 652,
653, 654
alkalosis following administration of,
709
amino acid metabolism and, 727, 728
antithyroid drugs and, 783
"B" hormone and, 421, 423–425
biosynthesis, adrenocortical steroids
and, 630, 652

17,21-Dihydroxy-Δ^4-pregnene-3,11,20-trione, see Cortisone
$6\beta,17\alpha$-Dihydroxyprogesterone, microbiological formation, 641
$11\alpha,17\alpha$-Dihydroxyprogesterone, microbiological formation, 608, 641, 642
3,5-Diiodo-4-hydroxybenzoic acid,
  derivatives, antithyroxine activity, 453, 475–476
  effect on metabolism of thyroxine, 453
  of triiodothyronine, 453
Diiodotyrosine,
  conversion to thyroxine, 443, 444–445
  hypophysectomy and, 445
Diisopropyl fluorophosphate, anticholinesterase activity, 117
3,11-Diketopregnane, 20-hydroxysteroids derived from, 529–530
2,3-Dimercapto-1-propanol (BAL), growth-inhibiting activity of lactones and, 24
1,7-Dimethylxanthine, as thyroxine antagonist, 476
Diosgenin,
  conversion to cholesteral, 561
  to 11-oxygenated steroids, 552
  structure, 551
Di-sec-butylcyclopentene, derivatives, see Auxin a
Diuresis, see also Water metabolism
  adrenocortical steroids and, 711–712
Dog, adrenaline and noradrenaline content of brain, 102
Doisynolic acid(s), 540–542
  configuration, 541
  estrogenic activity and, 540, 541
  synthesis, 541
Dopa decarboxylase, in adrenal medulla, 107
Dopamine, see Hydroxytyramine, 103
Drugs,
  effect on thyroid, 461–474, 496–497
  sympathomimetic, structural requirement, 134
Dwarfism,
  pituitary, 826–827
  symptoms of, 827
  treatment with growth hormone preparations, 270–273, 827

E

EPS, see Exophthalmos-producing substance
Ectohormone(s),
  occurrence, 80
  of termites, 77
Egg-diapause factor, of *Bombyx mori*, 142
Egg white, toxic effects in rat, adrenocortical steroids and, 757
Electrocortin, see Aldosterone
Electroencephalogram, effect of adrenocortical steroids on, 718
Electrolytes,
  dietary, effect on adrenal cortex of hypophysectomized animals, 278
  metabolism, adrenal cortex and, 688
  cortisone and, 704–705, 707, 708
  in Cushing's syndrome, 845–846
  effect of adrenogenital syndrome on, 851
  thyroid and, 486
  retention, growth hormone and, 290
  urinary excretion, assay of adrenocortical steroids based on, 702
Electroshock,
  mechanism of, 719
  threshold, adrenocortical steroids and, 702–703, 719
Elements, chemical, in thyroid, 436
Endocrine organs, effect of environmental changes on, 317
Endocrinology, clinical, 821–876
Enteramine, see also 5-Hydroxytryptamine, 78
  in insects, 77, 82
  in intestinal mucosa of tunicates, 79
  in invertebrates, 80
  in mollusks, 78
  as nerve transmitter in crustaceans, 67
Enzyme poisons, inhibition of root growth by, 23
Enzymes,
  action on growth hormones, 204–205
  adrenocortical hormones and, 723–724, 730–732
  auxins and, 41, 42
  effects of sex hormones on, 673, 674, 675 ff.
  activating, 677

3-Ketosteroids,
bromination, 548–549
inhibition of α-glycerophosphatase by, 676
11-Ketosteroids, reduction, 558
12-Ketosteroids, conversion to 11-oxygenated steroids, 556–558
15-Ketosteroids, configuration, stability and, 540
17-Ketosteroids,
androgenic, secretion in adrenogenital syndrome, 848
assay of, 667
formation, 650, 651
as metabolites of cortisol and cortisone, 638
of deoxycorticosterone, 635
of progesterone, 635
urinary, in adrenal cancer, 612
in adrenocortical hyperfunction, 860
chorionic gonadotropin and, 595
in Cushing's syndrome, 845
in pituitary hypogonadism, 855
of pregnancy, 861
20-Ketosteroids, bromination, 566–567
metabolism, differences between *in vitro* and *in vivo* experiments, 632
preparation, 566
Δ⁴-3-Ketosteroids, 547–551, see also individual compounds
configuration, 548, 549
effect of Δ-hydrogenases on, 648–649
formation, enzymatic, 628–629
from 3-ketosteroids, 548
labeled, preparation, 549
as metabolites of cortisol, 637
preparation, 548–549
protection during, 549–551
reduction of, 650–651
effect of nuclear substitution on, 650–651
Δ¹,⁴-3-Ketosteroids, synthesis of estrogens from 539
Kidney,
effect of estrogens on, 672
of pituitary extracts on, 397
function, adrenal cortex and, 704–712
parathyroids and, 153–155
as source of steroid hydrogenases, 647
Klinefelter syndrome, 866
Krebs cycle, adrenal steroids and, 730

L

LSD, see Lysergic acid diethylamide
LTH, see Prolactin
Lactation, see also Galactopoiesis, Lactogenesis
inhibition, by combined action of estrogen and progesterone, 361–362
maintenance, adrenocortical steroids and, 784
hormonal mechanism governing, 365
prolactin and, 363–365, 366–367
milk ejection, 363
posterior pituitary and, 363, 393, 399–400
onset at parturition, 359, 362–363
factors affecting, 353, 359
theories of, 359, 360–363, 367
parathyroids and, 169
role of pituitary-adrenal axis in, 351–352, 365
Lactogenesis,
experimental, effect of antagonism between ovarian hormone and prolactin on, 360
action of ovary on, 369
prolactin and, 351–363
Lactogenic hormone, see Prolactin
Lactones,
as growth inhibitors, 24
BAL and, 24
unsaturated, as germination inhibitors, 27
light and, 27
synergism with auxins, 24
Leaves, mature, role in fruit-set by auxins or pollen, 33–34
Lecithin,
linkage to protein components of cell surface, 126–127
acetylcholine and, 126
Leeches, adrenaline in, 103
Leprosy, effect of cortisone on, 778
Leucocytes, response to adrenal steroids, 747–748
Leukemia, effect of adrenocortical steroids on, 705, 748, 751, 752–753
Leukotaxine, 761

Leydig cells,
 function, hypogonadism due to failure
  of, 865, 866–867
  treatment of 867
 as source of androgens, 864, 868
  of estrogens, 868
  of progesterone, 864
 tumors of, 867
Licorice extract, beneficial action in
  adrenal insufficiency, 697
Light,
 effect on gonadotropic activity of anterior pituitary, 317–318
  on reproductive functions of animals, 317–318
  on thyroid, 460
Limulus, brain of, hormones in, 78
Lipids,
 blood, cortisone and, 733
  DCA and, 733
Lipogenesis,
 in lactating mammary gland, 353–354
  insulin and, 354
Liver,
 diseases, effect on ovarian function,
  859
 effect on thyroxine metabolism, 451,
  452
 estrogens and, 598, 600, 672
 fat, adrenals and, 733
  growth hormone and, 733, 744
 as source of steroid hydrogenases, 647
  hydroxylases, 646
 as target organ of glucagon, 193, 194
Lumiepiandrosterone, synthesis, 539
Lumiestrone, 537
Luteotropic hormone, see Prolactin
Luteotropin(s), see also Cyonin, Prolactin
 identity with prolactin, 369
 placental, 372
 prolactin and, 372
Lymphocytes, effect of adrenocortical
  steroids on, 703, 744
Lysergic acid diethylamide, action on
  Venus heart, 135
 central nervous effects, 136
 5-hydroxytryptamine and, 136
 structure, 135
Lumbricidae, "clitellogenic" factor in, 58

M

MCPA, see 2-Methyl-4-chlorophenoxy-
  acetic acid
Magnesium, blood, thyroid and, 488
Malaria, effect of cortisone on, 780
Malate, growth-promoting effect on
  flower ovary, 34
Maleic hydrazide, as antiauxin, 22, 36
Malnutrition, adrenal cortex and, 736
Mammals,
 brain, photosensitive areas in, 319
 effect of steroids on gonads of, 675
 metabolic effects of prolactin in, 373–
  374
 sexual activity, light and, 318, 320
Mammary duct system, response to prolactin, 348, 352, 378
Mammary gland,
 action of oxytocin on, 137
 calcium-concentration by, parathyroids and, 153
 development, prolactin and, 347–351
  somatotropin and, 348, 351
 lactating, enzyme systems in, 354
  lipogenesis in, 353–354, 357
   insulin and, 354
  oxidative metabolism of, 354ff.
   cortisone and, 356, 357
   "Dickens cycle" and, 354
   insulin and, 355
   prolactin and, 357, 358
 response to prolactin, 347–352, 355, 357,
  358
Mammogen, pituitary, 347, 349
 prolactin and, 348
Mammotropin, see Prolactin
Man,
 adrenalectomy in 696, 697
 corticosterone therapy and, 697–698
 toxic effects of chronic cortisone therapy in, 699
Manganese, in thyroid, 436
Marine worm, sessile (*Phoronis*), hormone in, 58
Mast cells,
 action of cortisone on, 743–744, 763
 production of hyaluronic acid by, 763
Mating behavior,
 androgens and, 673

symptoms, 861
treatment, 861
Pseudopregnancy, see Pseudocyesis
Pseudosapogenin,
structure, 561
synthesis, 561
Puberty, 868–869
anterior pituitary and, 869
precocious, 869
in adrenogenital syndrome, 652
pseudoprecocious, 869
Purines, effect of adrenocortical steroids
on, 732
Pyridoxine,
adrenal function and, 743
deficiency, cortisone and, 738, 739
effect on experimental lymphosarcoma, 752
effects of, 738–739
lymphoid tissue and, 743

R

Radioiodine, uptake by thyroid, adrenocortical steroids and, 782
Rat,
effect of growth hormone preparations
in, 242, 243, 244–245
luteotropic activity of prolactin in,
310, 349, 351, 362, 367, 369, 370
prolactin-like substance in placenta of,
372
Reichstein's Compound S, see 11-Deoxy-
cortisol
Reproductive organs,
male, effect of prolactin on, 373
stimuli from, effect on gonadotropic
activity of anterior pituitary, 332
Resorcinol, antithyroid activity, 470
Respiration, corticotropin and, 296
Reticuloendothelial system, effect of
cortisone on, 743
Rhenium, in blood and thyroid, 436
Rhinitis, allergic, cortisone and, 773
Riboflavin,
auxin destruction and, 28
thyroid and, 489
Ribonucleic acids, auxin and, 22, 35
Rodents, metabolism of testosterone in,
621–622
Roots,
in bioassay of auxins, 3

effect of antiauxins on, 38
of auxins on, 15, 23–24, 44, 128
geotropic responses, substances affecting, 24
growth, auxins and, 23–24, 44, 128
growth-promoting substances for, 3
Rotifers, subcerebral gland of, 59
Rutabaga,
inhibitory effect on thyroid, 461
isolation of goitrogen from, 461, 838

S

STH (Somatotropic hormone) see
Growth hormone, of anterior pituitary
Saline, intravenous, effect on adrenal
cortex of hypophysectomized animals, 278
Saliva, effect of adrenocortical steroids
on, 713
Salt hormones, 844
adrenogenital syndrome and, 851
formation in adrenal cortex of rodents,
851
Salt metabolism,
role of adrenal cortex in, 395
of neurohypophysis in, 394–399
Sapogenins,
degradation to 20-ketosteroids, 566
11-oxygenated steroids from, 557
Sarmentogenin, 551
conversion to cortisone, 551
structure, 551
Schizophrenia,
adrenals and, 717
following LSD intake, 136
Schwartzman phenomena, cortisone and,
771
Scopoletin,
auxin and, 29
inhibition of indoleacetic acid oxidase
by, 29
in plants, 24
Scurvy,
effect of cortisone on, 740, 741–742
rheumatoid arthritis and, 739
Seeds,
response to cold, 32
reversal of, 32
Semen,
estrogens in human, 595